BULK CARRIER PRACTICE

Second Edition

Captain Jack Isbester ExC FNI MCMS
Extra Master

Foreword (first edition) by Dr Frank Chao, Chairman, Intercargo
Foreword (second edition) by Robert Lorenz-Meyer, President and Chairman BIMCO
Managing Partner, Ernst Russ GmbH & Co. KG

First published 1993 by The Nautical Institute,
202 Lambeth Road, London SE1 7LQ, UK.
Reprinted 1997
Reprinted 1998
Reprinted 2000
Reprinted 2003
Reprinted 2008

Second edition published 2010
Reprinted 2013

ISBN 978 1 906915 10 0

Typeset by: Tradeset Ltd, 2 Burwood Ave, Eastcote, Pinner, HA5 2RZ

Printed in the UK by: Newnorth Print Ltd, Newnorth House, College Street, Kempston, Bedford MK42 8NA

Front cover photograph

A Cape-sized bulk carrier loading iron ore at Parker Point, Dampier, Western Australia. Holds Nos. 2, 4, 7 and 9 are open for loading. The loader, with a rated capacity of 7,500 tonnes per hour, appears to be located over Nos. 5 or 6 holds, probably moving from one loading position to another. Another Cape-sized vessel waits her turn to load while a third, in the background, appears to be deep laden and may be on the point of sailing.

The Parker Point terminal, and the nearby East Intercourse Island terminal, have a total capacity of 140 million tonnes of iron ore per annum.

Photo courtesy of Rio Tinto Iron Ore

CONTENTS

Notes on numbering of illustrations and appendices

The book starts with eleven pages of drawings (Drawings 1.1 - 1.11) of bulk carrier types. Thereafter all illustrations are to be found in appropriate chapters, numbered consecutively – eg Fig. 1.5 denotes figure 5 in Chapter 1 and will be found in the main text of the book. Appendix 10.1 denotes the first appendix relating to Chapter 10 and will be found in the collection of appendices at the back of the book.

APPENDICES AND REFERENCE MATERIAL

CONTENTS

FOREWORD
to First Edition

Dry bulk carriers, the workhorses of the sea, carry out the essential transport of commodities without which our modern society would not be able to function. The ships and their crews, together with the companies that operate them, do not enjoy the glamour attached to other sectors of the industry more in the public eye; the bulk shipping sector does, however, provide a highly cost-effective service for which proper recognition is due. This quiet matter-of-fact 'let us get on with the job' approach so prevalent in bulk carrier companies belies the professionalism implicit in the operation of bulk carriers and perhaps leads others to undervalue its major contribution to the world economy.

It is not until somebody of the calibre of Captain Isbester, supported by the Bulk Carrier Working Group of The Nautical Institute, puts operational practice into writing, that the reader becomes aware of the knowledge, expertise and skill necessary to run bulk carriers efficiently and safely. The 26 chapters of this book break new ground. They focus not only on operational requirements but also on the various decision-making processes necessary for successful operation.

This approach separates this publication from others in the field and provides its unique character. The task of compiling such a book is very much more difficult than simply writing a textbook on a specific theme, such as charterparties. But once achieved, it is essential for reference and study. Clearly it will be used both on board and in a company's daily operations. It will also be an effective training manual for all those joining the world's bulk fleet for the first time. More widely, it will be of particular value to shippers and charterers, terminal operators, surveyors, consultants and maritime lawyers.

The 400 pages of the book encapsulate the essence of good economic performance and professional awareness of all the contributory factors which go towards optimum stowage and discharge, and thus to a successful voyage. This entails meeting the charterparty requirements without claims arising, whilst still ensuring that the vessel is at all times ready to trade.

Operating successfully and profitably is no mean achievement in today's turbulent trading conditions. It therefore gives me great pleasure to write this foreword. The advice and information the book contains will not only ensure high standards of operation, but will provide a means for reducing claims and containing risk. Well presented, in straightforward language and intelligently illustrated, the book has a persuasive authority which will stimulate interest and commitment.

Dr Frank Chao
Chairman, Intercargo;
President, Wah Kwong
Shipping, Hong Kong
November 1993

FOREWORD
to Second Edition

SINCE THE FIRST EDITION OF *Bulk Carrier Practice* was published in 1993, the bulk carrier business has seen some significant changes. During the early 1990s the shipping world saw an alarming increase in the casualty rate within the bulk carrier fleet. Although there was no single common denominator in the casualties, it was predominantly elderly ships carrying heavy cargoes, such as iron ore, which foundered.

In 1994 the then IMO Secretary General William O'Neil took the unprecedented step of submitting his own paper to the Maritime Safety Committee proposing a new agenda item: Bulk Carrier Safety. After years of deliberation the IMO in 1997 adopted a new Chapter XII to SOLAS addressing the problem. A later Formal Safety Assessment study performed between 1998 and 2002 rounded off the task and the casualty statistics of later years have demonstrated significant improvements in the safety of the 'workhorses of the sea'.

The bulk cargo business is, like most other shipping sectors, subjected to variable demand and supply with the entailing fluctuations in freight rates. During the first decade of the 21st century, the business experienced peaks never seen before. The boom was mainly driven by China's unsaturated craving for iron ore which created positive ripples all the way down the bulk carrier industry. However, no peak lasts forever and here at the beginning of the second decade of the 21st century the world is suffering under the credit crunch albeit fortunately with some optimism picking up.

In 1993 the bulk carrier fleet consisted of approximately 5,000 ships. In the beginning of 2010 the number of bulk carriers was close to 7,500, with another almost 3,200 newbuildings expected to enter the market during the coming years. Not only is the number of ships growing, today's bulk carriers are generally significantly larger than their predecessors.

The shipping industry in general is expecting a significant increase in the number of ships in the coming years, which is giving rise to some concern about proper manning with qualified seafarers. The latest BIMCO/ISF Manpower Study from 2005 predicted a lack of 21,000 qualified officers by 2010. This prediction was based on a 1 per cent increase of the world fleet per annum. It was made before the boom in newbuilding orders kicked in and may well prove to be optimistic. The expected lack of qualified officers will not affect all sectors of the shipping industry equally hard, but the bulk carrier sector could well be one which will face a serious challenge in attracting skilled people to run the fleet.

Given this predicament it just emphasises how crucial it is to have someone of Jack Isbester's calibre to share a lifetime of bulk carrier experience with newcomers to the industry. Indeed, anyone in the bulk carrier industry will benefit from reading *Bulk Carrier Practice.* The publication has been updated with all recent, relevant rules and statistics and deserves to be on the bookshelf on the bridge of all bulk carriers, as well as in the offices of all bulk carrier operators.

Although the 'workhorses of the sea' are still mostly invisible to the public at large, they do provide a service without which the modern world as we know it could not function. No matter whether the times are of boom or of bust, successful and profitable business depends on skilful operation of the fleet and this publication should be considered an important tool to that end.

In spite of the complexity of many of the matters addressed in *Bulk Carrier Practice*, the plain language and excellent illustrations makes the publication easily readable and understandable, of vital importance also for seafarers who do not have English as their mother tongue.

Robert Lorenz-Meyer
President and Chairman BIMCO
Managing Partner
Ernst Russ GmbH & Co. KG,
Hamburg

INTRODUCTION
to First Edition

THIS BOOK is an attempt to gather into a single volume all the specialised knowledge and experience which a Master and his deck officers require if they are to operate bulk carriers safely and efficiently. The emphasis throughout is on the dry bulk trades, and matters such as navigation, ship handling and safety have in general been discussed only where they apply specifically to bulk carriers.

The reader has been assumed to have an adequate knowledge of ships, seamanship, navigation, stability and nautical terms, but no previous experience of bulk carriers. Every effort has been made to use plain English for the benefit of the many seafarers for whom English is a second language.

Whilst written primarily for the bulk carrier Master or officer who wants to increase his knowledge, the needs of shipowners, ship operators, nautical college staff, naval architects, marine consultants and surveyors, average adjusters, maritime lawyers and regulatory authorities have not been forgotten. The book contains much in the way of practical operating procedures which is likely to be useful to these categories of reader.

The methods and procedures described are those followed by shipping companies, Masters and senior officers who run hard-working ships with competent officers, adequate manning, and sufficient stores and spares. The standards described are high, but not unrealistic, and are necessary if ships are to be operated safely and efficiently and maintained in good condition.

For readers who have a thorough understanding of bulk carrier operations and simply require a reminder of good working routines, the checklists which end many of the chapters provide an easily readable summary of tasks and procedures. A full explanation of why and how each task is done is to be found in the body of the book, whilst the appendices provide worked examples of calculations and detailed treatment of some specialised matters.

The appendices containing the basic stability calculations have been prepared with care. Every effort has been made to give full guidance as to how these calculations can be completed. They have been provided because the explanations given in loading and stability manuals are often inadequate.

The mv *Regina Oldendorff*, a handy-sized geared bulk carrier has, by kind permission of her owners, been used as an example to illustrate points throughout the book. The range of cargoes for which she was designed and her excellent condition of maintenance made her very suitable for that purpose. My own background and those of the experienced bulk carrier Masters and officers who advised me have ensured that the working practices described in the book are appropriate for all sizes of bulk carrier and not limited to the handy-sized vessel or any other single category.

Several (in the second edition only one) of the builders' drawings of the *Regina Oldendorff* have been reproduced for reference. To fit them in this book they have been much reduced in scale. In general, the comments made about them can be understood without the need to read the small print, but readers who want to study the detail can do so with the help of a magnifying glass, or of an enlarged copy taken with a photocopier.

I had hoped to use standard abbreviations for the stability terms used in the book, but stability manuals from different sources use a bewildering variety of abbreviations for the same value, as is shown in Appendix 10.1. There is an obvious need for international standardisation of abbreviations for stability purposes. In most cases stability terms have in this book been stated in full to avoid confusion.

Metric units have been used throughout the book, with Imperial equivalents also given when they are often used. Although the Systême International d'Unitês (SI) has been the system of measurements adopted officially by the major maritime nations since the 1960s its introduction within shipping has been slow, and it remains normal in the industry to speak of 'weight' rather than 'mass'. I have followed common practice, and written of weight.

The title of this book, *Bulk Carrier Practice,* consciously echoes that of *Tanker Practice* written by Captain G A B King in 1956. Captain King's is an outstanding text book which was welcomed by generations of students, junior officers and newcomers to the business of operating tankers. With the encouragement and help of The Nautical Institute I have sought in this book to provide a similarly authoritative manual for those with an interest in bulk carriers.

There is one significant difference between the shipping industry in the 1950s and that of the 1990s. Captain King wrote for officers drawn, in most cases, from traditional maritime countries with well established schemes for officer training. Nowadays, most officers, particularly on bulk carriers, come from

Third World countries where traditions of training for the sea are more recent and diverse. When providing explanations in this book I have tried not to assume too much knowledge and experience in the reader.

The dry bulk trades, by virtue of the variety of ships used, cargoes carried and ports visited, make considerable demands upon the skill, experience, resourcefulness and determination of those who man the ships. Whilst talking to the many bulk carrier Masters and officers, past and present, who have advised me I have been conscious of their eagerness to pass on their hard-earned expertise, and to help those with less experience to operate their ships safely and competently. That is the main purpose of this book, and to those readers who are serving on bulk carriers, or preparing to do so I send my best wishes for voyages made safer, more efficient, more successful and therefore more enjoyable by a careful reading of the appropriate chapters!

There is always room for improvement in a book such as this and corrections and suggestions for new procedures or material to be included in any possible future edition will be welcome.

Jack Isbester
October 1993

INTRODUCTION
to Second Edition

The First Edition of ***Bulk Carrier Practice*** was three years in the writing but that period pales into insignificance when compared with the seventeen years which have elapsed between the publications of the First and Second Editions. Fortunately much of the book has stood the test of time very well and few amendments have been needed, but I believe that readers will find the Second Edition easier to navigate, better illustrated, updated to reflect changes in regulations and containing a lot of useful additional information.

In 2002 I chose a ship to replace m.v. ***Regina Oldendorff*** as a useful example to illustrate themes throughout the book and spent 17 days aboard her, gathering information with the blessing of owners and managers, only to be told that the builders refused permission for the ship's drawings to be used. ***Regina Oldendorff***, still trading recently under the Chinese flag, therefore remains the ship upon which the book is based and in most respects continues to be suitable. For examples of recent ship construction I have been fortunate to be given copies of the drawings and manuals provided for the Diamond 53 class of double skinned bulk carriers, reproduced on the CD attached to this book and available at www.nautinst.org/BCP and described in Chapters 3 and 18.

The Second Edition, like the First, has benefited considerably from suggestions and advice received from many seafarers and others involved in shipping and will, I hope, be useful to many readers. It continues to present what my colleagues and I consider to be best practice – procedures which are safe, prudent and efficient.

There is always room for improvement in a book such as this and any constructive comments or criticisms from users will be welcomed.

Jack Isbester
October 2009

ACKNOWLEDGEMENTS
to First Edition

A BOOK with the range and depth of *Bulk Carrier Practice* can only do justice to the subject if information is available from numerous sources. It has been my good fortune to write this book for The Nautical Institute, a body with an unrivalled wealth of experience amongst its membership in the operation of bulk carriers. Much of that experience has been put at my disposal by members who have provided information, contacts and advice, and I have been fortunate in receiving generous assistance from a number of very capable and experienced colleagues.

Captain Peter Roberts, BSc, FNI, and **Captain Les Hesketh, MNI,** both serving Shipmasters, have read the entire book chapter by chapter as it was written and provided me with a very considerable number of constructive comments which demonstrate their commitment to best operating standards and the practical approach they both employ. A third serving Shipmaster, **Captain François Hugo, FNI,** spent weeks of his spare time in designing a set of documents for all the standard deadweight, trim, stability and stress calculations, and supporting them with a comprehensive set of worked examples and explanations. He also checked all the other calculations which the book contains.

Captain Peter Boyle, FNI, and **Captain Eric Beetham, FNI, FRSA, FRMetS, FRIN,** like Peter Roberts and Les Hesketh, were members of the Bulk Carrier Working Group which guided the project and gave me much useful advice. In addition Peter Boyle provided much of the information for Chapter 21, whilst Eric Beetham wrote the text and provided the illustrations for the section on combination carriers. **Captain Peter Swift, FNI,** and **Dennis Barber, MNI,** were also members of the Working Group who could be relied upon for prompt information, assistance and support when it was needed.

When seeking a shipowner with a modern versatile handy-sized bulk carrier which I could use to illustrate the text of the book I was fortunate to meet **Mr Henning Oldendorff** of Egon Oldendorff. He and his staff, particularly **Mr D. Kannenberg,** were immensely helpful to me, and it was a pleasure to visit mv *Regina Oldendorff* in Liverpool and to note the immaculate condition in which she was maintained, as illustrated by the photos in the book.

Tony Vlasto and **Paul Dickie,** solicitors with Clifford Chance, provided very necessary advice about the legal aspects of charterparties and cargo documents, and **Captain Richard Evans** brought to my attention many commercial considerations for the same two chapters. **Keith Taylor, BSc, CEng,** managing director of MacGregor-Navire (GBR) Ltd, provided considerable assistance with Chapter 4. **Captain Geoff Cowap, ExC, MPhil, MRIN, MNI,** gave generously of his time to put the hydrostatic characteristics of the *Regina Oldendorff* into a computerised loading program.

I am indebted to many other people for their contributions on particular topics or their assistance in improving my text. Amongst former colleagues from Jebsens Ship Management Ltd I am particularly grateful to **Simon Evans, MIMarE,** for advising me from the chief engineer's point of view, to **Captain Derek Clements, MNI** and to **Captain Steve Barnet, MNI,** for practical information on a variety of topics, to **Captain Tony Gatt, MNI,** for welcoming me aboard mv *Telnes,* and to **Captain Allan Brown, MNI,** for the prompt provision of useful information.

Captain David Greenhalgh, MNI, revealed his experience of log carriers in a letter to *Lloyd's List* and was then prevailed upon to provide notes on that subject for the book. **David Phipps** of Arlona Engineering in Durban supplied notes upon the cocooning of cargoes and the use of grabs. **David Robinson, BSc, CEng, MRINA,** a principal surveyor at Lloyd's Register and chairman of the IACS working party on hull damages, and his colleagues provided much useful advice on safe loading procedures and the avoidance of damage to bulk carriers.

Dr Ian Dand, CEng, BSc, PhD, FRINA gave advice and encouragement on Chapter 8. **John Stott, CEng, MA, BSc, MIMarE, FInstR,** improved my words on ventilation and applied his usual scrupulous standards to the text. **Captain Ken Harper, FNI,** provided invaluable notes on the measurement and transportation of forest products, and for authoritative advice on the carriage of steel I was able to consult **Arthur Sparks, MNI. Jerry Colman, FRINA, MRIN, CEng,** and his colleagues provided advice on several stability matters, and on bulk carrier losses.

Captain Kelvin Ferries, MNI, supplied information about Munck gantries, whilst **Captains John Houghton, FNI,** and **Gordon Mackie, FNI,** gave me data and advice about weather routeing services. To **Captains Angus McDonald, FNI, François Baillod, MNI, Andrew Tinsley, MNI, John David, MNI,** and **Gordon Blythe, MNI,** I am indebted for thoughtful advice based upon their varied personal experience. **Douglas Foy, FNI,** has a long and creditable record of drawing attention to the scandal of bulk carrier losses, and I have been encouraged by his support and assistance. The Nautical Institute's *Seaways* magazine, and in particular its letters section, has also been enormously useful to me as a source of sound professional opinion.

For advice, information and encouragement I am grateful to **Captain Tim Lant, Mr O. H. J. Dijxhoorn** of the IMO, **Donald J. Sheetz, MNI, Captains Iain Steverson, MNI, Chris Colchester, MNI,** and **Sam Household, FNI,** to **David Ralph** of the DOT and **Derek Maidment** of BMT Cortec Ltd, to **Richard Clarke, BComm, MNI, Kenneth Long, BSc, FICS, FNI, MCIT, Phil Anderson, FNI,** and **Karl Lumbers, MNI**.

I am deeply indebted to **Julian Parker, BSc, FNI,** Secretary of The Nautical Institute, for his unfailing support and encouragement during the three years during which this project has matured, to **David Sanders, ExC, FNI,** production editor, for his skill in making the very best of the material provided, and to **Lieutenant-Commander Mike Plumridge, FNI, RN,** Deputy Secretary, for arranging for my attendance at several relevant seminars.

To **Captain Peter Lyon, FRIN, MNI,** my partner at Eagle Lyon Pope Associates, I offer my thanks for the patience and generosity with which he has accepted my extended absence from our consultancy–a period during which our office became, for me, hardly more than a photocopying agency! I am also grateful to him for improvements to Chapter 11–The Loading/Discharging Berth.

My wife **Audrey** is no expert on bulk carriers, and her contribution to the book cannot be identified within its pages. However, the book would never have been written were it not for the generosity, tolerance and equanimity with which she kept the household running during the last three years even accepting, with hardly a hint of protest, that when we went on holiday the word processor went with us! I owe her a very substantial debt of gratitude.

My debt to all those mentioned above, and to any others I may have forgotten, is considerable. If the book contains errors the fault is mine.

Jack Isbester
October 1993

Photographs and diagrams

Diagrams drawn by David Henderson. Additional artwork by Brian Mehl.

ACKNOWLEDGEMENTS for the Second Edition

THE SECOND EDITION OF ***Bulk Carrier Practice***, like the First, has benefited from the information and advice provided by many Nautical Institute members and also by numerous other well disposed members of the international shipping community during the long period that this work has been under revision. **Captain Les Hesketh, FNI,** a former bulk carrier Master now serving as a ship inspector with the UK P&I Club has repeated the work which he undertook for the First Edition and read and commented on every chapter as it was rewritten. A similar service has been performed by **Niels Bjørn Mortensen, Master Mariner, Naval Architect, BSc, MRINA,** Head of BIMCO Marine Department and formerly an officer serving in bulk carriers as well as designing bulk carriers at Burmeister & Wain Shipyard, who, besides providing many valuable comments and contacts, enabled me to consult his colleagues, in particular **Captain Nicholas A Mahony,** when they had relevant specialist knowledge. **Captain Nicholas Cooper FNI,** recently President of The Nautical Institute, and a former bulk carrier Master, also read and commented on almost every chapter. The interest, enthusiasm and commitment shown by these three gentlemen over a number of years has been a comfort and inspiration to me. **Mathieu Baehni,** Operations and Safety and Quality Manager, Enzian Ship Management AG, has thought critically about the ships and cargoes for which he is responsible and his searching questions and perceptive comments have helped to improve the book in a number of places. **Captains Ian Mathison FNI, Director Marine and Safety, Bibby Ship Management Ltd.** and **Graham Pepper,** Reviser of *Thomas' Stowage,* also read much of the text and provided useful comments for which I am grateful.

With the help of **Captain Kaare Lønningen,** recently of Star Shipping AS of Bergen, I was able to make voyages aboard mv *Star Istind* commanded by **Captain Phelipe Reyes** and mv *Star Sea Cosmos* – **Captain Bonofacio Gerochi Jr. Captain Richard Evans** of Mitsui OSK Bulk Shipping (Europe) Ltd arranged for me to sail with mv *Brilliant Arc* – **Captain Danilo G Faustino,** and **Chresten Boelt,** Marine Manager at Aalborg Portland, enabled my voyage aboard m.v. *Kongsdal* with **Captain Ole Espensen**. I was encouraged by **Dimitrios Fafalios** of Fafalios Limited to visit mv *Amazon* – **Captain Konstantinos Psaradakis,** in Barcelona and by **Gunnar Bjørknes** of Spar Shipping AS to spend time aboard mv *Spar Scorpio* in Tilbury, where my host was **Captain Saji Kurian**. To all these gentlemen I am much indebted for helping me to observe current equipment and procedures.

I am indebted to **Michael Schmidt**, Project Manager at that time with Carl Bro AS, for encouragement to use drawings and information relating to Diamond 53 double skinned bulk carriers and to **Jarle Ellefsen** Managing Director of Spar Shipping AS, for permission to use drawings and manuals issued to mv *Spar Scorpio.* **Henrik Vibe-Hastrup** of Carl Bro AS was generous with time spent to prepare manuals and calculations for reproduction and **N. Y. Wang** of TTS Hua Hai Ships Equipment provided plans of folding hatch covers. **Torbjörn Dahl**, Senior Naval Architect, Bulk Ships at MacGregor (Finland) Oy provided considerable advice and assistance with Chapter 4: Hatch Covers and **Peter Bryson**, now with Teekay Shipping, wrote an outstanding paper on maintenance of the structural integrity of bulk carriers on which I have drawn extensively in Chapters 23 and 24.

Captain M.G. Fothergill, FNI provided expert advice on lumber deck cargoes and **Karl Lumbers FNI**, Loss Prevention Director of the UK P&I Club gave me helpful access to the Club's advice on the carriage of grain. Invaluable practical advice on a variety of new or revisited issues was provided by **Tom Konow** of Jebsen Management AS; **Walter Vervloesem ANI** of IMCS; **Captain François Hugo FNI** of Warsash Maritime Academy; **Captain Robert W Sinclair MNI, MCIT, MRMetS, MIAMA** of Orion Marine Surveyors; **Captain Eric H Beetham FNI, FRSA, FRMetS, FRIN**; **Dagfinn Asmyhr** of the Torvald Klaveness Group; **Captain Richard Dixon MNI**; **Arthur Sparks** of Sparks & Company; **Jim Wallace**, Technical Manager of Sigma Coatings; **Simon W Evans CEng MIMarEST MCMS** of APB Marine; **Dr Ian W Dand** of BMT Sea Tech Ltd; **Captain Tom McLean MNI, MIIMS** of McLean Marine; **Ian Shipley MNI** of Captain G A Chettle & Associates; **Captain Richard Whistler, MNI**; **Mike Tysoe** of Jebsens (London) Ltd; **Captain Andrew Tinsley MNI**; **Captain David Greenhalgh MNI**; **Captain Thierry Rossignol** and **Captain Peter Bruce** of Tonand Marine (Aust) Pty Ltd.

The late **Captain François Baillod, FNI**, a thoughtful and committed Shipmaster, provided valuable insights on shiphandling in heavy weather and a number of other issues. The deaths of **Doug Foy** and **John Stott, CEng, MA, BSc, MIMarE, FInstR,** both significant influences in the First Edition are recorded with regret.

Julian Clark, now of Holman Fenwick & Willan, **Paul Dickie** of Prettys and staff at BIMCO provided helpful advice for Chapter 2: Charterparties, and **Anders Gustafson Swerke** and **Roald Vaarheim** of Det Norske Veritas provided detailed information on the carriage of steel coils. **Christian Strobel**, Senior Maritime Adviser to the same organisation, also provided much useful practical information.

Captain John R Knott BA FCMS FNI BACS; **Papoulidis Panagiotis MNI**; **Captain Mike Pickthorne, MNI**; **Captain L R Stewart MNI**; **Captain S Nandakumar MNI**; **Captain Peter Roberts BSc FNI** and **D Hachmann**, formerly with Expert Shipping Service Hans-Otto Ebner, all provided useful comments on the First Edition and these have been reflected in additions and amendments to the Second Edition.

Roger Holt, Consultant Director of Intercargo and **Colin Wright**, Principal Technical Officer, IACS Permanent Secretariat have provided welcome advice on a variety of topics and **Captain Shridhar Nivas MNI** of the MASSA Maritime Academy has given me useful feedback from officers serving in bulk carriers.

Captain Georgios Sakulias aboard m.v. *Thalassina Kyra*, **Vladimir Kis**, Chief Mate of m.v. *Stepan Razin*, **Vladimir Mel'nikov**, Chief Mate m.v. *Alexander Tvardovskiy*, **Captain Matti Viljakainen** of m.v. *Arkadia* and **Captain E Dovgal** of m.v. *Khudozhnik Moor* were all helpful and hospitable when I arrived unannounced aboard their vessels.

Captains Jim McNamara and **Philip Anderson, MNI, MIIMS** of the National Cargo Bureau and **Mark L. Kaminski** of the National Cargo Bureau, **Captains Jan Zwaan, MM** and **Alan Knight, FNI** of Transport Canada Marine Safety and **Nick Quarmby** and **David Foggie** of the Maritime and Coastguard Agency gave me welcome and willing assistance with the regulations of their respective administrations and **Captain Ashok Mahapatra MNI** assisted me at the International Maritime Organization.

I have gratefully received assistance and support from **Captain Chris Collings, MNI** and former colleagues at Eagle Lyon Pope, from **Bill Finnie** at TMC (Marine Consultants) Ltd, from **Captain Ian R Blair** with Brookes Bell, from **Captain Dennis Barber FNI**, with MARICO Marine Ltd, from **Captain Nic Paines MNI, MRIN, MBACS, FCMS of Newman Giles**, and from **Captain Tony Amoratis** of Scanautics Marine Experts SA.

For product information I am indebted to **Spiros A Malliaroudakis BSc MSc SNAME(M)** of S A Malliaroudakis Maritime Ltd.: to **Lars Austad** of Unitor Chemicals AS; to John Roberts of RBM HoldSolutions; to **Ross Freeman** of Wilhelmsen Ships Service (UK) and to **Jahn Stryken** of EMS Ship Supply (Norway) AS who gave me advice, encouragement and a variety of useful introductions.

The Nautical Institute has accepted the slow progress of the book's revision with patience and understanding and I am most grateful to **Julian Parker OBE FNI** for his friendship, support, advice and encouragement from the start of the project, over twenty years ago, to **Bridget Hogan, Director of Publishing and Marketing** for the speed with which she has adopted the flexibility and tolerance which I associate with The Nautical Institute, to **Philip Wake MSc FNI, David Patraiko MBA FNI** and to **Claire Walsh BA, MA, CNI** for their assistance and support over the years since 1994 when a second edition was first proposed. **Jim Judd**, typesetter, has been unfailingly patient and helpful in the long years during which we have collaborated and I have admired and valued his skills.

My friend **Dave Skinner** has lightened the administrative load elsewhere in my life to allow me time to complete the book and the help he has given with my computer problems has been invaluable. For this support I am most grateful.

My wife **Audrey** still knows little about bulk carriers except that everything connected with them seems to move at a boringly sedate pace. It remains true that without her tolerance, good humour and positive and practical support throughout our years together this book could never have been written.

My debt to all those mentioned above or in the Acknowledgments for the First Edition, and to any others I may have forgotten, is considerable. If the book contains errors the fault is mine.

Jack Isbester

October 2009

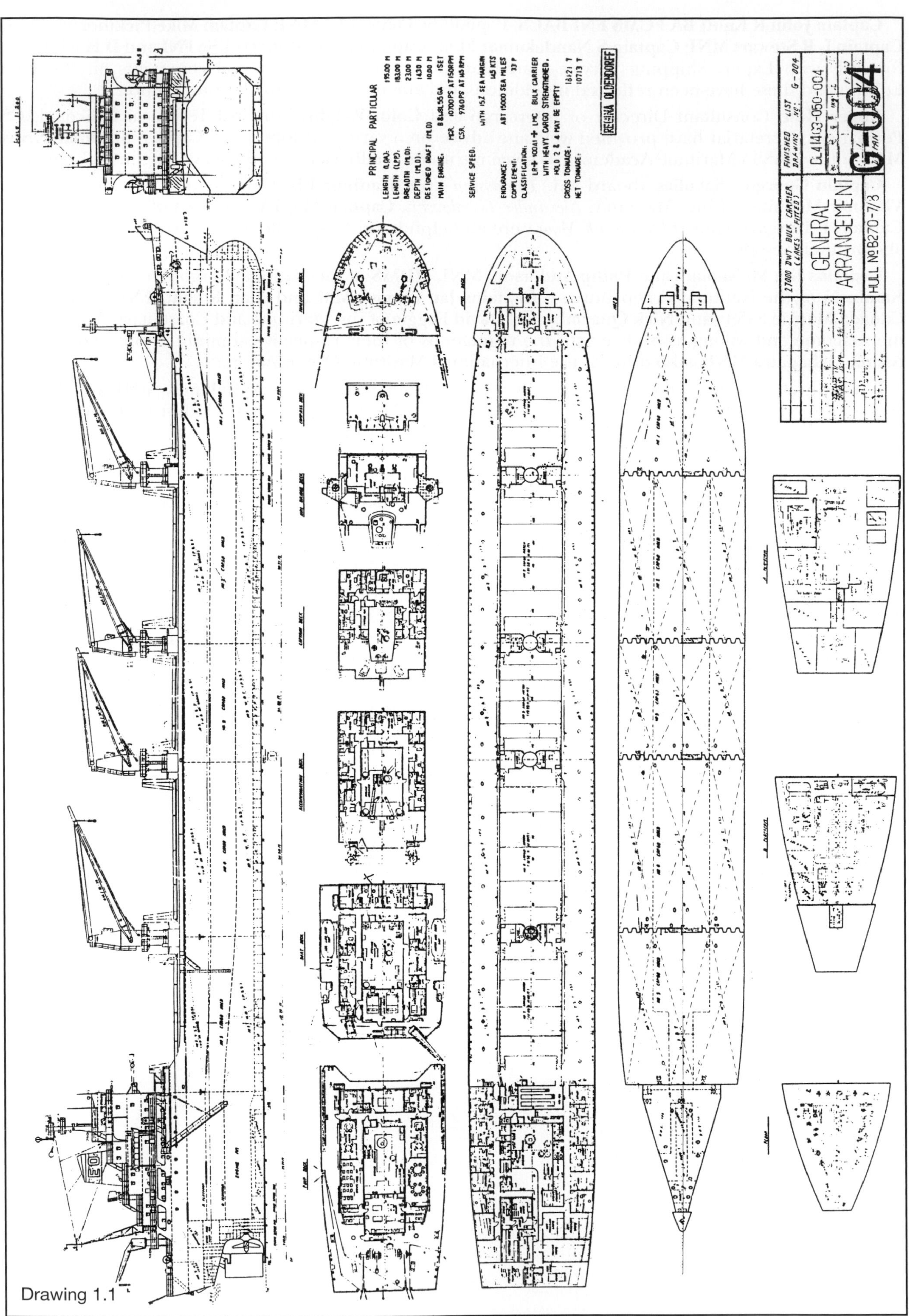
SCALE 1:200
PRINCIPAL PARTICULAR
LENGTH (LOA): 195.00 M
LENGTH (LPP): 183.00 M
BREADTH (MLD): 23.00 M
DEPTH (MLD): 14.30 M
DESIGNED DRAFT (MLD): 10.00 M
MAIN ENGINE: B&W 8L55GA 1SET
MCR. 10700PS AT 150RPM
CSR. 9760PS AT 145RPM
SERVICE SPEED: WITH 15% SEA MARGIN 14.5 KTS
ENDURANCE: ABT 15000 SEA MILES
COMPLEMENT: 33 P
CLASSIFICATION: LR✠100A1 ✠ LMC BULK CARRIER WITH HEAVY CARGO STRENGTHENED, HOLD 2 & 4 MAY BE EMPTY
GROSS TONNAGE: 18121 T
NET TONNAGE: 10713 T
REGINA OLDENDORFF
27000 DWT BULK CARRIER (LAKES-FITTED)
GENERAL ARRANGEMENT
HULL No B270-7/8
FINISHED DRAWING LIST NO: G-004
D.41403-050-004
G-004
Drawing 1.1

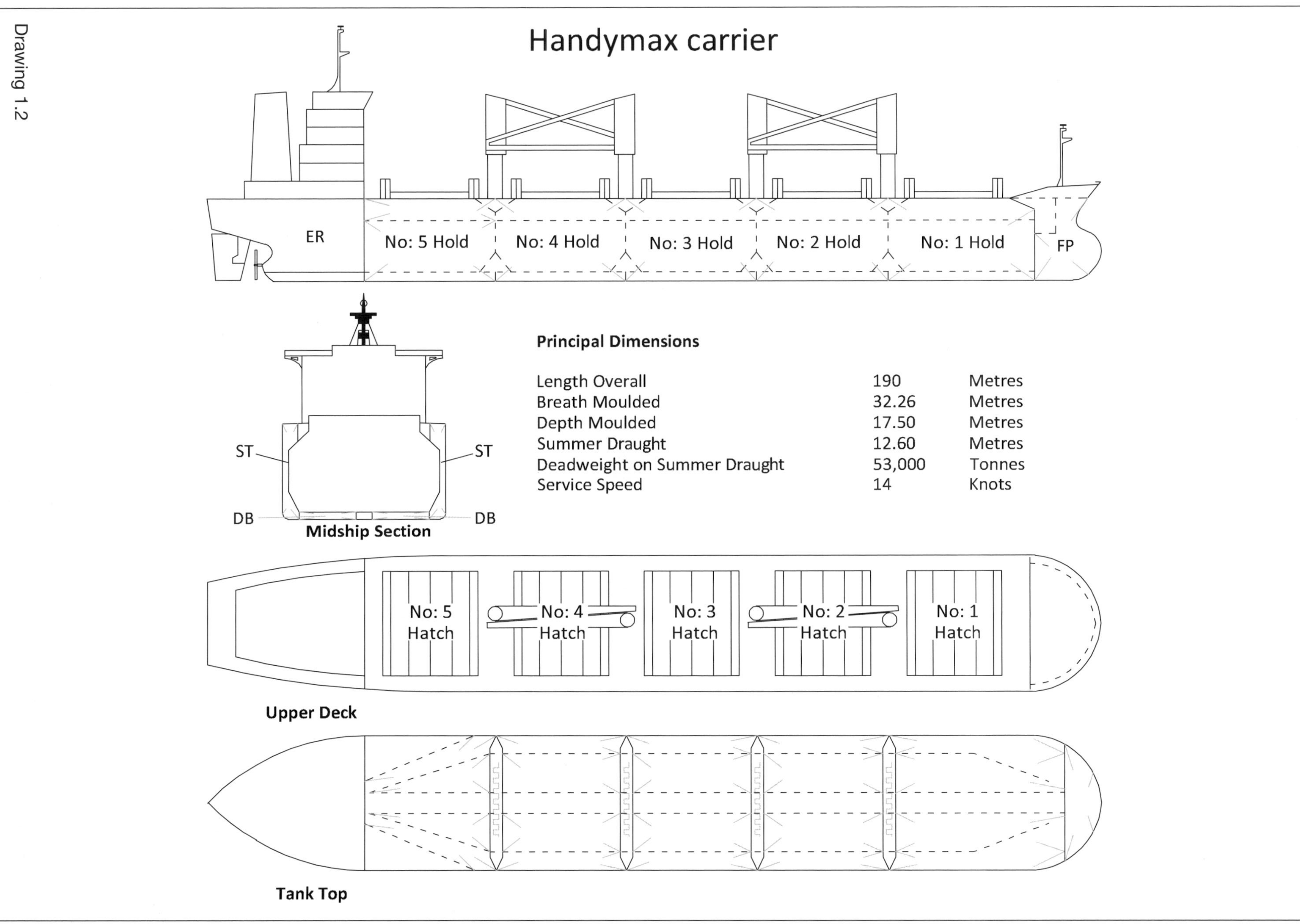

Handymax carrier
ER
No: 5 Hold
No: 4 Hold
No: 3 Hold
No: 2 Hold
No: 1 Hold
FP
ST
ST
DB
DB
Midship Section
Principal Dimensions
Length Overall 190 Metres
Breath Moulded 32.26 Metres
Depth Moulded 17.50 Metres
Summer Draught 12.60 Metres
Deadweight on Summer Draught 53,000 Tonnes
Service Speed 14 Knots
No: 5 Hatch
No: 4 Hatch
No: 3 Hatch
No: 2 Hatch
No: 1 Hatch
Upper Deck
Tank Top

Drawing 1.2

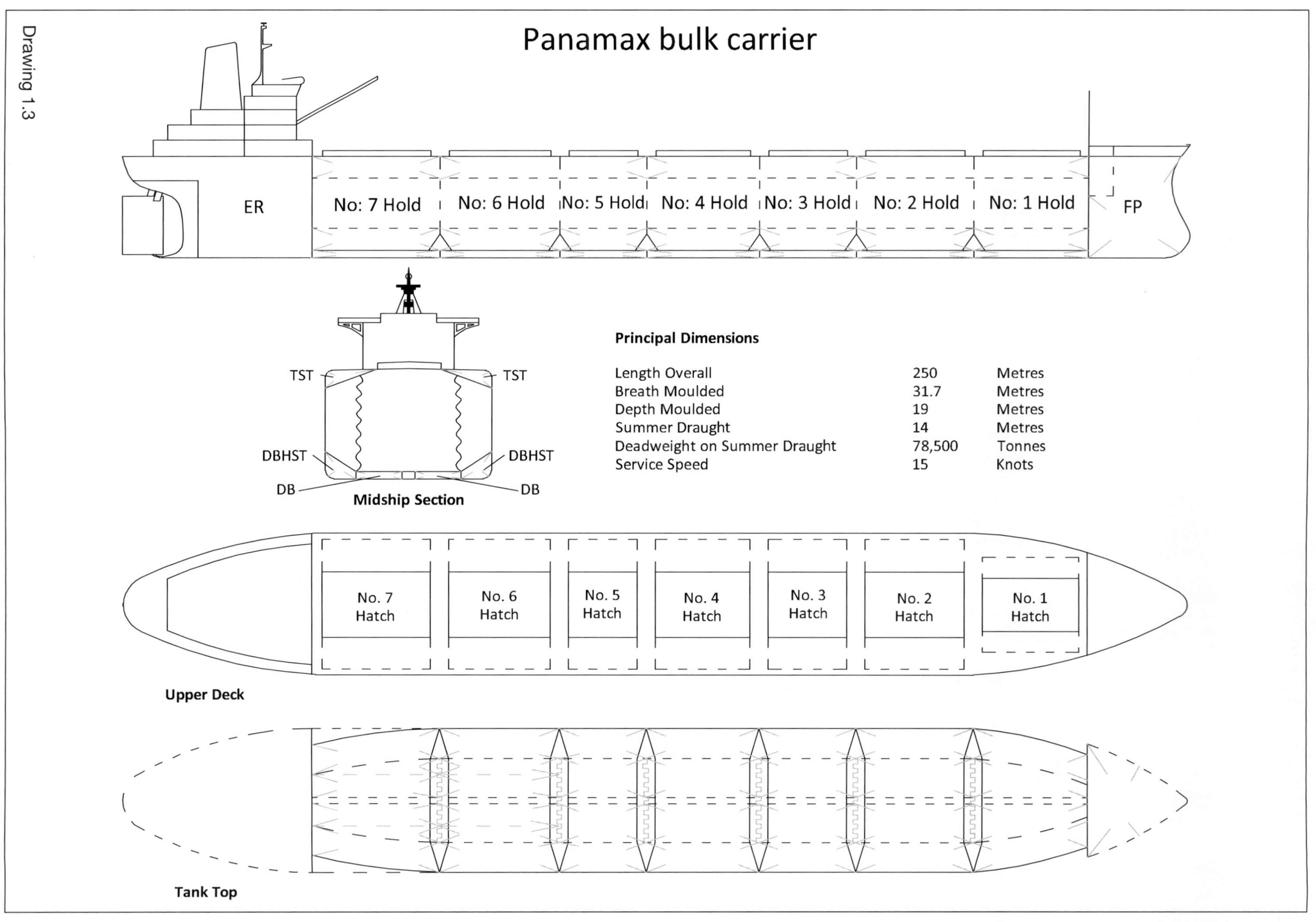

Panamax bulk carrier
ER
No: 7 Hold
No: 6 Hold
No: 5 Hold
No: 4 Hold
No: 3 Hold
No: 2 Hold
No: 1 Hold
FP
TST
TST
DBHST
DBHST
DB
DB
Midship Section
Principal Dimensions
Length Overall 250 Metres
Breath Moulded 31.7 Metres
Depth Moulded 19 Metres
Summer Draught 14 Metres
Deadweight on Summer Draught 78,500 Tonnes
Service Speed 15 Knots
No. 7 Hatch
No. 6 Hatch
No. 5 Hatch
No. 4 Hatch
No. 3 Hatch
No. 2 Hatch
No. 1 Hatch
Upper Deck
Tank Top

Drawing 1.3

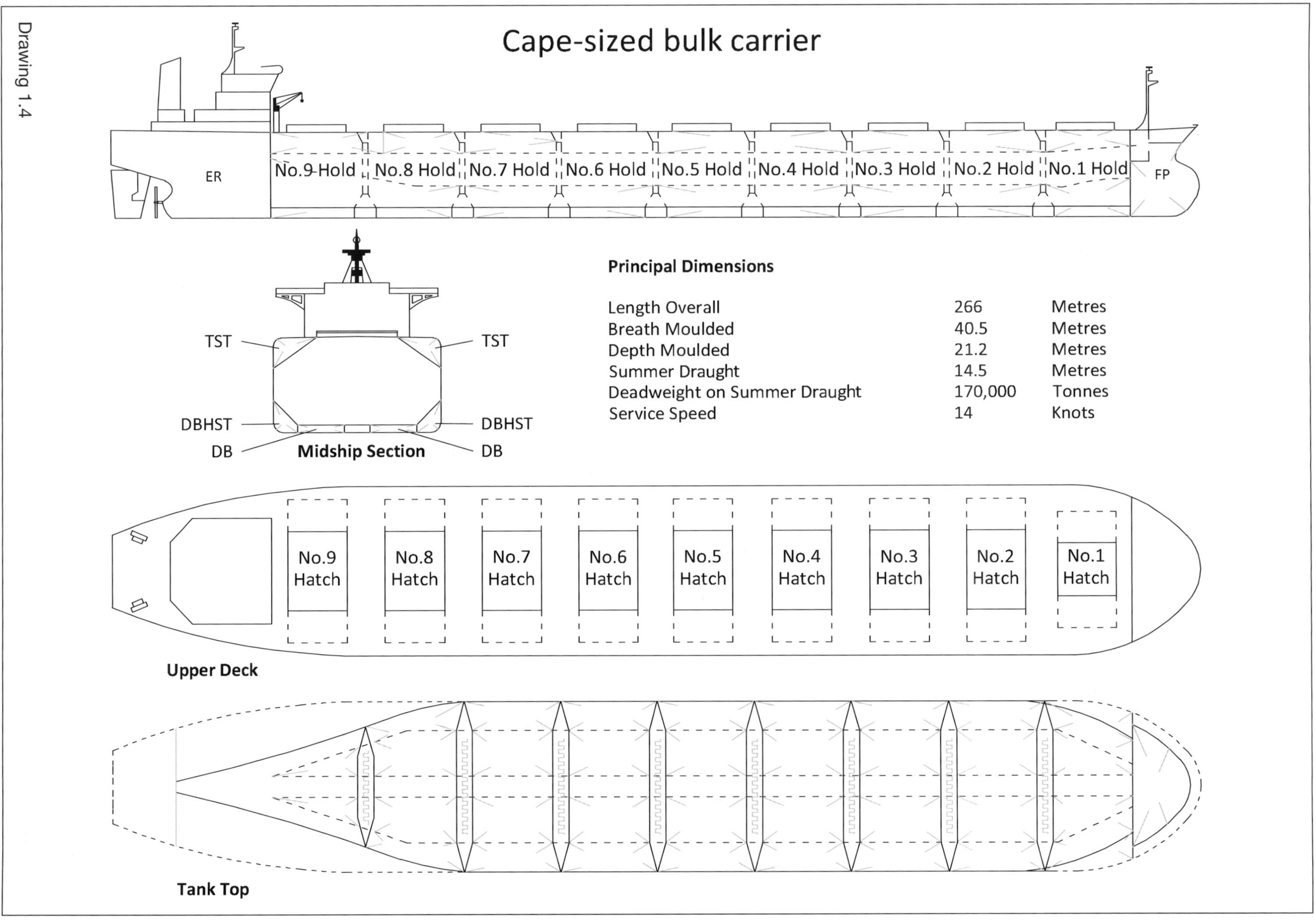
Cape-sized bulk carrier
ER
No.9 Hold
No.8 Hold
No.7 Hold
No.6 Hold
No.5 Hold
No.4 Hold
No.3 Hold
No.2 Hold
No.1 Hold
FP
Principal Dimensions
Length Overall 266 Metres
Breath Moulded 40.5 Metres
Depth Moulded 21.2 Metres
Summer Draught 14.5 Metres
Deadweight on Summer Draught 170,000 Tonnes
Service Speed 14 Knots
TST
TST
DBHST
DBHST
DB
DB
Midship Section
No.9 Hatch
No.8 Hatch
No.7 Hatch
No.6 Hatch
No.5 Hatch
No.4 Hatch
No.3 Hatch
No.2 Hatch
No.1 Hatch
Upper Deck
Tank Top

Drawing 1.4

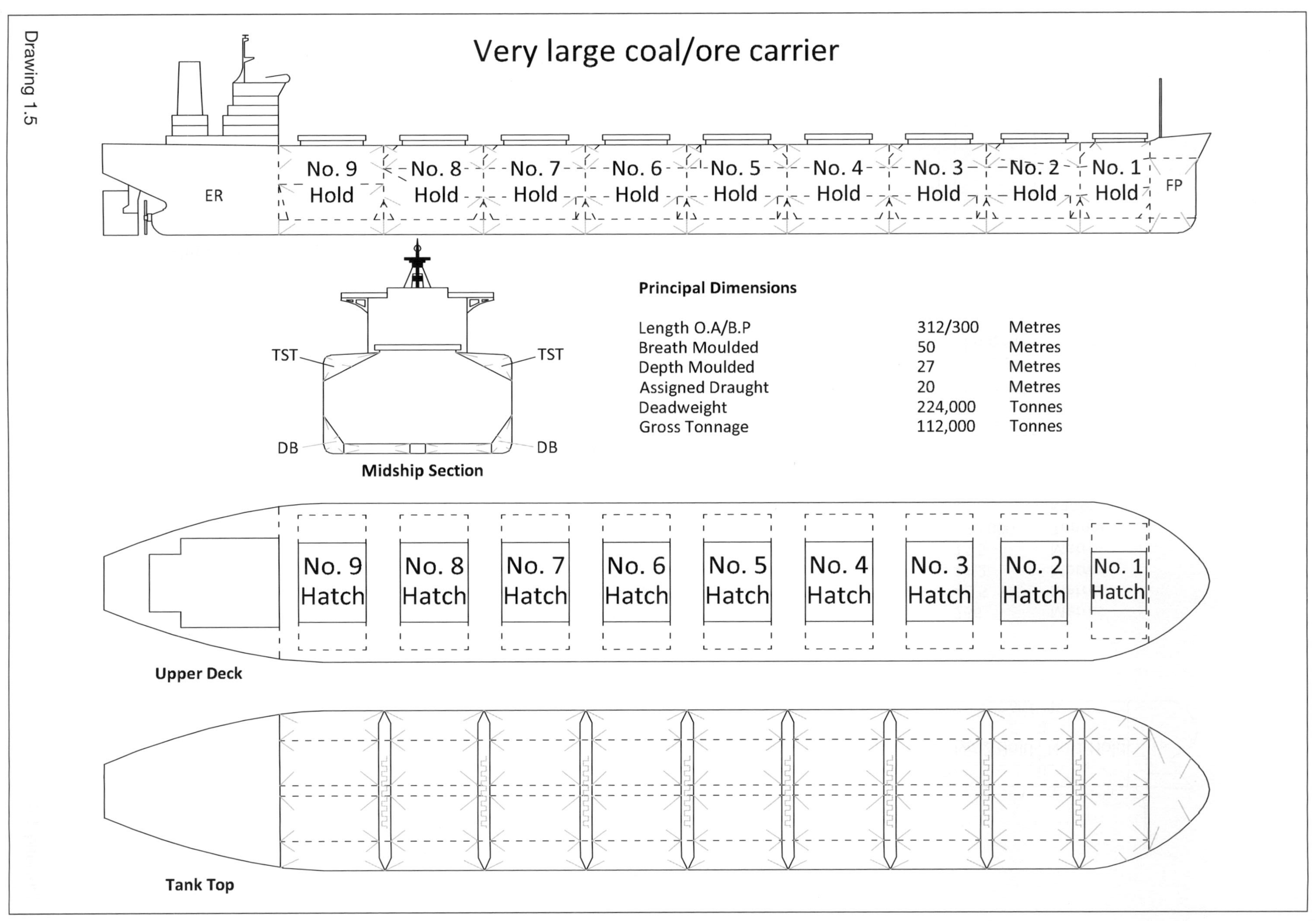

Very large coal/ore carrier
ER
No. 9 Hold
No. 8 Hold
No. 7 Hold
No. 6 Hold
No. 5 Hold
No. 4 Hold
No. 3 Hold
No. 2 Hold
No. 1 Hold
FP
TST
TST
DB
DB
Midship Section
Principal Dimensions
Length O.A/B.P 312/300 Metres
Breath Moulded 50 Metres
Depth Moulded 27 Metres
Assigned Draught 20 Metres
Deadweight 224,000 Tonnes
Gross Tonnage 112,000 Tonnes
No. 9 Hatch
No. 8 Hatch
No. 7 Hatch
No. 6 Hatch
No. 5 Hatch
No. 4 Hatch
No. 3 Hatch
No. 2 Hatch
No. 1 Hatch
Upper Deck
Tank Top

Drawing 1.5

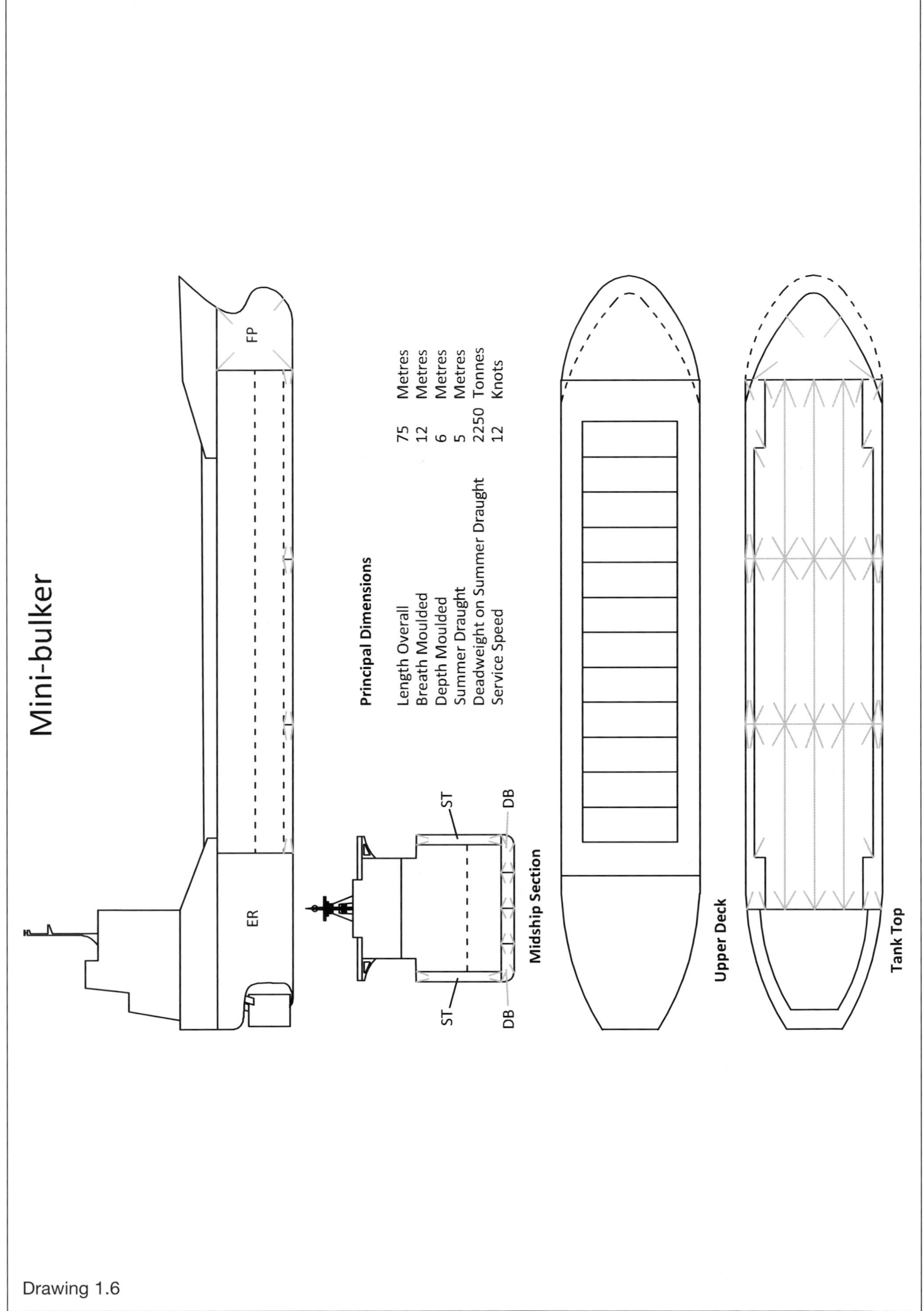
Mini-bulker
FP
ER
ST
ST
DB
DB
Midship Section
Principal Dimensions
Length Overall 75 Metres
Breath Moulded 12 Metres
Depth Moulded 6 Metres
Summer Draught 5 Metres
Deadweight on Summer Draught 2250 Tonnes
Service Speed 12 Knots
Upper Deck
Tank Top

Drawing 1.6

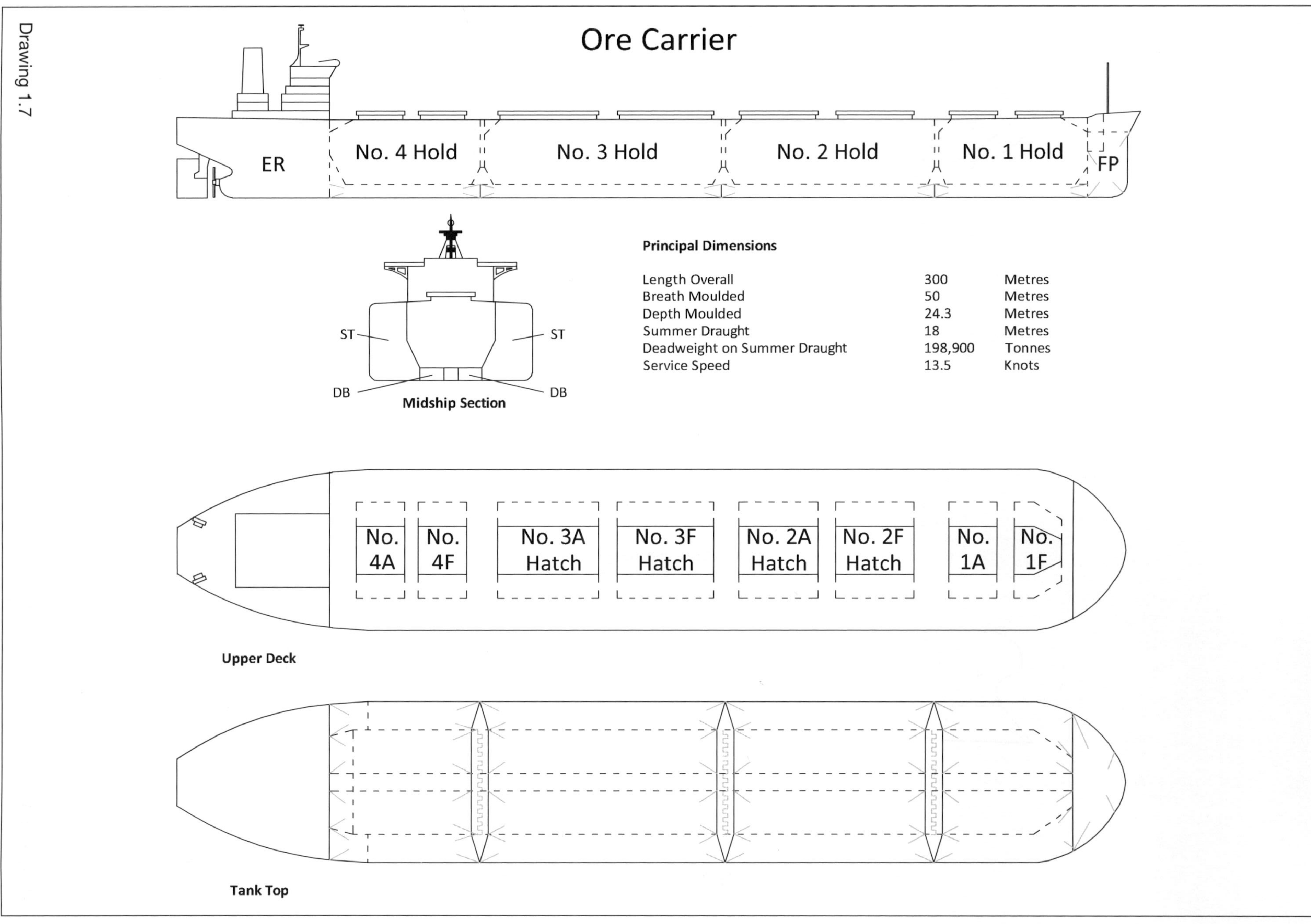
Ore Carrier
ER
No. 4 Hold
No. 3 Hold
No. 2 Hold
No. 1 Hold
FP
ST
ST
DB
DB
Midship Section
Principal Dimensions
Length Overall 300 Metres
Breath Moulded 50 Metres
Depth Moulded 24.3 Metres
Summer Draught 18 Metres
Deadweight on Summer Draught 198,900 Tonnes
Service Speed 13.5 Knots
No. 4A
No. 4F
No. 3A Hatch
No. 3F Hatch
No. 2A Hatch
No. 2F Hatch
No. 1A
No. 1F
Upper Deck
Tank Top

Drawing 1.7

Drawing 1.8

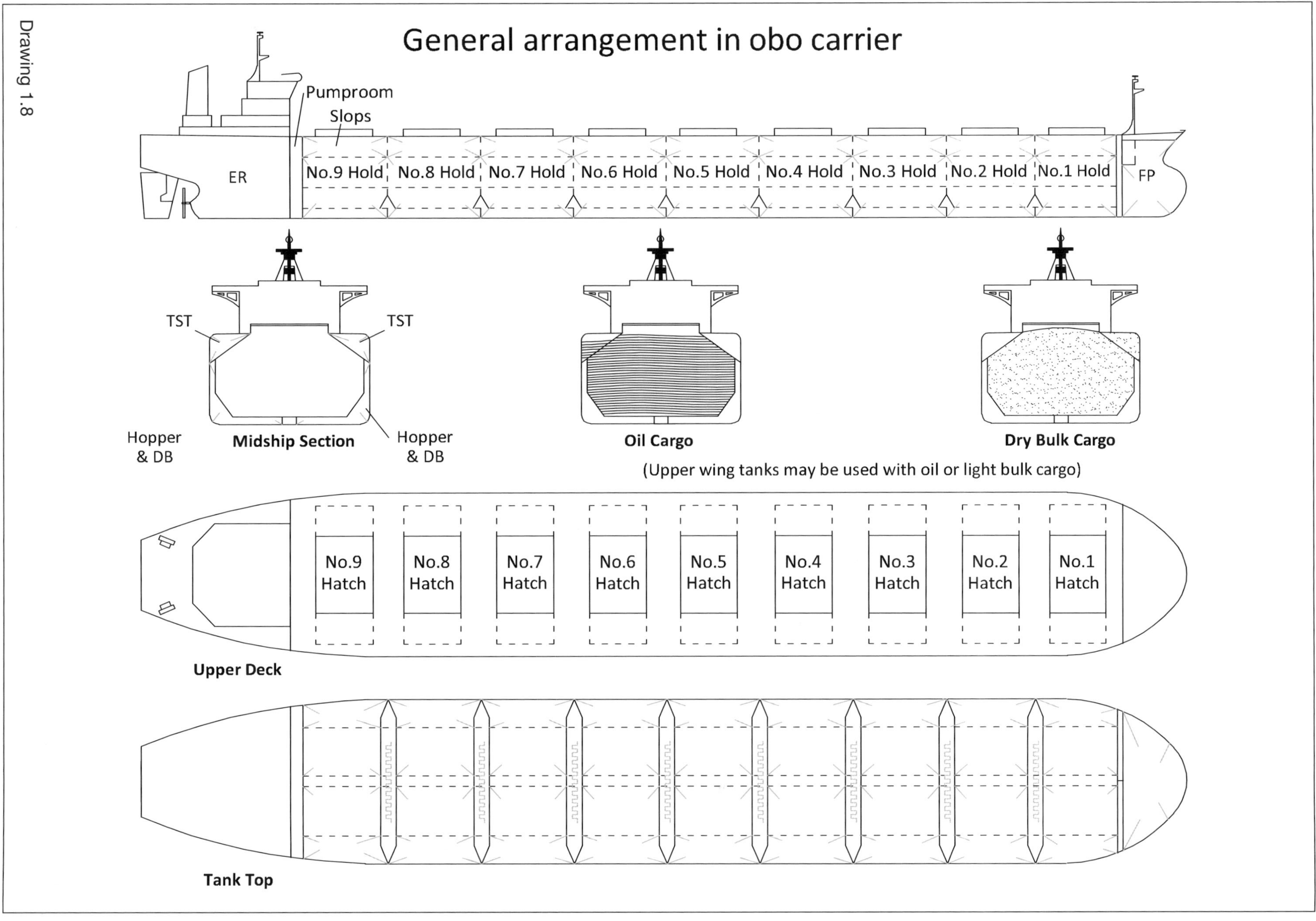

General arrangement in obo carrier
Pumproom
Slops
ER
No.9 Hold
No.8 Hold
No.7 Hold
No.6 Hold
No.5 Hold
No.4 Hold
No.3 Hold
No.2 Hold
No.1 Hold
FP
TST
TST
Hopper & DB
Midship Section
Hopper & DB
Oil Cargo
Dry Bulk Cargo
(Upper wing tanks may be used with oil or light bulk cargo)
No.9 Hatch
No.8 Hatch
No.7 Hatch
No.6 Hatch
No.5 Hatch
No.4 Hatch
No.3 Hatch
No.2 Hatch
No.1 Hatch
Upper Deck
Tank Top

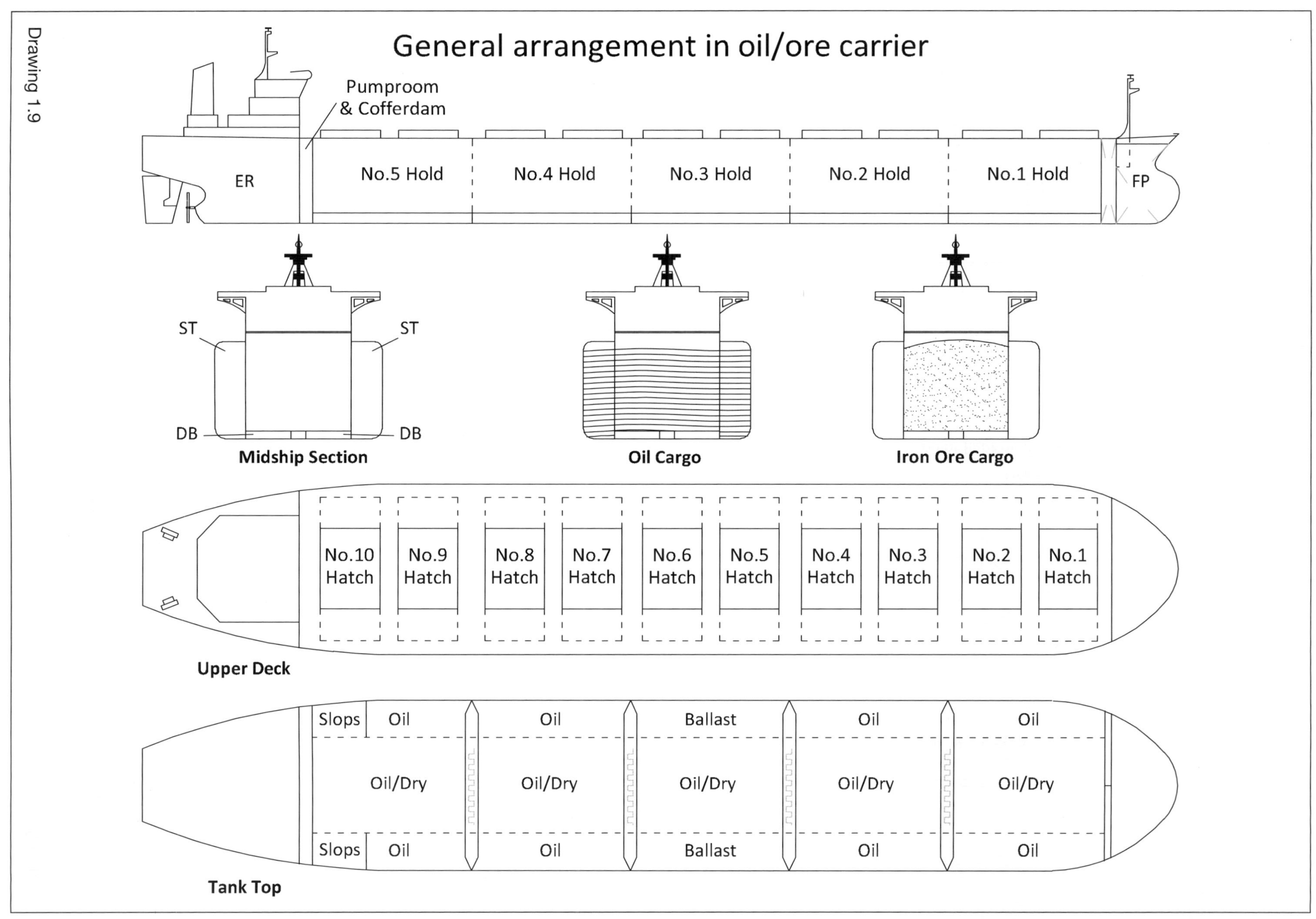
General arrangement in oil/ore carrier
Pumproom
& Cofferdam
ER
No.5 Hold
No.4 Hold
No.3 Hold
No.2 Hold
No.1 Hold
FP
ST
ST
DB
DB
Midship Section
Oil Cargo
Iron Ore Cargo
No.10 Hatch
No.9 Hatch
No.8 Hatch
No.7 Hatch
No.6 Hatch
No.5 Hatch
No.4 Hatch
No.3 Hatch
No.2 Hatch
No.1 Hatch
Upper Deck
Slops
Oil
Oil
Ballast
Oil
Oil
Oil/Dry
Oil/Dry
Oil/Dry
Oil/Dry
Oil/Dry
Slops
Oil
Oil
Ballast
Oil
Oil
Tank Top

Drawing 1.9

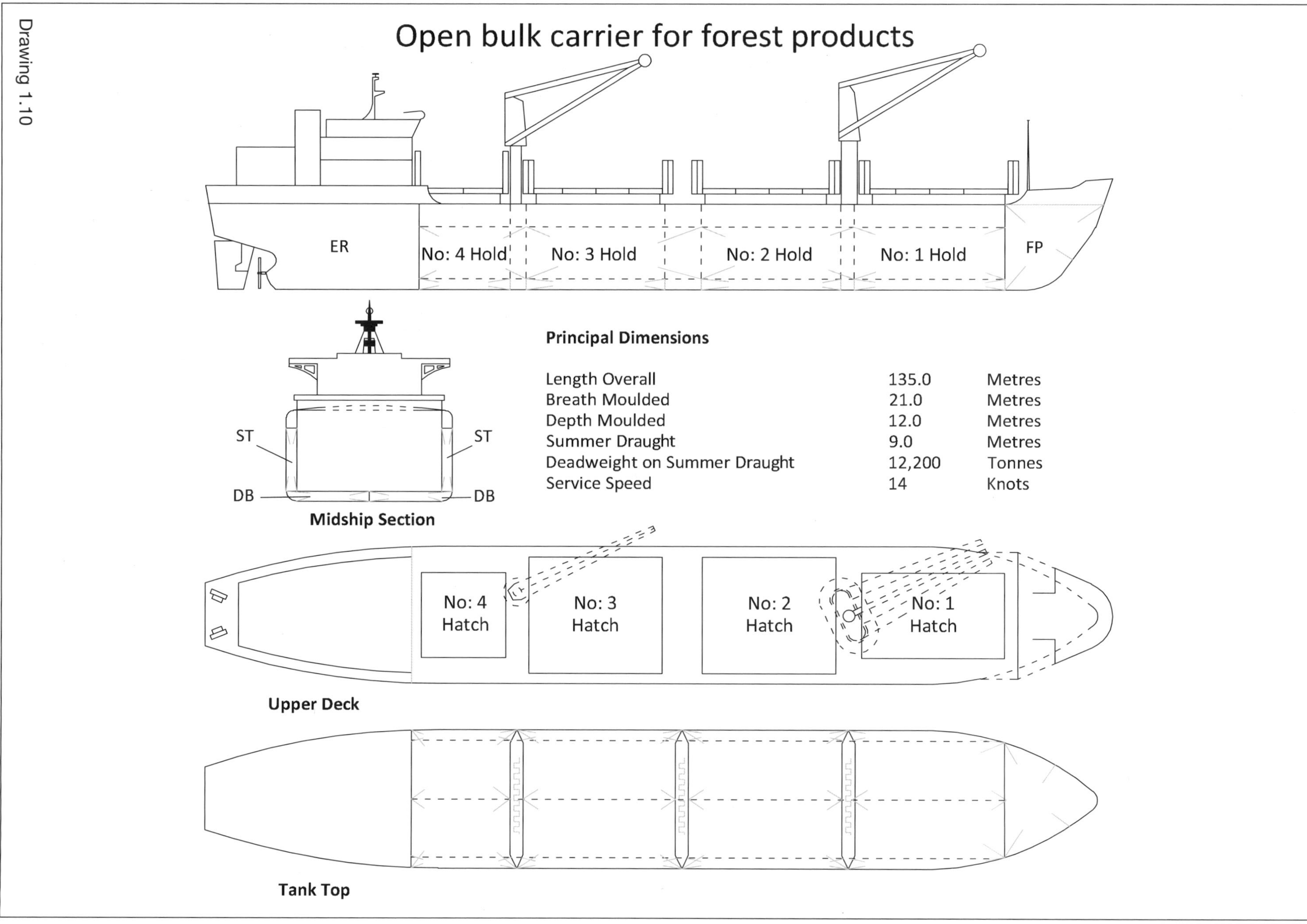
Open bulk carrier for forest products
ER
No: 4 Hold
No: 3 Hold
No: 2 Hold
No: 1 Hold
FP
Principal Dimensions
Length Overall 135.0 Metres
Breath Moulded 21.0 Metres
Depth Moulded 12.0 Metres
Summer Draught 9.0 Metres
Deadweight on Summer Draught 12,200 Tonnes
Service Speed 14 Knots
ST
ST
DB
DB
Midship Section
No: 4 Hatch
No: 3 Hatch
No: 2 Hatch
No: 1 Hatch
Upper Deck
Tank Top

Drawing 1.10

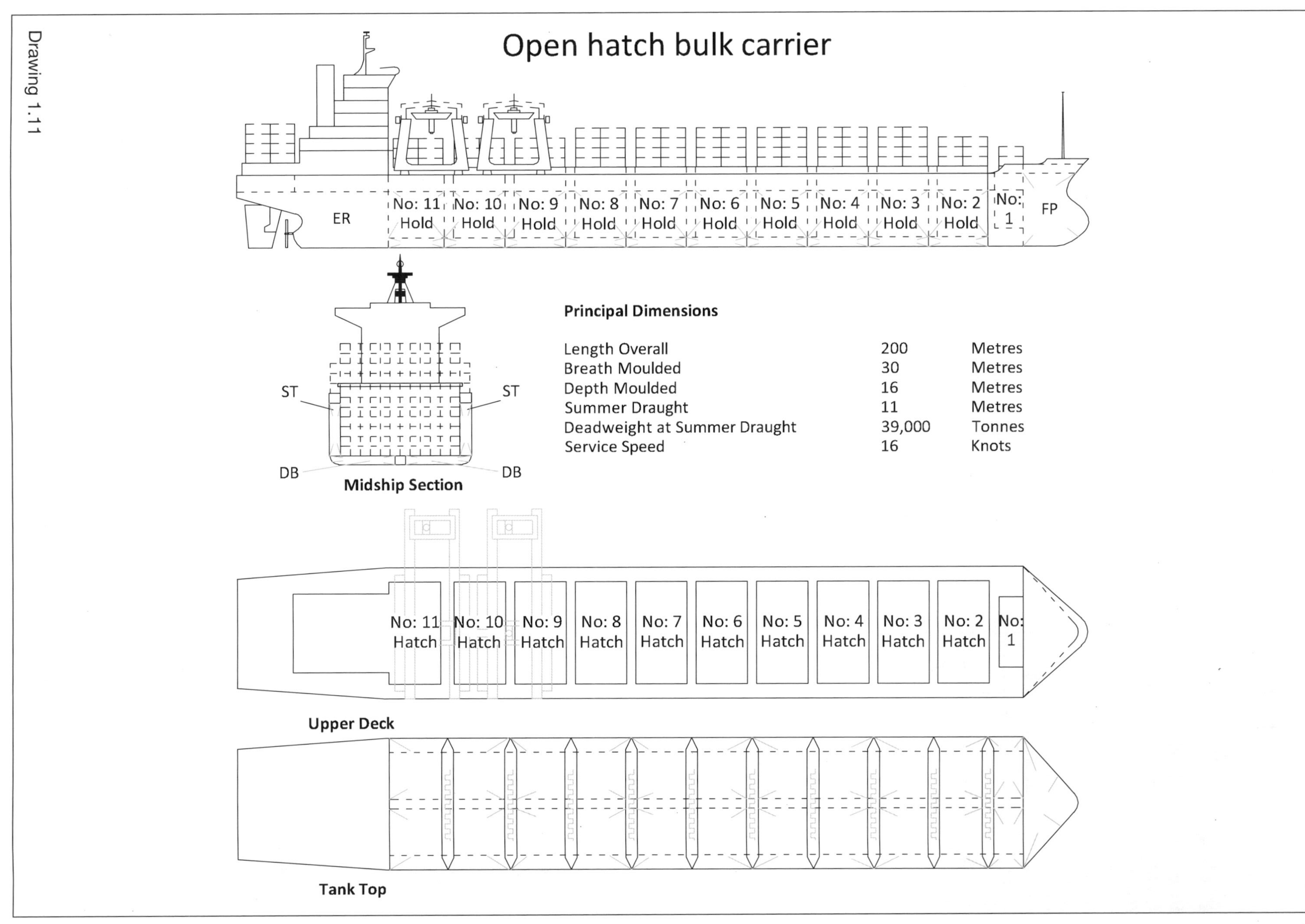

Open hatch bulk carrier
ER
No: 11 Hold
No: 10 Hold
No: 9 Hold
No: 8 Hold
No: 7 Hold
No: 6 Hold
No: 5 Hold
No: 4 Hold
No: 3 Hold
No: 2 Hold
No: 1
FP
ST
ST
DB
DB
Midship Section
Principal Dimensions
Length Overall 200 Metres
Breath Moulded 30 Metres
Depth Moulded 16 Metres
Summer Draught 11 Metres
Deadweight at Summer Draught 39,000 Tonnes
Service Speed 16 Knots
No: 11 Hatch
No: 10 Hatch
No: 9 Hatch
No: 8 Hatch
No: 7 Hatch
No: 6 Hatch
No: 5 Hatch
No: 4 Hatch
No: 3 Hatch
No: 2 Hatch
No: 1
Upper Deck
Tank Top

Drawing 1.11

CHAPTER 1

BULK CARRIERS PAST, PRESENT AND FUTURE

Bulk carriers and bulk cargoes, categories of bulk carrier, characteristics of a bulk carrier, typical bulk carrier layout and equipment, features of larger bulk carriers, future ships and trades

BULK CARRIERS, or 'bulkers', are described in The International Convention for the Safety of Life at Sea (SOLAS) as ships, including ore carriers and combination carriers, intended primarily to carry dry cargo in bulk. Such cargoes are 'any material, other than liquid or gas, consisting of a combination of particles, granules or any larger pieces of material, generally uniform in composition, which is loaded directly into the cargo spaces of a ship without any intermediate form of containment'.

SOLAS[220] distinguishes between two types of bulk carrier.

Single skinned bulk carriers are those in which any part of the cargo hold is bounded by the side shell (these ships are known informally as 'conventional bulk carriers'), or which have a double side skin too narrow to satisfy the regulations.

Double skinned bulk carriers are those in which all cargo holds are bounded by a double side skin of 1,000 mm or more in thickness (or 760 mm in older vessels). A double side skin is a configuration in which each side is composed of the side shell (the outer skin) and a longitudinal bulkhead connecting the double bottom and the deck (the inner skin). Hopper side tanks and topside tanks, if fitted, can be integral parts of the double side skin configuration. (Figs. 1.1 and 2) Ships which possess wing ballast tanks and holds of rectangular cross-section such as open bulk carriers and conbulkers, both described hereunder, are classed as double skinned bulk carriers.

The International Association of Classification Societies (IACS) defines bulk carriers, ore carriers and combination carriers in its Unified Requirements, an extract of which is at Appendix 1.2.

This book is concerned primarily with conventional bulk carriers which still form the largest part of the world bulk fleet though double skinned bulk carriers are, in 2008, being built in numbers. They are described, with other special types of bulk carrier, in Chapter 18. A proposal to require all new bulk carriers to be double skinned for safety reasons was, in

Figure 1.1 double skin with integral topside and hopper tanks. The after hold of a Diamond 53 vessel
Photo courtesy of Niels Bjørn Mortensen

Figure 1.2 Double skin construction. A midships hold of a Diamond 53 vessel
Photo courtesy of Niels Bjørn Mortensen

2004, defeated in the International Maritime Organization (IMO). It was argued that the double skin design had not been in existence long and widely enough to have demonstrated that the claims for its greater safety were valid and that there had not yet been time for recent measures to improve the safety of single skinned bulkers to demonstrate their effectiveness.

The range of cargoes carried in bulk carriers is considerable. Leading bulk cargoes in world trade are iron ore, coal, grain, bauxite/alumina and phosphate rock, along with substantial quantities of concentrates, petroleum coke, steel, ores, cement, sugar, quartz, salt, fertilisers, sulphur, scrap, aggregates and forest products.

In 2006 world seaborne trade[233] in iron ore was about 730 million tonnes, that in steam coal was about 750 million tonnes and about 325 million tonnes of grain was shipped. Seaborne trade in minor bulks such as cement, sugar and fertilisers totalled about 780 million tonnes in 2000[91].

The bulk carrier evolved from the closed shelter-deck cargo vessel (the 'tramp'), and the ore carrier, in the mid-1950s and thereafter developed rapidly in size and number. Whilst in 1960 only about one-quarter of bulk cargoes were carried in single-deck bulk carriers, the situation was transformed by 1980 at which time almost all bulk cargoes were transported by bulkers. Changes to international rules, such as the 1966 Load Line Convention and the IMO Grain Rules, enabled designers to take advantage of the inherent stability of the bulk carrier, and to develop its self-stowing characteristics. A further evolution in design took place in the 1980s with the conbulk vessel designed to meet the changing pattern of international trade, and to accommodate in particular the growth of containerised cargoes[6].

Categories of bulk carrier

Bulk carriers are normally described according to their deadweight tonnage (ie, their carrying capacity). A trend towards increasing size in all except the largest bulk carriers has continued and the limits to what are considered handy-sized, handymax and Panamax have all been raised in the last ten years.

Handy-sized bulkers: In July 2008, the world fleet of bulk carriers of 10,000 dwt and upward totalled approximately 6,500 vessels[228]. The most common size of bulk carrier was the handy-sized vessel with a displacement of 10,000-40,000 dwt and, usually, four or five holds. There were in 2008 about 2,600 vessels within this size range.

The handy-sized bulker (Drawing 1.1) is so called because her comparatively modest dimensions permit her to enter a considerable number of ports, world wide. Such vessels are used in the many trades in which the loading or discharging port imposes a restriction upon the vessel's size, or where the quantity of cargo to be transported requires only a ship able to carry 40,000 tonnes or less. They usually have four or five holds.

Handymax or Supramax bulkers: The increasing number of vessels in the 40,000-60,000 dwt range, although similar in layout and fittings to the handy-sized bulk carriers, have come to be recognised as a separate category, the handymax bulker (Fig 1.2), typically with five holds. There were in 2008 about 1,500 handymax bulkers. These ships are now becoming known to some as Supramax bulkers.

Panamax bulkers: Larger than the handy- classes of vessel is the Panamax bulk carrier (Drawing 1.3), so named because she is designed to the maximum dimensions, particularly the maximum breadth, which can pass through the Panama Canal. The limiting dimensions for canal transit are length overall (loa) 289.5 metres, extreme breadth 32.3 metres and maximum draught 12.04 metres. Some Panamax vessels have summer draughts in excess of the canal limit, so can only pass through the canal partly loaded. Panamax vessels usually have seven holds and are, in practice, usually no more than 225 metres in loa to meet the length restrictions imposed by many terminals. Plans to build new locks for the Panama Canal[221], increasing acceptable ship sizes to loa 366 metres, extreme breadth 49 metres and draught 15.2 metres by 2014 are expected to allow transit of bulk carriers of up to 135,000-140,000 dwt, and ships to take advantage of this development are being planned.

In 2008 there were about 1,400 Panamax vessels of 60,000-85,000 dwt. Panamax bulkers are extensively employed in the transport of large volume bulk cargoes such as coal, grain, bauxite and iron ore in the longhaul trades. The fact that most United States ports can accept no ships with draughts deeper than Panamax draught is an important factor in their continued popularity.

Kamsarmax bulk carriers: Kamsarmax bulk carriers are slightly larger versions of Panamax bulkers. With a length overall of 229 metres and 82,000 dwt they are the biggest ships that are able to load at the world's largest bauxite port, Port Kamsar in Equatorial Guinea. They will be able to transit the enlarged Panama Canal fully laden.

Cape-sized bulkers: Cape-sized bulk carriers (Drawing 1.4) have deadweights greater than 85,000 dwt. They include about 35 wide bodied vessels in the 80,000-100,000 dwt size designed with shallow draughts for trade with the United States. This group also includes a number of ships with Panamax beam, but in excess of 80,000 dwt. In 2008 there were about 790 bulk carriers, including ore carriers, in this category. Most had deadweights between 100,000-200,000 tonnes, with 140,000-170,000 tonnes becoming the most popular and numerous in recent years.

Cape-sized vessels, with loaded draughts usually in excess of 16.5 metres, can be accepted fully laden at only a small number of ports worldwide and are engaged in the longhaul iron ore and coal trades. The range of ports which they visit is increased by the use of two port loadings and two port discharges, the ship being only part laden when departing the first loading port and on reaching the second discharge port.

VLBCs: There were about 100 very large bulk carriers (VLBCs) in service in 2008, mainly employed on the Brazil/Europe and the Australia/Japan routes (Drawing 1.5). VLBCs are bulkers greater than 200,000 dwt. A number of these largest vessels are special types such as ore carriers, ore/oil carriers and OBOs, classes which are discussed below. In January 2008 another 118 VLBCs were on order, many exceeding

300,000 dwt. Many of these VLBCs will be employed in long time charters between Brazil and China[237].

Mini-bulkers: In addition to the 6,500 bulkers grouped into the handy-sized, Panamax, Cape-sized and VLBC categories already described, there are engaged in international trade a considerable number of small bulk carriers of less than 10,000 dwt which are employed primarily in the coastal, short-sea and middle trades in European waters and other parts of the world, carrying smaller consignments of bulk cargoes to smaller ports. Such vessels may have a conventional bulk carrier hold configuration with topside tanks and hopper tanks, or the hold or holds may be rectangular, and bounded by side tanks. They may be known as mini-bulkers (Drawing. 1.6), dry cargo vessels or multipurpose vessels and they probably number about 3,000. The rules and practice governing the classification of these vessels are complicated: consequently they may or may not be classed as bulk carriers, governed by rules written specifically for bulk carriers.

Reasons for varied sizes of bulk carriers: Receivers of bulk cargoes have very varied requirements for tonnes delivered per month or per year. The size of vessel that they choose to carry their cargoes and the frequency that such vessels are employed will be influenced by a variety of factors, including the receivers' storage capacity, depth of water in the berth, regularity of the demand for the commodity, and the financing of its purchase. Less frequently the size of vessel chosen will be governed by the limiting size for the loading port. This variety in demand has created a versatile world fleet of very varied ship sizes.

Geared bulk carriers: Many handy-sized, handymax and mini-bulkers and a small but increasing number of Panamax vessels are equipped with shipboard cranes or derricks for the loading or discharge of cargo: such vessels are described as geared bulk carriers. Loading or discharging by means of ships' cranes or derricks fitted with grabs is normally a comparatively slow means of cargo handling, most useful in ports which are poorly equipped for handling bulk cargoes and where the cargo is discharged direct into trucks.

Self-unloaders: Self-unloaders (Fig. 1.3 and 18.29) are bulk carriers equipped with conveyor belt discharging systems with booms which can be swung out from the ship to discharge directly ashore. Such systems are capable of achieving discharging rates similar to those of shore-based unloading equipment. This equipment is expensive to install and reduces the space available for cargo, but these disadvantages can be outweighed in the short-sea trades by the ability to reduce time spent in port substantially. No time is lost for rain, because the cargo is under cover throughout the discharging process. The numbers and sizes of self-unloaders have been increasing, (238 were listed[234] in 2008) and their role seems likely to continue to grow. Whilst most are found in the handy-size and handymax classes, or even smaller, recent buildings have been Panamax sized and in 2008 there were 11 self-unloaders above 80,000 dwt.

Fig 1.3 A self-unloader

Ore carriers: These vessels (Fig. 1.7) form a diminishing part of the Cape-sized fleet: there were about 50 in 2008[228]. They are single-deck vessels designed specifically for the carriage of iron and other heavy ores. They are characterised by small holds with high centres of gravity. Few ore carriers have been built in recent years, but those few have been amongst the largest bulk carriers afloat, and include the Berg Stahl, 364,768 dwt, built in 1986, which remains in 2006 the largest bulker in service[229].

Bulk/oil carriers: Bulk/oil carriers (Drawing 1.8), are designed with dual-purpose holds which can be used for the carriage of both dry and liquid bulk commodities. Most vessels of this type are also strengthened for the carriage of ore and are referred to as ore/bulk/oil carriers (OBOs). Most bulk/oil carriers are Panamax or Cape-sized.

Ore/oil carriers: Ore/oil carriers (Drawing 1.9) have centre and side compartments. When carrying oil both centre and side compartments can be used, whilst only the centre compartments are used when carrying ore.

Combination carriers: Ore/oil carriers and OBOs, known collectively as combination carriers, were developed to allow the vessel to trade in either the bulk carrier or tanker trades, according to seasonal or commercial demand, and to allow the proportion of time spent in non-revenue-earning ballast legs to be minimised. In the last ten years the decline in the number of these vessels has continued. The number built during this period is negligible and from a high point in 1975 when they comprised 43 per cent of the fleet by total deadweight they now in 2008 constitute less than 5 per cent.

In practice it has not been found easy to switch ships between oil and bulk cargoes on a voyage-to-voyage basis because of the effort required to clean holds to an acceptable standard after carrying oil, and the difficulty in matching discharge and loading ports without long ballast hauls. The declining popularity of combination carriers was probably hastened by their higher capital cost, and the fact that they have been prone, statistically at least, to the types of accidents experienced by both tankers and bulk carriers[6].

Open bulk carriers: Open bulk carriers (Drawing 1.10) are handy-sized or handymax and are designed for the carriage of packaged lumber and units of woodpulp. Some have hold lengths suitable for carrying standard length drilling pipes for the offshore industry. Such cargoes are best carried in rectangular cargo holds with an open hatch layout in which hopper tanks are replaced by straight hold sides, and the entire hold is open to the sky when the hatch covers have been opened; these are features of open bulk carriers. These vessels are usually geared, some being fitted with fixed cranes whilst others are provided with travelling gantry cranes.

Conbulkers: Bulkers fitted out for the carriage of containers were developed from open bulk carriers when it was realised that this type of bulker was well suited for container carrying when circumstances were right (Drawing 1.11). The necessary modifications consisted of suitable strengthening of tanktop and hatchcovers, and provision of container securing sockets. The shipboard cranes fitted to conbulkers are of a capacity appropriate for containers, and service speed is likely to be 15 or even 16 knots – higher than typical bulker speeds, as appropriate for the carriage of higher value commodities. Conbulkers are able to carry a wide range of bulk cargoes as well as forest products, drilling pipes and containers[6].

The characteristics and operation of some of the foregoing categories of vessel are described in Chapter 18.

Characteristics of a bulk carrier

What are the characteristics of a bulk carrier? In order to obtain a good deadweight carrying capacity such ships are given a full form. Many of them are very large, to take advantage of economies of scale and they usually have wide hatches and clear holds to allow easy loading and discharging. Alternate holds are often strengthened for the carriage of heavy cargoes.

The machinery spaces are situated aft, the accommodation block is located over the machinery spaces and the navigating bridge is also aft, above the accommodation. A bulbous bow, raked stem and transom stern are normal. The ship's main body containing the holds is single-decked, in other words, there are no horizontal subdivisions in the holds. The holds are closed with steel mechanical hatch covers.

Other characteristics of bulk carriers vary according to size, design and trade. Five cargo holds, is a typical number for a handymax vessel, but the number of holds can vary from as many as 11 in a very large bulker, to as few as one in a mini-bulker. It is not uncommon, though, for large ore carriers to have only four to six holds, but with two hatches to each hold. Conventional bulk carriers are provided with ballast tanks in the double bottoms and in the hopper spaces beneath and beside the holds. More ballast can be carried in the topside tanks above the holds, and in the forepeak and afterpeak tanks, at the ends of the vessel. Most bulk carriers are also able to carry water ballast in one or two holds situated near the midlength of the vessel.

The vessel is likely to be propelled by a diesel engine giving a service speed of 14-15 knots on about 110 rpm. Fuel tanks in recent tonnage are usually situated in centreline double bottom tanks where they are least exposed to damage in the event of collision although they are at risk when grounded. The most recent regulations on fuel tank protection determine that bulk carriers built in recent years usually have all fuel tanks in the engine room.

Typical bulk carrier holds are shown in Figs. 1.4 and 5. The sloping sides of the hopper tanks keep cargo in the centre of the ship, beneath the hatch openings, from where it can be more easily discharged. The topside tanks occupy the space into which bulk cargo would never flow, and remove the need for trimming of the cargo. This feature is particularly valuable in the grain trades, as it ensures that the vessel can comply with the grain regulations without the need for trimming or for shifting boards. The inclusion of topside and hopper tanks improves the handling of bulk cargoes and thereby reduces the overall cost of transportation. It also extends the range of positive stability options which are open to the Master. Whilst this hold configuration is by far the most common in bulk carriers, open bulkers, designed for the carriage of packaged lumber and/or containers, have holds with vertical sides (Drawing 1.10 and 11) bounded by side tanks which create a form of double side skin.

A bulk carrier's mechanical steel hatch covers are another area in which considerable variety is possible. The steel panels may roll to the hatch side or to the hatch end, they may hinge and fold to the hatch ends, they may lift and roll in piggy-back fashion or they may roll up like a blind. Folding covers (Fig.1.8) are nowadays common in handy-sized and handymax vessels. Panamax and Cape-sized vessels are most likely to be fitted with side rolling hatch covers (Fig.1.6). Hatch covers are described in detail in Chapter 4.

The hatch openings of a conventional bulk carrier usually extend for the maximum distance in the fore

Fig. 1.4 Hold of conventional bulker. Anticlockwise from top left: topside tank side plating; shell plating with vertical framing; DB hopper side tank; tanktop plating; bulkhead stool; corrugated bulkhead

Bulk cargo loaded in a traditional tweendeck vessel:
Trimming is required and discharge is difficult

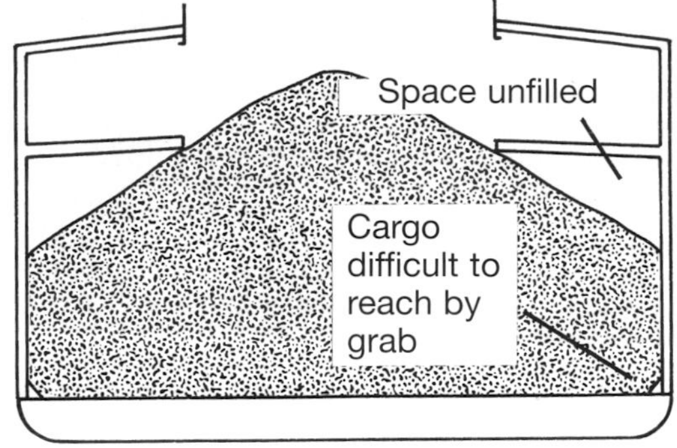

Low density bulk cargo loaded in a bulk carrier:
Little trimming is required and all the cargo is accessible for grab discharge

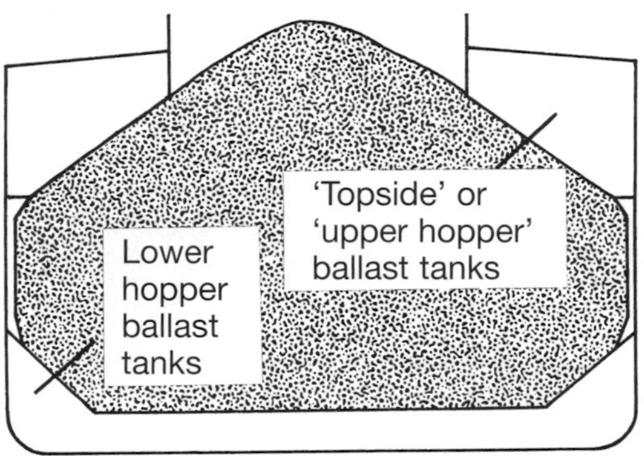

High density bulk cargo loaded in a bulk carrier:
No trimming may be required, but this depends upon the properties of the cargo.
Cargo is accessible for grab discharge

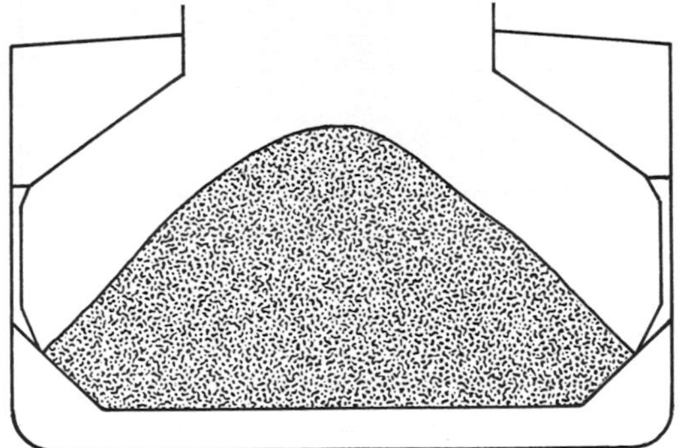

Fig. 1.5

and aft direction for optimum access to the hold, with minimum space between holds provided for essentials such as masts, crane pedestals, ventilators and hatch cover stowage where required. In the athwartship direction the hatch opening will normally occupy about 50 per cent of the ship's breadth, but special types may provide exceptions to this rule. In open type bulkers the hatches may occupy as much as 90 per cent of the ship's breadth, with this effect sometimes being achieved by installing twin hatch openings, side by side. Combination carriers which can carry dry bulk cargoes, or oil, will have smaller

Fig. 1.6 The No. 2 side rolling hatch covers are open, the No. 4 covers are part open and the remaining covers are closed while soya beans are discharged

hatches extending across about 35 per cent of the vessel's breadth.

Many bulk carriers, particularly large ones, are gearless. Geared bulkers may be fitted with swinging derricks, travelling gantry cranes, fixed cranes or boom-mounted conveyor for self-unloading. When cranes are positioned between the hatches (Fig. 1.7) four cranes can, between them, serve all five holds.

Aboard bulkers fresh water is used for domestic purposes such as drinking, washing and cooking. The sanitary (ie, toilet flushing) system uses fresh water on some ships and salt water on others. A fresh water system suffers less from corrosion, but requires the ship to provide more fresh water. Fresh water is used to fill the jackets which cool the main and auxiliary machinery and which are themselves cooled with sea water.

A mini-bulker will require some 5-10 tonnes per day (tpd) of fresh water, whilst a Cape-sized vessel will routinely use 15-20 tpd. Both will use much more when required to rinse holds with fresh water. Modern bulkers are normally provided with a fresh water generator, which manufactures fresh water from sea water. Such a machine is likely to be powered by waste heat from the main engine and will generate all the water the vessel requires for normal operations, so long as the engine is running at full service speed. Fresh water shortages may occur when a vessel is required to spend a long time at anchor with the main engine shut down, when she is operating at reduced

Fig. 1.7 Four cranes, placed between the hatches and able to rotate through 360°, can serve five holds

Fig 1.8 Folding hatch covers opening

(economic) speed and producing little waste heat, or when she is operating in coastal waters which may be polluted, and where it may be inadvisable to generate fresh water. Most Cape-size bulkers have a fresh water capacity of about 225 tonnes and plan to reach and to leave port with about 100 tonnes.

Typical bulk carrier layout and equipment

The descriptions which follow are intended to refer primarily to single skinned handy-sized and handymax bulkers. A section describing the special features found on larger bulk carriers can be found later in the chapter.

Forecastle deck: On most bulk carriers in service in 2008 the forecastle deck is flush with the remainder of the main deck although smaller and older bulk carriers may be provided with a raised forecastle, as will bulk carriers built since 2004.[236] The raised forecastle gives greater buoyancy forward and more protection to the hatch covers. The forecastle deck is provided with port and starboard windlasses for heaving in, paying out and holding on to the anchor cables. Two hawser drums and a warping end are often linked to each windlass (Fig. 1.9) so that the windlass shaft can be turned to haul or pay out any, or all, of the anchor cable and three mooring ropes simultaneously. In practice one or more of these units will be declutched and held on the brake if necessary, while the others are hauled or slacked. The windlass and associated hawser drums are driven by an electro-hydraulic motor situated in the forecastle space below deck. The motors on some ships can be linked to provide double power to one side if required, or for operating the opposite side in the event of equipment failure.

Most ships nowadays are equipped with sufficient powered hawser drums for the stowage and use of all the ship's basic mooring ropes. Additional ropes on such ships, and all ropes on ships without powered hawser drums, will be passed down through the access hatch into the forecastle store for the sea passage, and only brought back on deck in the approaches to the next port. Sounding pipe caps for the forepeak, the echo-sounder compartment and the chain locker soundings are sited on the forecastle deck (Fig.1.10) along with ventilators for forward storerooms and airpipes to the forepeak tank

Forecastle space: This space (Fig. 1.11) beneath the forecastle deck provides shelter for the windlass motors and also houses the motors for the hatch cover hydraulics, where fitted. There is space for the storage of mooring ropes, and for a heavy towing wire on a reel, less commonly found on recent ships. The hawse pipes and spurling pipes pass through the forecastle space. Access to the forepeak ballast tank is by a manhole in the deck of the forecastle space, and to the port and starboard chain lockers by doors (Fig.1.12) in the sides of the chain lockers, which extend from the forecastle space down into the forepeak tank.

A system remotely controlled from a readily accessible position is required[222] to drain a flooded forecastle space. This is often a bilge eductor system powered by water from the fire extinguishing/ washdeck line and also routinely used to pump out the forecastle space bilges and the chain locker bilges. It was reported[223] in 2005, that systems retrospectively fitted to ships were often unsafe and did not comply with the Load Line Rules. Water from the washdeck line for washing mud from the anchor cables is piped through the forecastle space to the hawse pipes. Forecastle spaces are provided with water ingress detectors (WIDs) positioned 0.1 metres above the deck, so that the officer of the watch on the bridge will receive prompt warning of the flooding of any forecastle space.

The forecastle space or forecastle deck will contain a valve wheel and extended spindle for the direct manual closing of the forepeak ballast line or a local manually operated hydraulic system, thereby ensuring the watertight integrity of the collision bulkhead between forepeak and No. 1 hold.

Forepeak tank: A forepeak tank can have a capacity of anything from 200 tonnes or less up to 9,000 tonnes or more, depending upon the size of ship. The space within the forepeak tank will be broken up by the horizontal stringer plates, and the vertical web frames, floors and wash bulkheads which reinforce the shell plating. These structural members are provided with lightening holes which reduce the weight of steelwork, and with drain holes that permit the flow of water necessary for the filling and emptying of the compartment. (Figs. 1.13 and 16)

The bulbous bow may form part of the forepeak tank, or may be separated from it and maintained as a sealed void space, accessible only through a manhole in the forepeak, although the former is more common. Like all ballast tanks the forepeak is provided with a ballast (pipe) line for filling and emptying the compartment and with a forepeak valve set in the line to control the process. This valve will probably be remotely controlled, and will be duplicated by the manual valve or manually operated hydraulic system already described.

Fig. 1.9 Windlass with anchor cable viewed from above, with a hawser reel on each side and a warping end to port

Fig. 1.10 Forepeak sounding pipe and tank valve just forward of the No. 1 hold access

The echo-sounder sensor is likely to be located in a separate watertight compartment at the base of the forepeak tank, accessible from the forepeak through a manhole, or in a more compact unit with a watertight access door. A second echo-sounder sensor may be provided somewhere near the stern of the ship, often in the engine room bilge, with provision for switching between forward and aft provided on the bridge.

Fig. 1.11 Forecastle store in handymax vessel

Fig. 1.12 Chain locker door in fo'c's'le store

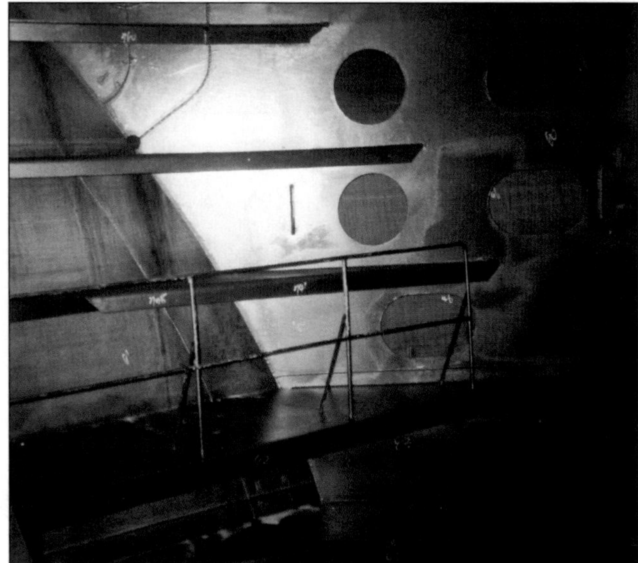

Fig. 1.13 Inside 2,000 tonnes capacity forepeak tank, middle level, port side

Fig. 1.14 The main deck, port side, conventional bulk carrier

Fig. 1.15 Main deck, port side, open hatch bulk carrier

Fig. 1.16 Inside forepeak tank, lower level looking toward the bulbous bow

Upper deck: The upper, or main, deck of a bulk carrier extends as an open deck from the forecastle to the bridge front, and includes the surrounds to all the cargo hatch coamings. (Figs.1.14 and 15). On flush deck ships it extends from bow to stern.

The hatch coamings are usually marked with the hold number, for ready identification by the operators of loading and discharging equipment (Fig.1.18).

Set into the upper deck are the covered manholes which provide access to the topside ballast tanks (Fig.1.17). Also set into the deck are the sounding pipe caps for the hold bilges and the ballast tanks. Ballast and fuel tank airpipes (Figs. 1.19 and 20) are to be found in protected positions against bulwarks, coamings, and masthouses, the latter provided with a saveall to catch any minor oil spillages.

Sockets and lugs for the vertical stanchions used with timber deck cargoes, when the ship is so equipped, are located at the ship's bulwarks (Fig. 1.21).

Masthouses (Fig. 1.22) so called even when they are below deck cranes, not masts, are situated between hatches and can contain hold access hatches, hold ventilation trunks and fans, hydraulic pumps for hatch operation, and storage spaces (Fig. 1.23) and workshops. Hold ventilators, described in Chapter 6, come in many varieties.

Cargo holds: These are entered through watertight access hatches (Fig. 1.24) usually located within masthouses or superstructures when such are fitted, as is common on smaller, geared vessels. On larger bulkers the access hatches are likely to be placed on the open deck, between adjacent hatches, since these vessels normally have no masts and no masthouses (Fig. 1.26). It is normal to find an access hatch and ladder at each end of each hold, symmetrically arranged so that, for example, all the forward ladders are to port of the centreline, and all the after ladders are to starboard.

Australian regulations require sloping steel ladders with an intermediate 'resting' platform when the height is greater than 6 metres, so each hold in larger bulk carriers trading worldwide is provided with at least one ladder which complies with the regulations (Fig. 1.25). Vertical ladders, fitted as second hold ladders aboard some vessels (Fig. 1.27), are sometimes provided with hoops at intervals, as required by some authorities. These allow those using the ladder to pause and lean back against the hoops. However, such hoops are easily damaged by grabs during the discharge of cargo.

The watertight bulkheads at the ends of each hold are usually constructed of vertically corrugated steel work. This is a simple method of providing the necessary strength and rigidity in a form which does not interfere with efficient loading and discharge, and without the need for additional steelwork. Such corrugated bulkheads are often stiffened horizontally with shedder plates (Fig. 1.28). These plates slope down at 45° to the horizontal so that cargo flows off them during discharge.

The hold tanktop is designed to present a completely flush surface for mechanical cargo discharging operations. Manholes giving access to the double-bottom tanks are provided with flush-fitting covers, as are the hold bilge wells. The tanktop plating

Fig. 1.17 '6UWBTP' is the sign on the manhole cover in the bottom RH corner of this picture. It means No. 6 Upper Wing Ballast Tank Port

Fig. 1.18 Number seven hatch, starboard side

Fig. 1.19 Ballast tank airpipe with quick-release lid to allow continuous overflowing of the tank when conducting a 'flow through' ballast change

Fig. 1.20 Airpipe for a fuel tank enclosed in a saveall to catch any accidental overflow of contents

Fig. 1.21 Fittings for timber stanchions

Fig. 1.22 Masthouse storeroom positioned below deck crane and between holds

Fig. 1.23 Inside a masthouse store

Fig. 1.24 No. 1 hold access hatch situated within the forecastle

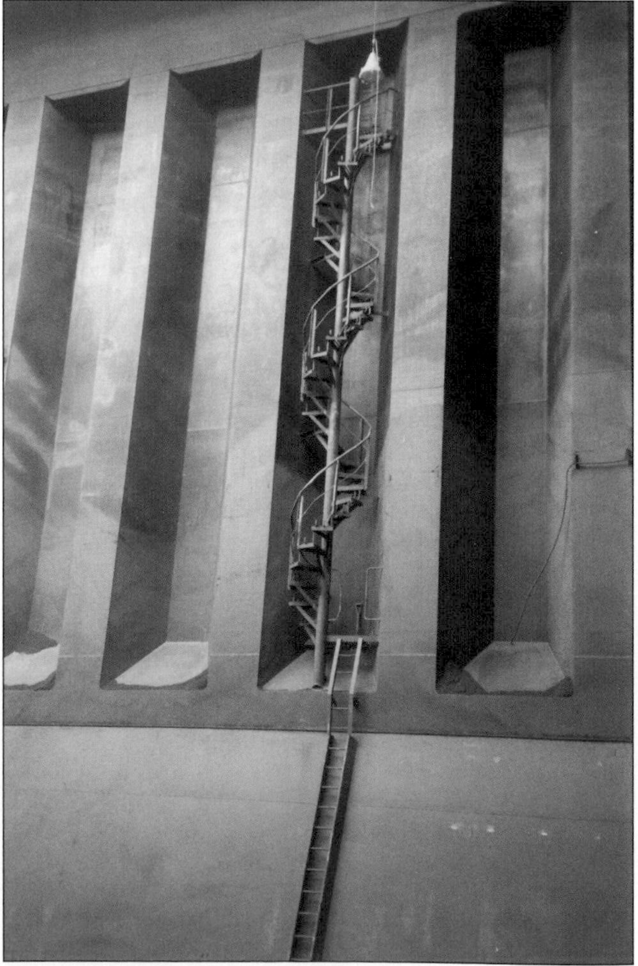

Fig. 1.25 An Australian ladder

Fig. 1.26 No. 7 hold access hatch sited on the open deck

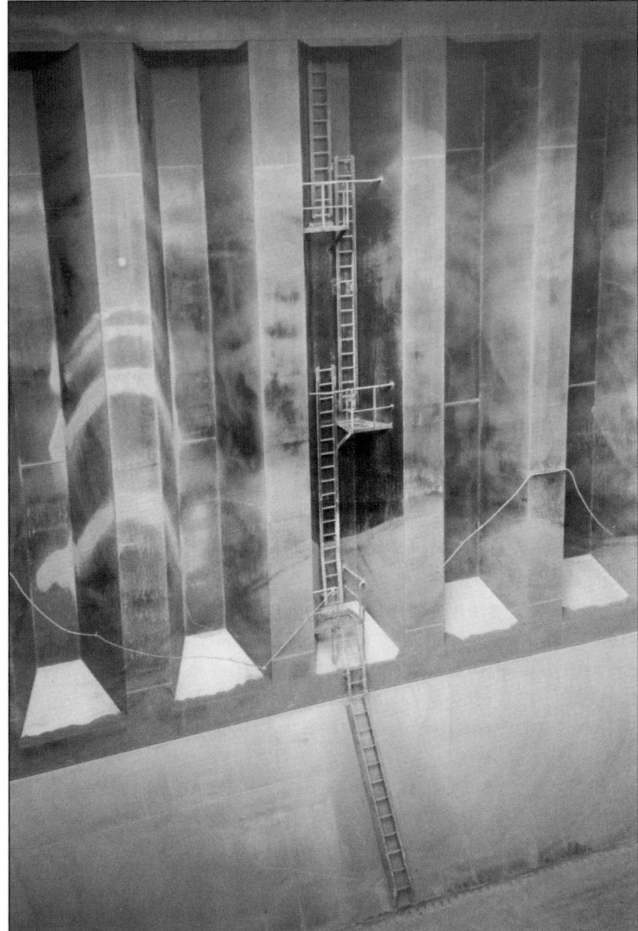

Fig. 1.27 A vertical hold ladder with platforms at intervals – Cape-sized bulk carrier

Fig. 1.28 Corrugated bulkhead with shedder plates which give strength but slope to 'shed' cargo
Photo courtesy of Mathieu Baehni MNI

Fig. 1.29 A heavily indented tanktop
Photo courtesy Captain L Hesketh FNI

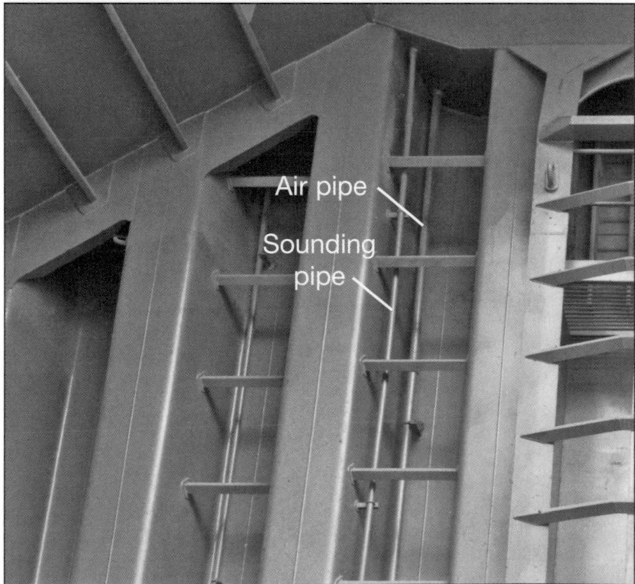

Fig. 1.30 Sounding and air pipes protected by horizontal steel bars

Fig. 1.31 Upper hopper tank with longitudinal framing in the hold, making the topside tank suitable for carrying grain

Fig. 1.32 Grain feeder ports in topside tanks

Fig. 1.33 Underdeck area at the end of a hold

Fig. 1.34 Stores crane able to lift 3 tonnes within a radius of 8 metres and when lowered to an inclination of no less than 30°

of most bulk carriers becomes dished and indented as the result of cargo loading and discharging activities (Fig. 1.29).

The two bilge wells in each hold are situated in the normal positions close to the after bulkhead in the port and starboard corners of the hold (Fig. 5.10). Each well is closed with a perforated plate. The hopper tank sides, featureless expanses of steel plating, slope up from the tanktop to the ship's sides (Fig. 1.4). The shell plating of the ship's sides is supported by vertical framing.

Airpipes and sounding pipes (Fig. 1.30) which run down the ship's side and the end bulkheads are protected with a heavy steel casing, or with an open webbing of heavy steel bar. The latter, as shown in the photographs, is preferable, as cargo can lodge behind casings, making hold cleaning difficult, especially for grain cargoes, when the highest standards of cleanliness are required. All ancillary steelwork, such as brackets, stiffeners, etc, should present no flat surfaces, but should slope down 45° from the horizontal so that cargo flows off during discharge, thus ensuring that no remnants are left behind to present difficulties for subsequent cleaning.

The sides of the topside tanks are usually featureless expanses of steel plating which slope upwards from the ship's side to the hatch coaming (Fig.1.4). Ships in which the longitudinal framing of the topside tank sides is in the hold instead of in the tank (Fig. 1.31) are rare. This is to improve the performance of the topside tanks for the carriage of grain. When these tanks are designed to carry grain, feeder ports are fitted at the base of the tank (Fig. 1.32). To allow the grain to flow from topside tank to hold the ports are unbolted and the plates removed before the grain is loaded. This allows the grain to feed into the hold as the cargo settles during the voyage and enables the balance of the contents of the topside tanks to flow into the hold during discharge.

Water ingress detectors to detect hold flooding are fitted in all holds of all bulk carriers[129]. As the lower of the two detectors is set at 0.5 metres above the tanktop (Fig. 18.16) an alarm shows that substantial flooding has occurred.

Piping for the injection of CO_2 gas, if fitted, may be attached to the topside tank sides, or the gas may be injected through piping set into the hatch coaming (Figs.18.18 and 19). Forward and abaft the hatchway are small areas of hold deckhead (Fig. 1.33) beneath the masthouses. These are the positions where the hold access ladders are situated.

Ballast systems: On handy-sized and smaller ships and others with no duct keels, the ballast valves are located in the engineroom and the ballast lines pass through the double bottom ballast tanks.

Accommodation, machinery spaces and poop deck: The CO_2 bottle room, the tallyclerk's office and the paint and gas bottle stores are all likely to be located in the accommodation block with doors opening onto the open deck. The ship's cargo and general office is likely to be located at the fore end of the accommodation with a view overlooking the main deck. Remote controls for the ballast system may be provided in this office. The conventional arrangement within an accommodation block is with senior ranks accommodated on higher decks and towards the forward end. Individual offices for the Master, the chief engineer and the chief mate are provided on larger ships.

The engineroom is normally entered by way of a changing room, while separate access for heavy loads is usually provided by means of a stores hatch. Other doors at various levels in the accommodation also give access to the engineroom.

Within the engineroom the main engine is centrally situated with, in most ships, a control room at a higher level. Ballast pumps and valves for the ballast and stripping systems will be situated at the forward end of the engine room at the level of the lower plates. The ship's steering gear is located right aft in a separate steering flat. Storerooms, workshops, storage tanks and auxiliary machines are distributed around the boundaries of the engine room at several levels as space permits. The emergency fire pump is located in a separate compartment which may be near the steering flat or may be right forward.

The poop deck is provided with port and starboard mooring winches often incorporating hawser drums similar to those associated with the windlasses (Fig. 1.36). Stores cranes, normally located at the after end of the boat deck, to port and starboard will be provided (Fig. 1.34) and containers for various categories of waste materials will be situated on or near the poop (Figs. 25.2 and 3).

Features of larger bulk carriers

Panamax and Cape-sized bulkers are often provided with features not found aboard handy-sized vessels. The following are some of the more common.

Duct keel: This is a tunnel which extends along the ship's centreline, within the double bottom, from engineroom to the after end of No. 1 hold, or occasionally to the collision bulkhead. It usually contains the pipelines which connect the ballast tanks, bilges and fuel tanks to the pumps in the engineroom, and the associated valves, allowing easy access to them for repair and maintenance. The duct keel can be entered from the engineroom, usually by way of an opening secured with a bolted plate, and from an access trunk situated at the fore end of the ship and opening on deck. One or two other access trunks may be distributed along the length of the ship. The duct keel gives access to bilge and ballast valves for overhaul, though its restricted height often makes it an uncomfortable place in which to work.

Stool spaces: Larger bulk carriers are usually provided with stool spaces at the bases of their transverse bulkheads. Stool spaces are created by replacing the vertical lower part of the bulkhead with sloping sections of plating (Fig. 1.37). These are similar to the side hopper tanks and fitted for a similar purpose, to feed the cargo closer to the hatch square (the area below the hatch opening) where it is more accessible for grab discharge. The stool spaces are void spaces, spaces which remain empty during normal operations. Stool spaces are entered from the duct keel (Fig.7.3) or from the deck, and contain manholes which provide access to the double-bottom tanks.

Fig. 1.35 Anchors housed on anchor pods

Fig. 1.36 Mooring hawser reels and warping end in use on the poop

Fig. 1.37 Draught marks in a hold, to measure the level of ballast water or cargo. At the foot of the corrugated bulkhead is the stool

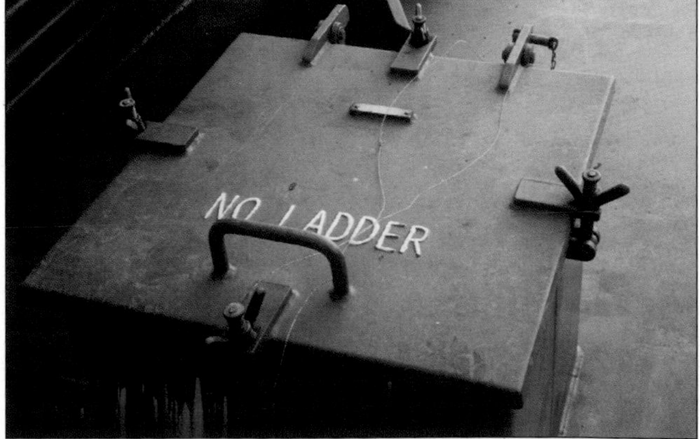

Fig. 1.38 A trimming hatch

Anchor pods: On many larger bulkers the anchors do not lie flush with the hull, but are stowed against pods, sometimes called 'frog-eyes' (Fig. 1.35). These are positioned to allow the anchor to be let go and run clear of the bulbous bow. They also aid easier stowage. Sometimes these pods form void spaces with manhole access from the forepeak or from the forecastle space. More usually they are common with the forecastle space or the forepeak tank.

Trimming hatches: These hatches, similar in size to access hatches, are often provided at the ends of holds to enable hold cleaning to proceed whilst the hatch covers are closed (Fig. 1.38). Drums of cargo residues can be removed with the help of a mucking winch and water hoses can be admitted through them without obstructing the access ladders.

Ballasting holds while in port: Panamax and Capesized bulkers may be designed and equipped to take a limited quantity of ballast in two holds besides the ballast hold, whilst in port, to reduce the air draught and permit the discharging equipment to plumb the hatch, allowing discharging to be completed. Draught marks are usually painted in such holds to allow monitoring of the level to which they are filled (Fig. 1.37).

Bulk carriers in the future

A number of improvements resulting from the investigations into the loss of the mv *Derbyshire* have been introduced or are being phased in[94]. Those improvements already introduced, such as water ingress detectors in holds and forward spaces, and restrictions on the use of alternate hold loading except in ships with adequate strength, are described in the appropriate chapters in this book.

Improvements being introduced on new ships built since 2004 such as enclosed forecastles on the freeboard deck, stronger hatch covers[237], safer access to forward spaces and strengthened ventilators and airpipes are welcome and should lead to a gradual improvement in safety as, over the lifetime of the bulk carrier fleet, they become universal.

Provided that the benefits of double hulls – the reduction in the danger of hold flooding, the reduction in discharge time and the improved efficiency of hold cleaning – are recognised and seen to outweight the disadvantages – increased cost of building, of inspection and of maintenance, and reduction in carrying capacity – the number of double hulled bulk carriers is likely to increase. These ships are described in Chapter 18.

Better means of access, either permanent or portable, to positions high in the hold for the purposes of close up inspections will gradually be introduced aboard larger vessels[93].

The trend for vessels in all classes except the largest becoming bigger is likely to continue, and more and larger vessels equipped for self unloading are likely to be built. The present small number of combination carriers will probably continue to decline.

The carriage, in special circumstances, of traditional bulk cargoes in containers is likely to increase[96].

A mandatory endorsement for deck officers serving on bulk carriers in recognition of the special skills required for the job was proposed some years ago and has much to commend it, but little has been heard of the idea recently[95].

Efforts to remove the need for mid ocean ballast changing, or to make it safer, more effective and economical will continue and, surely, more satisfactory systems will be found. Two systems have already been approved by the IMO Marine Environmental Policy Committee (MEPC)[235]. One involves the use of a biocide for treatment of ballast water and the other involves the disinfection of ballast water by electrolysis. The need to retain harmful cargo residues until outside special areas and well clear of land is likely to lead to the wider introduction of 'cargo hold washing water tanks' and similar holding facilities.

The vast majority of bulk carriers are properly equipped, as regulations require, to dispose of domestic and operational waste materials safely and efficiently. When waste reception facilities ashore, worldwide, match the standards set by shipping the environment will benefit.

Fuel efficient operation of ships is an area in which financial and environmental interests coincide. It is a subject which has recently been receiving a lot of thought in shipping circles and is likely to influence the way that ships are built and operated in the future.

It is to be hoped that the trend towards the 'overoptimisation' of bulk carrier design, which has led to ships being designed, built and equipped to absolute minimum standards with underpowered main engines, inadequate steering and with structure and fittings which are unlikely to remain effective much beyond ten years will be reversed[95]. There is some reason for optimism on this score. In 2005 influential shipowners in several parts of the world were calling for higher standards in the quality of ship provided, and were *'putting their money where their mouths were'*[224]. In 2006 the IACS Common Structural Rules (CSR) for bulk carriers and oil tankers took effect. The objective of the CSR is to prevent competition between individual class societies on scantlings. Instead, the CSR should ensure that all new bulk carriers are built to the same high standard.

Hatch covers, ballast tanks, ventilators and cranes are discussed in greater detail elsewhere in this book.

Sources

6, 91, 93, 94, 95, 96, 129, 220, 221, 222, 223, 224, 228, 229, 233, 234, 235, 236, 237. (See List of Sources, Page 497)

CHAPTER 2

CHARTERPARTIES

Charterparties, time charters, voyage charters, sub-chartering, vessel's description, voyage estimates, compliance with the charterparty, owners' and charterers' voyage orders, consultation with principals, Master's responsibilities including interruptions to the voyage, keeping full records, surveys, tendering of notice of readiness and new charterparty clauses

THE AGREEMENT whereby a shipowner or vessel operator agrees to carry goods or to supply his vessel to others to carry goods is the contract of affreightment, and is the contract under which he is paid freight or hire. The two principal types of contract of affreightment are charterparties and bills of lading. The former is between the shipowner and the charterers, and the latter is between the carrier (who may be the shipowner or the time charterer) and the owner of the goods.

This chapter is concerned with charterparties, but a bill of lading, waybill or other similar document will also be issued. Its potential significance as representing the goods and voyage described by it, and the fact that it will bind the shipowner or charterer, should be borne in mind by the Master.

Bulk carriers usually operate in the charter market. Whilst some are time chartered for a period of days, months or years, many are employed under a voyage charter, or a time charter for a single voyage or trip.

Charterparties

A charterparty (C/P) is a contract for the hire of a ship under which the shipowner provides the use of the ship for a specified period of time (a time charter) or for a specified voyage (a voyage charter), and the charterer pays for the hire or freight and, usually, finds the cargoes. (Occasionally the charter is by demise, or bareboat; under such conditions the charterer becomes in effect the temporary owner of the vessel and employs his own Master and crew. Such arrangements have not been discussed in this volume). Under a time or voyage charter the Master is employed by the owner, but will receive instructions from his owner in respect of the time charter and orders as to employment from the charterer. Under both types of charter it is always stated or implied that the ship will perform her services with reasonable diligence, and without deviation.

Time charters: A time charterparty is a contract to hire the ship for a stated period of time against an agreed payment (hire). The charterparty may allow the period to be extended or shortened, and there is likely to be some flexibility (within fixed limits) about the date for starting and ending the charterparty, to allow for the completion of the preceding and following voyages. Such time charters are known as short or long period charters. Alternatively, the time charter may be for a single voyage – for example, 'one time charter voyage', or 'one North Atlantic round voyage' – where the period of the charter is the time necessary to perform the voyage or trip, often called a trip time charter. For any time charter the hire of the vessel will be at a certain daily, weekly or monthly rate, and may be based on the tonnage of the vessel – eg, 'six thousand US dollars per day' – which will be stated in the charterparty. A lumpsum ballast bonus may also be paid to compensate the owner for part of the cost of delivering the ship at the loading port.

Under time charters the owner appoints Master and crew and normally pays for crew wages, hull and machinery and P&I insurances, provisions, stores and spares, lubricating oils, fresh water, repairs and maintenance and delays caused thereby. There will also usually be express obligations as to the seaworthiness of the ship, and the requirement to maintain her during the period of the time charter.

The owner is also required to pay for other items as agreed in the charterparty. Such items may include initial hold cleaning, off hire survey (or 50 per cent of joint on/off surveys), time lost due to plant breakdown, cost of temporary cargo equipment to cover breakdown of ship's gear, fuel for domestic cooking and lighting, deviation expenses, bunkers and diesel oil on redelivery at the end of the charter, fines due to the ship's operations, and non-compulsory tugs and pilotage. Pilotage which is 'compulsory' or 'customary' is usually stated clearly in the charterparty as being for charterer's account although this does not necessarily mean that the pilot is the servant of the charterer.

For cargo claims the charter may include the Hague/Hague Visby Rules regime of rights and liabilities. Also included may be provisions stating how liability will be shared between owners and charterers in respect of certain types of cargo claim, though such provisions are less common when dealing with bulk cargoes. In the case of time charterers on the New York Produce Exchange Form (NYPE) there will most likely be an additional provision incorporating the Inter Club Agreement (ICA). Devised by the International Group of P&I Associations this sets out a standard division of responsibility in relation to the most common types of cargo claim (shortage/damage/pilferage etc) under the most common circumstances (unseaworthiness/bad stowage etc). Other standard clauses make provision for salvage, general average, collision and was risks.

The charterer will normally be required to pay for daily hire, the cost of bunkers delivered and consumed during the charter period, port charges and canal dues, and stevedoring costs. In addition the charterparty is likely to require the charterer to pay for compulsory tugs and pilotage, additional insurance premiums for crossing International Navigating Limits, and trading in war zones, hold cleaning by crew during charter and on redelivery, bunkers and diesel oil on delivery, supply and labour for the application of special hold coatings, supply and fitting of special cargo fittings and dunnage, cargo fumigations, victualling of clerks and supercargoes, on hire survey (or 50 per cent of joint on/off surveys), radio communications and reasonable entertainment costs. The charterer may have the option of redelivering the vessel dirty if he makes a payment in lieu of hold cleaning.

A time charter invariably contains an off-hire clause for the benefit of the charterer. If the ship is not in full working order to provide the services required and there is a loss of time because of that failure, then the charterer is not liable for hire or the cost of bunkers for the duration of the failure. This provision is likely to be enforced in event of a failure of the ship's cargo gear, or an arrest of the ship for smuggling or some such offence.

A time charterparty will normally stipulate the service speed and fuel consumption to be achieved in good weather conditions, by the vessel when loaded and in ballast. Good weather is sometimes defined in the charterparty as 'Up to and including Beaufort 4', and the C/P may state that wind speed data provided by weather routeing organisations will be favoured over that contained in the ship's log book if there is disagreement. This arbitrary system takes no account of wind directions, or of currents and swell, despite the fact that these have the greatest effect on a vessel's speed. In addition to the service speed, many charterparties quote one or more economical speeds, with corresponding consumptions, these figures usually being 'without guarantee' (WOG) or 'about' meaning plus or minus half a knot or five per cent on the fuel consumption.

Apparent failure to achieve the speed and consumption required by the charterparty may be a cause of dispute (under-performance or over-consumption claims brought by the charterer) and it is important that the Master records accurately the speed, fuel consumption, weather conditions, stoppages, changes of course, currents, damage to the vessel, changes in trim or displacement and any other factors influencing the performance of the vessel during the charter period in the deck and engineroom logs, since there is scope for both owner and charterer to manipulate the situation to secure an advantage or conceal a deficiency. A Master should be alert to ensure that his ship is achieving the required performance, and should be ready to explain any failure to do so.

Stevedore damage is usually settled directly between the owner and the stevedore, with agreed assistance from the charterer. Under a time charter the stevedore is usually the servant of the charterer, so stevedore damage is ultimately the charterer's responsibility. However, most C/Ps state that written notice of liability must be tendered by the ship to the party causing damage within 24 hours of the occurrence, and it may be practical and indeed necessary for the Master to deal with the matter on the spot. In this way the charterer steps out of the procedure. However, if such notice is given and the stevedore fails to compensate for the damage, the shipowner will claim against the charterer direct. If notice of damage is not given to the stevedore, the charterer may escape his liabilities. If the damage caused by the stevedore is not discovered until later, because it is not apparent, the shipowner will claim against the charterer.

Voyage charters: A voyage charterparty is a contract to employ the ship for the carriage of specified goods on a defined voyage or voyages between specified ports or regions, for an agreed payment (freight) which may depend upon the quantity of cargo loaded or carried (for example, US$12 per tonne) or which may be lumpsum (for example, US$900,000), a gross sum paid for the use of the whole or part of a ship.

The voyage charter will almost always provide for a fixed time for loading and unloading the vessel. This is called laytime, and is paid for by the charterer with the freight. Laytime may be expressed as 'X thousand tonnes per weather working day', in which case the laytime will depend upon the tonnage loaded. (If no laytime is stipulated, then there is an implied agreement that the charterer will load and discharge the cargo within a reasonable time.) If the ship is loaded within the allowed laytime then the owners pay the charterers a bonus called 'despatch'. Despatch is usually calculated at half the demurrage rate.

Similarly, the voyage charter will almost always provide a rate at which the charterer must pay the owner if he fails to load and unload the vessel within her allowed laytime. This is called demurrage. If no demurrage rate is stipulated, then the charterer will be liable to damages for failing to load or discharge within laytime or a reasonable time.

The law relating to laytime and demurrage is complicated, and standard form charterparties contain different schemes which may lead to different results in different cases. It is not proposed to deal with those here. However, as disputes between owners and charterers frequently arise in this area, comment on the Master's role in giving the notice of readiness (NOR) which triggers the commencement of laytime, has been included below. The relevance of the statement of facts to this process is discussed in Chapter 14.

Sub-chartering: It is quite common for a vessel to be hired by a charterer from the owner under one charterparty (head charter) and then sub-chartered by the first charterer to a sub-charterer under a second charterparty (sub-charter). There may be one or more sub-charters and these may be time or voyage charters, although generally the last charter in the chain will be a voyage charter. In this situation the first (and any other intermediate) charterer becomes known as the disponent owner, and is responsible to the sub-charterer for the owner's obligations. The first charterer remains responsible to the owner for performance of the head charter, but the Master should be aware of the terms of both charters in case of conflicting instructions from disponent owners and sub-charterers. He should ensure that the instructions he receives are clear and unambiguous, and should have a clear understanding of the identities of the parties and the separate requirements of each with respect to reporting and consultation.

Vessel's description: It is usual for the charterparty to contain the vessel's detailed description, but in some cases the conventional description does not tell the whole story. For example it is insufficient to know that the ship has the hold capacity for 30,000 m^3 of bulk urea if it is not shown that without full bunkers this cargo, filling all holds, will put the ship two metres by the head. In that condition she may be unseaworthy and she will not be allowed to transit the Suez or Panama Canals. Similarly, a vessel with a deadweight of 40,000 tonnes may be able to carry only 20,000 tonnes of steel coils, because the tanktop plating and inner bottom longitudinals may be insufficiently strengthened for unevenly distributed loads[179]. Disputes arise when the vessel's description does not reveal a limitation in the ship's ability to carry a particular cargo and in such cases the Master should explain the difficulties to owners and charterers as soon as the cargo is proposed.

Voyage estimate

When a ship is coming to the end of a charter, the shipowner's commercial manager will instruct the company's shipbroker to find a charterer and fix the ship for further employment. The broker, knowing the owner's policy, the particulars of the ship, the state of the market and the movements of commodities, will seek to obtain the best return he can.

Once a potential charterer has been found to offer a particular cargo, the company will complete a voyage estimate to see if the voyage will be profitable. Even a loss-making voyage may be acceptable if it will take the vessel to a convenient area for a subsequent profitable cargo, or for other necessary ship's business such as a drydocking or crew change.

As noted above, the earnings of a ship employed under a time charter are governed by the rate of hire and the number of days for which the charter lasts, whilst those of a ship fixed under a voyage charter depend upon the tonnage carried and the rate per tonne. The costs which the shipowner must meet from these earnings also differ from one charter to another. In the case of a time charter it is generally only the owner's running costs which must be deducted to arrive at an estimate of the profitability of the business. In the case of voyage charters, however, the position is more complicated.

The object of voyage estimating is to calculate the approximate return on a voyage after deducting expenses from the expected income. In the case of a voyage charter it is usual to start by examining the time each section of a voyage will take, commencing with the ballast passage from the time of dropping the outward pilot at the previous discharge port. Time in the loading and discharging ports will be assessed, taking account of possible holiday periods, and time required for the laden voyage will also be considered. Factors to consider include the customs of the trade, the opportunities for obtaining bunkers, canal transits and seasonal conditions.

Estimating time for cargo loading and discharge requires much experience. It depends upon the quantity of cargo to be handled, the rate at which it can be delivered to or taken away from the ship, the capacity of the ship's or shore gear for cargo handling, and the likelihood of delays and interruptions to cargo work because of weather, or for other reasons.

Having costed the time, expenses have to be calculated. This involves bunkers, port charges, light dues, towage and pilotage fees, berth dues and other special items like canal tolls and extra insurance for Crossing International Navigating Limits. Charterers will often be required to pay the extra premium required by the ship's underwriters to trade the vessel outside International Navigating Limits or in war zones.

Running expenses take account of such items as crew costs, repatriation, repairs and maintenance to the ship, lubricating oils, fresh water, garbage and slop disposal, insurance premiums, depreciation and administration overheads. It is usual to calculate them separately as part of the company's normal budgeting procedures, and they will be known to the person completing the voyage calculation.

A typical voyage estimate (Fig.2.1) for a ship on voyage charter from Brazil to Iran with a cargo of soya bean meal is calculated in US dollars. It shows expected freight payable on 24,500 tonnes of cargo, plus demurrage payable for three days. Expected costs include commissions, fuel, port charges, insurance payments and payment for despatch. The anticipated time at sea, time in port, fuel consumption, fuel costs and port charges are summarised towards the bottom of the form. The voyage estimate shows net earnings of $8,929 per day. The calculations show that the voyage would be profitable if the ship's daily running costs (or overheads) were less than that figure.

The fixing of any charter is normally a process of negotiation, and it is likely that proposals and counter-proposals will pass between the brokers representing the charterer and the owner before the final terms of the charterparty are agreed.

The voyage estimate form has space for the insertion of 'Actuals', and the actual earnings and costs will be entered as they become known, so that the profitability of the voyage can be seen. Comparison of the estimates with the actuals also helps to improve the quality of future estimating.

Confirmation that proposed cargo can be carried: When attempts are being made to fix the ship, the broker may contact the Master to request his confirmation that a cargo can be safely carried and his calculation of the tonnage that the ship can carry between specified ports. This is particularly important, and particularly well advised, when the cargo is composed of several parcels to be loaded or discharged in different ports and to be carried in separate holds. The calculations in such cases can be complex and the limiting factor may not be obvious. Another possibility might be that the ship was unsuitable for a particular cargo because of hold configuration or dimensions, permissible stress limits or tanktop loadings, or amount of ventilation which could be provided. In addition the Master should consider whether any proposed cargo is listed in the charterparty as *'unacceptable for carriage'* as mistakes are not unknown.

Expensive mistakes can be avoided if the ship's Master and officers check any calculations which have been undertaken by the broker or head office staff. Although it may be frustrating for those aboard ship to be asked to investigate a succession of possible charter voyages which are never confirmed, the results which they produce can help to avoid mistakes. Prompt response to these requests by the Master can

VESSEL ____ DATE ____ COMMODITY Soya Bean Meal 52 ft

VOYAGE Rio G Do Sol + Iran CHARTER Irisl

		Estimate	Actuals
FREIGHT 24500 AT 40.00 $		980000	
DEMURRAGE 3 DAYS AT $7500 PER DAY		22500	
COMMISIONS 6¼% TTL	62656		
FUEL	178019		
PORT CHARGES	89000		
~~CANAL~~ WAR INS PANDI $7500; WAR CREW BONUS 27 days $50598	58098		
DESPATCH 2 DAYS AT $3750 PER DAY	7500		
TIME ✓ DAYS AT TTL ~~PER DAY~~	395273	1002500	
VOYAGE DAYS 68 — NET EARNINGS		607227	

TERMS OF CHARTER ETC.	
DATES	LAYCAN 12.7.88
RATE	40/41 $ + 0.50 $
LAYTIME	3500/2000
COMM.	6¼%
CREW WAR RISK $1874 per day	
1H KCS = 35 + 2.5 4.0 PORT	
CARGO 1,300,000 cu ft / 52 = 24500	
$8929 PER DAY	
—	

FROM	TO	MILES	DAYS AT SEA	DAYS IN PORT	EST. BUNKS. CONSUMPTION F.O.	EST. BUNKS. CONSUMPTION D.O.	$ COST/TON F.O.	$ COST/TON D.O.	ESTIM. FUEL COSTS	ESTIM. PORT CHARGES	ACTUAL ITEMS	ACTUAL COSTS
R G Do S	Paranagua	405	1	10	36	3	89	270	4314	15000 Para		
Para:	B. Abbas	8625	26	16	910	65	89	270	98540	4000 Para		
Lisbon	R G Do S	4934	15		480	37	90	105	47085	70000 Basas		
			.	26		104		270	28080			
TOTALS			42	36					178019	89,000		

Fig. 2.1. Voyage Estimate Form from 'Voyage Estimating' by William Packard

enhance the reputation of the owner and are usually very well received.

When the ship has been fixed: There are many different standard charterparty forms, and they are invariably used in amended form, with numerous additions to and deletions from the basic printed wording. Normally a charterparty also has attached to it a large number of additional typed clauses ('additional' or 'rider' clauses) as agreed by the negotiating parties. Sometimes a charter will contain the charterer's standard terms which will be more favourable to him.

Many of these clauses are concerned with methods of payment, settling of disputes, insurances and other matters with which the Master will have little or no involvement, but many other clauses deal with matters which are his responsibility and with which he will be directly involved. As a very general rule the additional clauses will prevail over the standard wording, and clauses specifically dealing with a particular circumstance will prevail over a general clause to the extent that there is conflict between them. Deletions may also play a part in determining the actual intention of the parties.

Knowledge of the terms of the charterparty and compliance with them

If a ship is to comply fully with the terms of her charterparty, she will need to be maintained in a seaworthy condition with all her equipment and fittings in good working order and operated efficiently and with her safety management system functioning correctly[107]. In addition, the Master and crew who must be certificated in compliance with the latest regulations[106], must act in accordance with the terms of the charterparty. In normal circumstances this can be achieved by carefully following the instructions contained in the voyage orders from owners and charterers. The Master and chief mate should both study the contents of the voyage orders with care, and all other officers should be informed of these orders as they affect them.

The Master of a ship on a period time charter should be provided with a copy of the charterparty as a supplement to the instructions from his owner. This will enable him to study the full contents of the document and he should not hesitate to question the owners about any relevant matters omitted from or contradicted by the instructions or orders he receives. For trip time charters and voyage charters the charterparty is, in general terms, not relevant to the Master. What is relevant to the Master for those charters is that he received appropriate instructions from the owners and properly written orders from the time charterers.

Sometimes even the owners sign a charterparty without fully appreciating the meaning of all the clauses. An alert Master may spot discrepancies between the charterparty and the voyage instructions from owners or charterers.

The Master will also receive from his owners and charterers extensive voyage orders by ship's mail or transmitted by facsimile, telex or email, which contain such extracts of the charterparty as each party considers it is necessary for him to know.

Owners' time charter voyage orders: The owners' voyage orders for a time charter voyage are likely to provide details of who the charterers are, the charterparty date, details of delivery, laydays and cancelling date, the voyage, and the date and place of redelivery. Instructions regarding speed of the vessel and consumption of fuel will be included, and these may be accompanied by notice of acceptable loading and discharging sequences of which the charterers have been informed.

The sense of charterparty clauses relating to important matters such as lying safely afloat (or in some cases safely aground), cargo to be loaded under the supervision and direction of the Master, appointment of charterers' supercargo, quantity of bunkers on redelivery and option of bunkering for owners' account, authority for charterers to sign bills of lading in accordance with mate's or tally clerk's receipts, and action to be taken in event of stevedores' damage will also be reproduced in the owners' voyage orders.

The owners' voyage orders may remind the Master to ensure that all invoices for the charterers' account are endorsed with a stamp stating: 'The goods and/or services being hereby ordered, acknowledged and/or receipted for, are being ordered and/or accepted solely for the account of charterers of the mv (name) and not for the account of said vessel or her owners. Accordingly, no lien or other claim against said vessel can arise therefrom.'

The orders may conclude with instructions to the Master to report at the time of redelivery on hold condition, fuel remaining and costs incurred by charterers in respect of subsistence and gratuities.

Charterers' voyage orders: Such orders are usually from time charterers as there is no requirement for voyage charterers to issue voyage orders to the Master. Since the charterers' interests and responsibilities are different from those of the owners, their voyage orders are likely to concentrate upon different matters.

After providing the same basic information as the owners with respect to their own identity, the charterparty date, details of delivery, laydays and cancelling date, the voyage, date and place of redelivery and instructions regarding speed and consumption, the charterers will normally provide details of the intended cargo, and ask the Master to prepare and submit a stowage plan. Requirements for reporting ETA (estimated time of arrival) will be stated, and details of the charterers' agents will be provided. Most importantly the authority, if any, to be given by the Master to charterers or their agents for the signing of bills of lading will be stated. Proposed bunkering intentions will be advised.

At some stage in the voyage the charterers will provide a list of discharge ports, and if appropriate they will state the maximum permitted draughts and cargo to be discharged in each, such information being necessary at an early stage if proper planning is to be achieved. They will also provide details of whether the quantity of cargo loaded and discharged is to be assessed by draught survey or shore scales, to determine bill of lading weight.

Arrangements for using a weather routeing service

may be described, and the requirement for reporting noon position, average daily consumption, speed, weather and ETA whilst at sea, and for providing an arrival report on completion of each passage will be stated. The Master will be advised of which radio stations to monitor and of the preferred method of sending and coding communications. He will also be told how to address both routine and emergency messages, and is likely to be reminded that he must provide the charterers with log abstracts.

Consultation with owners and charterers: Most Shipmasters know that they should consult their owners and charterers whenever an unusual situation arises. This permits the other parties to remind the Master of his rights and responsibilities under the charterparty, should that be necessary. Failure to comply with the terms of the charterparty can be expensive, so the Master should consult his documents and his principals whenever he is in doubt.

Master's responsibilities

The Master is, nowadays, almost always in a position to communicate with the owner and/or the cargo owner by telex, email, fax or telephone for instructions in difficult or extraordinary situations. For this reason, the Master's powers, in certain circumstances, to sell damaged goods, to transship goods, to raise money on cargo or the vessel, or to jettison goods have not been discussed although they still exist and can be useful in certain circumstances, for example when the ship has been abandoned by the owners.

General responsibilities: The Master's overriding obligation remains at all times to protect the lives of passengers and crew and to ensure the safety of the vessel and the environment. In addition he is responsible to international, national and local authorities for compliance with regulations, including the prevention of pollution and care for the needs of his crew. The commercial contracts entered into by the owner require him to preserve and care for the cargo on board, and to carry it safely and with reasonable dispatch. Thereafter the Master has to use his best judgement to ensure the optimum performance of the ship whilst complying with the various commercial contracts to which he or the owner is a party.

On a voyage the Master must do what is necessary to carry out the contract of carriage and to take reasonable care of the goods entrusted to him. In doing so he acts as the agent of the shipowner but, because of his possession of the cargo, he may also act as the agent of the cargo owner in protecting the cargo owner's interest in the cargo.

The Master is the owner's agent in providing 'necessaries' for the voyage which under the charter are to be provided by the owner, but he is the charterer's agent for providing 'necessaries' to be paid for by the charterers – for example, bunkers under a time charter.

The Master, in taking reasonable care of the goods entrusted to him, should do what is necessary to preserve them on board during the ordinary incidents of the voyage – for example, by ventilation, or by pumping bilges. In other words he should take reasonable measures to prevent or minimise loss or deterioration of the goods. He should also be aware of any special considerations which may apply to specific cargoes, especially dangerous goods, and follow the special guidelines for carriage set out in the International Maritime Dangerous Goods Code (IMDG).

Unless the charterparty expressly provides otherwise the Master should proceed by a usual and reasonable route without unjustifiable deviation or unreasonable delay. Leaving the route will, however, be justifiable if done to save life, to communicate with a ship in distress, or because of some other necessary reason such as to carry out repairs or to avoid perils. Alternatively, the charterparty may contain an express liberty to deviate but – beware! – such deviation may incur offhire, even when done to save life. Charterers will often have the right to direct the geographical route which the ship should take. Navigational matters are not the sole responsibility of the Master, although where a Master has genuine concerns for the safety of the ship, crew and cargo as a result of navigational orders which he believes are inappropriate, his decision will prevail. In such a situation the Master should seek confirmation from the owner and charterer and if necessary obtain independent confirmation of his preferred route by liaising with the ship's P&I club and/or the owner's office.

Interruptions to the voyage: Whether under time charter or voyage charter, interruptions to the voyage due to failure of the ship, her equipment or her personnel will be costly for the shipowner. The means by which the shipowner is required to bear the cost of the failure vary from one charter to another, but the conclusion to be drawn is the same: the ship's Master and officers should make every effort to ensure that no avoidable failures are allowed to occur.

In practice this means ensuring that the ship's machinery, both deck and engineroom, is maintained to a good standard and is operated with care by competent personnel who have received proper training in their tasks.

At the discharge port it is the duty of the Master to proceed to the place of discharge if the charter provides for one. The holder of the bill of lading is usually entitled to have the goods delivered to him direct from the ship, if existing liens are satisfied. A shipowner may have a lien – ie, a right to retain goods in his possession while he has unfulfilled claims against the charterer or the cargo owner. Such a claim might, for example, be for freight, general average contributions, or expenses incurred by the shipowner or Master in protecting or preserving the goods carried. (The discharge of cargo against bills of lading is fully discussed in Chapter 14.)

The Master may be asked to retain possession of the goods, either by keeping them on the vessel, or by maintaining them in the shipowner's possession – for example, by releasing them to a person or place where he retains control over them. The Master may be able to deliver the goods to the person entitled to them in the absence of a bill of lading, on receiving security or an indemnity against possible claims by others, but this is a matter which should be discussed with owners and their P&I clubs in advance. Most P&I clubs have standard Letters of Indemnity to meet these circumstances.

Maintenance of full records: Disputes can only be settled when clear factual evidence can be supplied. Charterparties commonly include a clause which gives charterers, their agents or supercargoes a right to inspect original deck and/or engineroom logbooks or to be provided with true copies of them. To satisfy this requirement it is a further responsibility of the ship to ensure that detailed and accurate records are maintained throughout the charter period, with supporting documentation up to date, so that the times and circumstances of significant events can be confirmed. Such records must be made contemporaneously and give as much detail as possible. Any original evidence (broken parts, fuel samples, photographs, video recordings etc) should be clearly labelled and retained to the order of the owners.

A checklist of data and records to be kept is given at the end of Chapter 3, and the subject is covered in detail in *The Mariner's Role in Collecting Evidence.*[89]

Surveys required by the charterparty: It is usual to have certain matters relevant to the charterparty, such as hold cleanliness and tonnage of cargo loaded, surveyed by independent surveyors, but ship's officers should always check the results obtained by surveyors and make their own assessment. Where they disagree with the conclusions reached by the surveyor, the Master may record this by endorsing the surveyor's report if he is required to sign it, by serving a notice of protest, or by making an entry is the ship's deck log book, as appropriate. He should consult his owners as far as is possible and should take great care before clausing bills of lading, mate's receipts or other documents evidencing the quantity, quality and condition of the goods loaded.

The start and finish of the charter period are normally marked by delivery and redelivery surveys. The purpose of these surveys is to observe and record the condition of the ship and to measure the bunkers aboard at both ends of the charter period. The results of the survey provide the facts required for settlement between owner and charterer of any claim for damage to the ship, or bunkers consumed or remaining. The survey is normally undertaken by a surveyor representing the charterer. A second surveyor, or the ship's Master or chief mate, will represent the owner or a single surveyor may represent both parties.

A delivery or redelivery survey requires the listing of every item of damage in the holds and adjacent cargo working areas, and the sounding of all bunker tanks and measurement of bunker temperatures in the company of the chief engineer. In cases where the redelivery survey takes place in the discharging port, but the charter ends on dropping the outward pilot, for example, the measured bunker quantities must be corrected for the quantity of bunkers to be consumed from time of survey to time when the charter ends.

On-hire and off-hire surveys can be the same as delivery and redelivery surveys, but can also be required during the course of a charter, if for any reason the vessel goes off hire.

Tendering of notice of readiness: The tendering of notice of readiness (NOR) is an important part of the process of making or resisting claims for despatch and demurrage, matters which were discussed in the paragraphs on voyage charters.

It is usual for a voyage charter to specify two dates and to provide that laytime cannot commence before an earlier date and that if the ship is not ready by the later date the charterers have the option to cancel the charterparty. The period between the two dates is called the 'laycan spread'. A valid NOR may be given at any time, but laytime cannot commence before the date given in the charter.

The Master does have an important role to play by tendering the NOR to load or discharge, and he and his officers can maximise the vessel's earnings by ensuring that no delays to loading or discharge can be blamed upon the ship.

Laytime will usually commence at a time dependent upon the time when the NOR is correctly tendered and/or received, depending upon the terms of the charter. It is the Master's responsibility to ensure that the NOR is correctly tendered, and the wording of the charterparty will normally state when, in what circumstances, and how the NOR is to be tendered, or given, and to whom it must be tendered. The owners' or disponent owners' voyage orders can be expected to confirm what is required, but if in doubt the Master should not hesitate to ask for clarification.

Under a voyage charterparty, an NOR will usually be required at every loading and discharging port and may have to be tendered when the vessel arrives at the customary anchorage at the port (a port charter), or when she reaches the berth (a berth charter). It may be sufficient to have the vessel in all respects ready to load or discharge, but the charterparty may contain specific requirements – for example, that the vessel has passed a preloading survey – before NOR is tendered.

The importance of the NOR makes it essential that the Master retains written evidence that he has tendered the NOR. This is normally achieved by endorsing the NOR with the date and time that it is handed to the charterer's agent, obtaining the agent's signature for receipt, and retaining a copy. Where it is not possible to tender NOR by placing the document in the agent's hand, because the ship is at an anchorage or because the agent has failed to visit the ship, then NOR should be tendered by radio telegraph, by telex or facsimile, using any method which provides proof of delivery. Email, although widely used for this purpose, does not provide proof unless an acknowledgement is received or unless this method of tendering is expressly specified in the charterparty.

A common provision is a requirement that the notice be given during office hours. If there is such a provision and the notice is given outside office hours, the notice will probably be treated as though it was given at the commencement of working hours on the next working day. In Muslim countries offices may be closed on Fridays and Saturdays, a point on which the charterparty will normally give guidance. In view of the commercial importance of the tendering of NOR, it is a widespread practice for Shipmasters to tender NOR on arrival in any loading or discharging port, provided that the vessel is ready to work cargo and regardless of whether or not they know the vessel to be on voyage charter. This is a safe practice to adopt.

If NOR is not received by the shore, the Master should keep tendering NORs until received. Each NOR after the first should include above the Master's signature the phrase: 'This NOR is tendered without prejudice to the validity of NORs previously tendered'. In these circumstances NORs should be tendered twice daily, and also at any appropriate time, such as when another ship berths or unberths at the intended berth. (An example of an NOR has been included in Chapter 14).

New charterparty clauses

New charterparty clauses are regularly introduced to meet new requirements. Examples are the BIMCO Bulk Carrier Safety Clause and clauses requiring Shipmasters to follow charterers' routeing instructions. Mention of the latter is made as appropriate later (see Chapter 15). Similarly the BIMCO Standard Scrap Metal Clause for Voyage Charterparties has been developed in response to demand for a 'soft loading' clause from owners concerned about the risk of damage resulting from light and heavy scrap being loaded simultaneously from a height.[103]

Summary

A Shipmaster cannot hope to control and to optimise the performance of his ship unless he is familiar with the contracts which govern her trading. If a Shipmaster is to do his job properly, he must know and understand the terms of the charterparties under which the ship is operating and ensure that his officers are well informed; he must operate and maintain the ship in an efficient manner and keep full and accurate records.

Sources

89, 103, 106, 107, 179. (See List of Sources, Page 497)

CHAPTER 3

LOG BOOKS, RECORDS, REFERENCE BOOKS AND PLANS

The records which should be maintained aboard bulk carriers because of their trade, ships' operations manuals, the plans required by deck officers and the reference books required for the trade

Records which should be maintained

NO MORE than brief mention is made in this chapter of routine records such as are required for all ships. The main purpose of the chapter is to draw attention to records and to log entries which may have particular significance for bulk carriers and their cargoes.

Log books – sea voyage: During the sea voyage, the deck log book (otherwise known as the bridge log book) should contain routine navigational information including positions at regular intervals and method of position fixing, courses steered, allowances made for compass error, leeway and set. These data should be recorded when observations are taken, or at the end of the navigational watch, as appropriate. The record of course, distance and speed made good, and course and distance to go should be completed daily and a full set of routine weather observations, with a report of sea and swell conditions, should be entered at the end of each watch.

Details of severe weather met and the action taken should be recorded. For example, the log book should record when the vessel has been hove-to in adverse weather, or when course has been altered to avoid a tropical storm. In addition, the log book should contain full details of any matters which might affect the cargo and its condition.

When a cargo which requires ventilation is being carried, ventilation of the holds should be recorded in detail, stating times of starting and stopping, and give the reason for stopping ventilation. Such a reason might be *Shipping water and/or spray over hatches,* or *High humidity of ambient air.* Where the ventilation programme is influenced by the air humidity, regular hygrometer readings (wet and dry bulb) should also appear in the log book once per watch. If a sensitive cargo requires more frequent readings or if, for example, humidity readings are taken within each hold with a whirling psychrometer, a full record separate from the log book can be maintained and after signature by Master and chief mate can be attached to the log book at the end of the voyage.

The nature of the ventilation should also be fully recorded, stating which ventilators are being used if there are alternatives, and whether the ventilation is mechanical or forced draught (ie, by fan) or natural draught (natural flow of air through the ventilation cowl). Where fans are used, the log book entry should show whether they are drawing air into the compartment (suction or inlet mode) or blowing air out from the compartment (exhaust or outlet mode), and whether they are being run at full speed, half speed or some other value. Differences between the ventilation given to different holds should be clearly recorded.

Suitable log book entries might read: *0800 Ventilation of holds Nos 1-7 commenced with after fans in all holds at full speed in inlet mode, and forward vents in all holds on natural ventilation. 1800 ventilation of holds Nos 1-7 stopped and all vent flaps closed in accordance with shippers' carrying instructions.*

Heavy rainfall and the shipping of water and spray over decks and hatches must also be recorded in the log book when experienced, as this may be relevant if cargo is subsequently discovered to have suffered wet damage.

The dates and times of any hold or hatch cover inspections during the voyage should be recorded, with the name and/or rank of the person making the inspection, the nature of the inspection and any findings. An appropriate entry for a cargo of steel coils might read: *1000-1200 Inspection of all holds and hatches by chief mate and bosun, to see if any cargo had shifted. All well.*

A more serious situation could be reported in the deck log book as follows: *1500. During routine cargo inspection by chief mate and bosun damage/shifting found in holds Nos. 2 and 5. Resecuring not possible. Course adjusted to minimise further damage.* Such an incident would, of course, also require immediate reports by the Master to his owners and charterers, and it would be necessary at the first opportunity to prepare a detailed report of the damage to ship and to cargo, and the circumstances in which the damage occurred. It would be prudent for owners to promptly inform their P&I club of such an incident.

Further information which should be recorded in the log book includes the records of cargo temperatures when observed, the pH readings of bilge water and the volumes or tonnages of bilge water pumped out, plus readings obtained with methanometers, O_2 meters and multi gas meters, etc

If there is insufficient space on the log book page for the clear entry of all the necessary detail, then additional sheets of paper must be attached to the log book with the extra detail which is required. Soundings of all compartments including hold bilges, ballast tanks, fresh-water and oil-fuel tanks, cofferdams, void spaces, chain lockers and other spaces should be taken and recorded in the log book or separate sounding book at least once daily.

It is not acceptable for an *empty* tank to be recorded simply as empty (often abbreviated to *MT*). The difference between a 10cm and a 20cm sounding in the ballast tank of a large ship can be considerable in terms of tonnes of ballast water, and any increase in water level needs to be detected and investigated in view of the possibility of leakage. This consideration is of particular importance when a ship is cargo laden, since the cargo may be exposed to the risk of water damage if water is entering some part of the ship undetected. A reader who finds *MT* recorded in the sounding book instead of a small sounding such a *5cm* or *12cm* will suspect that no soundings have been taken, and that the entry reflects the reported state of the tank and not the actual sounding.

During a ballast passage the testing of any cargo care systems should be recorded in the log book when carried out. Such entries might include the testing of hold bilge pumping systems, hold ventilation fans and hold CO_2 smothering systems. The testing of hatch cover watertightness by hose test or by chalk test should also be recorded, as should the result, and any remedial action taken.

A typical series of log book entries would be: *1030-1130 Hose tested Nos. 1 and 2 hatch covers for watertightness under supervision of chief mate. Leakage found only at No 2 starboard side. 1530 Following routine renewals and adjustments to fittings of No 2 hatch cover the covers were again hose tested, and were found to be watertight.*

The log book should contain records of such matters affecting the cargo and the operation of the ship as the inspection and tightening of cargo lashings and details of in-transit fumigation. Changing of ship's ballast to comply with pollution regulations, or for purposes of draught and trim should be recorded in the ship's ballast log.

Log books-in port: A *Statement of Facts* is normally produced by the ship's agent to cover the time spent in a loading or discharge port. The agent will often rely upon the ship's staff to provide some of the times and facts which are included in the statement, and the Shipmaster should satisfy himself before signing the statement that the information it contains is accurate, since it will be used to calculate the value of any demurrage or despatch payments or to settle any disputes which may arise regarding the voyage.

The deck log book will record significant times such as the times of dropping anchor off the port, reaching the fairway buoy, arriving at the berth and tendering notice of readiness. The log book will be supported by the more detailed and comprehensive entries contained in the bell book (also known as the movement book, or bridge note book), which is the working document in which events are recorded at the time they occur. An automated printout of engine movements may also be available.

It is essential that weather observations are continued whilst the ship is in port and they should be recorded at least three times daily – ideally at 0000, 0600, 1200 and 1800. When officers continue watches in port, the weather should be recorded at the end of each watch, throughout night and day. In addition, any exceptional weather conditions which may interrupt cargo work, damage the cargo or damage the ship should be recorded whenever they occur. Other incidents, such as ships passing at high speed, which disrupt or threaten the ship or activities aboard should also be logged.

The log book should record any surveys which are requested and which take place, and their result, and any protests which are made or received. Fumigation of cargo holds should be recorded, with details of the treatment given, the purpose of the treatment and who ordered it. The sealing of holds, if required, should be noted and inspections of the seals should be recorded.

Notebook or cargo log: Once in the berth, it is necessary to record details of starts, stoppages and completions of cargo work and transfers of cargo-handling equipment, along with tonnages and positions of ballast and fresh water loaded or discharged, soundings observed, and tonnages of cargo advised or calculated. The records should show the times that work started and stopped at each hold and the durations of all surveys and inspections. Tonnages of bunkers taken should be recorded, as should details of all accidents to ship and personnel.

These records are likely to be kept in the first instance in a note book in the possession of the duty officer, or in a cargo log book, or computer, kept in the ship's office or cargo control room. The cargo log book, when used, is similar to the bell book: it is the working document in which full records of all relevant data should be recorded. The use of a cargo log book providing a complete record of cargo, ballast and associated operations is to be recommended. Times of working cargo and reasons for stoppages will normally be copied into the deck log book from the cargo log or officer's notebook at the end of each watch, but the details of the working of ballast will not normally be transferred. All entries in log books and notebooks should be made in ink, not pencil and corrections should be made by putting a single firm line through the error, writing the correct version alongside and initialing the entry.

It is most important to ensure that stoppages are accurately timed, and that the reasons for them are discovered and recorded. This information can be most important for the ship in the event of a dispute. Draughts should be recorded on arrival and departure and at appropriate times throughout the port stay. During a discharging operation extending over several days, it is appropriate to take draught readings each morning and evening. When loading draught readings should be taken and recorded at the end of each stage in the loading, ie at the end of each pour. The importance of taking and recording the draughts regularly cannot be overstated. Draught readings provide the best and simplest warning when the ship is flooding or when the ballasting or cargo operations go wrong.

The cargo log or personal notebook is a document maintained by a duty officer who may be working in dirty and difficult conditions. The cargo log will best be maintained in a readable condition if immediate notes are kept in a notebook for transfer to the cargo log on next return to the ship's office or cargo control room. The cargo log and personal notebooks should always be retained, as they will be required as evidence in the event of a dispute and will carry more weight than a document which has been written up after the event.

Cargo documents: Copies of all cargo documents given to the ship, or presented for signature, should be retained. (The documents likely to be met are described in Chapter 14)

Damage records – damage to ship or cargo: It is vital that full records are kept of damage which occurs to ship or to cargo during loading or discharge. Some owners and charterers provide well designed 'stevedore damage' forms for such records but others are less suitable and a badly designed form may fail to provide all the necessary information, even when each space contains an entry. A well-designed form, such as the sample at Appendix 3.1, when completed will provide a full record of when, where and how the damage occurred and will contain a detailed description of the damage sustained.

As with all reports, sufficient information should be given to enable a reader with a professional knowledge of the subject to form a clear and accurate picture of the circumstances of the damage. Accurate measurements should be recorded, supported by photographs. (Actions to take when damage, particularly stevedore damage, occurs are discussed in Chapter 16). In the case of more substantial items of damage, when likely costs are to be measured in thousands of dollars, not tens of dollars, extensive detailed records will be required. The Nautical Institute's book ***The Mariners Role in Collecting Evidence***[89] provides full guidance for this situation.

Trim, stability and stress calculations: The trim, stability and stress calculations which are undertaken when planning the loading of a bulk cargo are usually done and stored on the ship's loading computer. It is prudent to print and retain hard copies of the calculations or to back up the computer records on disk in case the computerised records are destroyed. Cargo calculations which have been done by hand or by computers or calculators which are the personal property of ships' officers should also be retained for later inspection in event of an accident or dispute.

The records of the calculations should include the weights and assumed positions along with the values obtained from the calculations. Full details of the eventual departure condition on completion of loading or discharge should also be retained and filed for later inspection. These results may be useful in the planning of future cargoes or can provide answers to questions which may arise later concerning the present cargo.

The IMO BLU Code[110] requires completion of a Loading/Unloading Plan (see Chapter 9) and a Ship/Shore Safety Checklist, described in Chapter 11. The procedures for the calculation of stability are discussed in Chapter 10.

Draught survey calculations: The ship's calculations of the quantity of cargo by draught survey should be retained for inspection at a later date, if required. When an independent surveyor is appointed to make a draught survey, a copy of the results of his survey should be kept aboard along with the ship's own calculations, which should be done independently. (Procedures for the conduct of a draught survey are described in Chapter 13.)

Cargo book: It has become standard practice on some ships to include a note of cargo loaded or discharged on the ship's ports of call list or voyage memo, but more information can be valuable. On many bulk carriers it is the chief mate's practice to keep the details of previous cargoes readily to hand and this procedure can be strongly recommended. Considerable time can be saved and efficiency can be increased by studying the record of previous similar cargoes, particularly if carried between the same loading and discharge ports. One method of keeping such records is for the chief mate to maintain a cargo book.

Into such a book the chief mate will enter the principal details of each cargo with disposition of cargo (stowage plan), detailed list of bunkers and other weights aboard, departure and arrival draughts, dock water density, draught limitations, description of loading and discharging procedures, amount of cargo on conveyor belt, suggested trimming quantities and holds which were used for trimming, requirements of stevedores, reliability of shore weights, availability and price of fresh water, arrangements for access, and so on.

If these records are kept on a computer then ship, chief mate and any other interested parties can keep copies which will offer benefits in future efficiency.

The completion of such a record in the first day or two after the port visit will take no more than an hour or so. The chief mate's notes will include any information which could make a repeat voyage easier, such as which side is put alongside, tugs and moorings used, stevedores' hours of work, telephone availability, and arrangements for garbage disposal. If a local port information book has been obtained that fact also should be recorded.

Once a ship has gone beyond the first few voyages such a book or computer record needs a contents page, listing voyage number, date, cargo carried, loading port and discharging port: it makes good sense to maintain a contents page from the start. By reference to this book any similar previous cargoes can quickly be identified and their details inspected.

Voyage records: Whilst on charter the ship will probably be required to complete voyage abstracts for the charterers. If the ship is on voyage charter, the owners may require the Master to complete a proforma layday statement to enable them to check despatch or claim demurrage. Copies of these documents must be retained aboard ship.

Chain register/cargo gear register: The chain register is the register in which data concerning a ship's lifting gear must be recorded. The term 'lifting gear' includes derricks and cranes for the handling of stores, and also lifting gear used in the engineroom, and it is important that all such items of equipment should be properly tested, certified, marked and maintained.

The greatest practical importance of the chain register for a geared bulk carrier is as a register of all items of cargo-handling equipment. Such items, whether derricks or cranes, are used by stevedores for the loading and discharge of the cargo. Stevedores will expect to find that the equipment works efficiently and safely, and will, with good reason, complain about any defect in the equipment they are required to use. If they have any doubts about the condition of the equipment they will demand to inspect the chain register and it is vital that the register be kept fully and correctly up-to-date. In countries such as Australia and Canada union inspectors are likely to carry out spot checks aboard a ship to ensure that all the gear is safe, and also to verify that all items of gear are clearly marked and that test certificates can be readily located. Failure to have the chain register kept properly up-to-date can result in stoppage of work until matters have been put right, and the vessel will be put off hire in these circumstances.

There are two reasons for maintaining a chain register: it may be a requirement of the country with which the ship is registered and it may be a requirement of the country in which the ship is loading or discharging cargo. In theory a chain register issued in the form approved by any national authority or classification society will be acceptable in all countries which call for a register. In practice this is generally true, particularly when the ship is well maintained, but there are exceptions.

The chain register of one country is not always accepted at a local level in another country and some ship operators put aboard their ships chain registers from a number of the countries where difficulties are experienced in the ports. Thus a Liberian-registered ship may carry chain registers from Lloyd's Register and from the governments of Canada, Australia, New Zealand and India. Each country has its own requirements regarding frequency of inspection and these requirements differ one from another.

Some national administrations accept the chief officer as a 'competent person' whose signature for annual surveys is acceptable, but other countries such as India and Pakistan will accept a chief officer's signature only when he has a certificate issued by the government of the state whose flag the ship flies, stating that he has the authority to sign. The Panamanian register requires all surveys to be verified by a classification society surveyor.

Any chain register which the ship carries must be properly kept up to date. Before the register can be signed the following requirements must be satisfied.

- Every item of cargo gear must be of sufficient safe working load (SWL), and suitable design.
- Every item of cargo gear must be marked with a unique identifying number.
- There must be a certificate, in an approved form, for each item of cargo gear, identified by its unique number.
- A system must exist to produce the certificate for any item of cargo gear promptly.
- Every item of cargo gear must be in sound condition, and well maintained.
- Thorough inspections of the cargo gear must be carried out at the required intervals (annually for most authorities, but three-monthly for Australia).

When the inspections have been carried out the register must be signed in the appropriate places. Registers are normally divided into four parts to deal with four different categories of equipment. Careful study of the register will be required to identify where signatures are needed.

Quadrennial or quintennial examinations of lifting gear are carried out by competent persons such as surveyors from classification societies and foremen from marine engineering works or drydocks, who will sign the chain register upon completion of their work. If several chain registers are carried, the surveyor must be asked to sign all of them.

It will be apparent from the foregoing that national and local regulations for chain registers are varied, and their implementation is somewhat arbitrary. It may never be possible to comply with every requirement of every authority, but a ship aboard which the equipment is carefully maintained and renewed, properly marked and documented in accordance with the requirements of the flag State, and readily identified, will have done all that can reasonably be expected.

The Operations Manuals

Bulk carriers are provided with statutory manuals or 'booklets' usually prepared by the shipbuilders' naval architects and approved by the flag administration or a classification society appointed by them. A certified copy of each of these manuals, written in a language familiar to the ship's officers and, if that language is not English, also in English[150], must be kept aboard the ship and produced when required. The ship normally holds at least one additional working copy of each manual and the ship's operators normally hold another copy in their office. The manuals are essential reading for the ship's officers as they contain extensive instructions and guidance which are often not included in computerised versions of the information. It is vital that instructions regarding unsafe loading or ballasting plans and procedures are understood. The manuals deal with stability, grain stability, cargo loading and securing and ballast water management. If a working copy becomes badly dirty, dogeared or damaged a replacement working copy must be obtained. A certified copy must always be kept in good condition.

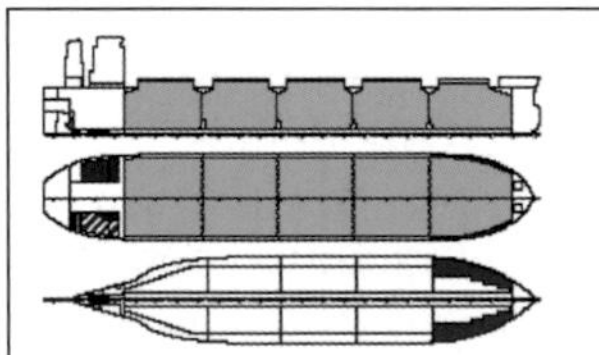

Stability Information Manual: This manual (see CD inside front cover), usually called the Stability 'Booklet' although it consists in this case of 381 A4 pages, opens with an Introduction and Instruction to the Master, reminding him that a stamped, legible copy of the booklet must always be readily available aboard ship and that stability calculations must always be completed before the vessel loads, to ensure that the ship is never overloaded, unstable or overstressed at any stage in the voyage. The booklet contains all the information necessary for longhand calculations of the ship's draught, trim and metacentric height (GM). A worked example is at ***Section 5*** and a blank form is at ***Section 14*** of the manual.

The Master is given a large number of useful warnings and reminders, including that he must exercise sound judgement and good seamanship, take precautions, ensure cargo is stowed securely, avoid excessive values of GM, close all watertight openings in adverse weather and ensure that closing devices are kept in good condition, not rely on automatic steering in adverse weather and maintain a seaworthy freeboard. He should reduce speed to avoid excessive rolling, frequent emergence of the propeller, too much water on deck or too frequent slamming.

He must exercise caution in following or quartering seas to avoid parametric resonance, broaching to, or loss of stability on the wave crest and excessive rolling which may occur singly, in sequence or all together, resulting in the danger of capsizing. Conditions are particularly dangerous when the wavelength is 1 to 1.5 times the length of the ship and course or speed should be altered to avoid these circumstances. (Ship handling in rough weather is discussed in Chapters 15 and 17 of ***Bulk Carrier Practice***.)

Stability whilst loading or discharging timber must be maintained, taking account of water absorbed or trapped by the cargo, ice, free surface effects and stores consumed. (See Chapter 10). All operations should stop if the ship lists for no known reason (Chapter 8). Before putting to sea the ship should be upright, have an adequate GM and satisfy all the required stability criteria.

Formation of ice on a vessel has an adverse effect because it increases the vessel's weight and reduces her freeboard, raises her centre of gravity, reduces her stability, increases her windage area and consequent heeling by the action of the wind, changes her trim and list and reduces her manoeuvrability and speed. Finally the Master is reminded that if the ship's structure is modified in a way that will influence the stability conditions new corrected stability information must be prepared.

The ship's main particulars appear in ***Section 2***, followed by necessary definitions and conversion factors in ***Section 3***. For example it is noted that the draughts given in the hydrostatic tables, the tables of form stability and the tables of maximum KG are measured from the ship's base line, which is the ***upper*** side of the 22mm thick keel plate whilst the ship's draught marks are measured from the ***lower*** side of the keel plate. This sort of inconsistency should be no problem for normal computerised calculations but would be an irritation in longhand computation.

Section 4 begins with a brief explanation of stability, curves of righting levers and free surface effect. The notes propose that when calculating free surface effect it should always be assumed that at least one transverse pair or single centreline tank containing each liquid (eg fuel oil, diesel oil, fresh water) has free surface and that the tank or tanks possessing free surface are the largest of their type. Provided that all 'slack' tanks are included these are safe assumptions.

The notes point out that the hydrostatic and isocline stability tables provide for trims between -1.00 metres and +3.00 metres. Extrapolation outside that range cannot be relied upon so the ship should not be trimmed more than 1 metres by the head or 3 metres by the stern. Trim and draught restrictions are stated, propeller immersion and air draught formulae are provided and requirements and formulae for the calculation of visibility ahead, over bows and deck cargo, are given. Draught and trim formulae for a loaded condition are provided as is actual displacement obtained from draught readings.

Paragraph 4.12 contains the information that all unprotected openings in the hull, deck or superstructure, which can affect the vessel's ability to withstand progressive flooding, will be immersed only when the vessel heels to more than 40°, thus satisfying IMO requirements. Any sailing condition has to satisfy IMO's intact stability requirements, given in ***Paragraph 4.13***, and compliance can be readily verified by use of the tables and diagrams of maximum allowable KG contained in ***Section 10***. The vessel should at all time comply with the tables of maximum allowable KG and/or minimum allowable GM. In doing so she will be satisfying the requirements for intact and for damaged stability as the tables take account of both. Because the vessel can carry cargo on deck IMO require that the effects of wind and rolling must be considered and the tables in ***Section 10*** take account of these factors.

Paragraph 4.15 states that the vessel is built in accordance with the SOLAS Convention, as amended up to and including the 1998 amendments. The vessel has been provided with a Ballast Water Management Plan as recommended by IMO. A copy is included with these documents. ***Paragraph 4.17*** states the vessel's allowable shear forces and bending moments and explains their origins in the limits imposed by the IACS Unified Requirements for strength in the flooded condition. The values are discussed in detail and readers are referred to the Cargo Loading and Securing Manual, a copy of which is included with these documents. A calculation to enable a comparison between allowable values and actual values of shear force is described.

In this vessel sloshing, which can cause serious damage to the vessel's structure, will only be a problem in the ballast hold, Hold No.3. ***Paragraph 4.17.5*** explains that the hold should never be left filled between 20-90% at sea and should only be filled or emptied at sea in calm conditions.

Ships carrying timber deck cargoes, ***Paragraph 4.17.6*** repeats, must have adequate stability, taking account of absorption of water, accretion of ice and free surface effects. The strength of the timber lashings should comply with the requirements of Code of Safe Practice for Ships Carrying Timber Deck Cargoes. ***Paragraph 4.17.7*** records that the vessel's lightship weight has been divided into several elements which are presented, with their distribution, in ***Section 12***.

Section 5 contains a worked example of a typical loading condition, 'as worked by hand'. Given the weights aboard, the calculations find the vessel's deadweight, vertical and longitudinal centres of gravity, free surface moments, draught, trim, allowable vertical centre of gravity and actual vertical centre of gravity. From this it is possible to see that the ship satisfies the required intact and flooded stability criteria. To assist users to follow the calculation the source of each argument is shown. The examples show how to use the formulae and interpolate the values. The calculation is a very cautious one: although no ballast is carried the free surface moments for the largest ballast tank have been included.

Section 6 contains plans and dimensions of all the vessel's compartments and ***Section 7*** contains a summary of 22 selected loading conditions with intact stability and longitudinal strength. Each condition is described in a nine page document presenting floating condition, weights aboard, visibility and air draught calculation, longitudinal strength without and with flooding and check of intact stability. In cases (for example Condition 19, departure with full bunkers and a full cargo of steel coils) in which ballast must be taken to satisfy the strength requirements as fuel is consumed an intermediate condition (Page 202) is provided.

Section 8 contains the vessel's hydrostatic tables for five different trims, ranging from 1 metre by the head to 3 metres by the stern, while ***Section 9*** contains stability data consisting of MS (stability lever MS as a function of draught and angle of heel) and KN (as a function of draught and angle of heel) data, both for the usual range of trims. ***Section 10*** provides the limit curves for maximum KG and minimum GM. The details of weathertight and unprotected openings used in the stability calculations as flooding points are given in ***Section 11***.

Section 12 contains details of the components of the vessel's lightweight and its distribution. ***Section 13***, headed 'Inclining Experiment' contains a letter authorising the use, for the lightweight test report, of the results (specifically the weight, and positions of the longitudinal and vertical centres of gravity) obtained from the inclining experiment for a sister ship. ***Section 14*** contains a blank set of forms for the intact and damaged stability calculations described in ***Section 5***. Drawings of draught marks and their positions, wind profile and area, freeboard plan and tank and capacity plan are provided in ***Section 15***.

Section 16 contains BC-A loading conditions. The section contains an explanation that these are not seagoing conditions, but simply strength conditions. They occupy the final 80 pages of the Stability Booklet.

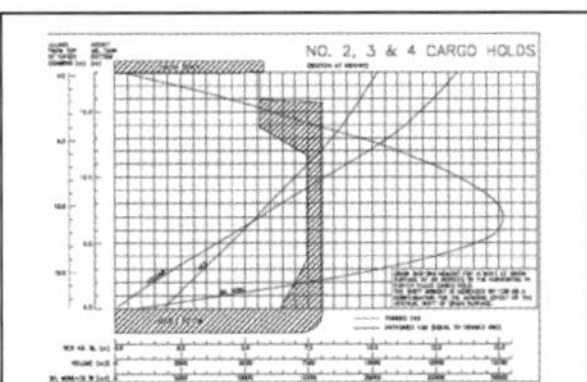

Grain Stability Manual: This manual (see CD inside front cover) is an appendix to the Stability Information Manual (see above) and readers are warned that it contains only information relating to grain stability. The early sections repeat warnings about the need for full and proper calculations, caution and seamanlike procedures. ***Section 2*** (Main Particulars) and ***Section 3*** (Definitions and Conversion Table) repeat the corresponding sections in the Stability Information Manual.

Section 4 describes the calculation of grain stability in general terms and ends by summarising the requirement by remarking that when the vessel is carrying grain, the Master has to ensure that the sum of the heeling moments due to grain shift is smaller than the value obtained from the limiting tables in ***Section 9***.

Section 5 contains a three page worked example, the first two pages of which are similar to the stability calculation provided in the Stability Information Manual and explained in ***Section 5 of that document***. The third page provides the additional calculations required to satisfy the Grain Regulations. The values for the grain shifting moments (or grain heeling moments) are taken from the tables and graphs in ***Section 8***, the quickest argument with which to enter the table being VCG, as this value had already been used in Page 1 of the calculation. For a filled hold there are, at the foot of the table, two sets of values: Filled or Untrimmed. In accordance with the Grain Regulations the example uses the Untrimmed grain shifting moments to match the untrimmed value for tonnage which the example assumes is in the hold. It should be noted that would be unacceptable to the Australian, United States and Canadian authorities who insist that full, trimmed tonnages are used with shifting moments for untrimmed ends, to take account of variations in the extent to which ends fill in particular cases and to introduce a greater safety margin (See Chapter 19). The worked example shows that the moments must be corrected to take account of the density of the grain, measured in tonnes/m^3. Maximum allowable grain heeling moments for the loading example are obtained from the tables in ***Section 9***, entered with trim, draught and KG.

Section 6 provides routine tank and capacity information for the ship and ***Section 7*** contains a range of six grain loading conditions, investigated for trim, stability and strength, with intermediate conditions provided in cases where the vessel has to ballast as bunkers are consumed. The examples include loadings with Nos 2 and 4 holds part filled and alternatively with No 3 hold part filled.

Section 8 contains the tables and graphs of shifting (or heeling) moments for each hold and ***Section 9*** presents tables of maximum allowable moments.

Empty calculation sheets are found in ***Section 10***.

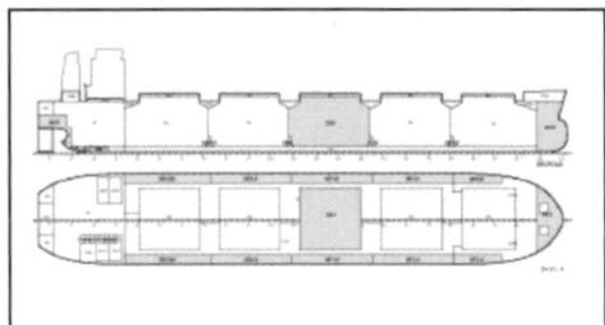

Ballast Water Management Manual: This manual (see CD inside front cover), written in 2006, with provision on Page 5 for recording updates, notes in ***Section 1*** that ballast water exchange is not yet mandatory throughout the world, but that it is already a requirement in a number of countries. Readers are advised to consult destination ports in advance, to keep records of requirements and to look for information on the internet and from the sources listed. The manual applies only to the ship for which it is written. The purpose of the Ballast Water Management Plan contained in the manual is explained. It is intended to provide guidance for ship's personnel and information for quarantine officers. A full and accurate Ballast Log should be maintained, even in places where it is not required, as the record may be useful at a later date.

Section 2 contains descriptions of the sequential and flow-through methods of changing ballast (see ***Bulk Carrier Practice*** Chapter 7) and summarises times when ballast should and should not be exchanged. The problems of taking ballast water in harbour are recorded in ***Paragraph 2.4*** and the desirability of removing sediment from ballast tanks is discussed. Factors to consider when planning a change of ballast are listed and readers are reminded that ballast in tanks which will remain full in the next port may not need to be changed. Port state requirements are likely to change, says ***Paragraph 2.8***, so Appendix 3 of the Manual, with contact addresses and data, should be kept up to date. Ship's personnel should understand the purpose of ballast water exchange and be familiar with the dangers of the process. They should know the locations of the ballast water sampling points (ie the sounding pipes). ***Paragraph 2.10*** lists the duties of the Ballast Water Management Officer who has responsibility for understanding, planning, supervising, reporting and recording the process of ballast exchange and training ship's personnel in their relevant duties. IMO forms for reporting ballast, for logging ballast operations and for recording sediment processes, with notes of guidance, are in Appendix 2 of the Manual.

Section 3 lists the vessel's principal particulars and provides a drawing of the draught marks. Details of the No 3 (ballast) hold airpipes and ventilators are provided and the need for them to be secured in the open position before commencement of ballasting operations is emphasised. Plans (drawings) providing information useful for ballast exchange are listed in ***Paragraph 3.3*** and extracts of some of the plans are provided. The ballast water management plans assume full heavy ballast (with No 3 hold ballasted) or full light ballast (No 3 hold empty). Programmes for other ballast conditions should be carefully planned on the ship's loading computer. Ballast water samples can be obtained from the sounding pipes. Ballast tank sediment samples can only be obtained via the tank manholes when the tanks are empty. ***Paragraph 3.11.1*** states that ballast exchange of all ballast except No 3 hold can be done using the sequential method. Exchange of ballast in No 3 hold must be done by the flow-through method.

Weather conditions should be stable, and no worse than wind Beaufort Force 4, and waves no greater than about 1 metre in height. The vessel's GM should be sufficient at every stage and to comply with damaged stability requirements should never be less than 1.2 m. Actual values for shear force and bending moments must always be within the permissible range (reproduced in ***Paragraph 3.11.6 and 7***). All these conditions will be satisfied if the ship's ballast management plans are always followed strictly. Unintended free surface should always be avoided and, in particular, the free surface which can arise in No 3 hold as a result of open ventilators.

Paragraph 3.11.8 describes the procedure for correcting the actual shear force. The draught and trim restrictions to which the vessel is subject when expecting to meet adverse weather and when in ballast are stated in ***Paragraph 3.11.9 and 10***. These restrictions also satisfy the need to keep the emergency fire pump suction below the surface and to immerse the propeller. Sloshing is a potential problem only in Hold No.3 which therefore should not be filled or emptied, nor kept filled to 20-90 per cent capacity whilst at sea, except in calm and stable conditions.

Paragraph 3.11.12 warns that tanks can suffer serious structural damage as a consequence of over or under pressurising. The ballast tanks are designed and dimensioned to ballast and deballast as far as possible by gravity and No.3 hold has a direct opening to the sea for this purpose. Hold and tank ventilators and airpipes must be fully open and ballast pumps, when used, should be one pump at most per tank, except for the ballast hold, on which two pumps can be used. Airpipes and ventilators used for the outflow of water when changing ballast by flow-through must be unimpeded. Any flame screens are to be removed and no ice must be allowed to form: this must be checked regularly. The ballast system is subjected to extra stress when ballast exchange takes place and components should be regularly checked for wear to avoid unexpected failure.

Guidance for ensuring that visibility ahead is always adequate is contained in ***Paragraph 3.11.13***. Time required for completion of a ballast exchange should be monitored and recorded for future reference. Time required to fill No 3 hold is about 4.5 hours and to achieve three flow-through changes will take about 15 hours. During ballast water exchange caution should be exercised in the vicinity of No.3 hold because for 15 hours large amounts of water pour out of the ventilation openings about 1.8 m above the deck (Fig. 18.8). Before and after each step in the ballast exchange the nearness of land, the weather forecast, crew fatigue, condition of equipment and any other relevant factors should be reassessed and if any are unfavourable the ballast exchange should be stopped or suspended.

Section 4 contains a full account of the two programmes for ballast exchange, in tabular form. ***Section 5*** contains IMO Resolution A868(20), which is a twenty page document on the subject of ballast exchange. A set of 4 blank forms is to be found in ***Section 6***. ***Section 7*** contains useful internet links and a list, dated 2001, giving information about ballast exchange requirements of several countries. Pages 72-215 contain the calculations supporting each step in the ballast water exchange plans.

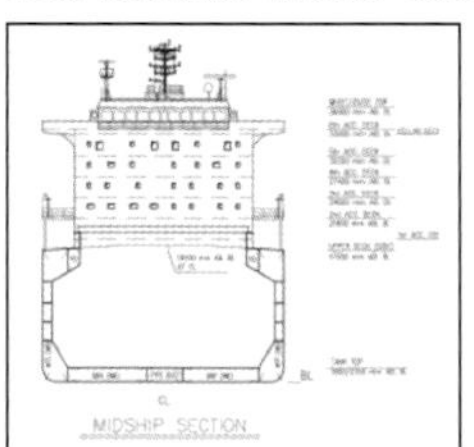

Cargo Loading and Securing Manual: This manual (see CD inside front cover), or 'booklet' contains 350 pages divided into three principal sections of which the first is General and Vessel Particulars. Second comes the Cargo Loading Manual and third the Cargo Securing Manual. The manual provides the Master with information and instruction about the ship's stability in various conditions of loading. In ***Section 1*** the rules requiring stability information are listed and the requirements to ensure that the ship will experience no excessive stresses, will float appropriately and will be stable at all stages of every voyage are affirmed. The vessel is intended to transport dry bulk cargoes, steel coils and timber so loading information for each of these commodities and also for metal scrap is provided.

The manual is valid only for the ship for which it was written and must be kept on board and made available to port/flag state inspectors, class surveyors and others with a legitimate interest. It is approved by Det Norske Veritas (DNV) and must not be altered or revised without the approval of DNV but it should be regularly updated and maintained with loading sequences for ports visited. Any cargo securing equipment must be properly certified. (When the manual was issued the ship carried no cargo securing equipment). If project cargoes (otherwise known as 'heavy lifts') are to be carried the manual is to be updated according to the requirements for ship specific accelerations and calculation examples. The guidance given in the manual, which should not overrule the principles of good seamanship, should be used in conjunction with the ship's loading computer.

Section 2 contains the ship's particulars supported by copies of several plans and by a list of documents providing additional information. Worthy of particular note is the fact that the vessel is designed to operate with holds 2 and 4, or hold 3 empty.

Section 3 is concerned with the ship's design loads and opens by listing the maximum permissible uniformly distributed loads on hatch covers, decks and tanktop. The words 'uniformly distributed' are vital. In a hold full of coal or grain the cargo is uniformly distributed. A cargo of iron ore, trimmed level, is uniformly distributed and a timber deck cargo, properly stowed, is uniformly distributed. However a project cargo ('heavy lift') is not uniformly distributed. Nor is a laden fork lift truck on the tanktop and nor is a cargo of steel coils. For these loads the maximum permissible loads stated in ***Section 3*** do not necessarily apply and other calculations must be made. For the carriage of steel coils in this vessel the calculations have been made and the results appear later in this manual.

The loading of any cargo hold, which for local and longitudinal strength purposes includes the loading of the double bottom tank below the hold, must comply with the ship's longitudinal strength as well as the local strength of the individual cargo hold. A set of five diagrams, entered with draught at the midlength of the hold, show the maximum and minimum tonnages which can be loaded in each of the holds. The diagrams take account of the fact that the ship is designed to load fully with certain combinations of holds empty. A sixth diagram gives the maximum and minimum tonnages of cargo/ballast for each pair of holds. It appears that this can be used for any pair of adjacent holds, for example 1 and 2 or 3 and 4 but this is not stated. It seems likely that this is a test that must be made when any hold is part filled, but this too is not stated.

Section 4 lists the IMO and IACS publications which specify how cargo should be loaded and states the ship's loading restrictions and limitations with regard to draught, trim, propeller immersion and view ahead, repeating the information contained in the Stability Information Manual.

Section 5 describes and illustrates the ship's ballast system, repeating the information contained in the Ballast Water Management Manual.

Section 6, Stability Information, refers readers to the ship's Stability Information Manual and summarises some of the contents of that manual. Because no IACS Unified Requirements for double skinned bulk carriers existed when the ship was built a description of the Damaged Stability criteria which were used is given. The ship is provided with an approved loading instrument and should use it to plan and monitor loading and discharge.

Section 7 records that the ship is designed to carry ordinary bulk cargoes as well as timber, logs and steel coils. The dangerous solid bulk cargoes that the ship can carry are catalogued and the precautions required for particular cargoes – surface ventilation, electric installations disconnected or explosion proofed and/or spark arresting screens to be fitted in ventilator openings – are listed. The electrical equipment in the holds, including the water ingress detectors, is of the certified safe type. The gauges, gas detectors, thermometers, protective clothing, etc with which the ship is equipped, are listed.

The loading patterns that the vessel is allowed to adopt are listed in ***Section 8*** which demonstrates her versatility by mentioning:

- Homogeneous full cargo loading at design and scantling draught.
- Heavy bulk cargo in holds No 1, 3 and 5 with holds No.2 and 4 empty and at scantling draught (Alternate or 'Jump' Loading).
- Light dry bulk cargoes in holds Nos 1, 2, 4 and 5 to full scantling draught (Block Loading).
- Packaged timber on weather deck hatches and side decks.
- Steel coils loaded in holds to full scantling draught.

The regulations requiring the shipper to provide the Master with information about the cargo are quoted and the Master is reminded of his duty to agree a plan to ensure safe loading, discharge and voyage of the vessel and to ensure that the cargo is trimmed reasonably level to the boundaries of the space.

Paragraph 8.5 describes the typical loading sequences provided in the manual. However some of these sequences have been amended to conform with the guidelines contained in IACS' Recommendation 83 (Appendix 3.2). The following amended comments should, therefore, be noted with regard to the calculations.

- All conditions shown are calculated with 100% consumables on arrival and on departure. When new, actual loading sequences are simulated on the vessel's loading instrument bunkering, etc should be taken into account.
- In the initial and final loading conditions seagoing moments and shear forces are used. During cargo operations harbour values are used.
- Although loading rates are unknown it has been assumed that they may be twice the speed of deballasting rates. For example it may be impossible to deballast more than 5,000 tonnes whilst 10,000 tonnes of cargo is being loaded.
- Only loading is shown in the examples. Unloading can be done by reversing the processes.

The loading conditions shown are:

- Light ballast to homogeneous cargo
- Light ballast to heavy cargo (Holds 1, 3 and 5 loaded)
- Light ballast to block cargo (Holds 1, 2, 4 and 5 loaded)

Later in the manual the following additional loading condition appears:

- Light ballast to full cargo of steel coils.

The ship's cargo washing and drainage system (ie the hold washing system) which features permanent pipelines in every hold to deliver compressed air and washing water and to transfer dirty washing water to the collecting tanks is described and illustrated in ***Paragraph 8.6***.

Section 9 is a general introduction to the Cargo Securing Manual. The information is general in nature because at the time it was written the ship was carrying no equipment for lashing timber deck cargoes or steel coils.

Section 10 provides generalised guidance for the carriage of timber. In ***Paragraph 10.2*** the ship's officers are instructed to insert in the lashing manual lashing plans showing use of the actual lashing equipment on board in compliance with the requirements of the Code (of Safe Practice for Ships Carrying Timber Deck Cargoes). Although *'lashing eyes for timber deck loads'* are mentioned in ***Paragraph 10.5.1*** no plan is provided, because the eyes are not fitted to this vessel.

Stowage patterns, stability, height and extent of timber deck cargo and lashing equipment are amongst the subjects discussed. ***Page 10-6*** is left blank for the insertion of a list of timber lashing equipment. After the blank page ***Paragraph 10.5.2*** continues with a useful description of tightening and caring for the lashings on a timber deck cargo and this is followed by ***Paragraph 10.5.3*** which deals with the inspection and maintenance of lashing equipment.

Layouts suitable for the recording of deficiencies in equipment, and routine inspection and maintenance logs are provided in ***Paragraph 10.5***. ***Section 10.6*** contains detailed guidance on the loading of a timber deck cargo dealing with basic principles, safety measures, before loading, when stowing, securing, before leaving port, during the voyage, tightening the lashings, voyage planning and ship handling and listing during the voyage. ***Paragraph 10.8*** consists of Appendix A from the Code of Safe Practice for Ships Carrying Timber Deck Cargoes and ***Section 11*** contains Appendix B from the same publication.

Section 12 deals with the carriage of steel coils and starts with the steel coil dimensions for which the ship is designed and the Det Norske Veritas (DNV) requirements for dunnage and spacing of the coils. Tables are provided which govern occasions when the coils are of sizes other than length 1,200 mm and diameter 2,000 mm. When loading standard coils the ship can carry a full deadweight cargo, something which many bulk carriers are unable to do (see Chapter 19). Plan and elevation views of steel coil stowages in all holds are provided.

Paragraph 12.5.1 contains a loading sequence for steel coils which satisfies trim, stability and strength requirements. In practice the steel coil loading sequence is likely to be governed by the number of loading gangs and the type or types of coils being loaded. The loading is most unlikely to be as fast as with an ore cargo and deballasting in step with the loading is not likely to be a problem.

Section 12.6 is based on the IMO Code of Safe Practice for Cargo Stowage and Securing[38] and describes the stowage and securing of steel coils.

Section 13 contains useful practical advice on the loading and stowing of metal scrap in bulk.

Computer printouts of every step in the strength and stability calculations for the five typical cargo loadings (see above) are contained in the 259 pages which form ***Section 14***.

Sections 15, 16 and 17 contain respectively empty loading/deballasting forms for agreement between ship and terminal, space for recording loading/deballasting programmes used in particular ports and blank log sheets for the recording of maintenance of cargo securing equipment

Tank calibration tables: These are tables which show for each of the ship's tanks the volume of liquid which corresponds to the sounding obtained. Calibrations are required for all ballast, fresh water, engine water, fuel oil and diesel oil tanks, and for ballast holds. These calibrations are normally calculated by the builders from the ship's drawings, in which case they may be marked 'as designed' or 'as built'. 'Enhanced drawing calibration' is a method of improving the accuracy of the calibrations. This is achieved by adjusting certain basic measurements taken from the ship's plans to correspond with the physical dimensions taken 'in tank'. A range of more accurate though more expensive methods of tank calibration is also available, but is unlikely to be used for the ballast tanks of bulkers.

The calibration tables will probably provide for trims ranging, say, from 1 metre by the head to 3 metres by the stern. When the actual trim is a value other than one of the quoted values, it will be necessary to interpolate to obtain the exact volume of liquid in the tank and if no trim corrections are provided the corrections to apply must be calculated by geometry. These are calculations which can be quickly done with the assistance of a suitable computer program, if provided.

The normal purpose of finding the volume of liquid in a tank is to discover its weight. If the weight is required, the volume obtained from the calibration tables must be multiplied by the density of the contents – fuel oil, diesel oil, ballast water or fresh water. (The use of calibration tables for the calculation of weights aboard ship is described in Chapter 13).

It is usual for the chief mate and the chief engineer both to have working copies of the tables, and a clean copy should be retained, perhaps by the Master, so that replacement copies can be produced when the working copies become dirty and worn.

Ship's plans or drawings

If the ship's officers are to deal efficiently with the problems that they are likely to encounter during the lifetime of a ship, and particularly as she becomes older, they will require at least two sets of ship's plans, or drawings, with the Master retaining a 'best' set, and chief mate and chief engineer keeping a working set. It is now a requirement[261] for as-built drawings to be kept up-to-date and retained on board with copies kept by the owners ashore. If these plans are to be of maximum value, the labels and summaries which they contain should be written in the language of the ship's officers. It may be acceptable for them to be labelled in English if the officers have a sufficiently good command of English.

For efficient use the plans are best stored in an indexed filing system and folded as originally supplied, with their titles visible. It is useful to maintain a book in which the removal and return of plans is recorded to assist in the tracing of missing plans. Plans should be checked annually against the index and missing plans located or renewed.

Occasionally the vertical scale of a plan is different from the horizontal scale: this should be remembered if it is necessary to take measurements from a plan. A triangular scale rule which can be used to read dimensions at six different common plan scales is a useful item of equipment.

Framed copies of some of the most important plans are likely to be displayed upon bulkheads within the accommodation, either on the bridge, in alleyways or in offices or control rooms. They are likely to fade and become unreadable over a period of years and should be replaced when this happens. Copies of plans can often be supplied by the builders, even many years after the ship was built, though the price for this service may be high.

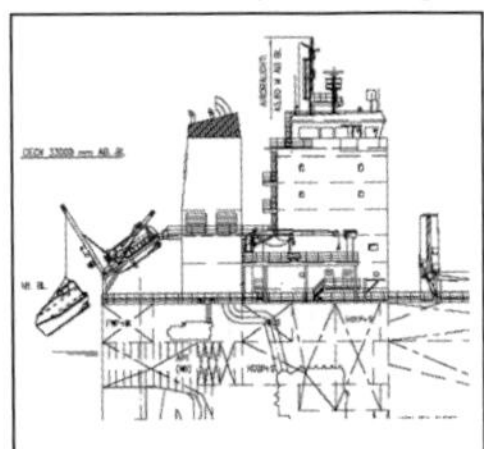

General Arrangement Plan: The General Arrangement (GA) plan (see CD inside front cover) is drawn at a scale of 1/400 although, when seen on a computer its size can, of course, be varied as convenient. It quotes the ship's main dimensions and class notation. Plan views of the ship are provided at tanktop and upper deck level, as are plan views of all levels of superstructures and of the machinery spaces. The entire ship is also shown in elevation and two transverse cross-sections are provided, one at midships and the other in way of a transverse bulkhead. The GA plan shows and names all the ship's main features and provides some principal dimensions. It is a plan which provides a quick general appreciation of the ship including the layout of the bridge, the accommodation, store rooms and machinery spaces. It shows the locations of holds, tanks, storerooms, cabins, main items of machinery and equipment, and the positions and heights of masts, antennae and radar masts.

The GA plan is a useful source of general information about the ship and can be used for the measurement of distances such as the air draught, or the distance from the centre of No.4 hold to the bows, should these be required.

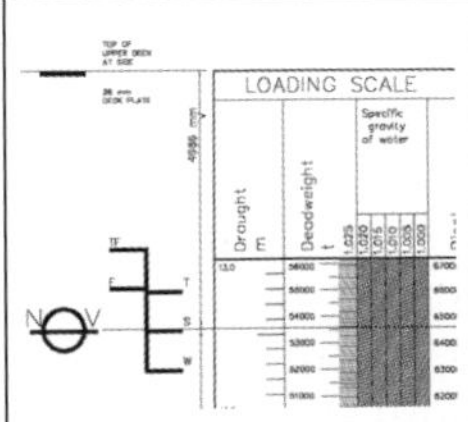

Tank and Capacity Plan: The Tank and Capacity Plan (see CD inside front cover) is a comprehensive source of the practical information needed to plan the loading of conventional and unusual cargoes. The ship's principal particulars and equipment are listed, dimensions, capacities and details of bunker and ballast tanks and cargo holds are provided. A full draught and deadweight scale, with readings for a range of sea water densities and for displacement, moment to change trim 1 cm (MCTC) and tonnes/cm immersion is shown. Details such as safe working load and maximum operating radius of cranes or derricks are provided. Loadline and freeboard information is listed though more accurate values can be obtained from the ship's stability tables, which should be used for all accurate calculations and surveys.

The vessel is shown in a number of elevation and plan views, focussing on structural details and dimensions and the list of hazardous cargoes that the ship is certified to carry is provided. In the capacity plans of some bulk carriers, though not this example, the bale capacity as well as the grain capacity of each cargo compartment is stated in cubic metres and/or cubic feet. Grain capacity is the total internal volume of the cargo compartment and is so called because it is the space which could be occupied by a cargo of bulk grain if trimmed to fill all spaces within the compartment. Bale capacity, by contrast, allows for the fact that bulky cargo such as bales or steel products cannot be stowed against the ship's shell plating, bulkheads and deckheads because of the frames, stiffeners and beams which, in a single hulled bulk carrier, are attached to these surfaces at intervals. Bale capacity is grain capacity less the space contained between internal hold fittings. Capacities of the hatch coamings are often given separately from capacities of the holds.

Cargo Washing and Drainage System plan: The plan (see CD inside front cover) shows the arrangement of permanent piping in each hold to provide the water and air for the system, and the detail of the collecting tanks to contain the used hold washing water. Details of the washing and stripping equipment are given.

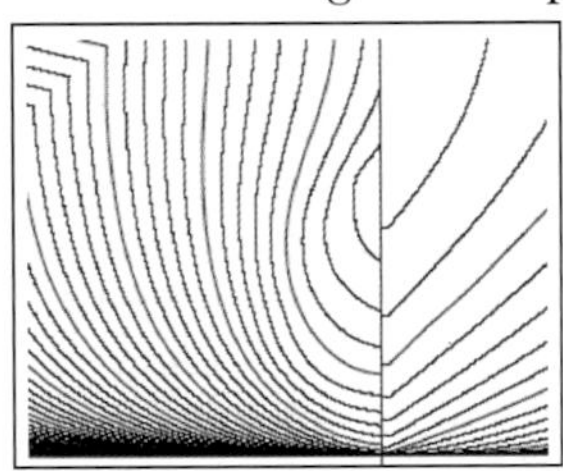

Docking Plan: The docking plan (see CD inside front cover), drawn at a scale of 1:400, provides information useful when drydocking the vessel. Besides measurements needed by the drydock personnel in order to position the blocks and sidebeds correctly the plan provides information such as docking draught and trim, air draught, hull paint areas, weights aboard to achieve docking trim, grades of steel used in specified areas and positions of bottom plugs, echo sounder and log sensors. The docking plan is a useful alternative to the general arrangement plan and the capacity plan when measurements are required. The lines plan/body plan often is not given to the ship to protect the shipyard's Intellectual Property Rights.

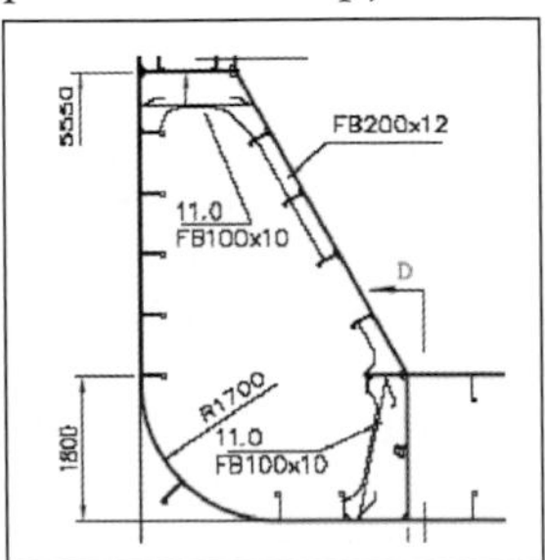

Midship Section: The midship section plan (see CD inside front cover) records the ship's main dimensions and class notation, and her design criteria. The construction details and scantlings are shown at various positions along the vessel's length and around her transverse cross-section. The structural details of the duct keel, double bottoms, bilge keel, side tanks, topside tanks, pipe ducts and hatch coamings can be seen.

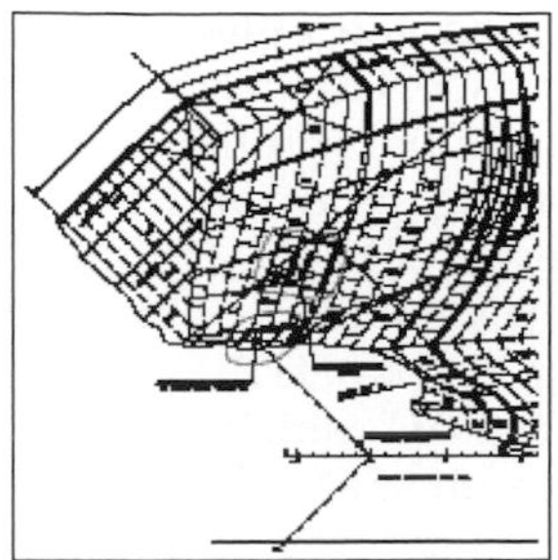

Shell Expansion (Aft) and Shell Expansion (Fwd): These plans (see CD inside front cover) are essential for describing the locations of damage to the ship's shell and connections to the shell. The boundaries of the shell plates are shown by thin continuous lines interrupted at intervals by a symbol like a $ and the thickness of each plate is shown in millimetres (eg '18.0'). Recent bulk carriers built to the IACS Common Structural Rules show Net Scantlings, on which the strength calculations are based, as well as Gross Scantlings which include corrosion addition plus owner's addition when applicable. In other words a minimum and a maximum value is shown for each plate thickness. The frames, floors, girders, longitudinals, bilge keels and stringers which make contact with the shell plating are shown by pecked lines, the more significant items such as girders, stringers and tanktop edge being labelled at the edge of the plan. The locations of other features such as sea chests and anchor pods are also shown. The labelling takes the form 'STRINGER, 5550 AB BL' meaning 5550 mm above baseline, ie the upper side of the keel plate, or 'GIRDER, 8800 OFF CL' meaning 8800 mm from the centreline. Bulkheads are shown by heavy pecked lines. The frame numbering appears at the bottom and again at the top of the plan, counting forward, and aft, from zero at the after perpendicular (at the rudder stock). The limits of each cargo hold are also shown at the top of the plan.

No system of numbering or naming strakes of plating or individual plates is shown on the plans. The convention is to name strakes of plating A, B, C, etc starboard or port, at midships where the greatest number of strakes of plating are found, with A being the keel plate. However this system does not work satisfactorily for this vessel because the strakes of plating are discontinuous at the engine room and forepeak bulkheads. Individual plates are traditionally numbered from the stern, 1, 2, 3, etc but frame numbers taken from the shell expansion plan are probably a simpler method of identifying position along the length of the vessel. A shell damage location could be described as follows: *Indentation, diameter 1,500 mm depth 40 mm, starboard side, between Frames 171 and 173 and just below stringer 5500 mm above BL.* The plans show that the bilge keel extends from the after bulkhead of No.4 hold to Frame 155 in No.2 hold. The areas of tanks adjacent to the shell plating are indicated by diagonal lines joining opposite corners of the tank in question.

Mooring Arrangement 1/2: The mooring arrangement plan (see CD inside front cover) shows the layout of mooring equipment on the forecastle, main deck and poop and should be consulted if problems with mooring are being experienced. The equipment requirements for Class and the ship's actual outfit of mooring lines are stated and fairleads, Panama chocks, bollards and other mooring furniture are specified.

Life-Saving Equipment: This plan (see CD inside front cover) provides an inventory for the ship's life-saving equipment and shows where the equipment is located. Of particular interest is the stores crane on the port side of the accommodation which serves also to launch the ship's rescue boat and/or a liferaft. The stores crane on the starboard side is similarly available to launch the liferaft which is stored beside it.

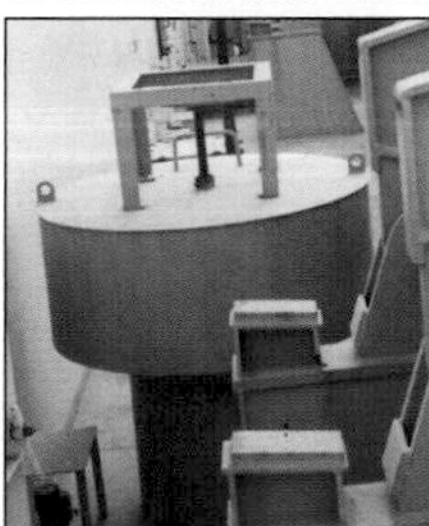

Natural Ventilation: This plan (see CD inside front cover), despite its name, shows all the ship's ventilation, both natural and mechanical. The hold ventilation is basic natural ventilation, with two ventilation openings in each end (fore and aft) of each set of hatch covers. Ventilation for the accommodation and store rooms is also shown. The statutory requirements with which the ventilators comply are listed and fittings such as spark arresting screens and rat proof nets are specified. On ships with more elaborate hold ventilation systems the plan will show the locations of hold ventilator cowls, of ventilator trunks and of ventilator flaps for opening or closing the trunks. It shows whether air can be delivered through grilles at the bottom of the hold or only at the top. If ventilator fans are fitted, their positions will be shown on the plan and the capacity of each should be stated. The plan should show the number of air changes per hour which can be achieved in each hold, when empty, if the fans are running.

The cargo ventilation plan should be consulted when the hold ventilation system is being tested and maintained and when a cargo which requires ventilation is to be carried. It is also of the greatest importance should a fire develop in the cargo. In these circumstances it will be necessary to ensure that all hold ventilation is sealed.

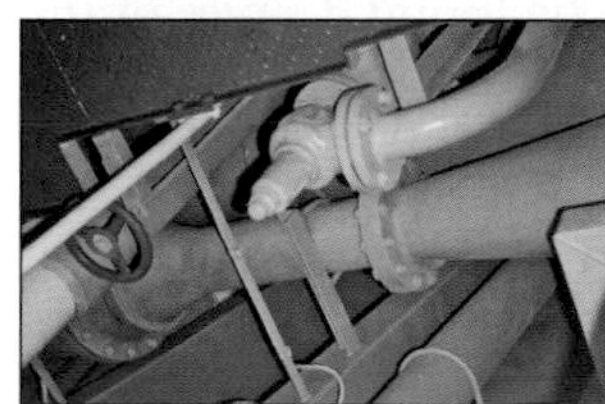

Ballast/Stripping System: The pumping of ballast and of bilges will normally be done by the duty deck officer who will himself operate the appropriate controls to set the valves and start the pump, or who will instruct a crew member to carry out these operations. These are the pumping matters described in this volume. The plan (see CD inside front cover) shows two main ballast lines and a ballast stripping line which run the length of the duct keel, from the engine room to the forepeak bulkhead. The port ballast line is connected to all the port double bottom and wing tanks and to the fore and after peaks. The starboard ballast line is connected to all the starboard double bottom and wing tanks. Both ballast lines are connected to the ballast hold, (No 3 hold) and the direct gravitating line between No 3 hold and the sea is also shown.

In the engine room a crossover line connects the two main ballast lines and enables the port ballast pump (labelled) to fill or empty tanks on the starboard side and the starboard ballast pump (labelled) to do the same for tanks on the port side.

The stripping line is connected to the ballast eductor on the port side of the engine room and serves all the ballast spaces except the forepeak, the afterpeak and No 3 hold. The two peak tanks presumably taper so much that stripping is unnecessary and No 3 hold can be stripped via the hold bilge pumping system. The plan shows that the forepeak valve in the forepeak is operated remotely, from the upper deck, with the assistance of a hydraulic hand pump. That valve is duplicated by a remotely controlled butterfly valve at the fore end of the duct keel.

A note states that 'The stripping suction on one side to be placed inboard of tank and for other side to be placed outboard to enable efficient stripping by suitable list of vessel'. To take advantage of this while deballasting and loading, the vessel would need to be listed, which would tend to encourage assymetrical pouring of cargo in the holds and the creation of cargo torque.

The plan of the ballast/stripping system is often useful when difficulties with ballast are met, or when an unusual ballasting or deballasting operation is planned. For example, is it possible to change trim quickly by pumping water direct from afterpeak to forepeak? The answer can be obtained from the plan.

The pumping plan can also assist in the study of ballasting or deballasting problems. Why does No 4 port double bottom tank fill when the forepeak is being filled? If the plan shows that the forepeak filling line passes through No 4 port double bottom tank, as it might do in a ship without a duct keel, it is likely that the filling line is holed in No 4 double bottom tank.

Fire and Safety Plan: The plan (see CD inside front cover) tabulates all the ship's fire and safety equipment, features and fittings and shows where they are to be found. Copies of the ship's fire and safety plan will be located in a number of prominent positions throughout the ship. On a longitudinal profile of the ship, supplemented by plan views of every deck, the position of every item of firefighting equipment will be shown. The plan will also list each item of equipment with brief details of sizes and types of hoses, hydrants, fire extinguishers, fire doors, firemen's outfits, breathing apparatus, safety lockers, lifebuoys and attachments, lifeboats, liferafts, ladders, emergency lighting, remote machinery stops, and so on. Colour coding of these plans makes them easier to read, and the symbols used must be internationally recognised.

Fuel Oil Service System: This plan (see CD inside front cover) illustrates the system linking storage tanks to settling, service, drain and sludge tanks and to the ship's main and auxiliary machinery.

Air, Sounding and Filling Pipes: The plan (see CD inside front cover) shows the position of air and sounding pipes and labels each one eg SD412/s412(40)C which presumably refers to Sounding No.412, and AP33/33(300)C which appears to refer to an air pipe. On the basis that sounding pipes are usually positioned over the deepest part of the tank, and air pipes are located over the highest point in the tank most of the items can be identified, but a list of air, sounding and filling pipes is needed. In bulk carriers in general it is not unusual for the sounding pipe for No.2 hold starboard bilge, say, to run down the forward bulkhead of No.3 hold. When looking for a sounding pipe it is useful to discover before leaving the accommodation that the search must be in No.3 hold or No.3 double-bottom tank, not No.2. It is also a loadline requirement (and good seamanship) to ensure that all the labels and markings on individual airpipes are correct, and the plan will assist in this process.

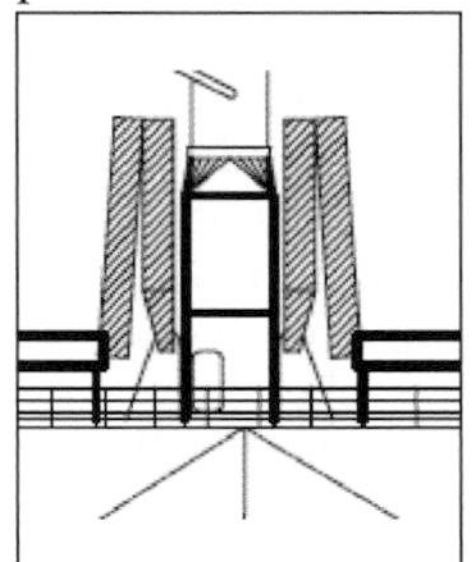

General Arrangement of Hatch Covers: This plan (see CD inside front cover) shows the positions of the vessel's double skin transfolding hatch covers in plan and elevation and provides detailed drawings of wheels, stoppers, a bottom hinge, a main cross joint, a snap lock and a pair of folded covers.

Sealing Plan of Hatch Covers: The plan (see CD inside front cover) identifies and names the appropriate rubber/neoprene seal for each position on the hatch covers and gives guidance on fitting and fixing them.

Fire protection plans: The provision of fire protection systems in cargo spaces is usually subcontracted to specialist fire protection companies who produce their own plans and booklets to describe the system. Such systems, which normally protect the machinery spaces as well as the cargo compartments, typically consist of provision for CO_2 smothering. From a bottle room pipes lead to every cargo and machinery space. If a fire occurs the appropriate quantity of CO_2 gas can by decision of the officer in charge be injected into the compartment which contains the fire. The same pipework may also be routinely used to continuously extract samples of air from each compartment and deliver them to a central point such as the navigating bridge. Here they pass across a photo-electric cell which detects smoke and activates an alarm. (The system is described in Chapter 6.)

Full plans of the system should be available and may need to be consulted when damage is being repaired or when the system is being tested. In addition, instructions for operating the system in event of fire will be posted in the CO_2 bottle room and in one or two other prominent positions such as the bridge.

Reference books required aboard bulk carriers

The following books which are recommended specifically for carriage aboard bulk carriers are listed, with publishers, at the end of this chapter.

The International Maritime Solid Bulk Cargoes Code (The ***IMSBC Code*** – previously the *BC Code*): The *IMSBC Code* is a carefully researched and detailed guide, developed over many years, to consider every aspect of the safe carriage of solid bulk cargoes. It should be consulted whenever unfamiliar cargoes or circumstances are encountered, and it should be read and reread regularly by ships' officers to ensure that they remain familiar with the principles of carrying solid bulk cargoes safely. The *IMSBC Code* states best practice and is scheduled to become mandatory on January 1, 2011 following entry into force of amendments to Chapters VI and VII of SOLAS. Some governments are likely to make the *IMSBC Code* mandatory before that date.

The primary aim of the *IMSBC Code* is to promote the safe stowage and shipment of bulk cargoes by highlighting the dangers associated with the shipment of certain types of bulk cargoes and giving guidance on the procedures to be adopted when the shipment of bulk cargoes is proposed. The *IMSBC Code* also lists typical materials currently shipped in bulk together with advice on their properties and handling, and describes test procedures to be employed to determine various characteristics of the bulk cargo materials.

Topics discussed include cargo distribution with reference to stress and stability, loading and unloading, the safety of personnel, assessment of the acceptability of cargoes for shipment, trimming procedures, methods of determining the angle of repose, cargoes which may liquify and materials possessing chemical hazards. Extensive appendices list the properties of many dry bulk cargoes and describe relevant laboratory test procedures. Non-cohesive cargoes are identified and the measurement of the density of solid bulk cargoes is described. Bulk cargoes exempted from carriage with a fixed gas fire-extinguishing system are listed and procedures for gas monitoring are described. Emergency schedules are set out for those materials possessing chemical hazards.

The *IMSBC Code* provides detailed advice on the characteristics, hazards, loading, stowage and carriage of an extensive list of dry bulk cargoes, along with the degree of hold cleanliness required, weather precautions, ventilation, discharge and cleanup. It is a useful source of stowage factors and properties of bulk cargoes.

The Code of Practice for the Safe Loading and Unloading of Bulk Cargoes (The *BLU Code*): The *Code*, discussed in detail in Chapter 11, specifies in general terms how ship and terminal should be equipped and prepared for the loading or discharging operation. It identifies the information that the terminal needs to receive from the ship and the ship needs from the terminal and describes in some detail the responsibilities of each party. The BLU Code is (in 2009) mandatory in much of the world and represents best practice in places where it is not yet mandatory. It is, in 2009, being amended to include bulk carriers loading or unloading grain.

The International Maritime Dangerous Goods (IMDG) Code: This *Code* lists the properties of a considerable number of hazardous cargoes and states the conditions under which they can be safety carried. The *Code* must be consulted and its recommendations for packaging, handling, stowage and carriage must be followed when they apply to cargoes carried. Latest corrections should be added when published and the record of corrections should be updated when they are made. Compliance with the *Code* is mandatory.

SOLAS Consolidated Edition with supplements: A number of chapters of the Consolidated Edition of SOLAS have particular relevance for bulk carrier operations. ***Chapter II-2, Reg.19*** and ***Table 19.2*** regulate the suitability of spaces for the carriage of dangerous goods. ***Chapter VI*** states requirements for the provision of cargo information, for gas detection equipment and for stowing and securing. Acceptability of cargo for shipment is discussed and safe procedures for loading, unloading and stowing are described. The Master's right to suspend operations if any safe limit is threatened is plainly stated. The documents, stowage and segregation required and the incident reporting for dangerous goods when carried in bulk are specified in ***Chapter VII*** while ***Chapter XI-1*** states the requirement for bulk carriers to undergo enhanced surveys. ***Chapter XII*** is entirely devoted to additional safety measures for bulk carriers. Compliance with SOLAS is mandatory.

Code of Safe Practice for Cargo Stowage and Securing: for stowage of containers, portable tanks, portable receptacles, wheel based cargoes, heavy items, steel coils, heavy metal products, anchor chains, bulk metal scrap, intermediate containers, logs and unit loads.

Code of Safe Practice for Ships Carrying Timber Deck Cargoes: for ships carrying timber deck cargoes.

International Code for the Safe Carriage of Grain in Bulk: for ships carrying grain.

Manual on Loading and Unloading of Solid Bulk Cargoes for Terminal Representatives: a version of the BLU Code for terminal representatives who may or may not be regulated by it, depending upon the decisions of their Administration. It contains useful Appendices advising how damage to the ship can be avoided and describing how damage, if it occurs, should be repaired.

Bulk Carriers: Guidance and Information on Bulk Cargo Loading and Discharging to Reduce the Likelihood of Over-stressing the Hull Structure: This booklet from the International Association of Classification Societies (IACS) was written with the object of reducing the number of bulk carrier casualties and explains with simple text and clear pictures the loading stresses to which a bulk carrier can be subjected. It forms IACS' Recommendation 46 and can be downloaded from their website.

Bulk Carriers: Guidelines for Surveys, Assessment and Repair of Hull Structure: This volume contains extensive and detailed guidelines for surveyors and other interested parties wanting to survey, assess and repair hull damage to a dry bulk carrier. It names and identifies all the component parts of the hull of a bulk carrier, and describes, illustrates and names likely damage. In addition to being available as a hard cover book it forms IACS' Recommendation 76 and can be downloaded from their website.

Sources

38, 89, 110, 150, 261. (See List of Sources, Page 497)

A heaving line – ready to throw

CHECKLIST-Records which should be maintained aboard bulk carriers

Following deck log book entries

- ☐ Routine navigational, weather, sea state and ship's performance data.
- ☐ Details of heaving-to, or action taken to avoid a tropical storm.
- ☐ Dew point readings of cargo spaces and on deck.
- ☐ Ventilation of holds – times of starting and stopping, reason for stopping, ventilators used, type of ventilation, direction of ventilation, speed of fans, hygrometer readings.
- ☐ Water, rainfall and spray over decks or hatches.
- ☐ Hold and hatch cover inspections – dates and times, names of person making inspection, nature of inspection, and findings.
- ☐ Temperatures, and methane and O_2 meter readings, of cargo.
- ☐ pH of bilge water.
- ☐ Pumping of bilge water – time, tonnage and origin.
- ☐ Soundings – full set daily, giving actual soundings, not 'MT'.
- ☐ Testing of cargo care systems such as hold bilge pumping system, hold ventilation fans, hold CO_2 injection systems, testing of hatch cover watertightness.
- ☐ Inspection and tightening of lashings on cargo.
- ☐ Details of any in-transit fumigation.

Following deck log or cargo log entries

- ☐ Surveys undertaken, with times, result and identity of surveyor.
- ☐ Protests made by the ship, and to the ship.
- ☐ Details of any fumigation undertaken.
- ☐ Starts, stoppages and completions of cargo work.
- ☐ Repositioning of cargo-handling equipment.
- ☐ Tanks ballasted and deballasted.
- ☐ Ballast valves opened and shut.
- ☐ Starts and stops of ballasting, and ballast pump readings.
- ☐ Soundings obtained.
- ☐ Cargo tonnages calculated or advised.
- ☐ Draught readings at completion of each pour during the loading, and at least twice daily during discharge.
- ☐ Details of shifting ship.
- ☐ Times of bunkering, and quantities taken.
- ☐ Weather observations.

Cargo documents

- ☐ Copies of all cargo documents issued or received.
- ☐ Authorisation to charterers or their agents to sign Bs/L.

Trim, stability and stress calculations

- ☐ Values used in calculations.
- ☐ Results obtained.
- ☐ Full details of departure condition.
- ☐ Copy of each cargo operations control form issued.
- ☐ Ship's own draught survey calculations.
- ☐ Draught survey calculations by independent surveyors, and results obtained.

Damage records

- ☐ When, where and how damage to ship or cargo occurred.
- ☐ Detailed description of damage sustained with photos where possible.

Cargo book

- ☐ Principal details of each cargo carried, with notes

Ballast log

- ☐ Changing of ship's ballast, to comply with pollution regulations, or for purposes of draught and trim.

Voyage records

- ☐ Voyage abstracts.
- ☐ Proforma layday statement if required by owner.

Chain register – cargo gear register

- ☐ Records of quadrennial inspections, and of thorough examinations of cargo gear, as required by regulations.
- ☐ Full set of certificates for the ship's cargo gear.

Publications necessary or useful in the dry bulk trades:

Title	Publisher	Date
International Maritime Solid Bulk Cargoes Code (IMSBC Code) [previously the Code of Safe Practice for Solid Bulk Cargoes (BC Code 2005)]	IMO	2009
Code of Practice for the Safe Loading and Unloading of Bulk Carriers (BLU Code)	IMO	1998
International Code for the Safe Carriage of Grain in Bulk (International Grain Code)	IMO	1991
Code of Safe Practice for Cargo Stowage and Securing	IMO	2003
Code of Safe Practice for Ships Carrying Timber Deck Cargoes	IMO	1992
International Maritime Dangerous Goods Code (IMDG Code)	IMO	2006
SOLAS Consolidated Edition, as amended	IMO	2006
MARPOL Consolidate Edition	IMO	2006
Manual on Loading and Unloading of Solid Bulk Cargoes for Terminal Representatives	IMO	2008
'Bulk Carriers: Guidelines for Surveys, Assessment and Repair of Hull Structure' (IACS' Recommendation 76)	Witherby Seamanship International Ltd,	2002
Bulk Carriers: Guidance and information on Bulk Cargo Loading and Discharging to Reduce the Likelihood of Over-stressing the Hull Structure (IACS' Recommendation 46)	IACS Rec.046	1997
Bulk Carrier Practice (Second Edition)	The Nautical Institute	2010

Fig. 3.1 Ship's cranes swung outboard, clear of the holds, while loading scrap
Photo courtesy of Walter Vervloesem

Fig. 3.2 Using a cactus grab to load scrap
Photo courtesy of Walter Vervloesem

Fig. 3.3 A front end loader used to push scrap into the ends and wings of the hold
Photo courtesy of Walter Vervloesem

CHAPTER 4

MAINTENANCE AND CARE OF HATCH COVERS

Development, hatchcover types, watertightness and weathertightness, general description and design, surveys, testing for watertightness, maintenance procedures, some defects, emergency opening and closing, hatch leakage – first aid

Development of steel hatch covers

THE DESIGN of steel hatch covers has evolved to meet new requirements since they were first introduced in the 1920s. In the 1950s hatch panel size and numbers had so increased that the ships' cargo gear, if fitted, could no longer provide the power required to open and close the hatch covers. The need for self-propelled or self-activated systems was met at that time by the introduction of hatch hydraulics. These in turn were superseded on geared bulk carriers by direct pull hatch covers where savings could be made by avoiding the use of hydraulics.

The last 30 years have seen the development of a variety of hatch cover types for different situations. These include folding, rolling, piggy-back, stacking and lift-away types with folding and side rolling being by far the most common.

Whilst hatch covers were evolving, the design of the ships to which they were fitted was also developing. Hatch openings were being increased in size to occupy a much larger part of the deck area, which created enormous problems with twisting, racking and bending moments of hatch covers and, of course, created problems of watertightness (For a discussion of weathertightness and watertightness see below). At the same time, developments in their design and construction resulted in vessels with hulls which are today much more flexible than was the case 30 or 40 years ago.

A modern set of hatch covers is likely to be of large dimensions, and must possess great strength to withstand high deck loadings from deck cargo carried and seas shipped. To meet these requirements they must be stiff, strong and yet flexible so that they can follow the bending and torsion of the hull girder. The challenge for the designer is to achieve a watertight fit between such hatch covers, and the 'flexible "U" shaped trough' which is the hull of the modern bulk carrier. It is safe in 2010 to assume that all bulk carriers have steel hatch covers of one type or another.

Hatch cover types

Single-pull (Figs. 4.2 and 4.3): Single-pull covers are sets of panels linked together by chains or rods at the coaming sides. Single-pull covers stow vertically at the hatch end or ends. They can be designed to be manoeuvred by wire led from crane or winch, or can be driven by chains powered by motors situated at the hatch end, or set into one of the hatch panels. Before they can be moved the panels must be raised, and the system to raise and lower them can be manual or automatic. Cleating is the process of clamping hatch panels firmly to the coaming and to each other to limit the movement, and cleating, too, can be manual or automatic. Very few vessels have in the last twenty years been built with single-pull steel hatch covers and it is likely that in 2005 they comprise less than 10 percent of the dry bulk fleet. Raising of the covers is by hydraulic means aboard most larger and newer vessels.

Folding (Figs. 4.1 and 4.8) The basic two-panel folding system, as fitted aboard the *Regina Oldendorff*, has hinges between the two panels, and hinges at the hatch end. One pair of panels folds to the fore end of the hatch and the other to the after end. More complex systems have three or four folding panels in a set. The system is usually hydraulically powered by external or internal hydraulic cylinders. Cleating is normally manual and jacks to raise the panels are not needed. Folding covers are widely fitted to handymax and smaller bulk carriers.

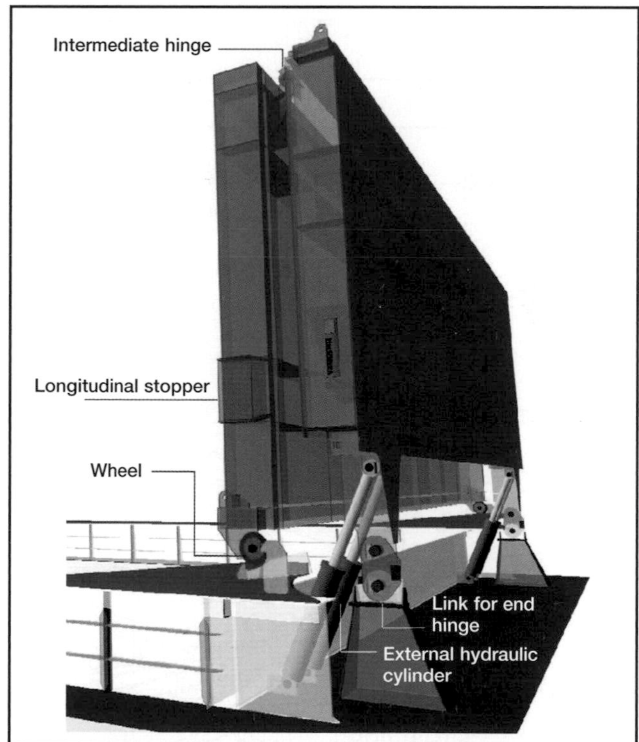

Fig. 4.1 Folding covers

Rolling (Fig.4.4): Side rolling covers roll transversely and end rolling covers roll longitudinally, both types rolling on rails mounted on and extended from the hatch coamings. Such covers are either single panel or two panel per hatch, in the latter case one panel normally rolls to each side. The panels are manoeuvred by positive drives of the rack and pinion (Fig.4.5), rack, pinion and wire, or chain drive type (Fig.4.6) and the panels are raised and lowered

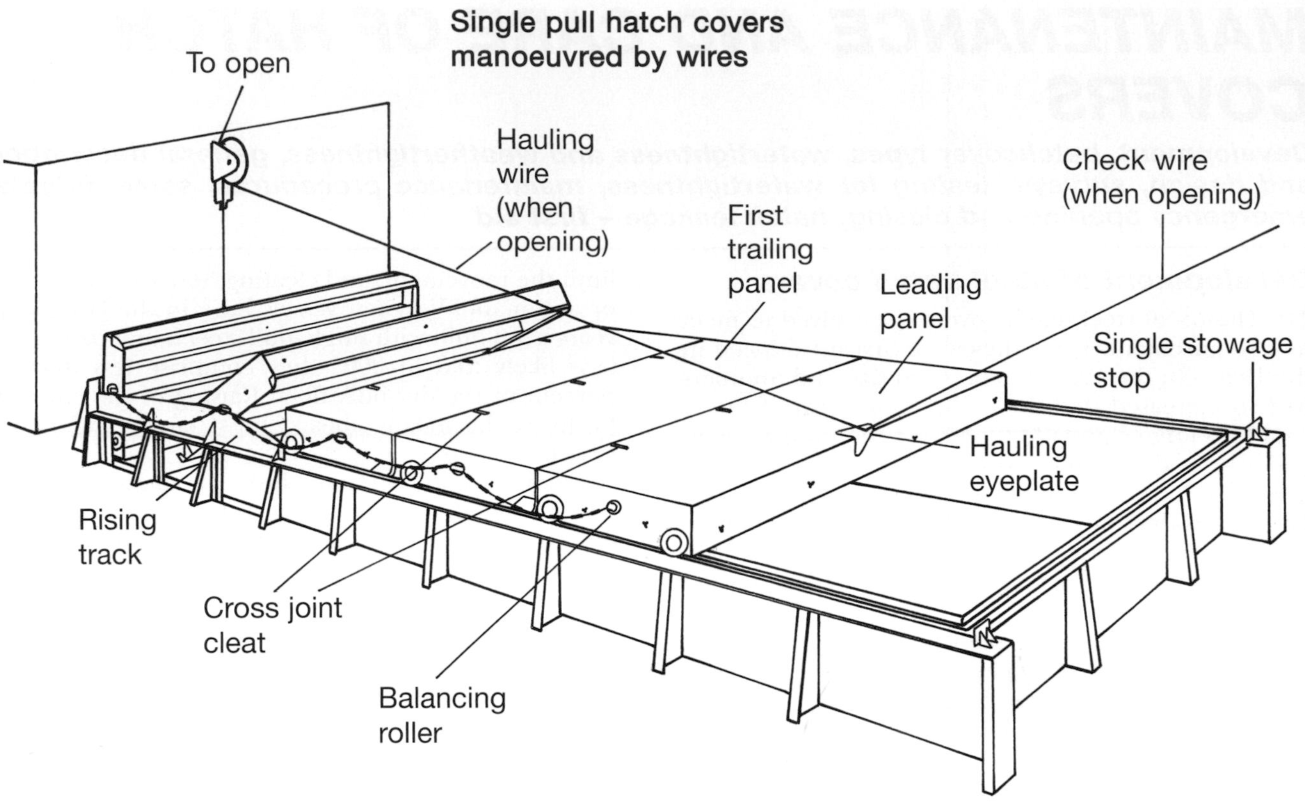

Single pull hatch covers manoeuvred by wires
To open
Hauling wire (when opening)
First trailing panel
Leading panel
Check wire (when opening)
Single stowage stop
Hauling eyeplate
Rising track
Cross joint cleat
Balancing roller

Fig. 4.2

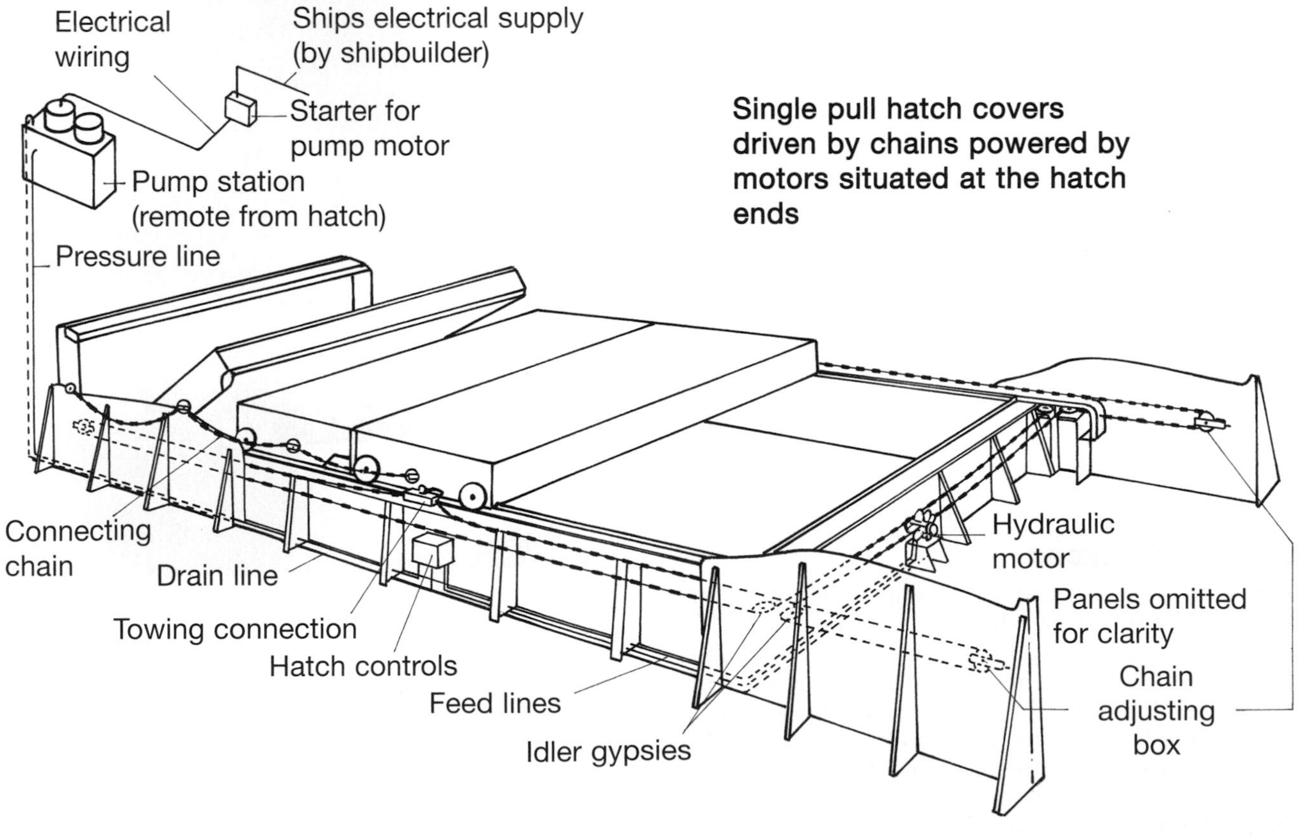

Electrical wiring
Ships electrical supply (by shipbuilder)
Starter for pump motor
Pump station (remote from hatch)
Pressure line
Single pull hatch covers driven by chains powered by motors situated at the hatch ends
Connecting chain
Drain line
Towing connection
Hatch controls
Feed lines
Idler gypsies
Hydraulic motor
Panels omitted for clarity
Chain adjusting box

Fig. 4.3

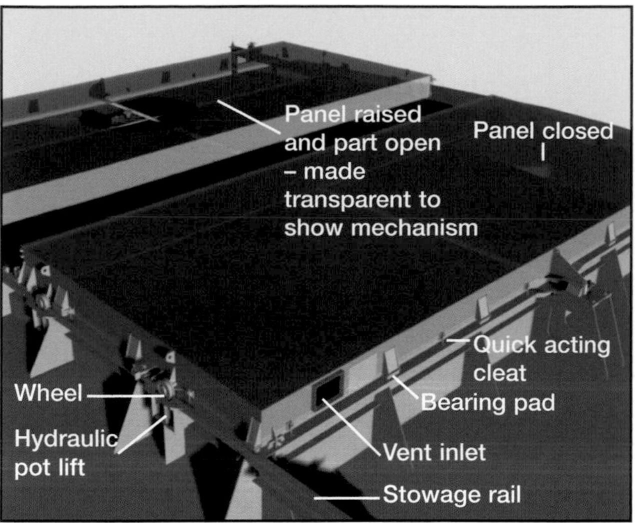

Fig. 4.4

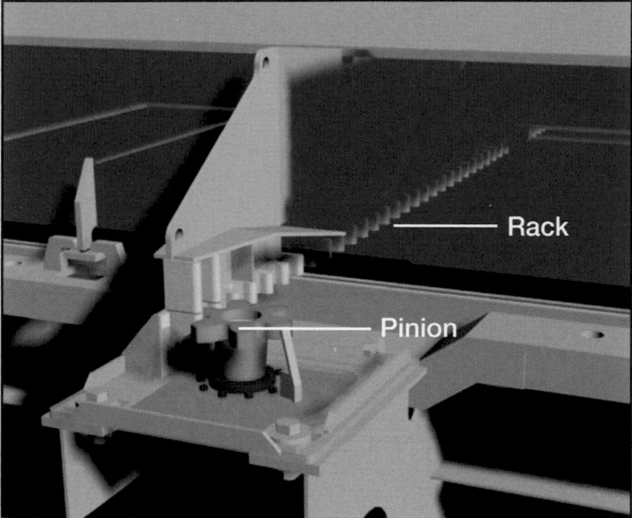

Fig. 4.5 Hatchcover shown transparent to show rack

Fig. 4.6 Chain driven side rolling covers. Both covers roll simultaneously

hydraulically, by jacks known as 'pot lifts'(Fig. 4.7) This system is widely used on larger bulkers, including Panamax, Cape-sized, OBOs, ore/oil carriers and dedicated ore carriers.

Piggy-back (Fig. 4.9). The piggy-back system involves the stowage of one hatch panel over another whilst the latter is in place covering a hold, or part of

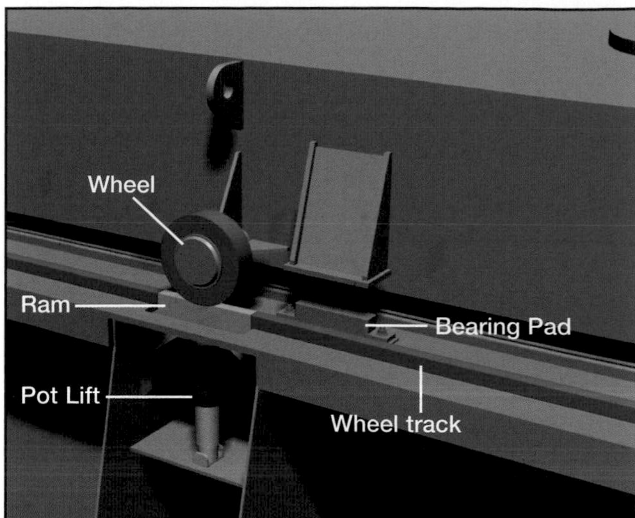

Fig. 4.7 Hydraulic Pot Lift with panel raised

a hold. An advantage of the system is that no deck space is required for the stowage of hatch panels, making it particularly suitable for open bulk carriers and conbulkers. With this type of hatch cover a number of alternative combinations of holds can be worked together.

For the piggy-back system one panel in each pair (the dumb panel) can be jacked up to permit the other (the motorised panel) to be rolled into position below it, where the upper panel is lowered onto it. The two panels can remain in the initial position, or can then be moved as a single unit. Piggy-back covers can be fitted as side rolling or end rolling, and the opening, closing and cleating systems are normally hydraulic. A variety of electric and hydraulic systems is available for the main drive of the covers.

A variant of this system found on some conbulkers such as forest product carriers, is for all panels to be dumb and to be raised, moved and lowered, for stowage over other panels, by equipment fitted to the travelling gantry legs.

Stacking (Fig.4.10): The stacking system is a development of the piggy-back system, with a number of panels being stowed and moved in a single stack. Initial stowage may be at the hatch end within the hatch, or alternatively off the hatch end, leaving the full hatch length clear. The stacking system is particularly suited to long and wide weatherdeck hatches such as are found on mini-bulkers with a single hold. Stacking weatherdeck hatch covers are usually all hydraulic in operation, the panels moving to stowage or closure in a specific sequence, powered by means of an endless chaindrive mechanism.

Lift-away: Lift-away hatch panels are completely removed for stowage on deck or ashore by the use of ship's or shore cargo handling equipment. This type of hatch cover is widely found on container vessels but is unlikely to be fitted to bulk carriers except a few mini-bulkers and forest product ships.

Watertightness and weathertightness

Most mariners speak of the *'watertightness'* of hatch covers to describe their ability to keep water out but, in fact, the Load Line Convention 1966 requires hatch covers to be weathertight, not watertight. That is because hatch covers, except in the special cases of

Powered folding
hatch covers
Securing
hooks
Cross joint
hinges
Rack back
hinge
Control
station
Tandem
cylinders

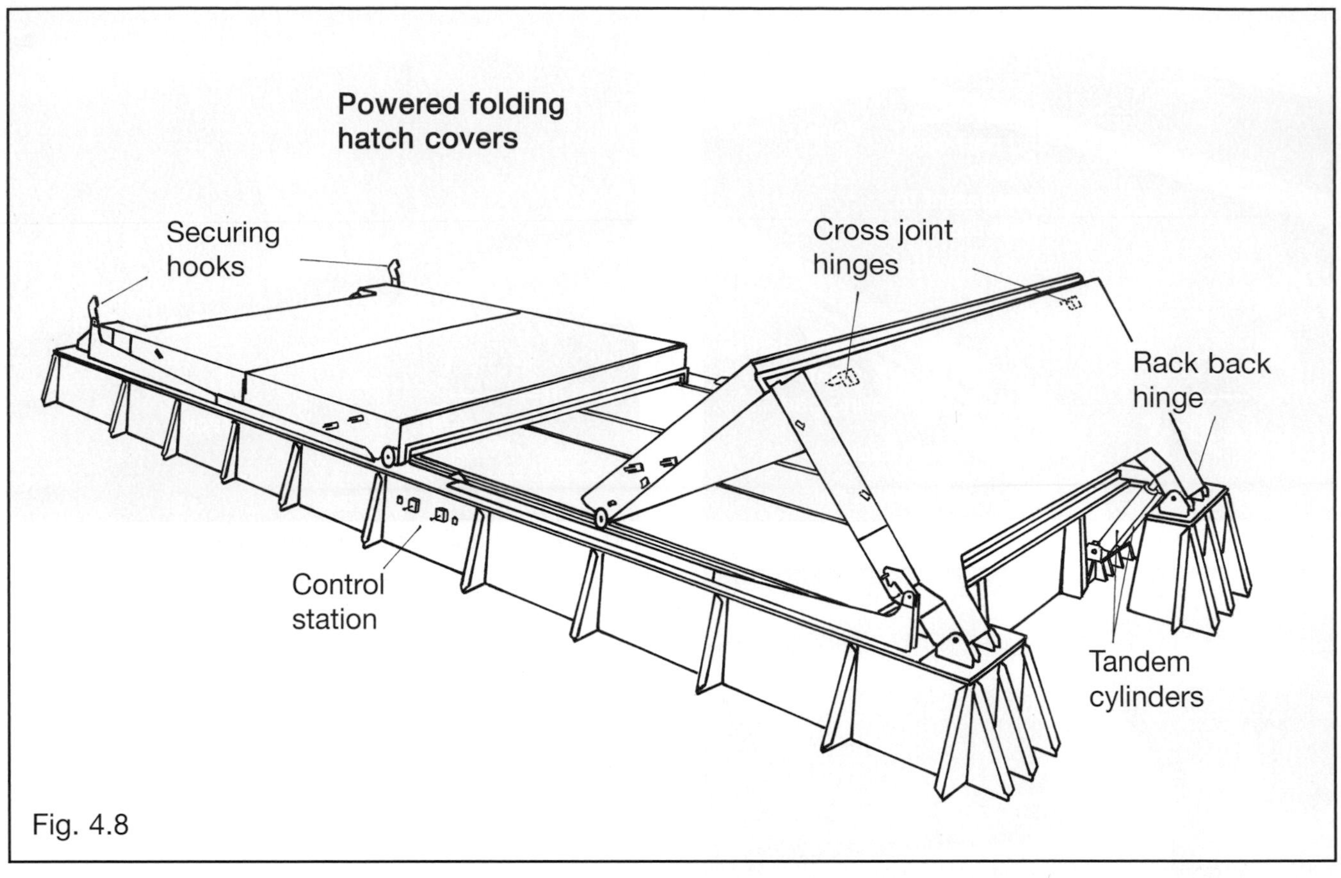

Fig. 4.8

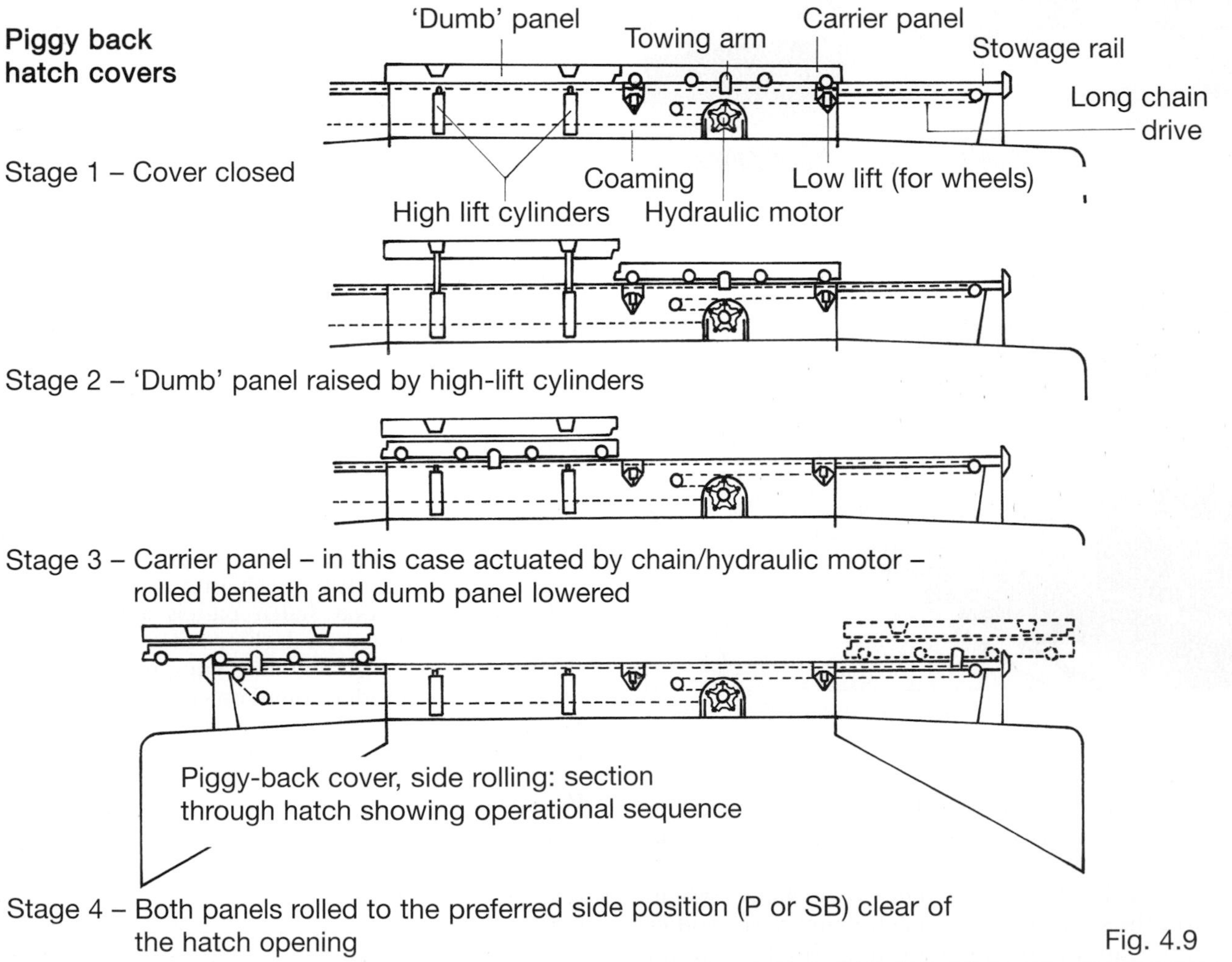

Piggy back
hatch covers
'Dumb' panel
Towing arm
Carrier panel
Stowage rail
Long chain
drive
Stage 1 – Cover closed
Coaming
Low lift (for wheels)
High lift cylinders
Hydraulic motor
Stage 2 – 'Dumb' panel raised by high-lift cylinders
Stage 3 – Carrier panel – in this case actuated by chain/hydraulic motor – rolled beneath and dumb panel lowered
Piggy-back cover, side rolling: section through hatch showing operational sequence
Stage 4 – Both panels rolled to the preferred side position (P or SB) clear of the hatch opening

Fig. 4.9

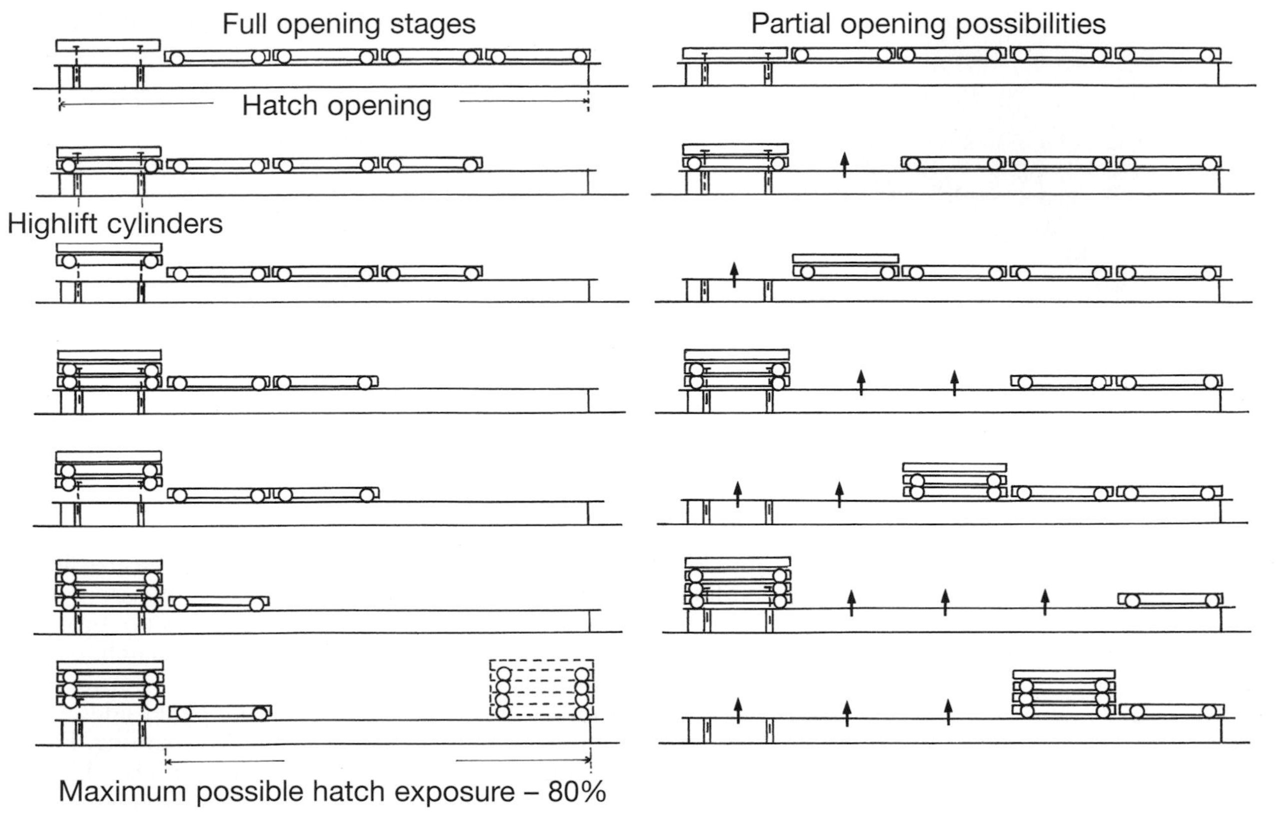

Full opening stages

Hatch opening

Highlift cylinders

Maximum possible hatch exposure – 80%

Partial opening possibilities

Fig 4.10 Stacking hatch covers

the covers for ballast holds and OBO holds, do not have to prevent liquid from escaping from within the hold; they only have to prevent water from entering the hold. They are required to resist intermittent external water pressure. This requires only what the legislators call weathertightness. Watertightness is the ability to withstand constant water pressure. Throughout this chapter references to *'watertightness'* are intended in the mariners' sense.

General description and design of hatch covers

Hatch covers in sound condition and properly maintained are required by a vessel's classification society, and by the authority which assigns her load-line. Amongst the factors which decide a vessel's free-board are the type of hatch covers and the securing arrangements.

Hydraulically operated hatch covers 'of steel or other material fitted with gaskets and clamping devices' are nowadays fitted to almost all bulk carriers. Whilst they may be made by different manufacturers and to a variety of designs, the principles of their construction are the same. The hatch opening is closed by one or several steel panels which rest horizontally across the hatchway. Each panel will consist of an upper surface constructed of steel plate, reinforced and supported on the underside by steel beams or stiffeners. The panel may be of open construction, or may be a sealed unit closed on its underside by plating similar to that on its upper sides (Fig.4.11). If sealed it may be treated inside with a rust inhibitor which removes the oxygen, or may be sealed hermetically, but untreated.

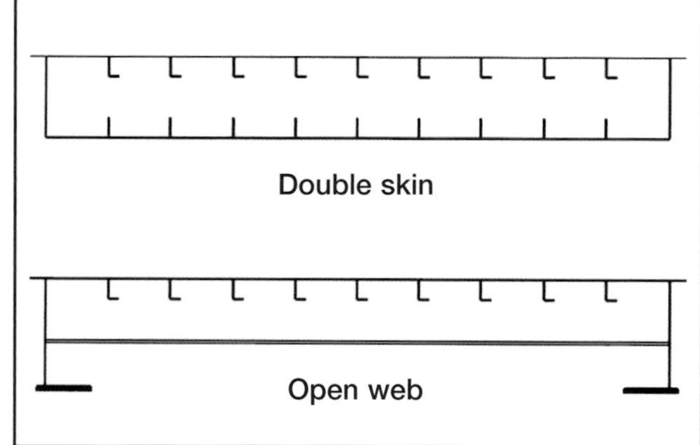

Fig. 4.11 Hatch panels

This double-skinned construction reduces the need for cleaning and maintenance, allows for reduced scantlings and panel depth, provides better insulation, and thus reduces condensation within the hold. However, a temperature differential can arise between the outer and inner skins which will cause thermal deflection which imposes additional loadings on the securing devices, and may give rise to problems, particularly in cases when the hatch panels are approximately square. The weight of a single hatch panel is likely to be 4-5 tonnes on the smallest vessel, increasing to over 100 tonnes on the largest vessels.

When the hatch is opened the panels will be moved

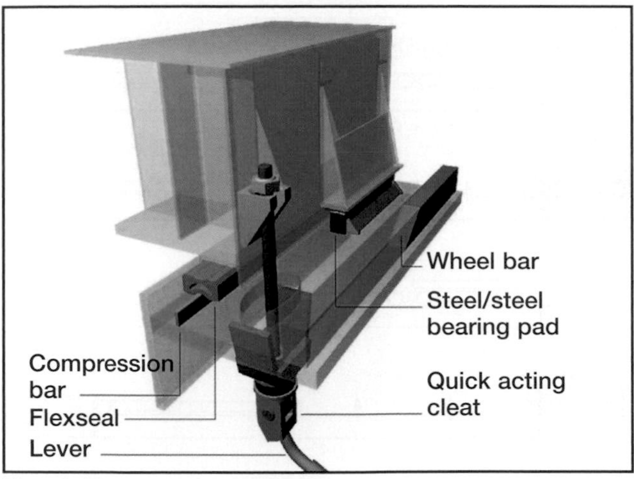

Fig. 4.12

to stowage positions at one or both hatch ends, or at the hatch sides, or over other hatch panels. There they may be placed or stacked vertically or horizontally in a variety of ingenious ways, depending upon the design fitted.

A ship at sea in a seaway moves and flexes. Different conditions of loading which cause the vessel to hog or to sag also lead to surprisingly large changes in the size and shape of the hatch opening. An 80 mm fluctuation in the size of the hatch opening has, for example, been measured in a 3,000 dwt single-hatch coaster. As a consequence of the rigidity of the hatch covers and the flexibility of the ship's hull, rigid connections between hatch covers and hatch coaming are impractical, and elastic joints are necessary. Such a joint is achieved in many vessels by a steel compression bar which projects above the coaming and which bears against a continuous rubber gasket strip set into the hatch panel (Fig.4.12) An alternative system used in some conbulkers eliminates the compression bar and uses special 'cat profile' sliding seals which are free to move across the stainless steel tightening surface, fitted flush in the coaming top, in response to fluctuations in the hatch dimensions (Fig.4.13).

The cross-joint between adjacent hatch panels is made watertight in a similar manner, the compression

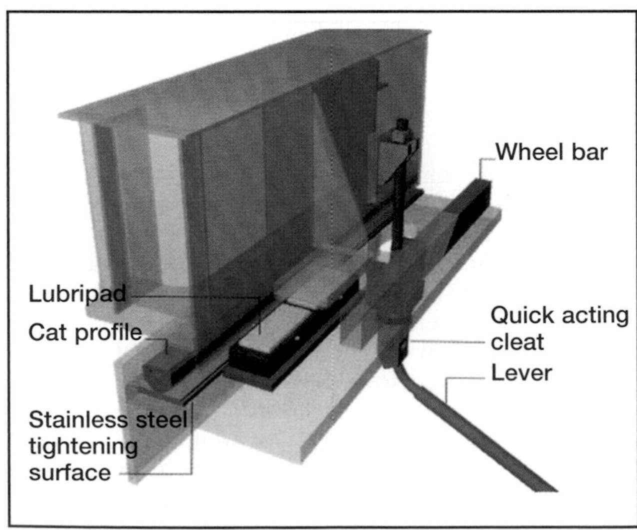

Fig. 4.13 Cat profile sliding seal

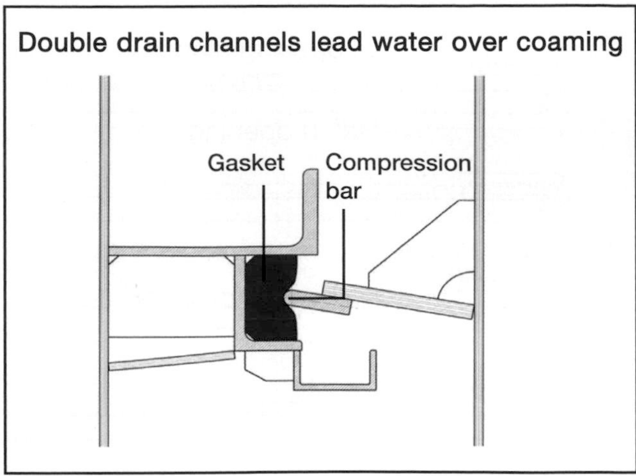

Fig. 4.14

bar attached to one panel bearing on the gasket set into the adjoining panel (Fig.4.14).

To ensure that the compression at the crossjoints is correct it is essential that hatch panels are correctly positioned on the coaming before they are brought to rest. Correct positioning of folding hatch covers is ensured when contact is made between the longitudinal stoppers fitted to the panel sides and the corresponding locator pads on the coaming. For side rolling covers a watertight meeting joint is achieved by the provision of transverse locators which guide the panels into the correct positions as they come to rest on the coaming (Fig.4.15). These locators are replaceable and have shim plates for easy installation and adjustment.

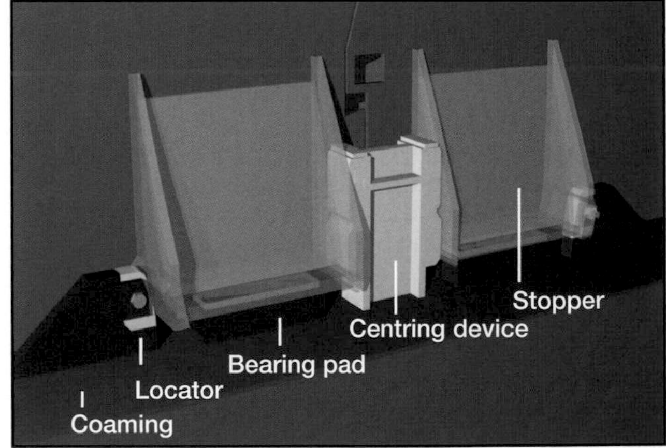

Fig. 4.15 Hatch Panel

In modern bulk carriers most of the weight of the hatch panels, when closed, is transferred to the hatch coaming by a number of bearing pads (Fig. 4.15) positioned at intervals along the coaming top. These ensure that the compression of the gasket strip by the compression bar is not excessive. It used to be said that 'steel-to-steel' contact was required between the bearing pads and the matching plates on the hatch panels but nowadays bearing pads are made of a variety of materials in addition to steel. The various designs offer easy installation, long life, corrosion resistance, low wear and other advantages in addition to preventing overcompression of the seals.

The hatch panels are held in position by cleats of varying design. Because of the need for an elastic joint between adjoining panels, and between panels and

Fig. 4.16 Hold ventilator set into hatch panel

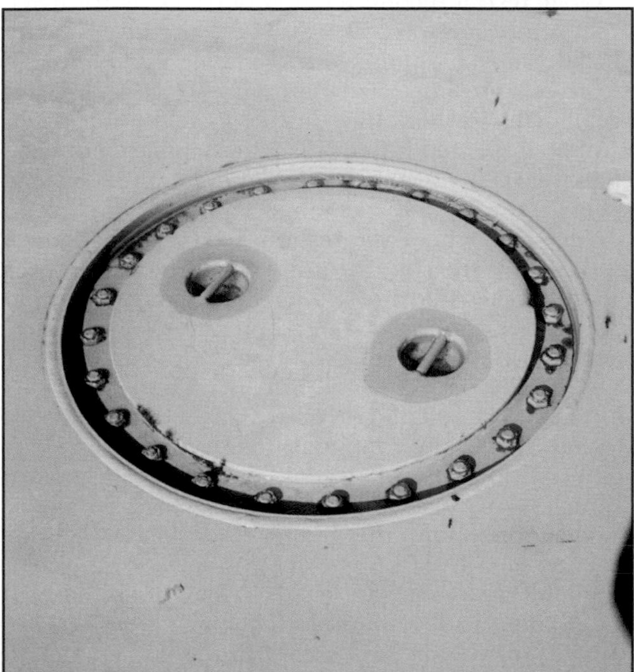
Fig. 4.17 Cement and grain loading port

Fig. 4.18 Gas sampling point

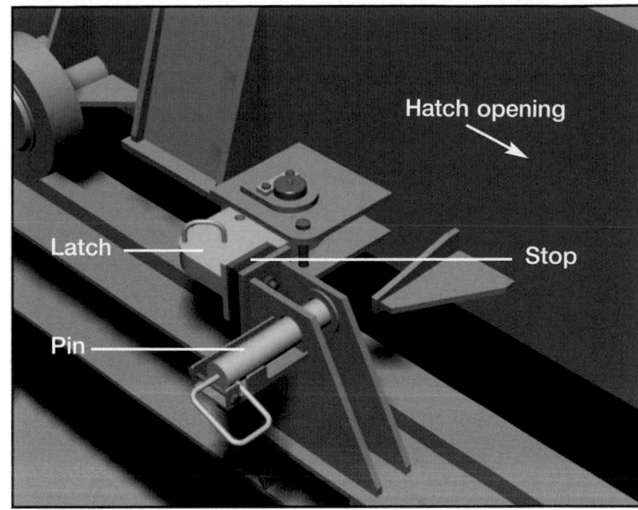

Fig. 4.19 Hatch panel securing device

coaming, the purpose of the cleats is to restrict the vertical movement of the hatch panels when the ship is rolling or pitching in heavy seas and also to achieve watertightness by physical compression of the gaskets in cases where the weight of the hatch panel is insufficient to achieve this (Fig. 4.12) Watertightness is maintained by keeping the gasket in contact with the compression bar, helped by the elasticity of the gasket and the cleat washer. This is achieved by ensuring that all the component parts of the hatch covers are undamaged, and are properly installed and adjusted. The responsibilities of ship's personnel in this matter are most important.

Hatch cover fittings: It has become increasingly common for hold ventilators to be built into the forward and after ends of the hatch panels (Fig. 4.16). Circular cement/grain loading ports, with lids bolted in position, may be fitted in the hatch covers (Fig. 4.17). Gas sampling points (Fig. 4.18) must be provided for any bulk carrier that will carry coal. Hatch panel securing devices (Figs. 4.19 and 20) are required for the covers when open. All these features are described in Chapter 6.

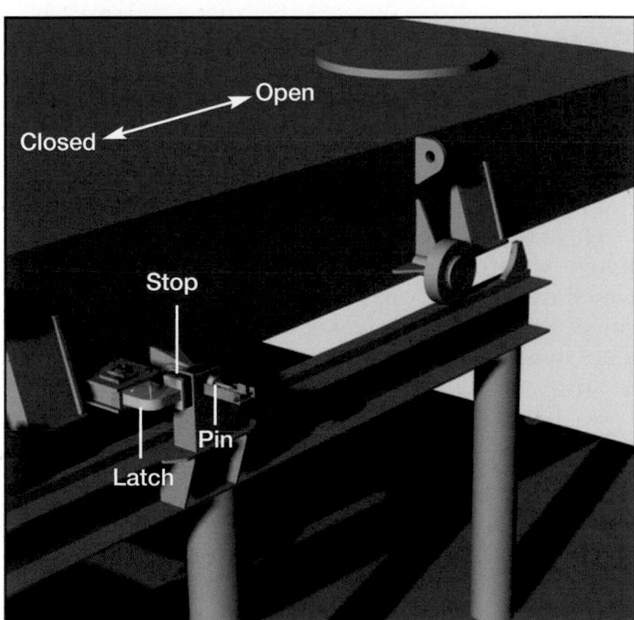

Fig. 4.20 Hatch panel securing devices

Survey of hatch cover arrangements

It is a requirement of the Load Line Convention 1966 as amended by the Protocol of 1988 that hatch covers and hatch coamings are surveyed annually. These surveys, which cover much the same ground as the annual and special survey of the classification society, are normally undertaken by the same surveyor at the same time as the Class surveys. The International Association of Classification Societies has drawn up a unified requirement[3] for these surveys and specifies that annual surveys for mechanically-operated steel covers shall consist of the following.

- General: Checking that no significant changes have been made to the hatch covers, hatch coamings and their securing and sealing devices since the last survey.
- Hatch covers and coamings: Checking the satisfactory condition of hatch coamings, hatch covers, tightness devices of longitudinal, transverse and intermediate cross-junctions (gaskets, gasket lips, compression bars, drainage channels), clamping devices, retaining bars, cleating, chain or rope pulleys, guides, guide rails, track wheels, stoppers, etc.

Special surveys shall, as a minimum, consist of the following.

- A general inspection with the extent of the annual survey as stated above and, in addition, random checking of the satisfactory operation of mechanically-operated hatch covers, stowage and securing in open condition, proper fit, locking and efficiency of sealing in closed condition.
- Checking the effectiveness of sealing arrangements of all hatch covers by hose testing or equivalent.
- Checking the residual thickness of coamings, steel pontoon or hatch cover plating and stiffening members as deemed necessary by the surveyor.

The *Record of Particulars Relating to Conditions of Assignment* (of Load Lines) is a document which is issued by the surveyor and normally kept with the Loadline Certificate. It provides a list of all the items that the surveyor will inspect when making his survey, and is a useful document for the Master and officers to use as a checklist when ensuring that all is ready for the survey.

Testing or assessing the watertightness of the hatch covers

When checking the watertightness of the hatch covers the opportunity should be taken to also check the watertightness of the associated ventilators and access doors and lids.

Hose test: A well established method of testing for hatch watertightness is by hose testing, a process which can only be carried out when the hold is empty since it may result in leakage of water into the hold. The method requires the hatch to be closed and secured as for sea. A powerful jet of water taken by hose from the fire main or deck service line is directed on to each part of every joint in the hatch cover in turn, and any point where leakage occurs is noted.

This process requires, in addition to the hose party, at least two responsible crew members, one of whom is likely to be the chief mate, equipped with walkie-talkie radios. The first person ensures that every part of every joint is hosed in turn and informs the second, located in the hold, which seam is being tested. The second views the appropriate seam and makes a note of any leakage. Observing the location of the leakage can be difficult in a closed and poorly-lit hold with the hatch covers anything up to 18 or 20 metres above the observer. A powerful light such as 300 watt floodlight or even an aldis lamp is essential and binoculars may be useful. Thorough hose testing of one hatch of a handy-sized bulk carrier can be expected to take 20-30 minutes. Hose testing cannot be carried out in freezing conditions, for obvious reasons.

A manufacturer of steel hatch covers specifies that hose testing should be undertaken under the following conditions:

- Water pressure — 4 bar.
- Nozzle inside diameter — 35-40 mm.
- Distance nozzle/object, maximum — 1.5 m.
- Rate of progress, maximum — 1 m per 3 sec.

Chalk test: A second method of checking for hatch watertightness is by chalk test. The procedure is to rub chalk from chalk lumps or sticks along the full length of the compression bars and then to close and secure the hatches. When they are reopened the gaskets must be inspected for any places which have not been chalk marked by contact with the compression bar. Where there is no chalk mark on the gasket no contact with the compression bar can have been made, and the joint cannot be watertight. This method of testing shows where the compression bar has touched the gasket, but it does not show how firm the contact has been. Nor does it prove that the compression bar remained in contact with the gasket in the final closed and secured state, and the value of this test is therefore limited though for the expert it offers evidence of the relative positions of compression bar and packing, which provides information about the hinge condition of folding hatches.

Silicon grease test: For hatch cover systems in which the packing rubber butts with the coaming flat, not with a compression bar, watertightness and alignment can be tested by coating the contact surface of the packing rubber with silicon grease. Alternatively chalk can be used but is less effective. The imprint mark left on the coaming flat after closing and battening down should be about 8mm wide. If it is not compression should be adjusted.

Ultrasonic test: Hatch watertightness can also be measured with convenient portable ultrasonic equipment powered by rechargeable batteries. One such item of equipment consists of a transmitter which is placed in the hold, where it emits ultrasonic waves when switched on. An operator on the hatch covers then takes a hand-held detector along the length of each joint in the covers. In any position where the seal is not tight the receiver emits audible sound and an accurate reading in decibels (dB) can be taken from the luminous display.

The sound emitted by the detector is like a low whine emitted by a badly-tuned radio. The noise will go up when a leaking area is found, at which point it is useful to hold the detector close to the joint to determine the exact limits of the leak. When these have been found the button can be pressed for a digital value, which gives a more accurate measure of the severity of the leak. At other times there is no need to hold the detector close to the joint.

At short ranges (for example, from 'tweendeck level) the signal strength will remain constant at a maximum value and the equipment can be used without calibration. When the range is greater, as when the transmitter is situated on the tanktop of a bulker hold, it will be necessary to calibrate the equipment before testing is carried out.

The instrument detects exactly the same leaks as would be found by an efficient hose test, it is claimed, but avoids many of the problems associated with the latter. Advantages claimed for ultrasonic test equipment are that it:

- Can be used by one man.
- Will not damage cargoes.
- Can be used when temperature is below freezing.
- Reveals the exact location of any leak.
- Is accurate.
- Requires calibration at intervals stated by the manufacturer.
- Can be used even when the hold is full.
- Is simple to use and requires no special training.
- Is compact and portable.

The equipment, marketed by MacGregor, also has numerous other uses for the monitoring of mechanical wear and pneumatic and hydraulic leaks.

Visual inspection of the covers: A visual inspection of the hatch covers can show defects which make it impossible for the hatches to be watertight. In bright daylight rays of light can be very obvious when seen from within a closed hold. Damaged compression bars and/or rubber gaskets which are permanently compressed are signs that hatch watertightness has been lost. 'Locating pieces' which guide the panels into the correct position may become damaged, worn away or built up with scale. As a consequence panels will not seat as intended – they may remain out of contact with one another, or one may be forced up out of contact with the coaming.

All of the above methods of testing and inspection relate only to the watertight integrity of the hatch covers at the time of the test, and cannot prove that the hatches remain watertight when the vessel is working in a seaway or is exposed to changed hogging and sagging stresses. Nevertheless, the tests and inspections are valuable in drawing attention to defects in the hatch covers, making it possible for improvements to be made.

Visual inspection of the cargo: A final way in which the ship's officers can assess the watertightness of the hatches is by careful inspection of the cargo in way of the hatch coaming immediately upon opening the hatches at the end of a sea voyage. No opportunity should be missed to make this inspection, since the information which it provides can be very useful. If spray or seas has been shipped, or even if there has been torrential rain, leakage will almost always show itself in markings in the surface of the cargo and sometimes in staining on the vertical sides of the hatch coaming. If the drip marks are very regular they are probably due to condensation, but if they are irregular and concentrated in certain positions they are almost certainly due to leakage.

Some cargoes are unaffected by sea water and in some ports the receivers are indifferent to signs that leakage into the holds has occurred. That is never an excuse for the ship's officers to ignore signs of leakage – they should always make a note of the positions of any signs of leakage which they see and report such leaks to their operators. At the earliest opportunity steps should be taken by ship's staff to carry out appropriate maintenance and renewals to eliminate the leaks.

Procedures for maintaining hatch covers in efficient condition

All steel hatch covers have four basic features – their strength, operating system, watertightness system and safety features.

Any loss of strength as a result of damage or corrosion is easy to see. A failure of the watertightness system is quickly noticed and becomes cause for concern when leakage occurs. Manufacturers state that operating systems, on the other hand, are often neglected and only cause concern when they have failed, usually in inconvenient circumstances. It should be cause for concern that safety features are frequently ignored.

Maintenance in general: There can be no doubt that inadequate maintenance is a major cause of many hatch cover defects. The marine environment is a harsh one and bulk carriers operate in conditions which are more punishing than those to which most other ship types are exposed. Damp salt-laden air, water on deck and dusty, abrasive cargoes all take their toll on a ship's structure and fittings, which deteriorate rapidly if proper preventive measures are not taken. Yet it is too often evident from the condition of ships presented for survey and repair that such measures have been neglected. This is inexcusable. Damage to cargo by the entry of sea water costs money, and in extreme cases leakage can be the cause of pollution, the loss of the ship and of seafarers' lives.

The increasing size of ships, coupled with their reduced time in port and their smaller crews, serves to make maintenance programmes more difficult to complete. There are limits set by time and by operating conditions to the amount of work that can be completed by ships' staff, and some ship operators nowadays make use from time to time of the maintenance services offered by hatch cover manufacturers.

It is essential that hatch covers receive regular maintenance and the workload becomes much heavier as the ship reaches 'middle age'. Work must be progressed whenever conditions permit, and this requires the chief mate to have a good understanding of the requirements for hatch maintenance.

It is impossible in a book such as this to foresee and to describe the precise maintenance requirements for the hatch covers of any particular ship, but certain advice can be offered and common problems can be described. MacGregor states that the maintenance tools which it would like to see used most often are grease guns and compressed air hoses! If the hatch covers and coamings are swept free of cargo and other rubbish, and if the moving parts are properly greased, the hatch covers should give many years of good service.

Leakage in way of hatches can be caused by faulty hatch operation, damage to hatches, excessive wear of components and neglect of maintenance.

IMO guidelines: In 2003 guidelines[118] for bulk carrier hatch cover surveys and owners' inspections and maintenance were issued. These guidelines, which should be onboard every bulk carrier, provide generic maintenance and survey procedures for hatch covers for ships' personnel.

Manufacturer's literature: It cannot be emphasised too strongly that the Master and chief mate should ensure that they possess full and legible copies of the manufacturer's literature for the hatch covers. The operation and maintenance manuals should be studied, and the procedures should be understood and followed. A chief mate who is not thoroughly familiar with the hatch covers on a vessel to which he has been appointed is well advised to give high priority to a study of the manuals, and also to study with care the operation of the hatch covers. In addition he should seek information from the ship's records and from his colleagues as to any problems met in the past. Hatch covers need regular attention and if they are neglected even for three or four months before the chief mate gives them his full attention the time which has been lost will be difficult to regain. The engineer officers can often provide good advice when it is needed, since maintenance of machinery is one of their specialist areas and deck machinery is, in principle, like any other machinery.

Safety measures: Whether hatches are open or closed they should always be secured in position. An unexpected roll as another ship passes, a gradual change of trim, a hydraulic failure – any of these things can cause hatch panels to move and to become dislodged if they have not been secured. Securing devices such as hatch retaining latches (Figs. 4.19 and 20) are always provided. They should be maintained in good condition, painted a distinctive colour and used. Their inspection in each port should be a requirement of the ship's planned maintenance system.

Before commencement of cargo work: Cargo escaping from loading conveyors or discharging grabs is likely to drop on a bulk carrier's hatch coamings and may fall into the drain pipes set in the coaming. This can be prevented by fitting temporary plugs in the mouths of the drain pipes. For example 40 cm lengths of broom handle, painted orange, can be used – they cannot be forgotten when the hatch is closed.

The need to sweep the hatch coaming channels will be reduced if the hatch coamings are covered with heavy duty canvas or plastic sheeting before commencement of cargo work, and this procedure is especially recommended in freezing conditions, when coamings are particularly difficult to clean.

Securing for sea – need to clean: Before closing hatches for a sea voyage it is necessary to ensure that all compression bars and gaskets have been thoroughly cleaned, to ensure uninterrupted contact between compression bar and gasket. Since cargo is almost always spilt during loading, the cargo residues and any other foreign matter will have to be carefully removed. This is done by shovelling and sweeping, then by 'washing' with a compressed air hose. Compressed air is most useful, both for speed and thoroughness, and should be applied with a compressed air gun which enables the air to be directed on to the area to be swept. This avoids wasting air and annoying the chief engineer! A compressed air gun on the end of a length of solid pipe is a useful tool for directing compressed air at the coaming from a safe distance. Care should be taken to avoid compressed air coming into direct contact with exposed skin, since this can cause cancer, can blind and can cause dermatitis if cargo dust is blown under the top skin layers. Operators must use goggles and dust masks when performing this task.

Quantities of cargo are sometimes spilt on hatch covers. This should be removed before the covers are moved, as they may be damaged by the extra weight. It is equally important to make sure that all drainage channels and drains are clear, to allow drainage of any water which penetrates the seal. Drain pipes are best cleaned with compressed air applied from below and directed up towards the coaming. If the drain pipes have been plugged, it is essential that they are unplugged before the vessel puts to sea. Long plugs painted orange cannot go unnoticed when closing the hatches.

This cleaning work must be done with equal care every time that the hatches are secured for sea, regardless of the time of day or night, or of the weather conditions. It is false economy to rush the closing of the final hatches on completion of loading; it is more important to ensure that they are properly and carefully secured for the sea voyage. Delay should be kept to a minimum, however, by ensuring that all other holds have been closed and secured before completion of loading in the final holds.

Securing for sea – correct hatch panel position: Every precaution must be taken to ensure that the hatch panels are correctly positioned when they are lowered onto the coaming. If a panel is wrongly positioned the cleats will not meet truly. They should not be forced; the panel must be correctly repositioned.

With single-pull covers it is imperative when closing the covers prior to battening down that the leading panel is properly located. Next, the hauling wire must be shifted from the leading panel to the trailing panel and again pulled tight to ensure that all of the sections are properly mated in relation to each other, so that the transverse compression bars are in the centre of the gaskets. Experience shows that leakage is likely to occur in way of the cross-joints as a result of the ship working if the compression bars are not placed centrally on the gaskets, or rubber seals. In Fig. 4.14 the panels are correctly located and the compression bar is centrally placed against the rubber seal.

The cleating systems on some recent ships are hydraulic but on most bulk carriers cleats have to be fastened manually. The manufacturer's recommended sequence for fastening the cleats, when stated, should be followed, since uneven tightening of cleats might alter the flexing and watertightness of the covers. Most manufacturers specify no particular sequence and any methodical approach should be satisfactory.

It is also necessary to guard against carelessness and negligence in closing hatches. The work will be shared between a number of crew members, possibly over a period of hours, and in these circumstances it is possible for some steps to be overlooked. It is normal for the chief mate and/or duty mate to satisfy himself that all hatches are properly secured before the ship puts to sea, and this procedure should be followed with commitment. Good practice is for the chief mate to check that all coamings, cross-joints, gaskets and drains are clean before the hatch is closed, and for the duty officer to ensure that the correct closing sequence and cleating procedure has been carried out as required by the ship's ISM system. This inspection is too important to be delegated to a crew member.

Prevention of damage to hatches by stevedores: Damage to the hatch covers, hatch coamings and associated fastenings is most likely to be caused by the discharging and loading processes. Fittings may be struck by grabs, by items of mechanical loading or discharging equipment, or by heavy items of cargo such as lumps of quartz or pig iron. The compression bars and those hatch rubbers and channels which are open to the hold are items which are often damaged. Ships' officers must be alert to the possibility of damage and must ensure that the person causing the damage is quickly served with a written notice, holding him responsible. This may ensure that the damage is repaired and may make the person who caused the damage more careful to avoid further damage.

Prevention of damage to hatches by crew negligence: A further possible cause of damage to hatch covers and their fittings is an accident when closing or opening the covers, perhaps resulting in broken or distorted fittings. Accidents of this sort are sometimes caused by a failure of crew members to make all the necessary checks to ensure, for example, that all cleats are disengaged, that all trackways are clear and that all chains, wires or cables are free to run before the panels are moved. Such accidents are most likely to occur when crew members are inexperienced, tired or working in difficult conditions. At such times their work should be more carefully supervised.

Prevention of damage to hatches by operation at sea: Another cause of damage can be the opening or closing of hatches at sea when the ship is moving in a seaway. When the ship is in ballast with a large freeboard and the seas are calm, it is convenient to open the hatches for maintenance purposes and often it is desirable to do so to achieve efficient hold cleaning. In principle this is no different to opening hatches during a sheltered river passage or in the approaches to the loading or discharging berth, but problems can arise if the seas get up a little during the course of the day and the ship is pitching or rolling perceptibly when the time comes to close the hatches, or if the hatch panels have not been secured whilst open.

The nature of the problem varies with the type of hatch covers fitted. Single-pull systems are vulnerable at the point where the panels tip into the stowage position, and any wire-operated single-pull or rolling system is dangerous if the ship's movement causes the panel to roll towards the hauling wire. A check wire leading in the opposite direction must be rigged and kept taut (Fig. 4.2). When hatch covers are open or partly open, all panels must be well secured. Wherever possible they should be lowered from their wheels or steadied with check wires, as appropriate, with all fastenings being symmetrical to ensure that panels cannot slew.

If a ship does start to move in a seaway with hatches open, the movements of the panels can become violent and uneven and hatch fittings can be damaged. This is a situation which needs continuous and careful watching. Hatches should not be opened when there is a danger of pitching or rolling which will disturb the hatch panels. If the ship starts to move noticeably when hatches are open, they should be closed with no delay, except to bring the ship on to a course with the seas astern if necessary to make her more steady.

If a hatch is damaged, the damage must be carefully assessed to decide whether the hatch can still be opened and closed and whether it remains watertight. The nature and timing of repairs will depend upon the circumstances. Some Masters, owners, makers and administrations make it a rule never to open hatches at sea and, when the ship's design, equipment and service allow it, the rule can be strongly recommended.

Treatment of wear and corrosion: Even when hatch covers and their associated fittings are all properly used and set up, the gradual processes of wear and corrosion will introduce changes. The exposure to salt water and to dust which is a feature of bulk carrier operations will accelerate these processes. Gaskets will become permanently compressed. Bearing pads, stoppers and locators will wear down. The amount of play in the hinges of folding covers will increase. Compression bars will become wasted, and corrosion will cause the retaining bars of the gaskets to swell and become distorted. It is necessary for the chief mate to inspect the hatch covers regularly for these gradual changes. Warning that the condition of the hatch covers is deteriorating may be given by small changes in the way that the hatch covers open or close. None of the foregoing can be neglected and worn items and slack fittings must be renewed, repaired or adjusted.

Lubrication: The condition of hatch covers will deteriorate very rapidly if they are deprived of routine lubrication. Parts which are not greased will quickly seize up. Seized parts which are hammered or heated to free them will be damaged and will eventually require expensive repair. A regular greasing routine must be followed, to ensure that moving parts are greased once a voyage or once a month, or at whatever interval is appropriate to the trade in which the ship is employed. Bearings (joints where two metal parts are fitted together and one rotates within the other) in hatch fittings, as elsewhere, require to be lubricated and are normally fitted with grease nipples to permit the injection of grease between the moving parts. Sometimes grease nipples are missing or broken and it is important to fit new nipples so that grease can be applied. The person applying the grease should look for signs that grease is being forced out of

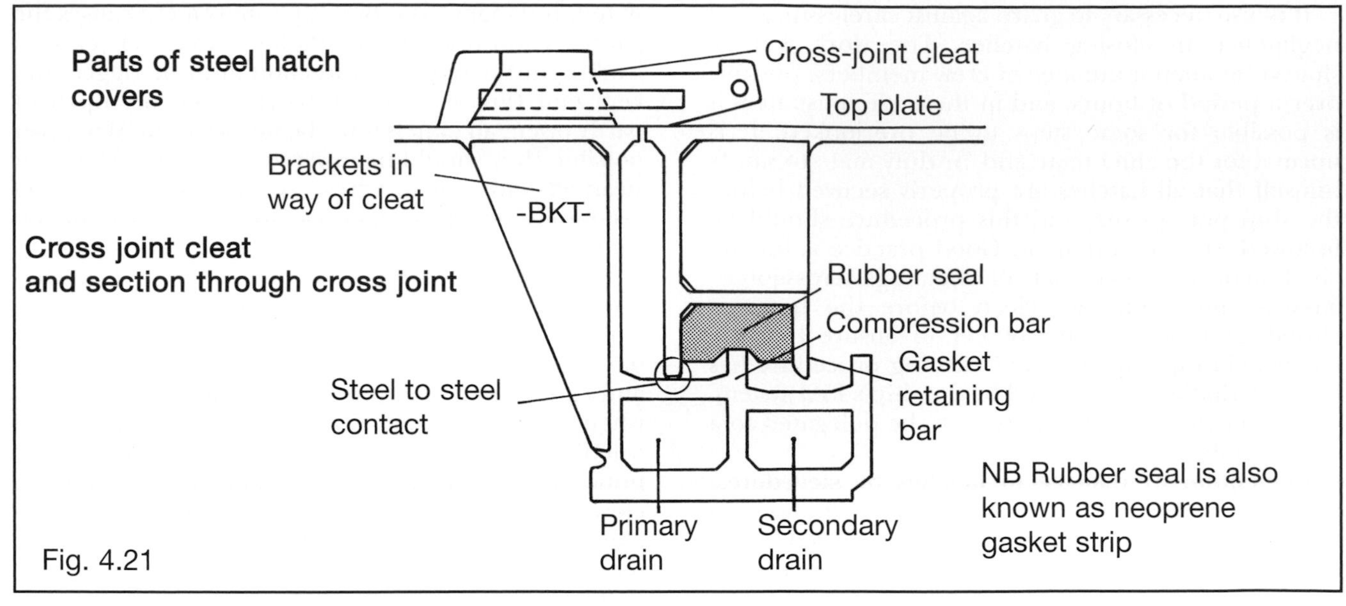

Fig. 4.21

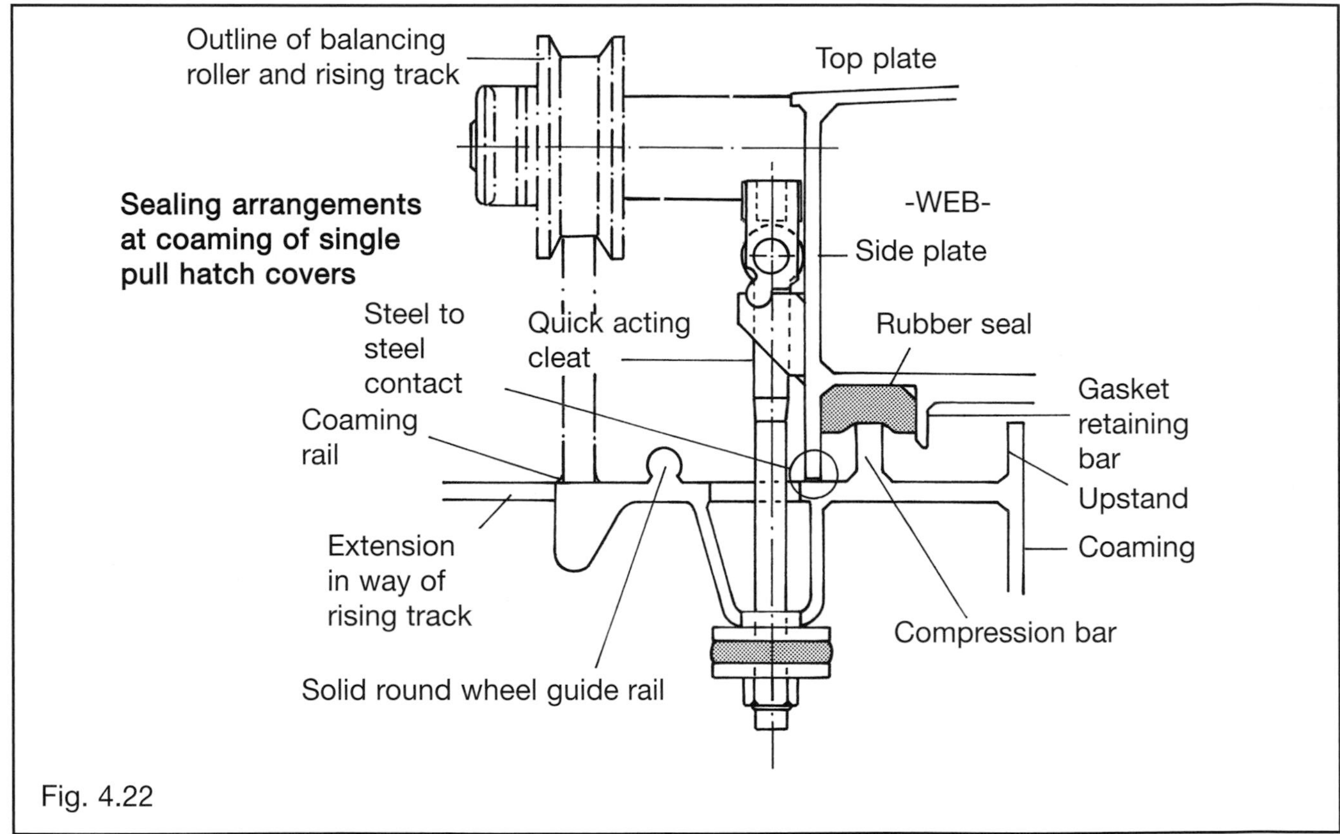

Fig. 4.22

the far side of the fitting which is being greased, as evidence that the process is working efficiently.

Care must be taken to use only the manufacturers' recommended quality of grease. Unsuitable greases may provide inadequate lubrication, with different tolerances, operating temperatures and pressures, and may also lead to the creation at the boundary between two non-compatible greases of a solid 'plug' which can completely block the grease channel.

Painting of hatch covers: The painting of those parts of hatch covers and coamings which are visible when the hatches are closed presents no special problems. The undersides of side rolling hatch covers, too, are readily accessible from the deck. Painting with airless paint spray is recommended, particularly for the hatch coaming sides, in view of the irregularity of the surface, though it may be better to use paint rollers when the crew are unskilled and the weather is rough. Before painting commences, all hydraulic pistons in jacks and automatic cleating devices must be suitably protected – for example, with plastic film held in place with masking tape. The back of all pipework secured to the hatch coaming must be painted as well as the front. The purpose of the painting is to protect the pipework from corrosion as well as to improve its appearance.

The scaling, wire brushing and painting of the undersides and ends of folding and single pull hatch panels presents greater problems. Normally this work can only be done whilst in port or at anchor and with the holds empty. The method adopted will depend upon the design of the hatch covers. It may be necessary to stand on one hatch panel whilst maintaining the next one in a stowed or partly stowed position. This work is potentially dangerous because it is done over the full height of the empty hold, and because the hatch panels may not be securely stowed and will have to be moved as the work progresses. Crew members must be protected, by the rigging of safety lines and the use of safety harnesses, from falling into the hold and from being injured by moving panels. The maintenance of the cross-joints with their drain channels, gasket retaining bars and compression bars is vital to the preservation of hatch watertightness, but favourable opportunities for this work will be rare. When an opportunity does arise this work must be given high priority.

At the time when hatch panels and coamings are painted, care must be taken to ensure that all drainholes are clear and than none is blocked and painted over.

Spare parts to carry: Spare parts for hatch covers are not available off the shelf in every part of the world; a minimum stock of spares should be carried for emergency renewals by ships trading worldwide. Such a stock should include sufficient gasket rubber for at least two hatch panels, including the specially moulded corner pieces, with the necessary adhesive. In addition, at least one specimen of every fitting in the entire hatch manual should be carried to fit following accidental damage, and a replacement should be ordered immediately the stock item is used. The foregoing is a minimum for emergency repair and takes no account of the needs of maintenance.

For maintenance purposes, a good supply of spares must be carried – the number required increasing as the ship grows older. For items such as the rubber washers in quick-acting cleats (with a life of perhaps two years) it will be necessary to carry 25 per cent of the full fitted stock. A good stock of all items exposed to heavy wear, such as quick-acting cleat units, seals for hydraulic units, and roller bearings for panel wheels, should be carried since such items can be difficult or expensive to obtain at short notice. An adequate stock would be 25 per cent of those fitted, or sufficient for one complete hatch, whichever is less.

A stock of spare hydraulic jacks and hydraulic cleating devices should be carried on ships that have these fittings so that replacements can be fitted whilst the discarded units are reconditioned. By the time the ship is ten years old it is likely that spares carried, new and reconditioned, will amount to some 10-20 per cent of the total installed.

It is not recommended that a large stock of rubber gasket material be carried, except when renewals in the near future are intended. The fitting of replacement gaskets is skilled work and is best undertaken by experienced staff such as employees of the hatch cover manufacturer. A number of spare joining shackles for hatch panel chains should be carried, along with sufficient hatch opening and closing wires for 100 per cent replacement, on ships with the wire-operated single-pull system.

Some defects found in hatch covers

Permanent setting down of gaskets: Many people believe that the tighter a cover is secured to its coaming, the better the seal that is made and the smaller the chance of leakage. This view is a mistaken one, since the hatch is designed to be closed with steel-to-steel contact. When this very important principle is not understood much money and effort can be wasted.

In recent tonnage so-called steel-to-steel contact is achieved with bearing pads (Fig. 4.12) although the bearing pads are often made of other materials which offer benefits such as harder wear, cost savings or easier renewal. Modern bearing pads are designed for quick and easy rebuilding or renewal.

Figs. 4.21 and 4.22 illustrate the manner in which steel-to-steel contact occurs in older hatch covers although these are now being phased out. When such hatch covers were newly installed the original dimensions of steel and gaskets (ie, rubbers) were such that gasket compression of more than 25-30 per cent was impossible. Modern gaskets are designed for a compression of no more than 13 mm ± 3 mm. Any gasket which has been permanently compressed or 'set' by 25% of its thickness is overcompressed and must be renewed. Provided that solid steel-to-steel contact has been achieved between hatch cover and coaming itself or a series of bearing pads fixed to the coaming, nothing can be achieved by overtightening the cleats. Overcompression of the gasket can only occur if the contact faces of the steel or the bearing pads have been worn down or corroded, as often occurs in older ships. In these circumstances it is pointless to renew the gasket before the full depth of the steel or the pad has been rebuilt.

Once gaskets have been permanently set down by overcompression, their characteristics are irretrievably changed and their sealing properties are lost. The length of life of a gasket depends upon the trade and the treatment to which it is exposed. Gaskets are

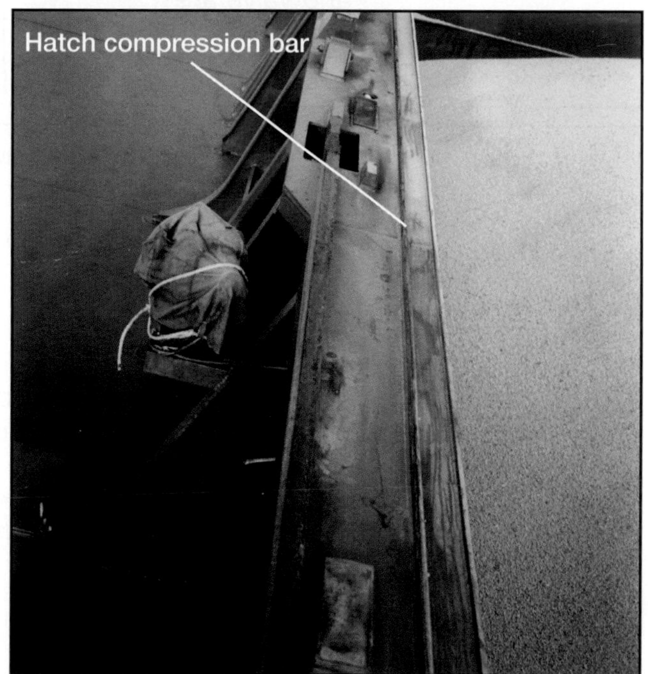

Fig. 4.23

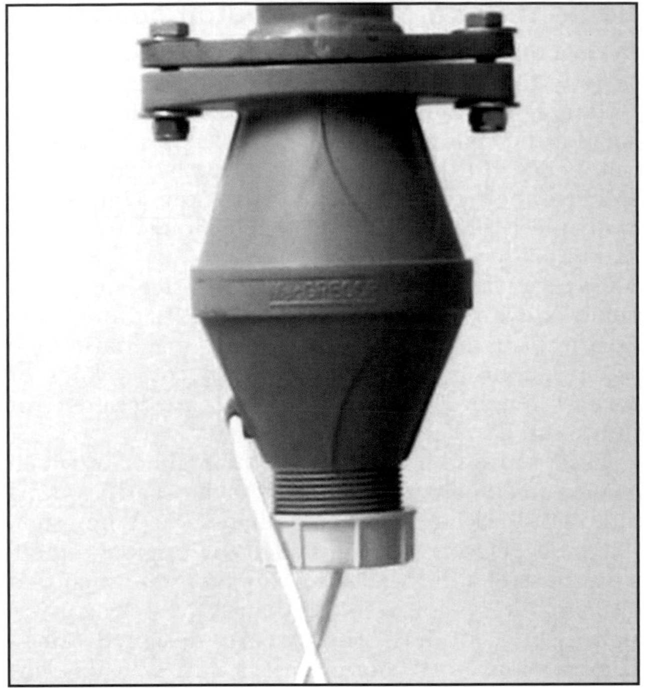

Fig. 4.24 Hatch coaming drain, closed

Fig. 4.25 Hatch coaming drain for ballast hold

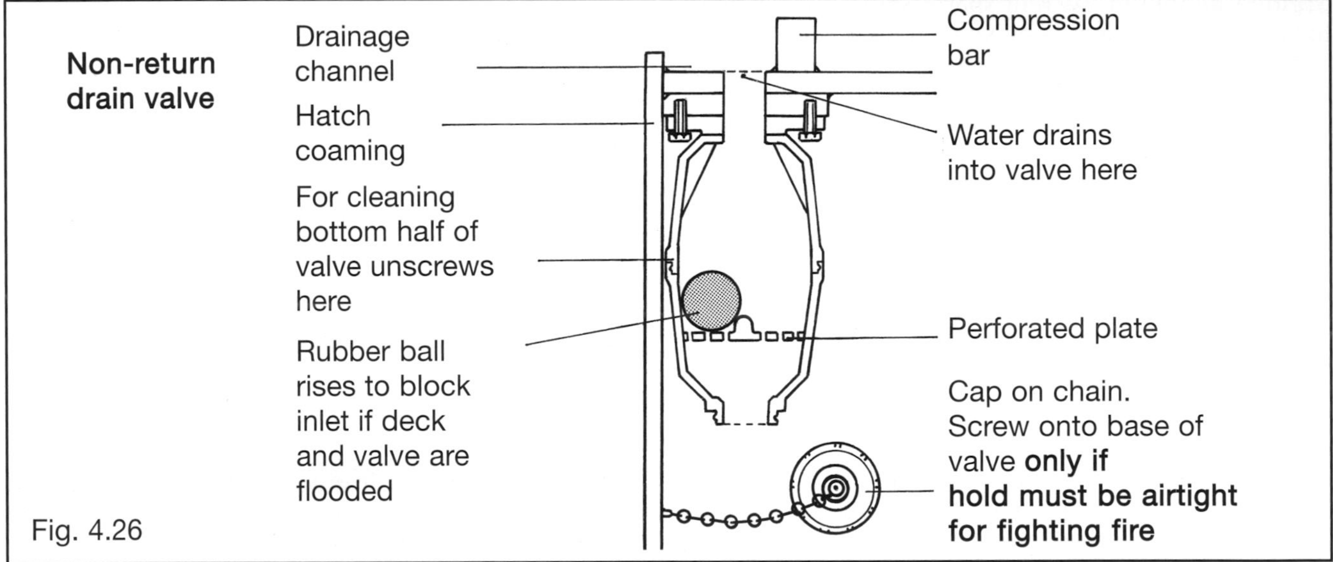

Fig. 4.26

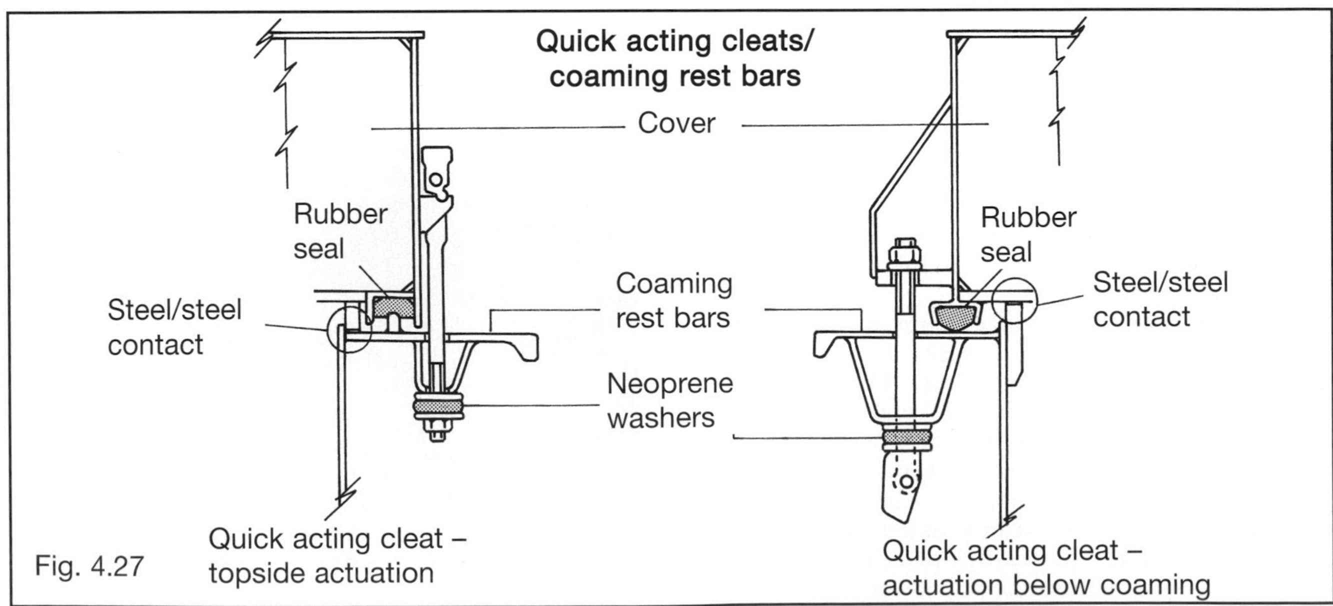

Fig. 4.27

designed to withstand a set number of operations rather than a life span in time, and hardening, cracking and failure of the gasket will result from a build-up of scale in the channel into which the gasket is set, particularly if the gasket has been over-painted, coated with grease and not kept clean.

When gaskets are renewed, it is recommended that replacement gaskets are purchased from approved suppliers since alternatives, although cheaper, are unlikely to be constructed to exactly the same specifications. If their cross-section or properties are different they will not give as good a performance.

It is unwise to insert short lengths of new gasket into a panel which is otherwise fitted with an old gasket because the compression will be different. This is almost certain to result in a poor fit, with leakage. Building up old gasket with lining strips is also not recommended and is rarely successful. It does not give back to the damaged gasket the qualities it previously possessed.

Damaged or corroded compression bars: Damaged and corroded compression bars are frequently met. Although stainless steel compression bars to reduce corrosion are now a Class requirement the quality of the material used remains variable. If the compression bar (Fig.4.23) is damaged and uneven it will permit leakage. Damage should be repaired at the first opportunity, probably with runs of welding, buffed to achieve a smooth and even finish.

Damaged or corroded gasket retaining bars: Gasket retaining bars (Fig. 4.21 and 4.22) when fitted are about 8-10 mm thick. They may easily suffer damage or wastage. If they do, the gasket will not retain its intended cross-section and the likelihood of leakage will be increased. Retaining bars should be kept free of rust and protected with paint. When they are damaged they should be repaired. If they become wasted they should be renewed.

Blocked drainage channels and drain pipes: If a hatch seal fails it is possible that the adjacent drainage channel will allow the water to drain away without doing any damage, but only if the channel and drain pipe are clear. Drainage channels on the hatch coamings and between adjacent panels must be cleaned as a matter of routine before the hatch is closed and secured and should be kept scaled and painted.

The hatch coaming drains are usually fitted with non-return valves (Fig.4.24 and Fig.4.26) consisting of a float in a chamber. If water shipped on deck starts to rise in the drain the float rises and blocks the inlet, preventing water from entering the hold. The bottom part of the non-return valve chamber can be unscrewed from the drain to permit cleaning of the valve as necessary. Instead of being fastened direct to the coaming the valve may be in a drainpipe, which must also be kept clean. If not dealt with as a matter of routine this cleaning can easily be overlooked. It therefore requires special attention from the ship's officers.

A screwed cap on a lanyard is normally provided at the base of each drain pipe. This is for achieving airtight sealing of the hold in the event of fire or fumigation, and should never otherwise be fitted except on ballast holds when ballasted. Inexperienced people often fail to understand this and mistakenly fit the caps, which makes the drainpipes completely useless. To prevent such mistakes, some operators remove the screw caps from the lanyards and leave clear instructions that they are kept in a conspicuous place such as the ballast control room, usually in a highlighted clearly marked and accessible box.

Fig. 4.28 Hatch coaming drain

The hatch coaming drains fitted to ballast holds may be more elaborate (Fig. 4.25).

Some recent ships are fitted with a simpler form of coaming drain, consisting of a rubberised spout (Fig. 4.28). A fault of this fitting is that no means is provided for sealing the drain in event of fire or fumigation of the hold. Canvas hose, sometimes fitted to the ends of coaming drains is also unsatisfactory[119].

Cleating devices: Cleating systems are designed to withstand dynamic forces on the hatch cover which may be subject to loading from above and, in the case of ballast holds and the hatches of OBOs and ore/oil carriers, to hydrostatic loading from below. (The special features of the hatch covers of combination carriers are described in Chapter 18). In recent years there has also been increasing recognition of the fact that green seas can impose very large horizontal forces on hatch coamings and hatch covers[113] but cleating systems are not designed specifically to resist these.

Different hatch cover systems use different cleating methods, with cleating located at key load transmission points throughout the coaming. These cleats are exposed to heavy use and hard wear. They must be regularly inspected, kept in good working order, properly adjusted and capable of further adjustment as required. It is good practice to keep a number of fully assembled spare cleats to fit in place of cleats which are found to be damaged or defective. When the neoprene (rubber) washers in quick-acting cleats (Fig. 4.27 and 4.29) have lost their elasticity and become permanently deformed they must be renewed.

Fig. 4.29 Hatch cleat with perished rubber
Photo courtesy of Captain L. Hesketh FNI

Connecting chains: On single-pull covers the connecting chains between individual hatch panels are subject to stretching in service and must be inspected for signs of this. With experience it is easy to see when stretching has taken place, as the chains then hang down to the level of the coaming rest bar, or below, whereas they should hang in a very shallow curve which does not reach as low as the coaming rest bar (Fig. 4.30). It is also important to keep a check on the amount of stretching which has taken place, since stretching weakens the chains. When they have stretched 15 per cent they should be renewed.

An efficient way to monitor the amount that each chain has stretched is to measure and mark a standard length (2 metres, for example) on each chain when it is new and to remeasure from time to time. When the distance between the marks, which could be wire seizings, has increased to 2.3 metres the chain must be renewed. When chains have been weakened by stretching it will be found that they stretch more rapidly and require more frequent adjustment, so there is no purpose in keeping them in service.

If both connecting chains have stretched, adjoining panels will fail, or will almost fail, to engage with one another as they drop to the horizontal when the hatch is being closed. If one chain has stretched, the panels tend to turn or 'crab' as they are pulled over the hatch. Manufacturers' adjustment routines for connecting chains should be followed, with all chains adjusted in pairs – port and starboard – and the chain lengths maintained to the original criteria. The lengths of connecting chains can usually be adjusted with bottlescrews, whilst bigger adjustments to chains can be made by cropping a link where necessary, using burning gear or an angle grinder, provided that the end link is not of special dimensions and that the shackle can be fitted to the new end link. Putting a twist in the chain is a device which has been used to reduce its effective length, but this is not recommended under any circumstances since it also reduces its strength and increases wear.

Hydraulic systems – moving parts: Manufacturers report that the operating systems for steel hatch covers are often badly maintained, and that poor maintenance combined with components of inferior quality and poor repair techniques cause a large number of accidents. Warning signs are leaking glands, noisy systems, slow operating cycles and dirty filters.

Hydraulic jacks are used in many hatch closing systems to raise and lower the hatch panels. Hydraulics are also used in some systems for the

Fig 4.30 Badly adjusted connecting chains

automatic cleating of the hatches. Dust and fine particles, mainly from cargo sources, are among the principal enemies of hydraulic systems. They lodge in the seals of jacks and pistons and these items eventually fail unless they are regularly overhauled, cleaned and renewed.

The cleanliness of the system is vital. Hydraulic systems are nowadays all fitted with filters in the return lines. These should be regularly cleaned or renewed and a sample of hydraulic oil should be submitted to the supplier of the oil, or to the service organisation of the hatch cover manufacturers, for analysis at least once every six months. It should be borne in mind that modern hydraulic systems are made to operate at up to 250-300 bar pressure. They deserve extreme caution, and safe procedures should be followed when personnel are close to hydraulic pipework.

Hydraulic systems – pipework: The failure of steel hydraulic piping as a result of corrosion, inadequate bracketing and vibration seems to rise to a high level in ships which are more than seven years old. Such failure is always cause for concern since it leads to the loss of quantities of hydraulic oil, possible pollution claims, decks which are dangerous and slippery, and delays to the ship as a result of the inability to open and close hatches as required. Pipework failure can be reduced by ensuring that the pipes are kept properly painted, at the back as well as in the visible areas, but a better method (though initially more expensive) is to wrap all pipework, particularly unions between mild steel and flexible hose, with a protective tape such as Densotape. Additionally, when pipes are renewed the new lengths must be secured with brackets, and brackets must be cushioned with gaskets to prevent wear resulting from vibration and flexing. After repairs or renewals have been made to a hydraulic system the section of pipework should be isolated, pressure tested and flushed through. Flushing in particular is most important and will often avoid a lot of later trouble. Experience shows that when pipes start to fail in numbers it is worth carrying an extra engineer or mechanic for a few weeks to carry out wholesale renewals.

Hydraulic failures at the union between mild steel pipe and flexible hose are common. They can be reduced by protecting the union with Densotape, as already mentioned, and by routine renewal of the flexible hoses at regular intervals, perhaps of five years. It is essential to have spare unions made up ready to fit. If necessary a new fitting can be welded on to the steel pipe and, if the ship's engineers are prepared, professional and experienced, the job can be completed within 30 minutes.

Hydraulic systems – loss of pressure: If a hydraulic system is not operating at the intended design pressure, the consequence may be a cleating system which does not fully engage or disengage the cleats, or a hatch cover manoeuvring system which fails to place the hatch panels in the fully open or fully closed positions. If the loss of pressure is due to a leak this will be obvious, as will the remedy. More likely causes of low pressure are pump wear and incorrect pressure adjustment of the system, whilst in older ships which have filters in the suction line these filters can easily become blocked, causing reduced line pressures.

If the ship is provided with a modern hydraulic system with a balanced pressure flow, and if the oil has been proved in good condition and the filters are clean but still a problem persists – call the manufacturer.

Hatch motors in exposed positions: Where electric hatch motors are installed in exposed positions – for example, when set into chambers within the hatch panels – it is essential that the seals to the chamber are maintained absolutely watertight and that the motor is inspected regularly to ensure that the chamber remains dry. If water is allowed to accumulate unnoticed in the chamber, the eventual result will be a motor which is burnt out and hatch panels which cannot be opened or closed.

Where motors are situated on the exposed deck they can be submerged when heavy seas are shipped. Check regularly, by inspection of the sight glass, that the luboil has not become contaminated with seawater. Regularly drain off any seawater which has been forced in through the bearings and check the oil for condition. Change the oil if it becomes milky or otherwise breaks down.

Hydraulic continuous chain drive to single-pull and side rolling hatch covers: When replacement continuous chains are fitted to hatch covers, it is necessary to ensure that the chains are a matched pair. In addition to being the same length, they must also both contain the same number of links. If they do not satisfy both these requirements they will when operated cause the hatch panels to slew, with the risk that the panels will leave the trackway and fall into the hold.

Emergency opening and closing of hatches

It is normal for the manufacturers to make provision for the mechanical opening and closing of hatches in the event of failure of the automatic system. Emergency raising and lowering of panels may be done by hand operated jacks and the moving of panels can be achieved with tirfors (lever-operated devices for hauling on wires). Elsewhere the ship's cargo-handling and mooring equipment may be brought into emergency use but this can be a slow process. Some ships are now provided with a portable hydraulic unit with electrical drive which can be wheeled on deck and plugged in to the ship's main or reserve electrical supply or even to a shore supply using a 50 m cable. The unit couples up to the local hydraulic controls and will successfully open or close the hatch in 15-20 minutes where normal operation would take 1-2 minutes.

Whilst the emergency procedure to be followed will vary from one design of hatch cover to another, there are some basic matters which deserve attention.

1. The emergency opening and closing of hatches calls for the use of equipment – jacks, emergency retaining pins, securing wires, tirfors – some of which is never otherwise used. This equipment should be clearly labelled and regularly checked, or it will be lost when needed in an emergency. Photographs showing how the equipment should be connected and used

are useful guides for ships' staff, especially if they are unfamiliar with it.

2. It is normally essential to keep the hatch operating levers in the correct position at every stage of the emergency process and to return the covers to the initial position by emergency means when they were first moved by emergency means.

3. The procedures must ensure that the panels are supported and/or secured at every stage. This is essential to guarantee safety and avoid damage when the operating system is not working.

The emergency hatch opening/closing procedures for *Regina Oldendorff* are described in Appendix 4.1 and those for *Spar Scorpio* in Appendix 4.2.

Hatch leakage – first aid measures

High adhesive plastic sealing tape: High adhesive plastic (Ram-nek) sealing tape is sold in strips 1.2 metres in length by 7 cm, 11 cm or 15 cm wide. It is designed to seal the joints of closed hatches, so as to prevent the leakage of water into them when it is known or feared that the hatch seals are not watertight. The fitting of high adhesive sealing tape, if done over the entire ship, is very expensive in cost of material and in crew time.

The process is by no means guaranteed to be successful. At its best the tape forms a bond so strong that it takes the paint with it when it is eventually removed, thereby causing increased corrosion. Even when adhesion is good, however, it is difficult to fit a continuous watertight strip over joints which were not designed to be taped and which are often irregular, though Ram-nek provide a second product, Koaming-Aide, designed to meet this requirement. One disadvantage claimed for high adhesive tapes by their critics is that they set up a condition in which electrolytic action can occur, since they create a sealed zone environment containing salt air, water, steel and possibly additional metals. This can cause severe corrosion and weakening of the joint areas.

Good bonding requires a surface which is free from salt and grease, conditions which cannot be guaranteed. If the hatch covers are salty they should be washed with fresh water before being taped. Good bonding also requires warmth in the tape (which can be achieved by storing it in the engineroom in cold weather), and in the surface to which it is applied. These are not easy to achieve and it has been found in sub-zero temperatures that an oxy-acetylene flame destroyed the hatch cover paintwork, but gave patchy adhesion.

Despite all the foregoing practical difficulties, the use of high adhesive sealing tape seems to be considered by cargo interests to show that the ship has made every effort to protect the cargo, whilst failure to use the tape is criticised in cases of wet damage to cargo as a neglect of seamanlike precautions. The use of high adhesive sealing tape is fairly common with sensitive cargoes such as grain, steel and woodpulp, but it must be stressed that the effectiveness is doubtful, the damage which it can cause to the hatch covers in the long term is substantial, and it can never be a substitute for ensuring that the covers are maintained to good standard, thereby ensuring watertightness.

Plastic sheeting spread over cargo surface: Plastic sheeting can be spread over the surface of a bulk cargo and, provided that adjoining sheets are spread in the same manner as the tiles on a roof with the higher sheet overlapping the lower one, any water which falls on to the sheeting will run to the sides or ends of the hold. Such an arrangement will catch leakage through the hatch covers and also any condensation which falls from the deckhead on to the cargo.

When the sheeting is removed, it may be possible to remove within the sheeting any water which has been caught in the 'trench' at the ship's side or at the end bulkheads, thus reducing or eliminating wet damage to the cargo. Any leakage which does reach the cargo, will damage cargo at the boundaries of the hold. Damaged cargo is likely to be rejected by the receivers. The cargo in the hatch square will be undamaged and can be grabbed directly out of the hold. The cargo at the hold boundaries is less accessible and is therefore less likely to be grabbed directly out of the hold. The damaged portions can more easily be sorted during the mechanical or manual stages of the discharge within the hold, particularly if the commodity is one which cakes when wet.

This system is used in the transportation of chemical fertiliser from Sweden to Belgium in winter, a voyage during which the ambient temperature increases, so that the outside water and air become warmer than the cargo in the hold. In these conditions cargo sweat (condensation taking place directly on the cargo) is likely to be formed. If the cargo is covered with plastic sheeting the sweat will form on the sheeting rather than on the cargo, thus preventing the caking which occurs very readily with this commodity.

The use of plastic sheeting in this manner is not suitable for cargoes which require surface ventilation. In addition it may cause condensation to form beneath the sheeting, and to form a caked surface layer on the cargo in circumstances in which ship's sweat is to be expected. Such circumstances occur when the cargo is a warm one, being brought to a cool climate.

Sources

3, 113, 118, 119. (See List of Sources, Page 497)

Figures 4.1, 4.4-4.7, 4.11-4.15, 4.19-4.20 and 4.24 by courtesy of the MacGregor Group.

Figures 4.2-4.3, 4.8-4.10, 4.21-4.22 and 4.26-4.27 by courtesy of MacGregor-Navire (GBR) Ltd.

CHECKLIST – Procedures for maintaining hatch covers in efficient condition

- ☐ Study the manufacturer's literature and gain a full understanding of the operating and maintenance procedures.
- ☐ Ensure that all hatch drain holes are clear.
- ☐ Clean coamings and cross-joints very thoroughly before closing hatches.
- ☐ Do not move hatch panels if spilt cargo is piled on them.
- ☐ Close panels in the correct sequence.
- ☐ Ensure panels are correctly positioned before securing them.
- ☐ Fasten cleats in the correct sequence.
- ☐ Officer to inspect secured hatches before proceeding to sea.
- ☐ Hold the stevedores responsible for hatch damage, and have damage repaired.
- ☐ Carefully supervise hatch opening and closing when crew members are inexperienced or working in difficult conditions.
- ☐ Avoid moving hatch covers when the ship is pitching or rolling.
- ☐ Whenever possible avoid opening hatch covers at sea.
- ☐ Inspect hatches regularly for items which are worn, slack or corroded and renew, repair or adjust them as necessary.
- ☐ Grease hatch fittings regularly.
- ☐ Ensure that all moving parts can be greased: fit nipples if needed.
- ☐ Protect hydraulic pistons before painting hatch coamings.
- ☐ Paint behind hydraulic pipework, or wrap it with Densotape.
- ☐ Give high priority to scaling and painting of cross-joint channels.
- ☐ Carry sufficient spares to permit emergency renewal of any fitting.
- ☐ Carry a good supply of spares for routine renewals.
- ☐ Ensure that equipment required for the emergency opening and closing of hatch covers is kept labelled and readily available.

Fig. 5.0 The painful process of removing coal stains from high on the ship's side

CHAPTER 5

PREPARATION OF HOLDS

General considerations, whilst discharging, preparation for cleaning, cleaning equipment, sweeping of holds, disposal of cargo residues, washing, exceptional cleaning, clearing blocked bilge suctions, drying, preparation of bilges and testing of fittings, hold inspections, time required for hold preparation, final preparations, hold coatings, ballast holds

Cleaning of holds – general considerations

WHAT CLEANING IS NEEDED?: When the discharge of a hold is completed, the chief mate will need to consider if, how and when the hold is to be cleaned. This will mainly be a commercial decision made by the vessel's operator, whether owner or charterer. In general terms hold cleaning is required where the next employment is not fixed and the ship must be ready for any permitted cargo, where the next employment is fixed and the holds must be prepared for the intended cargo or, for owners, as a matter of good practice in reducing corrosion in the vessel's holds. This means in practice that holds will always be cleaned in preparation for the next cargo except when the ship is engaged on a shuttle service carrying the same cargo. For example, on a coastal service carrying coal between two Danish ports the charterers found it cheaper to send the ship from the discharge port without employing trimmers to discharge the final sweepings. Turnround time was reduced by two hours and the cost of employing trimmers was avoided.

Similarly, a ship engaged on time charter for the carriage of iron ore may not clean the holds between cargoes, even if different grades are carried, though the holds will be 'shovel cleaned' by shore labour in the discharge port. When a ship is on voyage charter, the normal requirement is for the holds to be cleaned ready for any cargo, or for the particular cargo intended next voyage.

When on time charter the Master should ask charterers what they require by way of hold cleaning. If he fails to do so the charterers may refuse to pay for any cleaning. They object, understandably, to paying the owners for a wash which may cost US$1,000+ per hold in circumstances when all they require is a sweep, which is often free.

System for removal of water from holds: Bulk carriers are usually provided with a bilge suction system, which uses a pump or an eductor in the engineroom to extract water from the holds. The water is drawn through the bilge line, past a non return valve, to the engineroom and discharged overboard. Such a bilge system is usually operated with the same pump or eductor as is used for stripping ballast, a process described in Chapter 7.

Such a system cannot be used to wash large particles of cargo out of the holds as cargo residues will clog the suctions, non return valves and bilge lines. Nor can it be used to remove cargoes which may set solid in the bilge lines. The holds must be swept very thoroughly and the cargo residues must be lifted out of them before the holds are washed.

An alternative arrangement, found in some bulk carriers of all sizes, is the fitting of port and starboard bilge eductors (or 'ejectors') above the bilge wells in each hold. Water is usually taken from the deck fire/wash line to drive the eductor and the combined bilge and drive water is discharged through a pipe led directly overboard at deck level. Provided that the diameter of the discharge line is sufficient the system can discharge lumps of cargo the size of apples. As a result, thorough sweeping and removal of residues is much less necessary. Yet another variation is for bulkers to have a single eductor in each hold, specifically for hold cleaning, in addition to conventional bilge lines and suctions. Flooding of the hold by water from the eductor system is prevented by a non return valve in the bilge suction line. A non return valve is also fitted in the discharge line if the discharge opening is situated below the waterline.

Bulk carriers for several owners have been built without non return valves in the eductor's bilge suction lines because, if fitted, non return valves are frequently damaged by lumps of cargo which are sucked through them by the powerful suction of the eductor. Their owners accept that when the eductor is stopped the water remaining in the discharge line (the 'backflash') will return to the bilge well. The bilge wells are amply sized, provided with high level alarms and can be emptied by a mucking pump.

At the point where the branch line carrying the drive water for the eductor leaves the deck fire/wash line two valves with spectacle flanges and a spool piece are usually fitted to provide adequate separation to prevent accidental hold flooding when the deck line is pressurised and a gate valve is fitted at the open end of the discharge line 900 mm above the deck.

Ships equipped with portable eductors (sludge pumps) will use them for hold washing when the quantity of bulky or difficult residues to be removed justifies the time and effort required to lift the eductor into and out of the hold. From what is written above it is obvious that, when preparing to clean holds it is necessary to take account of which type of water removal system is installed. The first steps in the cleaning process should be taken whilst the cargo is being discharged.

Whilst discharging

Cleaning at high levels: When discharging cargoes such as grain, it is often worthwhile to send crew members into the holds to clean steelwork at high levels during interruptions in discharging. Whilst standing on the cargo during early stages of the discharge they can, using damped brooms or mops, reach places such as underdeck beams that later become inaccessible. Such work must always be carefully supervised to ensure the safety of crew members and is, of course, subject to safe access and local regulations.

Need for complete discharge: Cleaning the holds will be much more difficult if quantities of cargo sweepings have been left in the hold, particularly if the cargo is not soluble in water, so the ship's officers will do all that they can to compel or persuade the stevedores and trimmers to discharge all the sweepings. If a bilge cover plate has been displaced and cargo has filled the bilge, the trimmers will be unwilling to remove it. If they cannot be induced to do so it will be worthwhile to send the crew to get all the cargo out of the bilge before the finish of discharge, so that the contents of the bilge can be discharged along with the rest of the cargo.

Stevedores are often willing, if asked, to return to a hold where discharge has been completed, to remove sweepings gathered by the crew. They may even be prepared to leave a grab resting in the hold for a while into which sweepings can be shovelled. On a gearless bulker such help is very welcome.

Before closing the hatches on completion of discharge the hatch coaming top, the compression bars, the coaming drains and the hatch cover seals must be clean and free of residues, particularly if the hatches cannot be opened during the ballast passage. Hatches cannot be opened at sea when conditions are rough, because hatch panels may be dislodged or even lost overboard. For this reason some owners forbid the opening of hatches at sea. In the discharging berth this cleaning can be done with a compressed air hose or with hand held brushes. During these cleaning operations it is essential that ship's staff wear suitable protective equipment to prevent eye injuries or inhalation of the cargo dust.

Washing of hatch covers and coamings: At some point before loading the next cargo the hatch cover tops, bottoms and cross joints, along with the inner sides of the coaming should be washed to ensure that no residues can contaminate the next cargo. This is most easily done from on deck with the hatches partly or fully open and should, therefore, be done in sheltered or calm waters. Even if the holds are not to be rinsed with fresh water it is recommended[97] that hatch covers, coamings and underdeck areas are rinsed to ensure that any condensation which drips onto the next cargo will be free of salt. When hold ventilators are set into the hatch covers they must be thoroughly cleaned.

Preparation for hold cleaning

Many ships' officers have experienced the embarrassment of finding cargo residues on the tanktop when the hold is opened in the loading port, although a thorough hold cleaning, and inspection, have previously been undertaken. This can occur when full astern is ordered in the approaches to the berth, and the resulting vibration shakes down traces of old cargoes from inaccessible and undetected surfaces high under the deckhead.

To reduce this problem, some Masters put the engine to full astern, allowing the ship to vibrate and shake down the residues at the start of the ballast passage, before the holds have been cleaned. Even when this is done, it is prudent to reinspect all the holds a few hours before the loading port is reached, so that any unexpected problems can be found and corrected before loading is due to commence.

Cleaning equipment

The Torvald Klaveness Group, leading Norwegian operators of bulk carriers, require their owned and chartered handy-sized and Panamax bulkers to be equipped[105] with a minimum of one air/water Combi-gun and preferably a second Combi-gun and a Maxi-gun, the latter being a more powerful version of the Combi-gun. They must also carry one Spray Foam gun for applying chemicals to hold bulkheads and 1,000 litres of a cleaning chemical such as Aquatuff (an environmentally friendly product supplied by Unitor) for use when water washing gives insufficiently good results. Also required are a mucking winch and sufficient long ladders, scrapers, mops, brooms and bamboo or aluminium 'manhelps' (long poles) for knocking down cargo.

Five hundred to 1,000 litres of chemical will be required to clean a ship after a difficult cargo such as sticky coal. The required quantity of chemicals should always be maintained aboard ship and rapid re-supply can be made from depots in many parts of the world. Even with this equipment properly used, a perfectly clean hold after the dirtiest cargo cannot be guaranteed, but Torvald Klaveness consider that with the assistance of this equipment they have on many occasions been able to avoid having the holds rejected. A single instance of this sort, they believe, is sufficient to recover the cost of the equipment.

Digital cameras are used on board to report on the condition of the holds and ships' personnel are sent on training courses in hold cleaning skills.

Spray Foam guns are described in Chapter 22.

Sweeping of holds

Sweeping of holds is normally the first step in the hold cleaning process. On occasion it will be the only step as there are at least four situations in which hold washing is not required or cannot be carried out.

Sweeping of holds when washing is not permitted: If a ship is required to backload a bulk cargo in the same port as that in which she discharges, and if hold washing in the port is not permitted, it will be necessary to achieve the required standard of cleanliness by sweeping and then lifting the sweepings out of the hold to be stowed on deck until such time as they can be landed or disposed of legally at sea. This is work which the crew will be expected to do if time permits, so the chief mate will make every effort to ensure that the stevedores complete a good discharge and leave the minimum of sweepings in the hold. Shore labour must be employed for cleaning if there is insufficient time for the crew to complete the work before loading is due to commence. The quality of the required cleaning will depend upon the intended cargo and the danger of contamination, but as a general rule it is unreasonable to expect a very high standard of cleaning if washing is not permitted.

Sweeping of holds when washing is not necessary: Washing will probably not be required following a clean cargo such as steel coils or steel slabs. It will be sufficient to sweep up any debris and remove it from the hold.

Sweeping of holds in freezing conditions: Washing cannot be undertaken in freezing conditions. When the temperature is below freezing and the water is brackish, as it is in the Baltic and approaches, washing water will freeze on bulkheads and coamings. In these circumstances holds can only be scraped and swept clean, with all residues including ice having to be lifted from the hold. If early warning is given, massive fan heaters can be hired in some Baltic ports to dry out holds if the ship arrives with a coating of ice in the holds to load a sensitive cargo such as chemical fertiliser. The heaters are normally connected to a shore power supply. A mobile crane will be needed to place the heaters in the hold if the ship does not possess her own derricks or cranes and if there is no permanent crane at the loading berth.

Sweeping of holds when water will cause damage: Certain exceptional cargo residues must not be washed at all. It is reported, for example, that copper concentrate, if washed, will form a 'concrete' layer on the hold sides which can only be removed with abrasive discs on disc sander/grinders. This cargo must be cleaned by thorough blowing with compressed air and by sweeping.

Sweeping of holds in preparation for washing: Holds should be swept and the sweepings removed whenever the stevedores will accept and discharge the sweepings before the vessel sails from the discharge port. In addition the holds should be swept before washing, except when the residues are soluble or when fixed or portable hold eductors which can remove the residues are available.

Disposal of cargo residues and associated waste

Nature of cargo residues: The MARPOL regulations and national and local regulations govern the disposal of cargo residues and determine whether they are released at sea or landed in port. These matters are discussed in Chapter 25, while in this chapter each of the alternative procedures is described.

Soluble cargoes such as salt will normally present no problems for hold washing, and sweepings of granular cargoes like mineral sand or concentrates can usually be washed away without difficulty provided that the pressure of the washing water is maintained at 7 kg/cm^2 (100 psi) or better, and that the holds are drained by a direct overboard discharge bilge eductor system rather than a bilge pump system. Where cargoes come in larger lumps, like quartz, for example, it is particularly important to ensure a complete discharge of the sweepings since remnants cannot be drained from the holds and will have to be lifted out by the crew. Residues such as cement, which could set hard within the bilge system, cannot be washed through that system but must be discharged directly overboard from the holds by submersible pump, or dedicated hold eductor system using copious quantities of water.

Alternative methods of disposal: Most cargo residues are washed from holds, the washings being discharged into the water alongside the ship. When residues cannot be washed from holds they must be lifted from the holds for later disposal. A geared bulk carrier equipped with her own derricks or cranes will be able to use them if necessary to lift sweepings from the holds, provided that the ship is steady enough to permit the use of the ship's gear. If the weather is rough or if the ship is gearless, it will be necessary to use a mucking winch (described in Chapter 22, and sometimes known as a sediment hoist) and davit fixed to the hatch coaming, or access or trimming hatch, to raise sweepings from the hold. In most cases the use of the mucking winch will be the most convenient option.

Use of mucking winch: A mucking winch and the seamen who use it can only handle small quantities of sweepings – for example, a full bucket or 20 litre drum – at a time. The container is filled in the hold and carried to a position below the mucking winch where it is hooked on and raised to deck level. It is swung clear of the hatch coaming and landed on deck where it is immediately tipped over the ship's side, or is emptied on deck for later disposal, depending upon the nature of the sweepings and the location of the ship. Sweepings can be tipped on deck in front of an open hydrant, where the water from the hydrant can be used to wash them overboard. Inexperienced crew members must be reminded to tip or wash the sweepings over the lee side.

Sweepings left on deck: If the sweepings have to remain on deck they present problems for the ship, since residues are liable to be blown about the ship by the wind and they may stain the deck and the ship's side. For this reason they should where possible be retained in the hold until such time as they can be tipped overboard. When this is not possible the sweepings should be stowed on deck in drums. On larger vessels where the quantities involved are too great for the use of drums, the sweepings are usually stowed between hatches, slightly dampened down and temporarily covered with old tarpaulins and pallets to prevent them from being blown around the ship. Lifting of sweepings from the hold is a labour-intensive and potentially dirty process. It is always preferable for the ship to dispose of residues by washing, and this method is adopted whenever possible.

Sweepings left in hold: If it is not possible to remove sweepings from the hold before arrival at the loading port because of adverse weather or because of the weight and volume of the sweepings, they should be piled in an accessible part of the hold, in drums or sacks if possible, ready for rapid removal upon arrival. In the rare cases when this is done, it will be necessary to give owners or charterers maximum warning to ensure that facilities are ready on arrival and offhire time and costs are minimised.

Washing holds

Handheld hoses: The normal method of cleaning holds is by washing with water drawn from the sea. This involves hosing down every part of each hold with a water jet whilst the water is drained from the hold by the eductors or bilge pumps, and discharged overboard. Three alternative methods of hosing down the holds exist – using handheld hoses, water cannon, or a permanent installation.

The hosing may be done by handheld hose operated by a team of two or three seamen. One will

Fig. 5.1 Portable bilge basket

Fig. 5.4 Paintwork stained by coal

Fig. 5.2 20 litre drums for sweepings

Fig. 5.3 Brushes and shovels for hold cleaning

Fig. 5.5 Ready for hold cleaning

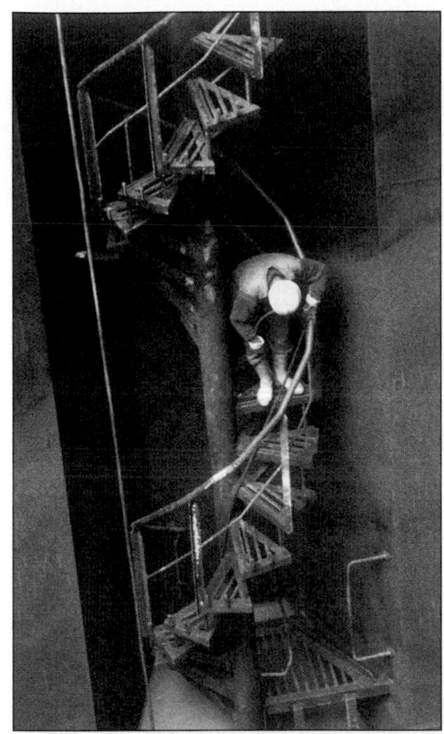

Fig. 5.6 Sweeping the Australian ladder with an air hose

Fig. 5.9 Using an air spanner to open the bilge well

Fig. 5.10 Bilge cover plate removed for bilge cleaning

Fig. 5.7 Sweeping the tanktop

Fig. 5.11 Bilge open and cargo residues removed

Fig. 5.8 Using scraper and manhelp to remove sweepings

Fig. 5.12 Ballast suction grille, turned end for end and sealed with cover plate when hold is cargo filled

Fig. 5.13 Washing hatch covers

Fig. 5.14

Fig. 5.15

Fig. 5.16 Washing the hatch coaming

Fig. 5.17 Washing the hold of a handymax bulk carrier after discharge of 6,600 mt of silicon dross, a dense cargo that only part filled the hold

be on deck to operate the control valve where the hose is connected to the deck service line (or fire main) and will oversee operations, whilst the others will drag the hose around the hold and direct the jet at each part of the compartment in turn.

On larger vessels it is important to use at least two men to handle the hose, since one will be unable to control the hose at full pressure and will do a poor job, either because the hose has been badly directed or because the pressure has been reduced. Aboard a small ship with holds which are not particularly dirty, a handheld hose is often the quickest and best method of completing the job. Handheld hoses are less satisfactory in larger ships – it is difficult to achieve good cleaning in the more remote parts of the hold and the method requires a lot of time and labour.

Water cannon: An alternative to using a handheld hose is to have the hose led to a high-pressure sea-water cannon, such as the Combi-gun or the more powerful Maxi-gun, on a tripod placed in the hold. These water cannon use compressed air from the ship's deck line to inject greater pressure into water from the fire main. This system, more likely to be used on larger bulk carriers, provides a more powerful jet of water than can be achieved with a handheld hose and results in better cleaning of the high extremities of the holds. The system takes longer to move from place to place and requires as much labour as does the handheld hose.

The washing sequence adopted when washing with handheld hoses or water cannon starts at the top of the hold and works towards the bottom. First, hatch covers are washed on all sides, as far as possible. Compression bars and rubbers may need scrubbing to remove cargo which is sticking to them. Next, the coamings, underdeck areas and hold sides are washed, paying particular attention to non-vertical surfaces such as hopper angles, pipe guards and brackets. Finally, the tanktop is washed and the bilges are flushed. Some ships use two washing teams, one on deck to wash hatch covers and coamings with a handheld hose whilst the other team uses the water cannon to wash within the holds. Within the holds a systematic procedure for washing is necessary to ensure that all parts and fittings are washed from at least two positions. Every frame and beam, for example, should be washed with a water jet first from one side and then from the other: this can be achieved by going round the hold twice, first clockwise, then anti-clockwise. It is necessary to be absolutely methodical in this work, to ensure that every centimetre of the hold is thoroughly washed. Where it is impossible to direct a jet of water directly onto one side of a beam from any position on the tanktop the beam must be hosed from a position on the hold access ladder, or 'splashback' (Fig. 5.18) must be used to ensure that washing is complete. Wet sticky coal can be very difficult to remove when compacted behind steel casings protecting ballast and air pipes. It can be dislodged by water cannon and/or beating the casing with heavy hammers.

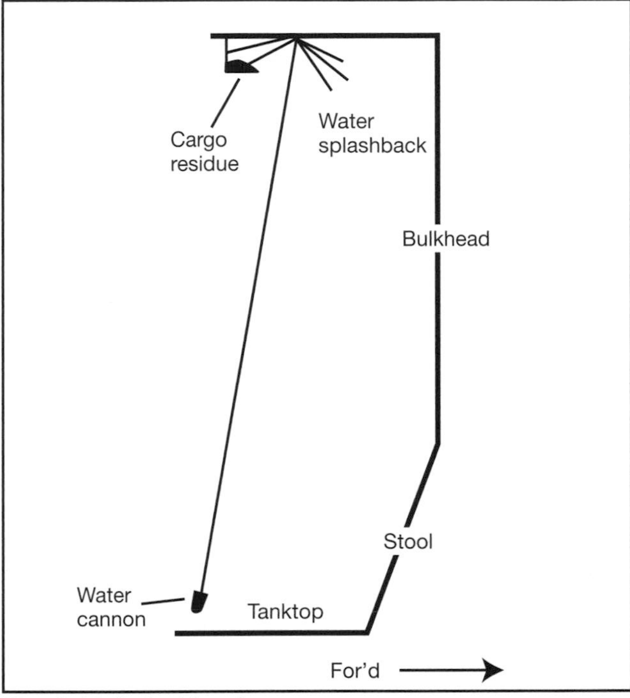

Fig. 5.18 Splashback

Permanent installation: The third option for washing the holds is to use a permanent washing installation with water guns installed under the deck-head in the hold. Aboard a mini-bulker the hold would be equipped with one water gun at each end. Each gun is wound down into the hold from a recess in the deckhead. Water at high pressure is provided by direct line from the engineroom. If the full washing program is selected, the gun will then automatically move through a full washing sequence with the nozzle directed first upwards to the deckhead, then more or less horizontally on to the bulkheads and finally down-wards towards the tanktop. Alternative washing programs can be selected. A bottom wash is a wash of the tanktop only. The program is designed to wash towards the after end of the hold, where the bilge suctions are located.

Butterworth systems: A few bulk carriers are fitted with butterworth systems similar to those used for tank cleaning on tankers. A rotating set of nozzles on the end of a heavy duty hose is lowered into the hold through a hole in the hatch covers, delivering water at high pressure at successive levels as, over a period of time, the hose is lowered deeper into the hold. Bulk carriers, unlike tankers, are not normally able to 'butterworth' with hot water.

Water must not be allowed to stand: All of the above systems of washing depend upon the flow of water to wash any dirt and residues down the bulkheads and across the tanktop to the bilge suctions. If the washing is to be effective, it is preferable that the water is pumped or educted from the holds continuously and that no pool of standing water is allowed to form on the tanktop. Whilst in ballast the ship will normally have a good stern trim, causing the water to flow across the tanktop and thereby assisting the washing process. On some ships the washing is found to be most effective if the ship is listed 1° with ballast water; if one bilge suction becomes blocked, the ship can be quickly listed the other way, allowing the use of the other suction to pump out the water. This will permit access to the blocked suction to clear it.

An exception to the above procedures occurs when it is necessary to wash holds in port because of lack of time, but the washings cannot be pumped overboard in port. In these circumstances the washings can be left in the hold to be pumped out when the vessel reaches the open sea. This procedure is often adopted with the ballast hold and can be followed with another hold, provided that it is safe to do so. It will be safe only provided that the water in the hold remains at a low level, say, up to one metre, and provided that calculations show that the ship's stability will remain adequate despite the reduction in metacentric height (GM) from the free surface of the water. The required calculation is described in Appendix 8.1.

Fresh water rinse: When holds are washed with sea water, traces of salt remain on all the surfaces within the hold. This is unacceptable to some grain surveyors and is liable to contaminate cargoes such as steel products and woodpulp. Salt traces will also encourage corrosion and are to be avoided if possible. For these reasons holds should be rinsed with fresh water after full washing. One method of achieving a fresh water rinse is to load fresh water in a suitable ballast tank, such as the forepeak or afterpeak, and then to pump the fresh water through the deck service line for use in hosing down the holds.

When using this method it is important that the crew members operating the hose understand that they are using fresh water from a limited supply and not the sea water which normally runs through their hoses. The water must be used efficiently and with care to provide a quick rinse of each compartment if all holds are to be properly washed with the available supply of water. On a handy-sized vessel, where the fire pump has a capacity of 200 tonnes/hour, two or three minutes spent rinsing each hold with fresh water will use a total of 50 tonnes for the entire ship and should remove most of the salt from the structure. Some ships routinely use much larger quantities of fresh water for final rinsing, and consider that the expense is justified. An alternative method of fresh water rinsing is to use a portable high pressure washing machine[98]. This will use less fresh water, but will take much longer.

Fresh water has a cost in most ports, so, if sufficient water for hold rinsing cannot be generated aboard ship, care should be taken to ensure that water for hold washing is obtained where it is cheap or free, the best sources of supply being those few places where the ship floats in clean fresh water. When appropriate the receipt for fresh water should be claused 'Hold Washing – For Charterer's Account', as it is the accepted practice in some trades for charterers to pay for fresh water washing when required for cargo purposes.

The practice of the routine fresh water rinsing of holds is becoming more widespread as the benefits are more widely recognised.

Precautions when washing within port limits: In most ports nowadays hold washing within the port limits is prohibited since the port authorities do not want cargo residues discharged into their waters, regardless of whether or not the commodity in question is a harmful or offensive one. If there is doubt as to whether hold washings can be discharged in port, it is prudent to obtain written permission via the agent. A spoken assurance from a stevedore is no guarantee that the ship will not be penalised later. Washing holds in port may be permitted when the washing water can be retained aboard, in the hold or in cargo hold washing water tanks.

When hold washing is permitted at the berth and the washing water discharge is above the surface it is usually necessary to discharge the washings only on the offshore side of the ship to avoid flooding the jetty. If hold washing is permitted within the port, arrangements must be made aboard ship to ensure that discharge of washing water can be stopped immediately if a pilot boat or other craft has reason to approach. This will ensure that accidental flooding of a boat can be prevented.

Washing of holds at sea: If holds are to be washed at sea with handheld hoses or water cannon, the process can be carried out most safely by leaving the hatch covers closed and passing the hose down the access hatch. Unfortunately this makes manipulation of the hose more difficult and provides poorer lighting. It also interferes with easy communication between the members of the washing party. In these circumstances there are strong reasons for opening the hatches 1 metre, if no more. Since the ship will be in ballast with a large freeboard, there is normally no realistic danger of foundering as a result of opening hatches. The danger lies in the hatch covers suffering damage or becoming unshipped whilst they are unsecured, as a result of the ship working in a seaway.

Hatch covers should never be opened at sea, except in calm conditions, and the hatch panels when open must be well secured. The ship's procedures should ensure that the opening and closing of hatch covers at sea is properly supervised and only occurs when it is safe to do so. Securing hooks ('safety latches'), provided for securing open hatch panels in port, are inadequate for use when at sea and should be supplemented by strong lashings. If conditions start to become rough whilst hatches are open, the vessel must be hove-to or her course must be adjusted to provide a steady platform whilst the hatches are closed.

Use of permanent installations and butterworth systems at sea: Permanent washing installations and butterworth systems are designed to be used with the hatches closed. There is no problem in using them when the vessel is at sea.

Exceptional cleaning

Washing stubborn dirt: When the holds are washed after particularly dirty cargoes such as petroleum coke (petcoke) and sticky coals, the washing time can be extended in an attempt to achieve a satisfactory standard of cleanliness. Coalstains (Fig. 5.4) or greasy or discoloured patches remaining after washing, particularly if they leave dirt on the hand when rubbed, are likely to cause surveyors to reject the holds for sensitive cargoes such as grain, so exceptional cleaning will be required. Suitable spray foam equipment[98] consisting of pressure tank, Minigun with extensions, hoses and air/water nozzles can be used to deliver chemical cleaning products to a height of 10-15 metres and this type of equipment is carried as standard by responsible owners[102]. Cleaning chemicals which are biodegradable and environmentally friendly[99] have been developed and are reported to be effective[105]. After a short period to allow the chemical to take effect the treated areas have again to be washed with water at high pressure after which the offending discoloured patches should be gone, except in the most difficult cases.

Spray foam equipment is not found aboard many bulk carriers and in its absence the cleaning must be done with the use of scaffolding, platforms or ladders, allowing crewmembers to work close up to the stains. Convenient and effective access equipment, capable of being used aboard a rolling ship is, if it exists, not well known or widely available. A consequence is that following the carriage of coal or petcoke a final cleaning by shore labour is often required before a sensitive cargo can be carried.

Cargoes to Australia: Holds must be cleaned extremely thoroughly, and absolutely all vegetable and animal products, particularly grain, must be removed from the ship before a cargo is carried to Australia. This measure, which is especially true for fertiliser cargoes destined for Australia, is designed to ensure that Karnel Bunt, a disease affecting grain, is excluded from the region. Failure to remove all grain from the holds and decks of the ship will, if discovered, result in exclusion of the ship and rejection of the cargo. (See Appendix 5.1)

Removal of taint by smell: An extreme case of problems arising from smelly holds involved a handysized bulk carrier which was fixed to load grain in a US Gulf port immediately after carrying a cargo of fishmeal[100]. She was finally passed as loadready when inspected for the tenth time, and after thirteen days of cleaning by crew assisted, in the later stages, by shore labour and equipment. Important lessons learnt were as follows. Cleaning and deodorising chemicals designed for use with hot water were ineffective when applied with cold water. The smell of fishmeal was only finally removed when the insides of the hold ventilator trunks, in the samson posts, were cleaned as thoroughly as the holds and when every trace of fishmeal was removed from decks, deck scuppers, hatch covers and masthouses and when equipment from the masthouses had been moved to the poop.

The equipment and products used for this cleaning

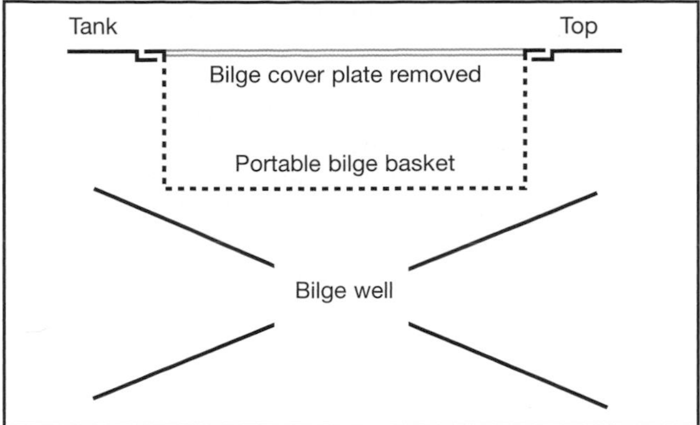

Fig. 5.19 Portable bilge basket

are described in Appendix 5.2. A remedy for the concealing of taint – the burning of coffee grounds in a bucket in the hold – cannot be recommended[101].

Difficult hold cleaning: When difficulties are experienced in hold cleaning or when doubt exists as to whether the hold condition will be acceptable for the intended cargo it is prudent to inform the owners as well as the time charterers. Digital photographs to accompany the report will be helpful. Owners will certainly want to know of any problems, in addition to which they may have a liability in respect of hold cleaning if owners' bills of lading incorporating the Hague-Visby Rules, have been used[97].

Clearing blocked bilge suctions

One suction blocked: Prevention is better than cure, and the blocking of bilges can be avoided by sweeping of holds and lifting of sweepings prior to washing and by the use of bilge baskets to catch larger lumps of cargo residue. Portable bilge baskets (which can be manufactured aboard if not provided – Figs. 5.1 and 5.19) are perforated steel boxes which are temporarily placed in the bilge wells to collect sweepings. They must be emptied regularly during hold washing. This is easily done during a manual wash and can prevent problems with blocked bilges and bilge lines.

Hold washing should be monitored at all times to detect any build-up of water. If such a build-up occurs, washing operations should immediately be stopped and the problem investigated. Directing a high-pressure hose into the bilge may be sufficient to clear the suction. Alternatively, if it is a hold eductor suction which is blocked, then 'flooding back' which is possible when there is no non-return valve between eductor and bilge well, may be the quickest way to clear it. This is achieved by temporarily shutting the eductor discharge so that the water which drives the eductor is forced through the bilge suction into the hold.

If the tanktop becomes flooded as the result of a single blocked suction, the hold can be pumped out by way of the other, with the ship given a small list towards the clear suction. Since the blocked suction will be located within a bilge well, and since the bilge well is likely to be from 1-2 metres in depth, it will be necessary to remove most of the water from the well before the suction can be cleared. If the bilge well is small in volume it is possible to bale it out with buckets, but if the bilge well is a large one a portable sump pump, powered by compressed air or water at high pressure, will have to be lowered into the hold and led to the blocked bilge where it will be used to pump the water across to the clear bilge.

Next, it will probably be necessary to unbolt one or more sections of the suction pipe to locate and remove the blockage, and make the suction ready for use again.

Both suctions blocked: If both suctions are blocked and the water is lying in the hold to some depth, a more serious problem exists. Portable sump pumps may be able to remove the water but the requirement to pump the water the full height of the hold for discharge on deck may mean that the process is a slow one, or that it proves to be impossible. One alternative in these circumstances is to open a manhole cover in the tanktop at the forward end of the hold to allow the water to drain into a double-bottom ballast tank. This can be done provided that the water at the forward end of the tanktop is not too deep to allow access to the manhole cover, and provided that the water drained into the double bottom will not contaminate it.

Drying of holds

The charterparty frequently requires holds to be presented 'Clean and Dry', and the requirement for a dry hold is not always easy to meet if the ballast passage is short and the hold has just been washed, or if sweat is forming in the hold. Holds can be dried by ventilating them when weather conditions are favourable and this is a useful test of the cargo ventilation fans, where fitted. Some ships are provided with ventilators for natural ventilation but not with cargo ventilation fans, and ships on bad weather routes may have the ventilators unshipped and blanked off. Two steps can still be taken. The crew can mop up all the puddles which form in the depressions in the tanktop when a hold is washed. If the weather is dry the hatches can be opened when the ship reaches smooth waters in the port approaches, and the flow of air over the ship will help to dry the holds.

It is clear that the requirement for a dry hold is unnecessary when the intended cargo is stored in a stockpile in the open air exposed to the weather and, when this is the case, shippers will normally be realistic and raise no objections if the hold is damp on arrival. This is not a reason to permit puddles of water in the hold and holds should not be presented for cargo in such a condition.

When commencing the loading of a cargo of grain in winter with holds which are sweating, it may be possible to persuade the operator of the grain elevator to blow some grain dust into the hold. This will stick to the moisture and will coat the hold, thereby reducing the contact between grain and moisture.

Preparation of bilges and testing of fittings

Cleaning of bilges: When hold washing has been completed, consideration must be given to cleaning of the bilges. Bilges are cleaned to ensure that they continue to function properly and do not become blocked with residues. In addition, they must be meticulously cleaned with every trace of matter removed and mopped dry, if foodstuffs such as grain or sugar are to be carried. Before carrying grain or other foodstuffs, the bilges should be sprayed with insecticide and rinsed with disinfectant. When presented for inspection they must be clean, dry and sweet smelling.

A bulk carrier bilge well normally consists of one or two bays of double bottom space, anything from 2 m^3 to 10 m^3 in volume. The space is usually cramped and uncomfortable to work in. Any accumulation of cargo should be removed and when hold eductors are fitted some of this can be achieved during the final stages of manual hold washing by a man standing over the bilge well and stirring the contents with a broom, so that the maximum is drawn away through the eductor.

Whatever remains in the bilge must be dug out with a hand shovel and lifted out of the hold by one of the processes described earlier. Traces of perishable cargoes must never be left in the bilges; they will decay and decompose, often with most unpleasant smells. On ships where the bilges are emptied with a bilge pump, each bilge suction is usually fitted with a perforated strum box to prevent large particles of cargo from entering the system and blocking the pump strainers. The strum boxes must be taken apart, cleaned and refitted.

When the bilge well is inspected for cleanliness the condition of the striker plate at the bottom of the sounding pipe must also be checked. Worn striker plates must be listed for replacement at the next opportunity to prevent damage to the ship's shell plating.

Flushing of sounding pipes and thermometer pipes: Hold bilge sounding pipes extend from the weather deck to the bilge wells in the hold, there normally being one on each side, port and starboard. Hold bilge sounding pipes are essential for the detection and measurement of any water in the bilges, even when remote gauges or alarm systems exist as well. Sounding pipes must be fit to be used when required; they must be kept clear at all times. It is regrettable that numerous instances can be quoted to show that sounding pipes are neglected and become blocked and unusable. This usually happens as a result of cargo residues being left in the bilge well and entering the bottom of the sounding pipe where, over a period of time, they dry out and solidify.

This problem can be prevented if the sounding pipes are flushed out – ie, hosed out with water from deck level after the hold has been washed and the bilge has been cleaned. This should be done as routine, with the water being removed from the bilge well by eductor or bilge pump. Some operators use an air line instead of a hose to flush out sounding pipes, sealing the mouth of the pipe with rags wrapped around the airline. The same alternatives are available for the flushing of hold thermometer pipes. Where fitted they must also be kept clear.

Testing of bilge suctions: If the hold has been washed out and the washing water has been discharged by eductors or hold bilge pumps, there will be no need for further testing of the hold bilge suctions. If the hold has only been swept or has not been cleaned at all, it is necessary to test the bilge suctions to ensure that water can be pumped out of the hold during the voyage if that becomes necessary. The testing of the bilge suctions can be combined with the flushing of the sounding pipes. Putting the water down the sounding pipe into the bilge well confirms that the pipe is clear, and pumping the water out of the bilge well confirms that the bilge pump or eductor is working satisfactorily.

The correct working of the non-return valves fitted in the hold bilge-to-engineroom lines (but not in the lines of hold bilge eductors which discharge directly overboard) can be tested by stopping the bilge pump or bilge eductor in the engineroom, and allowing water to flood back through the bilge line. If none enters the hold bilge the non return valve is working correctly. Non return valves must be overhauled on a regular basis. This should be a requirement of the ship's planned maintenance system. High level bilge alarms, when fitted, must be tested by raising the float and obtaining confirmation, usually by walkie-talkie radio, that the alarm has sounded.

Water ingress detectors: These must be tested as described in Chapter 6.

Hold inspections

The chief mate is responsible to the Master for ensuring that the holds are ready for cargo, and will normally inspect the holds himself when preparations are reported to be complete, if not before. If the crew members take an interest in their ship, it is quite likely that damage and defects noticed by crew members will already have been reported to him. The amount of supervision for the whole process of cleaning will depend upon the experience of the crew as well as their attitude.

During the ballast passage, loose scale may form in a cleaned hold, leakage into the hold from a ballast tank may occur or undetected cargo residues may fall from high in the hold. It is prudent to reinspect the holds at the end of a ballast passage, some hours before the vessel reaches the loading berth, to allow time for correction of any new problems which may have developed during the passage.

Cleanliness: The chief mate's first concern will be for hold cleanliness. If he has been instructed, or has read, or knows that the next cargo requires a particularly clean hold, he will inspect flat surfaces high in the hold, such as the flanges of beams visible from the hold ladder, for signs of cargo residues which must be removed. When at tanktop level he will find whether the bulkheads, hopper sides and tanktop are clean to the touch. He will look for residues beneath manhole cover plates and behind pipe casings. The bilge wells must be inspected. If the chief mate finds any fault he will know that a surveyor could use it as a reason to reject the ship for a sensitive cargo, and he will ensure that further washing or local cleaning is carried out to remove the fault.

Rusty steelwork or hard scale within holds is not a reason for rejecting a ship in normal bulk trades, but loose (rust) scale is not acceptable as it is likely to mix with the cargo and contaminate it. Loose scale should be removed by scraping and/or high pressure washing.

Insect infestation: Any trace of insect infestation in the hold or in the bilges is unacceptable with an edible cargo. The owners should be consulted as soon as possible for advice about the best way of eliminating the insects without making the hold unusable for the next cargo. Spraying with a suitable spray may be sufficient, or the hold may have to be fumigated (see Chapter 21).

Loose scale is a favourite hiding place for insects (otherwise known as bugs), and the inspection for them should be very thorough before perishable cargoes are carried. If detected by the inspectors, insect infestation can result in expense, delay and offhire whilst the ship is fumigated. If they are undetected, there is a danger that the cargo will be damaged and massive cargo claims will be experienced.

Leakage from ballast tanks or other sources: The ballast passage is probably the most favourable time to detect leakage from ballast tanks since such tanks will be full. Leakage from ballast tanks is a regular problem with middle-aged and elderly bulk carriers. Even if the leakage is minor it is still inconvenient. Ballast must be discharged from the leaking tank before any cargo is loaded, to avoid wet damage to the cargo, and this may be inconvenient. It will also be impossible to present dry holds at the loading port, except by keeping the ballast tank empty. If the leak is a major one it will be easy to detect. It will cause an additional difficulty; as water drains from the leaking tank into the hold the ship will develop a list.

When leaks are found, the chief mate will note their position with great care for subsequent repair and will arrange to pump out or drop out the ballast from the leaking tank as early as possible before arrival.

Hold damage: The hold should have been checked for damage during discharge and again upon completion, but when the hold is dirty it is still possible for damage to be overlooked. The chief mate, often accompanied by the Master, will inspect for damaged hold ladders, airpipes, thermometer pipes and sounding pipes and their casings, and damaged piping for any hold smothering system which is fitted. Local workers in many parts of the world insist that hold ladders, with platforms, handrails and protective hoops, are to be in perfect condition. It is imperative to make sure that all is safe for the ship's crew, too, if accidents are to be avoided.

Damage to frames, brackets and plating should also be recorded so that new damage can be shown to be the responsibility of the correct port and/or the charterers. Such damage should also be reported to Class in accordance with company procedures. The chief mate will also satisfy himself that no cover plates for manholes or gratings for bilge wells are missing. A good pair of binoculars and one or two powerful handlamps will assist in ensuring that areas high in the hold such as the tops of the side shell frames and the frames below the cross deck strips are properly examined.

Time required for hold preparation

The time required to clean a hold and prepare it for cargo will depend upon the dirtiness of the previous cargo, the volume of residues, the size of the hold, the resources available for cleaning, the standard of cleanliness required, and the number and experience of the seamen available. A reasonable estimate is that it will take five men one normal working day of 8-10 hours to clean one hold of a handy-sized or Panamax bulk carrier to normal cargo-ready standard from time of first entering the hold. Six men aboard a Cape-sized vessel will require about the same amount of time per hold. Cleaning to grain standard will typically take about 50% longer.

Cleaning of one hold of a two-hold mini-bulker and preparing for loading can normally be achieved by two or three men, to a grain-ready standard, in four-five hours, whilst a routine hold wash and rinse of the bilge wells can be completed in one-two hours. On most ships it is only possible to wash one hold at a time, though other tasks in an adjacent hold can be completed whilst the hold is being washed, if sufficient labour is available.

Final preparations

Burlapping of bilges: Bilge wells are usually provided with cover plates consisting of gratings or robust steel perforated plates set flush with the tanktop (Fig. 5.20) or recessed into it. They are so designed to reduce the likelihood that they will be dislodged by the bulldozers which will be used to shovel cargo into the centre of the hold in the later stages of discharge. These plates or gratings for drainage are intended to admit water from the hold to the bilge well and to prevent large particles of cargo from falling into the well.

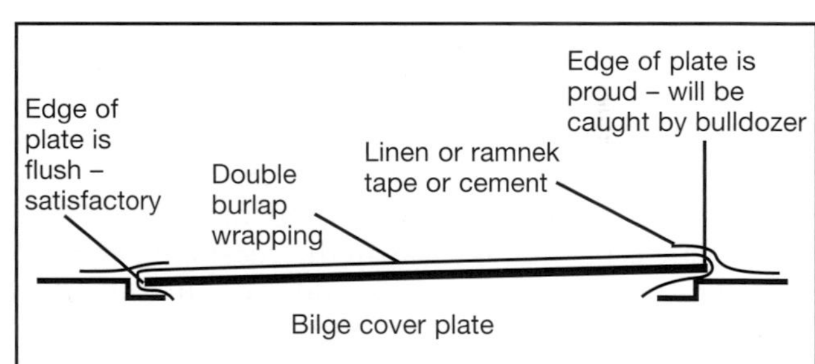

Fig. 5.20 Bilge cover plate

Smaller particles of cargo can still fall into the bilge well so whenever dry bulk cargoes are to be carried it is normal practice to line the bilge cover plates with burlap (sacking or gunnysack). This is achieved by wrapping the burlap around the cover plate, replacing the plate in its normal position and then sealing the edges of the burlap with cement or with Ram-nek or linen tape. After the fitting of the burlap the cover plate must remain flush with the tanktop. If the burlap is badly fitted and raises the cover plate proud of the tanktop (Fig. 5.20) it is likely that the plate will be dislodged, the bilge well will fill with cargo residues and the cover plate may be discharged by mistake. Very fine grained cargoes such as alumina will seep through burlap and fill the bilge well, setting hard after contact with water. For such cargoes the bilges must be sealed with tape thereby excluding even water.

Resealing of manhole covers: Double-bottom tanks are located beneath the cargo holds and they normally contain ballast water or fuel bunkers. The access to each tank is by manholes set into the tanktop or lower hopper sides in the hold, though larger bulkers have additional manholes in the stool spaces. Each manhole is closed with an oval steel lid fitted with a gasket and secured with nuts, tightened on studs. The lid will fit either directly above or directly below the manhole opening, according to design. To ensure that cargo cannot be damaged it is essential that when a manhole lid is closed a watertight and/or oiltight seal is achieved.

Such a seal is achieved by using a gasket which is in good condition, and by ensuring that the gasket and the steel surfaces of manhole and manhole lid are all absolutely clean, smooth and free of particles of rust or cargo. When this has been ensured all the nuts must be tightened hard. When closing of the manhole lid has been completed the tank, if a ballast tank, should be pressed up (ie, filled to overflowing) to test whether the closed manhole leaks.

It is not prudent to press up a fuel tank, except by gravity, because the consequences of an overflow would be so disastrous, so it may not be possible to pressure test the manhole lid of a fuel tank. For that reason it is all the more important to ensure that the lid is fitted carefully and expertly if there is reason to open it. Fortunately, reasons for opening fuel tanks are much more rare than are those for opening ballast tanks.

When a manhole lid is in place, a portable steel cover plate, flush with the tanktop, is normally provided to protect the recess. If the cover plate is in place it should be unshipped and any residues found beneath it should be removed. Grain has been seen sprouting from beneath these plates! During discharge it is easy for the cover plates to become dislodged and lost. If they are not fitted the manhole and its nuts and studs are in danger of being damaged. One method for protecting them if the cover plate is missing is to clean the recess thoroughly, spread old cloth over the nuts, and then fill the recess with cement, smoothed off flush with the tanktop. The purpose of the cloth is to prevent the cement from setting hard onto the nuts. Cement mixed to a strength of three parts sand to one part cement is suitable. When the manhole cover has next to be opened, the cement can be removed with a power chisel or with a cold chisel and mallet.

Isolation of electric circuits: If the intended cargo can burn or gives off gas which might explode, then any electric circuits such as hold lighting or forced ventilation circuits which pass into or through the holds or adjacent compartments should be isolated. In the case of cargoes which give off gas, the precaution must be extended to masthouses and other compartments connected in any way to the holds by access hatch, ventilator, or sounding, air or thermometer pipe. The most effective and reliable way of isolating such circuits is to remove their fuses and stow them in a secure place away from the isolated area. This will prevent accidental replacement. Suitable notices should also be posted when the fuses are removed.

Hold coatings

Limewashing: The shippers of most cargoes will be unconcerned about the condition of the coatings of the hold surfaces, provided that those surfaces are clean and free from loose rust, but for some cargoes rust can be a problem. One such cargo is salt used for water softening, chemical or industrial purposes such as the preserving of fish. Rust on the surfaces in the hold will discolour the salt with which it comes into contact. If this is a possibility it will be necessary to limewash the hold – to coat the bulkheads and the tanktop with lime – to prevent the salt from coming in contact with the rusty surfaces. Sulphur when not treated with sodium lauryl sulphate (SLS) is another cargo for which the holds have to be limewashed. Limewash and similar products benefit both ship and cargo: they reduce corrosion of the ship's structure and damage to the cargo.

Limewash is made by mixing one part by weight of slaked lime (hydrated calcium hydroxide – $CA(OH)_2$) with three parts fresh water. There have been reports that a small quantity of evaporated milk or soft soap added to the mixture will make the limewash easier to remove from the ship's structure at the end of the voyage but this has not been possible to confirm. This job can be done in the hold, the product being mixed in a 200 litre drum. The limewash can be applied to the bulkheads with the hose of a portable sump pump, the pump being used to draw the wash out of the drum. Alternatively a high pressure Spray Jet gun with a suitable nozzle or even paint spray equipment can be used. It will be necessary to limewash the bulkheads to whatever height the cargo is expected to reach in the holds, but the deckhead should not be limewashed as the limewash will be difficult to remove at the end of the voyage. The aim must be to cover bulkheads and tanktop with a good, thick even coat of limewash. The limewash will dry in a few hours. Surveyors often require the removal of limewash before the carriage of sensitive cargoes such as foodstuffs, fertilisers, mineral sands and concentrates and removal by washing is sometimes very difficult and time consuming. It is claimed that hold cleaning chemicals, applied by high pressure Spray Jet gun, can make the removal of limewash much easier.

RBM HoldBlock[99] is a biodegradable, environmentally friendly, semi-permanent coating or barrier developed to take the place of limewash for the carriage of sulphur, salt, sticky coal and petcoke. It is said to be easy to apply, over paint or rust, at heights up to about 13 metres using an application set consisting of air powered pump, spray nozzles, extendable power wand and appropriate hoses, which can also be used for hold washing chemicals. RBM HoldBlock is claimed to be much more effective that limewash and is easy to remove by washing down following the application of HoldWash-AP, another of the company's products. First reactions from the shipping industry appear to be favourable. It is not possible to paint over RBM HoldBlock and development work, to ensure that it can be seen clearly for removal, is continuing.

Painting of holds: Opportunity is sometimes taken, on ballast passages or during a period at anchor, to touch up hold paintwork or to repaint holds. When such work is considered it should be remembered that receivers and authorities in importing countries are becoming increasingly determined to ensure that foodstuffs are not contaminated with any harmful substance and that holds have been rejected because of taint from the smell of recently applied paint.

When foodstuffs are to be loaded and when a hold has been recently painted, the authorities in some countries insist on seeing evidence that the coating will not harm foodstuffs. The paint compliance certificate described and illustrated in Chapter 14 is an example of the sort of evidence that may be required.

If the ship possesses no certificate for the paint and there is doubt about the wisdom of painting, owners should be consulted. If they wish the ship to proceed with hold painting they can, if necessary, consult charterers and paint manufacturers.

Ballast holds

Ballast holds can be used either to hold ballast or to carry cargo. When cargo is to be carried it is essential that the proper steps are taken to ensure that ballast water cannot be admitted to the hold by accident. This is usually achieved by bolting a watertight coverplate over the ballast suction in the hold and this may be reinforced in the engineroom or on deck by fitting a blank, padlocking a valve or posting a notice. Blanks or cover plates which were fitted to the bilge, to the CO_2 smothering lines and to the hatch coaming drains must be removed so that these systems can operate whilst cargo is being carried.

These processes may have to be done, hurriedly, in the loading port since the hold may have been used for ballast during the previous ballast voyage.

There is likely to be a conflict of interests between the requirements for cargo and ballast, particularly when low density cargoes are to be carried, filling all cargo spaces including the ballast hold. At such times it may be difficult to find time and opportunity to clean the ballast hold at the start of the ballast voyage, before the hold is ballasted. Where possible the hold should be washed or, failing that, swept. If a hold is ballasted without removal of sweepings as a result of pressure of time, problems with blocked suctions will almost certainly be met at the time of deballasting, when the hold may be urgently required for loading.

Before ballasting it is, of course, essential to remove any blanks or coverplates which have been fitted to ballast suctions within the hold and to seal the CO_2 lines and the hatch coaming drains. The bilge suctions must also be sealed to prevent ballast from leaking through the bilge system. Aboard some ships, the same coverplate is used for the bilge and the ballast suctions and must be unshipped from one position and bolted in place in the alternative position.

Because of the time pressure which often exists when ballast holds have to be cleaned and ballasted, it is useful to consider the priorities:

- Before a ballast hold is ballasted the ballast line must be unsealed and the bilge line, the CO_2 injection and the coaming drains must be sealed.
- Any sweepings or rubbish which could block the ballast suction must be removed from the hold.
- If the next cargo will or may require a high standard of cleanliness, the hold should be meticulously cleaned.
- If the ballast water is dirty, there may be an opportunity to deballast the hold and clean it during the voyage, if stress limitations permit, refilling with clean sea water thereafter if necessary.
- If there is no opportunity to clean the hold of ballast sediment at sea and a clean hold is required quickly in the loading port, the crew can usually commence hosing down the open hold from deck level whilst the ballast is still discharging and can enter the hold to continue washing down when the water level reaches 30-40 cm over the tanktop. It is important to remember that written permission to commence deballasting is required in many ports.

When the ballast has been discharged and washing down, if required, has been completed, a fresh water rinse will be required for cargoes which require holds which are free of salt. On completion of washing and rinsing the bilge suction, the CO_2 injection and the hatch coaming drains must be opened and tested and the ballast suction must be blanked off. Sufficient time to complete these tasks must be provided in the loading plan.

Sources

65, 97, 98, 99, 100, 101, 102, 104, 105. (See List of Sources, Page 497)

CHECKLIST – Items for attention when preparing holds for cargo

- ☐ Decide how much hold cleaning is required.
- ☐ Encourage stevedores to discharge cargo sweepings as far as possible.
- ☐ Have crew or stevedores sweep down deckheads and bulkheads as discharge proceeds – for example, with grain cargoes.
- ☐ If cargo has filled a bilge have crew clean it before completion of discharge, so contents can be discharged.
- ☐ Clean coamings thoroughly with air hose before securing hatches for sea.
- ☐ Wash undersides of hatch covers and coamings, finishing wash with fresh water, in sheltered waters.
- ☐ Sweep holds before washing to remove bulky cargo residues, if required.
- ☐ Sweep holds instead of washing when washing is not necessary.
- ☐ Scrape and sweep holds and lift residues from hold when washing is not possible.
- ☐ Land cargo residues or store on deck for later disposal.
- ☐ Holds will not be washed if:
  - Vessel will remain in areas where discharge of washings is not allowed
  - Same cargo is to be carried again and charterers want no cleaning.
  - Clean cargo like steel coils has been carried.
  - Freezing conditions do not permit washing.
  - The cargo residues will react adversely with water, eg they will set hard.
- ☐ Decide if full wash or bottom wash is required, and if washing is to be done by automated washing or by portable hose.
- ☐ Decide if washing is to be done at berth, within port limits or outside limits, taking account of any restrictions on discharge of cargo residues and anticipated weather and sea state.
- ☐ Obtain written permission from port authority to discharge hold washings if intend to wash in port.
- ☐ Wash holds:
  - Wash hatch covers, top, bottom and sides.
  - Scrub hatch cover compression bars and rubbers if necessary to remove cargo traces.
  - Wash hatch coamings.
  - Wash underdeck areas.
  - Wash hold sides, paying particular attention to hopper angles, pipe guards, brackets and other non-vertical surfaces.
  - Scrub locally and/or rewash to remove stubborn dirt.
  - For stains or stubborn dirt apply cleaning chemicals and later rinse off.
  - Wash tanktop, scrape up loose rust scale.
  - Flush bilges.
- ☐ Rinse holds with fresh water to reduce corrosion and to prepare for cargoes which must not contact salt.
- ☐ Dry holds by ventilating, by opening holds and/or by mopping up puddles, as necessary.
- ☐ Clean and disinfect bilge wells.
- ☐ Flush sounding pipes and thermometer pipes.
- ☐ Test bilge suctions if not already used for washing.
- ☐ Test bilge non-return valves, when fitted.
- ☐ Test bilge high level alarms, when fitted.
- ☐ Test hold water ingress detectors.
- ☐ Inspect holds for cleanliness, insect infestation, taint, leakage and damage. Remedy defects where necessary.
- ☐ Wrap bilge cover plates with burlap and secure with tape or cement.
- ☐ Reseal any manhole covers which have been opened or disturbed.
- ☐ Isolate hold lighting and lighting in compartments connected to the holds, when this precaution is required for intended cargo.
- ☐ Limewash bulkheads and tanktop if required for next cargo.
- ☐ If holds are painted, or touched up, before a cargo of foodstuffs is carried, ensure that a paint compliance certificate can be produced for the paint used and that paint has sufficient time to dry.
- ☐ In ballast holds, close and secure cover plates for ballast suctions, and open bilge suctions, coaming drains and CO_2 injection lines.

CHAPTER 6

ENSURING SYSTEMS ARE OPERATIONAL

Ventilation, airpipes, hold bilges, water ingress detectors, soundings, hold temperature systems, deck and hold lighting, list indication lights, fire smothering systems, hatch coaming drains, hatch fittings, deck machinery, derricks and cranes

A BULK CARRIER exists to carry cargo, and is expected to do so safely, efficiently and without loss. To achieve this the ship's equipment must all be in good working order. This can only be achieved by regular maintenance, described in Chapter 23, and by methodical proving of all the systems every voyage. This chapter is devoted to the routines, tests and inspections which must be carried out regularly to ensure that everything is in good order before a cargo is loaded, and at other stages in the voyage, as required by the BLU Code, Section 2.2[110].

In general, every item listed in this chapter should be inspected or tested before each cargo is loaded and the hatches are battened down. This is particularly true for larger bulk carriers completing only six or eight loaded voyages a year. Some items, it will be obvious, must also be dealt with before the commencement of each discharge. On mini-bulkers performing one or more voyages a week most items must still be checked each voyage, but some can be left for regular but less frequent inspection.

Hold ventilation

The hold ventilators must be in good working order to fulfil two functions. First, they must provide adequate ventilation to the hold if required. Second, they must be capable of being completely sealed to prevent the entry of water in adverse weather conditions, and the entry of air if a fire occurs which must be smothered.

Chapter 15 contains more information about hold ventilators and the process of ventilation. Vents which are closed by doors (Fig.6.1) should be checked to ensure that the rubber seals have not been covered with paint, become permanently indented or cracked and brittle with age. Confirm also that the door closes properly, and that the sealing bar meets the centre of the door rubber. The hinges should be undamaged, and they and the butterfly nuts should move freely.

Fig. 6.1 Hold ventilator on masthouse

Located somewhere in the trunking of each ventilator, or at the point when it enters the hold, is a light metal grille which prevents sparks, insects and rats from entering. This can normally be reached by way of an inspection panel, set somewhere in the ventilator trunking. The grille must be renewed if it is damaged or wasted, and loose rubbish and scale must be removed from it.

Mushroom ventilators (Fig.6.2) are usually closed by turning the wheel which is set on top. This brings a damper plate inside the mushroom cowl into contact with the lip of the vent trunking. A 'rubber' (neoprene) seal is set into the damper plate, and it must be in good condition to ensure a watertight fit. The seal can be inspected when the vent is open by looking upwards into the vent cowl from a position on deck beside the ventilator. The grille in a mushroom ventilator is usually fitted in several parts, located in the position illustrated, and must be renewed if damaged.

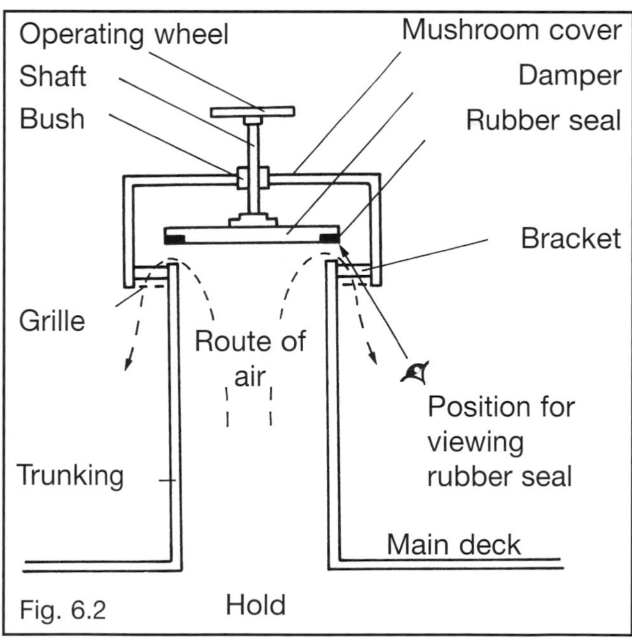

Fig. 6.2

The shaft of the wheel must be greased and working freely. If the shaft is coated with grease and the grease has become contaminated with dust and grit from the cargo the shaft is likely to jam. Before the vent is opened, the contaminated grease should be removed from the shaft. Then the threaded part should be wiped with a rag soaked in paraffin before the ventilator is opened and closed and the shaft is regreased. The wheel must be clearly marked with the 'Open' and the 'Close' directions, and the marks should be checked to be sure that they have not been reversed – mistakes can easily occur on older ships when the original plates have wasted, and been replaced by painted signs.

Ventilators which end in mushroom cowls at the heads of samson posts (Fig.6.3) are provided with ventilator flaps set in the trunking. When the lever is operated these flaps should move freely between the 'Open' and the 'Closed' positions, which must be clearly marked. The flaps should be inspected to confirm that the open and closed positions are correctly marked, and to ensure that the ventilator flap does turn with the shaft to which it is supposed to be attached. On some ships the flap is fastened to the shaft with bolted collars. Wastage can allow the fastenings to become loose. Such ventilator flaps are not always easily accessible but they and the grille can usually be inspected by torch from an access panel somewhere in the ventilator trunk.

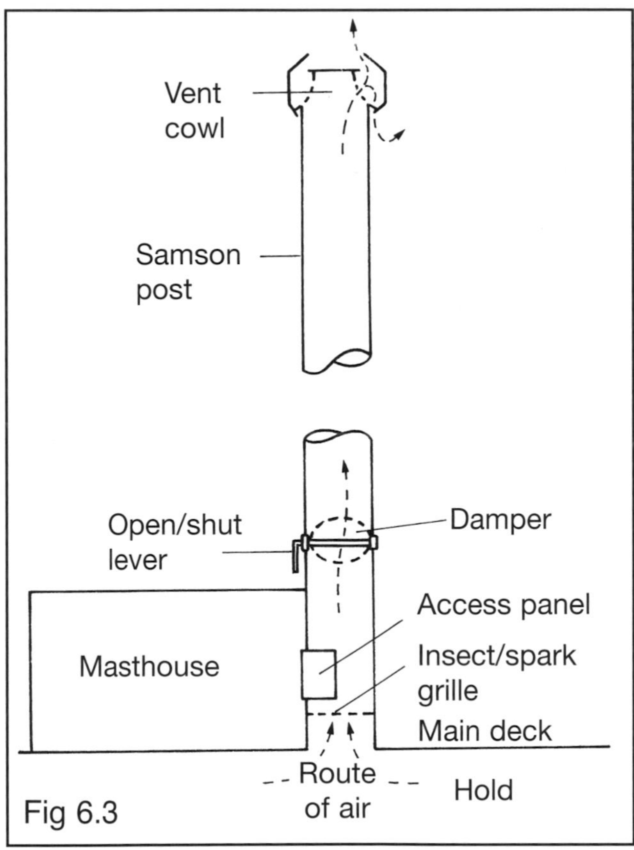

Fig 6.3

All ventilators should be correctly labelled to show the compartment which they serve. Ventilators set into the hatch panels (Fig.4.16) usually consist of rectangular openings closed by steel doors with neoprene seals. The seals must be in good condition, the hinges and butterfly nuts must be free and greased, and the grille must be intact.

Some vessels are provided with portable mushroom ventilators for bolting to the hatch covers when ventilation of the hatch square is required, as may be the case when coal cargoes are carried. Before the start of a voyage for which they are required such ventilators should be unshipped from their stowage positions, cleaned and freed as necessary to ensure that they are in good operating condition, and ready for fitting immediately when required. The bolted plates set into the hatch covers must also be freed, ready to receive the cowls. On other ships portable mushroom ventilators are recessed into the top of the hatch lid. These recessed units are raised after removing the securing bolts. The ventilator is lifted vertically out of its stowage position and turned to engage it onto a guide band. The guide band allows the ventilator to be trimmed to the required position. The guide band is prone to rusting and should be kept well greased[176].

If fixed fans are provided in the ventilator trunks for mechanical ventilation of the holds they should be tested whilst the holds are empty. First, they should be checked electrically to confirm that they are in good condition, and inspected by eye to ensure that nothing is lying on the fan blades. When ready to run all the options should be tested, including running fans in both directions where that is possible, and running them at full and at half speed. The fan trips and/or emergency stops should also be tested regularly.

On ships employed in areas where bad weather is common, such as north-west Europe, ventilators are normally kept permanently closed and sealed to prevent the entry of water. Despite this, it is still essential that all the working parts should be kept in good operating condition by following the procedures described above. It is only in this way that ventilators which work correctly can be guaranteed for the occasional voyage where ventilation is essential.

Ventilator trunks are liable to heavy corrosion in some trades, and sheets of loose scale can develop within them. From time to time the opportunity should be taken to remove scale from the trunks.

Tank airpipes

The airpipes (goosenecks) for ballast, fuel and fresh-water tanks must be kept in good order so that tanks can be filled and emptied without problem, and the entry of sea water can be prevented. Airpipes must be correctly labelled (Fig.6.4) to show the tank that they serve. Their non-return system, allowing liquids out of the airpipe but not in, must be working properly. When the system uses a float (Fig.6.5) it must be visually and manually inspected for damage, and to

Fig. 6.4 Airpipe for No. 5 port water ballast tank

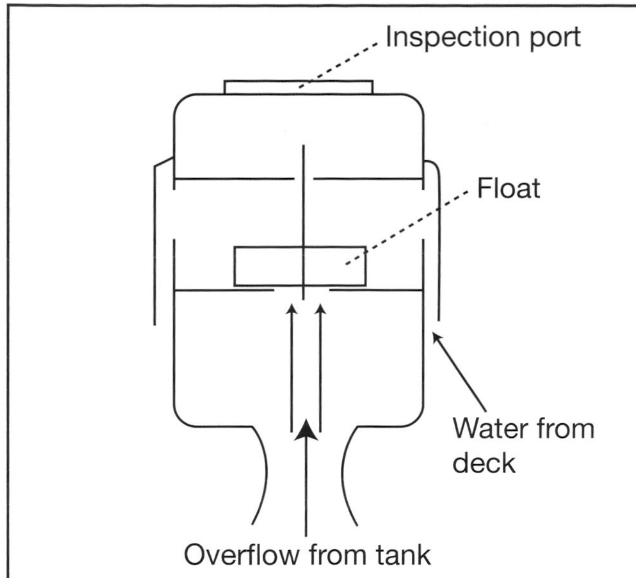

Fig. 6.5 Airpipe. When the tank overflows the float will lift and release the water. If water floods the deck and enters the airpipe the float will prevent it from going further

ensure that it seals the airpipe properly. A hand or finger can usually be inserted inside the airpipe to lift the float and ensure that it is free. Damaged floats must be renewed, and on older ships it is prudent to carry a few spares.

Savealls are provided around all fuel tank airpipes. Savealls must be clean and dry with their drain plugs free and greased. The height of the saveall must be less than the height of the airpipe

Hold bilges

The hold bilge wells must be thoroughly cleaned after every cargo, and all cargo sweepings must be removed. The bilge sounding pipes can be proved free by running water down them into the bilge, and the bilge suctions can be tested by pumping the bilge well dry.

The end of the bilge suction line is normally provided with a strum box (a perforated box, Fig. 6.6), which prevents rubbish from entering the line. This must be clean. The non-return valve, fitted in the bilge line to ensure that water cannot enter the hold through the bilge line, must be tested. The easiest way to test the non-return valve is to stop the pump and allow water to flood back into the bilge line. If it flows through into the hold bilge the non-return valve, normally situated in the stool space or the duct keel, is not working properly and must be opened up and cleaned. In any event all the non-return valves should be cleaned at regular intervals.

Fig. 6.6 Strum box in corner of bilge well

On completion of inspections the bilge wells must be correctly closed, and their perforated cover plates must be covered with burlap. High level bilge alarms, when fitted, should be tested by raising the float towards the top of the bilge and confirming that the alarm sounds on the bridge and/or in the engineroom. (These matters are described more fully in Chapter 5.)

Water ingress detectors

The detectors in the hold should be tested before each cargo is loaded. If of a moisture sensitive type (Figs. 18.15 and 16) they can be tested by applying a wet cloth to the sensor head. Pressure activated water ingress detectors can, in some cases, be tested by the temporary fitting of a pipe which is filled with water to the required level. In addition processes such as the cleaning of filters over pressure detectors, the inspection of cables, sensor glands and mounting flange bolts and the calibration of sensors should be carried out at the intervals specified by the manufacturers. The function test of audio and visual alarms must be carried out daily.

Soundings

The most reliable soundings of tanks and bilges are obtained with sounding rod and line when the depth is small, or sounding tape with water finding paste when the depths are large. These methods, of course, rely upon the sounding pipe being clear. A sounding pipe can become blocked with cargo residues which can float into a hold bilge sounding pipe when there is water in the bilge, or with cargo or rubbish which can fall into it if the sounding pipe cap is left off. Loose rust and parts of old sounding rods and lines can also block sounding pipes.

As noted above, sounding pipes can be proved clear by running water down them into the bilge or the ballast tank. They can also be checked by viewing, from a position at the base of the sounding pipe, the arrival of the sounding rod in the bilge well or in the ballast tank. A table of tank and bilge ullages (ie distance from striking plate to top of sounding pipe), prepared from careful direct measurements and checked against the ship's plans, can also be used to check if sounding pipes are clear.

Another quick and simple check is to compare the ullages found for similar soundings. The sounding rod should reach the same depth on the port side as on the starboard side. Similarly, aboard a large bulker the No.3 bilge or double-bottom tank sounding will, for example, probably be the same depth as the equivalent No. 4 soundings. If the depths are found to be different, it is likely that a false sounding is being obtained in the pipe which appears to be shorter, and the cause of this must be investigated and removed.

Fig. 6.7 Sounding pipe and dropout valve for topside tank

A blocked sounding pipe must be cleared as soon as possible, and various ingenious methods can be used to remove the obstruction and return the pipe to its former sound condition. Every sounding pipe should be provided with a cap which fits well, opens and closely freely, and has a watertight rubber seal in place. To prevent water or rubbish from entering the pipe the cap should be fitted at all times except when the sounding pipe is being used (Fig. 6.7) or the bilge is being pumped.

The accuracy of remote reading systems for ballast tank soundings should be checked by comparison with actual soundings obtained with sounding rod. Before each cargo is loaded a remote reading system for soundings, when fitted, should be given routine maintenance in accordance with the manufacturer's handbook. The air pressure used by the system should be set to the correct value, according to the manufacturer's handbook. All empty compartments, including void spaces, bilges and dry tanks should be sounded and/or inspected to confirm that they are empty.

Hold temperature systems

Cargo temperatures may be measured by gauge via the gas sampling points or by bimetal sensors embedded in the cargo, in which cases the necessary equipment must be checked and ready for use when required. Alternatively temperatures may be read from sounding pipes, but are sometimes read from separate pipes, similar to sounding pipes, positioned at the forward and after ends of each hold. Ensure that temperature pipes are correctly labelled. Their positions against the corrugated transverse bulkhead can mean that No.4 for'd is forward of No.3 aft, for example (Fig.6.8). The caps of temperature pipes must fit well, have watertight seals and be kept in position except when the pipe is in use. The base of the pipe must be checked to ensure that it is free of water, and that the opening in the base is clear, and guarded with light metal gauze or a similar product. Water standing in the pipe would produce water vapour, and might depress the temperature readings. Any damage to the pipes, sustained when discharging previous cargoes, should have been found and repaired.

Thermometers should be inspected for any apparent faults, such as breaks in the mercury or

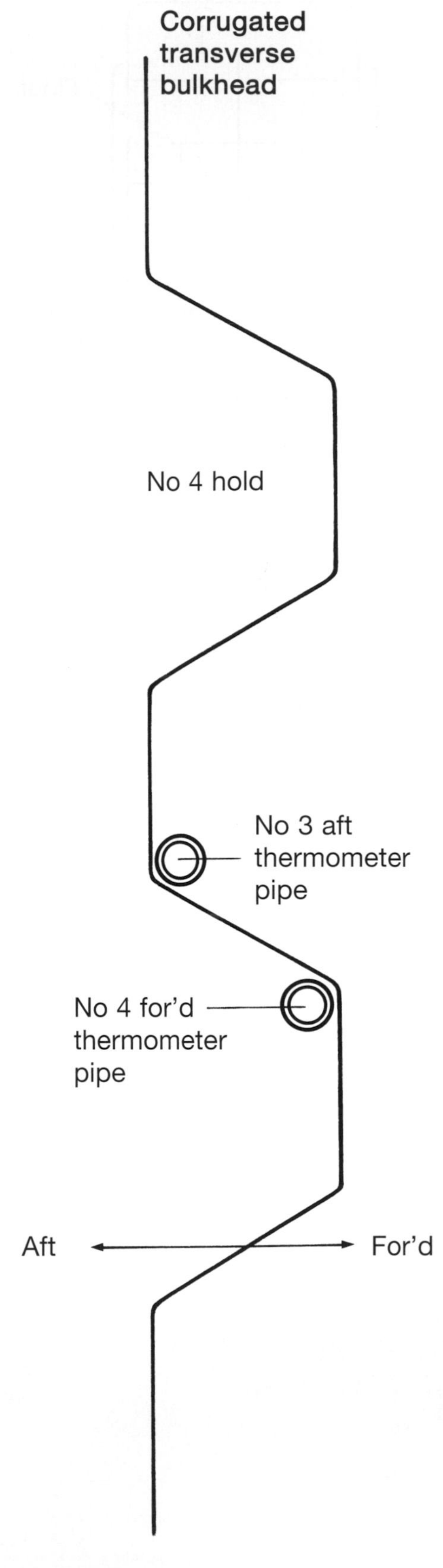

Corrugated transverse bulkhead

No 4 hold

No 3 aft thermometer pipe

No 4 for'd thermometer pipe

Aft ← → For'd

Fig 6.8

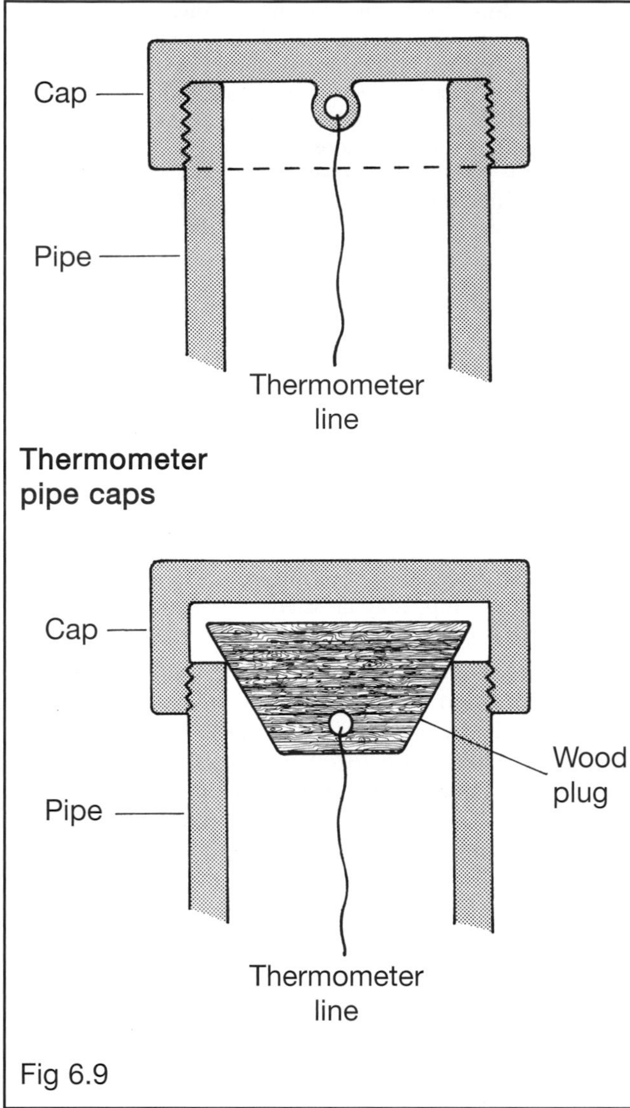

Fig 6.9

alcohol. They should be compared with the temperature gauge used for calibration or with other thermometers in use around the ship – for example, in the refrigerators, storerooms, engineroom and on the bridge – to confirm that their readings agree.

The lines used to lower the thermometers into the pipes should be in good condition, and of the correct length to reach the depth required. Usually the thermometers are left permanently hung in the temperature pipes, so that a set of temperatures can be taken quickly when required. The line can be fastened to the underside of the pipe cap, or attached to a plug placed in the top of the sounding pipe, provided that a watertight seal can be maintained (Fig.6.9). Some ships prefer not to leave the thermometers suspended in the temperature pipes. To obtain an accurate temperature reading one man installs all the thermometers into the temperature pipe and waits one hour for the thermometers to register a reading. Then he completes a round on deck taking the temperatures, removing the thermometers and resecuring the top to the temperature pipe. Although this is time consuming it is suggested that this way watertightness is better ensured and the thermometers suffer less damage.

Lighting

All deck and hold lighting should be switched on for inspection before the loading port is reached, and bulbs and tubes should be replaced as required. If the cargo is hazardous the hold and hold access lighting, if not of a certified safe type, must be isolated before the commencement of loading, and the circuit fuses should be removed to a safe place in the care of a responsible officer.

All lights should be maintained on a regular basis, such maintenance to include the greasing of moving parts, freeing of securing dogs, checking and renewal of glass covers and rubber seals as required, and inspection of wiring and conduits. Cable conduits in the holds should have already been checked for physical damage which may have occurred during the last discharge. Following rough weather, cable conduits on deck, if damaged, may contain water which should be drained. The electrician or a member of the engineering staff should regularly test the cables for 'earths'.

Portable deck and hold lighting (Fig.6.10) is required in any port where the shore lighting is inadequate, and also for security purposes. A ship committed to worldwide trading should hold a minimum of four portable floodlights or 'clusters' for each hold, two to light the hold and two to shine over the ship's side to illuminate the jetty or craft alongside. Ships engaged in regular trading between well equipped ports are unlikely to need so many portable lights, but should carry extra lights for security and anti-piracy purposes.

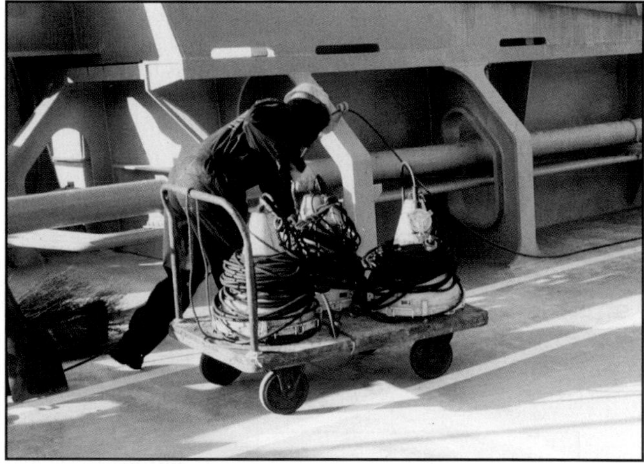

Fig. 6.10 Hold lighting being moved on trolley

Before reaching each port the portable lights should be tested, bulbs should be replaced and repairs should be made as necessary. The cables should be inspected for damage. Rope lanyards should be long enough to hang the lights in the correct position. A portable light should never be hung by its electrical cable. Light bulbs must always be protected by a wire cage or screen.

List indication lights

These lights are fitted on the bridge wings or on the centre line on the accommodation block forepart of some bulk carriers to show when the ship is listing. This information can assist the ship's officers and stevedores to ensure that the ship is not loaded asymmetrically. The system should be checked for accuracy against an inclinometer. Tests can conveniently be made by pumping some ballast whilst at a quiet anchorage.

Fire smothering systems

The basic components of the fire smothering system (Fig.6.11) are the battery of gas bottles in the bottle room, the mechanical control system for selecting the compartment to be smothered and for controlling the number of bottles released, the gas pipes which carry the gas to the compartment, and the nozzles which emit the gas. On modern ships the nozzles, four in number, are usually set in the hatch coamings, so that no pipework is within the holds (Figs 18.18 and 19). On older ships the gas pipes often enter the hold and lead to nozzles located under the deckhead.

If a smoke detecting system is also provided, as is often the case on handy-size and smaller bulkers, a fan will be used to draw air samples continuously from each compartment through the gas lines to a detecting cabinet, usually placed on the bridge, where a photoelectric cell will detect smoke and cause an alarm to sound.

Problems and their prevention: A number of problems can and do occur with these systems. The pipes which carry the CO_2 from the bottle room to the hold, the gas lines, can fill with water from condensation, or can be blocked by cargo residues when cargo such as grain is loaded up to coaming level. In the case of the ballast hold the lines can also be flooded with ballast water, while the gas lines within the holds of older ships can be damaged by cargo operations.

When the lines are blocked with water or residues, the smoke detecting system cannot work, and the CO_2 smothering may be ineffective. To prevent or correct some of these problems the manufacturers may include a variety of fittings in the system:

- Each gas line may be fitted with an individual drain valve for the removal of water. The drain valve may take the form of a spring-loaded plunger fitted at the after end of the gas line, just before it goes through the bridge front bulkhead. These should be operated regularly to ensure that the lines remain drained.
- Each CO_2 nozzle may be provided with a spring-loaded shutter which must be shut by hand when grain or similar cargo is carried, and opened after the cargo has been discharged.
- Each CO_2 nozzle may be provided with a removable dust cap which will be blown off if the CO_2 is released.
- Each gas line serving a ballast hold may be provided with an isolating valve, to be closed when ballast is carried and opened when cargo is carried (Fig. 18.19).
- Each gas line serving a ballast hold may have a 'spade', or 'spectacle', piece (ie, a blank) which can be used to seal the line in the same way that an isolating valve does.
- Each gas line serving a ballast hold may be provided with a non-return valve which will admit CO_2 gas to the hold, but will exclude ballast water from the gas lines.
- 'U' bends, placed in the gas lines at positions higher than the coaming top, may be used to prevent ballast water from entering the lines.

Shutters when fitted are spring loaded, and will be forced open by a gas pressure of more than $1.5kg/cm^2$. If the gas lines can be shut by a valve, there is often a bypass line fitted with a pressure disc, for each valve. The pressure disc will burst to admit the CO_2 gas into the hold in the event that smothering is required when the valve has been left shut, by mistake. Unfortunately, the pressure created by ballast water, pressed up or sloshing in the ballast hold, can also burst the disc and allow ballast water into the gas lines.

From the foregoing it will be clear that the CO_2 system must be properly understood, and correctly set for ballast or cargo. At the ballast hold the gas lines must be closed when the hold is ballasted and open when cargo is carried. At all holds it may be necessary to close the shutters or fit the dust caps over the nozzles to keep out dust or light cargo, and to open

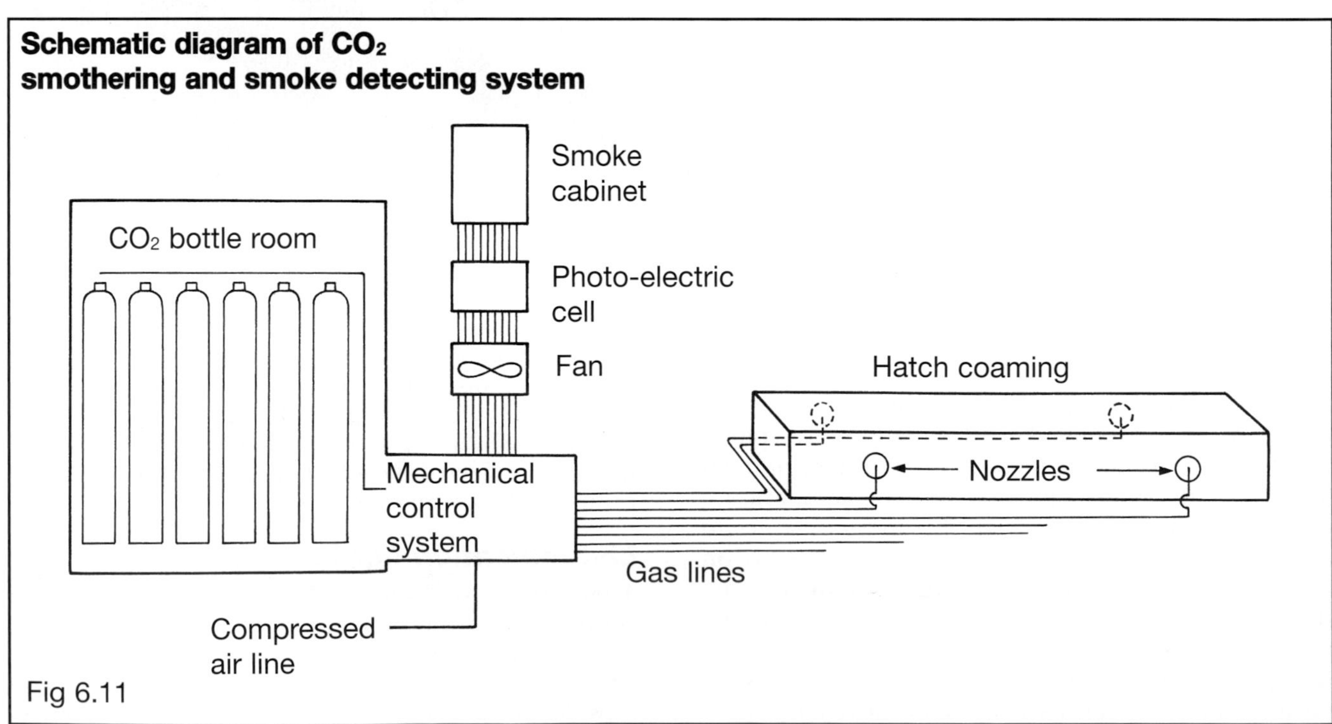

Fig 6.11

the shutters for other cargoes.

Routine testing – the gas lines: These problems, and the varied methods provided for their solution, make it easy for the gas lines to be blocked by waste matter, or by a shutter, valve or blank wrongly set. The most important rule, therefore, is to make absolutely sure before each cargo is loaded that the gas lines are not blocked or closed. This should be done by blowing through each line in turn with compressed air.

Most systems have a compressed air connection in, or near to, the CO_2 bottle room, so that compressed air can be blown into each compartment by operation of the appropriate valves. Often there are two blanks to be changed before the compressed air test is made: one blank is removed to admit compressed air into the system, whilst a second blank is fitted to protect the CO_2 bottle bank lines and trips, and the smoke detecting cabinet, if fitted. An observer should listen at the hold for the sound of the escaping compressed air, which will show that the outlet is clear. When the test is completed the blanks must be refitted in their original positions.

Oxygen must not be used to blow through the gas lines, as it can cause an explosion if it meets a trace of oil. Water should not normally be used to blow through the lines, since the object is to keep the lines free of water. If salt water ballast has entered the lines, however, they should be flushed with fresh water to remove the salt which will cause corrosion, and then blown through with compressed air to dry them. The CO_2 bottle banks must not be used to clear a blocked gas line. The CO_2 bottle banks are for emergency use and should only be used for extinguishing a fire, besides which short bursts of CO_2 will cause condensation in the gas lines and encourage rust.

Routine testing – the smoke detecting system: The smoke detecting system, when fitted, must be tested in each hold at the start of each voyage with a smoke-making device. These tests should be included in the vessel's planned maintenance routines. Smoke can be produced from an oily rag in a can, although chemical devices such as draeger tubes or smoke aerosols are preferred. Provided that the photoelectric cell and the fan which draws air into the cabinet are both switched ON, and provided that the gas lines are not blocked, the release of smoke close to a nozzle in the hold will cause the smoke alarm to sound at the smoke detecting cabinet.

Routine testing – for safety equipment certificate: In addition to the above-mentioned checks, to be carried out every voyage, the smothering system should be maintained in accordance with the manufacturers' advice, and the gas bottles should be inspected, have the level of their contents checked, be pressure tested and recharged as required by the authority issuing the Safety Equipment Certificate.

Hatch coaming drains

If the hatch coaming drains (Figs. 4.24 and 6.12) are blocked with cargo, as happens easily and frequently, the danger of leakage of water into the holds is increased. It is essential to ensure that the drains are checked and cleared, and that their non-return valves (Fig.4.26) – often containing a floating ball – are free before the loading of each cargo, and again after loading, and before battening down the hatches. Compressed air directed upwards from the bottom of the drain is a quick and effective method of clearing a blocked drain. If this doesn't work, the non-return valves must be dismantled and cleaned, and any blocked drain pipe must be cleared with a stiff rod, or even by the use of a drill if badly blocked. To prevent the hatch drains becoming filled with debris when loading a dusty or fine cargo, some ships temporarily fit half a broom pole into the top of each drain at the start of loading. This prevents the fine grains of cargo entering the drain and causing a blockage. The broom pole is usually painted a bright colour to prevent any careless hatch closure before it has been removed.

Fig. 6.12 Coaming drain

On long voyages, and in cold weather, the rubber ball of the non-return valve may stick. A quick poke with a rod or screwdriver will free it.

Hatch fittings

Gas sampling points set into the hatch covers or coamings (Fig. 4.18) should be provided with screwed caps to maintain the watertightness of the hatches. These should be greased, the rubber seal inside the screw cap should be in good condition and the cap should fit correctly and be watertight.

Cement/grain loading ports. Round bolted covers set into the tops of the hatch panels (Fig. 4.17) with one centrally placed for loading and a second perhaps in a corner, for the exhaust air, may be provided to allow cement to be loaded with the hatches closed (Chapter 19). Other possible reasons for the

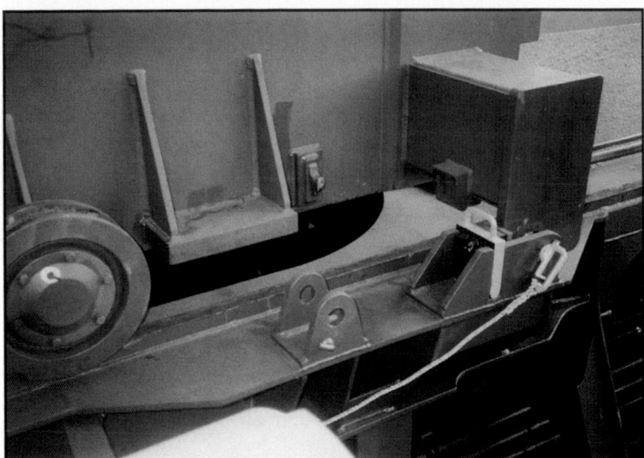
Fig. 6.13 Locking pin and locking plate for side rolling hatch covers

provision of bolted covers are to allow the fitting of portable cowls for the ventilation of the hatch square or to insert butterworth machines for washing the hold. These ports should be provided with a gasket in good condition, and great care should be taken when closing them after use to ensure that the joint is free of any dirt or particles and that the bolts are well tightened to achieve a watertight seal.

Hatch cover securing or locking devices (Figs. 4.19 and 6.13) are provided to ensure that, when hatches are opened the panels are prevented from moving if the ship rolls or develops a list. They should be distinctively painted, kept in good working order and used whenever the hatches are open.

Deck machinery

Deck machinery on a bulk carrier includes the windlass, mooring winches, capstans and hatch-opening motors. It also includes air motors used on deck, and cargo-handling gear, such as cranes or derricks and their winches, if fitted.

Before arrival in port, deck machinery should be tested in good time to ensure that it is operational. An exception must be made, of course, in cases where the vessel enters port directly from a bad-weather passage. In these circumstances the best that can be done is to inspect and test deck machinery as soon as possible after reaching sheltered waters.

Windlasses and winches on bulk carriers are usually electro-hydraulic, or occasionally electric. Problems are most likely to occur if they are not properly lubricated, and if the electric controls become wet. Bearings must be regularly greased using the grease nipples. The level of lubricating oil in the sumps of winches should be checked, which is usually done by looking through the glass viewing port, and they should be topped up as necessary. The lubricating oil will turn milky if water has been forced in and mixed with the oil. If that happens the seals must be renewed and the oil must be changed, which is a major task.

Motors in exposed positions, control pedestals for deck machinery, and emergency stop buttons can usefully be provided with canvas or waterproof covers to protect them from heavy spray or rain, and these should normally be fitted at sea. They can be temporarily removed in hot dry weather to give covers and equipment an airing. Heaters for deck machinery, when provided, should remain switched on at sea to provide a warm dry atmosphere for the electric control systems. Hatch opening chains and wires should be inspected for defects and regularly greased or coated as per the manufacturers' guidelines.

The hydraulic systems for operating the hatch covers and the deck machinery depend upon an adequate supply of hydraulic oil. The levels in the header tanks should be checked before entering port, and the tanks should be topped up as necessary from the storage tank in the motor room. This usually involves opening the valve in the supply line from the storage tank to the header tank, and using a hand pump to transfer hydraulic oil up to the header tank. A return line with a sight glass is usually fitted. When oil is seen in the sight glass stop pumping and close the valves. The return line also acts as an overflow line should the oil in a full header tank expand as it will do in hot weather or as it warms with high usage.

When the deck machinery and services are switched on, the decks should be checked for hydraulic and pneumatic leaks, which sometimes develop as a result of the ship working in a seaway or vibration during the passage. Any leaks which are found should be promptly repaired, and any leakage of oil cleaned up to prevent a pollution incident.

Air motors are likely to be used for accommodation ladders, for pilot hoists, for stores and bunker davits and for lifeboat hoists. It is prudent to confirm that they are all in good working order before arriving in port. The oiler/filter unit (Fig. 6.14) with which each air motor is provided cleans and lubricates the air before it enters the motor. The air is cleaned and dried as it passes through the filter: the filter must be cleaned or renewed as required. This should be part of the vessel's planned maintenance routines. The oiler unit adds oil to the air, thus ensuring that the motor receives the necessary lubrication. The level of oil in the oiler must be maintained, and the oil must be changed if it becomes milky due to water contamination.

A control valve on the oiler governs the amount of oil which is added to the air. The valve should be opened wider when the surroundings are dust laden, or if the motor is seldom used, though some operators play safe and always leave the control valve fully open.

The vanes of air motors can become chipped or corroded, and spare vanes should be carried. If the

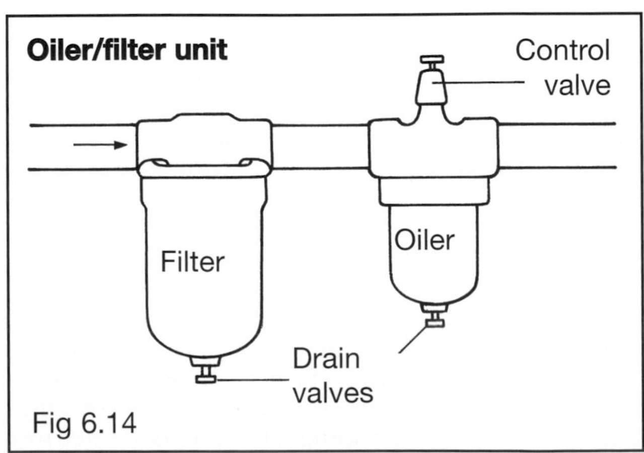

Fig 6.14

motor seems to have reduced power – for example, if it cannot lift the accommodation ladder – it should be dismantled and cleaned. The condition of the vanes should be checked and damaged vanes should be renewed. Vanes sometimes stick if the motor is not used for a long time – in these circumstances a sharp tap on the casing often frees them. Do not tap too hard, however, as the casings are often cast, and will fracture if struck too hard!

Cargo-handling gear

Geared bulk carriers are distinguished from gearless vessels by the fact that the former are equipped with derricks or cranes, which can be used to load or discharge cargo. It is quite common for handymax, handy-sized and mini-bulkers to be geared and even some 10 per cent of the Panamax bulk carrier fleet is crane fitted, whereas no Cape Size bulk carriers are geared. Geared vessels often visit well-equipped ports where the loading or discharge is carried out with shore equipment, which can handle cargo faster and with more flexibility, but such vessels really show their worth when required to serve poorly equipped ports and anchorages which have no shorebased gear.

Unexpected circumstances, such as a change of discharging berth, a failure of shoreside equipment or a strike, can result in the ship being instructed at short notice to work cargo with the ship's gear. Failure of even one derrick or crane will usually break the terms of the ship's charterparty, and result in loss of hire payments.

Cargo-handling equipment which fails when in use can cause death, serious injury or extensive damage as a result of a falling weight. As a consequence there are strict rules about the design, construction, testing, certification, marking, maintenance and inspection of cargo-handling equipment. Some countries are well known for their insistence that the ships which visit their ports comply scrupulously with the regulations, and in most countries a ship which was in breach of the regulations when an accident occurred would be held liable.

Before entering any port, the Shipmaster should ensure that all the cargo-handling equipment is in good working order, and that it complies with the regulations of the ship's own flag State and also, if possible, of the port State. Much of this can be achieved by complying with the requirements of the vessel's Safety Management System and by ensuring that the equipment is given the necessary regular maintenance, a subject discussed in Chapter 23. Regular maintenance is essential for keeping the cargo gear in good condition, but will not in itself guarantee that all will work well during a port visit. Deterioration of cargo gear is governed by how much it is used (too much use and too little are both bad for it), the extent to which it is mistreated, and the adverse weather met by the ship. There are a number of matters which must receive attention before the ship reaches port, and thereafter whilst cargo is being worked.

Maintenance of the cargo gear must be up to date, and every item of cargo gear must be permanently marked with a unique set of numbers and/or letters. A proper certificate must be held for every item of cargo gear, and must be readily available for inspection. Every item of gear must be clearly marked with its safe working load (SWL). All moving parts of the system must be working freely, and sufficiently greased or oiled. They may require oiling and greasing again after a rough weather sea passage, particularly if the vessel was deep laden. All shackles above eye level must be moused (fastened with lashings of seizing wire), or with split pins, to ensure that they cannot become accidentally unfastened. The gear must not include any damaged items of equipment. In addition, the following specific items should be checked.

The condition of wire ropes should be checked before commencement of cargo work, and those which are flattened, kinked, reduced in diameter, damaged or showing more than 5 per cent of broken, worn or corroded wires in any length of ten rope diameters should be renewed. Inspections of the wire ropes used in cargo gear should continue each day whilst cargo is being work. The anchorages used to fasten the ends of wire ropes to winch drums should be regularly checked to ensure that they are tight. It is prudent to carry a full set of spare wire ropes to avoid delays and off hire in the event that wire ropes must be renewed.

Derrick winches and crane machinery must be kept in good condition, following the same guidelines as already described for deck machinery. They must be greased, lubricating oil in sumps must be topped up as necessary and signs of contamination by water must be found and their cause and effects removed. Electric control pedestals and switch gear must be kept warm and dry.

When gear has been dismantled for maintenance it must be carefully inspected and carefully used after reassembly. It has been known for the more complex derrick rigs to be wrongly rerigged after the renewal of topping lift wires, with insufficient wire on one topping lift winch drum and too much on the other when the derrick was amidships, or with topping lift wires which failed to pass through a full set of topping lift sheaves! Such problems can sometimes be avoided by attaching the new wire to the old wire with seizing wire or a patent cable stocking and hauling the new wire into position whilst removing the old wire.

The manufacturer's operations manual should provide full instructions for the reeving of new topping or purchase wires and is likely to include instructions to ensure that no 'turns' or 'kinks' are introduced into the wire whilst it is being fitted.

Most derrick and crane systems are provided with limit switches, to prevent the derrick or crane from luffing too high or too low, from slewing too far to either side, or from hoisting too high or lowering too far with a load attached. These limit settings must be checked, tested and reset frequently to ensure that they continue to keep the movements of the derrick or crane within the limits for which it has been designed. Override keys are provided so that the derrick boom or crane jib can be lowered into the stowage position, or topped clear of the hatch when carrying no load. The override keys must be held by a responsible member of the ship's company, to ensure that shore drivers do not override the limits recklessly.

An emergency cutout may be provided so that an operation can be stopped instantly, by pressing a button and tripping the electrical supply. The emergency cutout can be used by the officer of the watch to immobilise the crane at the end of the working day, to prevent unauthorised use. To restart the crane the trip switch, usually placed in a locked cabinet, must be reset. The cutout should also be used when maintenance work such as overhaul of the electrics or greasing of the topping sheaves is being carried out. Cutouts should be tested frequently; their use for immobilising the crane is one method of doing this.

Some cranes and derricks are provided with overload cutouts. These cause the power supply to cut out if the load exceeds the value set, normally the safe working load. An overload cutout can prevent overloading when ship's gear is being used with shore grabs, or if lifting containers or logs where the weight may be unknown or wrongly declared. An overload cutout may also be designed to cut out the power supply if a motor becomes overheated because of lack of lubrication or because the ventilator is not open.

The brakes for crane and derrick winches are automatically applied by heavy springs whenever the winches are not being driven. They must be checked regularly. A quick indication of their effectiveness can be obtained by suspending a heavy load a short distance above the deck or quay. Any lowering will show that the brake is ineffective.

Other systems which must be operational

The maintenance and testing of hatch covers are described in Chapter 4. The preparation of the holds for cargo is described in Chapter 5.

Sources

110, 176. (See List of Sources, Page 497)

CHECKLIST – Items for attention before arrival at the loading port.

(The routine at the discharging port for lighting, deck machinery and cargo gear should be the same as is stated hereunder for the loading port)

Any item tested or inspected, and found defective, must be put in good working order.

Holds and hatch covers

- ☐ Maintain hatch covers as described in Chapter 4.
- ☐ Test hatch covers as described in Chapter 4.
- ☐ Prepare holds as described in Chapter 5.

Ventilators for holds and hatch panels

- ☐ Means of closing to be in good working order.
- ☐ Seals on closing plates to be in good condition.
- ☐ Grilles to be unbroken.
- ☐ All moving parts (hinges, spindles, flaps) to be well greased and working freely.
- ☐ Means of closing to be correctly marked Open/Closed.
- ☐ Ventilators to be correctly labelled for hold served.
- ☐ Prepare portable ventilators if required.
- ☐ Test ventilator fans.

Airpipes (goosenecks)

- ☐ Inspect airpipe non-return valves.
- ☐ Confirm airpipes are correctly labelled for tank served.
- ☐ Ensure that fire gauzes for fuel tank airpipes are intact and savealls are clean and dry with drainage plugs in position.

Hold bilges

- ☐ Bilge wells to be clean and dry.
- ☐ Ensure striking plates in hold bilge wells are not wasted.
- ☐ Strum boxes to be clean.
- ☐ Test bilge suctions.
- ☐ Test bilge suction non-return valves.
- ☐ Test bilge high level alarms.
- ☐ Fit bilge well covers and cover them with burlap.

Water ingress detectors

- ☐ Detectors in the holds to be tested by applying water pressure or wetness as appropriate.
- ☐ Filters over pressure detectors, when fitted, to be cleaned.
- ☐ Cables, sensor glands and mounting flange bolts to be inspected.

- ☐ Detectors to be calibrated at intervals specified by manufacturers.
- ☐ The function test of audio and visual alarms should be carried out daily.

Soundings

- ☐ Prove sounding pipes clear.
- ☐ Provide sounding pipes with well fitting watertight caps.
- ☐ Confirm the accuracy of any remote sounding system.
- ☐ Sound or inspect all empty compartments, including void spaces, to prove them empty.

Hold temperature system

- ☐ Pipes to be undamaged and proved clear, and free of water.
- ☐ Pipes to be provided with watertight caps which fit well.
- ☐ All temperature measuring equipment to be calibrated and in good working order.
- ☐ Thermometers to be sound and accurate, and provided with lines which are in good condition, and of correct length.

Lighting

- ☐ Test deck, access, hold and portable lighting.
- ☐ Inspect cable conduits for water and damage.
- ☐ Isolate hold lighting and hold access lighting before a hazardous cargo is loaded. Keep fuses in a secure place.
- ☐ Have sufficient portable lights ready.
- ☐ Inspect the cables of portable lights.
- ☐ Fit lanyards to portable lights, and do not hang lights from their cables.
- ☐ Test list indication lights against an inclinometer.

Fire smothering systems

- ☐ Blow through the gas lines with compressed air.
- ☐ Inspect the gas lines in the hold for damage.
- ☐ Test the hold smoke detector system, if provided.
- ☐ Shut off the CO_2 nozzles with shutters, where provided, when carrying cargoes such as grain or sugar.
- ☐ At each ballast hold: close the gas lines with blanks or valves when ballast is to be carried, and open them when the ballast hold is to contain cargo.
- ☐ Inspect pressure discs, if fitted, and renew any which have burst.

Hatch coaming drains

- ☐ Hatch coaming drains to be clear.
- ☐ Non-return valves in drains to be free.

Gas sampling points

- ☐ To be provided with well fitting, free moving watertight caps.

Hatch cover securing/locking devices

- ☐ To be kept in good working order and used whenever the hatches are open.

Deck machinery, including crane and derrick winches

- ☐ Test all machinery before arrival in port.
- ☐ Keep machinery greased and oil topped-up in sumps.
- ☐ Watch for water leakage into sumps.
- ☐ Keep electric controls and switch gear warm and dry. Remove canvas covers in warm, sunny weather.
- ☐ Keep hydraulic oil header tanks topped up.
- ☐ Inspect for hydraulic and pneumatic leaks.
- ☐ Clean or renew filters, and top-up or change oil as necessary, in the oiler/filter units of air motors.

Cargo-handling gear

- ☐ Maintain cargo gear in compliance with the rules of the vessel's flag State.
- ☐ Every item of equipment to be stamped with an unique identifying mark, for which there must be a certificate which can be produced immediately.
- ☐ All gear to be clearly marked with its safe working load.
- ☐ All moving parts to be well greased or oiled.

- ☐ All shackles above eye level to be moused.
- ☐ No damaged items of gear to be used.
- ☐ Inspect wire ropes and their anchorage points.
- ☐ Inspect gear carefully for rigging errors if it has been unrigged.
- ☐ Test limit switches frequently and reset them when necessary. Put override keys into safe keeping.
- ☐ Test emergency cutouts.
- ☐ Test overload cutouts.
- ☐ Test brakes.

Fig. 6.15 Tanktop with typical heavy indentations
Photo courtesy of Captain L. Hesketh FNI

CHAPTER 7

BALLAST MANAGEMENT

Basic pattern of ballast management, relevant regulations, ship's ballast layout, quantity of ballast required, ballasting whilst discharging, ballast management on passage, sequential and flow-through ballast changing, restrictions on deballasting, deballasting, achieving good results, maintenance of ballast tanks, removal of sediment and scale, patching of leaks, maintenance of coatings in tanks, inspections, closing of tanks

ABOARD BULK CARRIERS sea water is used as ballast to improve the ship's draught, airdraught, stability, trim and list. In terms of convenience and cost it is a great improvement upon the shingle which used to serve as ballast in 19th century sailing ships, but it brings its own problems, such as the damage which water can cause if it leaks into the wrong compartment, sloshes in a part filled tank, or contaminates the environment into which it is discharged.

The basic pattern of ballast management is familiar to most seafarers. As cargo is discharged ballast is loaded to maintain the vessel at an acceptable draught and trim. The voyage from discharging port to next loading port is then undertaken in ballast. It may be a requirement of the destination country that ballast is changed in the open ocean, to prevent the discharge of ballast water from the port area of one country into the waters of another country with different forms of marine life.

Ballast is discharged in the loading port before and whilst loading takes place. At other times small quantities of ballast may be loaded or discharged to achieve the required trim or list, and ballast may be taken to preserve positive stability.

Since most raw materials are exported from areas requiring little return cargo, larger bulk carriers spend 40-50 per cent of their time in ballast whilst the smaller vessels able to load a wider variety of cargoes are on average in ballast for 30-40 per cent of the time.[7]

Ballasting procedures which protect the ship from heavy weather damage, avoid infringing regulations, and use minimum power for ballast pumping and for propulsion are an important element in the competitive efficiency of the ship's operation.

Regulations governing ballast management

Before considering the ballasting processes in detail it is worth recalling the restrictions which are placed upon ballasting operations. These restrictions have two objectives: to protect the ship from damage and to preserve the marine environment.

- The appropriate 'in port' and 'at sea' limits for shear forces, bending moments and hull girder torque, as specified by the classification society and stated in the Loading Guidance and Stability Information Manual, must never be exceeded. To ensure that they are not exceeded the values must be calculated and taken into account when ballasting is planned.
- Vessels which have the option of ballasting to a light ballast draught or a heavy ballast draught must ballast to the heavy ballast draught when adverse weather is expected.
- A minimum forward draught for the vessel when at sea may be specified by the classification society. This figure will probably be 0.025L. (In a bulk carrier with L = 200m the minimum permissible forward draught would be 5 metres)
- Adequate positive stability must be preserved throughout the voyage.
- Ballast holds and topside tanks must not remain part filled throughout the sea voyage.
- Ballast tanks must not be overpressurised. The ballasting pressure will be too high and damage will occur if tanks are filled faster than the water can overflow from the airpipes when the tank is full. Such damage can occur if two pumps are used to fill a single ballast tank or if ballast tank airpipes are damaged or blocked.
- Ballast tanks must not be underpressurised. If tanks or ballast holds are emptied with airpipes and ventilators closed the resulting vacuum can cause severe damage to the deck structure, and hatch covers in the case of ballast holds.
- On January 1, 2008, the SOLAS requirements[181] entered into force that consideration is given, when changing ballast, to increased blind sectors which might impede a good lookout, that the exchange is in accordance with the ship's ballast water management plan and that the ballast exchange is logged.
- The IMO Guidelines[108] specify how and where ballast should be taken, exchanged and discharged, the precautions to take and the ballast records that must be maintained. These Guidelines are strengthened and made mandatory by the International Convention for the Control and Management of Ships' Ballast Water and Sediments[109] the requirements of which, depending on the willingness of the IMO member states to ratify the Convention, may be coming into force between 2008 and 2010. Some Authorities have their own requirements, which are mandatory and are more exacting than those of the Convention. Details of these can be found in national directories and port information on the internet, on the BIMCO homepage or Vessel CD, or in Guides to port entry. Details of the requirements at the intended ballast discharge port can also be provided by ships' agents in that port and should be studied before taking ballast to be sure that all requirements can be satisfied.

Ship's ballast layout

Ballast pipelines: Each ballast tank is connected to the engineroom by a ballast pipeline running from tank to engineroom, through which the ballast water passes as the tank is filled or emptied. Each tank may have its own separate line, or all starboard tanks may be connected to one common ballast main and all port tanks to another. If there is a duct keel the ballast lines will run along it. Certain bulk carriers and OBOs are provided with ballast ducts formed by the double-bottom structure, instead of ballast pipelines. Such ducts are approved as suitable for use with a stated static head of water which must not be exceeded in service.

In the ballast tank the line ends in a 'bell mouth', an enlargement of the line which terminates in the lowest part of the tank about 3 cm above the tank base. In the engineroom the line can be connected to a sea inlet by a choice of pipeline systems served by one or two ballast pumps, and a general service pump, so that the most suitable pumping option can be selected. In most cases, particularly in larger vessels, the line is also connected in the engineroom to an eductor or stripping pump for final stripping of the tank. Alternatively a separate stripping line is fitted

A plan of the ballast and stripping system of the *Spar Scorpio* is on the CD inside the front cover. This shows that each wing tank and double bottom ballast tank has its own separate suction/filling line connected to one of the main ballast lines and is also connected to one of the stripping lines. The fore and after peak tanks benefit from their tapering shapes and are connected only to the main ballast lines. The plan states, in effect, that in the double bottom tanks the suctions are to be placed inboard in the starboard tanks and outboard in the port tanks so that the most efficient drainage of the tanks can be achieved by listing the ship a little and, of course, keeping her trimmed by the stern.

Duct keel: In smaller ships the ballast pipelines to the forward tanks pass through the after tanks to reach the forward ones. In larger Panamax and Cape-sized vessels a duct keel – a tunnel running fore and aft to contain ballast and other pipelines – is likely to be installed below the holds on the ship's centreline. This provides space for all pipelines and for most of the valves serving the holds and forecastle, and allows access to them for repairs and maintenance. The duct keel is entered from the engine room via a watertight door and on larger ships is likely to be provided along its length with one or more additional accesses from the upper deck.

Airpipes: Each ballast tank is provided with at least one airpipe, and usually two – one forward and one aft – to allow air to escape as the tank fills, regardless of the ship's trim. The airpipes extend to sheltered positions on the upper deck. They come in a variety of designs which allow the passage of air, and the overflow of water, but which will not permit water to enter (Fig. 6.5). It is essential that this non-return arrangement (often a float) is well maintained and adjusted, if necessary, to ensure that accidental flooding of ballast or fuel tanks cannot take place. Inspection of the non-return arrangement in all the airpipes is a Load Line Survey item, and every airpipe should be regularly checked between surveys by ships' staff.

The positions of the air and sounding pipes of the *Spar Scorpio* can be seen on the 'Air, Sounding and Filling Pipe plan' on the CD inside the front cover. This shows each tank provided with two airpipes, one forward and one aft.

Sounding pipes: Every ballast tank is provided with a sounding pipe, normally located at the after end where the greatest sounding will be obtained, provided the ship is trimmed by the stern. At the base of the sounding pipe is a striking plate, a small section of doubled plating which protects the ship's shell plating from wear caused by the impact of the steel sounding rod, or the pipe, with openings cut near its base, may continue to the ship's shell. Striking plates must be examined whenever tanks are inspected and renewed when they are wasted, as they protect the shell plating from damage.

An unusual and practical feature aboard the *Regina Oldendorff* is the provision of additional hold sounding pipes on the masthouse tops. These make it possible to take soundings of the holds to detect flooding, even when the decks are awash.

Tank gauges: Ballast tanks are often provided with remote reading indicators which show whether or not the tanks are empty, or with gauges which show the volume of ballast which the tank contains. Such devices are useful indications of the progress of ballasting or deballasting but must never be trusted completely. Upon completion of any ballasting process the tank contents must be measured with sounding rod or sounding tape to obtain a reliable measure of the contents. If there is any suspicion that the sounding rod has not reached the base of the pipe, which may be blocked by an old sounding plumb or by scale or sediment, the ullage should be measured by taking the reading at deck level when the rod is at the deepest sounding. The ullage can then be compared with its known or listed value which, on large ships, is likely to be the same as that for a number of other tanks.

Centralised ballast controls: On modern ships the ballast controls are likely to be centralised in a single

Fig. 7.1 Centralised water ballast controls in a W/T box on deck

position, perhaps with duplicate controls elsewhere. Such controls are likely to include remote switches for the valves in the ballast system and for the ballast pumps, along with gauges or indicators to show the contents of each ballast tank. The centralised controls may be found in a cargo control room, in the engine-room control room, on the bridge, in a masthouse or within a watertight box on the open deck (Fig.7.1).

Double-bottom ballast tanks: It is normal for the double-bottom ballast tanks to extend into the lower hopper spaces, creating a tank with a tanktop which rises to a greater height in the wings beneath the lower

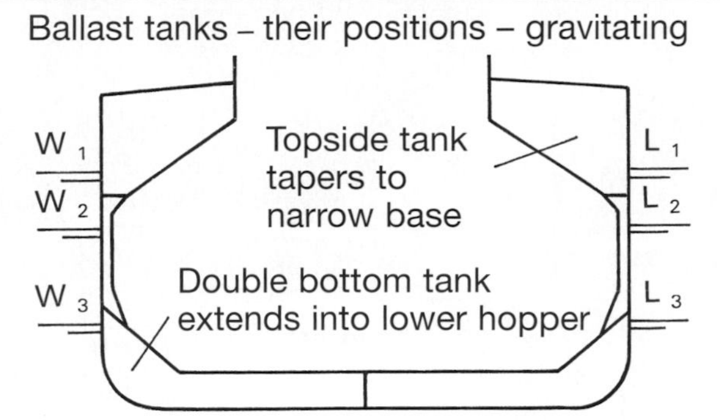

The topside tanks are high in the ship. When the ballast, lines are opened to the sea all the ballast in the topside tanks will gravitate to sea until the tank is empty, except, when the ship is floating at W_1L_1.
The double bottom tanks are low in the ship. When the ballast lines are opened to the sea the double bottom tanks will fill by gravity, except when the ship is floating at W_3L_3.

Fig. 7.2

hoppers (Fig. 7.2). Alternatively, in double hulled vessels, this area may be part of the wing ballast tanks. These double bottom tanks are subdivided for strength purposes into small steel cells formed by vertical steel plates running athwartships and fore and aft (Fig. 7.3). The athwartships plates (called floors) and the fore-and-aft plates (named side girders) have lightening holes cut in them at intervals to reduce the weight of steel used and to allow access. Drainage holes are provided at the base of the vertical plating to allow complete drainage of the tank, whilst similar holes at the top of plating allow free circulation of air. Movement through the tank for inspection or cleaning purposes is difficult in the smaller mini- and handy-sized vessels, because of the limited dimensions, though it becomes easier in large bulkers.

Topside ballast tanks: The topside, saddle or upper hopper ballast tanks stretch along the length of the ship's side and occupy the upper corners of the ship's hull (Fig. 7.2). There are several ways in which these tanks can be filled and emptied, and the method varies from one design of ship to another. The simplest method to describe is similar to that found in other ballast tanks: a ballast line runs to each topside tank from the engine room and is used to pump ballast water into or out of the tank, from or to the sea, via the engine room. This is the system installed in the *Spar Scorpio.*

Dump valves: The usefulness of the topside tanks is increased when they are fitted with dump valves. Dump valves (drop, or screw down overboard drain valves) are ship's side valves, usually one to a tank, which are used to discharge the ballast from the topside tanks by gravity directly into the water alongside the ship. This is very useful when there is a

Fig. 7.3. A Diamond 53 bulk carrier under construction in New Century Shipyard, PRC. The photo shows the double bottom and a lower wing tank with, in the background, the lower section of a hold bulkhead
Photo courtesy of N.B. Mortensen

requirement to discharge a lot of ballast quickly. A further advantage is that no pump is needed for the discharge. One exceptional situation in which dump valves are useful is when refloating a vessel after grounding. If all the topside ballast is dumped at one time the draught decreases rapidly and the prospect of overcoming the suction and refloating from a muddy bottom is increased. The facility is equally useful in routine deballasting when rapid deballasting is required, as is so often the case.

On older vessels when deballasting by way of dump valves, care must be taken not to discharge ballast into barges lying alongside or on to the quay where sensitive equipment, power lines or stocks of cargo are located. Where available and where required chutes should be used to guide discharged ballast water down the ship's side. On modern vessels the dump valve discharge openings are usually sited below the light waterline where they will cause no flooding.

Integrated topside tanks: Some topside tanks are fitted with no separate ballast lines, and with no dump valves, but are simply joined to the adjacent lower hopper and double-bottom tank by trunking. This system is clearly the cheapest to install and maintain, but is the least useful. The topside tank in this system is simply an extension of the lower hopper and DB tank. It can only be filled when the lower tank has been filled, and the DB tank cannot be emptied until all the ballast has drained from the topside tank. When there is a need to keep the lower tank empty for any reason – for example, to make the ship less stiff by raising the centre of gravity, or because the lower tank is damaged and leaking – the upper tank must be left empty, too.

An improved version of the combined topside and double-bottom tank is achieved when a gate valve is fitted in the trunking between upper and lower tanks. This permits the upper tank to be kept full while the lower tank is emptied.

Topside tanks for carriage of grain: A few bulk carriers, of which the *Regina Oldendorff* is one, are designed to carry grain in the topside ballast tanks. Loading grain in the topside tanks is an option which will be avoided where possible because of the great amount of careful cleaning which will be required both before loading the cargo, and after discharging it. (The carriage of grain in topside ballast tanks is described in Chapter 18).

Ballast pumping arrangements

Most bulk carriers are provided with at least two main ballast pumps (Fig.7.4). Normally one is used on starboard ballast tanks and the other on port ballast tanks, but these arrangements can be varied. The port pump can be used on starboard tanks, and the starboard on port tanks, and both pumps can be used together on large tanks such as ballast holds or the forepeak tank. For emergency use if a ballast pump fails there are usually other pumps such as a general service pump which can be used to pump ballast.

In addition to the main ballast pumps most bulk carriers except the smallest are provided with a ballast stripping system. This relies on a low capacity pump or eductor to pump out the strippings (the last few centimetres of ballast water) from the ballast tanks.

Fig. 7.4 Two main ballast pumps on a handymax bulk carrier

On Cape-sized or larger vessels a separate stripping line to each tank may be provided, but this is rare in other bulkers. More often on Cape-sized, Panamax and handy-sized vessels the stripping is done by way of the main ballast line.

Mini-bulkers may be provided with no separate stripping pump or system, all the ballast being discharged by careful operation of the main ballast pumps.

The bilge and ballast-pumps in the engine room of the *Regina Oldendorff* include a ballast pump, a similar ballast/bilge/general service pump, a fire/general service pump and a ballast stripping pump. (Fig.7.4 shows the two @ 500 m^3/hr ballast pumps of a 45,000 dwt conbulker).

Quantity of ballast required for voyage

Most bulk carriers have a light ballast condition for use in fair weather, with all double bottom, hopper, topside wing and peak non-fuel tanks filled. The displacement in light ballast condition is typically 40-50 per cent of loaded displacement.

Most bulkers also have a heavy ballast condition for use when rough weather is expected or met. In this condition the above tanks are filled and in addition one hold is, or several holds are, flooded giving a displacement of 50-65 per cent of loaded displacement.

It is possible to change the amount of ballast which the vessel is carrying during the course of the voyage, but the matter should be considered beforehand since a ship with insufficient ballast will be slowed by the weather and may suffer damage, whilst a ship carrying too much ballast will be incurring extra expense as her fuel consumption will be higher and her speed may be reduced.

When strong winds – particularly strong adverse winds – and a heavy swell are expected it is prudent to carry maximum ballast to prevent the bow slamming and the propeller racing when the ship is meeting the swell.

In fair weather, significant savings in fuel consumption can be easily obtained, it is claimed, by carrying minimum ballast, and a major study of this subject[7] has identified the optimum minimum ballast condition. The propeller need be only immersed to 90 per cent of its diameter when the vessel is at rest, since the stern wave will immerse the propeller fully when the vessel is under way. The optimum forward draught in fair weather is more difficult to specify. It is necessary to strike a balance between the benefit of reduced forward draught and the loss of efficiency which results from increased trim. In addition, there will usually be a loss of propulsive efficiency at the draught at which the top of the bulbous bow breaks the surface.

The study suggests that a ship provided with a reliable and accurate fuel meter and speed log can become its own testbed to tune draught and trim in varying weather states so as to maximise 'metres per litre'[7]. The benefits of tuning are likely to be greatest in fair weather conditions, whilst in moderate or heavy weather the vessel should be ballasted down. The transfer of bunkers is a more efficient way of improving trim than is the taking of additional ballast, since the former alternative requires no increase in displacement[14], but seafarers will treat this option with caution in view of the possible penalties for a mistake whilst transferring fuel.

A further study[14] by one of the same authors concluded that a very flexible and adaptable system of ballasting could be achieved if the ballast hold was always filled on ballast passages, with most other ballast tanks being kept empty except as required to avoid excessive bending moments and shear forces, to achieve optimum trim, or to increase displacement in the event of meeting adverse weather. An additional benefit of this method of operation would be the reduction of sediment taken into double-bottom tanks. This system of ballasting, with the ballast hold or holds always filled on ballast voyages, is only attractive in trades in which the hold or holds can become available for ballasting some time before the completion of discharge and where loading can proceed in other holds whilst the ballast hold is prepared for loading. It is particularly attractive for bulk carriers which have restrictions on filling or emptying ballast holds while at sea due to the risk of sloshing.

On some ships the filling of all ballast tanks for a ballast passage is forbidden because the longitudinal stresses are excessive when ballast holds, and adjacent ballast tanks, are all full. Such a ship is permitted to sail in the light ballast condition with all double-bottom and topside tanks full and the ballast hold empty, or alternatively in the heavy ballast condition with the ballast hold or holds filled but with specified adjacent topside tanks empty. Some bulk carriers have restrictions on the filling of their fore peak tanks, in particular in the light ballast condition, where it would cause excessive hogging. Any such requirement will be plainly stated in the ship's loading manual.

Ballasting whilst discharging

Preparations for ballasting: A full ballasting plan, consistent with the cargo discharge plan, complying with shear force and bending moment limits and taking account of any draught and airdraught limits must be prepared in advance in compliance with the *BLU Code*. (For a fuller account of this subject see Chapter 9).

Before commencement of ballasting it is necessary on some ships to open the ballast tank ventilators or airpipes to allow air to be exhausted as the ballast water enters the tank. It is also important to note where ballast water may overflow. Ballast water which can overflow into part-filled cargo holds or over the ship's side into barges or on to the quay can be a source of substantial claims, with the ship even being accused of causing pollution. For this reason when tanks are ballasted in port pumping must always be stopped before the tank overflows.

To ensure that this is achieved the ballast pumps should be singled up, or reduced to minimum speed, when the tank is nearly full and an officer should be stationed by the tank airpipe or sounding pipe with a walkie-talkie radio, which gives him direct contact with the ballast pump operator. When the officer sees from the sounding, that the tank is about to overflow or when he sees or hears the water nearing the top of the air pipe or sounding pipe he must instruct the pump operator to stop the pump. Alternatively, provided that the tank gauges are reliable, filling can be stopped when the gauges show the tank to be 95% full. To prevent sloshing the filling of such tanks should be completed (ie the tank should be 'pressed up') when the vessel is at sea.

It is important to remember that hold structures are regularly damaged by grabs during discharge. If a hole has been punched in a tank during discharge then ballast water will pour on to the cargo in the hold when the tank is ballasted. Before ballasting is started the holds should be inspected as far as possible to ensure that no damage has been sustained, and the tank boundaries should be regularly viewed to detect any leakage of ballast water whilst ballasting continues.

Precautions whilst ballasting: Instances have been recorded in which the internal structures of ballast tanks have been damaged as a result of ballasting at too high a rate. Damage can occur when a full tank is overpressurised, a condition which arises if water is pumped into the tank faster than it can overflow out of the tank through the airpipes. This is most likely to occur if the tank has an airpipe which is blocked through freezing, but could possibly occur if two pumps were used to fill a single tank, or if an airpipe were damaged. Risk of damage will be reduced if tanks are always topped-off at a reduced pumping rate.

When berthed in a river ballasting is best done on the flood tide, when there is less sediment in the water. This will result in less mud in the ship's ballast tanks. Other factors that may affect the quality of the ballast are shallow water, nearby sewage outlets, toxic algal blooms, cholera in the locality and the hours of darkness when bottom dwelling organisms rise to the surface. Often these circumstances cannot be avoided but they should be recorded[170].

Ballasting – the first stage: It is normal to commence ballasting by filling double-bottom tanks, and this can be done by gravitating – opening the sea valves in the ballast system and allowing the water to flow through the ballast pipes and into the chosen tanks under the effect of gravity. The speed of filling will depend upon the head of water: this corresponds to the draught of the ship. In the early stages gravitating may be faster than pumping. If the draught of the ship is less than the height of the tops of the lower hopper tanks (Fig. 7.2), then the tanks can never be completely filled by gravitating and it will be necessary to complete the filling by pumping. The benefits of filling a tank by gravitating are threefold. There is no possibility of the tank overflowing and causing damage, no power is required so there is a cost saving, and the filling will stop naturally when the level of the outside water is reached so it is not necessary to monitor the process continuously.

The sequence of filling the double-bottom tanks will be decided by the sequence of discharging the cargo holds. Where all holds are discharged simultaneously and where the cargo is of low density, the longitudinal stresses will be low and it will be possible to adopt any reasonable sequence of filling the double-bottom tanks, as will be apparent when the details are entered in the loading instrument.

Another factor to bear in mind is the vessel's trim. It is always preferable to maintain a trim by the stern so that reliable soundings can be obtained, for purposes of efficient drainage throughout the ship, and for the convenience of the engineers. Where possible this trim should be ensured by a suitable cargo discharging programme, but ballast may be needed to assist the process. Where all holds are not discharged at the same time and some remain full, it will usually be necessary to reduce the longitudinal stresses by taking full ballast in the double-bottom and topside tanks surrounding the holds which are first discharged.

Ballasting – the second stage: As the remaining quantity of cargo diminishes, and once the DB tanks have been ballasted, the topside tanks must be filled. They are at too great a height to be filled by gravitation so must be pumped full, taking the precautions already mentioned for the double-bottom tanks. The forepeak and afterpeak tanks will be filled as required during the first or second stage of ballasting.

Ballasting – the third stage: The third stage of ballasting is the filling of the ballast holds of ships which have them. Ships with no ballast holds are fully ballasted upon completion of stage 2 of the ballasting. Most other ships will, on completion of stage 2, be fully ballasted to the light ballast condition. Filling the ballast hold or holds is usually optional and is undertaken to achieve the heavy ballast condition. If this condition is chosen each ballast hold must be prepared for ballasting (a process which is fully described in Chapter 5).

When the hold has been cleaned as circumstances require any blanks and cover plates must be removed from the ballast line to allow ballasting and deballasting and the bilge line must be blanked off to prevent the flooding of other compartments. Some classification societies prohibit ships' Masters from operating their ships with ballast holds filled to between 20 per cent – 90 per cent of capacity, and holds if ballasted at sea should always be fully ballasted to avoid damage from sloshing. At the commencement of the voyage the ballast holds should be filled to the coaming, a process which is often achieved with the hatch covers still open for easy observation of the filling. When filling has been stopped the hatch covers must be closed and well battened down. The ballast hatch covers on some ships are provided with four pressure/vacuum valves which must be open when ballast is carried.

Ballasting – the fourth stage: Certain large bulk carriers are equipped with some additional ballast holds which can be ballasted only in port to reduce the airdraught. The bulkheads of such holds are not strong enough to allow the holds to be fully ballasted, and they can only be filled to a stated level, perhaps half the capacity of the hold. Soundings are often painted on the end bulkheads of such holds so that the water depth in the hold can be easily seen. The ballasting reduces the vessel's airdraught, so that the grabs and bulldozers can clear the coaming when being lifted in and out of the working holds. The ballast must be discharged from these holds before the vessel puts to sea.

Ballasting rates: Officers will quickly become familiar with the ballasting rates which can be achieved with one or with two ballast pumps or by gravitating. Nominal ballasting and deballasting rates, based upon installed pump capacity and ballast capacity, vary considerably from ship to ship, but a nominal time of 10-15 hours is typical for the full deballasting of a large range of ship sizes. Actual times are longer for operational reasons, though it is reported to be common for terminal operators and charter party clauses to require a vessel to deballast completely within 24 hours. Some Cape-sized vessels have ballast pumps with a pumping capacity of 2,000 m^3/hr or more, allowing two pumps to discharge ballast at more than 4,000 mt/hr when assisted by stripping pumps as is necessary for vessels with a ballast capacity of more than 70,000 m^3. Deballasting time is speeded when ships are fitted for gravity discharge through separate lines from topside tanks and ballast holds.

Ballast management on passage

Whilst on the ballast passage it is tempting to ignore the ballast tanks in the belief that nothing can go wrong with them, but this is not a prudent attitude to take. Ballast tanks when full should continue to be sounded or ullaged at least once a day as a means of detecting any leakage, and the soundings should be recorded as measurements, not simply as 'Full'. Leakage from ballast tanks into holds will usually be detected during hold inspections, but leakage from ballast tanks into void spaces or through the ship's side into the sea is not easily detected by any means other than the monitoring of soundings.

During the course of the voyage it is likely that a

small part of the contents of ballast tanks will slop out of the tanks by way of the air pipes, particularly if the ship moves in a seaway. For this reason it is common practice to press up (ie, fill and overflow) all ballast tanks before arrival in the discharging port. However, the pressing up of a tank does not guarantee that it is full, and it is still advisable to sound all tanks, to apply the appropriate corrections to the soundings and to take account of the density if the exact weight of the contents is required.

During the course of a ballast voyage there are several possible reasons for changing ballast. The most important of these is the requirement existing in a number of loading ports for ballast to be changed in mid ocean in accordance with the IMO Guidelines[230] before arrival in the port because the marine life can be harmed by the release of ballast water from another region.

A second reason for changing ballast arises when the ballast carried is fresh or almost fresh water and the ship is going to a loading port in a cold climate, where fresh or brackish ballast water is liable to freeze in the tanks and to block sounding and airpipes and ballast valves. Before reaching freezing conditions fresh water must be exchanged for salt water.

When a ballast hold has been filled at the start of the ballast voyage with dock water which is dirty or sediment laden and a clean hold is required in the loading port, for the carriage of grain for example, the hold should be emptied, cleaned and refilled at sea provided that the vessel is steady and it is safe to do so. Individual ballast tanks may be emptied or filled during a ballast passage, provided sloshing, stress and stability considerations permit, for purposes of adjusting draught, trim and list, or for tank maintenance.

When changing ballast in the open ocean a ballast water management plan which ensures that the at-sea stress limits are never exceeded and that adequate positive stability is maintained at all times must be used. All ships are supplied with such a plan in compliance with the IMO Guidelines[108], the plan normally being approved on behalf of the flag state by the ships' classification societies

Sequential and flow-through ballast changing: Two methods of making a full ballast change are recognised. They are the sequential method and the flow-through or continuous method. In the sequential method a ship's ballast tanks are emptied and refilled one or two at a time in a sequence which has been planned to ensure that the ship is not overstressed or unfavourably trimmed at any time. The benefits of this method are first that it removes most of the pollutants from the ballast tank, second that it requires less power and takes a shorter time than the flow-through method, third that it does not require the overflow of ballast water onto the vessel's decks and fourth that it minimises the risk of over pressurising ballast tanks and does not require the unshipping of the ballast tank manhole covers. Disadvantages of the method are that it increases structural stresses for the duration of the ballast change and that it requires more supervision and management. It is important to minimise the sloshing of water in part-filled tanks and holds. This requires that the changing of ballast is undertaken in the calmest weather available. Since swell is even more difficult to predict than wind, and since a full change of ballast may take 36-48 hours of continuous work, which may be spread over four normal working days, this will sometimes be a difficult requirement with which to comply. In addition the ballast change programme should be as simple as possible to execute, for the convenience of the ship's personnel responsible for the process.

The flow-through method keeps the ballast tanks full by pumping water into each full tank and overflowing it continuously. Its benefits are that if done properly it causes no increase to the structural stresses and it requires less supervision than the sequential method. A disadvantage is that on ships which were not designed and built for flow-through ballast change the ballast tank manhole covers must be unshipped to allow safe overflowing. Local structural damage to ballast tank ventilators or structures can occur if these precautions are ignored and tanks are overpressurised. Another disadvantage is that it is necessary to pump three times the tank capacity through the tank to achieve an acceptable standard of renewal of the tank's contents. Trials[20] have shown that the flow-through method does not achieve a complete change of ballast. Even after exchanging three tank volumes some 5 per cent of the original water and up to 25 per cent of plankton sediment is likely to be retained. This process takes longer and uses more fuel than the sequential method. Another disadvantage is that for the three or four days which the process requires the decks are awash with corrosive salt water, preventing maintenance work on deck and causing deterioration of deck coatings. Despite these disadvantages the flow-through method is nowadays preferred by most operators because it avoids increased structural stresses.

A successful ballast change requires deep water as far as possible from any land and sufficient time to complete the task. A sequential ballast change also requires calm weather but this is less important for a flow-through exchange.

When exchanging ballast the ballast tank sounding pipe caps should be removed to ensure that the ballast in the sounding pipes is exchanged. Neglect of this precaution could result in false samples later being obtained from the sounding pipes.

A programme for a complete change of ballast aboard a Cape-sized bulk carrier is at Appendix 7.1. A ballast tank on the port side and the matching tank on the starboard side should be emptied or filled at the same time. No. 2 starboard double-bottom tank should not be pumped out at the same time as No. 4 port DB tank, even if they have the same capacity. The ship will remain upright, but the uneven distribution of weight about the ship's centreline will risk twisting her hull and damaging her.

Restrictions on the discharge of ballast

Many ports and Administrations place restrictions on the discharge of ballast water in port or coastal waters. In some ports ballast water samples are taken by the local authority before deballasting is permitted. Before discharging ballast in port or coastal waters it is essential to find whether permission is required. If written permission is required it must be obtained.

Deballasting

Deballasting before berthing: A full deballasting plan, consistent with the cargo loading plan, complying with shear force and bending moment limits and taking account of any draught and airdraught limits, must be prepared in advance, in compliance with the BLU Code[110].

When planning the deballasting of their vessel, the Master and chief mate will take account of the possible need for permission from the authorities to discharge ballast – an important matter – and of several significant operational considerations. Important amongst these is the height of the loading arm (the height of the loader above water level, or the airdraught in the berth). If the ship discharges too much ballast before she commences loading she will rise too high in the water, and the loading arm will be unable to extend over the coaming to commence the pouring of cargo into the hold. The height of the loader, taken in conjunction with the ship's dimensions and trim, and the anticipated height of tide, will decide the maximum amount of ballast that can be discharged before arrival. In many instances the Master will decide to do no deballasting before berthing, to ensure that the vessel preserves a draught and trim which is safe for manoeuvring in all circumstances.

Stress and stability must be considered, as in all cargo and ballast operations, and if the ship has reached a sheltered anchorage or layby berth where she is not exposed to swell, then it is permissible to use the in-port stress limits for the calculations. However, The Nautical Institute recommends that the lower at-sea stress limits should where possible be used for all calculations to provide an increased margin of safety. A stern trim is essential for the taking of accurate soundings and for the efficient stripping of ballast tanks and must be maintained throughout loading.

Other factors will also influence the Master's decision as to how much ballast, if any, is to be discharged before berthing at the loading berth. If the winds are strong and the berth is not well sheltered or well orientated he may require to maintain maximum draught for the berthing manoeuvre. The port regulations may specify minimum draughts, trim and propeller immersion. On the other hand, a loading plan which calls for the loading of cargo in a ballast hold will require the hold to be deballasted and prepared for loading quickly. When sheltered waters can be guaranteed and an adequate draught can be maintained it may be possible to deballast the hold before berthing.

If other factors permit the discharge of ballast before berthing, it is always in the interests of a speedy loading that some ballast should be discharged. Loading at most berths can be accomplished faster than the deballasting rate, so deballasting delays can be reduced or eliminated if the ship is partly deballasted before berthing. Since it is sensible to meet and resolve problems as soon as possible, the best tanks to deballast before berthing are those which are most likely to present difficulties for the ship. These are the ballast holds, if they are to be loaded fairly early in the loading sequence, and then the double bottom tanks. The topside and peak tanks taper steeply to the tank bottom, which assists drainage, but the double-bottom tanks have extensive flat bottoms in which a small sounding (say, 15 cm) can represent a considerable tonnage of ballast. These double-bottom tanks are usually the most difficult to deballast and it is helpful if some or all can be pumped out before berthing when this can be done without risk to the ship.

Some of the factors mentioned above are reasons for the discharge of some ballast before berthing. Others are reasons for retaining ballast until the ship is berthed. The Master must seek to strike the correct balance in each loading port, having regard to the circumstances of the case.

Deballasting sequence: The deballasting sequence has already been indicated and is dictated by the requirements to limit stresses, maintain a stern trim and an acceptable air draught. Ballast holds, where provided and full, will be discharged first. Double-bottom tanks will be discharged next. Topside tanks will be discharged after double-bottom tanks, except where stress considerations or ship design dictate that they are discharged at the same time as the adjacent double-bottom tanks. Peak tanks will be discharged last. Within this framework it will generally be the case that double-bottom tanks and topside tanks will be discharged when the hold above or below is being loaded.

Keeping to the programme: A variety of operational problems can cause the speed of deballasting to slow, particularly with inexperienced operators and/or older ships. When this happens there is a danger that the deballasting will get out of step with the loading. This must not be allowed to happen; the deballasting must continue in step with the loading to ensure that the ship is not exposed to stresses which have not been calculated and that longitudinal stresses are not exceeded. If a deballasting step has not been completed the loading must be stopped until the deballasting is again in step although, if the quantity of ballast remaining in the tank is small, it is acceptable to move to the next step in the programme and to return to finish deballasting the uncompleted tank at a later stage.

It will always be easier to keep to the deballasting programme when that programme is a realistic one. When preparing the programme it is best to assume the highest possible loading rate and a moderate deballasting rate. This should ensure that there is adequate time for each deballasting step, even if minor problems are met.

Pumping ballast: On some bulkers the deck officers are responsible for ballast operations. On other ships they tell engineroom staff what ballast is to be pumped and the work is carried out by an engineer or pumpman. In both cases deck officers should have a good understanding of the processes involved.

As an example, the deballasting of the No. 5 port double-bottom tank of a Cape-sized bulk carrier is described, with reference to the schematic diagram of the ballast pumping arrangements of such a vessel (Fig. 7.5). (Safe practice is for the No. 5 starboard DB tank to be pumped out at the same time as the port tank, to avoid hull girder torque but for simplicity that is ignored in this example).

Ballast pumps are normally centrifugal pumps driven by electric motors. Gauges show the pump discharge pressure in kgs/cm^2, the pump load in amperes and the pump suction pressure in kgs/cm^2. The variable setting hydraulic valves can be set open, shut or part way between the two extreme positions. Each valve has a gauge which shows its setting. The manual valves can also be set in any position and have telltales to show their settings.

To deballast No. 5 port DB tank proceed as follows:

1. Before starting any ballast pumping operation inform the engineers of the intended pumping, and confirm that sufficient electrical power is available to commence and complete the operation.
2. Open fully valves 18, 23, 31.
3. Open discharge valve 26 until it is 15 per cent open.
4. All other valves on the port side and crossover valves 27, 28 should be closed.
5. Make the pre-pumping checks in accordance with the manufacturers' recommendations (Appendix 7.2).
6. Press the start button on the port ballast pump (a centrifugal pump which takes about six seconds to pick up speed) and when the pump is running open the discharge valve (26) slowly. As the discharge valve is opened the discharge pressure will decrease. Steady the discharge pressure by slowly opening the discharge valve until optimum pumping is achieved (with the manufacturer's recommended discharge pressure – 3.0-3.5 kg on this vessel).
7. Check that the ammeter shows maximum load (about 400 amps on this vessel), and confirm that the ballast suction pressure reading is steady.
8. Always check by sounding or by detecting air being sucked into the tank airpipes that the level of ballast in the tank is falling. Mistakes are common when people are tired, overworked or inexperienced, and it is impossible to tell from the pump's performance alone the origin or destination of the water it is pumping.
9. The discharge pressure should remain steady and not fluctuate. As the deballasting continues the water level in the tank will fall. This means that the head of water feeding the pump is reduced. Continue to adjust the discharge valve (26) by gradually closing it to maintain the maximum rate of pumping. This is indicated by a high amps reading, and a good, steady discharge pressure.
10. Do not close the discharge valve to below 15 per cent. Below this setting it becomes likely that the pump will overheat and trip out because of the high temperature, or will damage the pump casing.
11. When the discharge valve has been closed to 15 per cent, the amps are low and the discharge pressure is fluctuating, the tank is nearly empty. At this time another full tank should be opened and No. 5 port double-bottom should be closed, or the ballast pump should be stopped.

Stripping ballast: When No. 5 port double-bottom tank has been pumped out, a small quantity of water (the strippings) will remain in the tank. All but the smallest bulkers have a stripping pump or eductor to remove the strippings. Eductors rely upon the Venturi principle. They have no moving parts, and are operated by a powerful water jet which is passed through the eductor, and which sucks the ballast water with it. An eductor requires no filters and can be used to discharge water which is laden with sediment and mud. Another advantage of the eductor is that once it has been started it requires very little attention and will come to no harm if left to run on an empty tank.

The eductor in a typical Cape-sized bulker is situated in the engineroom and driven by a general service pump which can pump at two rates. The pump has two impellers which can be set in series (to pump at high pressure), or in parallel (to pump at high capacity). The series or parallel setting is selected by movement of an external lever at the side of the pump. The series setting should be used for driving the eductor. This gives a high discharge pressure from the pump, which causes a strong suction on the eductor intake and gives an eductor capacity on the Cape-sized vessel of 200 tonnes/hour.

The procedure for using the eductor to remove the strippings from the same No. 5 port double-bottom tank of the Cape-sized bulker can be followed in the schematic diagram (Fig. 7.6), and is as follows.

1. Choose to use the fire, and general service pump to drive the eductor.
2. The sea suction valve to the general service pumps must be open. It is normally kept open at all times, as these are also the ship's main fire-fighting pumps.
3. Open valves 39, 38, 65 and 32. (Alternatively, the fire, bilge and ballast pump can be used for this task. In that case the valves to open would be 36, 37, 65, 32).
4. Start the pump.
5. When the eductor is running read the pressure gauge at the eductor suction valve to confirm that a good suction has been obtained.
6. When a good suction has been obtained open valve 64 to the ballast stripping line. (Most bulkers except the largest have no separate stripping lines to the ballast tanks. The procedure followed is just the same, but when there is no stripping line the stripping is done through the main ballast lines.)
7. Check the tank sounding and confirm that the level of water is falling.
8. Tanks should be educted one at a time. If a pair of tanks is educted together the eductor will lose suction and pump air from the time that the first tank is empty.

On ships equipped with stripping pumps instead of stripping eductors, the stripping is similar to the main pumping but uses pumps of lower capacity. Two problems may be met with stripping pumps which do not occur with eductors. The pumps are equipped with strainers to prevent damage to the pumps by mud and grit which could enter them. If the ballast water is dirty the strainers may become blocked. This slows the pumping rate and the strainers must be changed or cleaned.

When a stripping pump is being used it must be watched in order to adjust its settings as the pressure changes and the tank must be watched to detect when it is empty, since the pump will be harmed if it continues to pump on an empty tank for more than a few minutes. In this case the stripping process requires more supervision than with an eductor.

Gravitating ballast: Gravitating ballast is the process of letting ballast which is high in the ship run out into the sea under the influence of gravity, without the need to use a pump. The same process can be used to fill tanks which are below the waterline, from the sea.

The process of discharging the ballast from No. 5 port topside tank in a Cape-sized bulk carrier can be followed from the schematic diagram (Fig. 7.5). No. 5 port topside tank in this ship is connected to No. 5 port double-bottom tank, and is filled and emptied

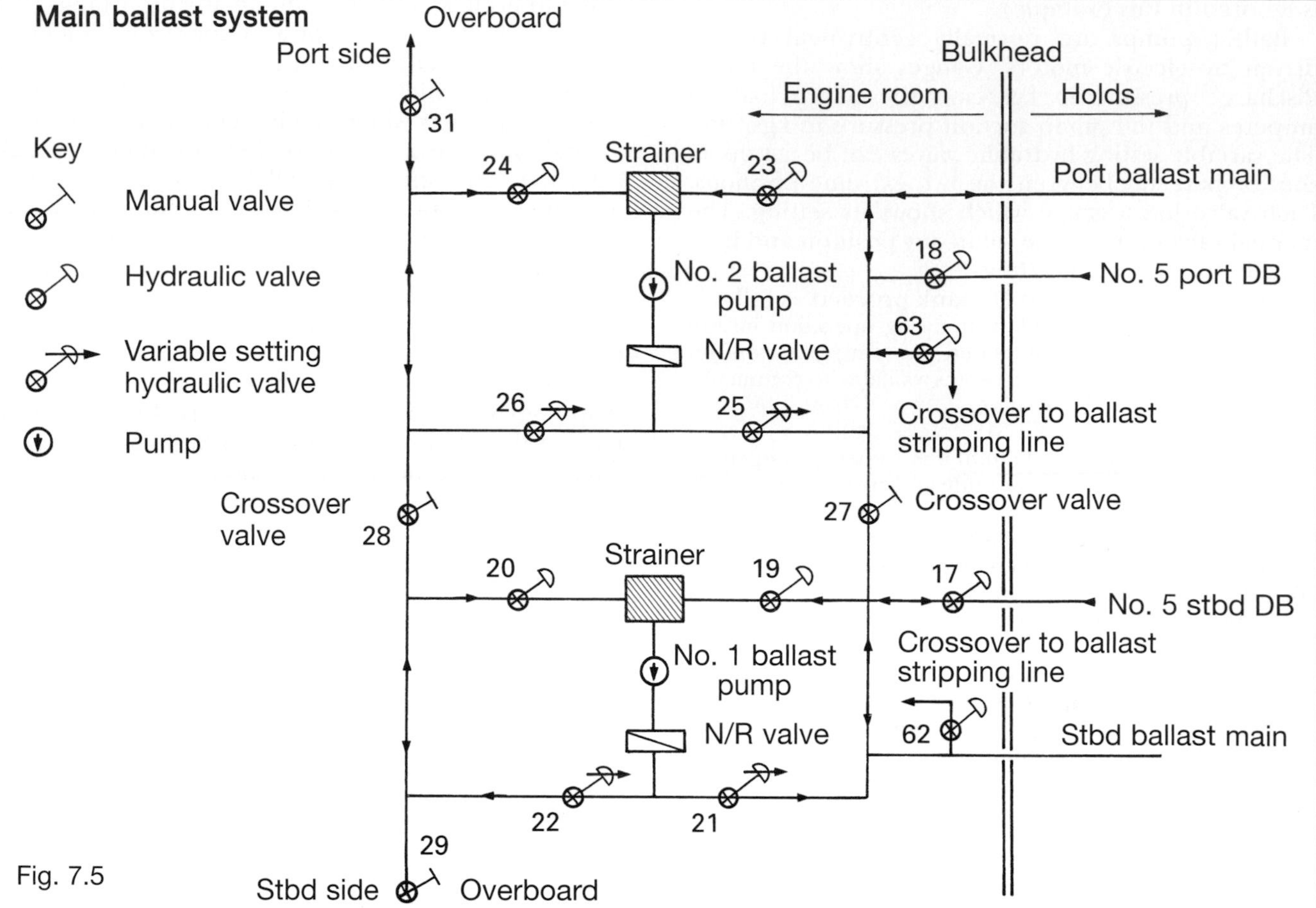

Main ballast system
Overboard
Port side
31
Bulkhead
Engine room
Holds
Key
Manual valve
Hydraulic valve
Variable setting hydraulic valve
Pump
24
Strainer
23
Port ballast main
18
No. 5 port DB
No. 2 ballast pump
63
N/R valve
Crossover to ballast stripping line
26
25
Crossover valve
28
27
Crossover valve
20
Strainer
19
17
No. 5 stbd DB
No. 1 ballast pump
Crossover to ballast stripping line
N/R valve
62
Stbd ballast main
22
21
29
Stbd side
Overboard

Fig. 7.5

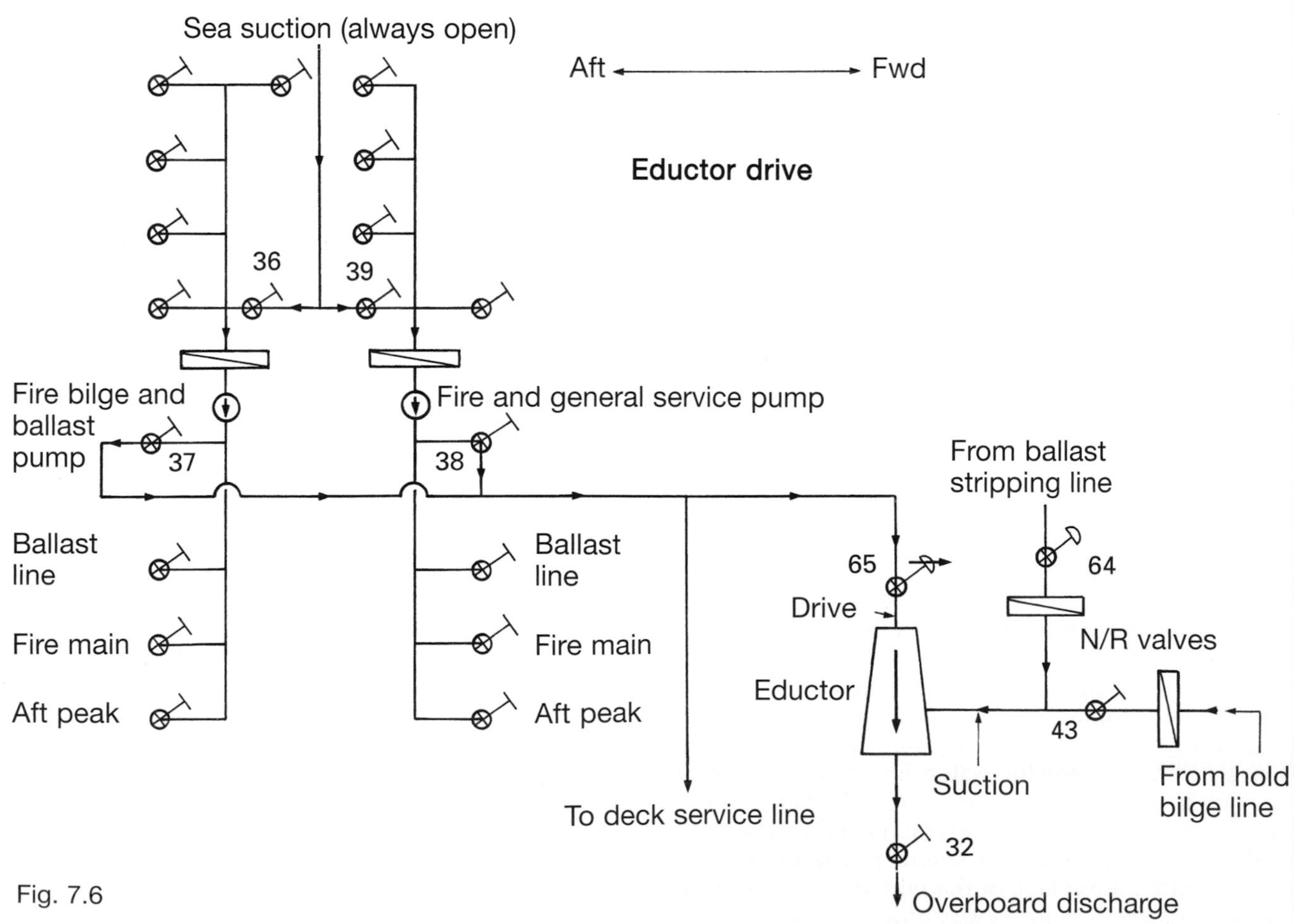

Sea suction (always open)
Aft
Fwd
Eductor drive
36
39
Fire bilge and ballast pump
Fire and general service pump
37
38
From ballast stripping line
Ballast line
Ballast line
65
64
Drive
Fire main
Fire main
N/R valves
Eductor
Aft peak
Aft peak
43
Suction
From hold bilge line
To deck service line
32
Overboard discharge

Fig. 7.6

through the double-bottom tank, by way of valve 18. If the tank was on a separate ballast line the valve for that line would have to be opened.

The procedure in this case is as follows.

1. Open fully the No. 5 port double-bottom tank valve, 18.
2. Open fully valves 25, 26, 31.
3. Valves 24, 23, 63, 27, 28 and all other port side tank valves must be closed.

This procedure runs the ballast through the discharge side of the main ballast pumps. The process is recommended because it avoids running ballast through the pump strainers on the suction side of the pump, and avoids unnecessarily pressurising the pump casing.

Achieving good deballasting

Opening of airpipe cowls: Before deballasting can commence, the ballast tank airpipes must be open. Aboard modern bulk carriers the airpipes are usually designed to be always open, but in older vessels the airpipe cowls may need to be raised, or opened, to admit air into the tank. If this is forgotten the ballast pumps will begin to labour as they try to remove water from a sealed tank, or the structure of the tank may be damaged as a vacuum is created within it.

Keeping ship upright: If the ship develops a list when loading and deballasting the effect may be caused by bad distribution of cargo, or it may be a fault with the deballasting, causing one of a pair of tanks to discharge more slowly than the other. If the fault is in the deballasting, the soundings will show that one tank is more full than the other and the fault must be found and corrected. If the list is the result of unbalanced loading of the cargo, the operator of the shiploader must be instructed to distribute the cargo so as to keep the ship upright whilst loading. An unplanned list will make deballasting more difficult and is likely to cause uneven discharge of ballast, thereby encouraging unbalanced loading of the cargo and exposing the ship's hull to additional stress.

Optimum trim and list: It is almost impossible to pump dry all the ballast tanks of a bulk carrier, but when such a vessel is carrying a deadweight cargo or is restricted to a limiting draught at some point in the voyage she ought to be carrying only the absolute minimum of ballast water, since the more strippings she carries, the less cargo she can lift. Achieving a good discharge of ballast requires a combination of competence, thoroughness and good organisation, and also a clear understanding of the physical positions of the ballast suction and the sounding pipe within the tank. The ship's pumping plan can be useful in providing an understanding of the layout of the tank, but a conscientious officer will seek an early opportunity to enter some of the ballast tanks to view the pumping arrangements for himself.

It is normal for the ballast suctions in double-bottom tanks to be situated in the inboard after corner of the tank. This is true for the *Spar Scorpio*, as can be seen from her ballast system (see CD). To achieve the maximum discharge of ballast from No. 2 double-bottom starboard wing ballast tank the vessel should be trimmed by the stern thus tipping any ballast which remains in the tank towards the after end where the suction is located. Drainage can be further improved if the vessel is listed (to port in this example) but this is not recommended. Ships should not be listed for stripping purposes when closeweight cargoes are being loaded because it is likely to lead to an assymetrical (unbalanced) distribution of the cargo which could overstress the ship. When loading low density cargoes such as grain or coal which will eventually fill the compartment assymetrical cargo distribution is less likely to be a problem, but there is less need to minimise the strippings if the vessel is not loaded to her marks. On the *Regina Oldendorff*, the sounding pipe is situated close to the ballast suction, so that an accurate measure of the depth of water at the suction can be quickly obtained.

The factors which govern the deballasting and stripping on most bulkers are the following:

- The ship should have a good stern trim throughout deballasting.
- The ship should be kept upright throughout the main discharge and stripping of ballast.
- On most bulkers stripping can only be done when main pumping is finished, or interrupted, because both processes use the same lines.
- Stripping can usefully continue so long as the tank sounding shows water.
- A list to port or starboard for the purpose of stripping is not recommended.

Good stripping of the double-bottom tanks takes time and cannot be done effectively at the end of loading, when the ship is normally trimmed even keel or nearly so. Every opportunity must be taken during interruptions to the main ballast pumping to continue with the discharge of the strippings, to reduce them to a low level before final stripping.

By the time that the final DB tank is stripped dry more water will probably have trickled through the tank floors and side girders to the suction in the first tank stripped. Any double-bottom tanks which are again showing a sounding should be stripped for a second time.

The topside and peak tanks taper down to a very small area at the base of the tank where the suction is situated and normally present no problems in stripping. Whilst loading and deballasting the ship should never be allowed to go by the head. In this condition the discharge of ballast is more difficult, final ballast strippings cannot be pumped out and accurate soundings cannot be obtained.

Preventing ballast pumps from tripping: Bulk carrier ballast pumps are usually centrifugal pumps driven by electric motors, with capacities appropriate to the size of ship, a Panamax vessel probably being provided with two x 1,000 tonne/hour pumps, and a handy-sized vessel with two x 500 tonne/hour pumps. When a ballast pump is given a tank full of ballast water to pump out it will operate efficiently until the tank is nearly empty, provided that its performance is monitored and adjusted as necessary. To maximise the pump discharge the load (the pump amperes) should be monitored regularly (say, every half hour) and maintained at the makers' recommended value by adjusting the pump outlet valve.

When the depth of water in a double-bottom tank is reduced to 15-20 cm the flow of water to the suction will start to be interrupted, as the ballast water cannot flow fast enough across the base of the tank, through the drain holes in the floors and intercostals. In consequence the pump will begin to pump a mixture of air and water.

Modern pumps are fitted with degassing devices which enable them to keep pumping when air is mixed with the water. The degassing is effected by a vacuum pump, which may serve one or several ballast pumps. When air starts to pass through the ballast pump the vacuum pump is switched on automatically and removes it. When the ballast pump is again pumping water the vacuum pump is switched off automatically. In older vessels, where the ballast pumps are not fitted with degassing devices, the pumps will race and then trip (ie, cut out, or switch off) when they gas up.

If the pump frequently cuts out, the deballasting becomes very inefficient and there are several methods by which the problem of gassing up can be reduced. One method is to provide the pump with a moderate flow of water from another source. For example a suitable sea valve in the engineroom or the suction valve from a full ballast tank can be cracked open (ie, opened a little), permitting a small flow of water to the pump which will be sufficient to prevent it from racing and the pump will continue to run and to take smaller quantities of water from the near-empty tank, as well as from the other source which has been cracked open. If this process is done carelessly, with the valve from the full tank or the sea opened too wide the result will be that water from this second source will flood back into the nearly empty tank, which is the opposite to the desired result!

Another cause for the ballast pump to trip is if the ballast suction in the tank becomes blocked with mud – the sediment which has settled out of the ballast water in the tank. Sediment in tanks can build up to substantial levels during a period of months or years. Where sediment is suspected of being the cause of a stoppage of discharge the quickest way to clear sediment from around the suction is to flood water back into the tank from another tank with a good head of water, or from the sea. The rush of water into the tank will wash the sediment away from the suction, but this, of course, is only a temporary solution. When sediment is causing problems in a tank, traces of mud will probably be seen on the sounding rod.

Leaking ballast line: A less common cause for difficulties in deballasting is a hole in a ballast line. So long as the hole in the ballast line is below the level of water in the tank, the system will perform normally, but once the water level has dropped below the hole, the system will start to take in air and the pump is liable to gas up and trip. Some vessels have expansion joints in the ballast lines, and if an expansion joint leaks the effect is the same as if the line has a hole in it. Such a leak should be suspected if difficulty is regularly experienced in pumping out the last 0.5-1.0 metres of ballast in a tank, and if the sounding in an after tank falls slowly whilst a forward tank is being discharged, or rises slowly whilst the forward tank is being filled.

The leak can quickly be found by inspecting the ballast line within the after tank whilst the forward tank is full and the tank valve is open. Under these conditions water will be squirting out through the leak. Repairs to a leaking expansion joint can be effected by tightening or renewing the bolts, or by wrapping the joint temporarily in plastic sheeting.

An unusual explanation for difficulties should only be considered once the common explanations have been tested and discarded. On most occasions the pump trips because the water cannot flow to the suction fast enough for the speed at which the pump is operating, or because mud is blocking the suction.

Investigation of deballasting problems: When difficulties with deballasting are experienced, time is often spent trying to deduce the cause of the problem. It is sometimes impossible to make a physical inspection and then it is necessary to rely upon experiment and experience, both of which are useful tools. Physical inspections are also valuable. Aboard a mini-bulker which had no stripping pumps and where all deballasting was done with the main ballast pumps, the pumps would lose suction when the sounding was still 40 cm – the height of the bottom of the lightening holes.

The engineers believed that the drainage holes in the floors and side girders were blocked with mud. The tank was opened up and the pump was started with the water height 40 cm, and the true problem was immediately seen. When the pump was pumping at full speed it emptied the small bay where the suction was located in two or three seconds, much faster than the water could flow into the bay through the drainage holes, which were not blocked. The only way that the tank could be pumped dry was by reducing the pumping rate.

Precaution when deballasting: When ballast is discharged from topside tanks by way of dump valves (otherwise known as drop valves) the process looks after itself. This is convenient for ship's personnel, but is thought to have resulted[12,13] on numerous occasions in personnel forgetting to close the dump valves after all ballast has been discharged. This can result in water re-entering the topside tanks, and flooding from there into the double-bottom tanks in ships where topside and double-bottom tanks are joined. At the worst this could result in serious difficulties or loss of the ship. At the least it could cause the carrying of unnecessary ballast, and reduction to the cargo lifted. It is recommended that the closing of all dump valves immediately on completion of deballasting be checked and logged.

A simple reminder of the setting of the dump valves is for each valve to be fitted with a rope lashing. When the valve is shut it must always be lashed loosely to the ship's side rail. When the valve is open the lashing must be left hanging loose. This system is recommended.

Importance of good records and thorough, methodical approach: Whilst deballasting, the object of the chief mate and his colleagues is to ensure that every ballast tank is empty, or as close to empty as is humanly possible, by the time that loading is complete. The prospect of achieving that objective will be greatly improved if each duty officer is competent, thorough and methodical. Communication with the loading foreman and with the ship's pumpman, if there is one, should be prompt and efficient. Records of soundings obtained and of stages in the deballasting should be carefully and accurately recorded, so that they can easily be checked by colleagues.

When the deballasting of a tank has been started the airpipe should be checked to verify that air is being sucked in, thus confirming that water is being pumped out. Tanks which have been deballasted and recorded as empty should be rechecked at a later time, preferably when there is a good stern trim. Water which was lying undetected at the fore end of the tank may have flowed to the after end, or the tank may have been partly refilled by mistake.

Often a draught surveyor will accept well presented records of this sort, so that the true ballast tonnage – measured accurately when there was a substantial stern trim-is used instead of the less accurate tonnage obtained from soundings taken when the vessel is near even keel.

Ballast residues: Typical ballast residues for well run ships in the laden condition, as measured by accurate surveys, are approximately: mini-bulkers, 20 tonnes; handy-sized bulkers, 50t; Panamax-sized bulkers, 100t; and Cape-sized bulkers, 200t.

Maintenance of ballast compartments

Requirement for maintenance: The maintenance required for ballast compartments includes the removal of sediment (mud), the removal of scale, the repair of leaks and the renewal of coatings.

Any time that mud-laden ballast is loaded into ballast tanks and held there for longer than a few hours, mud will be deposited on horizontal and near horizontal surfaces within the tank. A ship which regularly discharges and takes ballast in mud-laden rivers such as the Maas, the Mississippi or the Chinese rivers will quickly accumulate heavy deposits of mud. It is not unusual for such mud to built up over a period to a depth of 10 cm. It has been calculated that mud accumulated to an average depth of 7.5 cm in the ballast tanks of a 3,000-tonnes deadweight mini-bulker weighed about 50 tonnes. The weight of mud in a Cape-sized vessel with deposits of a similar depth would be considerable.

Mud accumulated within a ballast tank reduces the ship's cargo lifting capacity, makes inspection of the tank for damage and condition of coatings much more difficult, and makes draining of ballast from the tank a slower and more inefficient process. These are all good reasons for removing mud from ballast tanks and for preventing the build-up of mud as far as possible.

Entering ballast tanks: Entering any enclosed space can be dangerous and the procedures recommended by the International Maritime Organization and contained within the Company's safety management system should be followed when entering a ballast tank. (This matter is discussed in greater detail in Chapter 21.)

Immediately after a tank has been deballasted it is reasonable to expect the air within the tank to be as healthy as the air on deck, since all the air in the tank will have been drawn from on deck whilst the tank was being deballasted but the Permit to Enter procedures for entry into enclosed spaces must always be followed.

Removal of mud by shovel and bucket: There are several methods of removing mud. The most labour-intensive option is to remove mud by bucket and shovel. This is only a practical option when plenty of time and large quantities of cheap labour are available, as might be the situation in drydock or in layup. It may be worthwhile to remove mud from positions close to the ballast suction by shovel and bucket, but other methods will normally be found less expensive for a ship which is in service.

Hosing of topside and forepeak tanks: In compartments in which it is comparatively easy to move about, such as forepeak and topside tanks, the mud can be hosed towards the ballast suction and pumped out. Since these tanks can normally be entered at any time except when water is being shipped on deck this work can be undertaken at almost any time that the tanks are empty and the discharge of ballast is permitted. However, the hosing of mud from topside and forepeak tanks remains a slow and labour-intensive job because of the time required to wash all the mud to the vicinity of the suction, and the possibility of problems in keeping the pump running when the supply of water to the suction is small and uncertain.

Hosing of double-bottom tanks: The limited height and confined space within the double-bottom tanks of all but the largest ships make the hosing out of mud from these spaces, using a washdeck hose, not normally a practical proposition. However, the hosing out of the double-bottom tanks of a Panamax bulker was undertaken in drydock to remove 600 tonnes of mud. In this instance a number of holes were cut in the ship's bottom so that the mud could be hosed into the dock bottom, thereby reducing the distance the mud had to be hosed through the tanks and avoiding shipboard pumping problems.

Since double-bottom tanks of handy-sized and mini-bulkers are normally entered from the holds, it is only possible to enter these tanks when some at least of the holds are empty. This will occur in port, at anchor, during ballast passages or whilst part cargoes are being carried. The double-bottom tanks of Panamax and Cape-sized bulkers can normally be entered from the stool spaces. On some ships this allows access to the double-bottoms at any time that the tanks are empty.

High-pressure hosing of double-bottom tanks: The hosing out of a very cramped double-bottom tank in a mini-bulker has been achieved using a portable high-pressure washing machine, connected to a long lightweight hose no larger or heavier than the cable used with oxy-acetylene welding equipment. The work was illuminated by a gastight torch lashed to the probe of the high pressure hose. Washing was commenced at the after end of the tank, nearest to the suction, so that drain holes were cleared, permitting the liquid mud created by the washing to flow aft to the ballast suction. It was found that the water jet sliced up the 8 cm thick, claylike mud very effectively, and reduced it to a runny porridge in about 6 mins/sq. metre. This work is physically demanding and suitable only for active persons.

Use of sediment remover: Sediment removers are liquid compounds which hold mud in suspension, preventing it from settling on the tank surfaces and permitting it to be discharged with the ballast in which it was loaded. They remain efficient indefinitely. Since any chemical additive is expensive it is important to obtain the best value for money spent. To ensure that best value is obtained there are a number of practical considerations to take into account.

The most beneficial time to use a sediment remover is when the following conditions can be met:

- A double bottom ballast tank is heavily coated with mud.
- The passage can be made with the ballast tank 20 per cent full.
- A swell is anticipated, to make the ship pitch and roll.
- The ship can be brought to even keel.
- The tank can be emptied after a period of rough weather.

It is seldom that a passage can be undertaken with a part-filled double-bottom ballast tank, since longitudinal stresses or loaded draught often prevent it. Nevertheless opportunities do arise – for example, when the ship is carrying a full low density cargo such as grain, fertiliser, coke or coal, and is not loaded to her marks, or when she is loaded to winter marks, but passing through a summer or tropical zone. In addition, stress calculations may show that certain double-bottom tanks can be left empty, or part filled during a ballast voyage.

One reason for wanting the tank only 20 per cent full is that this will permit the maximum agitation of the water over the deposited mud as the ship pitches and rolls, thereby taking the greatest quantity of mud into suspension. In addition, the quantity of sediment remover to be used depends upon the quantity of ballast in the tank. A tank which is only 20 per cent full can be treated more efficiently, and much more cheaply, than a full tank. A tank which is half full is more liable to suffer damage from sloshing.

The scouring effect of the water in the tank, induced by the ship's motion, will be most effective when the water is surging in the same direction as the framing in the tank. Where longitudinal framing is fitted, a pitching motion will be more effective in raising the sediment than will rolling.

For best results it is important that the ship be exactly even keel when under way after the tank has been filled to the required level. It must be remembered that bulk carriers usually trim by the head when under way and allowance should be made for this. If the ship is not even keel whilst the sediment removal is taking place, it will be found that one end of the tank will be cleaned whilst the other end, which the water has hardly reached, remains thick with mud.

Every effort should be made to ensure that the sediment remover is thoroughly mixed with the ballast water in the tank. This is normally achieved by pouring it little by little into the tank by way of a sounding or air pipe adjacent to the ballast suction whilst the tank is filling.

Inspection of the tank before and after treatment is strongly recommended, to assess the results achieved and to gather information on how the process can be improved. The manufacturers of one product in this field, Rochem sediment remover, state that their product is polymer based, contains no acid, alkali or solvent, is completely biodegradable and has no flashpoint.

Removal of scale from ballast tanks: If the coatings in ballast tanks are allowed to deteriorate, either generally as a result of old age or locally as a consequence of mechanical damage, loose scale will be deposited and will tend to accumulate around drainage holes and near the ballast suction. Deterioration of tank coatings is aggravated by mechanical damage. The tanks which are most at risk depend upon the size of ship and the trades in which she is engaged. The topside tanks of mini-bulkers generally suffer most from grab damage and contact damage whilst berthing, whilst Cape-sized vessels sustain most of their damage in the tanktop which tops the double-bottoms. The loose scale will tend to reduce or prevent the flow of water to the ballast suction and should be removed. The only practical way of removing loose scale is with shovel and bucket, to be passed to the deck when filled. Provided that this process is done regularly the quantities to be removed will not be too great.

Patching of leaks in ballast tanks: It is quite common for small leaks to develop in the steel plating which forms the boundary between the holds and the topside tanks. In smaller bulk carriers such leaks are often the result of berthing impact on the vessel's port shoulder because such vessels normally berth port side-to. They occur primarily in the vicinity of the forward hold and appear to result from the transmission of the impact load through the transverse internal members of the topside tank.

Whatever their cause, small leaks in topside tanks interfere with the efficient operation of the vessel. If the leaking tank is filled a spray of water spurts into the hold which will not be dry when presented for loading. The leak may be sufficient to induce gradually a list into the vessel over a period of one or two days, which is inconvenient. Alternatively, if the affected pair of topside tanks are left empty, the forward draught may be unacceptably small, requiring the ship to slow down or causing her to pound. In larger vessels the longitudinal stresses may be excessive, making it unsafe to leave the tank unballasted.

The appropriate response to leaks of this sort is a professional repair undertaken by a qualified welder, but readers may be interested in the details of a method of quick temporary repair for small cracks and pinhole leaks. The method involves the use of patches of heated Ram-nek high adhesive plastic tape. The equipment required is a scraper, a blowtorch, a length of Ram-nek tape and shears or a knife to cut the tape.

The tank must be safe to enter, the required tests for oxygen and hydrocarbons having been completed. Within the tank the surroundings of the leak are scraped clear of loose paint and scale and a Ram-nek patch, measuring about 15 x 15 cm, is centred over it, perhaps being held in position with the scraper. A second Ram-nek patch, similar in dimensions to the first, is placed conveniently to hand. The patch which has been placed over the leak is heated to a molten, bubbling state with the blow torch and the second patch is then pressed firmly into place over the first. Provided that this is done quickly the patch can be pressed into place before the heat passes through it, making it too hot to touch with comfort. This forms a robust, flexible patch which seals the leak until a permanent repair can be made and which, unlike a poor run of weld, will not fracture again. Proper full repairs should, of course, be undertaken as soon as possible.

Maintenance of coatings: In most bulk carriers all the steelwork within the ballast tanks will have been coated when the ship was built and the coatings should be maintained in good condition throughout the life of the ship, to prevent excessive corrosion of the steelwork forming the tanks. It is now a SOLAS requirement[182] that the coatings in all dedicated seawater ballast tanks and double side skin spaces in bulk carriers built since 1 July 1998 are maintained in accordance with an approved ship maintenance system. Ships' personnel cannot hope to renew the coatings of ballast tanks without very specific support and assistance in the form of labour and materials from the ship operators since the job is a big one.

However, coatings within ballast tanks will deteriorate as a result of local mechanical damage caused by contacts with fenders, jetties and tugs, and damage caused by cargo, grabs and mechanical shovels. Damage of this sort can be made good without great effort and any opportunity should be taken to clean, prime and repaint any damaged areas, using the same paint system as was used previously.

As an example of what can be achieved by a well organised ship's crew, the case of a 16-month-old Cape-sized (115,000 tonnes dwt) bulker on a laden passage from Hampton Roads to Pohang, Korea, can be quoted. The vessel had sustained approximately 15 per cent breakdown of tank coatings, mainly below the double-bottom tanktop and lower hopper sides. All mechanical damage in all double-bottom and topside tanks was scraped clear of rust and flaking paint, wiped clean, coated with rust inhibitor, primed and painted with a recommended tank coating. The entire operation took 39 days and involved six men working eight hours/day, a total of 1,872 man/hours.

Inspections of ballast tanks: All of a ship's ballast tanks should be inspected regularly, say, twice yearly, or as required by the owners' management system, by competent ship's personnel, mindful of all the points which have been mentioned in this chapter. Matters to be noted and recorded are the condition of internal fittings such as ballast suctions, sounding pipes, airpipes and other pipework passing through the tank, quantities and locations of scale and sediment, condition of tank coatings and percentage break-down of coating, and details of any structural damage observed. The findings of ballast tank inspections should be recorded, and copies should be sent to the shipowners or managers. When ballast tank inspections are required as part of the Enhanced Survey Programme they are best done in conjunction with hold cleaning, at times when crew members are available to open and close manhole doors. The manhole recesses can be washed out at the same time.

Closing of ballast tanks: On completion of work in, or inspection of, ballast tanks care must be taken to ensure that they are properly closed with watertight seals to ensure that water cannot subsequently leak out of, or into, the tank. Correct sealing of manhole covers will be achieved by the use of a gasket which is in good condition and by ensuring that the gasket and the steel surfaces of manhole and manhole lid are absolutely clean, smooth and free of particles of scale or cargo. Once closed and sealed, the watertightness of the ballast tank should be tested by filling it and inspecting the closed manholes for signs of leakage. (This procedure is described in greater detail in Chapter 5.)

Sources

7, 12, 13, 14, 20, 108, 109, 110, 170, 181, 182. (See List of Sources, Page 497)

CHECKLIST – Reminders regarding ballast operations

- ☐ Comply with the requirements of the '97 Guidelines[108] and the International Convention[109].
- ☐ Calculate longitudinal stresses and do not exceed limits.
- ☐ Plan every stage of discharge/ballast or load/deballast programme before operations commence.
- ☐ Choose light or heavy-weather ballast, according to conditions.
- ☐ Increase or reduce ballast if weather conditions change.
- ☐ Maintain sufficient draught forward, at sea.
- ☐ Calculate stability and ensure it is always sufficient.
- ☐ Avoid part-filled ballast holds and topside tanks.
- ☐ Observe restrictions on filling/emptying ballast tanks/holds at sea.
- ☐ Do not overpressurise tanks. Ensure airpipes and P/V valves are not blocked. Do not use two pumps on one small tank.
- ☐ Close coaming drains and CO_2 inlets into ballast holds.
- ☐ Do not underpressurise tanks. Ensure airpipes and P/V valves are open when deballasting.
- ☐ Keep strictly to programme for discharge/ballast and load/deballast.
- ☐ Inspect holds, decks and overside for possibility of ballast overflow damage before commencement of ballasting, or dumping topside tanks.
- ☐ Reduce pumping rate, and then stop filling of ballast tanks before they can overflow.
- ☐ Lower/close airpipe cowls, if design requires it, when tanks are full.
- ☐ Check ballast soundings daily during voyage to detect problems.
- ☐ Change ballast at sea as required by destination port, or for a freezing destination.
- ☐ Where necessary empty and clean ballast hold at sea and then refill, when a particularly clean hold will be required for the next cargo.
- ☐ When changing ballast at sea comply with the Ballast Water Management Plan. Do not exceed longitudinal stress limits, and empty port and starboard tanks together, to avoid twisting the ship.
- ☐ Obtain written permission to deballast when written permission is required.
- ☐ Raise/open airpipe cowls, if design requires it, before emptying tanks.
- ☐ Commence deballasting before arrival in loading berth only if circumstances are favourable.
- ☐ Always maintain a good trim by the stern to help drain tanks while deballasting.
- ☐ Immediately on completion of deballasting the topside tanks ensure all dump valves are shut before draught is too deep and tanks start to flood. Log the closing of the dump valves.
- ☐ When dump valves are shut keep them lashed. When open leave them unlashed.
- ☐ Keep detailed and accurate records of all ballasting/deballasting and work done in tanks.
- ☐ Take safety precautions when entering ballast tanks.
- ☐ Maintain ballast tanks in good condition by preventing and removing sediment and scale, touching up paintwork in way of damage, and patching/repairing leaks.
- ☐ Inspect tanks twice yearly, and record conditions found.
- ☐ Close tanks properly and verify that doors are watertight.

CHAPTER 8

STRENGTH, STABILITY, DRAUGHT AND TRIM

Seakeeping strength, tanktop, upper deck and hatch cover loading, block loading, position of cargo in hold, alternate hold loading, shear forces and bending moments, ship movement in a seaway, springing, hull stress monitoring, stability, free surface effect, angle of loll, flooding, sloshing, hogging and sagging, squat, effects of list and heel, change of trim due to change of density

THIS CHAPTER contains reminders of the strength, stability, draught and trim considerations which must be taken into account when operating a bulk carrier if damage is to be avoided and operations are to be efficient. It is not intended as a primer in ship construction and stability, subjects which can only be adequately studied from books devoted to the subject. Such books are available and some are listed among the sources at the end of this chapter. Possible causes of bulker casualties are discussed in Chapter 26.

Seakeeping Strength

Studies reported in 2001[113] following the conclusion of the *'Derbyshire'* enquiry identified various weaknesses in some bulk carriers in service at that time. Cape-sized bulk carriers when built to the minimum (International Convention on Load Lines ICLL 66) strength standard and loaded to the B-60 freeboard are likely to suffer collapse of No.1 hatch cover when meeting wave heights of more than 10 metres. It has been suggested that casualties are not more frequent because it is rare for a Cape-sized bulker built to minimum strength standard and fully laden to meet extreme sea states.

The model tests also established that horizontal wave impacts on the forward face of the No.1 hatch coaming in severe conditions can be much greater than those for which ships were designed.

These findings have let the International Maritime Organization (IMO) to consider a number of amendments, such as increased design loads and mandatory fitting of forecastles on new bulk carriers, to the 1966 ICLL as well as the 1988 Protocol to the ICLL.

Tanktop loading

Maximum permissible tanktop loadings are normally shown in the ship's capacity plan and loading manual and must, of course, always be consulted and complied with. These values are calculated on the assumption that the loading is uniform, but this may not be stated. They are valid for cargoes heaped in bulk but not for commodities such as steel coils. The tonnage of steel which can be carried depends upon detailed calculations which take account of the spacing of the ship's double bottom floors and girders, the quantity and the positioning of the dunnage, the weight of each item of cargo and the size of the cargo's footprint. In a ship not provided with a Class approved loading plan for a steel cargo Class should be consulted. The ship must also be provided with an approved Cargo Securing Manual covering the intended cargoes. The carriage of steel is discussed in Chapter 19.

Upper deck and hatch cover loading

The maximum permissible loadings quoted in the ship's capacity plan and loading manual must not be exceeded when carrying cargo on deck or on the hatch covers. If the maximum permissible loadings are expressed in tonnes/metre^2 the loading must be uniform, meaning that the maximum permissible loading must not be exceeded at any point of the deck or hatch cover. It sometimes happens that the ship's loading instrument provides no way of calculating the effect on stability of cargo carried on deck. When this is the case the calculations shown in the ship's stability booklet must be completed to ensure that the ship will have sufficient positive stability and that any trim or list will be acceptable.

Block loading

A block loading condition is a loading in which two or more adjoining holds contain cargo (ie they form a 'block' of loaded holds) but the holds next to the block are empty.[111] (Fig. 8.1) The condition is likely to be proposed when the ship is part loaded or is carrying several different commodities or grades of cargo. The danger associated with block loading is that when high density cargoes are carried excessive local stresses can be imposed on the ship's hull even when the shear forces and bending moments are

Fig 8.1 Block Loading

Figure courtesy of IACS

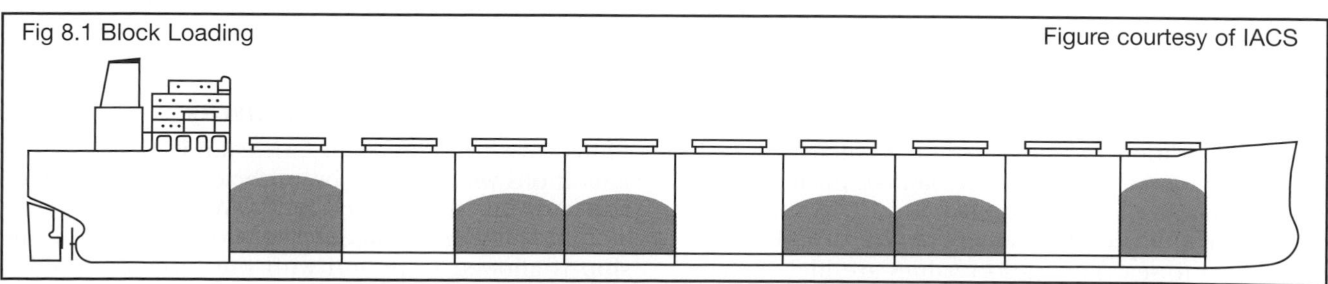

within permitted limits. Block loading should be adopted only when the ship's loading manual contains suitable conditions of loading or when the ship has been provided with a set of approved local loading criteria which define the maximum cargo tonnage with reference to ship's mean draught for each cargo hold and block of cargo holds, allowing calculation of the tonnage which can safely be loaded in each hold. In other circumstances the classification society should be asked to advise. (See also Chapter 9 and Appendix 9.4.)

The position of the cargo within the hold

The double bottom and cross deck structures of bulk carriers are designed on the assumptions that the cargo in the hold will be trimmed and distributed symmetrically in the hold space[111]. Cargo which is badly positioned within the hold will cause increased local stresses. If the cargo is poured too much towards one end of the hold the stresses in the nearer bulkhead and crossdeck structure will be increased. If poured too much to one side of the hold, with a matching tonnage poured to the other side in another hold, torsional loads causing twisting of the hull girder will be caused.

Alternate hold loading

Many bulk carriers of handy-size and larger are strengthened and classified for the carriage of heavy cargoes in alternate holds and there are commercial benefits to be obtained from this system In recent years, however, it has been recognised that the higher stresses which alternate hold ('jump') loading imposes on the ship's structure have been linked with a number of casualties. The majority of ship operators now voluntarily avoid using alternate hold loading for high density cargoes and for older ships of 150 m and upwards in length alternate hold loading is forbidden[167] unless certain conditions are met.

Shear forces and bending moments

All bulk carriers which are Panamax sized or larger, and all which are strengthened for loading in alternative holds, are provided by their classification societies with maximum allowable still water values for shear forces and bending moments. These values are stated in the ship's loading guidance and stability information booklet and are included in the programme of the ship's loading instrument, if she has one. These values, which are provided to ensure that the ship is not damaged by incorrect loading, must be calculated for every stage of loading and discharge programmes and for the complete sea passage. They must never be exceeded.

Normally two or three sets of maximum values will be stated. The 'in-port' or 'harbour' values for shear forces and bending moments are the maxima to which a vessel can be subjected whilst in the 'still' (ie sheltered) waters of a port, where she is not exposed to swell conditions. It is permissible to incur a higher level of stress, (up to the in-port limits), during stages in the loading or discharging provided that the stresses are reduced to lower at-sea levels before the vessel puts to sea. The in-port values are higher than the at-sea values because the latter take account of the additional stresses to which a ship is subjected when moving in a seaway.

A ship which is strengthened for heavy cargoes may be provided with two sets of maximum allowable values for bending moments in at-sea conditions, with one set being for 'Alternate Hold Loading Condition', and the second set for the 'Ballast or Uniform Hold Loading Condition'. The lowest bending moment values are allowed when alternate holds are loaded, since this is the condition in which the greatest stresses are created.

The shear forces and bending moments must be calculated before commencement of any of the following processes:

1. Planned loading and deballasting sequence.
2. Planned discharging and ballasting sequence.
3. Any change of ballast.
4. Any change in loading or discharging sequence.
5. Any instance when deballasting is delayed and becomes out of sequence with loading.
6. Any instance when ballasting is delayed and becomes out of sequence with discharging.
7. Taking of bunkers, step by step (ie, tank by tank).
8. Consumption of bunkers, step by step (ie, tank by tank).
9. Dry docking.

If the allowable values are exceeded there is danger that the ship's structure will be permanently damaged – it is even possible for the ship to break into two. The importance of completing the calculations and ensuring that the stresses are not exceeded cannot be stated too strongly. The most likely reasons for failure to comply with this requirement are the underlisted; they must be avoided.

- Failure to understand the calculations.
- Data provided in language which is not understood.
- Computer breakdown.
- Inability to make the manual calculations when the computer has broken down.
- Stability data unreadable.
- Change in loading/discharging programme.
- Failure to follow loading/discharging programme.
- Pressure of work.
- Negligent practices.
- Commercial pressure.
- Routine procedure undertaken without planning.

Small vessels up to and including handy size may be provided with no maximum allowable values or programmes for calculating shear forces and bending moments. This is because the short length and comparatively greater scantlings of a small vessel make it impossible to expose her to excessive values of shear force and bending moment unless she is jump loaded (loaded in alternate holds).

Ship movement in a seaway

Ships are designed to withstand the weather conditions which are to be expected at sea, provided that they are handled correctly. When heading into adverse weather damage is likely to be suffered if the ship is allowed to pound with the forefoot crashing down upon the sea surface, or to slam with the bows plunging into the swell. Shipping green seas over the bows in adverse weather should be avoided. It is likely to cause damage to deck fittings and hatch coamings and covers as a consequence of the weight of the water shipped and the violence of its impact, particularly in ships without raised forecastles. It is for this reason that all new bulk carriers over 150 m in length are, from 1st January 2004, required to be fitted with a forecastle.

A ship beam-on to a steep swell may roll very heavily. Such an attitude may occur as a result of the course being steered or as a result of an engine failure. In addition a ship which has had the weather astern may be caught in the trough of the swell if an attempt is made to turn into the wind in order to heave-to. Such heavy rolling may lead directly to damage to a vessel's hull and superstructure, and may cause the shifting of cargo which can also damage the ship or reduce her positive stability.

One result of rolling is that the side shell plating is repeatedly plunged into the sea and then removed. This results in repeated variations in the water pressure applied to the side shell. This panting effect may have a long-term weakening effect on the side shell plating, and the structure to which it is attached. The conduct of ships in heavy weather is described in Chapters 15 (loaded vessels) and 17 (vessels in ballast).

Springing

Seafarers report[21] having occasionally experienced abnormal 'springing' of the hull of their ships. This effect has also been named 'flexing', 'whipping' and 'wave excited hull vibration'. It may be visible as a succession of waves, flowing along the steelwork of the main deck of the vessel, associated with heavy vibration, or shuddering, of the structure of the ship. This phenomenon is sometimes the result of propeller damage or the isolating of one main engine unit.

Alternatively, it may be a dynamic response induced by waves or swell when the ship is loaded in a particular way. In this case it is usually possible to stop the flexing by an alteration of course. When course cannot be altered, a change of speed or a ballast change may stop the motion. Such violent working of the ship's hull is likely to damage it and every effort should be made to avoid it.

Hull stress monitoring

Since the early 1990s a few large bulk carriers have been equipped with hull stress monitoring systems, which measure longitudinal and slamming stresses.

Longitudinal bending stresses are measured by long base strain gauges situated at several selected points along the deck. This process is continuous at sea and in port, permitting stresses due to cargo operations and ballasting as well as the ship's movement in the seaway to be monitored.

Slamming stresses are measured by accelerometers usually placed so as to measure vertical accelerations in the fore part of the ship. High-pressure transducers, which detect the very high pressures experienced with slamming, are placed in positions near to the accelerometers.

The output from each of these instruments is relayed to a computer, usually placed on the bridge, where it provides the Master and watch officer with a visual indication of the stresses induced in the hull. If required, the data can be retained on a hard copy print-out or disc. Some ships also have audible aids and visual alarm settings which allow the Master to preset an alarm limit to give early warning of adverse weather and conditions. These aids remove the need for the officer to worry about when to call the Master and allow for an early alteration of course or speed to reduce weather stress conditions.

The highest levels of stress detected by hull stress monitoring of bulk carriers in service has occurred when they are engaged in mid ocean ballast changing using the sequential method[112].

Stability

A stable ship is one which will return to the initial position when inclined by an external force. An unstable ship is one which tends to heel still further when inclined to a small angle. One of the objectives of the ship's Master and officers is to ensure that their ship remains stable throughout her life and cannot capsize.

An approximate indication of the ship's stability can be obtained from the metacentric height (the GM), which can be readily calculated provided that the positions of all weights in the ship are known with reasonable accuracy. The GM must be corrected for free surface effect, described below, to obtain the fluid GM.

When the fluid GM is large the ship will be very stable, or 'stiff'. A stiff ship is uncomfortable in a seaway. She rolls violently and rapidly. Unfortunately, this condition is common aboard bulk carriers when they carry high density cargoes such as heavy ores and steel. A ship with a small fluid GM is less stable. She can be inclined more easily, and will roll more slowly. This condition, known as 'tender', is common when low density cargoes such as coal, coke and grain are carried.

The ideal stability condition for a ship lies somewhere between stiff and tender. Aboard a bulk carrier the ship's stiffness will be governed primarily by the design of the ship and the nature of the cargo carried. A ship is prohibited from undertaking a voyage in too tender a condition – she must satisfy the minimum stability criteria at all stages in the voyage – but there are no rules which forbid a ship from sailing in a very stiff condition, and bulkers are often required to do so.

Before a ship is permitted to go to sea she must comply with the requirements of the International Loadline Convention which call, amongst other things, for a more extensive assessment of her stability than is provided by the calculation of fluid GM alone. The ship's loading guidance and stability manual will provide details of the calculations required, which are also fully discussed in Chapter 10. The stability manual also states the minimum permitted values for areas under the statical stability curve for the righting lever and for the fluid GM.

The rules which require the calculation of a vessel's stability before she puts to sea are intended to ensure

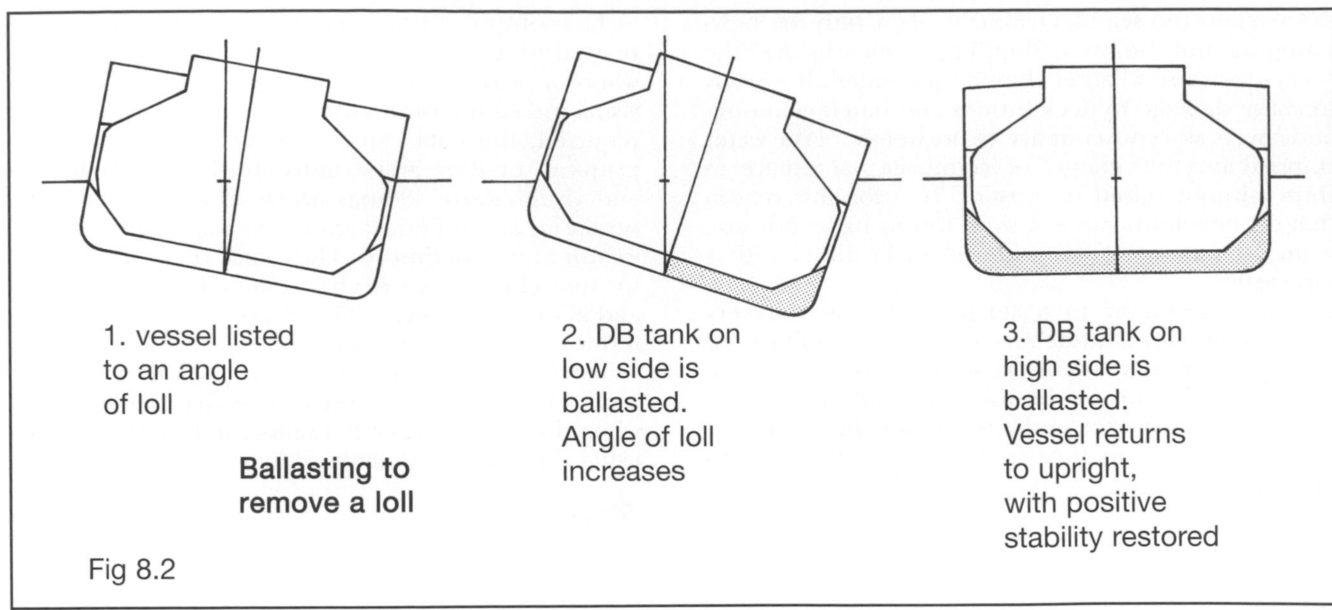

1. vessel listed to an angle of loll
2. DB tank on low side is ballasted. Angle of loll increases
3. DB tank on high side is ballasted. Vessel returns to upright, with positive stability restored
Ballasting to remove a loll

Fig 8.2

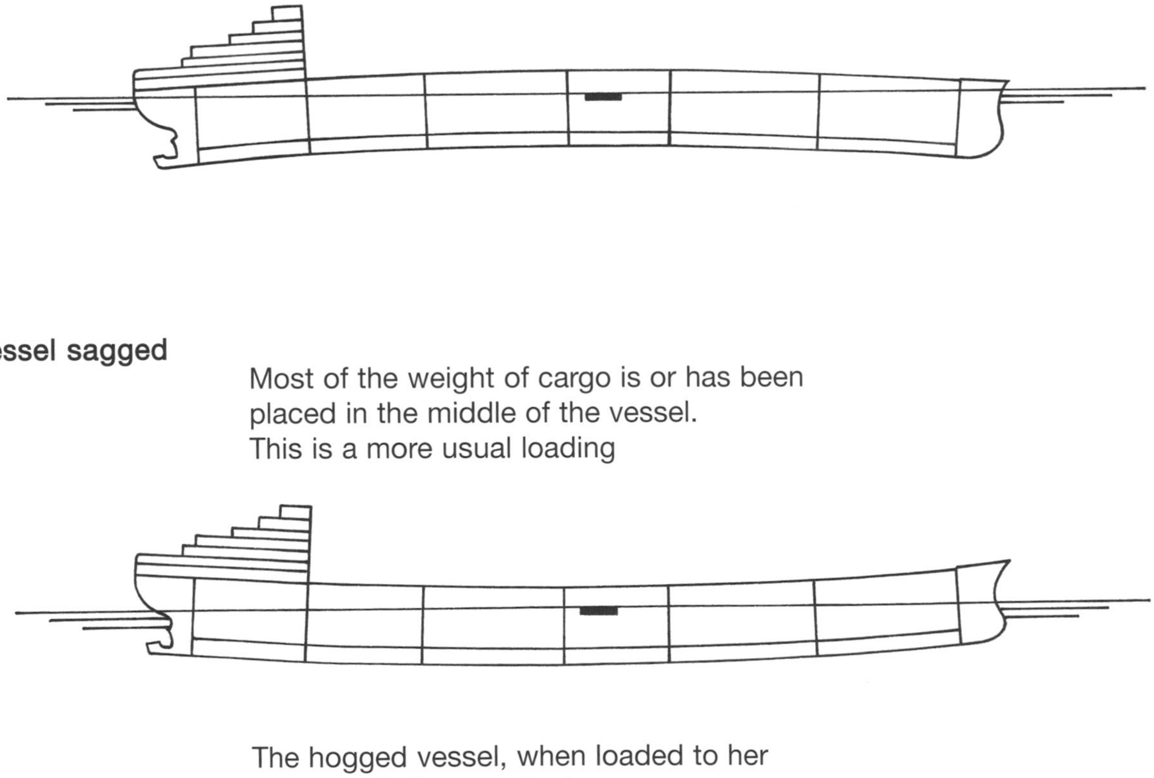

Vessel hogged
Most of the weight of cargo is, or has been, placed at the ends of the vessel
Vessel sagged
Most of the weight of cargo is or has been placed in the middle of the vessel. This is a more usual loading
The hogged vessel, when loaded to her marks, will lift a greater tonnage because she displaces more water at the forward and after ends

Fig 8.3

that no ship will go to sea in an unstable condition and subsequently capsize. They are in the best interests of every seafarer and must be followed with care.

If the calculations show that the ship has, or at some point in the intended voyage will have, insufficient stability, adjustments must be made. It may be possible to increase the positive stability by repositioning weight lower in the ship, by the addition of weight such as bunkers or ballast low in the ship, or by the removal of weight from high in the ship. Another option is the rearrangement of the contents of bunker and ballast tanks to reduce free surface effect. If all else fails it will be necessary to reduce the amount of cargo which can be accepted. (Planning of the loading is discussed in greater detail in Chapter 9.)

Free surface effect

When a tank in a ship is part filled with a liquid – normally ballast water, fresh water, fuel oil, diesel oil or lubricating oil – the liquid within the tank is able to 'slosh about' as the ship moves. This reduces the ship's positive stability by an amount which depends upon the dimensions of the tank, the density of the liquid and the displacement of the ship. Free surface effect must never be neglected; it can transform a stable ship into one which will capsize.

In many tanks the surface area of the liquid changes with the quantity of liquid in the tank. As a consequence the value of the free surface effect also changes. Some stability tables quote only the maximum value of free surface moment for each tank. If this value is used, any error in the result will be a safe one. The ship will be as stable as the calculations show or she will be more stable than they show.

When making any stability calculations it must be assumed that any tank which is not full, or which is to be used later, has free surface effect. There may be times when free surface occurs, or is proposed, in a cargo hold as a result of hold washing or flooding. Loading manuals usually provide no method of calculating the effect of such free surface.

When considering sea water in a hold the free surface moments (FSM) can be calculated from the formula:

FSM = $1.025 \times LB^3/12$ tonnes-metres, where
L = length of compartment, measured fore and aft, in metres and
B = breadth of compartment, measured athwartships, in metres.

The virtual rise of centre of gravity, in metres (G_1G_0) = FSM/Displacement(tonnes).

A worked example of this calculation is provided in Appendix 8.1.

Angle of loll

Ships which become slightly unstable will list to an angle of loll. This condition can often be recognised by the fact that the ship will 'flop over', which is to say that she will list quite noticeably first to one side and then to the other depending on such factors as the direction from which the wind is blowing, and the way the vessel heeled when the last alteration of course was made. If derricks or cranes are topped up when a ship is resting at an angle of loll that angle will increase.

A loll has in the past often been associated with ships carrying lumber or woodpulp on deck. If the stability calculations have been inaccurate it is possible for such ships to complete their voyage with no positive stability and to commence to loll as more bunkers are consumed and negative stability develops. However, there are often other possible explanations for any list which such a ship develops towards the end of the voyage. The list may be due to the quantity of water which has been absorbed by the deck cargo on one side of the ship, perhaps because that was the weather side for most of the passage. Alternatively, the list may simply be due to an imbalance between the weights of bunkers and cargo to port and starboard of the centre line. In these cases, of course, the ship will remain listed to one side and will not flop from side to side.

The occurrence of loll must always be taken very seriously, since it shows that the ship has become unstable, and the reason for it must be sought with care. On one notorious occasion the Master and crew of a dry-cargo vessel which developed a large list were so convinced that the list was caused by the large tonnage of cargo on deck that they completely overlooked 400 tonnes of water which had flooded one of their holds!

If a ship is found to be at an angle of loll the following steps should be taken to improve her stability.

- Slack tanks should be filled where possible to eliminate free surface effect.
- Weights should be lowered in the ship where possible, for example by transferring bunkers from deep tanks to double bottom tanks.
- If empty double-bottom (DB) tanks are available the stability can be improved by filling them with water ballast or with fuel oil, as appropriate and as available. When filling such tanks there are two important rules to remember: pairs of small DB tanks should be filled before pairs of large DB tanks; and in each case the tank on the low side must be filled before the tank on the high side.

For example, if the vessel has taken up an angle of loll to starboard (Fig. 8.2) the starboard double-bottom tank must be filled before the port one. This will initially result in a further increase in the list to starboard, but the increase will be gradual, and well controlled. Thereafter, when the opposite double-bottom tank is filling, the list will diminish and eventually disappear, provided that the filling of the first pair of double-bottom tanks is sufficient to eliminate the negative stability.

If these rules are ignored, and the double-bottom tank on the high side is mistakenly filled first the ship will, at some time during the process, roll over violently from her angle of loll to starboard to take up a similar angle of loll to port. The object of filling pairs of small tanks before pairs of large tanks is to ensure that the temporary increase in list is kept to a minimum.

Flooding

Accidental flooding of a compartment will almost invariably cause an unexpected list to develop.

Flooding is also often associated with sudden increases or reversals of list, and any of these effects should ring warning bells in the mind of the duty officer and prompt him to make an urgent search for an explanation.

When an empty compartment such as a cargo hold is flooded the free surface effect will be the maximum for that compartment. If the compartment contains cargo the free surface effect will be reduced until such time as the water surface rises above the level of the cargo.

Sea water which enters a hold may do so by a number of routes. Water may enter direct through holes in the ship's side or deck, it may pass through leaky hatch covers or through ventilators which are damaged or inadequately closed. Ballast water may leak from ballast tanks, and water may pass into the hold through eductor systems or bilge lines with faulty valves or as a result of faulty procedures.

The flooding of one hold of a bulk carrier which is loaded with a low density cargo such as coal is unlikely to cause such a vessel to capsize. Since the hold will be filled with the cargo the loss of buoyancy and the increase in free surface effect will not be excessive. If the bulker is loaded with a high density cargo, the level of flood water is more likely to rise above the surface of some or all of the cargo and the free surface effect will be larger. However, a ship carrying a high density cargo will have a much larger initial GM so this vessel, too, is unlikely to capsize as a result of the flooding of a single hold.

Sloshing

A bulk carrier which experiences flooding is more likely to suffer structural damage from sloshing than to capsize. Sloshing is the violent movement of liquid within a compartment as a result of the ship's motion in a seaway. If the natural frequency of sloshing approaches that of the ship's motion frequency then resonance will occur, large wave amplitudes and pressures will be set up in the tank, and damage can occur[7]. If a ship suffers flooding there is a danger that sloshing of the flood water will cause the collapse of watertight bulkheads, permitting the flooding to spread to adjacent holds.

Sloshing effects are likely to be most violent when a compartment is half full; a compartment which is almost full or almost empty is less at risk. This is recognised in the restriction sometimes imposed by classification societies upon the filling of ballast holds. Such a restriction is likely to be that the ship must not operate with the ballast hold filled to a level which lies within the 20-90 per cent range of full capacity.

Sloshing within ballast tanks is likely to be less of a problem than sloshing within holds, as the internal structure of the ballast tanks has a substantial damping effect. Nevertheless, partly filled ballast tanks, particularly large ones, should be avoided as far as possible in rough weather, unless a 'sloshing investigation' has been carried out by a classification society, and its approval has been given.

Hogging and sagging

A ship will experience hogging stresses when weight is concentrated at her forward and after ends. On a ship which is hogged the mean of the forward and after draughts will be greater than the mean draught amidships. (Fig. 8.3) When the weight carried by a ship is concentrated amidships that ship will experience sagging stresses. The mean midships draught will be greater than the mean of the forward and after draughts when a ship is sagged.

Any ship which loads to her marks must load to the midships draught specified in her international loadline certificate. If such a vessel is hogged her forward and after draughts will be deeper than will the draughts of the same vessel, if sagged. Thus a vessel when hogged can legally lift a greater deadweight than the same vessel if sagged. This fact has been known for very many years and is said to have caused Masters in the past to 'bend' their ships with successive cargoes to make them permanently hogged, and thereby to increase the tonnage of cargo they could carry. This can never have been a prudent action to take, but may have been tolerable when ships were smaller and ships' structures were built with larger safety margins than is the case today.

Nowadays, with the assistance of calculations to find the values of shear force and bending moment, it will be found that when stress values are minimised the vessel will be sagged. This is the natural consequence of the fact that the cargo spaces are located along the middle body of the ship; cargo cannot be loaded in the machinery and storage spaces which occupy the bows and stern. The result of this is that a vessel which is loaded to minimise stresses will fail to lift the 'full' deadweight cargo which corresponds to a level trim, and which the charterer expects.

If an attempt is made to improve the tonnage of cargo lifted by introducing a hog, or even by eliminating the sag, it will be found that stresses increase, with highest values of shear stresses occurring immediately forward of the bridge and at the forepeak bulkhead. Provided that the shear forces remain within the maximum allowable limits this condition is not forbidden, but ship operators must consider whether it is advisable to load a ship, time after time, to stress values which are higher than normal and close to the maximum permitted, as is the case when bulkers are loaded in alternate holds.

Squat

When a ship is under way she pushes her way through the water. The water which is pushed away will travel down the sides and under the keel of the ship. This moving water causes a drop in pressure beneath the hull and the ship is drawn vertically down in the water. The ship will also trim until equilibrium is obtained. Squat is the mean increase in draught – ie, the sinkage – plus any contribution due to trim, and is usually measured forward or aft, whichever is greater[8].

Bulk carriers are full bodied ships with block coefficients of 0.8 upwards. Ships with a block coefficient greater than 0.7 can be expected to trim by the head as a consequence of squat. Thus a bulk carrier which is trimmed to even keel on completion of loading will trim a little by the head when under way. Similarly the stern trim of a vessel trimmed by the stern when at rest will be reduced by squat when she is under way.

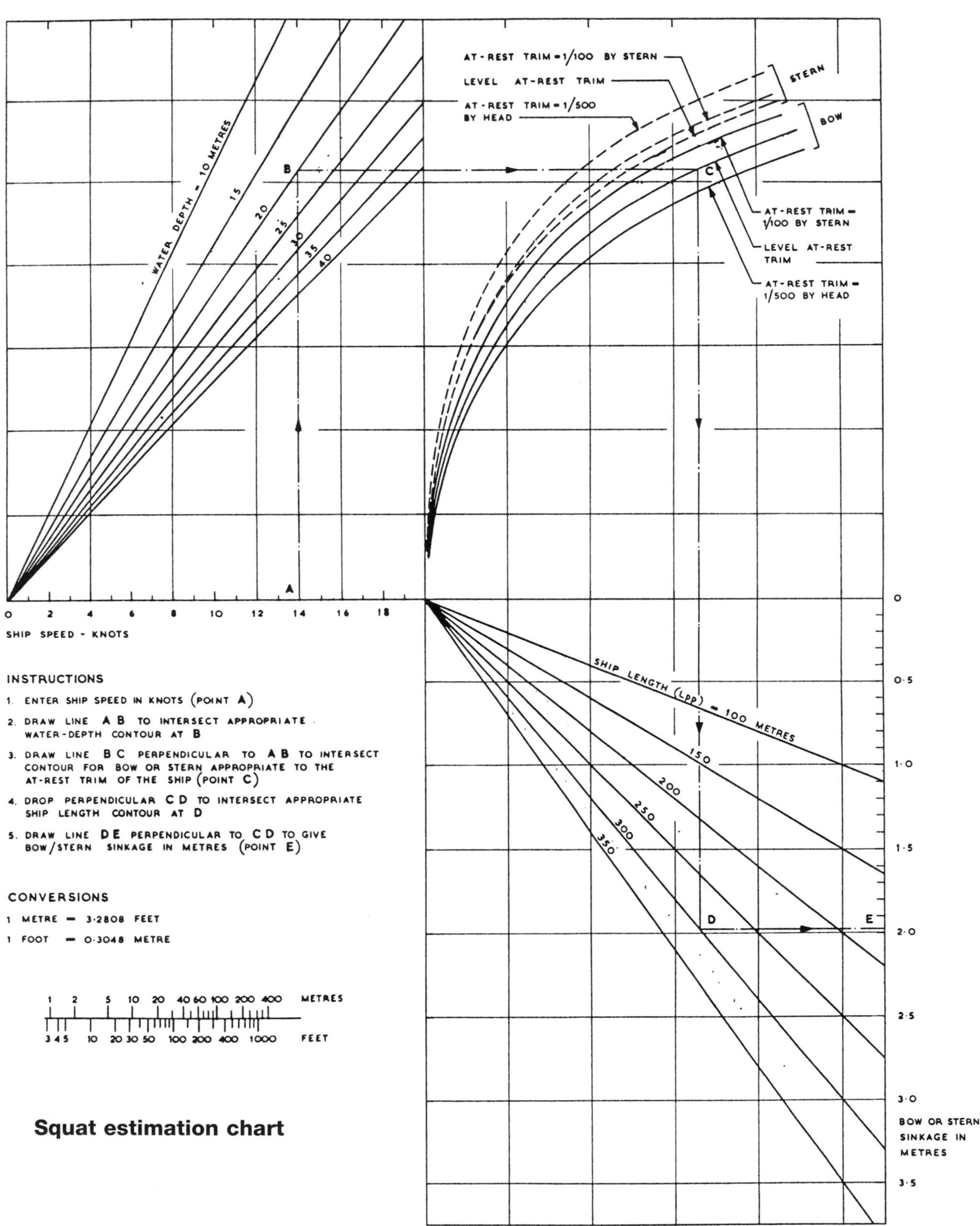

Squat estimation chart

Fig 8.4 *(Courtesy Dr Ian Dand)*

The amount of squat experienced increases considerably in shallow water and also where the width of water available is limited. Since bulk carriers are often required to visit ports where underkeel clearances are small, a good knowledge of the values of squat to be expected is essential.

Squat in narrow and shallow waters is greatest at high speed and is zero when the ship is at rest in the water. Squat varies approximately as the square of the vessel's speed through the water, so the value of squat can be quickly reduced by reducing speed, when required to avoid grounding.

When water depth is restricted approximate values for squat for bulk carriers can be obtained from the NMI Squat Chart (Fig. 8.4). Typical values for standard bulk carriers trimmed to even keel when stationary are quoted hereunder. These assume a depth of water equal to draught +10 per cent, and a speed made good of 10 knots, both of which are extreme conditions for normal operations in shallow water. The actual values of squat which occur during normal operations in port will usually be less, because the ship's speed will be less and/or the depth of water below the keel will be greater.

Class of Bulker	Length BP (m)	Draught (m)	Water Depth (m)	Squat (m) Aft	For'd
Mini	99	6.8	7.5	0.7	1.0
Handy-sized	183	10.2	11.2	0.8	1.1
Panamax	224	14.0	15.5	0.6	0.8
Cape-sized	292	17.3	19.0	0.6	0.8
VLBC	315	20.0	22.0	0.5	0.8

Effect of list or heel upon draught

When a vessel is listed by an uneven distribution of weights or when she is heeled by an external force, her draught will be increased beneath the low side of the deck. A useful approximation of the increase in draught can be obtained from the ship's geometry (Fig. 8.5), and examples are quoted below which serve to draw attention to the substantial increases in a ship's draught which result from a list or heel. If a precise measure of the increase in draught is required it will be necessary to take account of the change in the waterplane area when the vessel heels and of the measurement of the hull in way of the turn of the bilge.

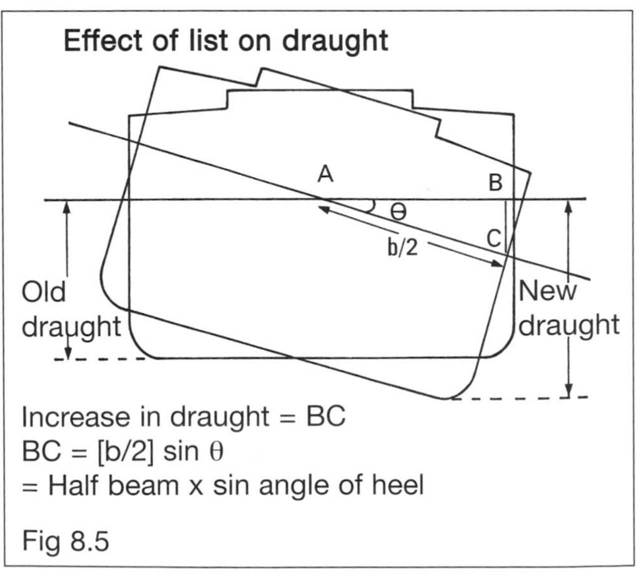

Fig 8.5

Class of Bulker	Beam (m)	Draught Increase (m) for list 1deg	3deg	5deg
Mini	16.4	0.14	0.43	0.72
Handy-sized	23.0	0.20	0.60	1.00
Panamax	32.2	0.28	0.84	1.40
Cape-sized	43.8	0.38	1.14	1.91
VLBC	47.0	0.41	1.23	2.05

Change of trim when passing from salt water to fresh water

When a ship passes from water of one density to water of another density her mean draught is changed, and if the longitudinal position of the centre of buoyancy changes the ship's trim will change. As the draught changes, the longitudinal position of the centre of buoyancy *will* change if the bows and stern of a ship are different shapes, as is usually the case.

Draught and trim are usually of most concern when the vessel is laden, and operating at her deepest draught. Deep-laden vessels are usually trimmed even keel, or nearly so. A useful illustration of the importance of the matter is provided by a particular Panamax-sized vessel requiring to pass through the Panama Canal at the usual maximum draught (ie, 39ft 6in = 12.04 metres).

She must be on the maximum permitted draught and even keel when transiting the main section of the Canal where density is 995 kg/m³. Her increase in draught when passing from density 1025 kg/m³ to density 995 kg/m³ is 36 cm, and change of trim can be calculated to be 12 cm by the head, an amount which cannot be ignored. To achieve 12.04 metres even keel in the canal (when in water with density 995 kg/m³) it can be calculated that the vessel must be floating at 11.62 m forward, 11.74 m aft in salt water, with a trim 12 cm by the stern, before commencing the Canal transit.

Formula for change of trim with change of density: The formula for trim change when passing from water of one density to that of another is:

Change of trim (cm)	=	Displacement x Shift of CB/MCTC, where:
Displacement	=	Displacement in tonnes, at initial draught.
MCTC	=	Moment to change trim 1 cm, in tonnes-metres, at initial draught.
Shift of CB	=	Shift in position of Longitudinal Centre of Buoyancy = ($LCB_1 - LCB_2$), where LCB_1 is distance of LCB from midlength, in metres, at initial draught, and LCB_2 is distance of LCB from midlength, in metres, at final draught.

If the position of the CB moves aft, the change of trim is by the head. A worked example of the calculation is contained in Appendix 8.2.

Stability of ships carrying grain and forest products

Both grain and forest products provide particular stability problems. (Their carriage is discussed in Chapter 19, and the associated calculations described in Chapter 10 and illustrated in Appendices 10.11-10.14).

Sources

7, 8, 21, 111, 112, 113, 167. (See List of Sources Page 497)

CHAPTER 9

PLANNING THE LOADING

Orders for loading, permissibility of the proposed cargo, general approach, maximum lift, limiting point in voyage, factors which govern the distribution of cargo, the loading/deballasting plan, two berth and two port loading and discharge, block loading, two and multi-loader operations, the trimming pours, loading the optimum amount of cargo, the unloading/ballasting plan, when cargo cannot be carried safety

Orders for loading

LOADING ORDERS may reach the Master from the owners or direct from time charterers. To minimise misunderstandings orders should be written in plain English and should avoid the excessive use of abbreviations, particularly when the recipient is not a native English speaker. Despite this, the use of abbreviations will undoubtedly continue from force of habit although, thanks to modern communications, the resultant savings in costs are unlikely to be significant.

Loading orders should contain all the information which the Master will require to enable him to plan the voyage and calculate the quantity of cargo to be carried. The information needed will depend upon the nature of the voyage; a complicated voyage involving several cargoes and ports will require more information than will a single consignment from one loading port to one discharge port.

Loading orders are likely to contain some or all of the following: loading port(s); discharging port(s); port rotation; loading dates; proposed cargo and its characteristics; proposed tonnages; tonnage limits; manner of segregation of different commodities; limiting draughts and air draughts; intended bunkering ports and quantities; intended routes and speed; and/or details of fuel and diesel oil consumptions proposed.

The Master will normally be asked to confirm that he has received and understood the orders. To emphasise that the Master must only accept the orders if he is satisfied that they are safe, he should also be asked to confirm that he has completed the necessary calculations and ensured that the vessel can safely comply with the orders. When the Master receives the orders they must always be considered carefully. All questions which the orders contain must be answered, and any orders which are not clear and fully understood must be questioned. The Master must satisfy himself that the orders can be safely executed. A prudent Master who has the interests of his owner and charterer at heart will also consider whether the orders appear to make operational and commercial sense and will query orders about which he has doubts.

The loading orders quoted below are for a Cape-sized bulk carrier.

> Re: Next voyage
>
> Intention is to load full cargo coal Hampton Roads/Richards Bay for discharge Kwangyang or Kwangyang and Pohang. Your v/l will be supplied with capacity bunkers at Flushing after completion discharge Redcar, thereafter will top off to capacity with bunkers at Hampton Roads.
>
> Routeing Richards Bay – Korea will be via Malacca Straits with possibility additional bunkers up to max loadable supplied at Singapore. Will revert with confirmation Singapore bunkering during voyage once price diff for bunkers Singapore/Korea established.
>
> Please advise your bunker requirements Flushing.
>
> Charterers request you load following:
>
> AA About 60,000 Ltons Clintwood grade coal at Norfolk
>
> BB About 40,000 Ltons Pittston grade coal at Newport News
>
> CC About 38,000 Ltons Witbank grade coal at Richards Bay
>
> Assume SF 42 all grades.
>
> HamptonRoads/Newport News holds to be filled to capacity.
>
> Assume V/l proceeds 46/47 mt per day ballast/laden.
>
> Please advise soonest provisional holdwise/gradewise stowplan.

In the foregoing, Hampton Roads is the US East Coast port complex which includes both Norfolk and Newport News, and Richards Bay is a South African port. The SF (Stowage Factor) of all the coal is given as 42 (cubic ft/ton), and the daily fuel consumption in ballast is to be 46 tonnes per day and laden is to be 47 tonnes per day.

The Master is requested to provide, as soon as possible, his provisional stowage plan, showing the tonnage and grade to be allocated to each hold.

The Master's reply to the orders is given below. It states the heavy oil and diesel oil bunkers required at Flushing, and indicates the tonnages and grades of cargo planned for each hold, and the total quantities to be loaded. Departure draughts for each loading port are given, with the departure from Richards Bay being planned to be even keel.

> Re your message NoXXX
>
> Next voyage require 2650 mt HO + 40 mt DO at Flushing
>
> Proposed stowplan

Hold	MT	Grade
1	12980	Clintwood
2	16680	Witbank
3	15440	Pittston

4 16420 Clintwood
5 15460 Pittston
6 16420 Clintwood
7 15650 Pittston
8 16670 Witbank
9 14355 Clintwood

Clintwood = 60175
Pittston = 46550
Witbank = 33350

Total = 140075

Est Dep Draught HRoads F14.1 m, A 14.3 m
Est Dep Draught RBay 17.2 m e/k

Another proposed loading for a Cape-sized bulker is given in the email quoted below. This shows greater interest in the anticipated stresses, because the proposed cargo is iron ore, a high density cargo which will give rise to higher stresses and loadings than will coal. COB is 'close of business', and 10 PCT MOLOO means '10 per cent more or less, in owner's option'. This phrase is often used in charter-parties, and repeated in voyage orders. It allows the Master the freedom to take the maximum tonnage of cargo his ship can safely and legally carry.

For possible future trading pls advise soonest – latest COB London 27/7 – if your V/l is able comply gradewise/stresswise with following loading requirements:

V/l loading Tubarao 75,000 mtons 10 pct moloo iron ore then shifting in seaworthy condition to Sepitiba Bay where load addition 75,000 mtons 10 pct moloo ore. grades to be segregated holdwise.

Assume V/l then proceeds Indonesia range for discharge with bunker ROBs sufficient to overtake discharge port.

Maximum arrival draught Tubarao 14.0 m.

Maximum air draught Tubarao 16.5 m.

The ship's reply to the foregoing was as follows:

Your message 26/9 Re Possible Future Business

No problems encountered gradewise or stresswise

Tubarao

	MT
1	11000
3	16500
5	19000
7	19000
9	10370
	75870

Dep Draught F 9.35 m A 12.40 m

Sepitiba

2	18500
4	13000
6	15000
8	21000
	67500

Dep Draught F 17.40 m A 17.60 m
Arr Draught Indonesia range F 17.30 m A 17.50 m

Some loadings are much more complex. Loading orders for a Panamax vessel, illustrating this point, are at Appendix 9.1.

Is the proposed cargo permitted?

This is the first question a Master should ask himself. Some cargoes are excluded by the terms of the charterparty under which the ship is operating. In addition, some older ships of 150 m and upwards in length are forbidden by SOLAS regulations[217] from carrying high density cargoes (density > 1,780 kg/m^3) or are restricted in the ways that the cargo can be distributed within the ship. Some are required[218] to obtain a density declaration from an accredited testing organisation if the intended cargo is declared to have a density within the range 1,250 kg/m^3 to 1,780 kg/m^3. Bulk carriers to which the SOLAS restrictions apply will have the restrictions recorded in the ship's stability booklet and will be permanently marked on the side shell at midships, port and starboard, with a solid equilateral triangle[219].

General approach to planning

Whether planning the loading of a VLBC or a mini-bulker, the basic principles are the same. First, it is necessary to determine the maximum amount of cargo the ship can carry if restricted only by the loadline regulations. Then, the voyage must be studied, stage by stage, to identify any limiting point which will further restrict the amount of cargo which can be carried. Next, the disposition – ie, the positioning – of the cargo in the ship must be decided and when this has been done a loading plan must be devised, to place the cargo safely in the required positions. Finally, the discharge programme must be planned to ensure that the cargo can be safely discharged.

To discuss this process we will consider first the simplest case: a ship loading a single bulk commodity in a single berth for a single discharge port. As an example an imaginary voyage of the *Regina Oldendorff* is taken, loading a full cargo of calcined phosphate rock in Fremantle for discharge in Avonmouth. The voyage is to be by way of the Suez Canal, with bunkers to be taken at Aden.

Maximum amount of cargo the ship can carry

On any particular voyage the amount of cargo that the ship can carry may be decided by her deadweight or by the volume of her cargo spaces. A high-density cargo such as ore will bring the ship down to her marks before the cargo spaces are filled. With low-density cargoes like most varieties of coke and agricultural products, the opposite is true – the cargo spaces will be filled before the ship is down to her marks.

Cargoes such as coal and grain are likely to be borderline cases, depending upon the grade of the cargo and the characteristics of the ship to determine whether she will be filled before the marks are reached, or vice versa. Where the slightest doubt exists, stowage factors (expressed as cubic metres to the tonne – m^3/mt; or cubic feet to the long ton – cf/lt) must be obtained and used to calculate the tonnage of cargo which the holds can contain. For most bulk carriers the ratio Grain Capacity (m^3)/Deadweight (mt) is about 1.2 and it is cargoes with a stowage factor (SF) round about 1.2 m^3/mt which will be on the borderline between deadweight and volume cargoes. For individual ships the ratio may be anything from 1.0 to 1.4 and should be known to the Master and his officers. Each loading must be carefully considered because particular factors such as the quantity of bunkers carried will influence whether the cargo is a deadweight or volume cargo.

In the example it is assumed that the calcined phosphate rock to be carried by the *Regina Oldendorff* is reported to have a stowage factor of 1.10 m^3/mt. This figure would normally be provided by the shippers via their agent, or by the operators, or obtained from the ship's own records of previous cargoes carried. The stowage factor (SF) will always be an approximate figure, since it is influenced by the shape of a ship's holds and the condition of the cargo upon loading, and these can vary from one ship and one parcel of cargo to another.

The total capacity of the cargo holds of the *Regina Oldendorff* (excluding the topside tanks, which can be used for grain) is 34,977.9 m^3. From this we can calculate that the ship can contain 34,977.9/1.10 = 31,798.1 tonnes of phosphate rock. This figure exceeds the maximum summer deadweight (28,031 mt), which demonstrates that this is a heavy cargo which will bring the ship down to her marks before the holds are filled. The maximum cargo which can be carried will depend, in this instance, upon the maximum acceptable draught and upon the maximum permissible load for each hold as stated by the vessel's classification society.

Besides the cargo the deadweight tonnage includes bunkers, stores and other items carried. These items have to be taken into account when the maximum cargo lift is calculated. The method of listing and labelling these items may vary from ship to ship; what is important is to ensure that all weights are listed, and that the tonnages carried are kept to a minimum.

In the case of the *Regina Oldendorff* the weights to be carried will include sufficient bunkers to take her to the next bunkering port, plus a quantity in reserve. For the passage to Aden, the bunkering port chosen for this voyage, the ship will require at least 650 tonnes of fuel and 50 tonnes of diesel.

The following list contains typical figures for other weights. Weights on board:

Fuel	650 mt
Diesel	50
Fresh water	70
Crew and Stores	37
Ballast residues	50
Ship's Constant	120
Sag allowance	50
	1027 mt

The ship's constant is described in Chapter 13.

(Strictly speaking, the sag allowance is not a weight carried, but a reduction in deadweight capacity which results from the ship's normal sag when loaded. It is prudent to include a sag allowance in all deadweight calculations, so that the charterer is aware from the beginning of the voyage of the cargo lift which can be realistically anticipated. The value used for sag allowance should be the average of capacity lost because of sag in previous voyages when loaded with similar weights and with the weights distributed in a similar manner between the holds.)

Some of these values are likely to change during the course of the voyage as bunkers are consumed and replenished, and must be recalculated for any limiting condition. Because the maximum amount that the ship can carry depends, in this example, upon the vessel's draught one cannot in this case state the maximum amount of cargo that the ship can carry until the limiting draught for the voyage has been found.

Limiting point of the voyage

At various points in the voyage, limits may restrict the amount of cargo the vessel can carry. Such limits include the ship's maximum permitted draught at each stage in the voyage, dependent upon the geographical zone and the time of year, draught restrictions in the loading port, discharging port or some intermediate point such as a canal or waterway, and the requirement to carry changing quantities of fuel and water during the course of the voyage. Charterers or owners often advise the Master of limiting draughts to be expected at loading or discharging ports, but mistakes are sometimes made and he should always confirm the limits from the information available to him. It is necessary to consider all these limits and to identify which is the most restrictive.

In the imaginary voyage undertaken by the Regina Oldendorff from Fremantle, Western Australia, to Avonmouth, United Kingdom, in February, the limits which she will meet are the following:

Limits for the Voyage

Point in Voyage	*Limit*	*Maximum Draught(m)*
Load a full cargo	Summer marks	10.24
Departure Fremantle	Max for berth/port	12.65ek
Enter Tropical Zone	Summer marks	10.24
Arrive Aden	Max for berth/port	11.50ek
Depart Aden	Tropical marks	10.45
Suez Canal transit	Max for canal	16.20ek
Departure Port Said	Summer marks	10.24
Seasonal Winter Zone	Winter marks	*10.03
Arrive Avonmouth	Max for berth/port	10.38ek

(ek = even keel) *limiting draught

The above limits fall into two categories. The limits imposed by the Loadline Rules are concerned with the ship's freeboard and draught amidships, but impose no restrictions upon her trim. The limits imposed by the depths and densities of water available in the ports and the canal, on the other hand, are absolute, and the maximum draughts can only be achieved if the vessel is even keel.

Another possible limit upon the amount of cargo to be carried must be mentioned – the tonnage to be carried may be stipulated in the charterparty. If the charterparty states that the *Owners undertake that the vessel shall load 25,000 tonnes of 1,000 kilos, 5 per cent more or less in their option,* then the tonnage to be loaded should not exceed 25,000 tonnes + 5 per cent, or 26,250 mt. This tonnage, carried with the bunkers and stores listed, would produce a deadweight of 27,277 mt, corresponding to a mean draught of 10.06 m as read from the deadweight scale, on departure Fremantle. For the purposes of the example we assume that the charterparty places no upper limit upon the tonnage of cargo to be carried.

At first sight it appears that the most exacting limit which the vessel will meet is the requirement to be on winter marks when entering the seasonal winter zone off Cape Toriñana, Spain. The object will be, therefore, to arrive off Cape Toriñana precisely on winter marks, but to achieve this it will be necessary to carry and consume sufficient bunkers to reach this point, and calculations must be made back from the ship's condition at Cape Toriñana to earlier points in the voyage to ensure that no unacceptable draughts are required earlier in the voyage.

Before checking back to earlier stages in the voyage it is necessary to determine how much of the deadweight aboard at Cape Toriñana will be cargo. The fuel and diesel totals will depend upon how much was taken at Aden and that, in turn, will depend upon the orders that the ship was given regarding bunkering. We have chosen to assume that the Master was instructed to reach Avonmouth with sufficient fuel for three days' steaming, and that it was normal to keep fuel for two days in reserve. To arrive in Avonmouth with fuel for five days it would be necessary to pass Cape Toriñana with fuel for seven days. The weights aboard upon passing Cape Toriñana would be:

Fuel	273 mt
Diesel	25
Fresh water	70
Crew and Stores	37
Ballast residues	50
Ship's Constant	120
Sag allowance	50
Total weights:	625 mt
Winter deadweight	27,212
Cargo tonnage	26,587 mt

The next step is to ensure that this tonnage of cargo can be carried at earlier stages in the voyages, without exceeding the limits. An inspection of the table of limits for the voyage (above) suggests that the ship will have no difficulty in staying within the limits for the canal transit, for arrival Aden and for entering the tropical zone, provided that she complies with the maximum draught restrictions on departure from Fremantle and Aden, since her mean draught will reduce day by day at sea as bunkers are consumed. However, the ship's draught and trim on departure from Port Said and Aden and upon loading in Fremantle must be calculated with care.

Approximate distance and times required between successive points on the voyage are as follows, with times based upon a steaming distance of 350 nm/day:

Fremantle – Aden	4,920 nm	14 days
Aden – Suez	1,310	4
Suez Canal	100	1
Port Said – Cape Torinana	2,475	7
Cape Torinana – Avonmouth	630	2

On the basis that the *Regina Oldendorff*'s consumption is 37 tonnes of fuel and 2 tonnes of diesel per day (not her real consumption – see Appendix 1.1) and that she maintains her supply of fresh water by manufacturing it whilst on passage, the difference in displacement between Cape Toriñana and Port Said will be 39x7 = 273 mt. Given that the tonnes per centimetre immersion value for the *Regina Oldendorff* at loaded draught is 38.5, mean draught on departure from Port Said will be 7 cm greater than draught at Cape Toriñana. The difference between summer and winter marks is 21.3 cm, so the vessel should have no difficulty in complying with the limit when leaving Port Said. Her summer marks will be well above the water.

From this it follows that keeping the tropical marks above the water will present no problems when leaving Aden, only five days earlier. The mean draught will be 5 cm deeper, well within the tropical allowance of 21.3 cm.

If the *Regina Oldendorff* had left Fremantle with 26,587 mt of cargo and with 1,027 mt of other weights as itemised above, her draught on sailing (from the ship's hydrostatic tables) would have been 10.13 m. These results, all calculated from the limiting condition at Cape Toriñana, can be summarised as follows:

Point	**Limit**	**Limiting Draught**	**Actual Mean Draught**
Load Fremantle	Summer marks	10.24	10.13
Depart Fremantle	Port limit	12.65	10.13
Arrive Aden	Port limit	11.50	9.99
Depart Aden	Tropical marks	10.45	10.15
Suez Canal	Canal limit	16.20	10.11
Port Said	Summer marks	10.24	10.10
Cape Torinana	Winter marks	10.03	10.03
Avonmouth	Port limit	10.38	10.01

Since the actual mean draught is always shown to be less than the limiting draught, this confirms that entering the winter zone off Cape Toriñana is the limiting condition for the voyage, provided that the ship can be operated without an excessive stern trim throughout the voyage so that she can arrive at Avonmouth substantially even keel. An additional reason for needing to avoid an excessive stern trim is the requirement that the visibility ahead should be obscured for no more than two shiplengths[92]. Some canals such as the Panama have more severe visibility requirements.

With experience, the limiting point in the voyage will often be obvious without the need for detailed investigation such as shown above, but it is essential that every stage in the voyage is considered to ensure that the maximum cargo is carried, and that the vessel is not loaded too deeply at any stage.

Disposition of the cargo

Deciding the tonnage distribution: Having calculated the total tonnage of cargo to be loaded (in the example it is 26,587 mt), it is necessary next to decide upon the tonnage to be loaded into each hold. Many factors have to be taken into consideration when making this decision. Given the right combination of circumstances such as the ship's past record carrying the same cargo the decision can be a very easy one but when the requirements are more exacting skill, experience and patience will be required to find the best solution. The steps in the calculation are as follows.

1. **Decide how many holds are to be loaded.** If a full low-density cargo is to be carried, all holds will be loaded, though some may not be full. If a full high-density cargo is to be carried and the ship has been suitably strengthened the loading may be in alternate holds although this option is nowadays chosen less often because of the high sheer forces involved. In addition bulk carriers of 150 m in length and upwards, after reaching 10 years of age, when carrying a full high density cargo, must distribute the cargo between all holds unless their superior construction excludes them from this SOLAS requirement[167].
2. **Share the total cargo between the holds.** The first tentative (ie, experimental) sharing of the cargo between the holds can be based upon a standard condition from the ship's stability manual, the tonnages used on a previous voyage, or a sharing based upon proportion. A hold which contains, say, 30 per cent of the ship's cubic capacity can be given 30 per cent of the total cargo. The calculation for the *Regina Oldendorff* looks like this:

	Grain Capacity (m^3)	Per cent	Tonnage (mt)	Rounded (mt)
Total	34,978	100	26,587	26,600
No.1	6,848	19.57	5,205	5,200
No.2	7,867	22.49	5,980	6,000
No.3	5,503	15.73	4,183	4,200
No.4	8,061	23.04	6,127	6,100
No.5	6,699	19.15	5,092	5,100

The table shows that the capacity of No.3 hold (5,503 m^3), for example, is 15.73 per cent of the vessel's capacity, so 15.73 per cent of the total tonnage (4,183 mt) can be carried there. The rounded distribution shown in the final column is simply a convenient starting point for the calculations which must follow.

3. **Place fuel, fresh water and other weights in the positions intended for departure from the loading port.** A position for the centre of gravity of each item of weight must be used in the calculation. This raises important considerations (See Chapter 10, Stability calculations – practical considerations).
4. **Calculate the ship's draught and trim on departure and ensure that they are acceptable.** The mean draught will be as required, unless a mistake has been made. If the trim is not as required a rearrangement of the cargo between holds must be made.
5. **Calculate the ship's stability characteristics on departure and ensure that they are acceptable.** They will not be acceptable if they fail to meet the minimum requirements stated in the ship's loading manual – these will normally be the requirements stated in the International Load Line Convention 1966, Regulation 10, Annex I, or the equivalent national regulations.
6. **Calculate the shear forces and bending moments on departure and ensure that they are not excessive.** The maximum allowable still water bending moments and shear forces will be stated in the loading manual. The in-port values do not apply when the ship goes to sea; the at-sea values must be used. Where two alternative values are provided, one set for alternate hold loading and the other for ballast or uniform loading, the appropriate set must be used. In the longhand calculations of longitudinal strength for some vessels a separate 'bulkhead factor' is used to reduce the calculated values of shear forces. This correction should be applied strictly in accordance with the instructions in the stability booklet. The bulkhead factor takes account of the fact that some of the load caused by cargo in adjacent holds is transferred to the transverse bulkhead through the double-bottom structure instead of the side shell plating. Computerised loading programs offer the operator the opportunity to make this correction. If he chooses not to apply the correction the resulting error will be a safe one; the shear forces will appear higher than they really are.
7. **Check that the tonnage allotted to each hold is not greater than the classification society permits.** This check is important to ensure that the ship is not overstressed, but often the requirement is not clearly stated in the loading manual, particularly on older ships. The maximum tonnage, when plainly stated, may be a single sum, or the permitted tonnage may vary with the draught of the ship. In some loading manuals the permitted tonnage is not stated. In such cases the ship may be put at risk if any hold is loaded with more cargo than is shown in any of the standard conditions of loading contained in the loading manual. When such a loading is proposed, Masters are advised to consult the classification society, through their owners. This matter is fully discussed in Appendix 9.2. The unintended overloading of a hold is most likely to occur when loading a high-density cargo in alternate holds and when loading to tropical marks. Unintended overloading may also occur when extra cargo is carried because only a small quantity of bunkers has been loaded, or when several parcels of cargo are loaded, requiring uneven distribution between holds.
8. **Check that the hold tanktop, or double-bottom, loadings are not excessive** when the cargo is one such as steel coils or slabs. This important and complicated matter is discussed in greater detail in Chapter 19. Confirm that deck and hatch cover loadings are not excessive when deck cargoes are being carried.
9. **If the ship is to be block loaded ensure that the loadings for individual holds remains within the special block loading limits set by the classification society.** A block hold loading condition refers to the stowage of cargo in a block of two or more adjoining cargo holds with the cargo holds adjacent to the block of loaded cargo holds empty[111]. Block loading is likely to be proposed when several parcels of closeweight cargo are to be loaded or discharged at different berths, or in different ports. It may also be proposed as a means of reducing the longitudinal stresses which occur when a vessel is loaded in alternate holds. The problems associated with block loading are described later in this chapter, and full details appear in Appendix 9.4. Block loading is permitted only when the proposed loading is described in the ship's loading manual, or if the ship has been provided with class approved local loading criteria which define the maximum cargo weight limit as a function of ship's mean draught for each cargo hold and block of cargo holds. If one of these conditions is not met, approval must be requested from the classification society, through the owners.
10. **Work through the voyage stage by stage**, adjusting bunker quantities to reflect bunkers consumed and taken, and repeating the calculations at steps 3, 4 and 5 for arrival at and departure from each port.
11. **If any of the above steps gives an unacceptable result the cargo tonnages or other weights must be redistributed**, and the calculation must then be repeated.
12. **When an acceptable cargo distribution has been produced it must be carefully reconsidered to see**

whether any errors have been introduced. For example, is there room in the hold for the amended tonnage allotted to it? Can the tonnage distribution between holds be further amended in any way that will help to speed loading or discharge?

Reasons to amend the tonnage distribution: Results that would be unacceptable include insufficient positive stability, excessive shear forces or bending moments, or excessive tanktop or hold loadings. Also unacceptable would be a large trim by the stern which makes the ship's draught too deep to enter or leave a port, or any trim by the head which is likely to make the ship steer badly and which usually makes it difficult to draw fuel from forward bunker tanks to the engine room, if required.

For sea passages a trim by the stern is desirable because ships are designed to operate with a trim by the stern. When by the head any water in the holds will flow to the fore end and not to the bilges. Tank soundings with be unreliable because residues will lie at the forward end of the tank where a sounding rod or tape in the sounding pipe at the after end of the tank cannot detect them. A bulk carrier which is loaded to even keel when she leaves port will trim by the head when proceeding on voyage at sea speed. This is a consequence of squat (see Chapter 8). For this reason a ship should, where possible, leave port with a trim by the stern or adopt a stern trim when clear of the port.

In the case of a bulk carrier which is normally sagged when fully loaded, it is worth examining the possibility of putting increased tonnages of cargo in the end holds and reduced tonnages in the centre holds to reduce the sag, provided that this does not take bending moment and shear force values close to the limits.

It is sensible to respect the wishes of the chief engineer, as far as possible, with regard to the most convenient bunker tanks in which to carry the bunkers. Such tanks will usually be close to the engine room. The voyage plan should not involve the transfer of bunkers, except from bunker tank to engine room, since any other transfer of fuel increases the risk of spillage and pollution.

Guidelines for amending the tonnage distribution: It is most unlikely that the first attempt at distributing the cargo between the holds will satisfy all the requirements. It is much more likely that the calculations will show that the ship's trim, stability or stresses will be unacceptable at some stage in the voyage. When this occurs there are several useful guidelines to keep in mind when redistributing the weights throughout the ship:

1. Wherever possible an unacceptable trim should be corrected by repositioning cargo, not bunkers. If the cargo can be positioned so that the draught and trim throughout the voyage are acceptable, then the possibility of repositioning bunkers can be kept in reserve for emergencies.

2. A ship on passage often has spare lifting capacity, except at the limiting point of the voyage. At such times it may be possible to take ballast, in the forepeak or afterpeak tank, to improve the trim or stability without exceeding the permitted draught. The temporary ballasting of double bottom tanks or topside tanks to improve trim is not recommended except when continuing calm conditions, permitting a safe and complete discharge of ballast when required, can be relied upon.

3. Transferring bunkers within the ship should be avoided as far as possible to reduce the risk of a spillage. If bunkers must be transferred, the transfer should be by gravitation if possible and preferably in a calm sea. Preplanning which ensures that the bunkers are loaded into the most suitable tanks and consumed in the optimum sequence is better than the transferring of bunkers. However on a long sea passage such as from Australia to Europe the transfer of bunkers may be unavoidable so careful planning and monitoring of the transfer, in accordance with the Company's Safety Management System (SMS) is essential. If the bunker tank is situated forward a prudent Shipmaster will ensure that the fuel is suitably heated well in advance to expedite the planned transfer.

4. Insufficient positive stability in seaworthy bulk carriers is a problem which is normally met only in vessels carrying forest products. In brief this problem is countered by keeping the number of slack tanks to a minimum, keeping bunkers (both water and fuel) as low as possible in the ship, keeping ballast tanks filled, and if necessary carrying additional bunkers in double bottom tanks to act as ballast.

5. When rearranging the cargo aboard a vessel to alter the ship's trim or stresses a few simple rules may be useful.

- To reduce trim by the head, or increase trim by the stern, move a weight aft.

  To reduce hogging stresses move weights from forward and aft towards midships.

- Aboard Panamax and Cape-sized bulkers where alternate holds are the same length, it is usually possible to reduce longitudinal stresses whilst maintaining the same trim by moving two equal weights in opposite directions at opposite ends of the ship. For example, to reduce a shear force at No. 9 hold, move 200 tonnes of cargo from No. 9 to No. 7 hold, and balance that by moving 200 tonnes from No. 1 to No. 3 hold. This may have unexpected effects upon bending moments so they must always be rechecked after weights have been moved.

Loading/deballasting plan

The Loading Plan: When a satisfactory distribution of cargo has been obtained, a plan must be devised for loading the cargo whilst keeping stresses within the permitted limits throughout the process and always maintaining a sufficient stern trim to assist efficient deballasting. Limited depth of water and height below the loading arm may restrict the draught and air draught which can be accepted.

The plan should provide all the information required by deck officers and loading personnel, presented in a clear and logical manner. The IMO form[110] for this purpose (Appendix 9.3) is based upon one devised by The Nautical Institute. Copies of the completed plan should be available as working documents ashore and aboard, and a copy should be filed aboard ship as an actual record of the cargo and/or ballasting operation.

The loading plan lists each step in the deballasting, and the corresponding cargo pour. (A pour is the quantity of cargo poured into one hold as one step in the loading plan. Other expressions sometimes used for a pour are a 'run', a 'shot' and a 'drop'.) A pass is composed of a pour into each of the holds to be loaded. Thus a ship loading five holds with 30,000 tonnes of cargo might load with a first pour of 3,000 tonnes in each hold. When the first pass was completed 15,000 tonnes would be distributed between the five holds. The second pass would be composed of a second pour of 3,000 tonnes into each of the five holds.

Information required for preparation of loading/deballasting plan: If a realistic loading/deballasting plan is to be devised, the following information is required:

- Maximum safe draught in berth.
- Minimum depth in the approach to the berth.
- Water density at the berth.
- Tidal range.
- Maximum arrival trim and propeller immersion required by the port.
- Maximum permitted sailing draught.
- The minimum air draught beneath the ship loader.
- Characteristics of loading equipment.
- Limits of movement of the loading equipment.
- The maximum theoretical loading rate.
- Any restrictions on the ship's freedom to load in any sequence and hold.
- Any restrictions on deballasting.
- The number of ship loaders to be used.

(These requirements are discussed in greater detail in Chapter 11.)

Guidelines for preparation of a loading/deballasting plan: As a starting point it is normal to assume that each pour will consist of about half the total tonnage to be loaded into the compartment in question. On occasions when it is particularly desirable to minimise longitudinal stresses three pours, each consisting of about one third the total tonnage for the compartment, will be used. The loading sequence (or loading rotation) depends upon the size of ship and the number of holds to be loaded, but some guidelines can be offered.

1. The first pour should where possible be into a midship or after hold to provide or maintain a reasonable trim (say 0.005 ship's length) by the stern for ballast stripping purposes.
2. If the air draught is restricted it will be necessary to make the first pour into a hold which causes some increase in forward draught to ensure that the loading spout can continue to clear the hatch coamings of the forward holds.
3. If the air draught is restricted the effect of a rising tide must be considered and deballasting may have to be stopped or the rate reduced if the clearance approaches the minimum clearance permitted by the port or the terminal.
4. Successive pours should alternate between forward and after holds to maintain a reasonable trim by the stern. Where safe to do so the trim by the stern should be 0.01 ship's length, or more, when stripping double bottom ballast tanks.
5. The end holds (ie, the foremost and aftermost holds) have the biggest effect upon trim. Where possible they should receive the last pours of the first pass, and the first pours of the second pass, because the resulting large changes in the trim and maximum draught are likely to be least inconvenient at that point.
6. The ballast which is likely to present most problems should be discharged first, the normal sequence commencing with ballast holds, continuing with double bottom tanks and wing tanks and concluding with peak tanks.
7. Ballast should normally be discharged from a position close to the one where the cargo is being loaded at that time. For example, No.3 double bottom tank should be discharged whilst No.3 hold is being filled, if No.3 double bottom tank is below No.3 hold.
8. The time required for a deballasting step should be matched with the time required for a loading pour. A pour of 3,000 tonnes at a loading rate of 1,500 tonnes/hour will take two hours. This should be programmed with a deballasting step which will take less than two hours, so as to reduce the likelihood that the deballasting will overrun, and become out of step with the loading.
9. The deballasting should be programmed to be completed several hours, at least, before completion of loading, and at a time when the vessel still has a good stern trim, to assist the deballasting and stripping. When the anticipated loading rate is so high that the deballasting rate cannot possibly keep up one or several loading stops must be written into the loading plan, and the Master must resist any attempts or threats from the terminal or charterers to put the vessel off hire or to remove her from the berth for these periods. The SOLAS regulations[190] give the Master the authority for this action.
10. On some bulk carriers trim can be quickly and conveniently changed by pumping ballast directly from forepeak to afterpeak, or vice versa. However, the afterpeak is often used to hold fresh water for cargo hold cleaning.
11. Rules imposed by the Classification Society and quoted in the loading manual may restrict the sequence of loading: they must be strictly observed. For example the manual may state that no hold can be completely filled until the mean draught is at least two thirds of the intended sailing draught or that no hold can be completely empty at full draught.
12. In exposed berths the ship should be maintained at a draught, trim and condition of positive stability at which she can put to sea at short notice if required. This precaution is essential in areas where ports must be evacuated on the approach of a tropical storm.

Calculation of the loading/deballasting plan: From a starting point with the ship in ballasted condition and ready to commence loading, calculations must be undertaken for each step in the loading programme. These calculations are similar to those already undertaken for each stage in the loaded voyage, and are intended to find the ship's draught, trim, stability and longitudinal stresses at each stage in the loading. They are essential to ensure that the ship is not subjected to excessive bending moments and shear forces during the course of the loading, and their importance cannot be overstated.

Whenever the calculations show that the draught, trim, stability or stresses at the end of a stage are unacceptable, the plan must be changed by changing the loading or deballasting sequence or quantities. Unfortunately it is sometimes necessary to amend a number of earlier stages to remove a problem which is found in the later stages. When this occurs the data for all the stages which have been amended and those which follow must be recalculated.

When rearranging the ballast and the cargo pours aboard a vessel to alter her trim or stresses the rules quoted earlier are still applicable:

- To reduce trim by the head, or increase trim by the stern, load cargo aft or discharge ballast from forward.
- To reduce hogging stresses load cargo amidships or discharge ballast from the forward and after ends of the ship.
- To reduce shear forces and bending moments whilst maintaining the same trim move two equal weights in opposite directions at opposite ends of the ship.

Ways of adjusting the loading/deballasting plan: Sometimes it will be found very difficult to devise a loading/deballasting plan which remains within the stress limits. This is most likely to occur when loading a high density cargo in alternate holds (jump loading), or when planning the loading of a segregated part cargo which is not to be distributed between all holds. Difficulties are more likely if the ship is observing the at-sea stress limits whilst in port to increase the safety margin, to reduce the danger of structural damage to the ship during the loading process and to retain the option of leaving the berth and putting to sea in emergency such as an approaching tropical storm.

Several steps can be recommended to reduce the calculated stress values and improve the program.

- The pour sizes can be varied. Better results may be obtained if 60 per cent, say, of the tonnage is loaded in the first pour, and 40 per cent in the second, or vice versa.
- The number of pours can be increased, using three pours in holds where two give difficulties. Since each shift of the loading spout will take 10 minutes or so, this will slightly increase the time required for loading, making this option less attractive than safer loading achieved by varying the size or the sequence of the pours.

Loading when the ship is too long for the berth: If the ship is too long for the berth, so that the loading spout cannot reach all holds without the vessel shifting, the plan should require the ship to shift along the quay as seldom as possible. This can probably be best achieved by commencing loading in an after hold, the forward hold being beyond the end of the berth. Then, after about one-third of the cargo has been distributed between holds except No.1, the vessel should be moved astern to allow a first pour into No.1, followed perhaps by a second pour into an after hold – though not the aftermost one, which would be beyond the end of the berth. This could be followed by a second pour into No.1 hold, after which the vessel would be moved ahead and loading would be completed in the remaining holds. Loading the forward hold is likely to cause a bigger change of trim than loading the after hold, so it is better for the former to be loaded midway through the programme.

A possible loading sequence for a nine-hold bulk carrier loading alternate holds is:

3, 9, 5, 7,
move astern
1, 7, 1,
move ahead,
9, 3, 5, trim.

Planning two-port or two-grade loadings

It is quite common for bulk carriers of all sizes to be instructed to load several different grades of cargo, to be stowed in separate holds. Such different grades may be for loading and discharge at separate berths or even in separate ports. The loading orders quoted at the start of this chapter refer to such cargoes.

This sort of requirement can usually be satisfied by using a distribution with grade A shared between forward and after holds, and grade B treated similarly. If there is a bigger quantity of one grade than of the other, that grade can be allotted to an additional hold, amidships. Possible distributions include:

Hold	9	8	7	6	5	4	3	2	1
Option 1	A		B		A		B		A
Option 2	A	B	A	B	A	B	A	B	A
Option 3	A	B	C	A	C	A	C	B	A

These and any other distributions are acceptable provided that draught, trim, tanktop loadings, hold loadings, shear forces and bending moments are within acceptable limits throughout the loading, the voyage and the discharge. There is another condition which must be satisfied: if block loading is used it must only be used in a manner which is approved by the classification society.

Planning should take account of the fact that it is usually desirable (and sometimes essential) to load all of one grade of cargo before commencing to load a second grade, even if both grades are to be loaded at the same berth. One reason for this is that there may be a requirement for a draught survey on completion of each grade to obtain a ship's figure for tonnage loaded. Furthermore, when grades are changed, it is usually necessary for the conveyor belts to be cleaned after completion of one grade and before commencement of loading the second grade. Even if it is possible to switch back and forward from one grade to another time will be lost and inconvenience will be suffered whilst the belts are cleaned.

When planning the loading of several parcels of cargo the discharge must also be planned and checked to ensure that every stage in the voyage will satisfy all the requirements. If grade A is to be loaded and then grade B, and if at the discharge port grade B is to be discharged and then grade A, it is likely that the discharge process will be as safe as the loading process, since one is the mirror image of the other. Even in this case it will be necessary to take account of the effect of differences in the bunker quantities carried.

When the discharging sequence is not a mirror image of the loading sequence the discharging programme must be calculated, before loading, with the same care as the loading programme. If this is not done it may be discovered, too late, that the cargo cannot safely be delivered and discharged in the sequence required.

Block loading

Block loading is the name given to a loading in which adjacent holds are heavily loaded whilst one or more remaining holds are empty. The requirement to load and discharge a number of parcels of closeweight cargo in several loading and discharge ports or berths sometimes leads to the use of this method of distributing the cargo between holds. The decision to use one or two extra holds when carrying a high-density cargo in alternate holds has the same effect. Block loading places an increased load on the transverse bulkhead between the two full holds and this, in turn, increases the load on the cross-deck structure.

Block loading was commonplace in bulk carrier operations for many years. Naval architects had not realised that block loading was being used and has issued no warnings against it. In 1993 it was reported by the International Association of Classification Societies (IACS) that a number of large bulk carriers had experienced structural damage affecting the cross-deck structure which separates adjacent cargo hatchways at the upper deck level. All the damaged ships had completed a voyage with two adjacent holds heavily laden.

The attitude of IACS to the question of block loading is stated in Appendix 9.4. Their advice can be summarised as:

- Never exceed the maximum permitted load in any hold.
- When using alternate hold loading use only the holds specified in the loading manual.
- If it is necessary to depart from the above, and if the ship has not been provided with approved block loading conditions, consult the classification society.

Classification societies have provided some ships with approved plans for block loading with closeweight cargoes. A feel for the factors involved may be obtained from the example quoted in Appendix 9.4. This demonstrates that the maximum permitted load for two adjoining holds is much less than the sum of their individual maximum permitted loads.

Two-loader and multi-loader operations[15]

When two loaders are available the ship is divided into two, and each loader works its own end. The loading plan devised for a single loader is normally suitable for two-loader loading, provided that the rate of deballasting is sufficiently high and that the original deballasting plan can be followed in step with the loading. As with loadings with a single loader, stern trim should be maintained, but extremes of trim that may cause clearance difficulties should be avoided. Appendix 9.5 contains a typical loading for the mv *Iron Somersby* for one-loader operation and the same loading adapted for two loaders.

It must be remembered that a second loader does not necessarily mean a doubling of the loading rate, that two loaders are seldom available for the entire loading and that variations in the pouring rate are likely. Extra vigilance is required when different grades are being loaded.

When loading with two loaders both must plumb the centre line to avoid twisting the ship's hull. This is most important as a ship which is kept upright by loading to starboard of the centreline in No.3 hold, say, and to port of the centreline in No.7 hold will be subjected to cargo torque, or twisting of the ship, which may cause serious damage to her structure. If troubles with ballast occur the first response should be to stop one loader.

Because of their size, loaders usually require at least one hold separation between them. This should cause no problem to the ship as it is generally undesirable to load adjacent holds. When it is not certain whether one or two loaders will be used it is prudent to plan for two, adopting a plan which is also suitable for one loader. At some grain terminals up to five spouts may be used to load. Loading a low-density cargo in so many positions simultaneously will eliminate trim and longitudinal stress problems provided that a sensible distribution of cargo loaded is adopted.

Trimming pours

Reasons for the trimming pours: It is normal to complete the loading of a bulk cargo with the trimming pours, a final quantity of cargo kept in reserve to be loaded partly into a forward and partly into an after position as necessary to bring the vessel's mean draught and trim to the desired values. The trimming pours are necessary to compensate for inaccurate quantities loaded, failure to load the cargo in exactly the positions intended (Fig.9.1), inaccuracies in the loading calculations and/or error in the assumed position of the ship's constant. It is essential that all deballasting is completed before the trimming pours are calculated and performed.

Tonnage set aside for the trimming pours: If the tonnage set aside for the trimming pours is too great, new errors may be introduced and the results of the pours may differ a little from those intended. On the

Fig. 9.1 The longitudinal position of the centre of gravity of the cargo is unlikely to coincide with the longitudinal position of the centre of gravity of the hold

other hand, if the tonnage allowed is too small and at the same time the tonnage supplied by the loader is inaccurate, as it often is, the ship may be brought very close to her marks before trimming commences, leaving insufficient cargo for whatever adjustment of trim is needed. Typical tonnages allowed for trimming are:

Vessel	Dwt	Trimming (mt)
Cape-sized	170,000	5,000
Panamax	75,000	2,500
Handymax	50,000	2,000
Handy-sized	27,000	1,000
Mini-bulker	3,000	300

Other authorities[15] recommend as much as 20 per cent of the total cargo.

Choice of holds for the trimming pours: The basic requirements for trimming pours are two loading positions, one of which will cause trim by the head and the other trim by the stern. Provided that only one grade of cargo has been loaded, a number of options for trimming are likely to be available, with Masters of some larger ships favouring the end holds (Nos.1 and 9) and others arguing that the end holds are usually of different shapes and preferring to use another combination, such as Nos. 2 and 8 or 3 and 7. When the loading berth has a limited draught, holds Nos.3 and 7 are likely to be preferred as they will cause smaller changes in the draught during the final stages of the loading and create less risk that the vessel will touch bottom in the berth.

Aboard mini-bulkers with only one or two holds, it is normal to load in several positions in each hold and the trimming can be done using a single calculated position within the forward hold. Unlike the trimming aboard a larger vessel, which offers the choice of applying trim by the head or trim by the stern, the trimming aboard a mini-bulker always starts with the ship trimmed well by the stern, so that trimming is concerned simply with the calculation of how much trim by the head is required to bring the vessel to the desired trim. Put another way, trimming on larger bulkers requires a decision as to how much cargo to put in a fixed position forward and how much in a fixed position aft. On a mini-bulker the question is different: how much is to be loaded in the forward hold, and where in the hold must it be loaded?

In general terms a trimming pour in the fore end of the No.1 hold of a mini-bulker will eliminate the stern trim and bring the vessel to an even keel, whilst a trimming pour in the after end of the hold will cause a smaller trim change. The ability to choose intermediate positions along the length of the hold permits more precise adjustments to be made to the trim. An example of this calculation is to be found at Appendix 9.6.

Apportionment of the trimming pours: The tonnage set aside for the trimming pours must form part of the tonnage already planned for the ship, and must therefore be deducted from the tonnages allotted to the holds where the trimming pours are to be delivered. It is necessary to decide what proportion of the trimming quantity is to be deducted from the hold total of each of the two holds. Simply put, the rule is: take the larger quantity from the hold with the larger trimming moment.

The explanation for this approach is as follows. If there are no trimming errors to correct and the draught and trim are exactly as required, then the quantities set aside for trimming will be loaded in the positions originally chosen for them. If, however, there are errors in trimming to correct, it will be necessary to transfer some of the cargo planned for one trimming position to the other. In that case a greater tonnage will be needed to obtain a given amount of trim change in a position with the smaller trimming moment, and that tonnage must be available from the tonnage intended for the position with the larger trimming moment.

For example, in a Panamax vessel: 1,000 mt in No.3 hold causes trim change of 47.5 cm, and 1,000 mt in No.7 hold causes trim change of 27.0 cm.

If the trimming quantity is to be 2,500 mt:

The No.3 trimming moment will be 2,500 x 47.5/(27.0 + 47.5) = 1,594 m, say 1,600 mt;

The No.7 trimming moment will be 2,500 x 27/(27.0 + 47.5) = 906 mt, say 900 mt.

In this example No.3 hold has the larger trimming moment, so 1,600 mt will be taken from No.3 for trimming, and 900 mt from No. 7. This will ensure that the same amount of trim change can be achieved, if necessary, by the head as by the stern.

Trimming pours in the loading programme: When the quantities intended for the trimming pours have been chosen, the loading programme must be adjusted to show the trimming quantities. If hold No.3 was planned to load 16,000 mt, with a first pour of 8,000 mt and a second pour of 8,000 mt, this would be adjusted to give: first pour, 8,000 mt; second pour, 6,400 mt; and trimming pour, 1,600 mt. After this, the amended pours into the two trimming holds must be checked to ensure that they still provide acceptable draught and trim, and values for longitudinal stress, at every stage in the loading.

Implementation of the trimming pours: Trimming pours are included in the loading programme because experience shows that the ship's draught and trim in the later stages of loading are seldom exactly in accordance with the calculated values. When the time for the trimming pours is reached loading is halted and a draught survey is performed to determine precisely the tonnage of cargo remaining to be loaded.

This survey may be done by an appointed surveyor, who will then agree the final tonnage for the trimming pour, or more usually will be done by the chief mate perhaps in consultation with the terminal supervisor, to ensure that the ship is given the tonnage required to ensure the correct final draught and trim. In the latter case, the draught surveyor, if appointed, will only attend when all loading is completed. It is quite normal for the draught survey to show that the actual tonnage required and the trim observed are both slightly different from those previously calculated.

There are several manual methods for calculating the trimming quantities to be placed in each hold when it is time to make the trimming pours, though surprisingly the calculation is not normally to be found in computerised loading programs.

A reliable and accurate calculation is to be found at Appendix 9.7. If the available figures are pre-entered, the calculation can be completed quickly with the aid of a computer or hand-held calculator when the draughts have been obtained. The tonnages calculated for trimming can then be double-checked against the ship's trimming tables to confirm the tonnages required, in a process which need take no more than ten minutes.

Another method for calculating the quantities required for the trimming pours is simply to use the trimming tables, using a trial and error approach. For example, if the trimming quantity was 1,770 mt an officer would take from the trim tables the trim changes resulting from placing 1,000 mt in No.7 hold and 770 mt in No.3 hold. If, when totalled, they showed too great a stern trim he would try again, using 900 mt in No.7 hold and 870 mt in No.3 hold, and so on, until the correct figures are obtained. This method is not recommended as it is cumbersome and its accuracy depends upon the degree of accuracy contained in the trimming tables and the care with which they are interpolated.

Changes in hog or sag during trimming: When calculating the tonnage required for the trimming pours it is normal to assume that any existing hog or sag will remain throughout the trimming pours, but this may not be so. If the trimming pours are placed in the end holds (eg, Nos. 1 and 9) any existing sag will probably be reduced. On completion of the trimming pours it will be found that a little more cargo is still required to bring the vessel to her marks. If the trimming pours are made into amidships holds such as Nos.5 and 7, in a 9 hold ship, any sag is likely to be increased by the trimming. If this happens the vessel will be found to be overloaded on completion of trimming.

When using midships holds for trimming on larger vessels it is prudent to subtract a small quantity of cargo from the trimming tonnages to allow for sag which increases during trimming, and so to avoid overloading. This quantity can be loaded by additional trimming pours if draught readings on completion of the first trimming pours show that there is still capacity for it.

Some terminals in Brazil and Saldanha Bay are reported to be ready to deliver trimming pours in successive pours of 100 tonnes or more[189].

Trimming in end holds or in midships holds makes no difference to the tonnage lifted by a vessel which loads exactly to her marks. The tonnage lifted is governed by whether the vessel is hogged or sagged and this depends upon the total tonnage loaded in each hold. The total tonnage in the hold is unaffected by whether it is loaded in, say, two pours, or two pours plus a trimming pour.

Fig. 9.2 No room to load more cargo to trim the ship

Trimming in marginal conditions: Difficulties in trimming are likely to be experienced with borderline cargoes such as some grades of coal and grain, which have stowage factors very close to that required to fill the ship homogeneously whilst also bringing her to her marks. Such a ship may reach her marks before all spaces are filled, or alternatively may be filled before she is down to her marks. The chief mate trying to trim the ship may find that he has run out of space in which to place the cargo required for the trimming (Fig.9.2). A similar problem can arise if attempting to load a full deadweight cargo such as dolomite, limesand or clay in alternate holds.

To avoid being caught in this situation it is recommended that the loading is interrupted with about 70 per cent of the cargo loaded. By this time at least one hold should be completely filled. The stowage factor should be recalculated for a full hold, provided that a reliable figure for tonnage loaded in that hold can be provided by the stevedores, and the remaining loading of the cargo should be recalculated and if necessary replanned. In the absence of a reliable figure from the stevedores, with some holds part filled and with discharge of ballast probably not completed there is no way that an accurate stowage factor can be calculated and loading must proceed cautiously to ensure that if either space or freeboard is exhausted the ship is at the required trim.

Loading the optimum amount of cargo

Requirement: From time to time bulk carriers are required for commercial reasons to carry less than a full cargo. The Master will find that although his vessel can lift 27,000 mt she is instructed to carry only some lesser tonnage or, when loading a low-density cargo, space remains when all the cargo allocated to the ship has been loaded.

However, such occasions are rare and it is more usual for the earnings of the owner and/or the charterer to depend upon the tonnage lifted. When that is the case it is the responsibility of the Master to do his best to ensure that the maximum amount of cargo is carried.

To achieve this the ship must be loaded to the appropriate limiting draught, or all her cargo spaces must be efficiently filled, but in addition to such practical matters careful planning is required to keep other weights to a minimum when a high-density cargo is being carried since every extra tonne of fuel or water carried means one tonne of cargo rejected.

Bunkers: The Master often controls the quantity of bunkers which the vessel carries, since on most voyages he is instructed to order sufficient bunkers for the forthcoming voyage, plus a specified tonnage in reserve. If the Master, in consultation with the chief engineer, underestimates the tonnage of bunkers required the ship will be forced to proceed at slow speed, to purchase bunkers in a more expensive alternative port, or to burn expensive diesel oil. Otherwise she will run out of fuel. Since all these options are unattractive, there is pressure on the ship's officers to overestimate their bunker requirements rather than to underestimate them, and there is a danger that this process can be carried to excessive lengths.

There is one acceptable reason for appearing to carry extra bunkers. The ship's bunker tonnages usually include an unpumpable quantity of fuel which will be left in bunker tanks after they have been drained as much as possible. Since the unpumpable tonnage cannot be used, it must be excluded from the calculation of tonnage required.

Such a calculation for fuel oil for the *Regina Oldendorff* might look like this:

Voyage: 32 days at 31 tpd		992 mt
Reserve: 3 days at 31 tpd		93
Total required for voyage		1085 mt
Quantity aboard	327 mt	
Unpumpable	35	
Usable fuel aboard	292 mt	292
Tonnage to order		793 mt

The usual convention is that fuel in the settling and service tanks, normally equal to about one day's consumption, is not included in the quantity aboard. This provides an additional reserve.

The foregoing figures justify an order for 800 mt of fuel oil bunkers. This would provide for the intended voyage with the required margin of safety, plus the small additional margin provided by the contents of the settling and service tanks. It would be bad practice to order more than 800 mt of fuel oil since that would be to shut out cargo to carry unnecessary bunkers.

The requirement for diesel is less easy to predict since it is used in port as well as at sea, and since time in port, the working of ship's cargo gear, and port manoeuvring are not entirely predictable. For that reason, and because diesel can be used to fuel the main engine at sea, it is quite common to carry 30-50 mt of additional diesel aboard ships where daily consumption of this fuel is only 2-4 mt.

There are occasions when it makes good economic sense to carry extra bunkers, because the opportunity to purchase cheap bunkers is worth more than the freight earned by carrying an equal quantity of cargo. This is a decision which will be taken by the owners or charterers since it is unlikely that the Master will have sufficient facts at his disposal to enable him to propose such a line of action.

The figures quoted previously illustrate the considerations which must be taken into account when calculating fuel figures, but the actual allowances used depend upon the size of ship, her normal performance, the trade in which she is employed and owners' policy.

Fresh water: Aboard bulk carriers fresh water is used for drinking, cooking and washing, and it may be used for toilet flush systems. It is also used for machinery cooling systems. Most bulk carriers are provided with fresh water generators of one kind or another, and these are designed to manufacture all the fresh water that the ship will require in normal service whilst under way. This means that vessels equipped with reliable fresh water generators need only leave port with sufficient fresh water to last until the vessel is clear of coastal waters which may be polluted, plus a margin for safety. Additional fresh water may be required if a period at anchor is a possibility.

Some charter parties are claused on the reasonable assumption that the vessel does have an efficient water generator, and stipulate that the vessel must leave the loading port with no more than five days' consumption of fresh water aboard. There should be no difficulty in complying with this provided that consumption is normal and the equipment is working well.

Ballast strippings: Careless or inefficient discharge of ballast, or sediment filled ballast tanks, can lead to the retention in the ballast tanks of much larger tonnages of ballast water and sediment than are acceptable. (Measures to reduce ballast strippings and sediment to a minimum are discussed in Chapter 7.)

Miscellaneous weights: The ship should be checked regularly for the accumulation of unnecessary weight. It is good practice to ensure that chain lockers, void spaces and engine room bilges are all regularly pumped out using the oily water separator and it is particularly important that these are checked towards the end of the ballast voyage before reaching the loading port.

Charterparty constant: Some charterparties contain a clause in which a tonnage is specified to cover consumables and miscellaneous weights other than fuel. Such an allowance, say, of 400 mt for a Panamax vessel, covers fresh water, stores, unpumpable ballast, the ship's constant (see Chapter 13) and any reduction of the ship's lift due to sag. The charterparty constant has the effect of giving the charterer a guarantee as to the cargo the ship can carry, since deadweight minus fuel minus c/p constant equals cargo capacity.

Old bulk carriers which have defective water generators, an accumulated tonnage of spare gear, thick coatings of paint and ballast tanks clogged with sediment will have difficulty in keeping weights within the permitted figure unless it is set at a realistic level.

Hog and sag: A vessel is said to be hogged (Fig.8.3) when the mean draught amidships is less than the mean of the forward and after draughts. This occurs when the hull is curved, with the highest point of the curve occurring amidships. Of a vessel which is sagged, the opposite is true. The mean draught amidships is greater than the mean of the forward and after draughts and the hull is curved with the lowest point of the curve occurring amidships.

Although a ship is built with her keel forming a straight line, her hull possesses flexibility and the distribution of weight that she carries usually causes some curvature in the keel and other longitudinal members once she is afloat. This curvature will vary with changes in the sizes and positions of weights carried and also with time. It has often been observed that the value of a vessel's hog or sag alters during the course of a voyage and this may reflect the conversion of loading stresses into hull deflections as the vessel works in a seaway.

Careful measurements taken aboard large bulk carriers have shown that curvature or distortion of the hull due to distribution of weights aboard is not parabolic and can be quite complex, with some parts of the hull sagging deeper than others. This is particularly true when the ship is loaded in alternate holds, or block loaded. These facts have a bearing upon the calculation of cargo tonnage by draught survey, particularly for the largest vessels, and the best way of taking account of them in draught surveys remains a matter for discussion.

The subject (discussed more fully in Chapter 13) is mentioned here because a vessel which is hogged can legally lift a greater tonnage of cargo than the same ship if sagged, as the former vessel has a greater displacement when loaded to her marks than has the latter. Fig. 8.3 illustrates this point. Bulk carriers when loaded conventionally are normally sagged. This comes about because all space amidships is available for cargo and can be filled, whilst spaces forward of the collision bulkhead and abaft the engine room bulkhead are empty or only part filled when the vessel is loaded.

A bulk carrier's 'official' deadweight is calculated assuming no hog or sag. If the vessel is sagged she will lift less than the 'official' figure, and this has been known to cause disputes between owners and charterers. The value of a vessel's sag can be reduced by reducing the tonnage of cargo carried in midship holds, and increasing the tonnage carried in the vessel's end holds, always provided that shear force and bending moment values are never excessive.

A Panamax bulk carrier when sagged 10 cm – and this is a modest figure – can lift about 150 mt less than she could lift if in the 'official' condition, neither hogged nor sagged. Reduction of this loss of lifting is a good reason for attempting to reduce the amount of sag, but will never justify exceeding the permitted values of shear forces and bending moments.

When a bulk carrier has a history of being sagged when fully loaded, as most bulk carriers do, it is realistic to recognise the fact, and to take account of it in deadweight calculations prior to loading by including a sag allowance when calculating the tonnage that the vessel can lift. This ensures that the charterers are informed of the ship's actual capacity. The appropriate sag allowance is the average or typical figure observed for sag for recent previous full cargoes. (ie, it is the average of negative corrections to the displacement in respect of deflection).

Unloading/ballasting plan

The unloading/ballasting plan must be prepared in the same way as the loading/deballasting one, and the IMO Form (Appendix 9.3) provides a useful way of recording the results of the calculations. Provided that a single grade of cargo is carried there will normally be no difficulty in preparing an unloading/ballasting plan which satisfies the requirements for draught, trim and longitudinal strength.

If a two-berth or a two-port discharge is required, it may be found difficult to comply with all the requirements. It is essential to make sure before the cargo is loaded that the ship will be safe and can comply with all the requirements from commencement of loading to completion of discharge.

When the cargo cannot be carried safely

Sometimes it will be found that there is no way that the proposed cargo can be safely and legally loaded, carried and discharged, because it is not possible to comply with all the requirements listed above. This is most likely to occur with segregated part cargoes for two-port, or two-berth, loading or discharge.

Whilst ship operators are usually well informed about a ship's dimensions and cargo capacity, they may not have the information or the knowledge to plan each step in the loading and to appreciate the insurmountable obstacles which can arise. In these circumstances the Master has no alternative but to inform his owners and charterers as soon as possible that the proposed cargo cannot be safely carried. He should be prepared to offer advice as to the best options which can be offered by a change of tonnages or port rotation.

Sources

5, 15, 92, 110, 111, 189, 190, 217, 218, 219. (See List of Sources, Page 497)

CHECKLIST – Procedure for planning the loading

Find maximum the ship can carry when fully laden

- ☐ Deadweight cargo or volume cargo?
- ☐ Decide values of other weights which must be carried. Keep the total weight of bunkers, ballast, bilge water, stores and miscellaneous weights as low as possible.

Identify any limiting stage in the voyage

- ☐ List maximum permitted draught for each stage in voyage.
- ☐ Select point where lightest draught is required (the limiting point).
- ☐ Calculate back and calculate forward from limiting point to ensure no other limits are met.
- ☐ Calculate maximum cargo which can be carried at limiting point.

Devise loading distribution

- ☐ Decide how many holds are to be loaded.
- ☐ Share the total cargo between the holds.
- ☐ Place fuel, fresh water and other weights in the positions intended for departure from the loading port.
- ☐ Calculate the ship's draught and trim on departure and ensure that they are acceptable.
- ☐ Calculate the ship's stability characteristics on departure and ensure that they are acceptable.
- ☐ Calculate the shear forces and bending moments on departure and ensure that they are not excessive.
- ☐ Check that the tonnage allotted to each hold is not greater than the classification society permits.
- ☐ Check that the hold tanktop loadings, and when carrying deck cargo that the deck and hatchtop loadings, are not excessive.
- ☐ If the ship is to be block loaded ensure that the loadings for individual holds remain within the special block loading limits set by the classification society and request limits if none has been provided.
- ☐ Work through the voyage and the proposed discharge, repeating the checks upon draught, trim, stability and longitudinal stress for every stage.
- ☐ If any results are unacceptable move cargo or other weights and recalculate. Check the results for errors.

Prepare loading/deballasting and unloading/ballasting plans

- ☐ For the plan use a suitable form, such as the IMO BLU Code form.
- ☐ Take note of the features of the berth, including least depth of water, least airdraught, number of loaders, distance loaders can travel.
- ☐ Plan for two or more pours into each hold.
- ☐ Commence loading amidships/aft to maintain a stern trim.
- ☐ Load alternatively aft, then forward, then aft, etc.
- ☐ Load the end holds midway through the loading.
- ☐ Discharge ballast from holds, then double bottoms, then topside tanks, and finally peak tanks.
- ☐ Discharge ballast from part of ship where cargo is being loaded.
- ☐ For each stage of the loading, match the time required for loading with the time required for deballasting.
- ☐ Plan to complete deballasting well before completion of loading.
- ☐ Observe any Class rules for loading/discharging.
- ☐ Observe any port rules and ballast water management plans for deballasting.
- ☐ Throughout loading keep ship in condition to put to sea in emergency, if required.
- ☐ Plan suitable trimming pours.
- ☐ Plan the discharge in the same manner and with the same objectives as the loading.
- ☐ Ensure that the ship complies with requirements for stability and for longitudinal stress at every stage throughout the loading and discharge.
- ☐ Inform owners/charterers as soon as possible if calculations show that the proposed cargo cannot be loaded, carried and discharged with safety.

CHAPTER 10

LOADING CALCULATIONS

Loading instruments, the use of loading manuals, their deficiencies and contents, displacement, stability and longitudinal strength calculations, choice of methods, practical considerations, grain stability, timber stability

It is an unfortunate fact that a great variety of abbreviations are used for stability expressions in the documents supplied to ships. In most cases abbreviations have not been used in this book to avoid confusion, but a table of abbreviations which are commonly used is at Appendix 10.1.

Equipment required for planning the loading

Planning the safe and efficient loading of a bulk carrier is a vitally important process, which makes it essential that the documents, information and equipment for planning the loading are easy to use and readily available. All bulk carriers over 150m of length are required[149] to be equipped with an approved loading instrument and it is increasingly likely that almost all smaller vessels are equipped with one too. Guidelines for the design, provision and use of shipboard computers, and for loading and stability computer programs, have been issued by the IMO[114]. They represent good practice and are being adopted throughout the industry.

Loadicators and loading computers – the equipment: Loadicators and loading computers are similar instruments, the principal difference between them being that a loadicator is made only for loading calculations and cannot be used for ship's accounts, spare parts records or word processing whilst a loading computer is a conventional PC which could be used for a variety of tasks, including loading calculations, depending upon the software used with it, though in practice it is often used only for loading calculations. Redundancy is achieved in some systems by having the program installed on the 'C' drives of at least two separate PCs so that failure of one will not compromise the other. Hardware and software will both be recorded on the Type Approval Certificate.

Older hardware may consist of a plan of the ship with lights to indicate percentage bending moments and shear forces, and a small digital panel to display the values at a chosen frame. More modern equipment will consist of a monitor, a keyboard, a printer and a hard disc or processor, and in the case of the loadicator all these may be assembled in a single unit (Fig. 10.1). The loadicator's memory or the hard disc of the computer contains past and present records and all the data necessary for calculating the ship's stability.

Rules and procedures to be observed: A ship equipped with a loadicator or loading computer should have evidence that the instrument has been approved by her classification society. This may consist of a brass plate, firmly attached to the side of the equipment, showing the classification stamp and the surveyor's initials, or of a certificate issued by the classification society and displayed on the bulkhead by the equipment. The instruction book for the instrument is usually one of the listed plans for the vessel and will normally contain either the classification stamp or a statement that the loading computer has been approved. At least two copies of the instruction manual and of the test conditions or test report should be available, one of these to be a fair copy to be kept in the Master's care, available for copying when the working copy becomes damaged and difficult to use.

It is recommended[114] that at least two copies of all constant data in computer files, such as ship geometry and tables, should be available on independent storage units such as CD-ROMs, tapes or floppy discs. A Master copy of the disc should be kept by the Shipmaster in a safe place. The working copy should be treated with care and protected from abrasion, dirt, heat and sunlight. A further recommendation is that careful procedures should be established so that revisions to the program, required if the ship is altered, are properly tracked and forwarded to the ship. Each revision delivered to the ship should include replacement pages for the user's manual and instructions on how to delete obsolete files and install replacement (revised) files. The process should include an 'action complete' report back to shoreside management.

To prevent a virus attack, all ships' computers containing loading programs should be equipped with a regularly updated anti-virus program. CD-ROMs, discs or floppies from unknown or non virus screened sources should not be used in a computer containing the stability program. It is always preferable that the ship's loading computer is used only for ship's stability and its use is restricted to authorised ship's personnel.

In 2007 a ship operator reported three instances of misuse of the shipboard computers[200]. In one case the officer of the watch, at sea, had been found playing a computer game on the bridge computer. On a second ship a non-approved program had been installed on a chart correcting computer, which immobilised it. The ship's staff on a third ship, trying to remedy a perceived fault, fitted an incompatible 'uninterrupted power supply' to the computer which caused it to malfunction. The fleet in question was reminded about the following company policies which are well worth noting.

1. No unauthorised program should be loaded on any of a ship's computers.
2. All ships' computers should be regularly checked for unauthorised programs and viruses.
3. The bridge computer is installed only for chart correction and watch-keeping programs and to assist deck officers in administrative tasks and should only be used in port, or by off-duty staff while at sea.

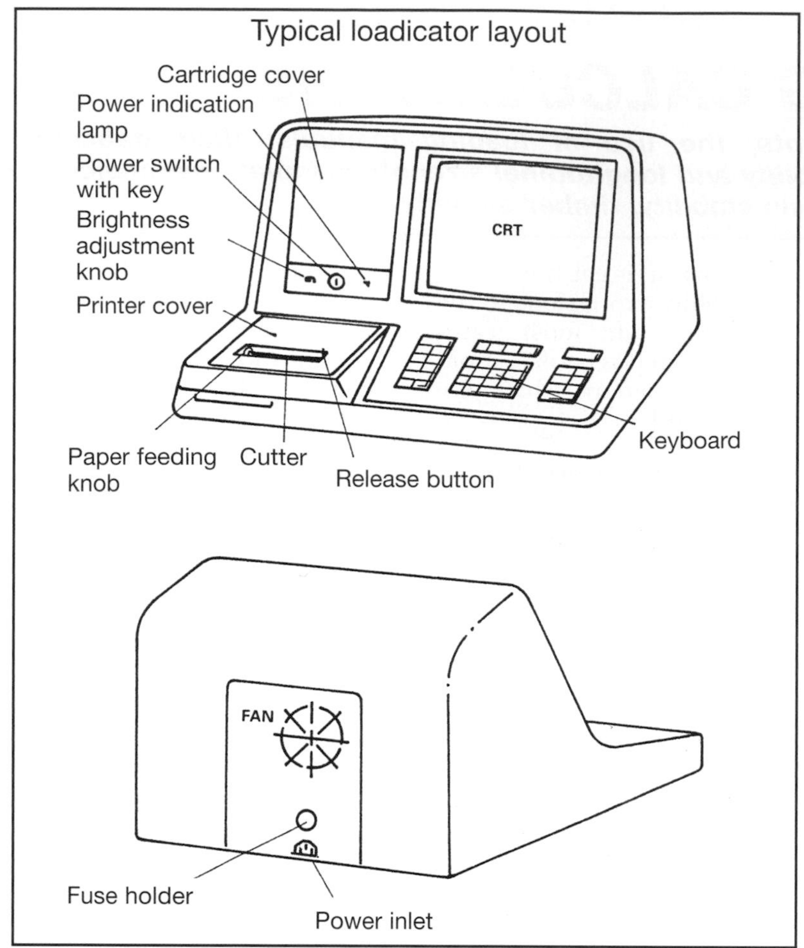

Figure 10.1

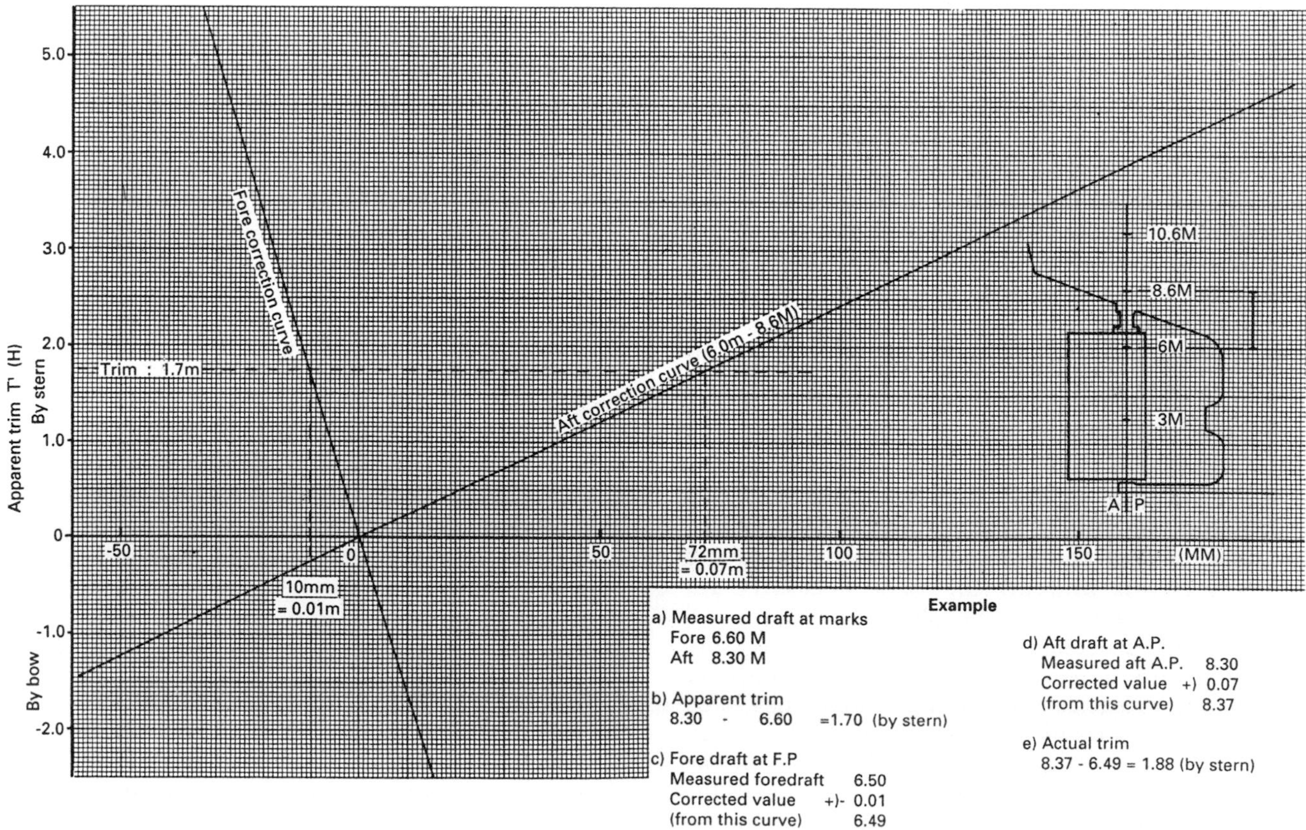

Figure 10.2

4. If any unauthorised software is detected, the company is to be consulted to determine a safe method of uninstalling such programs without damage to equipment or loss of data.
5. The company should be consulted in case of any software or hardware defect or deficiency and hasty, unilateral action must not be taken.

Using a loading instrument: A method for independently verifying that the program is working correctly should be provided. Ideally the opening screen which appears when the program is started should present a self-diagnostic report on program functioning. Alternatively a range of sample loading conditions can be furnished on paper which can be manually entered into the program for comparison with correct draughts, trim and available GM. These checks should be made regularly, particularly when a new series of calculations is being started.

When the instrument is a computer, a succession of 'pages' can be displayed on the monitor, providing the opportunity for the user to enter or change the details of any proposed loading, which the user inputs with the keyboard. The data which the user enters are displayed on the monitor. When so instructed the instrument calculates the trim, stability and strength characteristics of any proposed loading. The instrument is connected to a printer and can print out a full standard printout of the results (Appendix 10.2). The instrument calculates the results almost instantaneously. There is normally a facility for saving at least ten calculated conditions in the memory, and modern machines can save hundreds of conditions. Shear forces and bending moments, when displayed, are usually expressed as a percentage of the maximum permitted values as well as tonnes and tonnes/metres (or kN and kNm), as they would be if calculated manually.

Care of computerised loadicators and loading computers: When not in use the instrument and the printer should be switched off and they and the printer paper should be covered over to protect them from dust. Ships carrying bulk cargoes are not clinically clean places. The data in the memory (hard disc) will be retained even though the power is switched off. The cooling fan, usually situated at the back of the instrument, must be left clear. Under no circumstances should food or liquids be allowed near the computer. Spilt coffee or bits of bread can cause many problems with the computer keyboard. The computer printer should be kept in good working order and an adequate stock of printer spares such as cartridges should be held. If the loadicator or loading computer breaks down this should be immediately reported to owners or managers as it is a Class item and its repair should be treated as a matter of urgency even if an alternative computer is available.

It is not acceptable for ships to use dirty, dog-eared and illegible loading manuals for planning the loading, nor for officers to be provided with loading instructions and guidance which are badly composed and written in broken English or in another language that they cannot understand. The value of a loading computer or loadicator is much reduced when its instruction manual has been lost, and problems are likely when all copies of the ship's stability software are on CD-ROMs or floppy discs, loose and unprotected, in a dirty drawer in the ship's office.

Approved stability booklet and loading manual – the essentials: The ship's stability information is provided in one or several booklets, often running to more than 200 A4 pages. These approved stability booklets and loading manuals, which are referred to hereafter as loading manuals, are usually prepared by the shipbuilder and stamped with a seal of approval by a classification society or Flag State Administration. In addition to at least one volume containing general stability information, examples of loading calculations and details of standard loadings, there may be additional volumes dealing with such subjects as grain and timber loading. One full set of loading manuals is likely to be securely fastened with permanent rivets or with seals to prevent the removal or addition of pages, and should be kept by the Master for production to the authorities when required.

The chief officer should be provided with a second full set of loading manuals, in good condition as a working set. Better still, if he is provided with two full working sets, one for him and a second for the surveyor, then draught surveys will be completed more quickly. A fourth set should be available in the company head office to photocopy, or on disk to print, when a replacement set is required aboard ship since the chief mate's set may become dog-eared and dirty with frequent handling over a period of years.

The *Instructions to Masters* and the *Notes for Guidance* which the loading manuals contain should be available to the Master and his officers in a clearly written form in a language with which they are familiar and if that language is not English then also in English[150]. Included with the documents should be blank copies of the stability and stress calculation forms for use in making longhand stability and stress calculations.

Loading manuals

Use of loading manuals: When using the working copy of the loading manual for the first time after joining the ship, the following checks are recommended.

- Confirm that the master copy has been stamped by the current classification society and/or national administration and that the information is 'final' and not 'provisional'.
- Look for any indications that the manual under inspection is only part of the full stability information. For example, a note on the cover might read 'Vol.1 of 3' to show that the full information was contained in three volumes. Bring together the full set of loading manuals.
- Ensure that the working copy is complete with no pages missing and that its contents are the same as those of the master copy. Officers should never enter any comments or amendments in the loading manuals.
- Inspect the manual carefully from cover to cover for any restrictions on loading. Instructions similar to those quoted below, but varying from ship to ship, should be at the front of the manual but may in practice be found anywhere in it:
    - The draught forward in rough sea should not be less than 7.32 m (24 ft) when slamming is expected. (*Seven-hold Panamax vessel*)

- Cargo holds Nos. 4 and 5 are permitted to be used as ballast tanks under either full or empty conditions during the ballast voyage. The holds have sufficient strength for a temporary partial filling between 20 per cent and 90 per cent only when weather conditions are fair and heavy rolling is avoided. (*Seven-hold Panamax vessel*)
- For short-range coastal voyages, No.3 hold need not be ballasted, but propeller must be 100 per cent immersed and shaft revolutions must not exceed 89 rpm. (*Five-hold handy-sized vessel*).
- Allowable values for shearing forces and bending moments are...etc.
- Maximum permitted uniform loads on tank top, decks and hatch covers are...etc. (*Handy-sized vessel*)
- Where cargo is loaded and unloaded in two ports, it is preferable to load cargo in Nos. 2 and 4 holds at the first loading port and to discharge from Nos. 1, 3 and 5 holds at the first unloading port. If it is required to load cargo first in Nos. 1, 3 and 5 holds, or discharge first from Nos. 2 and 4 holds, No. 3 double-bottom tanks must be filled to reduce the excess hogging moment. (*Five-hold handy-sized vessel*)
- When ship is fully ballasted with No.6 hold filled, No.4 topside tanks (adjacent to No.6 hold) must be empty. (*Nine-hold Cape-sized vessel*)
- No.2 hold and No.8 hold are only to be used for in port 'slack' ballast. These holds are not to be used for sea going ballast. (*Nine hold Cape-sized vessel*)

Deficiencies of loading manuals: The loading manuals supplied to most ships are, unfortunately, not user friendly. Many of them are bound in a manner which causes them to close unless they are being held open. This method of binding may be an efficient way to prevent the removal of pages, but it makes the manuals very difficult to use as working documents. The quality of the English used in manuals is often very poor, stumbling and inaccurate. Text which is difficult for a native English speaker to understand must be even more difficult for someone who speaks English only as a foreign language.

Essential instructions about the ways in which the ship is **not** to be loaded are often not given sufficient emphasis. All restrictions upon the way the ship can be loaded should appear prominently at the front of the manual. They should not appear as item 28 in a contents list of 52 items, appearing on page 176 of the manual, as was found in one loading manual.

Since loading manuals are produced by naval architects in many countries and each one is approved by one of many classification societies, it is perhaps not surprising that their contents are not standardised. It is, however, a cause for regret that they differ so widely in the layouts adopted and the expressions used. There are great differences, too, in the amount of data presented, and the manner of their presentation, with one loading manual adopting tabular presentation and the next graphical display for the same data.

These differences and deficiencies create unnecessary difficulties for ships' personnel who still require to use the loading manuals to learn about the ship's basic characteristics, to find explanations for what the loading instrument is telling them and to make non-standard calculations. For example some of the programs provided on loading instruments for bulk carriers assume that all cargoes will act through the geometrical centre of the hold and make no provision for cargoes, such as steel products, which may be positioned away from the centre. When this is the case accurate strength, trim and stability calculations can only be made separately from the loading program. The loading manual will continue to be needed in these circumstances and also when the loading instrument has broken down, or when an officer wants to complete the calculations manually.

Contents of loading manuals

(See CD inside front cover)

Although the titles given to the graphs and tables will vary from manual to manual the information discussed below is to be found in most – perhaps even all – loading manuals. The basic information which the manual contains (and its purpose) is described. This commentary draws attention to common problems and is intended to help readers to use a loading manual.

Ships's principal particulars: These may be accompanied by a copy of the general arrangement plan, or the capacity plan. This information is for general reference and can usually also be found elsewhere.

Abbreviations used in this manual: This list, of which five examples are summarised in Appendix 10.1 is important since different manuals use a wide variety of different abbreviations which may be unknown to the user, and it is often difficult to guess the meaning of a particular abbreviation. Unfortunately, these lists are often incomplete.

Capacity tables for tanks and holds: These tables (Appendix 1.4) list the cubic capacity of every hold and tank and the longitudinal and vertical positions of its centre of gravity. The transverse position of the centre of gravity may also be given. The weight of the normal contents (fresh water, salt water, fuel oil, etc) of the tank when full is also given. This information can be useful when listing weights and levers for trim and stability calculations, but the position of the centre of gravity must be corrected if the compartment is not full, and the weight of the contents must be corrected if the specific gravity of the contents is other than that assumed in the table.

Draught correction due to trim: The ship's stability data are compiled on the basis that the draught measurements are taken at the forward and after perpendiculars, and exactly amidships. In practice the draught marks are often not marked in these positions. When the ship has a trim the readings must be corrected to obtain the values at the perpendiculars and amidships, and an explanation of the correction is normally provided. (Fig.10.2)

Worked example for displacement calculations: The displacement calculation (Appendix 10.7) starts with the draughts as read and corrects them for trim and deflection of the hull to give the mean of mean draughts. The displacement which corresponds to the mean of mean draughts is read from the hydrostatic tables. The displacement is corrected for any list, for first and second trim corrections (layer correction and form correction), and for density of the water in which the ship is floating. These corrections, for which tables may be provided in the loading manual, are described in greater detail in Chapter 13.

Hydrostatic tables: These tables (Fig.10.3) provide values for each item of the ship's hydrostatic data for a range of possible mean draughts. Hydrostatic tables normally show displacement in salt water of specific gravity 1.025, but occasionally other values (for example, 35 cubic ft/long ton = 1.02518) are used. The tables should be carefully inspected to confirm, if possible, that the SG used is 1.025 and to note whether weights are given in long tons or metric tonnes.

Worked example of trim and stability calculation: The basic trim and stability calculation, to calculate how the ship will be trimmed and the value of her fluid metacentric height (G_OM) when certain weights have been loaded, is familiar to most seafarers and each case is normally shown on a single page in the loading manual. The calculation is shown in Appendix 10.8. All the intended weights for cargo and bunkers, etc, are entered along with the ship's lightweight, as are the vertical (VCG) and longitudinal (LCG) positions of their centres of gravity, measured upwards from the keel and horizontally from a reference point which is usually amidships, but occasionally the after perpendicular (AP) as in the case of the Diamond 53 class.

The values of LCGs are measured either forward or aft from the reference point, forward measurements being distinguished from aft measurements either by entering them in separate columns or by giving them different signs. The sign convention used – (–) sign shows forward from the reference point and trim by the head, and (+) sign shows aft from the reference point and trim by the stern – is reversed in some loading manuals, so it is always necessary to be sure which convention is adopted in the manual in use.

Values for the LCG and VCG can be taken from the capacity tables for tanks and holds, but it may be necessary to use corrected values. (See below under 'CGs of part-filled compartments'.)

Free surface moments (inertia moments, moments of inertia, I or i) must also be entered in respect of any part-filled tanks. These data may appear in special tables of free surface moments (Appendix 10.4), or may be included in the information provided for each tank, either in the loading manual or the tank calibration tables. (See below under 'Free surface moments'.)

When weights, CGs and free surface moments have been entered in the trim calculation sheet, the vertical moments (product of weight and VCG) and longitudinal moments (product of weight and LCG) must be calculated and entered and the columns must be summed to provide total weights (the displacement), total vertical moments, total longitudinal moments and total free surface moments. From these the values of VCG, LCG for the loaded vessel and virtual rise of the centre of gravity due to free surface (GG_0) are calculated by dividing each of the moments by the displacement.

Draught, moment to change trim 1 cm (MTC), position of longitudinal centre of buoyancy (LCB), position of longitudinal centre of flotation (LCF) and transverse metacentric height (TKM), all corresponding to the calculated displacement, are to be obtained from the hydrostatic tables. With this information the trim and the forward and after draughts are calculated. GG_0 is used to amend the VCG to obtain G_0M, the fluid metacentric height. (For the detailed working of a trim and stability calculation see Appendix 10.8.)

Worked example of construction and use of the statical stability curve: The ability of a ship to return to the upright when inclined by an external force is of considerable importance. It is this which governs the ship's capacity to avoid capsizing in adverse swell and weather. The ship's statical stability curve (the GZ or righting lever curve) provides a measure of the ship's range of stability, (the range of heel over which she will return to the upright when inclined), and of her stability characteristics.

The International Load Line Convention, 1966, Regulation 10, Para. 2, requires the Master of every ship to be provided with sufficient stability information to ensure that the ship remains stable under varying conditions of service. Under this regulation, maritime administrations specify minimum stability criteria which all ships must meet, in any sailing condition (Appendix 10.5). Most of these criteria are measured from the statical stability curve, so the curve must be constructed, measurements must be taken and calculations completed in respect of each critical stage of the voyage.

This process, fully described in Appendix 10.9, is a complex and tedious one which is seldom clearly described in loading manuals. When there is no alternative the longhand calculations must be undertaken for the worst condition of each voyage. The worst condition of the voyage is, of course, the condition in which the ship possesses the least positive stability. When a single cargo for one-port loading and discharge is carried, the worst condition usually occurs upon arrival in the discharging port or upon arrival in a bunkering port before discharge. However, a number of other factors such as the distribution of part cargoes and free surface effects in bunker or ballast tanks can create worst conditions at other stages, and it is prudent to check the stability for all departures and arrivals and for intermediate conditions when stability is small.

Simplified stability information: As already stated, the construction of the statical stability curve and the completion of the associated calculations are complicated procedures. Aboard ships which are suitably equipped, the process can be avoided by using a loading instrument. Alternatively, simplified stability information has been included within the loading manuals of some newer ships and this information (when properly presented) provides a comparatively quick and easy method of finding if a particular loading will satisfy the minimum stability criteria.

The simplified stability information may be presented as a diagram or as a table in one of several different ways, of which three are mentioned here.

Maximum 'deadweight moment': An example of a diagram used for this method is attached (Fig. 10.3). Using the arguments *Displacement* or *Draught* on the

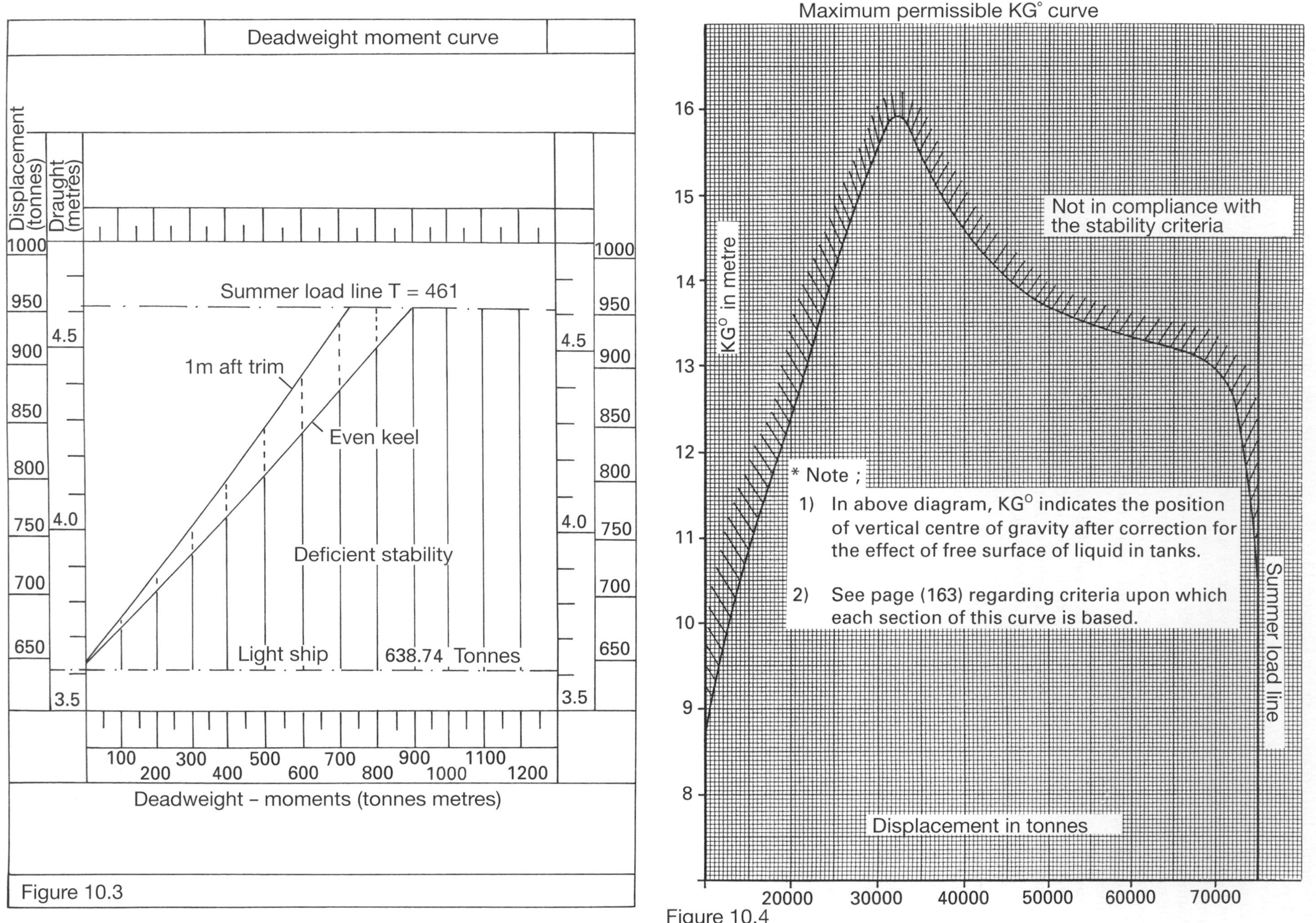

Figure 10.3

Figure 10.4

vertical axis and *Deadweight moments* on the horizontal axis, a position is plotted. The deadweight moments required for this plot are the total vertical moments, including the free surface moments. The diagram shows a sector in which the stability is deficient or unacceptable, with the boundary of this sector varying according to the vessel's trim. Inspection of the diagram shows whether the plotted position in any particular case falls within the deficient stability sector. If the plot shows that the stability is deficient, the minimum criteria have not been satisfied and the ship must not go to sea or be at sea in the condition examined.

Maximum permissible KG: An example of a diagram used for this method is attached (Fig. 10.4), the vessel in question being a Panamax bulk carrier. British shipping industry sources are reported[17] to prefer this approach, using maximum permissible KG with a graphical presentation. The diagram is entered with arguments KG (corrected for free surface effect) and displacement, and the stability is acceptable provided that the plotted point does not fall in the area marked 'Not in compliance with the stability criteria'. One limitation of the diagram (Fig. 10.4) is that it stops at the Summer Load Line. Bulk carriers frequently load to tropical marks in West African, Indian, South American and North Australian ports and could not use this diagram to check their departure stability.

Minimum permissible GM: This simplified method, used by the Diamond 53 ships but not illustrated here, is similar in its general approach to the two methods described above, but plots the value of GM.

Simplified stability information like the three methods listed above has been provided in some loading manuals since the 1980s or even earlier, but its purpose has seldom been clearly explained. When well designed, the simplified stability information provides a quick means of ensuring that the minimum stability criteria are satisfied, as required by international regulations. Such diagrams or tables, if provided, should be found and used. Where the information is poorly presented, as is too often the case, owners and builders should be informed so that improvements can be achieved in the future.

Longitudinal strength: For many small and handy-sized bulk carriers the calculations already listed – namely, the calculation of draught, trim and stability – complete the basic calculations required. For larger bulk carriers and for those strengthened for loading in alternate holds there is, in addition, a requirement to calculate the longitudinal shear forces and bending moments in order to ensure that the maximum permitted values stated by the classification society are not exceeded. For such vessels the loading manuals will contain appropriate data, which are discussed below.

Longitudinal strength calculations

Nature of longitudinal stresses: Longitudinal shear forces are forces which tend to break or shear the ship across. Longitudinal bending moments are those moments which tend to bend a ship along her length, causing her to hog or sag. Both are a consequence of the irregular way that the hull weight, cargo and buoyancy are distributed along the length of the ship (Fig. 10.5).

Values to be calculated: Values for shear forces and bending moments are normally calculated at the positions of the ship's transverse watertight bulkheads, although computerised calculations often consider a larger number of stations. The shear force acting at a bulkhead (or other station) is the algebraic sum of the loads acting on either side of the bulkhead, whilst the bending moment acting at a bulkhead is the algebraic sum of the moments acting on either side of the bulkhead.

When a ship is in equilibrium in still water, values of shear force (SF) and bending moments (BM) at a specified bulkhead can be expressed as follows:

SF = W1 + W2 – W3

BM = M1 + M2 – M3

where

W1 = the constant lightship weight abaft the specified bulkhead, in tonnes

W2 = the deadweight carried abaft the specified bulkhead, in tonnes

W3 = the buoyancy acting abaft the specified bulkhead, in tonnes

M1 = the moment of W1 about the specified bulkhead, in tonnes-metres

M2 = the moment of W2 about the specified bulkhead, in tonnes-metres

M3 = the moment of W3 about the specified bulkhead, in tonnes-metres.

Of the foregoing, W1 and M1 are constant values reflecting the ship's light weight and are contained in tables provided in the loading manual. W3 and M3, the values of buoyancy, depend upon draught and trim and must be extracted from tables provided in the loading manual. W2 and M2 depend upon the weights loaded and their positions. These values must be compiled and entered by the person making the calculation.

Simplified calculation of longitudinal strength: In the more user-friendly loading manuals, the corrections to SFs and BMs for lightweight and for buoyancy have been combined to produce two tables instead of four. When the tables are entered with bulkhead frame number, displacement and trim, it is possible to extract a single correction for the shear force and another for the bending moments.

These combined corrections are sometimes known as S-values. Some manuals divide all the values in this calculation by 1,000 at the start of the calculation, and multiply by 1,000 at the end, apparently to make the numbers more manageable. Whilst some loading manuals require the user to use the weights and moments *abaft* the specified bulkhead, others use the weights and moments *forward* of the bulkhead.

Procedure for the calculation of shear forces and bending moments: It is not possible to provide explanations for all the different methods found in loading manuals for the calculation of shear forces and bending moments. To illustrate one approach, a description of the process for the *Regina Oldendorff* is provided. Aboard other ships where the information

Shear forces and bending moments

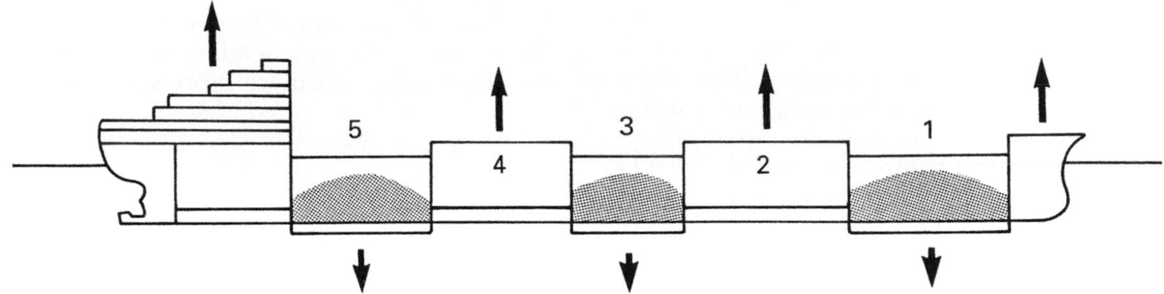

Shear Forces are those forces which tend to break or shear the vessel across.

The vessel is exposed to forces due to the weight of the structure, the weight of the cargo, the forces of buoyancy, and direct hydrostatic pressure. When these forces are not in balance at every point along the length of the vessel shear forces will exist.

Shear forces are normally expressed in tonnes.

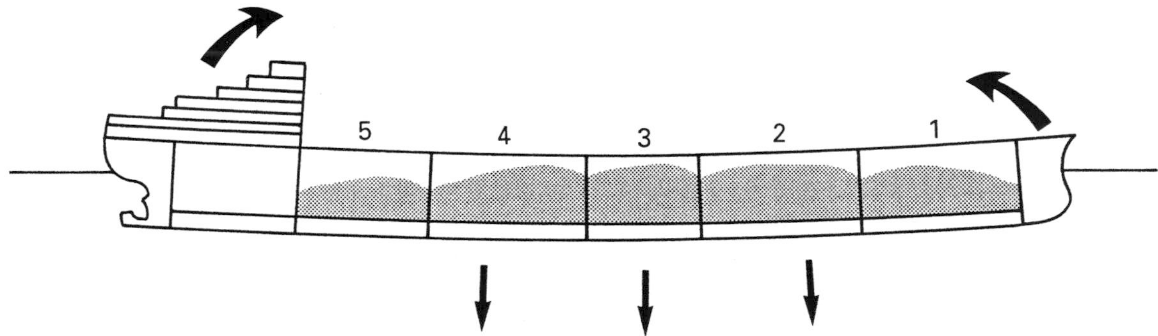

Bending Moments are those moments which tend to bend a vessel along its length, causing it to hog or sag. The bending moment at any point along the length of the vessel is equal to the algebraic sum of the moments of all loads acting between that point and one end of the vessel.

Bending moments are normally expressed in tonnes-metres.

Figure 10.5

in the loading manual is presented in a different manner, it may not be possible to use this method of calculation.

The procedure, summarised below, is fully explained in Appendix 10.10. First, appropriate values are entered in a calculation sheet. The sheet is divided into columns with a column for each of the ship's transverse bulkheads, which are identified by their respective frame numbers. All the weights abaft (ie, aft of) each bulkhead must be listed and totalled. The moments of each of these weights must also be listed and totalled and for this the distance of the centre of gravity (CG) of each weight from the relevant bulkhead is required. This distance is obtained by comparing the distance of the CG and of the bulkhead from midships.

For example: all the holds and almost all the tanks are abaft the collision (forepeak) bulkhead; all loaded compartments except those forward of the collision bulkhead are listed in the column for the collision bulkhead (frame 219 on the *Regina Oldendorff*). Each of the weights is then also entered in each of the remaining columns if it is abaft the bulkhead under consideration. The No.1 fresh water tank (FWT), for example, is located in the stern abaft every bulkhead in the ship, so a weight in the No.1 FWT is listed in every column. A weight in No. 1 hold, on the other hand, is abaft only the bulkhead at frame 219 (the collision bulkhead) so it is listed only in that column. The result of this procedure is that a decreasing number of weights is listed in each column as one proceeds from collision bulkhead towards engine room bulkhead. Very few weights are carried abaft the engine room aft bulkhead (frame 12 on the *Regina Oldendorff*), so very few items are listed in Column 12.

The distance of each weight from the bulkhead must be recalculated for each column, since the weight is a different distance from each of the bulkheads considered. When the weights and moments in each column have been totalled, they must be adjusted in a series of steps which take account of the lightweight of the ship and its distribution, the vessel's buoyancy when even keel and its correction for trim, to produce the values of SF and BM at the bulkhead under consideration. For correct results in these as in other stability and stress calculations, the signs (+ or –) of the numbers used must be shown and used correctly in the calculations.

Bulkhead correction: When the values of the shear forces have been obtained from the above calculations they can be reduced by a correction known as the bulkhead correction. The correction allows for the fact that some of the load caused by cargo in adjacent holds is transferred to the transverse bulkhead through the double bottom structure instead of through the side shell plating. Because this is so the stress on the ship is reduced: the bulkhead correction is recognition of this fact. The correction is only significant when the ship is loaded in alternate holds. When she is loaded in all holds the correction will be small and will not be needed.

The value of the correction is calculated by comparing the shear force at a bulkhead with the shear forces at one of the adjacent bulkheads (Fig. 10.6), and then with the shear force at the other adjacent bulkhead. The difference obtained in each comparison is multiplied by a factor obtained from the loading manual, and the lesser of the two values so obtained is used to reduce the value of the calculated shear force. If the bulkhead correction is ignored, the longitudinal stresses appear to be greater than they really are, so the correction can safely be ignored if the stresses are within the permitted limits.

Calculated values of SF and BM: The purpose of calculating the values of SF and BM is to ensure that any proposed loading does not exceed the values specified by the classification society. The maximum permitted values are listed in the loading manual and should be shown prominently, though in practice they are sometimes difficult to find. Several sets of maximum permitted values may be stated for different conditions. For example, the permitted values are higher when the ship is in port than when she is at sea; they may be higher when the ship is loaded homogeneously than when she is jump loaded in alternate holds with a high-density cargo; and they may be higher when she is sagged than when she is hogged. If it is found that the proposed loading does exceed the maximum permitted values, it is unsafe and cannot be used and an alternative distribution of weights will have to be tried.

SF and BM diagrams: When the values of shear forces (SF) and bending moments (BM) have been obtained a SF and BM diagram can be drawn. Whilst this is not essential to a safe loading, it will help to show the distribution of longitudinal stresses, and irregularities in the diagram may draw attention to errors in the calculation.

In the diagram the shear force curve should be drawn by joining the calculated values with straight lines. The calculated values of bending moments should be joined by a fair curve. Peak and trough values of bending moments will occur in positions where the shear forces are zero. A typical diagram is at Fig. 10.7, whilst the diagram which accompanies the worked example at Appendix 10.10 draws attention to an interesting fact. When a bending moment curve is obtained by joining the values for BM at each bulkhead in a smooth curve, the curve does not appear to comply with the rules. It does not have peak or trough values in each position where the shear force curve is zero. The explanation for this is that, when additional values of BM are plotted between the bulkheads, it becomes clear that the BM curve is an undulating one with peak or trough values which coincide with the zero values of SF. It does not matter that the normal plot, taking values only at the bulkheads, does not detect the peaks and troughs. The classification society will have taken account of this when setting the limiting values at the bulkheads.

SF and BM diagrams produced by loadicator or computer (Appendix 10.2) may look rather different from hand-drawn diagrams which should look more like the example in Appendix 10.10. This is because the loading instrument may be used to calculate stress values at much more frequent intervals, thus producing a more complex curve.

SF and BM diagrams are usually plotted against scales which show actual values. Alternatively, it is possible to plot them as a percentage of the maximum

Method of shear force correction using the bulkhead factor (according to ABS rules and regulations 6-3-3-C)

1. The shear force correction

   Q correction = Q difference * bulkhead factor

   Q difference = The net buoyance (or load) of a hold, derived from the change in shear forces along the length of the hold.

Hold No.	Bulkhead correction factor
1	0.1311
2 thru 6	0.2394
7	0.1891

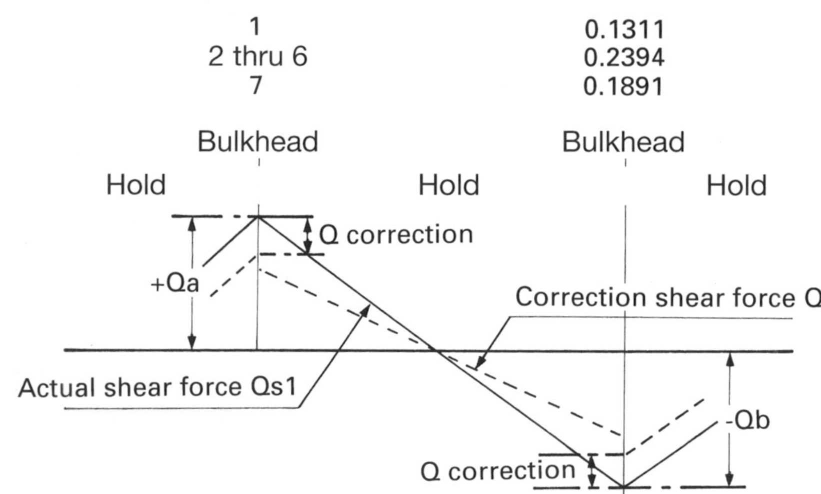

When Qa and Qb are of different sign
Q difference = Qa - (-Qb) = Qa + Qb

When Qa and Qb are of the same sign
Q difference = (Qa - Qb)

2. The corrected shear force : QF

   Qf = Qsl - Q correction

   * Qsl : The actual shear force at the bulkhead under consideration
   * Q correction to be used is the lesser of the values derived for adjacent holds.

Figure 10.6

Example of use of bulkhead correction factor to correct the shear force

Fr. / BULK Fac1 / Fr. / BULK Fac2 / Fr.	Shear Force ② / Shear Force ① / Shear Force ③	④=①-② / ⑤=①-③	⑥=④ xBulk Fac1 / ⑦=⑤ xBulk Fac2	⑧=①-⑥ / ⑨=①-⑦	⑩
47	3870				3870
0.1891					
77	-234				-234
0.2394					
107	-2892				-2892
0.2394					
137	-5470	-2578 / -9379	-617 / -2245	-4853 / -3225	-4853
0.2394					
167	3909				3909
0.2394					
197	1794				1794
0.2394					
227	-510				-510
0.1311					
258	-1716				-1716

①,②,③ : Actual shear force at each Fr.
④,⑤ : Shear force difference value
⑥,⑦ : Shear force correction value
⑩ : Corrected shear force (the greater of the value between ⑧ & ⑨

permitted value, a method which provides a less cluttered graph (Appendix 10.10). Since different limiting values are provided for different conditions of loading, it is essential to specify the limits used.

Manual calculation of longitudinal stresses: Such methods as the foregoing are often optimistically described by those who produce loading manuals as 'simplified methods of calculation' or 'rapid and simple hand calculations' for longitudinal strength. In reality some of the systems presented are poorly constructed, complicated and difficult to follow. Even the best of them require the extraction from tables of a substantial number of figures which must then be entered on the calculation sheet along with a further large number of figures from other sources. Finally, to obtain the SFs and BMs, a large number of additions and subtractions must be made accurately. When this process has been completed, the stresses arising from a single distribution of weights have been calculated. The entire process must be repeated whenever the consequences of an alternative weight distribution are required.

The most successful way to approach this repetitive work is to extract and enter the data systematically, starting from the forward bulkhead and transferring data across the columns where possible. A blank form constructed on chart paper with data entered in pencil may save time if the form when completed is then photocopied to preserve a record of the calculation. Thereafter the data which have changed can be erased and the form can be used again.

At its best the procedure is slow and cumbersome and it is most unlikely that it is always used, as it should be on ships without loading instruments in working order, to verify that every stage in the proposed loading programme lies within safe limits.

Stability and stress calculations – options

Possible methods of calculation: There is a requirement, described above, for a number of calculations to be made to establish the ship's draught, trim, stability and longitudinal stress values for successive steps during the loading and during the voyage. The calculations may be done on a computer or loadicator or with pencil and paper, although if there is no dedicated instrument with specialist software many of the necessary calculations can still be done by computer or calculator.

Calculations by computer or loadicator: Calculations by computer or loadicator use software which is tailor-made for the ship on which it is being used, with the ship's dimensions and hydrostatic data already entered. Such calculations are quick and easy when compared with the alternatives, but they still call for the accurate keying in of all the weights loaded and discharged at every stage in the loading and the voyage.

For most ships the software provided for stability and stress calculation has been designed to show the final condition before sailing, using a layout similar to that used for the standard conditions in the ship's loading manual. This makes it possible to confirm that the ship's condition is satisfactory before she puts to sea. This calculation can be repeated for each stage in the loading, giving results suitable for insertion into the mandatory Loading/Unloading Plan (Appendix 9.3).

Regrettably, many software packages do not provide a printout which summarises on a single sheet all the steps in a loading/deballasting or discharging/ballasting programme, but most packages do allow the Master to check that every stage in the loading or discharging programme is safe and give immediate warning to the operator if he keys-in a weight which will cause stresses or trim in excess of allowable limits.

Longhand calculation: Calculations with pencil and paper are very time-consuming and for more difficult loadings many hours may be needed to complete them properly. To avoid error they should be completed in a standard format, using blank copies of the ship's trim and stability calculation form and shear force and bending moment form. Completed samples of these forms should be, and normally are, provided in the ship's loading manual. Blank forms should be available aboard; if they are not they must be made.

Copies of the completed calculations should be retained and filed. They will be useful if similar cargoes are carried again and will provide evidence as required by the International Safety Management Code that the ship has been operating safely[152].

Stability calculation – practical considerations

It is good practice for the Master to inspect and sign a copy of the stability calculation printout, to be kept by the chief mate, before commencement of loading or discharging. This ensures that he sees it and can consider its detail as far as he finds necessary, as required by Safety Management Systems.

Centres of gravity of full compartments: Positions of centres of gravity (CGs) for grain space and for bale space within the holds may be stated in the loading manual. Provided that compartments are full, the CGs for grain space should be used for all bulk cargoes except for unitised cargoes such as timber or woodpulp, for which the bale space CGs are appropriate.

Vertical CGs of part-filled compartments: When a compartment is only partly filled the position of the vertical centre of gravity (VCG) of its contents will be lowered. If the reduction in height of the centre of gravity is ignored in calculations the inaccuracy is a 'safe' one which makes the ship appear less stable than she really is. This error will have no effect upon the accuracy of the calculation of the ship's trim and longitudinal stresses and can be ignored provided that the calculations still show that the vessel has adequate stability. In cases in which the ship's positive stability is small, it will be necessary to take account of the actual height and distribution of each weight. This will lead to the use of an amended height of the VCG.

For bunker and ballast tanks and grain loaded holds, the position of the CG of the compartment when part filled may be provided in the form of a graph or table in the ship's loading manual or tank calibration tables. If not available from graph or table, it must be calculated or estimated using prudent approximations. For a VCG it is prudent to assume a position a little higher than its actual position. It is

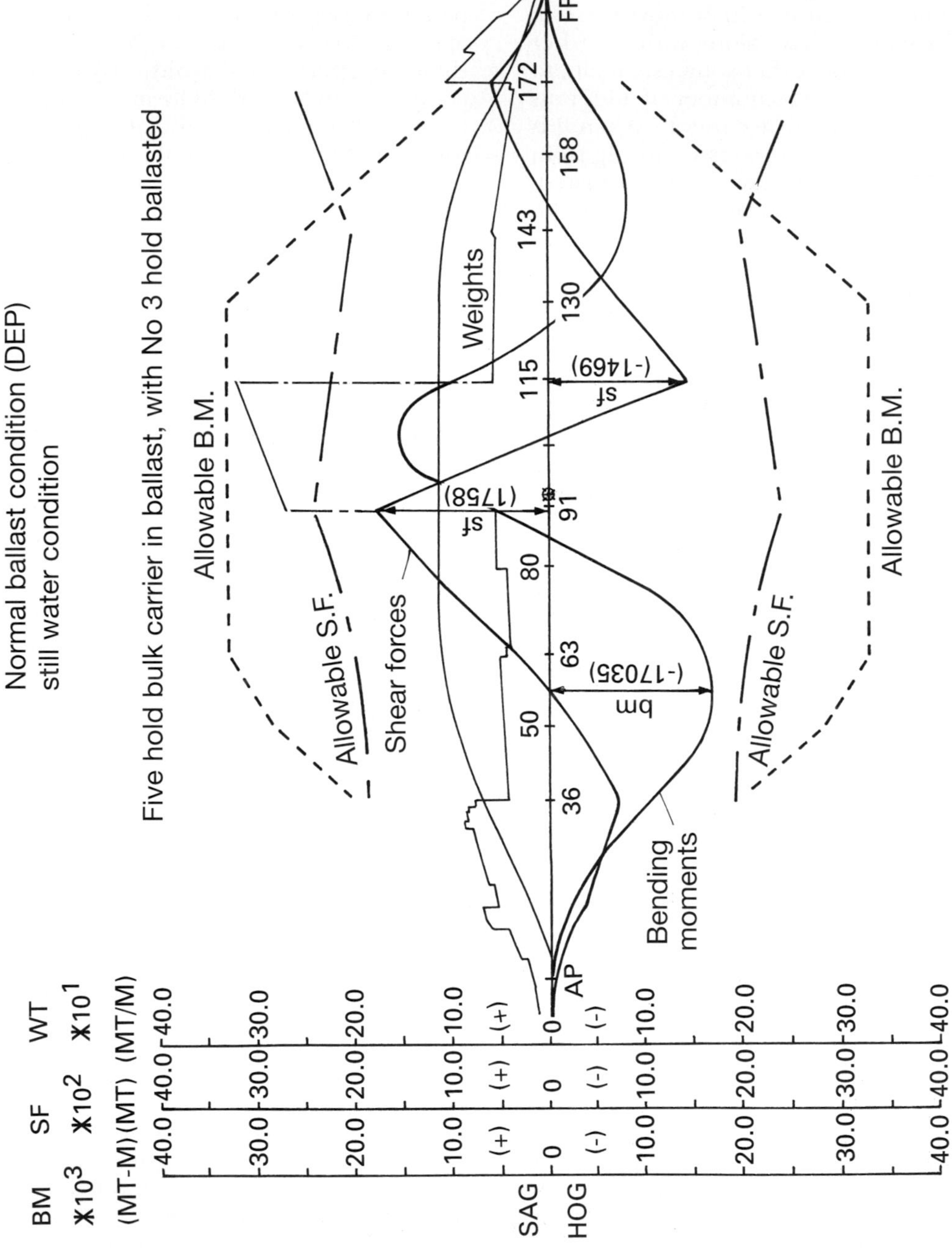
Bending moment and shearing force diagram
Normal ballast condition (DEP)
still water condition
Five hold bulk carrier in ballast, with No 3 hold ballasted
Allowable B.M.
Allowable S.F.
Shear forces
Weights
Bending moments
sf (17758)
sf (-14469)
bm (-170035)
AP
36
50
63
80
91
115
130
143
158
172
FP
BM
SF
WT
(MT-M)
(MT)
(MT/M)
SAG
HOG
40.0
30.0
20.0
10.0
(+)
0
(-)

Figure 10.7

reckless and unprofessional to assume a VCG lower than its actual position.

Longitudinal CGs of part-filled compartments: The position of the LCG of a ship's tank can be accurately predicted since it depends upon the geometry of the tank and the volume of liquid it contains, adjusted slightly to take account of any trim or list. The position of the LCG of a hold containing a quantity of bulk cargo cannot be predicted with equal accuracy, except when the cargo is trimmed reasonably level to the boundaries of the space as required by the *IMSBC Code*[5]. In practice, the cargo is frequently higher in the centre of the hold than at its boundaries and it is impossible to position a pile of bulk cargo in a hold with absolute accuracy. This has several practical implications for those planning the loading of dry bulk cargoes.

The port and starboard sides of each hatch coaming of some bulk carriers are paintmarked with conspicuous marks with which the loading spout is to be aligned. This practice is used particularly aboard small bulkers with long holds, where several pouring positions in each hold are often used. This is no more than an approximate method of positioning a large tonnage of bulk cargo in the hold, but if the same paintmarked points are used voyage after voyage, the ship will be able to place some reliance upon the trim that is calculated on the basis of the planned cargo distribution. When required, it is possible to change the positioning of the cargo within the hold to some extent by directing the loading spout to pour in a position x metres forward or abaft the paintmarked position.

Whatever point of loading is chosen, it is not possible to guarantee that the cargo will be distributed around that point in an absolutely regular manner, since the distribution will be influenced by the shape of the hold, the sequence of pouring, the trim of the ship and the change of trim whilst the cargo is being loaded, in addition to the accuracy of the method of pouring adopted by the loading foreman. As a result, the eventual LCG of the cargo in the hold is unlikely to be exactly that which was planned.

When the cargo is distributed more widely and evenly in the hold by moving the loader or by spout trimming it is even more certain that the position of the centre of gravity of the cargo will not be precisely at the geometrical centre of the hold. The trimming pour (described in Chapter 9) is used to correct the trim as necessary, but this does not alter the fact that even if the correct tonnage is loaded into each hold it is unlikely that its longitudinal distribution will be exactly that assumed in calculations.

Free surface moments: Free surface moments (moments of inertia, measured in m^4) represent the effect of a part-filled tank upon the ship's stability and must be included in the calculation for each tank which is part full. Many loading manuals simply record a maximum value for free surface moments (FSMs) for each tank and there is no alternative to using that figure. Whilst this is inaccurate, it is safe, as in most cases it will result in an overestimate of the loss of stability. The most comprehensive loading manuals, however, provide a graph of values for free surface moments for each tank and the appropriate value to match the tank sounding can be extracted. For some ships the free surface moments are printed not in the loading manual, but in the tank calibration tables, where a full set of values corresponding to soundings is provided.

In a forepeak tank or topside tank the value of FSMs increases with the sounding (because the surface area of the ballast water increases), whilst the double bottom tanks which extend into the lower hopper sides have FSMs which fall to zero as the liquid level rises to the top of the hopper side.

Free surface moments vary according to the specific gravity of the liquid. In some loading manuals the FSMs have been corrected by multiplying them by suitable values of specific gravity such as 1.025 for water ballast, 1.00 for fresh water, 0.98 for fuel oil and 0.85 for diesel oil. In cases where they have not been corrected appropriate corrections should be applied, though their values will usually be small.

Grain stability

When it is intended to carry a cargo of grain, the Master must first satisfy himself that the ship is able to comply with the requirements of the IMO Grain Rules at all stages of the voyage. (See Chapter 19.) They include the requirement to ensure that the vessel can maintain sufficient stability throughout the voyage to satisfy the stringent demands of the Grain Rules.

Fig. 10.8 is a flow chart which shows the sequence of calculations which must be undertaken. These calculations are the same as those required to complete the grain stability calculation forms issued by various national authorities (described and illustrated in Chapter 19). Appendix 10.11 contains a worked example for the *Regina Oldendorff*. This is from the same voyage with grain from Three Rivers to Oran as has been used to illustrate the computer printout (Appendix 10.2 (1-5)) and the grain stability forms (Appendix 19.1).

The detailed steps in the Calculation of grain stability can be followed in the worked example. For those who require a reminder of the objects of the calculation the process is summarised in the flow chart and is explained below.

Grain stability calculations will be required for a number of different events during a grain voyage to ensure that the vessel remains stable throughout. A calculation must be completed for departure from the loading port and for arrival at the discharging port. Calculations must also be made for arrival at and departure from any bunkering port and for the worst condition of the voyage. The worst condition normally occurs immediately before arrival at the discharging port, when bunkers are at their lowest level. However, the occurrence of large free surface effects in bunker tanks or the taking of bunkers or ballast could mean that the worst condition occurs at some other point in the voyage, and this possibility must be kept in mind.

After loading grain in Three Rivers, the *Regina Oldendorff* was to cross the Atlantic to the Straits of Gibraltar. She was to bunker at Ceuta and then proceed the short distance to Oran. Bunkering at Ceuta would improve the vessel's stability by placing weight in the bunker tanks, situated low in the ship.

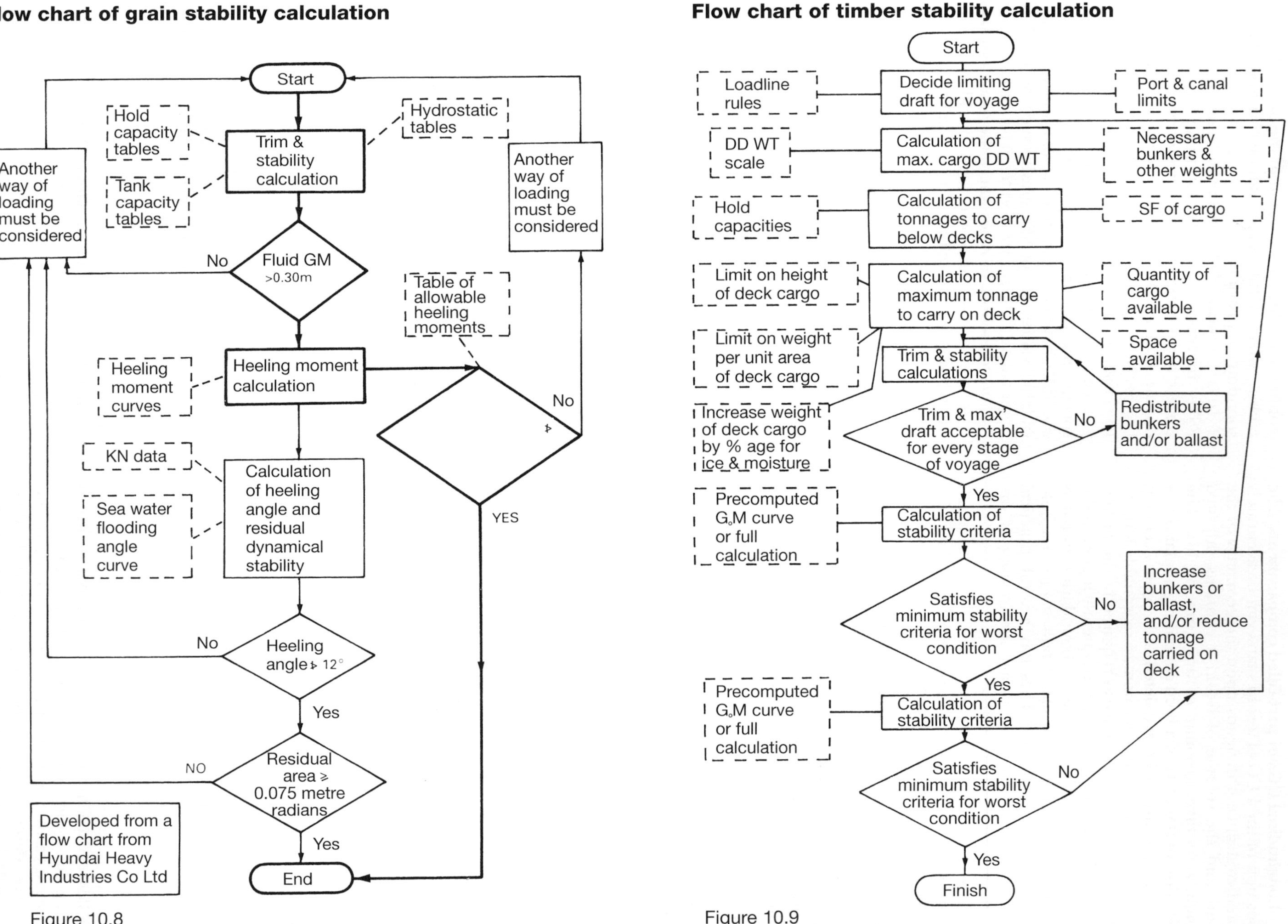

Figure 10.8

Figure 10.9

Thus the worst stability condition would occur on arrival at Ceuta, before bunkering. This is the condition used in the calculation in Appendix 10.11. The procedure for the calculation is as follows.

Complete a normal trim and stability calculation of the kind shown in Appendix 10.8. When the hold ends are untrimmed the hold capacity is reduced. This reduced capacity, which is shown in the loading manual, would normally be used to calculate the tonnage which each compartment can contain and the stowage factor. However US[116], Australian and Canadian authorities now insist that the full capacity of the hold be used to calculate the tonnage, which must be used in conjunction with the heeling moments for untrimmed ends. In other words, when calculating the tonnage assume that the ends are filled but when calculating the heeling moments assume that the ends are not filled. This apparent contradiction is justified because it uses a set of conservative (ie cautious and safe) assumptions.

The approach of the US' National Cargo Bureau, the Canadian Coast Guard and of the Australians is safe and satisfactory for the purposes of ensuring that the ship will have adequate stability at every stage in the voyage but it can introduce uncertainty into other aspects of the voyage planning. It can cause inaccurate values to be precomputed for the tonnages in holds which remain part filled on completion. This, in turn, could cause a ship to fail to achieve her intended final trim, particularly if completing with only one part filled hold. For that reason amongst others readers are advised to monitor the density/stowage factor during loading.

Is the fluid G_0M less than 0.3 metres? If the calculations show that the fluid metacentric height (G_0M) in the worst condition is less than 0.3 metres the intended loading does not comply with the Grain Rules, and calculations must be restarted with an alternative cargo distribution. Provided that the fluid GM in the worst condition is more than 0.3 metres, proceed to the next step.

Obtain corrected volumetric heeling moments (VHMs) for each cargo space: The heeling moments (sometimes called the shifting moments or upsetting moments) for each cargo space are obtained from tables or graphs in the loading manual. Appendix 10.13 contains a full explanation of the corrections to heeling moments, and Appendix 10.12 illustrates how the values were obtained for use in Appendix 10.11. The procedure is complicated as the correct tables must be used, and corrections must be applied as necessary to take account of the following considerations:

- Have ends been trimmed?
- Have volumetric or true centres been assumed for cargo?
- Is compartment full or part filled?
- Was ullage of cargo calculated or measured?
- What corrections have been included in tables?

Correct VHMs to obtain grain heeling moment: All VHMs must be corrected for the density of the cargo, according to the following formula: actual grain heeling moment = VHMs x density. An alternative way of making this correction is to divide the VHMs by the stowage factor of the cargo.

Whichever method of calculation is used the units used must be consistent. If the VHMs are expressed in m^4 they must be amended by the density in tonnes/m^3 or stowage factor in m^3/tonne (and not in tons/ft^3 or ft^3/ton). Actual grain heeling moment = VHMs/ stowage factor (or VHMs * density).

Calculation of permissible grain heeling moments: Permissible (or allowable) grain heeling moments for any condition of loading must be read from the ship's loading manual from a table which is entered with a displacement and fluid vertical centre of gravity (fluid KG). An accurate result must be obtained by interpolation between the values given.

Comparison of actual and permissible grain heeling moments: Provided that the actual corrected grain heeling moments are less than the permissible (allowable) grain heeling moments, the ship when loaded in the manner proposed complies with the stability requirements of the Grain Rules. If the actual moments are more than the permissible moments, an alternative loading plan must be devised and the calculations repeated.

Reduced values of VHMs can be achieved by rearranging the cargo in any of the following ways:

- reduce the number of holds which are part-filled
- use a smaller capacity hold as the part-filled hold
- change the level of cargo in the part-filled hold to avoid the half-filled condition where VHMs are greatest
- trim hold ends; and if topside tanks are designed for grain, consider using some of them

Alternatively, a greater KG and larger values of permissible heeling moments can be achieved by a better distribution of bunkers and ballast in the ship.

Grain density/stowage factor monitoring: The preloading calculations for a grain cargo depend upon an assumed figure for stowage factor or density for the cargo and also, when loading in the US[151], Australia or Canada, on an assumed hold capacity. The stowage factor is normally provided by shippers or loading stevedores. It may prove to be inaccurate for any of a number of reasons. The grain or the ship may not be typical or the information from the shippers may prove to be unreliable. If the figure proves to be wrong, the ship's actual VHMs and corrected grain heeling moments will be different from the figures calculated beforehand and the ship may not be safe to undertake the voyage.

Throughout loading, any opportunity should be taken to obtain an accurate measurement of the stowage factor and/or density of the cargo. Completion of loading of the first hold is an obvious opportunity to divide tonnage loaded by the volume of the hold in cubic metres to calculate the stowage factor. For consistency the hold volumes must be treated in the same manner as in the earlier calculation, including or excluding the voids in any untrimmed ends. If the stowage factor or density found is different to that used in preplanning the loading, the calculations must be reworked to ensure that the ship will still satisfy the stability and trim requirements throughout the voyage.

Simplified stability calculation: The method of calculating grain stability by the use of actual and permissible grain heeling moments (described above) is a simplified method of stability calculation, and is the only calculation which needs to be completed aboard ships provided with tables of grain heeling moments.

Aboard a ship which is not provided with appropriate tables it is necessary to complete full stability calculations. In the statical stability diagram the net or residual area between the heeling arm curve and the righting arm curve must be measured. The area to be measured extends up to the angle of heel of maximum difference between the ordinates of the two curves, or 40°, or the angle of flooding, whichever is the least. In all conditions of loading this must not be less than 0.075 metre radians. In practice this calculation is seldom required, since most grain carrying vessels are provided with tables of permissible and volumetric heeling moments, and it has not been described in this book.

Timber stability

The carriage of timber and lumber (ie sawn timber) cargoes is described in Chapter 19, and the operation of a log carrier is described in Chapter 18. These notes describe stability calculations for timber cargoes. The procedure is the same whether done by computer or by longhand calculation, though the latter process is much more time consuming.

Timber is a low-density cargo which fills the ship long before she is loaded to her marks. To increase the cargo lift, timber is usually carried on deck; but, as the height of the deck cargo rises, so the ship's positive stability is reduced. In cases where lack of stability prevents the vessel from carrying a full deck cargo the following steps must be taken to ensure that the maximum cargo is carried. They are depicted in the flow chart at Fig. 10.9, and a worked example of the planning of a timber loading is at Appendix 10.14. The main considerations when planning a timber loading are the following.

Identify the limiting point in the voyage in terms of draught following the procedure described in Chapter 9 and calculate the deadweight to correspond with the limiting draught.

Obtain the stowage factor of the cargo and use it to calculate the tonnage of cargo which can be accommodated in each hold: Where cargo of several different stowage factors is available the heaviest cargo should be carried as low as possible in the ship. (Timber does not normally stow between the frames and beams in the hold, so the weight in each hold should be considered to act at the CG of the bale space of that hold)

From the calculated deadweight deduct bunkers, miscellaneous weights and the cargo to be carried in the holds: The remaining deadweight can be carried on deck, provided that there is sufficient space, and provided that sufficient positive stability can be maintained. These matters are examined below.

The space available on deck is limited by the available area of deck and hatch covers and by any restrictions upon the height of the stow. Permissible height of timber deck cargo is limited by the 1966 Loadline Convention to one-third the vessel's beam for vessels in seasonal winter zones and may be restricted at other times by the classification society. The maximum permitted loadings on deck and hatch covers are other matters which limit the height to which deck cargo can be carried. The final restriction upon height of deck cargo is that which ensures a good view from the bridge for navigational purposes, the SOLAS requirement (Ch.V, Reg.22) being that visibility ahead should be obscured for no more than two shiplengths[92] though canals such as the Panama have stricter requirements. Taking account of all these considerations calculate the maximum height of cargo permitted.

Using the stowage factor of the timber and the height and area of the deck cargo, calculate the weight of the maximum amount of cargo for which there is room on deck. The total deck and hatch top areas may be stated in the loading manual or it may be necessary to calculate them. The necessary measurements can be readily obtained from the ship's capacity plan. It is prudent to check the result obtained: the total deck area available for cargo is likely to be 10-20 per cent less than the product of maindeck length and maximum beam. The stowage factor (SF) for timber on deck is usually slightly better than that for timber below decks, since no space is lost above deck cargo, as there is above cargo in the holds. For example, the loading manual for the *Regina Oldendorff* proposes an SF for timber below decks of 76 cuft/mt and a figure of 66 cuft/mt for timber on deck, whilst another loading manual suggests 82 cuft/mt below decks and 77 cuft/mt on deck. These figures will vary with the measurements of the timber, the configuration of the ship and the quality of the stevedoring, so can be no more than approximations.

Choose a height (KG) for the centre of gravity for the deck cargo. Where a full volume of deck cargo is being considered the KG given in the loading manual – for example, in an appropriate worked example of timber loading – can be used, although it should be checked for accuracy. When planning for less than a full volume of deck cargo the KG of the deck cargo must be reduced. As an approximate rule of thumb, a 1.0 metre reduction in the height of the deck cargo will lead to a 0.5 metre reduction in the KG of the deck cargo. Reductions of other amounts will be in the same proportion.

For calculation of the vessel's trim and stability at the end of the voyage, the calculated weight of the deck cargo must be increased by 10 per cent to allow for absorption of water from spray and rain during the voyage. If the additional weight due to absorption will overload the upper deck, the hatches or the ship then the tonnage of deck cargo must be proportionately reduced to prevent overloading. (The vessel's worst condition for stability purposes will normally occur at the end of the voyage, except when the vessel takes extra bunkers at an intermediate port, when worst conditions will occur at commencement of bunkering).

Weight of the deck cargo at the end of the voyage must also be increased to allow for ice accretion – the formation of ice on the deck cargo – where this is likely to occur. Guidelines vary considerably as to the figure to allow for ice accretion, with recommendations ranging from 2-10 per cent of weight of deck cargo[163]. In high latitudes in winter the total allowance for absorption plus icing should lie within 12-20 per cent.

Excessive initial stability should be avoided as it will result in rapid and violent motion in heavy seas, which will impose large sliding and racking forces on the cargo, causing high stresses on the lashings. It is recommended[4] that the metacentric height should not exceed 3 per cent of the vessel's breadth, so a ship with a beam of 22 m should have a fluid metacentric height no greater than 0.66 m. This will rarely be a problem as excessive stability seldom occurs on forest product ships.

Complete a set of trim and stability calculations and confirm that the vessel's draught, trim and fluid metacentric height (G_0M) will be acceptable at every stage in the voyage.

Check the vessel's stability at the worst condition she will experience during the voyage. If a criteria curve for fluid GM (G_0M) for timber loading (Fig. 10.10) is provided, the Master can confirm that the vessel complies simply by plotting the calculated G_0M against displacement on the curve. If no such curve is provided the Master must complete a full statical and dynamical stability calculation. (Appendix 10.9).

If the loading does not satisfy the vessel's stability criteria bunkers or ballast must be increased or tonnage of deck cargo must be reduced and stability must be recalculated. The first and cheapest option is to carry additional ballast and where possible this method will be used to improve stability. Bunker distribution will also be rearranged to minimise free surface effect in the worst condition. If the improvement achieved by ballast is insufficient there is the possibility of carrying additional bunkers. This has a cost, since bunkers must be purchased earlier than would otherwise be required and possibly at a higher price.

If stability is still inadequate when all possible has been done with ballast and bunkers, the tonnage of deck cargo must be reduced. This is best done by reducing the height of the deck cargo overall by removing a layer of the planned deck cargo from the top of the stow. Alternatively, it can be achieved by stepping the cargo down at one end of the stow. The creation of vertical faces of cargo in the stow which could present a barrier to seas sweeping the decks should be avoided.

Check the vessel's stability for the commencement of the voyage using a G_0M criteria curve or a full calculation of all the stability criteria, as before. When a satisfactory worst condition has been devised, it is possible to work back to the initial condition on departure from the loading port. This condition must be checked to ensure that it satisfies the stability criteria and any draught requirements. In the initial condition the G_0M for most vessels must be at least 0.1 metres. It is not necessary to assume any water absorption or icing in this condition.

Check the arrival condition at the discharge port, if that is different from the worst condition, and check any other intermediate stages to ensure that all comply with the stability criteria, and with draught requirements.

The illustration of the planning of a timber voyage (Appendix 10.14) uses an imaginary voyage of the *Regina Oldendorff* from Umea, a Swedish port in the north Baltic, to Alexandria, Egypt, by way of the Kiel Canal. This provides an opportunity to consider the issues which can arise with timber cargoes, including the need to shut out some deck cargo in order to achieve adequate stability.

Sources

4, 5, 17, 18, 85, 114, 116, 117, 146, 149, 150, 151, 152, 163, 200. (See List of Sources, Page 497)

3) G_0M criteria curve for timber loading

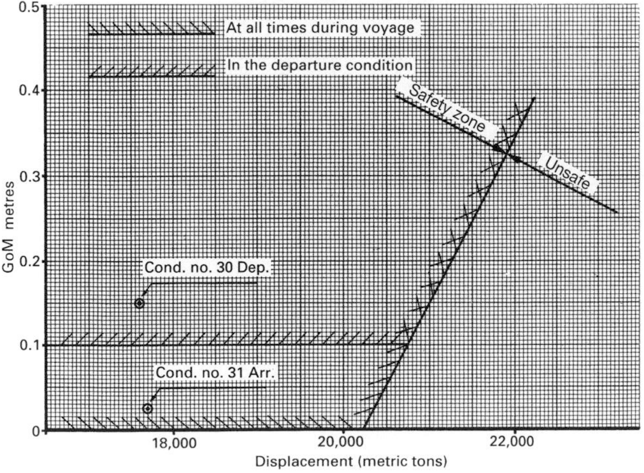

This curve shows the permissible minimum G_0M for each displacement based on the stability criteria recommended by IMCO (IMO) Resolution A.206(VII)

Figure 10.10

Fig. 10.11 Bundles of eucalyptus stowed below decks
Photo courtesy of Mathieu Baehni

Fig. 10.12 Bundles of eucalyptus logs carried on deck
Photo courtesy of Mathieu Baehni

CHAPTER 11

LOADING OR DISCHARGING BERTH

Final authority for decisions, need for exchange of information, maximum safe draught, tidal range and sailing draught, air draught, cargo handling equipment and rate, positions of structures on quay, mooring requirements, systems of fendering, systems of access, restrictions on deballasting, ship/shore safety checklist, items requested by Master, communication with berth operators, tonnage on the belt, hours of work, effects of weather, methods of trimming, pollution avoidance, methods of loading, methods of discharging, ship's information for the berth operator including typical mooring arrangements, the implementation of the BLU Code, methods of information exchange, storing and handling of cargoes ashore, offshore transshipment

Final authority for decisions when vessel is berthed

WHEN A VESSEL is at a berth decisions made by the Master and his officers will have consequences for the berth operators, and decisions made ashore by the operators of the berth will affect the workings of the ship. This raises the question of who has the final authority when Master and berth operators cannot agree on cargo operations, a question which is answered plainly in the IMO's BLU Code[110] which states "The Master is responsible at all times for the safe loading and unloading of the ship..."

In practice, the number of occasions in which reasonable Shipmasters and berth operators cannot agree is very small. Options which are impossible or damaging can be recognised and rejected by reasonable people, and the remaining options must then be weighed according to the benefits or disadvantages which each gives to each party. Both Master and berth operators will seek efficient cargo operations.

The Master's responsibilities are for care of the ship, her equipment and the cargo, once it has been placed aboard. He must never give his agreement to proposals which will harm the ship or the cargo she carries and he must vigorously resist any attempt to impose such proposals. The berth operator can be expected to be equally firm in defending the interests of the berth, the cargo-handling equipment if based ashore and cargo in his care from damaging actions by the ship.

Need for exchange of information

If the time which a ship spends alongside a loading or discharging berth is to be used safely and efficiently, it is necessary for the Master to be provided before the ship berths with information about the berth. This requirement is recognised and stated in detail in the IMO's BLU Code[110]. The Code is mandatory in much of the world and represents best practice in places where it is not yet mandatory. Provided that the ship is given the necessary information the chief mate can devise a loading or discharging programme which takes account of any limitations of the berth. If the chief mate is required to produce a programme without the benefit of such advance information his calculations will probably have to be reworked when he eventually discovers that the air draught is limited or the ship is too long for the loader to reach all hatches without shifting ship.

There is a similar need for the berth operator to be provided with information about the ship in order that preparations can be made ashore to load or discharge the ship in the most efficient manner and provision of this information, too, is a requirement of the BLU Code. The information which each party requires about the other can be divided into two categories: that which is essential for efficient planning; and that which is useful. The information to be exchanged between ship and terminal is detailed in the Code.

In recent years the need to make terminal operators active partners in the safe loading and unloading of ships has been recognised and the IMO has involved port and terminal representatives in the formulating and implementing of the BLU Code.

In practice, standards of efficiency throughout the world vary considerably from berth to berth and from ship to ship. Well organised ships and berths will exchange information in a practical and professional manner. This will enable them to preplan the entire loading or discharging process, although they will be ready to adapt their plans if unforeseen circumstances occur. At the other extreme are a diminishing number of ships and berths which do not exchange information, which engage in no preplanning, and which merely react to the requirements imposed upon them when the ship has berthed.

Essential information for the ship about the berth

Maximum safe draught in berth: The Master first needs to know the maximum draught at which he can safely remain in the berth at all times. This figure will take account of the need to keep a safe depth of water under the keel and of any rise and fall of tide.

When a vessel is under way in the sheltered waters of a port approach, a minimum safe depth below the keel is usually considered to be D/10, where 'D' is the vessel's maximum draught, although particular ports and individual shipowners may have their own rules. A clearance of 1 metre below the keel is often required for Panamax vessels when anywhere within the port. A smaller allowance below the keel – for example, D/20 – may be considered acceptable for a vessel in the berth or entering or leaving it as she will be at rest or moving slowly and this figure is also used in the approaches to some ports in which the bottom is entirely mud and sand. It is prudent to allow a greater margin of safety when the bottom is rocky than when it is mud or sand, since accidental contact with the former is more likely to cause serious damage. Of course the requirements of the shipowner's management system must be adhered to. If these differ from the requirements of the port the owners must be advised

It is normal for the berth operators to decide upon the maximum safe draught. They are not likely to consult the Shipmaster for his view as to a safe figure. Unfortunately the figure provided by the berth operators is not always reliable. Depths in the berth may have been reduced by deposits of silt or by cargo residues dropped from grabs or swept from the jetty or from the decks of ships. Low rainfall may have reduced water levels in a river or abnormal meteorological conditions may have caused a reduction in sea level. The berth operators may be under a contractual obligation to provide a certain depth of water and may be reluctant to admit that the actual depth is less than that which they are guaranteeing. Depth survey records may be out of date or inaccurate.

For all these reasons the Master must treat the operators' figure with caution when his ship is visiting a berth where a limiting draught will apply. He will be well advised to question the pilot and the berth operators' representatives closely about the frequency with which the berth is surveyed and dredged and the reported water depth available. When there is doubt if sufficient depth of water is available it will be prudent to keep the echo-sounder in operation producing a sounding trace whilst entering the berth, although the results obtained must be treated with caution since echo-sounders are liable to suffer from a variety of errors at very low underkeel clearances. In addition, soundings with a hand leadline should be taken around the ship once she is berthed. The hand leadline sounding should be adjusted for any tidal range to give an accurate minimum depth alongside. If any doubt exists, frequent hand leadline soundings should be taken at critical stages of the loading. Whilst a berth which is well maintained and smartly run by competent staff inspires greater confidence, even the best run operations can be guilty of errors and there have been a number of instances in which bulk carriers have unexpectedly grounded in the berth.

A few berths exist where the depth is greater at one end than at the other, ships normally being berthed with their sterns in the deeper water. In this case it is necessary to know the maximum depth of water which can be guaranteed at each end of the berth or of the vessel.

Occasionally the water is deeper in the berth than the minimum depth in the approaches to the berth. Such a berth is known as a 'berth box', where a vessel can stay afloat at all states of the tide, but cannot enter or leave the berth in certain tidal conditions. When these conditions are found the Master needs to know the minimum depth in the approaches and also the minimum depth in the berth as loading or discharging may be easier to arrange if, whilst working cargo, the vessel can reach a draught at one end which is deeper than her sailing or arrival draught. There will be times when the vessel cannot leave such a berth in the event of an emergency such as a fire ashore and the Master should take note of those times.

Tidal range and sailing draught: Where a rise and fall of tide is experienced at a loading berth and the ship is a large one for the berth, loading may be suspended before low water and then completed on the rising tide before the vessel leaves the berth at high water. Similarly, a vessel may berth at a discharging berth at high water, requiring to discharge sufficient cargo during the fall of tide to remain afloat at low water. When operations of this sort are intended, the Master will require to know the tidal range and the maximum safe draught for arrival or departure on the top of the tide.

Air draught: A vessel's air draught is generally understood to mean the height of her highest point above the surface of the water at the relevant draught, this information being of interest when deciding if a vessel can pass safely below a bridge or overhead power cable. It is this air draught for the light condition, when the air draught will be maximum, which is sometimes quoted in a ship's particulars.

The expression has a second meaning when applied to bulk loading berths where a principal matter for concern is whether the loading arm is high enough or the vessel low enough for the arm to clear the hatch coaming and where necessary the hatch covers and be positioned over the hold to commence loading. It is when the hatch covers are 'side rolling' that the loading arm must clear them as well as the coaming. The measurement which the Master needs to reassure himself on this point is the minimum air draught beneath the ship loader, measured from the bottom of the loader spout to the water surface. Such an air draught will be least when the river or tidal level is at its highest.

When this figure has been provided the Master or chief officer will compare it with the height above water level of the coaming top, or when fitted the side rolling hatch cover top, of the hatch where loading is to commence (Fig. 11.1). This can be measured with reasonable accuracy from the vessel's general arrangements or capacity plan, but it must be remembered that when the vessel is trimmed by the stern the air draught increases from aft to forward. The air draught at a forward hatch will be greater than that at a midships or after hatch.

If loading is commenced in after holds and deballasting takes place, it is possible that the forward draught will decrease during the early stages in loading and the air draughts of the forward hatches will increase. When preparing the loading program, the air draughts of these hatches must be checked to ensure that the ship loader will be able to reach the loading position over the hold.

Details of loading or discharging equipment: To devise an efficient programme for loading or discharging, it is necessary to know whether the loading or discharging equipment is fixed or mobile. If the equipment is fixed or if its movement is limited, it is necessary for the ship to move back and forth along the length of the berth. It is normal for discharging equipment to travel almost the full length of the berth, so that only the largest ships visiting the berth are required to shift to permit discharge from

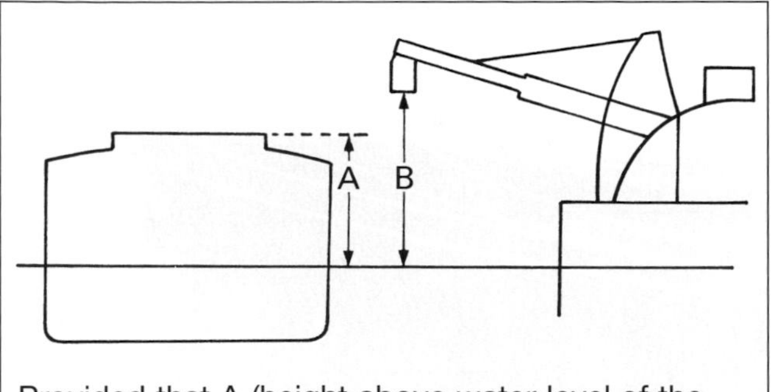

Provided that A (height above water level of the hatch coaming) is less than B (minimum air draught beneath the loader) the vessel can berth to commence loading

Fig 11.1

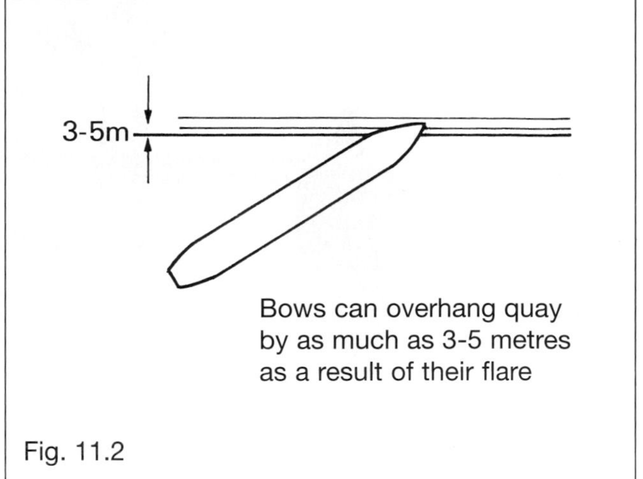

Bows can overhang quay by as much as 3-5 metres as a result of their flare

Fig. 11.2

Typical mooring arrangements for bulk carriers

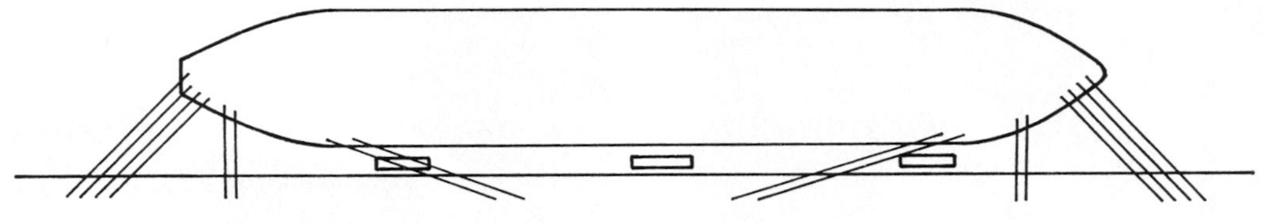

Cape-sized
4 headlines, 2 forward breastlines, 2 forward springs
4 sternlines, 2 after breastlines, 2 after springs

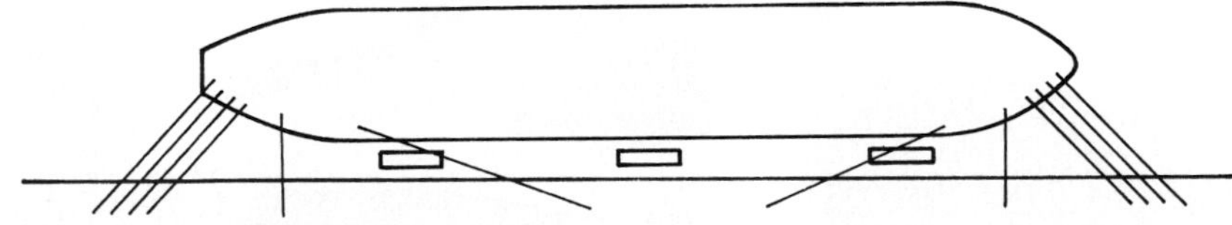

Panamax
4 headlines, 1 forward breastline, 1 forward spring
4 sternlines, 1 after breastline, 1 after spring
or other combinations giving 6 ropes at each end

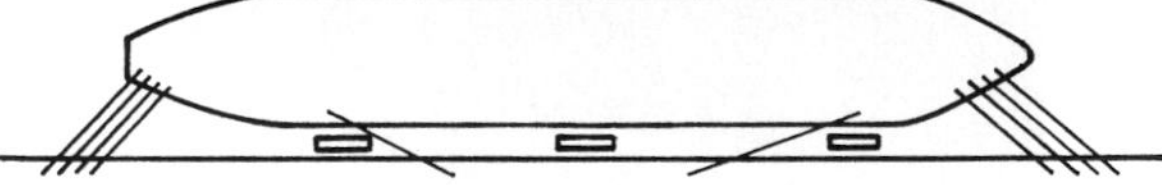

Handy size
4 headlines, 1 forward spring
4 sternlines, 1 after spring

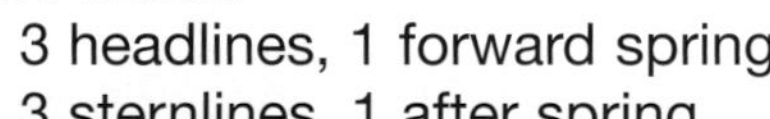

Mini-bulker
3 headlines, 1 forward spring
3 sternlines, 1 after spring

Typical mooring arrangement for a handy sized bulk carrier required to shift back and forward in the berth during loading

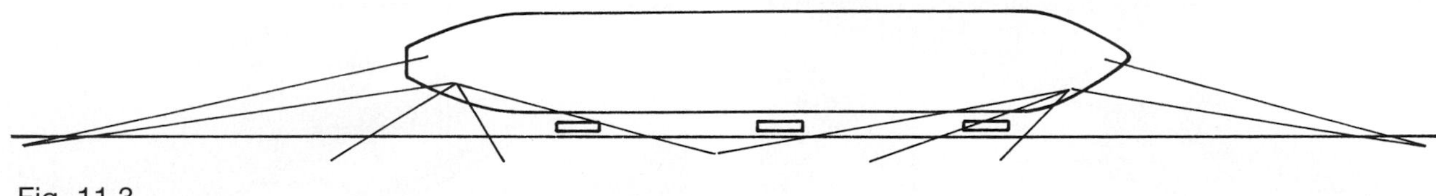

Fig. 11.3

Fig. 11.4 After moorings of Cape-sized vessel

Fig. 11.5 Forward moorings of a Cape-sized vessel

Fig. 11.6 Forward moorings of a Panamax vessel

Fig. 11.7 After moorings of a Panamax vessel

Fig. 11.8 After moorings of a handymax vessel

Fig. 11.9 Forward moorings of a handymax vessel

all holds. Ship loaders are also normally designed to move along the length of the berth, except in berths for the smallest ships (mini-bulkers) where fixed loading installations are often encountered. Fixed installations are occasionally used in berths for larger ships. The largest ships which visit a loading berth are likely to have to shift to allow loading in the end holds, since the ship loaders will not be able to reach holds positioned beyond the end of the berth.

The Master also requires to know the loading or discharging rate so as to calculate whether the ballasting or deballasting can keep up with the cargo and to decide whether it is desirable to commence ballasting operations prior to berthing. Some terminals quote the maximum theoretical loading rate, even though they know that such a rate is never achieved in practice. This is a useful 'worst case'. If the ship can keep the ballast in step with the maximum loading rate, no problems will be experienced if the actual loading rate is found to be erratic and slower on average than the rate quoted, as is usually the case.

In some loading berths the ship is given a time allowance during which the ship can interrupt loading without penalty, in order to achieve full deballasting before loading completes. In other ports the ship is penalised for all delays caused by the ship. When the ship's deballasting rate is sufficiently high to ensure that the terminal's loading rate can be comfortably accommodated the loading/deballasting plan should be prepared on the basis that no delays will be required, but an allowance for interruptions without penalty is very welcome and helps to ensure that decisions regarding proper deballasting are made for the right reasons and without undue pressure. The Master needs to know what penalty-free time allowance is given, if any. Also needed is information as to the number of ship loaders or discharging units to be used, as this will have a significant effect upon the programme. If the terminal's proposed loading rate is too high for the ship's intended deballasting programme, reportedly a regular problem at some terminals, the Master and chief mate must make this clear to the terminal, and insist on programming one or several stops during loading to allow timely completion of the deballasting. In cases in which the chief mate may need his support it is well worth while for the Master to be present when the chief mate meets the terminal representative to agree the loading/deballasting plan.

If the ship is prevented from keeping to the loading/deballasting programme by pump failure or other problem and there is the slightest danger that permissible stress limits may be exceeded the Master has the authority of SOLAS to suspend loading[190] and he should not hesitate to do so.

Positions of structures on quay: Mini-bulkers or handy-sized vessels berthing without the assistance of tugs or with only limited tug assistance will normally approach the berth bows first, with the ship's fore-and-aft line making an angle of about 30° with the berth (Fig. 11.2). This often leads to the bows overhanging the berth until the vessel has been swung into alignment with the berth and moored.

For this reason, the Master will want to be assured that any travelling loading or discharging gantries and structures on the quay have been moved well clear of the position where the bows of his ship are to be moored, and this matter will be of particular interest to him if he is doing the pilotage, as is more likely on a smaller vessel. Such equipment should be moved completely clear of the berth or alternatively to a position one-third the ship's length from the point where her stern is to be placed, since this is the position where the ship is least likely to overhang the quay during the berthing process.

Similar considerations should not apply to larger (Panamax and Cape-sized) vessels as standard berthing procedures for large vessels require them to be brought to rest parallel to the berthing face, from which position such a vessel is moved bodily sideways by tugs. Most large berths are designed for a zero berthing angle, though a few are designed for a maximum berthing angle of 5-10°. Despite this, it is not uncommon in practice for Panamax vessels to be berthed at greater angles and with inadequate tug assistance in ports where insufficient tugs are available.

A further requirement for ships of all sizes is that any gantries which project over the ship when rigged for cargo work and which could be fouled by the ship's masts or aerials must be raised or moved clear of the berth whilst berthing or unberthing takes place. When there are fixed structures near the edge of the quay a clear description of their positions will be required.

Mooring requirements: Before berthing the Master requires to know whether the vessel is to berth port side-to or starboard side-to and what mooring lines will be required. If clearly stated, this information can usefully be passed to the ship before her arrival. Alternatively, it is sufficient if the pilot upon boarding informs the Master of requirements, provided that the pilotage is long enough for the ship's company to receive the information and make whatever preparations are needed.

Conventional moorings systems, such as are illustrated in Figs.11.3-11.9 for a range of vessel sizes, should cause no problems to bulk carriers but unusual mooring configurations or unfamiliar shore fittings may require a rearrangement of the ship's mooring lines. Maximum prior warning is advisable for any arrangement which requires ships' personnel to do anything other than land the eyes of the mooring lines of their choice to bollards on a quayside adjacent to the ship.

If lines are to be sent to buoys and require lashings or shackles, if lines are to be doubled and require messengers for hauling the ends back aboard, or if light rope tails are to be attached to the eyes of ropes to facilitate their transfer from mooring boat to quay or dolphin, the ship may need to make special preparations. The same is true if exceptional lengths of mooring line are required for mooring to distant points or if the ship is to provide towing lines for tugs.

There are a few bulk carrier berths where ships are moored with shore lines on shore winches. In these berths, shore personnel can move the ship back and forward along the quay to enable a fixed shiploader to load in a succession of different holds. In these circumstances the officer of the watch must always be informed before the ship is moved by shore personnel.

On Cape-sized bulkers, the expectation will be that lines will be sent ashore by mooring boat, with the first lines ashore being fibre ropes and later lines also being fibre or else wire ropes with nylon tails though the latter will not be accepted at some terminals. Panamax vessels using the same types of moorings as Cape-sized will be met by mooring boats in the better equipped berths, but in many berths they will be required to land their moorings with the help of heaving lines. Handymax and handy-sized vessels and mini-bulkers will normally be moored entirely with fibre lines, with the first lines on mini-bulkers normally being put ashore by means of heaving lines. On handymax and handy-sized vessels the first lines may be landed either by mooring boat or by heaving line or may be passed directly ashore.

The normal rules of mooring apply. Wires and fibre ropes must not be sent through the same lead. Moorings forward and aft must match, wire springs forward must be matched with wire springs aft and fibre headlines must be matched with fibre sternlines. All moorings should either remain on winch barrels or be turned up correctly on bitts. Moorings should never be left on drum ends. If wires are used with rope pennants they must be connected by a patented joining shackle such as a Tonsberg mooring link or a Mandal mooring shackle, (a stainless steel mooring shackle with a sleek shape designed to pass through fairleads).

Systems of fendering: Berths designed for vessels of less than about 20,000 dwt berthing unaided by tugs will generally have fenders spaced at intervals of no more than 5-10 per cent of the vessel's length. For much larger vessels berthing with tug assistance, fender spacing can be at intervals of about 25-50 per cent of the vessel's length. A small vessel is likely to experience difficulties when berthing at a berth designed for large vessels and a large vessel is liable to cause damage when berthing at a berth which has been fendered for small vessels. Before a vessel berths details of the fendering should be advised by agent or pilot. The details required may include the type of fenders, whether they are fixed, floating or hanging, their distance apart, and whether any are damaged or missing.

Smaller vessels should always have their own fenders ready as some berths are found on arrival to be insufficiently fendered or with a fender broken or missing in a vital location.

System of access: If the ship's accommodation ladder or gangway is to be used for access when the vessel is berthed, advance warning of what is required and where will help the ship to make suitable arrangements in good time. The alternative is for the berth to provide the means of access, usually in the form of a gangway or system of gangways suspended from the loading or discharging equipment. Information about the access requirements can usually be provided by the pilot in sufficient time to allow the ship's crew to make the necessary preparations. Guidance for the provision of safe access is contained in Chapter 21.

Restrictions on deballasting: In an increasing number of areas throughout the world there are restrictions, either compulsory or voluntary, upon the discharge of ballast drawn from the inshore waters of other countries for reasons which are discussed in Chapter 7. Provided that ships satisfy the requirements for clean ballast and, where required, the port has authorised deballasting there will be no restrictions upon deballasting. If they do not satisfy the requirements, deballasting and loading cannot take place and the ship will be sent back to sea to change ballast.

Other information: The BLU Code[110] also requires the ship to be informed of the name of the berth at which loading or unloading will take place, the estimated times for berthing and completion of loading or unloading and the availability of tugs, their type and bollard pull. The maximum allowable speed of approach is to be advised. The ship is also to be informed of the water density but as this can vary from point to point and from hour to hour it will be prudent for ship's staff to check the value given.

Also to be provided is the loading sequence for different parcels of cargo, advance information on proposed cargo handling operations and, importantly, the properties of cargo to be loaded which may present a hazard when placed in contact with cargo or residues on board.

Ship/Shore Safety Checklist: After berthing the Master and his officers will require more information about facilities, procedures and programmes and the Ship/Shore Safety Checklist, to be found in the BLU Code, has been created to formalise the exchange of safety related information between ship and terminal. Completion of the checklist with input from both parties is an important and useful routine designed to ensure that each party is fully prepared for events during the vessel's stay.

A Ship/Shore Safety Checklist is, of course, required in every port and can, if care is not taken, become an unthinking routine in which a computer printed document is produced and signed without any discussion between ship and terminal. Surveyors report that the Checklist, prepared before arrival, is sometimes seriously wrong; even failing to show that the ship has grounded when entering the berth and could not be hauled alongside! Blunders of this sort can be dangerous and expensive and will seriously damage the credibility of the ship's Master and officers in the event of a dispute.

Items requested by the Master: Also required by the BLU Code are any other items related to the terminal requested by the Master. These can usefully include all the items discussed hereunder, in *Helpful information for the ship about the berth*, as appropriate.

Helpful information for the ship about the berth

The preceding paragraphs have discussed the information which is essential to the Shipmaster before arrival at the berth if he is to ensure that his vessel's stay is a safe one and that cargo operations are conducted with maximum efficiency. After berthing there is more information which the Master will find useful and the following paragraphs discuss the information which is particularly relevant to the operation of bulk carriers. Safety issues covered by the Ship/Shore Safety Checklist and items of general information, such as port emergency communications, port services and the provision of stores, bunkers and fresh water, have not been discussed.

Cargo work–the loading berth: The Master or chief officer will want to know how he can make contact quickly with the loading supervisor to discuss any problems or to stop the loading in an emergency. At most loading berths a man with a VHF radio will be stationed on deck close to the hold being loaded, but occasionally such people disappear when most needed and it is essential to know the location of the supervisor's office or to establish a VHF link with him.

Tonnage on the belt: The normal tonnage of cargo on the belt (ie, on the loading conveyor belt) is an important fact. If an unplanned stop is ordered it will be normal practice to continue loading until all the cargo has been cleared from the belt, because the belt cannot be restarted when it is laden. If the belt is a long one, the tonnage on the belt can be very considerable, being as much as 1,000 tonnes in some berths where Cape-sized vessels are loaded.

Hours of work: The Master will want to know the hours of work of the loading or discharging gangs and the timing of any routine interruptions for change of shift, shunting of rail wagons, routine maintenance of equipment or other purposes.

Effects of weather: The Master needs to know the customs of the port with regard to working cargo in adverse weather – for example, in rain, snow, fog or high winds. Discharging cranes may be prohibited from working in winds above Beaufort Force 6 or 8 and when fog restricts visibility to less than 50 metres. The Master will want to ensure that he is in agreement with the policy of the port or the cargo representatives regarding the stopping of cargo work and the covering of holds in the event of rain or snow. In ports where objections are received on environmental grounds when dusty cargoes blow over residential areas, work is liable to be stopped in any strong winds. He will also want to know if there is any possibility that he will be ordered to leave the port in event of exceptional weather.

Methods of trimming: Trimming, when mentioned in connection with the loading of a cargo, is understood to mean the levelling or part-levelling of the cargo. Trimming is undertaken to reduce the danger of cargo shifting (ie slipping into a new position) and thereby putting ship's stability at risk or to ensure a better filling of any empty spaces to increase the quantity of cargo carried. Trimming may also be carried out to reduce the surface area of cargo exposed to air and to level the cargo in the hatch square to permit the hatch covers to be closed.

When loaded, high density cargoes such as ores and mineral sands may be spout trimmed, mechanically trimmed or untrimmed. If the maximum reach of the loading spout is only to the ship's centreline and if the spout is not fitted with any device for spreading the cargo, it is not possible to spout trim the cargo. Devices used to improve the effectiveness of spout trimming include a loading shoe (Fig. 11.10) which shoots the cargo off at an angle, and a spinning head

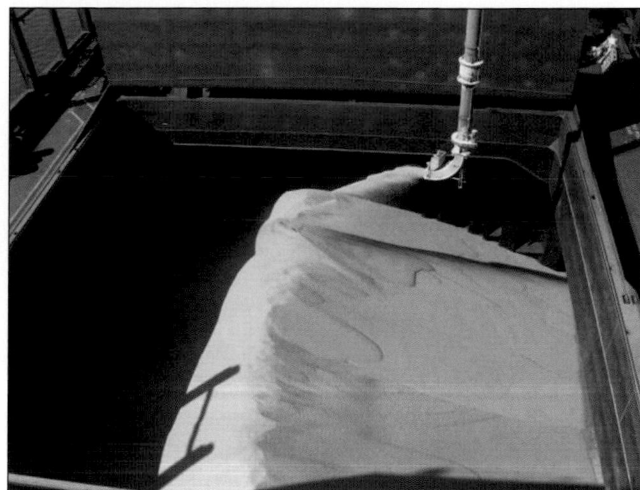

Fig. 11.10 Loading fertiliser with a mechanical loader and loading spout

Photo courtesy Walter Vervloesem

(Fig. 19.5) which flings cargo out all round, thus trimming reasonably level at all stages of the loading. Deflector plates, separate from the loading spout, can also be used to direct cargo into the sides and end of the hold.

It is also possible to trim ore cargoes level by mechanical means, such as the use of bulldozer or front-end loader placed in the hold after completion of loading. This practice is becoming more common, particularly with concentrates. Trimming is a requirement of the IMSBC Code[232], which gives detailed instructions for the trimming of non-cohesive bulk cargoes and recommends that cohesive bulk cargoes are also trimmed reasonably level to reduce the likelihood of cargo shifting and to minimise the air entering the cargo

Low-density cargoes such as grain may be shovel trimmed by trimmers – men or women who shovel the cargo into the empty spaces around the hatch coaming. The trimming of cargo holds during discharge is the removal of such residues of cargo as cannot be removed by the main means of discharge, usually the grabs. (This process is discussed in Chapter 16.) When the Master knows the method of trimming to be employed in loading or discharging, he will know what precautions will be required to ensure that the process is done efficiently.

Pollution: It is always desirable that pollution by dust or by odour from the cargo is kept to a minimum and this is particularly true where bulk terminals are situated near to private housing. This may call for special precautions such as keeping hatch covers partly closed during strong winds or winds from certain directions, or at all times.

Methods of delivering the cargo to the vessel: Some of the lighter and more dusty cargoes such as grain and cement are loaded direct from the silo using enclosed systems, and bulk cargoes are occasionally loaded by grab, but it is more common for dry bulk cargoes to be loaded by mechanical ship loaders in which the cargo is brought over the ship by a conveyor belt contained within a suitable boom framework (Fig. 11.11). A variety of systems allow the ship loader to deliver the cargo to a range of positions along the

Fig. 11.11 A mechanical ship loader with self propelled gantry, rotating boom and enclosed conveyor belt
Photo courtesy of Vigan Engineering s.a.

Fig. 11.13 Continuous bucket unloader lifting front end loader from hold

Fig. 11.12 A two-spout pneumatic suction unloader
Photo courtesy of Coperion GmbH

Fig. 11.14 A grab unloader being used to discharge a handymax vessel

Fig.11.15 A continuous screw-type cement unloader
Photo courtesy of MacGREGOR Group

Fig.11.16 Vessel at buoys, using floating crane to discharge to barges
Photo courtesy of Walter Vervloesem

Fig.11.17 A three spout pneumatic suction unloader
Photo courtesy of Coperion GmbH

length and breadth of the hold. The boom, or arm, may be able to rotate and may carry an adjustable conveyor belt as in the figure and the gantry may be self propelled. The loading spout is likely to be telescopic and modern systems will provide dust reduction. Alternatively the boom may be telescopic, capable of luffing (ie, being raised and lowered), and slewing (swinging round in the horizontal plane). The entire ship loader is normally designed to travel along the quay on rails or tyres. When the cargo has been brought over the ship's hold by conveyor belt it is directed into the hold by a spout or chute which may allow it to fall vertically, or where it may be mechanically distributed to port or starboard.

Cargo work – the discharging berth: Solid bulk cargoes are removed from the holds of ships by grabs, by continuous mechanical unloaders or by suction unloaders (Fig.11.12), each of which is normally able to travel most of the length of the berth.

Grab unloaders (Fig. 11.14) can transfer cargo direct from the ship's hold to a barge or to a stockpile next to the berth. Alternatively, they can drop cargo into a hopper built into the structure of the unloader or placed alongside it. From the hopper the cargo is fed on to a conveyor belt or into a road truck or rail wagon for transfer to a place of storage.

Dockside cranes and floating cranes (Fig.11.16) equipped with grabs can perform much the same variety of tasks as the grab unloaders within a smaller area.

Continuous unloaders may take the form of an endless chain of buckets (Fig. 11.13) or an Archimedes' screw delivering cargo to a conveyor system (Fig.11.15). Such systems result in less dust and spillage than grab systems and provide a more steady flow of cargo on the conveyor.

Pneumatic suction unloaders (Fig.11.17) are used to draw cargo out of the hold (Fig.11.18) through the suction pipes and on to a conveyor system for delivery to the silo or transport system. Alternatively, suction discharge can be carried out by vacuvators (Fig.11.19), which are portable units powered by diesel motors. These units can be placed on a ship's deck and used to draw cargo from her hold and deliver it through a discharge pipe to a smaller vessel moored alongside or a rail wagon or road truck placed close by on the quay.

Fig. 11.18 Pneumatic suction unloaders discharging grain

Photo courtesy of Walter Vervloesem

Fig. 11.19 Mobile vacuvators placed on hatch covers and used to discharge into trucks

Photo courtesy of Walter Vervloesem

Essential information about the ship for the berth operators

The BLU Code[110] lists information considered essential for the ship to pass to the terminal operators before arrival and in cases where the terminal does not provide the Master with a list of their requirements he should be guided by the Code. In addition to routine ETAs, draughts and ship's particulars the specific bulk information which may be required includes the following.

Extreme dimensions: To plan the ship's visit, the berth operators will normally require to know some or all of the ship's extreme dimensions, (length overall, extreme breadth, maximum draught, air draught to highest point on ship and air draught to coaming or, in the case of side-rolling hatch covers, to the hatch cover top of first hold to be worked). Of course if two holds, for example Nos.2 and 8, are to be loaded simultaneously, the airdraught for each hold will be required. For planning the ship's position in the berth, the distance from stem to navigating bridge may be required, as all the cargo holds fall within this distance. Some berths request the length from the forward end of No.1 hatch to the after end of No.9 hatch, as this will determine the travel distance for the loader.

Distribution of cargo, and loading or discharging programme: Before commencement of cargo operations the berth operators will require to know the ship's planned loading rotation, or loading sequence. The document which shows the loading rotation will list the pours in order, showing for each pour the tonnage to be poured and the hold which is to receive it. The berth operators may have no need to know the planned deballasting sequence and the planned draught and calculated longitudinal stresses at the end of each pour, but it is recommended that they be given a copy of the entire loading/deballasting programme, set out on the IMO Loading/Unloading Plan (Appendix 9.3). This document lists the loading rotation. In addition it shows the berth operators that the plans and calculations necessary for the loading have been completed, reassurance which will sometimes be welcome.

If the purpose of the visit is to discharge cargo, the stowage plan listing the commodity, tonnage and consignee of the cargo in each hold will be required as will the ship's planned discharging sequence. This information, too, should be presented on the IMO Loading/Unloading Plan.

When the information is available the loading quantities and sequence should be passed to the terminal before arrival.

Time required for deballasting: There are a number of factors to consider when declaring the time required for deballasting or the ballast pumping rate, values which may be required by the terminal before arrival or for the loading/unloading plan. It is only in most favourable conditions that the theoretical pumping rate of the ballast pumps can be achieved and there may be tanks on which only one pump can be used. Pumping rates will diminish as the ship gets older and sediment accumulates in the ballast tanks. Gravitating rates will vary as the head of water diminishes. Adequate time for stripping must be allowed and the amount of trim, as well as the availability and efficiency of stripping pumps or eductors will have an effect. If a time required for deballasting is stipulated in the charterparty the Master will want to use that value and should inform his owners if he thinks it unachievable.

Ship's cargo-handling equipment: When the ship is equipped with cranes or derricks and when that equipment is to be used for cargo operations, the berth operators are likely to require details of the equipment. Information required may include the number and capacity of the cranes or derricks, their cargo working rate in tonnes/hour, the holds which each serves, their maximum outreach and whether they are equipped with grabs.

Access: If the ship is to provide the means of access, the berth operators may require to know the preferred position of the ship's gangway, or the position of the ship's accommodation ladder. The latter may be installed adjacent to the accommodation or on larger ships part-way along the length of the ship's parallel body.

Ship's mooring lines: The berth operators may want to be sure that the ship is equipped with suitable mooring lines which will hold her safely alongside throughout her stay and which will prevent ranging which might result in damage to loading or discharging equipment. Large vessels may be asked to report in advance the number and types of lines which they intend to use and they may be provided by the berth operators with recommended mooring layouts. Whilst the berth operators do not normally have the authority to instruct the Master what lines he must use, they do have the authority to refuse to bring his vessel in or to keep her alongside if they do not consider her moorings satisfactory.

Bulk carriers can be found with all synthetic mooring ropes, with mixed moorings (synthetic ropes and wire lines) and with all wire moorings (with and without synthetic tails). Rated brake capacities can vary from 30 to 90 tonnes. Winch and fairlead locations can vary significantly from ship to ship. Ship crews will have differing degrees of expertise in mooring matters and varying philosophies concerning maintenance and/or replacement of critical items of mooring equipment.'

The following notes on the mooring of bulk carriers are intended as general guidance for those unfamiliar with the dry bulk trades. No attempt has been made to provide detailed and precise advice, which would depend upon the ship, the berth and numerous other factors. For detailed recommendations on mooring large vessels readers are referred to a specialist publication[283].

- Typical mooring arrangements for bulk carriers moored with fibre ropes of appropriate size in good condition are shown in Fig. 11.3. They assume moderate weather conditions and no significant current or swell.
- A bulk carrier's minimum outfit of mooring lines is governed by the equipment letter allotted to her by her classification society.
- Bulk carriers of all sizes up to and including Cape-sized are usually equipped to moor entirely with fibre ropes.
- The largest fibre ropes in general use for mooring are 84 mm diameter, though 64 mm-72 mm are more widely used.
- A mini-bulker is likely to use 32 mm-40 mm fibre ropes.
- On modern Cape-sized and Panamax bulk carriers, all the mooring ropes used in a normal tie-up will usually be stowed on powered reels. A Cape-sized bulker will have as many as 16 powered reels.
- Powered reels may be fitted with self-tensioning capability, though nowadays this is unusual. The self-tensioning device causes the reel to take up or pay out on the line until the selected tension has been obtained. If the same setting is used for every reel, all the ship's lines will have the same tension.
- When lines have been satisfactorily tensioned they should not be left in the self-tensioning mode, but should be put on the brake. This ensures that if the forces acting on the ship change, she will not start to creep along the berth.

- Older and smaller ships will probably not have ropes or wires on powered reels. Without powered reels the work aboard ship during mooring will be slower and will require more labour.
- If a ship uses wire ropes as mooring lines each will normally be provided with a nylon or other fibre tail of length about 11 metres.
- The largest size of wire rope likely to be used for routine mooring is 44 mm diameter.
- Provided that all lines are of a suitable size and are in good condition, a ship that is moored with wire ropes will require about 25 per cent fewer lines than will the same ship if moored with fibre ropes.
- Mixed moorings, comprising full-length synthetic ropes used together with wire ropes, are not recommended. When it is necessary to use mixed moorings, wire ropes should be used for one type of mooring and synthetic ropes for another. For example, all spring lines can be wire ropes and all headlines, sternlines and breastlines can be synthetic ropes. It is not acceptable for some headlines to be synthetic and others to be wire, as the wire, which stretches less, will take most of the load.
- A vessel which is required to shift along the berth during the course of cargo work will have some of her moorings led to more distant mooring points to assist the shifting.
- In a berth which is exposed to strong tides or currents or where bad weather is expected, additional moorings will be required to supplement those normally used.
- Moorings with a short scope, or length of line used outside the fairlead, must be adjusted more frequently that those with a long scope to correct for the effects of working cargo and ballast and for the rise and fall of tide.
- All-wire mooring lines must be adjusted more frequently than wires with synthetic tails to correct for the effects of working cargo and ballast, and for the rise and fall of tide.

Other information: Additional information listed in the BLU Code must be provided by ships which will arrive partly loaded and by combination carriers. In particular cases there is much other information which berth operators may require to know about a bulk carrier, but there are too many possibilities associated with the loading or discharge of particular bulk carrier types or specific cargoes to do more than to list a few examples here. Information required might include cargo compartments suitable for grab discharge, maximum dimensions of clear deck areas, dimensions of hatch coamings and maximum permitted tanktop, hatch cover or deck loadings.

The implementation of the BLU Code

Inconsistencies: It is worth noting that there have been inconsistencies in the implementation of the Code. In some areas such as the European Community (EC) the Code is mandatory and terminals as well as ships are bound by its requirements. Even within the EC the manner in which the Code is applied varies[120]. Worldwide there are some countries which have not yet made the Code mandatory and where there is no local requirement for ports and terminals to comply with the Code. Despite that the BLU Code represents best practice and all dry bulk shipping should comply with its requirements as far as possible.

Methods of providing information

Information for Master: The information which the Master needs regarding the berth and the intended loading or discharging operation may be given to him in writing, by means of an email or facsimile message from the terminal operator or ship's agent, or may be delivered in the form of a port or terminal brochure, or a data sheet prepared by the port, terminal or agent. The most effective means of passing information is likely to vary from port to port and information provided in any of the above forms will be acceptable if it is clearly written, accurate, relevant and timely.

Information passed verbally, in conversation between the Master and the pilot, agent or port official is useful, too, to emphasise important matters and help with understanding if there is a language difficulty, but verbal advice is best when supported by written information which can be left with the Master.

Information for berth operators: The berth operators can obtain information about the ship from the owners and charterers and from published works of reference such as *Lloyd's Register-Fairplay* and *Clarkson's Bulk Carrier Fleet CD*. However, for information which is up to date and accurate the most reliable source ought to be the vessel's Master and any information upon which the berth operators intend to rely should be provided and/or verified in writing by the Master.

Storing and handling of bulk cargoes ashore

A basic knowledge of the methods used ashore for the handling of bulk cargoes can help with understanding of the reasons for interruptions in the loading or discharging process.

Stockpiles: The cargo may be stored in a stockpile in the open air. Stockpiles are large heaps of bulk cargo (Fig.11.20), often weighing thousands of tonnes, stacked upon an area of level land, the base of the stack resting upon hard packed soil or a concrete or tarmac surface. The largest European storage yards have a stockpile capacity of more than 5 million tons in an area of 80 ha (200 acres). If the commodity is of high value, or if there is concern about the pollution which would result from dust blown away, the stockpile is likely to be protected by fresh water sprays. The Richards Bay Coal Terminal, for example, uses sprays to maintain a surface moisture content of 6-9 per cent in its stockpiles[16].

Cargo arrives at the stockpile by rail wagon, by barge, by conveyor belt or ropeway transportation system direct from the mine or quarry or by road truck if the quantities are relatively small. The cargo is likely to be placed in the stockpile by grab (from a crane) or by stacker (Fig. 11.22). A stacker is an arrangement of conveyor belts and booms similar to a mechanical shiploader. It can be used to deliver the cargo to the stockpile after it has been tipped from the rail wagon or road truck, or grabbed from the barge into a hopper which pours it onto the conveyor belt.

Bulk cargo is removed from the stockpile by a reclaimer, which feeds the cargo onto a conveyor belt

Fig. 11.20 Stockpiles at Maasvlakte, Rotterdam
Photo courtesy of Europees Massagoed-Overslagbedrijf (EMO) BV

Fig. 11.21 Cement silos at Aalborg Portland A/S

Fig. 11.22 A stacker taking ore from the conveyor belt and stacking it in the stockpile
Photo courtesy of Sandvik Mining and Construction

Fig. 11.23 The circular framework of two tipplers in tandem contains wagons which have been upended to pour their contents into hoppers below
Photo courtesy Richards Bay Coal Terminal

Fig. 11.24 A reclaimer taking ore from the stockpile and loading it onto the conveyor belt
Photo courtesy of Sandvik Mining and Construction

Fig. 11.25 *Bulk Irony* using cranes to load coal from a Panamax vessel, for later discharge to a smaller vessel via hoppers, conveyers and discharging boom
Photo courtesy of CoeClerici Logistics

Fig.11.26 A stacker/reclaimer can deliver ore to the stockpile and also remove it
Photo courtesy of Sandvik Mining and Construction

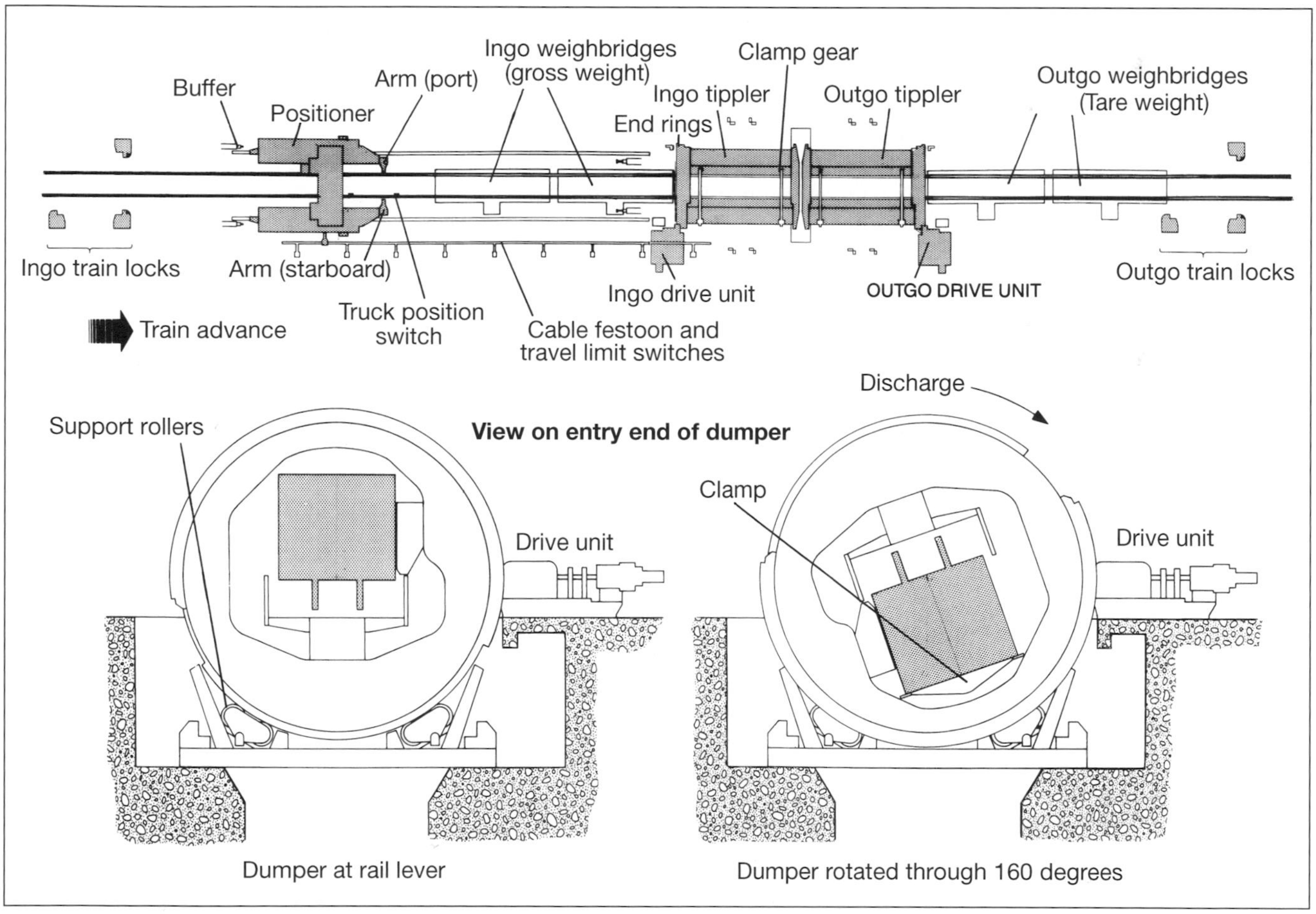

Buffer
Positioner
Arm (port)
Ingo weighbridges (gross weight)
Clamp gear
Ingo tippler
Outgo tippler
End rings
Outgo weighbridges (Tare weight)
Ingo train locks
Arm (starboard)
Truck position switch
Cable festoon and travel limit switches
Ingo drive unit
OUTGO DRIVE UNIT
Outgo train locks
Train advance
Discharge
Support rollers
View on entry end of dumper
Clamp
Drive unit
Drive unit
Dumper at rail lever
Dumper rotated through 160 degrees

Fig. 11.27 Rail dumper system turns rail wagons upside down to tip out contents
(Courtesy of Strachan and Henshaw)

for delivery to the ship. A reclaimer (Fig. 11.24) is a machine which uses a bucket wheel or a scraper belt to remove cargo from a stockpile and feed it onto a conveyor. Often a single unit is built to operate as a combination stacker/reclaimer (Fig. 11.26) which will put cargo into a stockpile or remove cargo from the stockpile. At some loading terminals such as in Stjernøy in Norway, where the mine is adjacent to the loading berth, the stockpile is underground within the mine.

Silos: These are used mainly for bulk grain, animal feeds and oilseeds, and for mineral cargoes such as cement with high values or dusty characteristics (Fig.11.21). Filling and emptying them can be achieved by mechanical means assisted by gravity or by pneumatic means. Handling capacities of 1,000 t/h or more can be achieved. When a ship is loaded from a silo the cargo will normally be delivered by means of a pipe or hose suspended from a boom (Fig.19.22). Whilst silos are large structures they may be subdivided into a large number of bins. The full contents of a bin may be the minimum pour that can be delivered.

Rail wagons: When bulk cargoes are brought direct to the loading berth by rail wagons it is normal to use a railcar dumper ('tippler') system (Figs. 11.23 and 11.27) to capsize the wagons, sometimes two at a time, and tip out their contents into the hopper or hoppers situated below them. From the hopper the cargo will be delivered by conveyor to the stockpile or to the ship. Theoretical tippling rates can be as high as 7,300 t/h achieved with 75 wagons on single rail line, but this is dependent upon the faultless operation of an extensive marshalling yard and it is unlikely that it is often achieved in practice. Richards Bay Coal Terminal, however, has three railcar dumper systems in tandem, giving a theoretical rate of delivery to the stockpiles of more than 15,000 t/h.

Road trucks: Road trucks delivering bulk cargo to a terminal will normally back up a ramp and tip their contents into a hopper, feeding a conveyor, serving the ship loader.

Barges: When bulk cargoes are delivered to the loading terminal by barge or by ship for transhipment, transfer to the loading ship or stockpile will often be achieved by grab unloaders, otherwise known as gantry cranes (Fig.11.14), though fixed or floating cranes (Fig.11.16), or vacuvators (Fig.11.19), can also be used. Grabs with a capacity of 30-50 mt are common in the major bulk transhipping ports, and grabs with capacities as great as 85 mt have been built. Grab unloaders can also be used to load vessels by transferring cargo from the stockpile direct to the ship's hold.

Offshore transshipment: When trade develops faster than port capacity, as in the coal trade between Indonesia and India, there is a place for offshore transshipment of cargoes from larger ships to smaller vessels or lighters and transshipment is achieved by using geared bulk carriers, self unloaders or self propelled transhipping units[231] designed to discharge and load cargo and to provide some storage (Fig.11.25).

Sources

16, 110, 120, 121, 190, 231, 232. (See List of Sources, page 497)

CHAPTER 12
LOADING PERIOD

Importance of the loading period, arrival in berth, preloading surveys, acceptability of offered cargo, duties of ship's officers, loading/deballasting programme, monitoring loading and deballasting, supervision of work of the crew, liaison with loading staff, damage to ship or cargo, maintenance of full records, chief mate's role as troubleshooter, Master's role, shifting ship by warping, safe procedures for working cargo

THE LOADING PERIOD is a most important one for the Master of a bulk carrier and for his officers. Loading is usually more rapid and concentrated than is the carrying or discharging of the cargo. Events happen quickly. Unexpected problems can arise if the cargo is unfamiliar or the port unknown and will require prompt attention to ensure that the cargo is loaded in a safe and satisfactory manner and that the ship and cargo are protected from damage throughout. A high level of alertness will be required from the start to the end of the loading period.

The system used by the deck officers for sharing the supervisory work during loading will be governed by the number of officers carried, their experience and the normal procedure for ships of their flag or ownership. There will always be at least one deck officer on duty during loading, under the direction of the chief mate. The chief mate will himself usually take charge of all important steps in the loading, such as draught surveys, the completion of deballasting and the calculation and execution of trimming pours. In smaller ships with only one or two mates he will also take his turn on cargo watch, as he may also do on larger vessels. The Master will hold himself available to advise where required or will take a more active supervisory role if his officers are inexperienced or unreliable, or when the manning provides only a Master and one mate.

Arrival in the berth

The required sequence of tasks when a vessel arrives in a loading berth is as follows. First secure the vessel in the berth. Next provide a safe access. Then obtain a full set of draughts for a draught survey. Simultaneously or immediately afterwards agree the Ship/Shore Safety checklist and the Loading/Deballasting Plan with the terminal representative as required by the BLU Code[110]. Receive and consider the Declaration by Shipper as required by SOLAS[128] and note the characteristics of the cargo. Where necessary deballasting must also be approved by the quarantine or other ballast authorities. When the weather is adverse or the approaches to the berth are exposed, or when required for an on-hire survey, hatches should remain closed until the vessel is secured alongside. When the approaches are sheltered, the weather is fair and it is safe to do so the cleats can be removed from the hatches before berthing but they should not, unless special circumstances justify an exception, be lifted on the rams or opened until the vessel is secured in the berth. In most cases the opening of each hatch will take no more than a few seconds and being a symmetrical process, will not affect the trim but if more panels are moved forward than aftwards, or vice versa, the opening of hatches should not be done at the same time as the reading of the draughts. Only when the above steps have been completed and a preloading or on-hire inspection or draught survey, if required, has been passed can loading commence.

There can be a case for amending the above sequence of tasks when the declaration by shipper has been transmitted to the ship before berthing, the loading programme has been fully agreed in advance between ship and terminal, when tonnage is to be decided by shore scales, when no preloading or on-hire inspection is required and when the approaches are sheltered, the waters are calm and the weather is good. On the rare occasions when all those conditions are satisfied it is reasonable to berth with all hatches open to demonstrate the vessel's readiness to load, and an officer should read the draughts for the ship's draught survey immediately the vessel has berthed.

On vessels which are required to change position under a fixed loader, the pilot before berthing will require to know the first loading position so that he can position the ship ready for commencement of loading.

Preloading surveys

Before the commencement of loading there will often be a requirement for a preloading survey of the holds and for a draught survey. Where the vessel is a regular trader employed on a period time charter carrying the same commodity every voyage, preloading surveys of the holds are less likely to be required except when the cargo is easily contaminated. Draught surveys by independent surveyors are not required when the charterparty states that the tonnage carried is to be established by some other means such as shore weighing, although the ship's personnel should always make their own survey to calculate a ship's figure for cargo loaded.

Normally the ship's agent will be able to advise the Master whether surveys will be required, if there is any doubt. When surveys are undertaken it is sensible to treat surveyors with courtesy and consideration. A surveyor undertaking a preloading survey of holds should be accompanied by an officer, preferably the chief mate and a seaman, and should be helped to gain access to holds and assisted with lighting and ladders, if required. Radio contact between the hold inspection team and ship's staff on deck will expedite the inspection and also provide instant communication should an accident happen or any defects be found. Engineers should be on standby for the testing of bilge suctions, if required. (Survey requirements in Australia are particularly strict, see

Appendix 12.1) Careful note should be taken of any items which the surveyor notes for attention and the officer must be sure that he has a clear understanding of what the surveyor requires. Any work required by the surveyor should be given top priority, since failure to pass the survey will normally mean that the ship goes off hire until such time as she is passed as ready to load. A hold inspection certificate is at Appendix 14.1.

The draught surveyor should also be accompanied by an officer when taking his readings. For soundings of bunker tanks the chief or second engineer is usually the appropriate person, whilst the chief mate should accompany the surveyor to read the draughts and to check the bilge, ballast and fresh water soundings. It is fairly common for the draught surveyor to board the vessel and announce that he has already read the draughts, but this should not be acceptable to a conscientious chief mate. An officer should check and agree the readings obtained, and should independently complete a set of calculations to obtain figures for bunkers, ballast and ship's constant.

Condition of cargo offered

When the vessel is berthed and the Master has satisfied himself that she is safely secured alongside, information will be exchanged, as described in Chapter 11. A copy of the Ship/Shore Safety Checklist specified in the BLU Code[110] must be completed and the loading programme, which can be set out in the IMO form[(232)] for this purpose (Appendix 9.3), should be confirmed. Thereafter the Master and his officers must satisfy themselves that the cargo is acceptable.

Where possible the cargo should be inspected ashore in the stockpile, silos, trucks or wagons or in the lighter before it is loaded, as it is always easier to object to unacceptable cargo before it has been loaded and many bulk ports do not have the facilities to discharge cargo from a ship's holds once it has been loaded. Officers must be on the lookout for any defects which would make the cargo unacceptable or which might later be blamed on the ship if not seen, recorded and made the subject of a protest. Bulk grain which is wet, sprouting, mouldy or infested would be unacceptable, as would wet or caked fertiliser, rusty cold rolled steel coils or bulk ores contaminated with a different cargo or containing excessive moisture. Coal contaminated with iron ore, wheat in a cargo of corn, and timber stained with oil have all been found and rejected by alert officers. The great number of possible cargoes, each with many possible causes of damage, make it impossible to do more than provide examples here.

Excessive moisture is a particularly dangerous feature of a fine grained bulk cargo and in a number of instances moisture content has been greater than declared, allowing the cargo to liquefy and threatening the survival of ships or caused their loss. In one case a cargo of copper concentrates, frozen when loaded in Arctic Russia, liquified when it melted during a North Atlantic voyage causing the ship to list dangerously.

The *IMO SOLAS Convention*[92] requires the shipper to provide the Master with details of the nature of the cargo so that any safety precautions which may be necessary can be put into effect. The shipper must also provide a document stating the transportable moisture limit (TML) of the cargo and a certificate of moisture content showing the average moisture content of the material at the time that the certificate is presented to the Master. In practice all this information is normally contained in a single document, the declaration by shipper (Appendix 14.10), described in Chapter 14. The moisture content stated in the Shipper's Declaration should not be accepted without question particularly if the cargo appears wet. The value may have been falsified or the cargo may have been exposed to heavy rain after analysis. If there are any doubts samples of the cargo should be tested for moisture content using one of the methods described in the IMSBC Code[153].

The Master should request the contents of the Shipper's Declaration by email before arrival and should insist upon receiving it before loading commences[216].

Where the cargo cannot be inspected ashore it should be regularly inspected at the point of delivery aboard ship, where officers will hope to avoid the painful experience of a certain pair of chief and second mates. They were standing by the hold at 0200 hours on a winter morning to watch the commencement of loading aboard a bulk carrier in Chicago. What they saw was 50 tonnes of ore poured into the hold and then rapidly covered with the cargo of petcoke. This seems to have been a case in which the shiploader operator cleaned the conveyor belt of a previous cargo into the ship's hold, a practice which is completely unacceptable. It was not possible to stop the loading when this incident occurred because the operator of the shiploader was out of sight (perhaps deliberately), but the fact that the incident had been observed made it possible for the ship to issue a letter of protest.

Duties of the officer of the watch

During the loading period the officer of the watch (OOW) must be concerned with a number of matters, some of which are common to all ships and others which are specific to bulk carriers.

Loading/deballasting programme must be studied and understood: A copy of the loading/deballasting programme prepared by the chief mate will be provided for the officers of the watch and will, if necessary, be the subject of discussion at a meeting of those involved. This may be the same programme as has been passed to the loading foreman or it may contain extra details, of ballasting for example, which the chief mate considers that it is not necessary for the shore personnel to know. Each OOW must make sure that he understands every item in the programme and what must be done at every stage.

Cargo loading process must be monitored: Monitoring of the cargo loading must have the highest priority because it is better to get things right the first time, since it can be very difficult to correct mistakes in loading. Ships' personnel must keep in mind the fact that the interests of the shippers of the cargo and of those employed to load it are not necessarily the same as those of the ship's personnel. What is convenient for one party may be quite the opposite for another.

Figure 12.1 Hold ballasted in port to the marked level (white line) to reduce air draught

Photo courtesy of Walter Vervloesem

The initial positioning of the shiploader arm must be watched to ensure that the calculated airdraught is available in practice. If the shiploader has insufficient height to plumb the hold it may be necessary to alter the ballast. Alternatively, if the extra height needed is small, it may be possible to allow access to shiploader by using ballast to list the ship towards the quay. If the ship is already fully ballasted the list should be created by discharging ballast from an after topside or double bottom tank to avoid any decrease of the forward mean draught. As soon as sufficient cargo has been loaded to achieve the required increase in draught, ballast should be used to bring the ship upright again.

Air draught is unlikely to be a problem in those bulk carriers which are provided with extra holds which can be ballasted in port (Fig.12.1). Where necessary, and when conditions are favourable, such holds can be ballasted in sheltered waters before berthing to ensure that the ship's air draught is sufficiently low.

Any contact between ship and shiploader should be avoided as it is likely to lead to damage to one or both. Contact is most likely if the shiploader is left unattended whilst the ship moves as a result of swell, rising tide, ballast changes, slack moorings, winches left in automatic mode allowing the ship to creep, or the shifting of the ship to a new loading position.

The OOW must regularly check that the loading is continuing in accordance with the loading programme. Each pour must be loaded into the correct hold and into the correct position in that hold. Ideally the cargo should be poured across the breadth and along the length of the hold to satisfy the requirement of the IMSBC Code[5] that the cargo should be trimmed reasonably level to the boundaries of the cargo space and to ensure that the load is distributed evenly throughout the hold. This can be readily achieved when the loading head is able to travel to positions in which it can plumb the full length and breadth of the hold. Provided that the loader keeps moving from port to starboard and back again, and does not dwell on one side of the centreline, the ship will be kept upright and the cargo will be symmetrically distributed. If there are valid reasons why the cargo need not be trimmed reasonably level the IMSBC Code requires the shippers to inform the Master in writing giving full details prior to loading.

When the loader is fixed and unable to travel along the hold or reach beyond the ship's centreline the cargo should be poured at the geometrical centre of the hold. This requirement is often achieved by ensuring that the loader is aligned and remains aligned, say, with a white mark painted on the hatch coaming. On smaller bulkers with long holds the chief mate may have planned a different cargo distribution, requiring the cargo to be poured in another position – eg, '2 metres forward of the mark' – and such instructions must be strictly followed.

It is also necessary to ensure that the correct cargo is being loaded. If the loading programme calls for iron ore fines in No. 3 hold and iron ore pellets in No. 5 hold, the OOW must ensure that the cargo being loaded in No. 3 does look like fines, not pellets. From time to time during the pour he must confirm that the cargo continues to have the same appearance and that there are no signs of contamination, or of excessive moisture.

The method of loading must be kept under survey and the ship's requirements must be enforced. If the ship is to be kept upright and all cargo is to be poured amidships, the shiploader operator must be reminded as necessary of the requirement. If the cargo is to be spout trimmed in the hold involving some listing of the ship first one way and then the other, the operator must be warned if he exceeds an acceptable amount of list. When a list develops as a result of uneven deballasting, the shiploader operator must be informed so that he does not try to eliminate it with cargo. Some bulk carriers are fitted with list indicator lights on the bridge wings. For example, a row of lights, green to starboard and red to port, with a single white light amidships, may be fitted. When the ship is listed 2° to starboard two green lights will be lit. When indicators of this sort are available it may be necessary to bring them to the attention of the operator of the shiploader.

If the cargo is not evenly distributed in each hold – if the ship is kept upright by balancing the excess cargo on the starboard side of one hold with the excess cargo on the port side of another hold – the ship will be twisted and may suffer serious structural damage. It is essential that a ship which develops a list because there is too much cargo to starboard in No.2 hold is brought upright with cargo poured to port in the same hold. The ship should be upright at the completion of each pour.

The OOW will find it useful to have a reasonable idea of the loading rate. The time taken for the first pour will provide an indication of the rate in tonnes/hour. This can be checked against whatever rate the loading foreman or ship's agent has predicted. A slower rate than that predicted will be unsurprising since it is common practice to quote the best rate rather than the average rate. A faster rate than that forecast needs careful examination to confirm that it is correct and to consider its effect upon the rest of the loading/deballasting programme. If loading continues at this rate, will the deballasting be able to keep up?

It will also be useful to observe whether the loading

rate is a steady or a fluctuating one. That can often be determined by watching the flow of cargo from the spout or by observing the method of delivery of the cargo to the loading conveyor. Once the loading rate and any variations in it have been observed, it can be used to predict the time when each pour will finish. Pours which finish unexpectedly early or continue excessively should be carefully checked to confirm that the correct tonnage has been delivered.

The quantity of cargo loaded in each pour must be monitored as far as possible. A useful check can be obtained by taking a set of draught readings and checking the soundings of the working ballast tanks when the loader moves from one loading position to the next. Provided that the readings can be obtained quickly whilst loading is stopped, the results can be studied after loading has resumed and should be in good agreement with the values shown in the loading programme. If they are not in good agreement, there must be a mistake in the tonnage loaded, the quantity of ballast discharged or the loading/deballasting programme and it will be a matter of urgency to recheck everything and find the mistake.

Most bulk carrier officers know of one or two occasions in which serious errors in loading have occurred – when a hold has been overloaded by as much as 1,000 tonnes and the ship has finished up excessively trimmed by the stern or, even worse, by the head. It is very difficult for such errors to occur if the OOW is thoroughly alert and regularly checks the draught readings. Errors of this sort sometimes occur when officers are inexperienced and find themselves with too many problems to solve. On other occasions they occur when officers believe that everything is going well and their conscientious supervision is unnecessary. There is never a good excuse for overloading: draught readings, carefully taken, will always show the tonnage loaded and provide warning of possible overloading.

Deballasting must be monitored: Aboard many bulk carriers the deck OOW will personally implement the deballasting programme by operation of the appropriate control switches at a ballast control station. On other vessels the deballasting will be carried out by engineroom personnel on instructions from the OOW. In both cases it is good practice for the OOW to satisfy himself by direct observation that the deballasting is proceeding and a flow of air into the airpipe on deck provides a clear sign that ballast is being removed from the correct tank. Before deballasting starts the OOW or someone assisting him must where necessary ensure that airpipe caps (on older vessels) and manual valves (for forepeak tanks) have been physically opened.

As the loading continues, the OOW must check regularly to ensure that the deballasting continues without problem, a problem being anything which prevents maximum discharge from both pumps. First warning of a problem in deballasting may be the ship listing as a port tank pumps out whilst a starboard one fails to do so or vice versa. The pump gauges should be watched, and will provide a similar warning. A normal reading on the amp meter shows the pump is pumping and this can be confirmed by a normal reading on the discharge pressure gauge.

By itself, evidence that the pumps are pumping efficiently is not sufficient to guarantee that the deballasting is going well. Mistakes do occur and equipment does fail. It is essential to make regular checks by sounding or by observing the flow of air into the airpipe to confirm that the ballast is being drawn from the correct tank. Direct manual soundings of ballast tanks must be taken with sounding rod or steel sounding tape, particularly as the tank approaches empty, to check how much ballast remains and whether the tank has been properly drained.

As the deballasting continues, the OOW (if he is directly responsible for the pump controls) will have to adjust them as necessary to maintain optimum discharge rate as per the makers' instructions. On a large vessel – say, a Cape-sized bulker – the ballast pump controls are likely to require checking and adjustment at intervals of about 30 minutes, a frequency which increases in smaller vessels.

Deballasting of a compartment normally continues until the ballast pump finally loses suction with only a small sounding (0-30 cm) remaining in the tank at that time. Stripping is the process of discharging as much as possible of the final small tonnage of ballast which remains in the tank. If the ship is equipped with a separate stripping pump or eductor, that will be used to continue the discharge of any remaining tonnage of ballast in the compartment with the OOW monitoring the sounding in the tank. If there is no separate system for stripping, a further attempt will be made to reduce the strippings remaining when trim and list conditions are most favourable.

Work of crew members must be supervised: The OOW must be prepared to organise and supervise the work of the crew when they are engaged in cargo-related work, particularly if they are required for the cleaning and preparing for loading of ballast holds and for the shifting of the ship from one position of loading to another. To ensure that no time is lost unnecessarily the OOW must co-ordinate the work of the crew with the deballasting and the loading, and must ensure that the crew members are kept informed of the programme and any adjustment to its timing. For example, the crew must be kept informed of any changes to the anticipated time when the ballast hold will be nearly empty and ready for cleaning.

As loading progresses and the loading of some holds is completed, the OOW will inform the crew when each hold is ready to be secured for sea. As the securing proceeds he will supervise it as necessary to ensure that the work is done correctly and with the required degree of thoroughness. Particular emphasis must be placed on the thorough cleaning of coamings and hatch drain channels.

Liaison with the loading foreman: Liaison must be maintained with the loading foreman to ensure that a good understanding is maintained between shore and ship personnel. The chief mate will normally take the responsibility for informing the loading foreman if deballasting or hold cleaning is behind schedule and an interruption in loading is required. It will be the duty of the OOW to keep the chief mate informed so that he can act in good time to arrange for an interruption in loading.

In the few ports where ships are moored with shore lines on shore winches and where the ship can be shifted along the berth by shore personnel, it is essential that the OOW is always informed before the ship is shifted.

Damage to the ship: Damage to the ship whilst loading is less common than damage whilst discharging, and can occur as a result of contact between the shiploader arm and the ship's structure or as a result of careless loading. For example, the tanktop can be damaged by the pouring of pig iron on to the unprotected tanktop and some coal spouts are reported to deliver the cargo at such a high rate that the hold coatings are blasted off. Wherever possible the OOW should anticipate the possibility of damage and take steps to prevent it. When damage occurs the details must be noted, digital photos obtained where possible and the stevedores must be held responsible by a written notice. Normally it will be the responsibility of the OOW to pass the details of the incident promptly to the chief mate so that the latter can serve the notice on the stevedores. (Stevedore damage is discussed more fully in Chapter 16).

Damage to the cargo: Damage to the cargo or loss of cargo through spillage whilst loading is a possibility and should be treated in the same manner as damage to the ship. Damage should be anticipated and prevented where possible. When it occurs the details should be noted and promptly passed to the chief mate. If damage or spillage continues to occur it may be necessary to stop loading until better methods can be introduced.

Loading with ship's gear: When cargo is loaded with the ship's cargo-handling gear, a high level of alertness is required of the ship's officers. They must ensure that the equipment is properly used. Where necessary they must insist that winch or crane drivers from ashore follow the ship's rules for safe operation. They must inspect the gear before cargo operations commence and also observe the equipment in operation and inspect it frequently to ensure that it remains in good working order at all times.

Moorings must be tended: The tending of moorings is necessary to ensure that the ship remains firmly alongside in position, despite the disturbing effects of loading of cargo, discharge of ballast, passing of other shipping, or change in level of tide, rate of current or strength or direction of wind.

If experienced seamen are on duty and the ship is well equipped with mooring gear, the duties of the OOW will consist of little more than ensuring that the tending of the lines is effected as required. But if crew members are inexperienced and untrained, the mooring equipment is inadequate, the berth is a difficult one or the conditions are exceptional, the work will require much of the officer's attention and he will have to be ready to decide when to initiate action such as putting out additional lines or calling the chief mate.

Means of access must be tended: The gangway or accommodation ladder will be subject to all the same disturbing factors as will the moorings and must receive all the attention required to ensure that it remains safe and in compliance with the regulations throughout the vessel's stay in port. This is a task which requires continuous attention if loading rates are high and tidal range is large. (See Chapter 21.)

Pollution avoidance: Pollution must be avoided. This requires the OOW to be alert to prevent any overflow of oil on deck or overside and to prevent any discharge of ballast where harm can be done. Most bulk carriers when in port fit all the scupper plugs to contain any accidental oil spills from hatch hydraulics or accidental overflows of ballast. Pollution from the ship's domestic garbage and from hold sweepings, from discharge of contaminated bilge water, and by discharge of thick smoke from the funnel must also be avoided. Pollution by dust from the cargo can also be a problem and is one about which the terminal operators can be expected to give advice. Pollution avoidance is discussed more fully in Chapter 25.

Weather must be observed and recorded: The basic weather data (wind direction and force, barometric pressure, temperature, amount of cloud, and description of weather – eg, 'heavy rain', snow showers', 'fair') must be recorded at least three times daily, and are best recorded at the end of the watch of each OOW. In addition humidity readings should be recorded when the cargo is one which requires ventilation. More frequent weather reports should be recorded when the weather is bad and when it interferes with cargo work or threatens to cause damage to the cargo. Times of starting and stopping of rain must be recorded to allow the Master to verify the statement of facts which may be significant for the laytime calculation.

The role of the OOW with respect to weather is far from being a passive one. When he observes the weather he must consider its effect upon the ship and cargo and must have no hesitation in taking action if the possibility of damage to ship or cargo exists. With some cargoes and in some ports the shore personnel may enforce sensible rules to protect the cargo and the loading process when adverse weather occurs, but it is never prudent for the OOW to rely upon anyone else to take the necessary action.

Loading must be stopped and the hatches closed if it starts to rain or even if it threatens to start to rain or snow upon a cargo, such as chemical fertiliser or grain, which can be harmed by water. If the cargo is being loaded from a stockpile which is in the open and if the permitted range of moisture content is large, then some rain during loading is unlikely to be critical, although this must be reconsidered if the rain is prolonged and heavy. The IMO *IMSBC Code*[5] provides advice on measuring the moisture content of bulk cargoes.

If the loading foreman insists upon continuing to load during adverse weather when the Master considers that loading should stop then company policy should be followed. This may call for a standard letter of protest to be issued, holding the shippers liable for any damage consequent upon loading during rain, or the Master may be instructed to insist that a responsible person signs a standard letter of indemnity provided by his owners. If no satisfactory response is received the hatches must be closed. The decision as to what to do if it rains is best taken and agreed between all the parties before the rain occurs, when the vessel first arrives in port.

Loading may be stopped by shore personnel if high winds or fog interfere with the process, although problems are more likely during discharge. Furthermore, there are ports where loading in high winds from certain directions is prohibited because of the unacceptable quantities of cargo dust which are blown over residential housing.

Maintenance of full written records: The OOW must maintain a full and accurate written record of all the events which occur and the readings which are obtained during his period of duty. This information will be recorded in the port log, with the significant items being transferred to the deck log book. It is nowadays the practice on some ships for the port log to be typed directly into a computer. This practice cannot be recommended because the record can be altered at a later date and may arouse suspicion in the event of a dispute. Whilst this topic is fully discussed in Chapter 3, it is worth repeating that a written record should be kept of:

- Times of commencing and stopping loading, and tonnages loaded as calculated by ship and shore.
- Times of inspecting cargo gear.
- Times of transferring loading operations to another hold.
- Reasons for interruptions in loading or deballasting.
- Times of starting and stopping ballast pumps.
- Times of opening and closing ballast tank valves.
- Values and times of soundings obtained and tonnages remaining in each ballast tank.
- Values of ballast pump amp meter and discharge pressure readings at regular intervals.
- Values of draught readings obtained.
- Times of shifting ship.
- Details such as name, time alongside, time of departure of any barges used in cargo operations.
- Times of start and end of surveys, names of surveyors, results of surveys.
- Times of bunkering fuel and water and tonnages taken.
- Details of any damage to ship or cargo.
- Weather observations at regular intervals, at least three times daily, but preferably every four hours.

Chief mate's role during loading

draught survey: Before the start of loading the chief mate will normally undertake a draught survey. If an independent surveyor has been appointed the chief mate will accompany him on his survey, agree soundings and draught readings with him and then complete a separate set of calculations before comparing the final results with the surveyor. If no surveyor has been appointed the chief mate will simply take his own readings and complete his own calculations. Similar procedures will be followed on completion of loading.

Instructing junior officers: It is the chief mate who normally prepares the ship's loading/deballasting plan, and who is answerable to the Master for its implementation. The chief mate will have supervised the cleaning and preparation of the holds and will normally take personal charge of any of the more critical steps in the loading programme. The second and third mates, and engine room staff if necessary, will be provided by the chief mate with copies of the loading/deballasting plan and will be instructed by the chief mate as to his requirements. If there are any special matters to which he wants to draw particular attention, the chief mate will be well advised to put them in writing. When in writing they are available to the OOW for further reference and study as the loading progresses.

Commencement of loading: The chief mate will normally be in attendance at the commencement of loading to ensure that a swift response can be made to any unexpected problems which occur. He will double-check that the loader can plumb the hold and that the cargo is the correct product being loaded in the intended position.

Monitoring of tonnages delivered: Problems can be expected if the tonnages of cargo delivered by the shore installation are inaccurate. Unfortunately, shore personnel are not always certain of the accuracy of their measuring equipment or honest in informing the ship of the reliability of the tonnages loaded. When possible it is prudent to make an accurate check of the tonnages loaded at intervals during the loading, and this is something that the chief mate should try to do by undertaking informal draught surveys from time to time, without interrupting loading.

Such surveys are useless unless the precise ballast condition is known, so they are best undertaken at the end of a stage in the deballasting when a full and up-to-the-minute set of soundings of any working tanks can be obtained at the same time as a full set of draught readings at a time when loading is interrupted and the shiploader is moving from one position to another. This informal survey is less important than an actual draught survey, so it is acceptable to use earlier soundings for ballast tanks which have not been pumped in the meantime.

With the information obtained from the informal draught surveys, the chief mate can calculate whether the shiploader is loading the planned tonnages or whether it appears to be loading too much or too little. If the errors are consistent a percentage error can be calculated, but it would be unwise to assume that the errors are consistent unless this is found in a succession of calculations. If the figure is consistent and significant (and errors of up to 10 per cent have been reported on occasion) it can be used to amend the quantities required for the tonnages in each pour.

Departure from the loading plan: Quite often it happens that the loading and deballasting cannot follow the intended programme exactly. The chief mate should be informed when that occurs and may be able to adjust the loading/deballasting plan to take account of the new circumstances. This is only acceptable provided that he satisfies himself that the new plan remains within any limits imposed by the classification society and that it is acceptable to the terminal representative.

It may be necessary to stop the loading if problems occur. This is a decision which the chief mate will normally take, perhaps after consultation with the Master. Any interruption in loading is an important matter, which may cost owners or charterers money, so it is essential that the information provided by the ship is clear and unambiguous. It must be made absolutely clear if the ship is ordering a stop in loading or is merely giving advance warning that a stop may be required. It is also most important that any order to stop should be given in writing and should be claused 'due to failure of shore loader to keep to Master's load plan' if the problem has indeed been caused by a failure of the shore installation and not of the ship. The reason for the stop and where possible the duration of the stop should be stated, and similar clear information should be provided when loading is to resume.

Final stripping of ballast tanks: The chief mate will normally take the opportunity at a time when the main deballasting is complete and the ship has a good stern trim, to satisfy himself that all the ballast tanks have been stripped to the fullest extent possible. This is an opportunity for him to use his experience to pump out a further tonnage of strippings, thereby enabling the ship to lift a corresponding additional tonnage of cargo. The final soundings to which the strippings in the ballast tanks are reduced should be carefully recorded for inspection by any independent draught surveyor. Soundings obtained when the ship has a substantial stern trim and properly corrected for that trim will provide a measurement of the contents remaining which may be more accurate than later soundings taken when the vessel is trimmed even keel prior to sailing.

Trimming pours: The chief mate will calculate the quantities required for the trimming pours when he has obtained a full set of draught readings and has verified that all pumpable ballast has been discharged (See Chapter 9). To speed the process and to minimise the interruption in loading he may rely upon officers with VHF handsets to report some of the draught readings to him. The tonnages required for the trimming pours and the holds in which they are to be loaded will normally be passed to the loading foreman in writing, to avoid misunderstanding.

Topping off of holds: When the ship is loading a low-density cargo such as coke or grain, where the holds have to be completely filled, the chief mate will try to view the completion of each hold to satisfy himself that it has been entirely filled and that no space has been lost. Where a cargo requires trimming to provide a level stow or to ensure the maximum tonnage loaded, the chief mate should satisfy himself that the work has been properly done. Where a hold is part-filled on completion of loading a low-density cargo he may wish to observe the ullage or to measure or estimate the space remaining. When the space remaining is known the space used can be calculated, permitting an accurate calculation of the final stowage factor for the cargo.

Special requirements for particular cargoes: Many bulk cargoes require special attention. The lashing of steel cargoes and of timber deck cargoes, the separation of small parcels of bulk cargo, and the protection of chemical fertilisers from condensation require particular supervision, but no attempt has been made to deal with such matters here. The general point is that whenever the cargo requires special attention the chief mate will be actively involved, either by his presence in person or by the detailed instructions that he gives to his junior officers.

Damage claims: It is essential that stevedores are warned immediately when they have caused or seem likely to cause damage to the ship or cargo. The chief mate should regularly emphasise the importance of this to his junior officers and should ensure that they issue the appropriate warnings, and/or report to him immediately, when damage occurs or is likely to occur. When damage occurs the chief mate will probably speak to the stevedores immediately to ensure that they are aware of the matter and should always follow this up immediately with a digital photo or photos and a written notice (which can be a standard stevedores' damage form, or cargo damage form) when damage has occurred.

Securing for sea: The chief mate will superintend the securing of the ship for sea, rechecking for himself where necessary the work of the crew as supervised by the officers of the watch. In some trades, hatch covers and accesses must be sealed by an official, who issues an appropriate certificate (Appendix 14.23). (Some grain cargoes are fumigated on completion of loading, a process which is described in Chapter 21.)

Master's role

When provided with competent officers, the Master can expect that his involvement with loading a familiar cargo will be limited to the receiving of regular reports from the chief mate as to how the work is progressing and the offering of advice where appropriate.

When the cargo is more unusual or when the officers are inexperienced or unreliable, the Master will find it necessary to monitor their work more closely and to undertake or recheck some of the more critical duties normally undertaken by the chief mate.

On occasions it may happen that a problem arises with the loading which is outside the Master's experience. For example, he may be assured that a procedure to which he objects is 'normal practice' in the port. In such circumstances the Master should not hesitate to stop the loading if necessary and to consult his owners and/or charterers. They have a strong interest in the safe carriage of the cargo and will expect to be informed and consulted when doubt arises.

Shifting ship by warping

Shifting ship by warping is a procedure which is rarely required in many sectors of modern shipping, but which continues to be relatively common in the dry bulk trades. When the loader is fixed or limited in its movement the ship must be moved to place each hold below the loader in turn. When the ship is too large for the berth and overlaps its ends, she must be moved to allow the loading or discharging of the end holds. In addition, bulkers are sometimes required to move along the quay from one berth to another.

Mini-bulkers in the European trades obtain considerable experience of shifting ship. On average they visit 50 loading ports a year. At least half of those ports are likely to be fitted with fixed loaders where the loading normally requires four shift-ships per loading.

Handy-sized bulkers are required to shift berth or

to shift within the berth at many loading and discharging ports, and Panamax and Cape-sized bulkers are also occasionally required to shift-ship within the berth.

The ability to shift-ship efficiently is a requirement in the bulk trades, but sometimes presents difficulties. If experience is lacking it is well worthwhile to make careful preparations and to ensure that a full mooring party is available aboard ship. There are two distinct and different warping operations, the first being a move within the limits of the berth with mooring ropes remaining on the same bollards, and the second being a move along the quay with mooring ropes transferred to new bollards.

Warping within the limits of the berth: Warping within the limits of the berth (called here for convenience a Type 1 shift) is normally considered to be an undemanding routine operation. On many bulkers, particularly smaller ones, the manoeuvre is conducted by the duty officer assisted by crew members without Master and perhaps without chief mate being in attendance. No pilot, no tugs and no main engines are normally used.

It would be expensive and time-consuming to use a mooring gang for such a manoeuvre, which must be repeated several times during a ship's stay. Normally no mooring gang is used and the mooring lines remain on the same bollards throughout the duration of the ship's stay. To permit the ship to move back and forward along the length of the berth, at least one rope at each end of the ship must extend well beyond the ship's extreme positions and the forward and after springs must be secured at the centre of the berth. A suitable layout of moorings for use with a fixed loader is shown in Fig. 11.3. Where the loader is mobile but the ship is too long for the berth, the distance to shift will be less and the ropes need not extend so far.

Many ships have sufficient manpower and deck machinery to allow them to control no more than four ropes, two forward and two aft, at a time. Before the start of the manoeuvre, one rope leading well forward and one leading well aft must be chosen on the forecastle head and a similar pair of ropes must be chosen on the poop. The two ropes which have to be hauled must be led to winches or capstans, or will be on powered reels, allowing them to be hauled or slacked as required. The two ropes which must be slacked to allow the ship to move can also be led to winches if manpower permits or can be slacked from the bitts. The remaining ropes must be left slack, hanging down into the water.

To warp the ship ahead, the rope which leads ahead from the poop (the after spring) must be hauled. The two ropes leading aft must be slacked. The slack on the headrope must be picked up as the ship moves ahead, but the headrope must not be hauled (Fig. 12.2). If the headrope is hauled as a ship moves ahead the bows will be pulled towards the quay and the headrope will hold the ship against the quay. She is said to be bowsed in, and stops moving ahead (Fig. 12.3). The same difficulty occurs if the stern ropes are hauled when the ship is moving astern. Bowsing the ship in is an easy mistake to make, partly because those positioned in the bows and stern do not always have a good view of the ship's alignment. It must be avoided, because the ship cannot shift when bowsed in.

The shift-ship manoeuvre may be conducted by the OOW located with a walkie-talkie radio on the forecastle head or beside the next hold to be loaded, where he can confirm that the ship has been positioned correctly. This arrangement will work when all the members of the mooring parties are experienced, but it is better to direct operations from

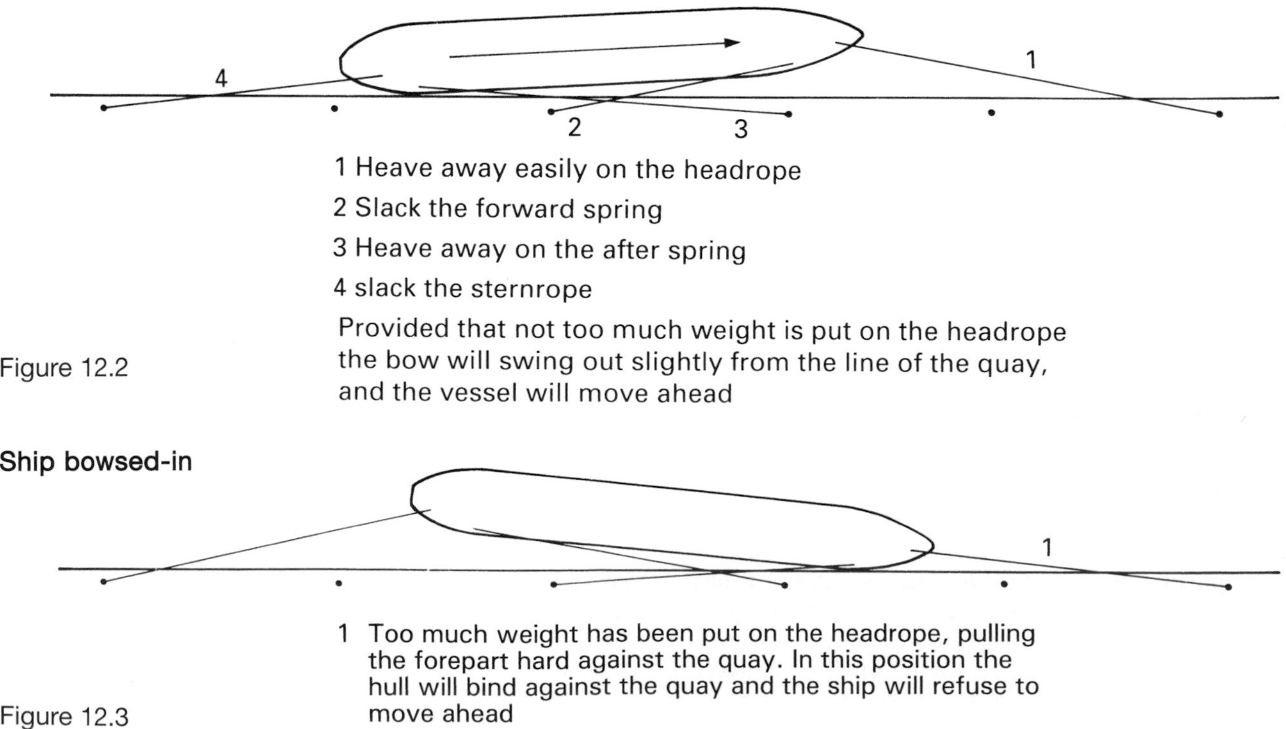

Figure 12.2

Figure 12.3

the bridge, which gives a better overall view, if the mooring parties are inexperienced.

Warping from one berth to the next: Warping from one berth to the next (a Type 2 shift) is generally considered to be more hazardous than shifting ship within the berth. A failure to transfer the ropes competently could result in contact with the quay being lost at one end of the ship and the bow or stern swinging out into the harbour. Normally the Master will conduct the manoeuvre, assisted by all the officers and full mooring parties on forecastle head and poop. A mooring gang will assist on the quay. There will be no pilot, no tugs and no main engines, except when the weather conditions are difficult. If there is any doubt as to the abilities of the crew and shore line-handlers to perform this operation efficiently and safely the ship's engine should always be ready for use. Consideration should be given to employing a tug, which will be an essential requirement if the tide, current or wind is strong.

Warping ahead from one berth to the next is conducted as follows in calm conditions or light winds from anywhere but onshore:

- Single up to a headrope and a spring forward and a sternrope and a spring aft, with the headrope and the after spring led well forward.
- Take the remaining lines inboard.
- Slack down forward spring and sternrope. Heave away on after spring. Pick up the slack on the headrope.
- Mooring men carry the ends of the two slack ropes along the quay, with just a short length outboard, the men walking abreast the fairlead.
- As the headrope and after spring are reduced to short lengths, the other two ropes are carried well ahead by the mooring men and the process of hauling the ship ahead is repeated.

The most serious problem met with this process is when the mooring men have strong views on how the operation should be conducted and those views do not coincide with those of the Master. Mooring men who refuse to put the rope on the bollard when it is necessary to check the ship's motion can cause havoc with a shift!

If winds are strong, a Type 2 shift is achieved by making a succession of Type 1 shifts, with several ropes carried forward and secured in positions further ahead before the commencement of each shift.

Warping – general remarks: If it is necessary to alter the vessel's alignment as she is being warped along the quay, one of the ropes which is being slacked must be held (Type 1 shift) or one of the ropes which is being carried along must be put on a bollard and set taut (Type 2 shift). This is a skilled operation requiring judgement and experience – if too much weight is used the ship will sheer more violently than intended.

When a ship has started to move along the berth impelled by heaving on a spring with all other ropes just picking up the slack or paying out easily, a single mishandled rope with the weight applied at the wrong moment can cause the ship to sheer violently and spoil the whole manoeuvre.

Often the man at the controls of the winch, windlass or powered reel cannot see that part of the rope he is controlling which lies beyond the fairlead and does not know if it is slack or taut, although he can see if it is excessively taut. He is dependent upon orders or hand signals from the officer.

If a ship moves off the quayside during a shift-ship the process becomes increasingly hazardous because: the bow can swing in to the quay, with damage to the bulb or to the quay; the stern can swing in to the quay, with damage to the rudder, propeller or quay; the scopes of rope become longer and more dangerous to handle; and there is increased danger of reaching the end of a rope. For all these reasons a seaman's instinct and training condition him to keep the ship alongside during a shift-ship, and to shift at slow speed.

On many ships the hauling power of the windlasses on the forecastle head is greater than that of the winches on the poop. As a consequence, when a ship has to be hauled alongside from a position some distance off the berth difficulty is experienced in bringing the stern alongside, unless the main engines and/or tug are available. Even when eight or 12 ropes are on powered reels, it is unlikely that the officers in charge at the bows and the stern can exercise effective simultaneous control over more than about three ropes at each end.

As the length of rope outside the fairlead increases, so its elasticity increases. This makes it increasingly likely to surge on the winch drum end. When it surges it is likely to snatch itself out of the hands of the man who is controlling it on the drum end. This can cause injuries, and can lead to the remainder of the rope disappearing over the ship's side. When shifting ship long scopes of rope are hazardous, but are sometimes unavoidable.

A bulk carrier in ballast presents a large profile to a beam wind. The effect of the accommodation block at her stern is to make the stern fall off the wind. Adverse weather makes a shift-ship operation more difficult. A strong offshore wind is the most difficult condition in which to shift ship. It is also the most unusual. The ship is often sheltered from offshore winds by buildings or high land and even if this is not so winds off the land are less strong than winds from the sea because of the greater frictional resistance they meet.

Safety during cargo working

No-one should be allowed to stand or pass beneath the path of the cargo. Anyone passing along the deck should use the side opposite to that on which the cargo handling gear is working. It is good practice to rope-off the working side of the deck and to display 'NO ENTRY' signs.

The gangway or accommodation ladder should be clear of the cargo working area if at all possible. The design of some ships and the positions of their accommodation ladders make this guideline impossible to follow.

It is a requirement of most, if not all, safety management systems (SMSs) that Personnel Protection Equipment (PPE) including boilersuit, safety shoes, gloves and hard hats must be worn on deck. Goggles and dust filter masks must be worn when the cargo is dusty and requires these precautions.

A hold should never be entered when cargo is being worked except with the authority of the duty officer and the knowledge of the signaller for the cargo working equipment. Extra care must be taken when slippery cargo residues are on the deck particularly when dust from cargo such as grain lies on top of early morning dew or ice.

Hatch covers, whether open or closed, must always be secured so that they cannot roll in the event of a change in trim or list. Stevedores must be required to observe the same standards of safety as are required of ships' personnel. (The subject of safety is discussed more fully in Chapter 21.)

Sources

5, 92, 110, 128, .153, 216. (See List of Sources, Page 497)

CHECKLIST – Tasks on arrival in the loading berth

- ☐ Secure vessel in berth
- ☐ Establish safe access
- ☐ Obtain a full set of draught readings
- ☐ Agree Loading/Deballasting programme with terminal representative
- ☐ Agree Ship/Shore Safety Checklist with terminal representative
- ☐ Obtain and consider the Declaration by Shipper which describes the characteristics of the cargo
- ☐ Obtain approval where necessary from quarantine or other officials for deballasting plan
- ☐ Satisfy the requirements of Draught, On-hire and/or Preloading surveyors if appointed
- ☐ Open hatches when safe and appropriate to do so
- ☐ Commence loading and deballasting

CHECKLIST – Duties of the officer of the watch in the loading port

- ☐ Study and understand the loading/deballasting programme.
- ☐ Ensure that all hatch covers are secured in position, whether open or shut, and cannot move by accident.
- ☐ Monitor the position of the loading arm, the loading sequence and the loading rate.
- ☐ Ensure that the correct cargo is loaded and cargo is in good condition.
- ☐ Keep any list within acceptable limits.
- ☐ Watch the draught to ensure that no overloading occurs.
- ☐ Monitor the deballasting to ensure that the best deballasting rate is maintained, problems are identified and corrected and maximum discharge of ballast is achieved.
- ☐ Co-ordinate and supervise the work of the crew to ensure efficiency in shifting of the ship, preparing ballast holds for loading, ensuring that ship's cargo gear is properly used and maintained in perfect condition, and securing of holds on completion.
- ☐ Keep the loading foreman informed of any developments, particularly of potential problems which may affect the loading.
- ☐ Note any possible causes of damage to ship or cargo and make every effort to prevent them.
- ☐ Note and record any damage to ship or cargo, and immediately pass details to the chief mate who will hold the stevedores responsible.
- ☐ Ensure moorings and means of access are tended as necessary.
- ☐ Prevent pollution from ballast, bilges, leakage of oil, garbage, cargo residues, funnel smoke and dust from cargo.
- ☐ Record full weather observations at least three times daily.
- ☐ Maintain full written records in the port log book and/or deck log book of all relevant events and data (items as detailed in the body of Chapter 12)
- ☐ Ensure that safe working procedures are followed.

CHECKLIST – Duties of the chief mate in the loading port

- ☐ Keep the Master fully informed of progress in the loading and problems encountered.
- ☐ Distribute copies of the loading/deballasting plan to the loading foreman and the OOWs and ensure that it is understood.
- ☐ Give the OOWs additional written instructions regarding the loading if the circumstances require it.
- ☐ Keep the loading foreman informed regarding requirements for trimming, and possible causes of delay.
- ☐ Conduct ship's draught surveys or undertake draught surveys with an independent surveyor, when appointed.
- ☐ Monitor the commencement of loading, and act promptly to deal with any problems.
- ☐ Use informal draught surveys to monitor the tonnages delivered from time to time during loading.
- ☐ Supervise the final stripping of ballast tanks to ensure minimum ballast is retained.
- ☐ Calculate and supervise the trimming pours.
- ☐ Supervise the trimming of holds filled with low-density cargo to ensure that no space is lost.
- ☐ Supervise the trimming of holds when a level stow on completion has been stipulated.
- ☐ Check space remaining in part-filled holds for the calculation of stowage factors.
- ☐ Ensure that appropriate matters receive attention when particular cargoes are loaded.
- ☐ Provide verbal warning, quickly followed by written notice, to stevedores when the ship or the cargo is damaged.
- ☐ Ensure that the ship is properly secured for sea.
- ☐ Obtain digital photos of damage to ship or cargo.
- ☐ Ensure that safe working procedures are followed.

Fig. 12.4 Steel slabs in a stepped stow to match the shape of the hold

Photo courtesy of Mathieu Baehni

Fig. 12.5 Starting to stow steel slabs. Note the heavily indented tanktop

Photo courtesy of Mathieu Baehni

Fig. 12.6 Stowing steel slabs

Photo courtesy of Mathieu Baehni

Fig. 12.7 Using wire lashings and bottle screws to secure a stow of steel slabs

Photo courtesy of Mathieu Baehni

CHAPTER 13

ESTABLISHING QUANTITY OF CARGO LOADED OR DISCHARGED

Methods of weighing bulk cargoes ashore, draught survey procedures, reasons for unexpected results

Shorebased methods of weighing

THE QUANTITY of cargo loaded aboard a bulk carrier can be measured in a variety of ways. The only method which directly involves the ship's personnel is the draught survey, but before considering this method in detail it is worth giving brief consideration to methods which may be used ashore. An understanding of these methods will help in assessing their reliability.

Electronic weighing of cargo on conveyor belt: The most common method of weighing used at modern loading terminals is the belt scale. This device continuously weighs the material on a selected length of the loading conveyor belt and multiplies this instantaneous weight value by the belt speed. The signal thus obtained is at all times proportional to the rate of material flow on the belt. Some commercial belt scales rely on magneto-elastic load cells. These devices rely upon the fact that the magnetic characteristics of steel are affected by mechanical stress.

The accuracy of a belt scale depends largely on the design of the conveyor and the way it is used, calibrated and maintained. Provided that the conveyor conforms to specified basic requirements for design and operation, an accuracy of better than ±1 per cent of nominal capacity within the flow rate range is claimed by one manufacturer. Others state that belt weigher systems are capable of achieving an accuracy of up to ±0.1 per cent of true weight for capacities of 10,000 tonnes/hour and can be relied upon for an accuracy of 0.5 per cent. Accuracy is likely to diminish to ±1.0 per cent if the system is not used to capacity and other causes of inaccuracy are frequent stopping and starting, or calibrating whilst handling a variety of materials[209]. Shipboard observers consider that inaccuracies rise on occasions as high as 10 per cent of true weight, presumably as a result of failure, or faulty calibration and maintenance.

Electronic weighing of cargo in grab: Cargo being discharged or loaded by grab can be weighed whilst in the grab by an electronic system. A computerised system can then record and total the tonnage handled. A working accuracy of 0.1 per cent is claimed by the manufacturers, but this is dependent upon the crane being motionless and in windless conditions when the weight is recorded. In practice these conditions are rarely met.

One manufacturer of electronic weighing systems for cargo in grabs uses a load cell mounted on the hook block. The magneto elastic load cell is built into a load-bearing part of the lifting system. When there is no load on the load cell, the magnetic flux lines around the windings do not influence each other. When the load cell is subjected to a load, the flux lines will cut each other and a voltage proportional to the applied force is induced in the secondary winding. The transducer which transmits the reading has low internal impedance and produces a powerful output signal, which is insensitive to interference, making the system reliable and accurate. The system is only suitable for use with grabs which are operated electro-hydraulically.

Tallying of number of grabloads: It is reported[240] that receivers have taken delivery of a part cargo with the claim that each grabload discharged, filled to capacity, weighed two tonnes. This could not possibly be a reliable basis for measurement of the cargo and completion of discharge at the next port revealed a shortage of 514 tonnes.

Weighing of trucks on weighbridge: For accuracy this method depends upon all trucks passing over the weighbridge with the results being accurately recorded and upon the tare weight (ie, the unloaded weight) of each truck being accurately known. This is best achieved by weighing the unloaded vehicle on its return journey. Accuracy also depends upon the truck fitting fully onto the weighbridge and this requirement has been ignored on occasion[239]. Weighbridges have a potential accuracy of ±0.2 per cent. Most weighbridge systems can be indexed in the control house for any debris, water, ice or snow which may accumulate, but if the correct indexing is not applied (or is deliberately ignored or wrongly set) the weights recorded will be in error to a greater degree than would be expected by the manufacturers or the licencing authority.[2]

Automatic bulk grain weighers[2]: These machines are suitable for weighing grain and free-flowing materials fed from elevators, conveyor belts, storage hoppers or silos. They are produced in various sizes and can record weights in cycles from 30kg up to 5 tonnes. They can deliver at rates of up to 1,000 tonnes per hour. When this machinery is correctly installed and maintained by the manufacturers and regularly inspected by a reliable local regulatory authority an accuracy of ±0.1 per cent is to be anticipated. Such a degree of accuracy is a general requirement within the grain trade. It should however be stressed that the degree of accuracy attained depends upon the regularity of inspection, servicing and maintenance. It is reported[1] that some manufacturers are more realistic and suggest that operational accuracy is more like ±0.3 per cent.

Shorebased systems in general: At best, all the foregoing methods can be only as accurate as the design of the weighing equipment allows. At worst, if the equipment is not regularly calibrated and if not all cargo is weighed, the results may bear little relationship to reality[241,242].

Cargo which drops on to the deck or into the dock

from partly closed grabs or which leaks out of insecure or overloaded trucks can form a significant percentage of the total, and it is worthwhile keeping a record of occasions when this is a problem backed up with photographic evidence where possible. Even cargo which blows away from open grabs, trucks or stockpiles represents a loss of weight and should be noted. Cargo residues which remain aboard will also not be included in outturn weight if measured ashore. In addition, such residues (if substantial) present a real practical disposal problem for the ship's small staff, unless the ship returns uncleaned for a further load of the same commodity.

The operations departments of shipping companies with ships engaged on regular trades receive separate cargo figures from shippers, receivers and ship and can over a period of time build up a reliable picture of the accuracy of cargo measurements. The Masters of such ships are often told by their operations department 'It is our experience that the shore weight in this port is always 1 per cent high', or some such figure, and this can be a useful point of reference.

There is no doubt that the operators in the loading or discharge port quickly obtain a feel for the accuracy of the measurements they obtain. They may choose to disregard the protests of a single ship, but if they are told by a succession of ships of different owners and nationalities that their cargo totals are too high or too low, they will begin to accept that there is truth in the allegation. Persuading them to pass this information to future ships attending the berth is another matter. Often informal questions to the loading foreman produce more accurate and reliable statements of known errors than do enquiries directed to management, who are reluctant to admit to the shortcomings of their system.

Shore measurement can be useful, but the importance of independent measurements made by the ship cannot be too strongly emphasised. Mistakes are sometimes made by operators ashore or instruments develop faults, and some spectacular and embarrassing errors in loaded quantity have resulted from failure by ship's staff to take their own accurate independent measurements. It cannot be emphasised too strongly that the ship must make regular draught checks during loading to avoid ending up loaded too deeply. Two final pours must be reserved at the end of loading for accurate trimming and to achieve the intended draught.

Draught survey

The ship's method of determining the amount of cargo loaded is by means of draught surveys taken before and after the loading is carried out. With the data so obtained the ship's displacement (the volume and therefore the weight of water displaced by the ship) before and after loading can be calculated. In simple terms the increase in displacement after loading, adjusted for any change in weights such as ballast, equals the weight of cargo loaded.

The draught survey may be the method of measurement specified in the charterparty for deciding the quantity of cargo carried, in which case one or several surveyors are likely to be employed to carry out the survey. When the charterparty specifies that shore measurement is to be used for deciding the quantity of cargo carried, the Master will still be expected to calculate a ship's figure to provide a check. It is in his interests to do so and to ensure that the results are as accurate as possible. In special cases, the surveyor will have the benefit of equipment and instruments not found aboard the normal bulk carrier, but in most instances the ship's Master or officer with careful attention to accuracy and procedure can obtain results quite as good as those of the surveyor.

In this chapter the procedures for making draught surveys before and after loading, and for calculating the quantity of cargo loaded are described in general terms. For those who require it a complete displacement calculation, fully explained, is to be found at Appendix 10.7. In addition, the United Nations draught survey code[24] can be strongly recommended for the clarity and detail with which it describes good procedures, and for the well-designed survey forms which it provides.

Conditions for the commencement of survey

1. Vessel afloat.
2. No cargo being worked.
3. No ballast, fuel, fresh water, etc, being pumped or run.
4. No hatch covers being opened or closed.
5. No spares or stores being shipped or landed.
6. All ballast tanks full or empty.
7. Ship upright.
8. Little or no tide or current running, where possible.
9. Seas not unduly rough where possible.
10. Temperature difference between sea water and ship's decks not excessive where possible.

From the foregoing list, items 1 and 2 are essential, whilst items 3, 4 and 5 are equally important unless the ship is large and the tonnages involved are very small. For example, the loading, discharging or moving of stores or bunkers weighing no more than 5 tonnes would not be detectable aboard a Panamax-sized vessel but would have a measurable effect on the draught of a handy-sized vessel.

Subsequent calculations are simplified if ballast tanks are either empty or full (item 6). It is often suggested that ballast tanks should be pressed up and overflowed prior to survey, to demonstrate that they are full. If the ship possesses no trim corrections for the tank calibration tables, pressing up the tank may be the best option, but this method has its disadvantages. In many ports the overflow of ballast water on deck is prohibited. Even when overflowing is permitted it is possible for a tank to overflow without being completely filled. This problem occurs particularly with topside wing tanks, when the ship is heavily trimmed.

Most accurate results are likely to be obtained if the topside wing tanks are filled to just below upper deck level at the sounding pipe, and if the tonnage of ballast is then calculated using the tank calibrations to take account of sounding and trim. Use of a correction can be avoided if the vessel is upright when the survey is undertaken (item 7).

Items 8, 9 and 10 are beyond the powers of ship's

staff to influence unless the time of the survey can be delayed, but they should be remembered, and strong current, rough seas or great temperature differences should be recorded in the survey remarks.

A strong current can lead to squat, which will affect the accuracy of both mean draught and trim. Rough seas will make accurate draught readings difficult or impossible to obtain, and a ship with decks heated by the sun at a time when the underwater body is relatively cool will be distorted, which will introduce inaccuracies into the stability data. Fortunately extreme examples of these problems are rarely found in practice, so that accurate results can usually be obtained.

Full set of draught readings: The first step in the survey is to obtain accurate readings of the six required draughts – namely, forward, amidships and aft on both port and starboard sides. An active person can obtain these readings easily with the help of a rope ladder on the outboard side if the vessel is small or medium sized, but for a large ship a launch or ship's boat is useful.

It is possible to obtain a good approximate reading of the draughts of a small ship from on deck, but this method will not be sufficiently accurate for the purposes of a draught survey because of the oblique angle at which the marks are then viewed. For illumination, a powerful torch or portable Aldis lamp may be required in conjunction with binoculars, as it may be necessary to read some draughts from a distance of 10 or 20 metres. Draughts are normally read to the nearest centimetre or half inch, any greater degree of accuracy being unrealistic.

When there is a substantial sea running and the waterline is rising and falling a simple device can be use to find the actual water level. A 5-10 metre length of clear plastic hose about 2.5 cm in diameter, open at both ends, has a magnet fastened close to one end. The magnet, put in place from a boat or from a ladder, holds the top of the hose well clear of the surface and close to the draught marks while the length of hose is allowed to hang vertically into the water. The water level inside the hose is calm and steady, making an accurate reading of the draught easy. If no clear hose is available the mid-point between the highest and lowest readings should be observed over a period of several minutes or longer. Highest and lowest readings can be read from a weighted tape – for example, a sounding line – dangled overside close to the draught marks. In these conditions it is recommended[122] that a total of, say, twelve readings are obtained, preferably by several observers and, after discarding the highest and lowest, the remaining ten should be averaged.

Complete set of soundings: Next, soundings must be taken of all spaces including compartments such as cofferdams, chain lockers, duct keel and void spaces in addition to all bilge and ballast spaces. The ship's swimming pool should preferably be empty. There have been plenty of instances in which compartments which the ships' personnel thought were empty were found to be full.

Additional soundings of 'empty' tanks should where possible be obtained later during the course of loading or discharge, when the vessel has a good trim. When this is done, the sounding is less affected by minor errors and the calibration tables can be used to obtain a tonnage of remaining ballast. A tonnage obtained by these means will be much more accurate than one obtained when the ship is on an even keel as she is likely to be when fully laden. A surveyor will often accept these ship's figures if he can see during the draught survey that the ship's approach is professional.

A full set of fuel tank soundings should also be obtained, but this requirement is often avoided by simply obtaining from the chief engineer the total quantity of fuel aboard. If the purpose of the survey is to measure the quantity of cargo aboard it does not greatly matter whether or not this fuel total is accurate. The ship's constant (described below) will absorb any inaccuracies in the fuel total as an automatic consequence of the routine deadweight calculations. The total weights aboard ship will be unchanged.

It is important that the quantity of fuel consumed and loaded between the initial and final draught surveys is accurately known. In many cases the in-port consumption will be no more than two or three tonnes and no bunkers will be loaded, so an accurate figure for fuel consumption presents no problems. In cases when this is not so, a full set of fuel soundings must be obtained. A full set of all soundings, including fuel soundings, is also required when the purpose of the draught survey is to obtain an accurate value for the ship's constant.

The purpose of the set of soundings is to discover the volume and thereafter the weight of all liquids aboard the ship. It is good practice to note the reading on the rod/tape/line at the level of the sounding cap, too. Provided that the sounding to the cap is known or can be verified, a correct reading will show that the sounding pipe is not blocked – for example, by a broken link of a sounding rod or by mud. It will usually be found that similar tanks to port and starboard and along the length of the ship have soundings with the same total depth from the sounding cap. If any sounding gives unexpected or uncertain results it is necessary to recheck. If doubt remains and the compartment can be entered, this is often the quickest way of finding exactly what its contents are. Alternatively, it may be possible to sound or to ullage it through a different opening, such as an airpipe, to obtain a rough check on its contents.

Where soundings are taken with sounding rod or tape the signs of a suspect sounding are the failure of the rod to land cleanly on the striking plate, or a dirty rod without a definite waterline on it. The use of water finding paste will provide a clean waterline on a sounding tape.

Beware of false sounding which can be taken when the water or oil in the tank is surging because the ship is moving.

When a sounding is read from a gauge, the accuracy of the gauge should first be confirmed by ensuring that the reading is zero when the gauge is switched to 'null', or by obtaining the correct test readings when the gauge is switched to 'test'. Gauge readings are not considered sufficiently reliable for draught surveys and should not be used for this purpose.

Density of water: The final measurements which are required at the time of the survey are measurements of the density (in air, not in a vacuum) of the water in which the ship is floating and of any ballast water carried aboard ship. Unfortunately, accurate measurements of density are more difficult to obtain and to interpret than many seafarers will realise. If traditional routines are followed it is quite likely that unsuitable hydrometers will be used to measure incorrect water samples.

If the water density is measured as 1.025 when it is actually 1.020, the error in calculated tonnage of cargo aboard a laden 65,000 tonne deadweight (75,000 displacement) Panamax bulk carrier will be 317 mt. Even 1.024 instead of 1.025 will result in an error of 63 mt in the calculated figure. Clearly, it is important to obtain an accurate density. Unfortunately this is not easy, for reasons explained below.

Water sampling: Harbours are often filled with water of different densities as a result of a mixture of sea water and fresh water from a river and this condition can vary with the state of the tide. When water of different densities is present, it tends to form layers, with the most fresh (least dense) water on the surface. A sample of water taken from the surface is unlikely to be typical of water over the full depth of the vessel and water density may also vary between different positions along the length of the ship. For best results it is necessary to obtain a number of samples, from at least three positions on the offshore side of the vessel and from a number of different depths. Several patterns of sampling bottle are available (see Chapter 22).

The problem of obtaining reliable water samples can be a real one, particularly for big ships at deep draught, but this is an extreme case quoted to draw attention to the problem. If, on the other hand, the port is wide open to the sea and if no rivers flow nearby, it is likely that the water density will be constant or nearly so over the full draught of the ship. In those circumstances a water sample taken from the surface will be adequate. Officers who are eager to build up an accurate set of measurements of the ship's constant will try to obtain careful measurements in places where the water is likely to be completely salt or completely fresh.

Density of ballast water: In addition to the density of sea water it is also necessary to measure the density of any ballast water carried aboard at the time of the survey. It is quite possible for the density of water within a ship's ballast tanks to vary from tank to tank if the tanks were filled at different stages of the tide or at different points on a river passage, so samples should be obtained from a number of tanks if accurate results are required. Samples taken from the top of the sounding pipe may not be typical of the tank as a whole and should be avoided where possible. To take an extreme case, if the ship's full ballast is assumed to be salt water when it is actually fresh water the resulting error in the calculated full cargo lifted would be about 1.0 per cent.

Density measurement: The next problem arises with the hydrometer supplied to the ship to measure density. A great variety of instruments using an assortment of scales, units and standard temperatures are supplied to ships. In addition to the fact that hydrometers are manufactured in various parts of the world where different units are used, part of this confusion arises because there is really a need for two different ship's hydrometers, each for a different task.

Most ships are (or should be) provided with a loadline hydrometer (Fig.22.1) which measures *specific gravity* (also known as relative density). The specific gravity of fresh water is 1.000, and that of salt water is 1.025. This number has no units – it is the ratio of the density of the measured water with the density of fresh water. The loadline hydrometer is intended for use in the calculation of fresh water allowance. It enables the ship's officer to calculate how much the loadline can be submerged in fresh or brackish water and for that purpose it provides a direct ratio between water of different densities.

Surprising as this statement will be to many, a loadline hydrometer is not suitable for the calculation of displacement unless a correction is applied. For an accurate calculation of the weight of water displaced by the vessel it is necessary to know the *apparent density in air* of the sea water, in kilograms/litre or equivalent units. Draught survey hydrometers (Fig.22.2) made of glass and calibrated in these units have been available for some years but their use is not yet widespread. Their readings extend from 0.990 kg/1 to 1.040 kg/1.

Many ships carry a loadline hydrometer and few carry a draught survey hydrometer, so it is helpful to know that a reasonably accurate conversion of the reading taken from a loadline hydrometer can be made. If the hydrometer is marked with graduations of *g/mg at 15C* or *Spec. Grav. 15C/4C* then 0.0011 must be deducted for the reading obtained. If the hydrometer is marked with graduations of *Spec. Grav. 60F/60F* then 0.0020 must be deducted from the reading obtained.

		Example	
Hydrometer Graduations	**Correction to Apply**	**Reading Obtained**	**Corrected Reading**
g/mg at 15C	–0.0011	1.023	1.0219
Spec. Grav. 15C/4C	–0.0011	1.023	1.0219
Spec. Grav. 60F/60F	–0.0020	1.023	1.021

The corrected reading should be used for the calculation of displacement.

Calculation of the displacement: On completion of the readings and observations described above the calculation of displacement can be undertaken. The procedures and formulae used are given in full in Appendix 10.7. They are also fully and clearly described in the UN code for draught surveys[24], a detailed publication which provides much additional information and can be recommended to anyone who wishes to obtain a comprehensive knowledge of draught surveys for bulk cargoes.

Described below is the purpose of each step in the calculations. The numbering used refers to the relevant line in the Appendix.

- *(L23/26) Correction of the draught readings*

  The ship's stability data will have been compiled using draughts at standard positions – namely, at the ship's forward and after perpendiculars and at the ship's midlength between the perpendiculars. The ship's draught markings are not usually placed at the perpendiculars. If they do not coincide there will be a discrepancy between the draught as read, and the draught at the perpendicular, except when the ship is at an even keel (Fig. 13.1). The corrections, which may be obtained from the ship's tables or from formulae must be subtracted from the observed reading to obtain the corrected reading when the ship is trimmed by the stern and the draught markings are located abaft the perpendicular. Formulae should be used in preference to the ship's tables to avoid the risk of errors in interpolation.

- *(L32) Correction for hull deformation: calculation of mean of mean, or quarter mean, draught*

  If a ship's hull is completely undeformed (ie, not distorted) the midships draught will equal the mean of the forward and after draughts. In practice, this is rarely the case. The ship is normally either hogged (with the midships draught less than the mean of the forward and after draughts) or sagged (with the midships draught greater than the mean of the draughts at the extremities). A ship which is hogged will displace more than an undeformed ship at the same midships draught, whilst a ship which is sagged will displace less. The purpose of this correction is to take account of these facts.

  The formula for mean of mean draught (or quarter mean draught – an alternative name for the same calculation) assumes that a ship deforms in a parabolic fashion. This is not strictly correct, but is accepted as being a sufficiently good approximation for practical purposes and is used almost universally. The formula, when evaluated, gives a corrected mean draught with a value which takes account of hull deformation.

  (Alternative methods for correcting for hull deformation are: [a] use of ship's approved table of corrections: [b] integration of the transverse section areas representing the immersed portion of the hull as actually trimmed and deflected, using approved parabolic coefficients: and [c] correction related to the waterplane area with use of approved hog and sag correction factors. Whilst each of these methods is valid and is described in the UN code none is widely used in practice.)

- *(L33) Displacement (in tonnes)*

  Displacement is obtained from the ship's hydrostatic tables (stability data) entered with the corrected mean draught. This requires further corrections, described below.

- *(L39) First correction for ship trimmed (layer correction)*

  This correction is necessary because the longitudinal centre of flotation (LCF) about which the ship trims is not a fixed point and does not normally coincide with the ship's mid-length, the point for which the corrected mean draught is calculated. The correction is positive when the ship is trimmed by the stern, and the LCF is abaft midships. (For a loaded Panamax vessel – displacement 75,000 tonnes – with a trim of 1 metre the correction has a value of about 65 tonnes.)

- *(L46) Second correction for ship trimmed (form correction)*

  This correction is necessary when the trim is large to take account of inaccuracies which arise in the layer correction in these circumstances as a result of the flare[255]. This correction is always positive because the waterplane area increases with increasing draught. (For a loaded Panamax vessel – displacement 75,000 tonnes – with a trim of 1 metre the correction will have a value of about 12 tonnes. If the trim is 2 metres the correction will be about 50 tonnes.)

- *Trim correction by ship's tables*

  It is quite likely that the ship's trim correction tables will be based upon the first correction, but will not take account of the second correction. This can be readily checked by working some examples by tables and by the formulae provided, to see whether the tables give a correction which equals the first correction or the sum of the two trim corrections. In addition, the use of tables permits errors of interpolation and the tables themselves may contain errors. It is advisable to calculate the trim corrections by formulae and to avoid the use of the tables except as a check.

- *(L52) Correction for ship listed*

  A ship when listed experiences a reduction in mean draught. This is because the effect of the list is to increase her waterplane area. Because her actual displacement remains constant the mean draught when listed is reduced. Therefore the correction is always positive to reflect the greater displacement which corresponds to the deeper draught at which the ship would float when upright. This correction is approximate: when a high level of accuracy is required the vessel must be brought upright[255]. (For a loaded Panamax vessel – displacement 75,000 tonnes – with a list of about 3° the correction has a value of about 15 tonnes.)

- *(L55) Density correction*

  When the ship is floating in water of a different density to that assumed in the ship's hydrostatic tables the displacement must be corrected for density. When the water is less dense (eg, fresh water) the ship's displacement at any draught will be less. The hydrostatic tables for most ships are compiled for a density of 1.0250 mt/m^3 (equivalent to an SG of 1.0250), but occasionally other values such as 1.000 (fresh water) or 1.02518 (= 35 ft^3/long ton) are found.

Completion of the foregoing corrections provides the ship's true or actual displacement. When all known weights have been deducted from the displacement, the weight remaining will be that of an unknown quantity – for example, the cargo when the ship is loaded, or the ship's constant when the ship is in ballast. Calculation of the ship's constant normally precedes calculation of the cargo loaded.

Calculation of the ship's constant: The 'ship's constant' (or, occasionally, the 'lightship constant') is the name commonly given to the unidentified weights and inaccuracies which remain when all listed weights have been deducted from the true displacement. It is called the ship's constant because when it has been calculated with the ship empty of cargo it is assumed to be unchanged (ie, constant) for the purposes of the calculations when the ship is loaded. Some people find it confusing that the ship's constant is found to vary from voyage to voyage. This probably arises from differences in quantities in engineroom tanks and bilges, changes in the tonnage of stores and spares carried, and minor inaccuracies in the draught surveys.

No opportunity should be lost to recalculate the ship's constant as accurately as possible, and to maintain a full record of values obtained. If the ship's records are carefully and fully maintained they are more likely to be accepted and used by a surveyor when something goes inexplicably wrong with a draught survey and taking the readings again is no longer possible. A recommendation of the UN draught survey code[24] is that the ship should keep a record of all constants on a *Light Ship Correction Certificate* which

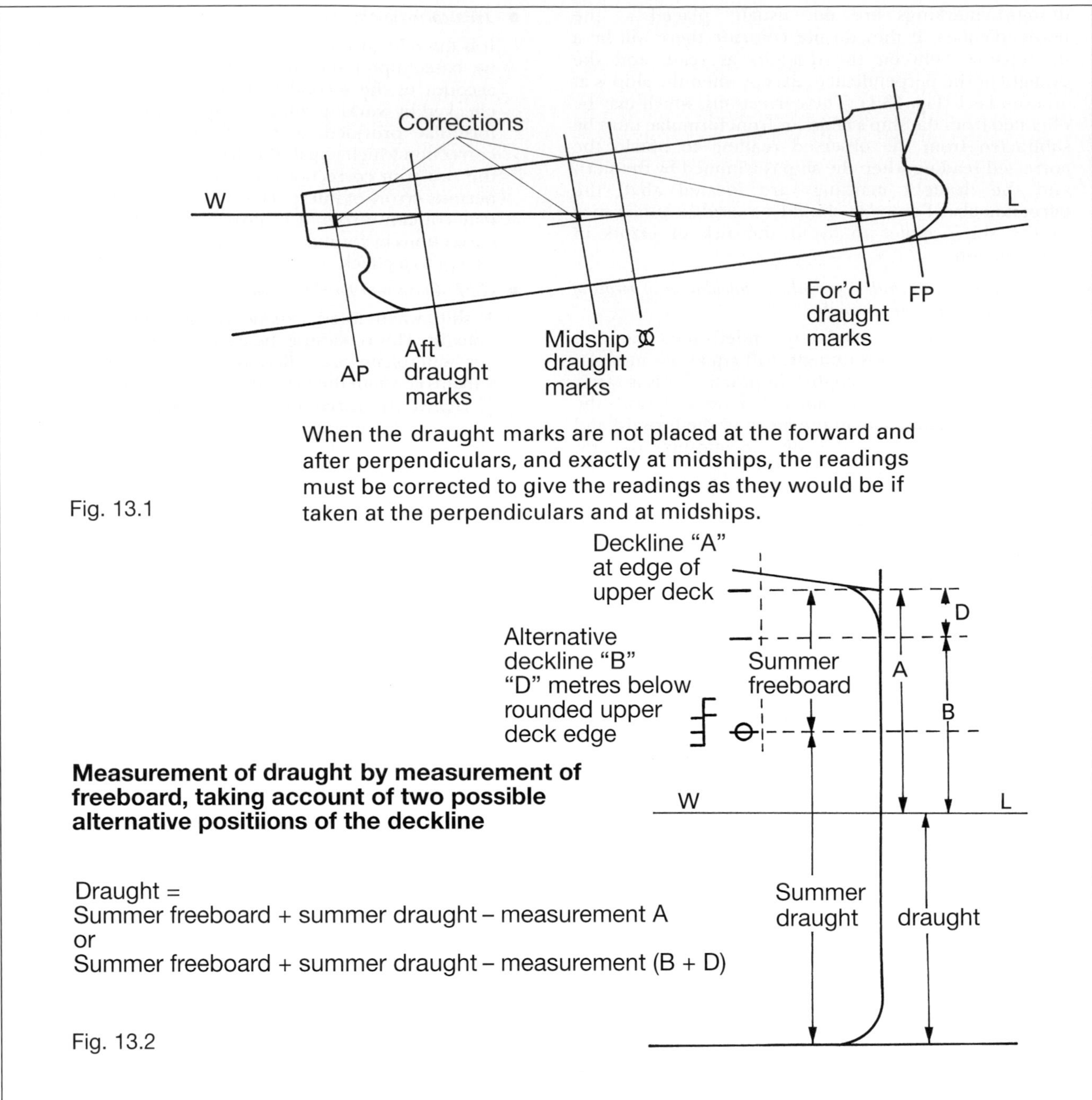

Fig. 13.1

Measurement of draught by measurement of freeboard, taking account of two possible alternative positiions of the deckline

Fig. 13.2

should show date, place, constant in metric tonnes and signatures of chief mate and surveyor, with the surveyor's stamp. If this recommendation is followed, it will be important to ensure that the calculation is consistent and that the same items are always deducted from the displacement.

In practice, the weights which are separately itemised vary from ship to ship, surveyor to surveyor, owner to owner and time to time. Usually the itemised weights will include fuel oil, diesel oil, fresh water and ballast water. Sometimes stores and spares will also be separately listed, but they may alternatively be included in the ship's constant. The ship's light weight (her weight as built before being stored or bunkered) will always be a separate item. Luboils may be a separate item, and other items such as ER water (water for engineroom purposes) can be itemised separately if convenient.

If the ship's constant is to be calculated simply as part of the process of calculating the tonnage of cargo aboard, it will only be necessary to make accurate calculations of the ballast which will be discharged whilst the cargo is being loaded. Any inaccuracies in the values given to the other weights will be absorbed into the ship's constant. If the ship's constant is to be calculated as accurately as possible, then all the other weights must be calculated with care.

The soundings must be used with the ship's calibration tables to find the tonnage of water or fuel in each tank. Corrections must be applied to take account of trim. If no corrections are included in the tables themselves, it will be necessary to use a formula (Appendix 13.1) to correct the sounding to an even keel value.

When using the calibration tables, ship's staff are well advised to look critically at them since they occasionally contain obvious errors. It has been known for similar double-bottom tanks to be provided with the same calibrations, despite the fact that in one tank the sounding pipe ran vertically down a bulkhead amidships, whilst in the other it followed the ship's side and sloped at an angle of 45° in way of the turn of the bilge. The procedure mentioned earlier of taking a reading of the sounding line at the level of the sounding cap would lead to the detection of this discrepancy.

The volume of water or fuel in each tank must be multiplied by the density (NB: the apparent density in air) of the liquid as measured to obtain the tonnage contained therein, and readers are reminded of the importance of accurate measurement of the density.

The ship's light weight is obtained from her stability information. It changes only if the ship's structure is modified. There is no easy way of measuring the weight of stores and spares carried aboard ship. This will vary with the size of ship and the nature of her trade, and will tend to increase as the ship grows older one authority[122] suggesting that this increase is about 0.2% light displacement per annum. An estimated figure will be used for this item, a figure probably based upon that used in past voyages.

Once all these weights have been calculated or estimated, and deducted from the true displacement, the weight which remains is the ship's constant, a figure which can be expected to range from 30 or 40 tonnes aboard a relatively new mini-bulker of 3,000 tonnes deadweight to 300-400 tonnes for a Panamax bulk carrier. Actual values will vary substantially for individual ships, depending upon many factors which are examined in greater detail in Chapter 9 where the maximising of the tonnage of cargo lifted is discussed.

The ship's constant will probably include the accumulation of paint on the ship's structure, the build up of mud in the ballast tanks, the increasing weight of stores, spares and equipment carried, the water in the engineroom bilges and the fuel in the engineroom settling and service tanks. It may also include ballast residues and luboil. Because of the manner in which it is calculated the ship's constant will also inevitably include tonnages to match any deliberate or accidental overestimates or underestimates in the itemised weights. If the figure for fuel bunkers is 50 tonnes too low, the constant will be 50 tonnes higher than it would otherwise be.

Calculation of the cargo loaded: Once the ship's constant has been calculated, it is possible to list all the weights aboard the vessel on completion of the loading of her cargo. Some of the weight totals will have to be amended from those used at the start of loading. Almost all of the ballast will have been discharged and some fresh water and fuel will probably been consumed. Additional bunkers, fresh water or stores may have been loaded.

A second draught survey is undertaken and a new true displacement will be calculated. All the itemised weights, correctly updated, will be deducted from the displacement. The light ship weight, and the ship's constant will be deducted. The tonnage remaining is the cargo tonnage by draught survey, often known as the ship's figure.

Possible sources of error

Occasionally it will be found that the results obtained from a draught survey are unexpected. The ship's constant may be found to be much larger than the normal value for that ship, or a negative constant may be calculated. The ship's figure for the tonnage of cargo lifted may differ from the shore figure by an unusually large amount. If the ship's officer and surveyor work independently, but compare figures at each stage of the calculation, then calculation errors are minimised. Since the discrepancy may be the result of a mistake in the draught readings or soundings, these should be rechecked, if still possible.

If the result remains unchanged it will be necessary to look further for an explanation. All the information used in the calculations must be studied to assess its reliability. Where possible data should be rechecked by a different method. It is useful to consider whether the discrepancy has occurred once only, or occurs every voyage. If it occurs every voyage, then it arises from data which are used every voyage. If it occurs once only, then it is more likely to be caused by something specific to that voyage.

Always investigate any substantial changes in the calculated value of the ship's constant. Accurate and reliable draught surveys are more difficult to achieve when a vessel has a large stern trim, such as may occur when a vessel has been partly deballasted to permit a quick loading. The Master should hesitate to berth his vessel with an excessive trim if he knows this will make the draught survey less reliable and should use whatever means are available to persuade the terminal manager to accept his vessel with more ballast. The interests of ship and terminal do not always coincide, and the Master should ensure that an accurate draught survey is made, which will enable him to produce the correct amount of cargo at the discharge port.

Examples

Vessel aground: A Panamax vessel was completing loading a cargo of iron ore in a West African port at 0300 hours with the final trimming pour being loaded in a forward hold. The chief mate was on the quay watching the forward draught. While loading continued the forward draught stopped increasing. Loading continued until the tonnage calculated for the trimming pour had been loaded. The final draught was found to be less than expected, with a trim by the stern. The explanation for this was not immediately realised and it was thought that there had been an error in the calculation of the trimming pour. Since departure from the port was governed by a limiting draught of 45 ft, ballast water was put into the forepeak tank to bring the vessel to an even keel, but the trim by the stern persisted. Finally, it was realised that the vessel must be aground forward and the ballast was pumped out. Fortunately for those involved the vessel refloated at high water, although the tidal range was small. When afloat she was found to be a little by the head and listed a little to starboard.

Grounding in the berth is a possibility where the bottom is mud or sand and has to be dredged, particularly if the port authority is inefficient. Partial grounding is also liable to occur on a shallow patch which may occur close to the quay, where cargo may have been spilt. If the vessel is aground on completion of loading the final draught and trim will be wrong. If the vessel grounds at an earlier stage – for example, at the time when the tonnages for the trimming pour are calculated – then the final draught and trim will be accurate if the vessel is afloat by that time, but they will not be the draught and trim intended.

Inaccurate draught marks: Following drydocking on a mini-bulker, the ship's figure for tonnage lifted was lower than expected for several voyages in succession. The draught marks were carefully measured from a dinghy and it was found that the upper port after draught marks (painted on the sloping surface of the stern) were several inches in error. The lower marks, cut into the sternpost, were easier to see and to verify and were used as a datum. The ship was ten years old, the hull was rusty and thickly coated with paint in the vicinity of the draught marks, and the original lines cut into the hull to mark the upper draughts were almost invisible.

Raised draught marks are unlikely to be wrong and inaccuracies in draught marks painted on the vertical or near vertical surfaces amidships and at the bows can easily be noticed. The after draught marks painted on a sloping surface are the only ones which are difficult to verify. Suspicions should be aroused if the draught readings suggest that the ship is twisted between midships and the stern. If the midship draughts are equal, port and starboard, but the after draughts suggest a list to one side, or vice versa, it is possible that the draught marks are incorrectly marked.

Deck line not placed at deck level: Where a ship has no draught marks amidships, the midship draughts are obtained by measuring the freeboard from the waterline to the top of the loadline, or deck line, with a steel sounding tape or tape measure. When the draught is light it is often easier to measure from the deck line, with one person descending to water level whilst the other takes the reading at deck level. Freeboard is normally converted to draught by adding the deepest summer draught to the summer freeboard, and then subtracting the measured freeboard. (Fig. 13.2) In some cases this will give a false draught.

On some ships – for example, those with a rounded deck edge – the deck line is likely to be located on the vertical ship's side, at a distance (d) below the freeboard deck. Distance 'd' will be stated on the loadline certificate and in the ship's plans. In this case the midships draught is obtained by subtracting the measured freeboard, plus 'd', from the sum of the deepest summer draught and the summer freeboard.

Ballast retained by mistake: Ballast has on occasion been retained by mistake aboard a ship loading a deadweight cargo. This has occurred as a result of a misunderstanding at change of watch or as the result of a tank being refilled or part filled by mistake through a leaking ballast line or an open valve. If no draught surveyor is in attendance, and if ship's staff do not follow sound procedures, such an error may not be detected.

The soundings of all ballast tanks should be rechecked before the final trimming pours are calculated and loaded. If this procedure is followed without fail any remaining ballast will be detected and can be discharged before completion of loading.

When completing the discharge of ballast from a compartment the valve should be closed before the pump is stopped. If these operations are carried out in the reverse order water will gravitate back through the stopped pump and past the valve, until such time as the latter is fully closed.

When there is any possibility of a misunderstanding of orders about ballasting all orders should be given in writing and acknowledged with a timed signature.

Sources

1, 2, 24, 122, 209, 239, 240, 241, 242, 255. (See List of Sources, Page 497)

CHAPTER 14

CARGO DOCUMENTS

Hold inspection certificates, mate's receipts, bills of lading and authorisations to sign them, phytosanitary certificates, certificates of compliance, UN approval, origin, declarations by shipper, certificates of transportable moisture limit, moisture content, Master's response sheet, lashing, readiness to load, fitness to proceed to sea, loading, fumigation, weight and quality, stowage plans, cargo manifests, dangerous cargo manifests, material safety data sheets, hatch sealing certificates, statements of fact, letters of protest, empty hold certificates, trimming certificates, certificates of loading/discharging and stevedores' time sheets, clean ballast discharge permits, paint compliance certificates, certificates of IMO classification, IMSBC Code fitness certificates, certificates of compliance for bulk and dangerous bulk cargoes, hatch closing certificates and no damage certificates

THIS CHAPTER considers the documents which a Master may be required to hold, to issue or to receive in connection with the carrying of dry bulk cargoes and other cargoes such as steel and forest products which may be carried by bulk carriers.

A Master should be aware that there is very often a complex financial background to the physical carriage of the cargo with which he is concerned. There will often be a chain of sellers and buyers with many sale contracts relating to the same cargo. Payments under such contracts will often be made by means of letters of credit whereby banks will make payment against documents presented to them by the party seeking payment. The documents presented will include many with which the Master has been directly concerned.

Because the actual documents presented to banks must comply strictly with the description of those documents in the letter of credit, there may be intense pressure on the Master to issue documents which comply with the description of the documents in the letter of credit. It is a statement of the obvious, but still well worth remembering, that where possible damaged cargo should be rejected. Issuing a clean bill of lading for a clean cargo is the easiest option. It is vitally important that the Master resists pressure to issue documents when the effect of doing so will be to misrepresent the true situation. He must refuse to issue clean bills of lading, for example, when damaged cargo has been tendered, which should lead to the clausing of mate's receipts and bills of lading to reflect the actual damage condition. Failure to observe this rule is likely to expose the owner to claims such as for shortlanding or cargo damage. A Master should always consult his owner in such situations and should be aware of the dangers of signing or issuing documents whose authenticity he doubts or whose contents he cannot verify.

Master to receive maximum information: The Master cannot hope to represent the owners, managers and charterers efficiently and reliably unless he is provided with proper information. It is in the best interests of all parties to ensure that the Master receives full information about his commercial responsibilities and is provided with clear guidance and clear orders. These should reach him in good time to ensure that he is able to act in their best interests.

Signing of documents: In certain cases a Master may wish to acknowledge receipt of a document without binding himself to its authenticity or to the accuracy of its contents – for example, when he is asked to sign a statement of events following a collision. In such cases he may sign the document and add the words 'for receipt only' or 'without prejudice'. Under English law, that would prevent his signature being taken to denote an admission of liability or acceptance of the document as true or correct. He should be very careful to ensure that when placing his signature on a document, even when marking it 'for receipt only' as is prudent, he is not taken under the laws of the country where he is to be accepting the authenticity or the accuracy of the document. If he is in doubt he should always consult his owner, his manager and/or his owner's P&I Club.

Hold inspection certificate

The hold or hatch inspection certificate, or preloading survey certificate, is issued by a surveyor after inspecting the holds to ensure that they are suitable for the intended cargo.

A preloading survey is required when the local authorities at the loading port or the shipper demand it or when it is a charterparty requirement. Surveys are more likely to be required for sensitive and valuable cargoes such as grain, alumina, fertilisers, pulp and paper, steel and high-value ores. Such a requirement may be stated in the charterparty. When a survey is required, loading cannot commence in a hold until the surveyor has passed it. Often the vessel cannot present notice of readiness until the hold inspection certificate has been issued, as the vessel may not be 'in all respects ready to load'.

If any holds fail the survey, a vessel on time charter may be placed off hire and a vessel on voyage charter may fail to start time running against charterers until such time as the holds have been resurveyed and passed, although it may be possible to have some holds passed so that the vessel can submit a valid notice of readiness and/or commence to load in suitable holds. The Master or his representative (for example, the chief mate) should take careful note of any criticisms offered by the surveyor and should try to obtain a clear idea of the work that must be done to bring unacceptable holds up to standard as quickly as possible.

The thoroughness of the Australian government survey prior to the loading of grain can be seen from the document (Appendix 14.1).

The surveyor will provide the hold inspection

certificate for whoever instructs him, but a copy will normally be given to the Master. The Master has no powers, except the power of reason, to require the surveyor to alter a negative conclusion. If the Master considers that the surveyor's conclusions are unreasonable and if the consequences are likely to be costly, the Master can set out his views in writing in a letter of protest (see below) or he can obtain the services of another surveyor, perhaps with the help of the ship's P&I club. A second surveyor cannot overrule the first, but can provide evidence of the facts for use in a dispute.

Mate's receipt [34]

A mate's receipt is usually a printed form, often with handwritten entries, which acknowledges on behalf of the ship the receipt of the goods. In the absence of a printed form the receipt can be handwritten. It is evidence that the goods specified in it have been delivered to and received by the ship. Usually the person to whom the mate's receipt is given is the person entitled to a bill of lading in exchange for the return of the mate's receipt.

When any damaged or deficient cargo is delivered to the ship it should immediately be brought to the attention of the shippers or their agents so that it can be removed and undamaged cargo supplied in its place. This requirement should be confirmed in writing to provide a record in the event of a dispute.

Alternatively, qualifying words ('clausing') can be inserted to describe the condition of the goods at the time of delivery. As it is a common requirement that bills of lading should be issued in accordance with mates' receipts, if damaged cargo is not removed it will be necessary to clause the mate's receipts which will then lead to the clausing of the bill of lading.

Very careful consideration should be given to the wording of any clausing intended for mate's receipts to ensure that it is accurate. As explained above, the Master's primary concern is that no claims should lie against the owner – for example, for cargo damage or shortlanding when damaged or insufficient cargo has been tendered by the shipper. If possible the Master may wish to use a form of words which is acceptable to the shippers, but this is not his primary concern or obligation.

When in doubt as to suitable wording for clausing, the Master should consult the owners or managers, giving them as much notice of the enquiry as possible. They may instruct him to take advice from a surveyor recommended by the P&I club for the purpose.

The sample mate's receipt attached (Appendix 14.2) is taken from the papers of a handy-sized bulk carrier which carried a full cargo of soya bean meal pellets from Sao Francisco do Sul, Brazil, to Iranian ports. The chief officer has endorsed the document 'said to be, said to weigh', 'quantity and quality unknown'. These are common endorsements where the condition and quantity of the cargo is difficult to ascertain or where the ship's figures do not agree with the shore figures. However, this practice will not necessarily protect the owner from claims where there are very large differences which should have been noted.

A mate should not sign a mate's receipt nor a Master a bill of lading which he knows is incorrect as the shipowner may be held liable if, for example, the signatory states 'weight and quantity unknown', in a situation where he knows the figures submitted are incorrect. It is better for the Master to insist on using the ship's figures or to call for an independent survey to establish the true figure. Provided that he is acting reasonably owners will not be liable for any delay caused. In bulk trades mate's receipts are not always issued, particularly when the Master himself signs the original bill of lading.

Authorisation to sign bills of lading

Under a time or voyage charterparty the Master in signing bills of lading (Bs/L) acts as agent for the shipowner. Similarly, if a loading broker or charterers' agent signs bills of lading it will be as agent of the shipowner. However, both time and voyage charterparties often contain a demise clause' which will state whether the Master or another is signing on behalf of the owner or the charterer.

Under the terms of many time charterparties and some voyage charterparties the owners transfer the authority to sign bills of lading to the charterers, thereby cancelling the authority normally held by the Master. In these circumstances the Master should not sign bills of lading and cannot delegate authority to others to do so. The Master should take great care in understanding who is authorised to sign as the owners' and charterers' requirements are often slightly different. If in doubt he should request specific instructions first from his owners and secondly from the time charterers. If the time charterers tell the Master to do nothing they have retained their own authority to sign bills of lading. If they instruct him to authorise a named agent they have, in so doing, passed their own authority back to the Master. Voyage charterers cannot give this authority to the Master.

In any case in which the agent will be signing bills of lading on behalf of the Master, the Master should ensure that the agent receives appropriate instructions in the form of an authorisation which he should issue. The wording of any such authorisation is often dictated by owners' or charterers' voyage instructions and the Master should consult his owner if he is in any doubt as to the form of instruction to be issued.

The authorisation should be given to the agent and a copy should be retained by the Master, with the agent's signed acknowledgement. A difficulty can arise when the vessel has been time chartered and sub chartered and owners have no knowledge of, or contract with, the end users of the ship. Owners will want to ensure acknowledgement of the head charterparty while subcharterers will be interested only in the voyage charterparty. A suitable form of words intended to deal with this problem is given in Appendix 14.3 where reference to the voyage charterparty is contained in the second paragraph and reference to the head charterparty is included in the final paragraph. A completed letter of authorisation which mentions only the voyage charterparty for a soya bean meal pellet voyage is at Appendix 14.4. This is appropriate when there is no time charter.

It is common practice for agents to present Masters with letters of authorisation which are worded to the agents' own advantage. The Master is never obliged to use such forms. He can always use the owners' wording. If the agents refuse to accept such an authority the Master should inform owners and time charterers accordingly.

In some trades, such as the grain and agricultural products trades, it is common to have 30 to 40 bills of lading. In these circumstances it is advisable for the Master, always acting under instructions, to delegate his authority to one or several named individuals in the agency and to obtain copies of their signatures on all copies of the letter of authority. This will help to reduce opportunity for fraud when bills of lading are presented to the Master at the discharge port.

It is important to stress that the Master should always be aware of the precise terms of any relevant charterparty clauses and should consult his owners if he is in any doubt as to the existence or extent of his authority to sign bills of lading, whether on behalf of owner or charterer.

Bills of lading

Normally bills of lading (Bs/L) cause few problems, particularly when ships are employed on long-term contracts of affreightment and the parties to the contract are well known to one another. However, the experience of one major operator of bulk carriers in the early 21st Century is that bill of lading fraud is widespread in the tramp trades, particularly in some western Pacific countries, and that it is getting worse. Other commentators report that fraud is even more widespread. In these circumstances safe and rigorous practices are to be strongly recommended. It is good commercial practice for Shipmasters to take nothing on trust.

The advice given by different owners varies because such advice is coloured by the particular problems which each has experienced. When there is a problem the consequences can be so serious that the Master requires to be guided by his owners and their solicitors. He should not hesitate to consult his owners and operators when in doubt.

A bill of lading (Appendix 14.5) may perform three functions. It is usually very good evidence of the terms of the contract for the receipt, carriage and delivery of the cargo. It is often a negotiable document of title to the goods carried, providing evidence of ownership of the cargo, and it acts as a receipt for cargo loaded aboard the vessel. The Master's role in signing bills of lading has been described[26] and can be summarised as follows.

Before signing the bill of lading, the Master should ensure that:

1. The goods are actually aboard and the bill of lading is correctly dated.
2. The description of the goods complies with the mate's receipts, failing which the bill of lading should be claused accordingly.
3. That he only ever signs the same number of originals as is shown on the face of the bill of lading. If three originals are shown on the document, as is usual, only three should be signed. Particular care is needed when the Master has to sign ten or 15 sets of three. (NB. The bill of lading shown [Appendix 14.5] was issued in four originals, which is unusual.)

The Master should also ensure that:

4. The bill of lading contains a clause referring to any relevant charterparty, and includes the protection clauses specified in that charterparty. Very specific wording is often required in order to achieve the protection of all relevant charterparty provisions, and if in doubt the Master should consult his owners. However, the Master is usually required to sign bills of lading as presented and there is little that he can do except bring the matter to the notice of owners and charterers if the bills of lading do not contain the specific clauses.

The Master should not:

1. Sign a bill of lading which is in any respect inaccurate.
2. Be persuaded to sign clean bills of lading against the offer of a letter of indemnity.

Signing the bill of lading: When the Master is asked to sign a bill of lading there are six main aspects which he should examine for accuracy. However, it should be emphasised that there are no set rules.

Quantity of cargo: The Master cannot be asked to sign for goods which he knows have not been loaded. It is quite common for there to be a small discrepancy between the figure obtained from shore weighing, and the draught survey by ship's officers. The charterparty, or the practices of the trade, will dictate which figure is to be used in the bill of lading and the voyage instructions send to the Master by owners will normally state what is required. If the shore figure is used, and the ship's figure by draught survey is less, the Master will fear that he will be unable to deliver the full quantity stated in the bill of lading. Procedures for dealing with this situation vary from company to company and from one trade to another.

- A discrepancy of up to 0.5 per cent (one owner will reluctantly accept 0.25 per cent) between the bill of lading figure and the ship's figure is considered acceptable in some trades, and it is normal for the Master to sign the B/L as presented in those circumstances. The requirement is, however, that the quantity of cargo signed for in the bill of lading must be delivered to the consignees.
- One owner advises his Masters to sign bills of lading as presented when the difference lies between 0.1-0.5 per cent in excess of the ship's figure, but then to inform charterers and shippers in writing.
- If the discrepancy between the ship's figure and the bill of lading figure is greater than 0.5 per cent some owners expect the Master to endorse the bill of lading with the remark 'x tonnes in dispute', whilst other owners adopt this wording for any discrepancy.
- Another option is for the Master to leave the total blank, insert the remark 'quantity loaded in dispute', and attach a note of protest on a separate sheet of paper, stating what he believes to be the correct figure. When the dispute has been resolved, usually after the vessel has sailed, the note on the bill of lading can be deleted by an authorised agent, the protest removed from the bill and the correct figure entered as appropriate. Once the bill of lading has been corrected and the protest has been removed the bill is acceptable to a bank because it is not considered to be 'dirty', or non-negotiable. If this practice is adopted it is very important that the agent is properly authorised and instructed.
- Other options are open to the Master, but may be considered unnecessarily provocative, and should be avoided unless the circumstances are exceptional. For example, he can delete the bill of lading figure and insert

the ship's figure, initialling the alteration, or he can tear up the bill of lading and issue his own.

- Endorsements such as 'said to be, said to weigh', 'quantity and quality unknown', or 'weight and quantity unknown' may be, and often are, used when the ship's figures do not agree with the shore figures, but this practice will not necessarily protect the owner from claims where there are very large differences which should have been noted. A Master may be held liable if, for example, he states 'weight and quantity unknown' in a situation where he knows the figures submitted are incorrect.
- What the Master should not do except when the discrepancy is very small (see above) is to sign the bill of lading as presented and then issue a letter of protest.

Description and condition of the cargo: The Master cannot be asked to sign for a description or condition of the cargo which he knows is misleading or of which he has no knowledge. He should ensure that if any part of the cargo is not in good condition, that will be obvious to anyone who reads the bill of lading. If in doubt about clausing the bill of lading he should consult his owners, some of whom will refer him to the local P&I club representative whilst others consider this too important a matter for anyone but themselves.

Date of the bill of lading should be a date on which the vessel completed the loading of the named cargo. If the Master is prevented from correcting the date on the bill of lading he should protest in writing to shippers and charterers and leave the bill of lading unsigned, reverting to owners or managers for advice.

Description of the voyage: The Master must not sign bills of lading which name a destination which is outside the range named in the charterparty or in the voyage orders or which the vessel cannot physically reach. He must not sign a bill of lading which explicitly forbids transhipment if the vessel's draught will make transhipment unavoidable.

Terms and conditions: As stated above, the background to the carriage of the cargo in question will often be financial, involving a letter of credit. The letter of credit will normally specify clean bills of lading, but will not specify a charterparty, so banks do not normally accept bills of lading containing charterparty terms.

When the Master is able to insert charterparty terms in the bill of lading the correct wording is governed by rules of law. When in doubt as to the wording in use, the Master should consult his owner or manager.

If the Master takes particular care to fill in the relevant clause there should be little doubt as to which charterparty provisions are incorporated. The charterer may have authority to instruct the Master to sign the bills of lading as presented, with respect to its terms and conditions. However, subject to the above comments, the Master will usually wish to ensure that the blanks are correctly filled when the bill of lading contains words such as 'This shipment is carried under and pursuant to the terms of the C/P dated … between … and … and all terms clauses exceptions and conditions thereof apply to and govern the rights of the parties concerned in this shipment.'. Some forms of bill of lading contain no such provision, but this does not matter if the document includes the Hague Rules or Hague-Visby Rules as these displace the charterparty provisions.

When there are two or more charterparties covering the vessel's employment, ie when the vessel is chartered and sub chartered, the Master should consult his owner as to whose terms are to be incorporated in the bill of lading contract.

Payment of freight: A bill of lading which has not been transferred (sold to third party) is a receipt only for cargo, but a bill of lading marked 'Freight Paid' or 'Freight Prepaid' is a receipt for both cargo and freight money. If it refers to 'freight payable as per C/P', the owners will retain their right to exercise lien on the cargo for unpaid freight.

The Master should only sign 'Freight Paid' or 'Freight Prepaid' Bs/L where he is specifically instructed to do so by owners or managers (but not by charterers), or he is specifically instructed to do so by time charterers if the charterparty allows them to do so, or the charterparty explicitly requires him to do so, or he has good evidence that the freight has indeed been properly paid and received by owners or managers or time charterers, but this should always be checked.

If none of the above conditions is satisfied the Master should delete the words 'Freight Paid' or 'Freight Prepaid', and should initial this amendment before signing. If this proves impossible the Master should pass the bill of lading to the agent with a written instruction not to issue it without explicit instructions from his owners and should notify owners or managers of what he has done.

It should be noted that voyage charterers cannot insist on a 'Freight Paid' bill of lading being signed before payment of freight unless the charterparty explicitly allows it. In any event the position should be checked. Signature of 'Freight Paid' bills of lading in a situation where freight had not in fact been paid may lead to the loss of the owner's right later to exercise a lien for unpaid freight.

Time charterers can insist on a 'Freight Prepaid' bill of lading being signed unless the charterparty specifically forbids them from doing so, but the Master should assume that they do not want such a bill of lading signed unless they have given him specific instructions to sign.

Alternative courses of action: If the Master finds it impossible to reach agreement with the shippers about the signing of the bill of lading which they present, there are three courses of action which he can follow. All are perfectly legitimate. He can:

1. Delegate the signing of the bill of lading to the ship's agent, instructing him to sign only after receipt of written authority from the owner. The Master should immediately communicate with the owner to inform him of the action he has taken. Passing the responsibility to the agent in this manner allows the ship to sail without delay, and buys time for the solution of the dispute. This is a discreet and informal solution to the problem.
2. A second possibility is to follow the procedure described earlier – namely, to endorse the bill of lading with a remark that it is the subject of a dispute, attach a note of protest and authorise the agent to delete the endorsement when the dispute is resolved.
3. Issue his own bill of lading.

The threat of any of these courses of action may be enough to obtain shippers' consent to modification of the bill of lading which they have prepared.

The Master may wish to clause the bills of lading, but he may find that he is threatened with arrest of himself or the ship or heavy financial penalties for delay to the ship if he refuses to sign the bills of lading as presented. In those circumstances, if all other proposals fail, he may in the last resort sign the bills of lading as presented. If forced to do this he should, as soon as he has cleared the port, inform all parties that he signed the bills of lading under duress (ie, he was forced to sign them) and that he repudiates them. He should then issue new bills of lading. Alternatively, he may issue a report/protest and have it authenticated by the local notary public.

General considerations at time of sailing from the loadport: On no account should the Master sail without either issuing a bill of lading under his own signature or else delegating the signing to the agent. On sailing from the loadport the Master should notify the discharge port agents that he will require to see original bills of lading for the cargo before he will authorise its discharge and he should insist that they acknowledge and confirm his instructions in writing unless, as is often the case, owners or managers have instructed him in writing that they consider this procedure unnecessary.

It is good practice for the Master to instruct agents to forward to his owners or managers copies of both sides of a signed non-negotiable bill of lading so that they can read their contractual obligations and liabilities. If the Master should at any time discover that he has issued an incorrect bill of lading, he must notify owners immediately, giving full details of its particulars, including names of shippers and consignees. He must also notify those parties.

Negotiable and non-negotiable copies of bills of lading: Most bills of lading issued in the bulk trades are negotiable, to enable the cargo to be traded while *en route*.

It is normal for three negotiable copies of the bill of lading, stamped 'Original' to be issued. Historically, this allowed the owner of the cargo to despatch copies by different routes to ensure that at least one copy would reach the discharge port in sufficient time to be presented when delivery of the cargo was claimed. Although this is rarely a problem nowadays, the practice still continues. When one negotiable copy of the bill of lading has been presented, the other copies of the same bill of lading are thereby cancelled (null and void). The existence of three copies of the bill of lading does give opportunity for error or fraud and a variety of precautions are recommended to reduce the risk.

In some trades, to ensure that a set of original bills of lading are available in the discharging port, a sealed envelope containing one set of negotiable bills of lading is left in the Master's care for delivery to the agents at that port. When this is done it is recommended that all the original bills of lading should be endorsed with the words:

One original bill of lading retained on board against which bill delivery of cargo may properly be made on written instructions received from charterers.[90, 127]

A non-negotiable bill of lading, stamped 'Copy', is evidence of the contract to carry the cargo and of the cargo loaded on the ship, but it is not proof of ownership of the cargo.

Delivery of cargo in return for bill of lading

When the ship has arrived in the discharging port, the cargo must be safely discharged into the care of the correct person before the voyage can be considered successfully concluded.

When the cargo has been received aboard ship and the Master has issued a bill of lading in respect of it, he becomes responsible for ensuring that it is delivered to those whom he reasonably believes to be entitled to its possession. The Master is not compelled to give delivery of cargo without production of the original bill of lading unless specifically instructed by owners. The Master should not agree to deliver cargo without production of the original bill of lading. It is extremely bad practice to assume that the agent has attended to this matter on the owner's behalf, as this is often not the case.

As noted earlier, the Master should give plenty of advance warning to the discharging port agent that he will require to see the original bills of lading unless owners or operators have told him that they are attending to this matter. This ensures that the agent has time in which to arrange to comply.

When original bills of lading have not reached the discharge port the owners may agree to discharge the cargo against letters of indemnity provided by the receivers, shippers or charterers, but that is a decision for the owners and not for the Master. When the owners or managers instruct the Master to accept a letter of indemnity (LOI), they will take steps to ensure that the wording of the LOI presented to the Master is the same as that which they have proposed. The Master should then check carefully that the LOI presented matches the one supplied to him by owners. It should be kept in mind that the LOI in these circumstances is a *substitute* for the P&I cover.

In one reported instance the Master released the cargo against a perfect colour photocopy of the bill of lading and, although the fraud was clear, the owners were ultimately held responsible for misdelivery.[127] Fraud of this sort must be very difficult to detect but inspection of the back of the bill of lading might have revealed the absence of indentations in way of the signature and other entries.

'Accomplished' bills of lading: An 'accomplished' bill of lading is one which has been cancelled, upon delivery of the cargo to its owner. The fact of the delivery accomplishes all the original bills of lading for that cargo. To make the situation clear and to reduce opportunities for fraud, shipowners often instruct Masters to write or stamp 'Accomplished' on each side of each bill of lading which is presented to them, to stamp them with the ship's stamp and to sign below this endorsement.

Strictly, the bills of lading are only accomplished when the cargo has been discharged, but if it is acceptable to the receivers it is convenient to endorse them as accomplished when they are first presented. Accomplished bills of lading should be retained by the Master for the owners or, failing that, photocopies should be retained.

Proper delivery of cargo against bill of lading

There are three situations in which the Master must be particularly alert to ensure the proper delivery of the cargo. These are change of destination, transhipment/lightening, and split bills of lading and/or part cargoes.

Change of destination: If the Master receives an instruction to proceed to some port or place other than the one which appears in the bill of lading, he should draw this fact to the attention of all concerned as soon as possible. This rule applies regardless of whether the instruction comes from owners, managers, time charterers, voyage charterers or agents.

There is no P&I cover for misdelivery of cargo, so change of destination is usually the subject of a letter of indemnity (LOI). Provided that the change of destination is confirmed, the Master should contact the agent at the new destination to ensure that he has in his possession at least one original bill of lading. Although this document names the original destination, it will still be delivered to the Master and accomplished in the normal way, provided that the LOI has been issued and accepted by the owner. The owner will retain the LOI. The International Group of P&I Clubs (IG) has issued standard LOIs to cover such situations.

Transhipment/lightening: On receiving the instruction to tranship or lighten all or part of his cargo, the Master should always ask himself whether this instruction is consistent with the bill of lading. If it is not, he must immediately notify all concerned.

On parting with all or part of his vessel's cargo other than at its final destination, the Master should ensure that he receives a clean and plainly worded receipt for it, signed by a qualified person such as the Master or chief mate of the other vessel. The Master should ensure that the receipt states the full quantity transferred, this being particularly important in the case of part discharge or lightening, as if the vessel has actually discharged more cargo than stated in the receipt there will be a shortage at the next port.

In the event that there is some dispute concerning the quantity transferred at such lightening or transhipment and the Master feels that the receipt reads low, he should note this in protest at all subsequent ports of discharge.

Split bill of lading and/or part cargoes: There are two types of split bill of lading. The first occurs where a consignment of cargo described in one bill of lading is split at the discharge port and sold partly to one receiver and partly to another. In these circumstances, delivery is given against delivery orders to which all the conditions of the original bills of lading apply. Usually, the required number of delivery orders is issued by the owner's agent when all the original copies of the bill of lading are presented to him. The Master will give delivery of the cargo against production of all the originals plus all the delivery orders. Delivery orders are made out in original only, with no copies, and are often unacceptable to banks, which severely limits their use.

More difficult is the situation in which the charterers require bills of lading for several parcels of cargo when the Master originally issued a single set of bills of lading for the entire consignment. For example, it might be that one set of bills of lading was issued for the entire cargo, but the charterers and their traders require three sets of bills of lading, each for one-third of the total cargo. This differs from the first case because three sets of negotiable bills of lading are required. The procedure for dealing with this is simple in theory and difficult in practice. The one set of originals is collected and delivered to the owners or their nominated agents, together with the required number of replacements. The owners destroy the original set and sign and issue the replacement sets. If the Master is requested to authorise the issuing of split bills of lading, he should refer the matter to owners or managers and await orders.

The practical point for the Master to remember when a cargo has been divided into separate consignments for different ports is that, as with transhipment or lightening, the receiver who receives too much cargo will usually say nothing, whilst the receiver who is short will always claim. Even if the discrepancy can be traced, owners may still find themselves responsible for shortlanding. Every effort should be made to keep an accurate check on the tonnages discharged and to maintain full records of measurements taken, calculations completed and precautions adopted to ensure correct delivery. A ship which relied upon a stated grab capacity of 2 tonnes to measure a parcel of bulk peas for discharge found a shortage of 514 tonnes of peas when the second parcel was discharged.[141] When discharging the first consignment the ship failed to take account of the stowage factor and angle of repose of the peas and the impossibility of ensuring that every grab load was filled to exactly the same level.

In the iron ore trades it is common that in charterers' option freight is paid less an allowance (0.5% or 1%) 'in lieu of weighing' (ILOW). In some ports, particularly Rotterdam, the charterers' agent will exercise this option by passing the Master a letter stating either that charterers will pay freight less this ILOW allowance or by shore scale. This is a curious practice because of the purely commercial nature of the matter. The Master should take care to sign such a letter without prejudice and subject to the terms and conditions of the prevailing charter party, and make sure that a copy of the letter is included with his documentary returns[126].

Phytosanitary certificate

Most countries of the world have plant health regulations which seek to regulate the import of products such as grain, plants, seeds and fruit. Importing countries require such products to satisfy certain requirements, which vary according to the country and the product.

To meet these requirements, exporting countries must ensure that their exports satisfy the regulations of the importing country. Phytosanitary certificates are issued by inspectors in the exporting country to certify that the requirements of the plant health regulations of the importing country have been met. The inspectors are normally members of the country's plant protection service which, in the UK, is part of the Department for Environment, Food and Rural Affairs.

In some cases the importing country issues an import permit which specifies the information which the phytosanitary certificate must contain. In these cases the import permit is the primary document to which the phytosanitary certificate is attached. With effect from mid-1993 phytosanitary certificates are not required for trade within the European Community. Instead, a plant passport scheme operates.

The phytosanitary certificate (Appendix 14.6) was issued by the Primary Protection Department of the Republic of Singapore, in respect of a cargo of rice. The certificate informs readers of the details of the consignment, and certifies that the plants or plant products described have been inspected according to appropriate procedures and are considered to be free from quarantine pests and practically free from other injurious pests, and that they are considered to conform with the current phytosanitary regulations of the importing country. If the cargo had been disinfested or disinfected that information would also be given.

It is normal for the Master to receive a copy of the phytosanitary certificate with the other cargo documents. This should be retained and presented to the authorities at the discharge port, if requested.

Certificate of compliance with exemptions to trade sanctions

When trade sanctions have been imposed on a country, it may still be allowed to import certain commodities such as food and medicines. Ships carrying such exempted cargoes will be required to produce a certificate of compliance to the authorities enforcing the sanctions to demonstrate that the cargo qualifies for exemption. Certificates of compliance are issued by the exporting government. The example provided (Appendix 14.7) is a permission to export issued by the Government of Australia. A UN approval certificate is also required.

UN approval certificate

The example attached (Appendix 14.8) takes the form of a letter from a UN official to the government of a country which proposes to export exempted goods to a country which is the subject of UN sanctions. The letter states that the prohibitions in respect of these shipments no longer apply and that the captains of the ships engaged in the trade should be provided with copies of the letter. Particularly, this letter is provided so that it can be produced to the naval ships operating the blockades against countries against whom sanctions are in force.

Certificate of origin

A certificate of origin of a cargo may, for example, be required when the authorities in the destination port are applying an embargo against another country and require to be satisfied that the cargo does not originate there, or where the origin of the cargo must be documented for the purposes of the underlying sale contract.

The certificate of origin, often issued by a government department, states the country of origin of the cargo. It should be issued to the Master and will be required by the authorities in the discharging port and possibly in transit ports if they are also applying an embargo. The example (Appendix 14.9) is issued by the République de Guinée in respect of a cargo of bauxite.

In some cases the authorities will accept the ship's cargo manifest as evidence of the origin of the cargo, but it is important that the Master knows in advance what is required.

Declaration by shipper

The declaration by shipper (Appendix 14.10) is made in compliance with the requirement of SOLAS[128] that before loading the shipper or his appointed agent should provide to the Master details, as appropriate, of any bulk cargo in order that any safety precautions which may be necessary can be put into effect. The layout of the declaration and the information it contains will vary with commodity and with shipper, but is becoming increasingly standardised in some trades.

The information which the declaration contains is necessary for the safe planning and supervision of the loading of the cargo. The Master should, if necessary, demand the declaration in writing and insist on being provided with it before commencement of loading. The information contained in the declaration will help the Master to make decisions such as whether it is necessary to trim the cargo reasonably level to the boundaries of the cargo space and whether cargo work should be stopped and the hatches should be closed during periods of rain.

The Master or his representative should sign for receipt of the declaration, and should when planning, loading, carrying and discharging the cargo take account of the information provided. The Master and the shipper will each retain a copy of the declaration.

Certificate of transportable moisture limits

The transportable moisture limit of a cargo which may liquefy is the maximum safe moisture content of the cargo when carried in a conventional bulk carrier. In practice this figure is normally included in the declaration by shipper.

Certificate of moisture content

The moisture content of a sample of cargo is the quantity of water, ice or other liquid which the sample contains, expressed as a percentage of the total wet mass of that sample.[5] In practice, this figure is normally included in the declaration by shipper. If the moisture content is higher than the transportable moisture limit, the cargo may liquefy and cause the ship to become unstable. In these circumstances the cargo cannot be carried safely.

Complete reliance should not be placed upon the certified value of moisture content. As mistakes in providing the figure can be made and cargo can be wetted by heavy rain whilst stored in the open or during loading, the moisture content of the cargo should be monitored. If there is any reason to fear that it may be close to the transportable moisture limit, the moisture content should be checked using one of the methods described in the *IMSBC Code*.[5] Particular care should be taken when the climate is moist and temperatures are below zero.

Master's response sheet

This document (Appendix 14.11) is issued by some coal shippers to encourage Masters to comply with General Requirement 15 of the coal section of the *IMSBC Code*. This states: 'If the behaviour of the cargo during the voyage differs from that specified in the cargo declaration (ie the declaration by shipper), the Master should report such differences to the shipper. Such reports will enable the shipper to maintain records on the behaviour of the coal cargoes, so that the information provided to the Master can be reviewed in the light of transport experience.'

For the safety of ships and their crews there is a need to know more of how consignments of coal behave during the voyage, and Masters should be encouraged to complete and return these forms to report any unexpected experiences with coal cargoes, although reports[125] indicate that co-operation from shippers is sometimes inadequate.

Certificate of lashing

The Master or his representative may be required to sign a certificate of lashing to state that the securing of a timber deck cargo or a cargo of steel coils or other cargo which requires lashing has been to his satisfaction.

Before signing he should be satisfied that the deck cargo is securely stowed and lashed. If in doubt as to how the cargo should be stowed and lashed he should consult the ship's *Cargo Loading and Securing Manual* and the *Code of Safe Practice for Ships Carrying Timber Deck Cargoes*,[4] or that for *Cargo Stowage and Securing*.[38]

After signing the certificate the Master retains one copy and the other copies go to the foreman responsible for the lashing.

Certificate of readiness to load

The certificate of readiness to load (Appendix 14.12) is issued by the marine authorities (such as the Canadian Coast Guard, the National Cargo Bureau in the USA, and the Australian Maritime Safety Authority) in respect of cargoes of grain and concentrates and timber deck cargoes, each of which has special loading requirements.

The certificate is issued after satisfactory inspection of the cargo spaces and the pre-loading calculations, and contains reminders of restrictions that must be imposed upon the loading. The restrictions in question are those imposed by international regulations and by the *IMSBC Code*.[5] The Master must ensure that all the restrictions are observed.

Copies of the document go to the Master, the port authority, the ship's agent and the port warden. The Master cannot present notice of readiness until the certificate of readiness to load has been issued.

Certificate of fitness to proceed to sea

The certificate of fitness to proceed to sea (Appendix 14.13) follows the certificate of readiness to load, being issued by the marine authorities after satisfactory completion of loading of a cargo of grain or concentrates, or a timber deck cargo.

The certificate records the manner in which the cargo has been stowed and provides reminders of precautions which must be taken during the voyage. It also contains details of the vessel's draught, trim, weights carried and stability on sailing. Copies of the document go to the Master, the port authority, the ship's agent and the port warden.

Certificate of loading

A certificate of loading (bulk grain only) (Appendix 14.14) is issued in the USA by the National Cargo Bureau to certify that a cargo of bulk grain has been loaded in accordance with USCG regulations. The document is similar to the Canadian certificate of fitness to proceed to sea. The Master signs the certificate to acknowledge receipt. One copy of the certificate is retained by the Master, and another by the surveyor.

Certificate of fumigation

A certificate of fumigation is issued by the relevant agricultural or other responsible authority and provides details of the fumigation of cargo, and/or cargo or other spaces.

The specimen certificate (Appendix 14.15) was issued by the agronomist engineer from the Agricultural Authority at Sao Francisco do Sul, Brazil. It records the fumigation of the cargo of '(soya bean meal) pellets in bulk' in the holds of a handy-sized bulk carrier, notes the fumigant and dosage used, and records that fumigation was to continue on passage, the fumigant to be exhausted by ventilation after 72 hours.

A certificate of fumigation is required for two reasons. It will satisfy the local department of agriculture that the cargo is free of infestation and it provides the information which enables an authorised chemist to carry out a gas free test.

A clearance certificate is issued by the chemist when tests show that the residual fumigant has been dispersed from spaces containing cargo or adjacent working spaces and any residual fumigant material has been removed. Such a certificate, when required and issued, is usually provided by a chemist in the discharging port to ensure that cargo spaces can be safely entered.

The Master and the fumigator or chemist each retain a copy of any certificate which is issued and copies may be required by the shipper, the receiver and by the port authorities in the loading and discharging ports.

Certificate of weight and quality

A certificate of weight and quality is issued by suitably qualified surveyors and samplers and testifies to the quantity of cargo loaded and to its physical description and analytical specification. The example (Appendix 14.16) is issued in respect of a cargo of grain and also records the clean condition of the holds prior to commencement of loading.

In grain trades this is the document on which the mate's receipt and bill of lading are based. It is therefore of vital importance to all concerned with the cargo. In some cases the certificate of weight and quality may be treated like a mate's receipt. If asked to countersign such a document the Master may sign 'for receipt only' if he cannot verify the accuracy of all the information which it contains.

Stowage plan

The stowage plan, otherwise known as the cargo plan or the hold distribution plan, shows the commodity, tonnage and/or measurement of cargo in each hold. The plan may be produced by one of the ship's officers (Appendix 14.17) to provide a record of the loading as observed and measured by ship's personnel, in which case it may also provide information about the bunkers carried and the vessel's draught, trim and stability. Where there is a discrepancy between the cargo tonnages as calculated by different people using different methods, the ship's plan is likely to show the bill of lading tonnages, though the ship's figure may also be stated.

Alternatively, the stowage plan may be produced by someone from the loading installation (Appendix 14.18) to record the quantities loaded in each position. A stowage plan provided by shore-based staff will normally show the shore values for the tonnages loaded, regardless of whether or not these are the figures used in the bill of lading.

The simplest plans are produced for the simplest cargoes. When the cargo is provided by a single shipper and consists of a single commodity for a single consignee, the stowage plan need show little more than the tonnage loaded in each hold. The stowage plan must be more complex when the cargo consists of several commodities for several consignees in a number of ports, as may happen when the cargo consists of a number of parcels of forest products, steel, ores or different grades of coal. The plan must show the different commodities, and the tonnages and B/L numbers of each parcel.

When the cargo consists of several different parcels in a single hold, it is essential that the cargo for the second discharge port does not overstow the cargo for the first discharge port and the stowage plan must show clearly which parcels of cargo overstow which others. This is necessary so that the sequence of discharge of the cargo can be planned and amended if necessary. The accepted practice is that the parcel shown (on the plan) nearest to the top of the hold is the first parcel to be discharged and the parcel shown lowest is the last to be discharged. When two parcels are shown side by side, either can be discharged first.

For example, in the plan at Appendix 14.17, No. 2 hold is shown as containing cargo for Cleveland, Toledo, Detroit, and Chicago. The cargo for Chicago is shown standing on its own ground, and with nothing overstowing it. Consequently, it can be discharged either before, or after, the cargo in the after end of the hold. In the after end the Detroit cargo is overstowed by the Toledo and the Cleveland cargo, and the discharging sequence must be Cleveland, then Toledo, then Detroit.

When several parcels of similar cargo – it could be timber, woodpulp or steel products – are stowed in the same hold they must be separated by a distinctive separation material. Materials used for cargo separations include polythene netting, plastic sheeting, coloured ropes, plywood, wire netting and separation quality burlap. The separations should be carefully and accurately shown on the stowage plans. The cargo of logs carried by a handy-sized bulker (Appendix 14.19) from the USA to three Japanese ports was separated, port by port, with coloured ropes, and the separations are shown on the plan.

When stowage plans are drawn by the loading stevedores, they are intended as a record and to provide information for the ship's staff and for the discharging stevedores. Similarly, stowage plans prepared aboard ship are for the ship's records and for the discharging stevedores, and possibly also for the loading stevedores. Copies of stowage plans may also be sent routinely to the owners, managers and/or charterers of the vessel.

Cargo manifest

A cargo manifest (Appendix 14.20) is issued by the shippers or their agents in the loading port and is based upon the information contained in the Bs/L. It provides brief details of the ship and the loading and discharge ports and lists details of the cargo carried. Details include the B/L number, shipper, consignee, marks and numbers, contents, gross weight and freight.

Copies of the cargo manifest, if available, are retained by the Master, who will give copies to the authorities in the discharge port and ports visited *en route*, if required. In some trades the manifest may not be completed and available to the Master before the ship sails, but if required to produce one he can complete his own from the information in the Bs/L.

Whilst the Master may not be required to sign the manifest produced by the charterer he should satisfy himself as far as possible that it is an accurate statement of the cargo carried.

Dangerous cargo manifest

A dangerous cargo manifest (Appendix 14.21) is issued by the shippers or their agents in compliance with the regulations which apply at the loading port. The document states the quantity of hazardous material carried and certifies that it is properly named, prepared and otherwise in proper condition for bulk shipment.

The name and description of the hazardous material as given in the dangerous cargo manifest can and should be used to confirm the stowage requirements for the cargo, as stated in the *IMSBC Code*[5] and/or the *IMDG Code*[33].

The document will be presented to the Master for his signature, and before signing he should satisfy himself, as far as is reasonably possible, that the stated quantities and positions of the cargo are correct, and that the cargo has been stowed in accordance with the requirements of the codes.

Correct stowage is necessary to ensure safe carriage of the cargo. Failure to carry the cargo in the manner specified in the codes could expose the ship and those aboard her to hazard and could weaken a claim for compensation in the event of loss. Indeed, it could lead to a claim against the ship if the cargo is lost or damaged through incorrect stowage.

The Master and shipper will each retain one copy and a further copy or copies may be required by the authorities in the loading and discharging ports.

Material Safety Data Sheets

Material Safety Data Sheets (MSDS) (Appendix

14.22) provide detailed information about hazardous cargoes and stores carried on board. All hazardous materials carried on board must be accompanied by an MSDS. They are issued in the USA. The data include useful information about the health hazards and other dangers associated with the commodity, protective equipment to use, additional precautions, and emergency and first aid. When local regulations require that such information must be available for shore workers, it is reasonable to obtain it for ships' personnel, too.

Hatch sealing certificate

Cargo hatches may be sealed to prevent theft of cargo or because the holds have been fumigated and are unsafe to enter. When hatches have been sealed by a shorebased organisation a certificate recording the fact is usually issued. The example (Appendix 14.23) lists the compartments which have been sealed and the type and serial number of the seal used. When countersigning, the Master or chief officer will ensure that the information entered in the certificate is correct.

Statement of facts

A statement of facts (SOF), sometimes known as a port log, is prepared by the ship's agents in each loading and each discharging port. It is intended to provide a full record of the times of those events which may be required for the preparation of the laytime statement and which may affect claims for dispatch and demurrage or for offhire.

The example (Appendix 14.24) is for a handy-sized bulker loading soya bean meal pellets in Sao Francisco do Sul, and provides a good example of the information which should be included in such a document.

The SOF should detail the vessel's arrival at the pilot station, the anchorage and the berth, and should note the time of pilot boarding and the arrival of tugs. Tendering and receipt of notice of readiness and granting of free pratique should be recorded, as should the clearing (ie passing) of the holds by the pre-loading surveyor.

Periods of loading or discharging should be recorded, as should the times of stoppages, with their reasons. Weather which interrupts cargo work and adverse weather at any other time should be noted.

Cargo tonnages, bunker figures and draughts should be recorded. The time of sailing should finally be entered with other significant times, such as time of completion of fumigation, and any unexpected delays with their reasons.

The Master should check the accuracy of the SOF before he signs it. He should insist on correction of the statement of facts when it is inaccurate, or should add remarks stating the correct facts if the agent refuses to amend the document to his satisfaction. The SOF is signed by the Master and sometimes by representatives of both owners' and charterers' agents. It may also be signed by a representative of the shipper. Copies are retained by each party.

In some trades, particularly from the USA, the presentation to the Master of incomplete SOFs is said to be an increasing problem. The first page, with arrival data, is presented and the Master is asked to sign a final page, permitting later insertion of more data on a middle page. The reason given may be that the times from the loading facility are not yet available. The Master should never sign such a blank cheque.

When presented with such a proposal the Master should insist that the SOF is as complete as possible, and should then draw a line beneath the data entered and attach his signature. He should then formally delegate to the agent the responsibility for ensuring that the remainder of the SOF is completed correctly.

There is no justification for a mad rush to prepare and sign the SOF in the last minutes before sailing. If the SOF is a complex document the Master can ask the agent to send it to him by email for checking and confirmation. The Master can then delegate his authority to the agent to sign the SOF on his behalf after receipt of his confirmation as is done by at least one major ship operator.[126]

A trick sometimes used by unscrupulous agents is to present an SOF top copy with the final details handwritten, along with five copies with a blank last page on which the agent promises to type the manuscript entries copied from the top copy. When the blank pages have been signed the agent discards the top copy and types whatever suits him on the signed pages. Masters should avoid signing blank or incomplete SOFs whatever the circumstances.

Letter of protest

A letter of protest is a document used to provide a written record of a dispute. The Master should write a letter of protest whenever he considers that shippers, stevedores or any other parties are responsible for an event or circumstance which will cause a loss to the ship. For example, the Master should write a letter of protest to the shippers if they fail to provide a full cargo in accordance with the voyage charterparty. He should write a letter of protest to the stevedores if the ship is unable to work cargo because they have failed to inform him of special requirements and cargo work is delayed while the cargo gear is adjusted, for example.

The Master is liable to receive a letter of protest if the vessel fails in some way to perform in accordance with the charterparty. For example, a letter of protest is likely to be issued if the vessel is unable to accept the quantity of cargo stipulated in the charterparty or if loading or discharge of cargo is interrupted because of a fault of the ship.

When writing a letter of protest, it should be remembered that its meaning must be clear to whoever may be asked to resolve the dispute as well as to the person to whom the letter is addressed. The facts of the matter should be stated plainly and in sufficient detail to make clear why the protest is being made. The letter should include a clear statement of why the addressee is considered responsible for the problem reported and of the action he must take to remove or minimise the problem.

A Letter of Protest should be supported by photographs when they are available.

An example of such a letter is at Appendix 14.25.

Empty hold certificate

When there is any doubt as to the outturn of the cargo – for example, if the receiver is claiming that his cargo has been short-landed – the Master can issue an empty hold certificate. Such a certificate will say that all cargo has been discharged and that the holds have been emptied. The stevedore supervisor will be asked to sign the certificate (Appendix 14.26) to confirm that no cargo remains aboard.

The Master will keep the original of this document and can give copies to the stevedore who signs it and to the ship's agent. Some owners instruct Masters to obtain empty hold certificates for every cargo carried and this is a safe commercial practice to adopt.

Trimming certificate/Certificate of Loading/Discharging

The trimming certificate (Appendix 14.27(1)) is a document which the Master or his representative may be asked to sign to confirm that he is satisfied with the manner in which the cargo has been trimmed.

One serving Shipmaster advises his colleagues to add a clause saying 'The cargo has not been trimmed in compliance with the *IMSBC Code*, as the cargo has not been trimmed reasonably level to the boundaries of the cargo space' when this is the case. He reports that the stevedores presenting the document usually withdraw it rather than accept the endorsement. The Master will give the original of this document to the stevedores' representative or to the agent and will retain a copy.

The certificate of fitness to proceed to sea issued by the port warden, coastguard or similar authority also testifies to the trimming of the cargo, but the trimming certificate is issued by the Master, not the authorities.

The certificate of loading/discharging (Appendix 14.27(2)) goes rather further and requires the Master or chief mate to state that the cargo has been properly loaded, stowed, trimmed and separations laid according to the signatory's satisfaction. The Master of this self trimming bulk carrier was able to insert the remark 'no separation or trimming required'.

Stevedores' time sheet

The stevedores' time sheet normally shows the number of gangs employed, the hatches worked and the equipment used, with dates and hours worked and times and reasons for stoppages. If asked to countersign this document the Master should, of course, ensure that it is correct. He should insist on correction of the stevedores' time sheet when it is inaccurate, or should add remarks stating the correct facts if the agent or stevedore refuses to amend the document to his satisfaction. Alternatively, he can sign 'for receipt only'.

Clean ballast discharge permit

A clean ballast discharge permit is a document which is becoming more widely used in many parts of the world. The example (Appendix 14.28) authorises the vessel to discharge clean ballast in the Port of Long Beach and stipulates the conditions which must be observed whilst ballast is being discharged.

The permit is issued by the port authority following application from the ship's agent and a copy has to be posted at the ship's gangway, with a record of 'checks and condition of discharge'. In Vancouver, a certificate is issued by the port warden at the time when the vessel is first boarded, after the first discharge of ballast has been sighted and found acceptable. A similar permit is required in some parts of the world for the discharge of bilge water.

Paint compliance certificate

If holds have been repainted shortly before a cargo of grain or other foodstuffs is to be loaded the shippers may demand to see a compliance certificate for the paint used. Such a certificate, (Appendix 14.29) issued by an independent laboratory, states that all the materials used to make the paint are approved for use on surfaces which are in contact with foods. The details of the relevant regulations appear on the certificate.

Stevedore damage form

These documents are issued by the Master or his representative, to hold the stevedore responsible for damage to ship or cargo. (They are described in Chapter 3.)

Notice of readiness

The procedures associated with the tendering of notice of readiness are described in Chapter 2. A sample notice of readiness is attached (Appendix 14.30).

Certificate of IMO classification

A certificate of IMO classification of a cargo must be issued to the Master by the shipper before shipment of a cargo which is listed in the *IMDG Code*. This is essential so that he can apply the correct emergency procedures, should they be necessary. Such a certificate is usually in the form of a standardised dangerous goods bill of lading.

On receipt of a certificate of IMO classification, the Master should study the emergency procedures, ensure that the ship can carry the cargo safely and confirm that the proposed stowage complies with IMO recommendations. Such precautions as are necessary for the safe carriage of the cargo must be observed throughout the voyage.

Copies of the certificate of IMO classification may be required by the receiver and by the port authority in the port of discharge and also in ports visited *en route*.

Certificate of compliance/IMSBC Code fitness certificate

These certificates (Appendices 14.31(1), 31(2) and 32), issued by an Administration or a classification society on behalf of an Administration to every ship constructed since 1st September 1984,[123, 238] state the dry bulk cargoes that the ship is constructed, equipped and permitted to carry. The certificates demand careful study because there is reportedly some variation in the permitted cargoes listed in different certificates, even for sister ships. The certificate at Appendix 14.31.(2) permits Appendix A and C cargoes from the edition of the *IMSBC Code* valid at that time (ie cargoes which may liquefy and cargoes without hazard) but excludes hazardous cargoes. The certificate at Appendix 14.31.(1) permits Appendix A and C cargoes and also coal (an Appendix B cargo).

The certificate at Appendix 14.32, a certificate of compliance for the carriage of dangerous goods, shows that the ship is suitable for carrying dangerous goods as listed on Page 2 (not shown), including goods designated class MHB (materials hazardous only when carried in bulk). The list of permitted cargoes is likely to be similar to that given on the sample capacity plan (see CD inside front cover).

In addition to listing permitted cargoes the certificates or their supporting documents list the conditions that must be satisfied and the equipment that must be carried if the certificate is to remain valid. The certificate of compliance for the carriage of dangerous goods must be renewed at each periodical survey.

Such certificates must be studied with care to note the holds (often the hold nearest to the machinery spaces) in which particular dangerous goods cannot be carried and the special requirements for the carriage of particular cargoes. Requirements for particular cargoes include 'Not to be loaded adjacent to fuel oil tanks heated above 45°C', and 'All electrical installations are to be disconnected'.

Hatch closing certificate

The hatch closing certificate (Appendix 14.33), issued by an attending surveyor, reports on hatch covers which appear to be in good condition and which have been properly closed, and has provision for recording hatch covers or fittings which appear to be defective, or which have not been properly closed. This appears to be a document used by shippers or charterers who want to ensure that their cargoes are well protected.

The Master or chief officer, when countersigning the document can, if necessary, insert a remark rejecting the report.

No damage certificate

In some regions, particularly India, the Master will be required to sign a 'no damage' certificate releasing the stevedores from liability after completion of discharge. The ship may be prevented from sailing until the certificate has been signed[127]. One owner instructs Masters to sign the certificate with the endorsement 'without prejudice'.

Sources

4, 5, 26, 33, 34, 38, 90, 123, 125, 126, 127, 128, 141, 238. (See List of Sources, Page 497)

CHAPTER 15

LOADED VOYAGE

Departure from the loading port, trim for the loaded voyage, choice of route, cargo ventilation, soundings, action to take when flooding is detected, acidity of bilges, cargo temperatures, sampling of air in holds, checking and tightening of cargo lashings daily, inspections in fair and rough weather, conduct of the voyage in rough weather, reporting, arriving at the discharging port

Departure from the loading port

IN Chapter 12 it was noted that it is normal for all the hatches to be secured for sea and their securing checked by the chief mate before the vessel leaves the berth. An exception may be made when a vessel has a long passage to complete from the loading berth through sheltered waters before the open sea is reached. In these circumstances, if the paperwork can be completed promptly, and if the securing of most of the hatches has been completed when they finished loading, time can be gained by completing the securing of the final one or two hatches after the vessel has left the berth. For Cape-sized vessels the ports of Ponta Da Madeira, Narvik and Dampier come into this category, and the grain loading port of New Orleans is an example of a port where this approach is justifiable for Panamax-sized vessels. Many more examples could be quoted for handy-sized and mini-bulkers. If there is a high tide to catch or if daylight is required for the transit, there is an added reason for departing as quickly as possible and completing the work of securing whilst proceeding towards the sea.

Once the berth has been cleared and tugs have been released, mooring lines must be secured on their reels and covered or passed below decks into the rope stores. Anchors must be secured and spurling pipes cemented or covered when deep water is reached and there is no realistic possibility of using them.

Cargo residues lying on deck should not be washed or swept overboard whilst the vessel is in the port approaches or coastal waters. Light residues such as grain are liable to blow over the ship: they should be swept into piles between the hatches and damped down or covered for disposal once international waters are reached. Heavy residues like iron ore can be left on deck to be swept or washed overboard in international waters. (The regulations for the disposal of cargo residues are described in Chapter 25.)

Essential cleaning should be done. For example, a clear path along the deck to the pilot ladder must be swept or washed, and if the pilot is to be discharged by helicopter the helicopter landing hatch cover and the two adjacent covers must be washed down. This is to prevent dust being drawn into the helicopter engine, where it might cause failure, and to avoid the creation of a dust fog. Permission from pilot, terminal or port authority to wash down the helicopter landing area must be obtained.

Trim for the loaded voyage

Bulkers frequently leave the loading port trimmed even keel or nearly so and when at full sea speed in the open sea will trim by the head (See Chapter 8, 'Squat'). This is inconvenient at best: at worst it can be dangerous. Bulk carriers are designed to operate at even keel or trimmed by the stern. The hold bilge wells are situated at the after ends of compartments but when a ship is trimmed by the head water leaking into the hold from any source will flow or seep towards the fore end where, with cargoes such as steel or forest products in particular, it will lie on the tanktop. In these circumstances the bilges will remain empty and the leakage will be undetected until sufficient water has entered to cover the entire tanktop and reach the after end of the hold.

Wherever the ship's loadlines permit the ship should be trimmed by the stern for the sea passage, for example by filling the afterpeak with sea water ballast. In addition to improving the reliability of the hold bilge soundings this will make easier the transfer of fuel, and drainage in washrooms and ship's stores will become more efficient.

Choice of route for the loaded voyage

The obvious first choice of route for the loaded voyage will be the most direct one and often this will be the best, but there are various reasons for considering alternatives. When choosing the route, the Master should take into consideration the ship's loading and operational requirements, plus climatic and weather data.

Loading and operational requirements: A ship which has been soundly built and properly maintained ought to be able to face normal heavy weather without suffering structural damage, but there is no benefit to be gained from meeting adverse weather on the direct route if more favourable conditions can be found on an alternative route. Furthermore, no Master should let his vessel remain in the path of exceptional weather, such as is met near a tropical cyclone, when there is an alternative.

The ship's loading and operational requirements are dictated by such facts as the cargo the vessel is carrying and, where applicable, the way it is secured. The Master of a ship carrying a deck cargo of steel pipes, timber or woodpulp, or with holds loaded with steel coils lashed with strapping bands, for example, will want to avoid heavy adverse swell as far as possible. Heavy seas shipped on deck can dislodge deck cargo, and the ship's violent motion can cause steel coils to break adrift in the holds. If the cargo requires ventilation the Master should try to avoid weather which makes it impossible to ventilate.

A strong case can also be made for choosing a route to avoid troubles. Coasts where civil strife has led to the shelling of passing ships, areas where pirates are known to operate and areas where large concentrations of fishing vessels can be expected are all well worth avoiding.

Climatic data: Climatic data include the observations of currents and wind and wave height and direction taken over a period of years. In low latitudes within the tropics, the weather and wave conditions remain stable for long periods except when tropical cyclones occur, and these data published by hydrographic authorities are very reliable. In low latitudes a choice of route which takes account of prevailing currents, winds and swell conditions is likely to be successful. It is reasonable for a Master to set courses which increase the distance over the ground, provided that the extra distance is outweighed by benefits such as a favourable current, or a better speed through the water.

If the arithmetic shows that on indirect route 'B' making good 14 knots, the vessel will arrive in port earlier than by direct route 'A' where only 13 knots can be expected, then the decision to use indirect route 'B' is justified.

It is climatic data which influence a Shipmaster when he chooses an indirect route across the Arabian Sea during the SW monsoon or remains further from the South African coast when rounding the Cape from west to east to avoid the adverse effect of the Agulhas current.

The routes recommended in *Ocean Passages of the World*[36] are based on climatic data, and such data can be found in routeing charts, current atlases, tidal stream publications and sailing directions.

Weather forecasts: In higher latitudes the weather is less stable than in the tropics, being regularly disturbed by the depressions which cross the oceans. In these areas the use of weather forecasts is essential when choosing the best route to follow: swell and wind conditions can be very different over a distance of no more than a few hundred miles.

A departure from the direct route (ie, from the great circle route) in higher latitudes is most likely to result in a saving when the route runs easterly or westerly because that is the direction in which the weather systems travel. It is mainly in east-west crossings of the North Atlantic, North Pacific and the three southern oceans that savings in time and/or fuel can be made by good route choice.

Experienced Masters can learn to recognise the weather patterns over the oceans and to choose their route accordingly. During periods when conditions are favourable the planning of the route is easy, but ocean voyages may take 10-30 days and there can be few Shipmasters who have the resources to plan optimum routes so far ahead through adverse conditions.

The difficulties for a Shipmaster of forecasting, days in advance, the nature and effects of adverse weather on his ship and the desire for voyages completed economically and without losing time or damaging cargo, have led to the development over the last 40 years of ship routeing services. Improved communications and data acquisition and processing have made such services possible.

Ship routeing services: Ship routeing services serving the whole world or more limited areas are provided by several commercial organisations including fleet managements which have the resources to predict the weather and to forecast a ship's progress along alternative routes so that the most suitable one can be chosen. The size of their data bases and the power of their computers enables them to assess the options and choose the best route in a way that no mariner could hope to match consistently. The International Maritime Organization has issued advice on minimum standards for weather routeing services[260].

The weather routeing services receive regular and frequent weather reports from numerous sources situated all round the world, including data from satellites, and use operational computer models which produce detailed forecasts of winds and waves for a number of days ahead.

These services normally ask the purpose of the routeing – to minimise fuel consumption, or to minimise adverse weather and swell, for example – and recommend an appropriate route. The route is chosen on the basis of the forecast weather and the ship's anticipated performance. The ship's performance is forecast on the basis of her particulars and the experience which the forecasters have in their computerised records of routeing similar ships. The ship reports her position at intervals during the voyage or is tracked automatically so that her progress can be monitored and the route amended when changing conditions require it. The routeing services also monitor sea ice and the recommended routes take vessels clear of ice infested waters.

After the voyage the routeing organisation can provide a comparison between actual and possible alternative routes to demonstrate the benefits of the routeing advice. The routeing organisation can also provide comparisons between actual speeds achieved and charter speeds, after taking account of the weather and currents experienced. These comparisons can be provided regardless of whether or not the vessel was routed on the voyage in question. A fuel consumption monitoring service is provided by most routeing services as an optional extra and is used by many charterers.

When to use a ship routeing service: It is common for charterers to insist on the provision of a ship routeing service for the loaded voyage, particularly for east west crossings of the oceans outside the tropics. Since the *Hill Harmony* case some charterers have adopted the BIMCO Weather Routeing Clause for Time Charter Parties which states:

(a) The Vessel shall, unless otherwise instructed by the Charterers, proceed by the customary route, but the Master may deviate from the route if he has reasonable grounds to believe that such a route will compromise the safe navigation of the Vessel.

(b) In the event the Charterers supply the Master with weather routeing information, although not obliged to follow such routeing information, the Master shall comply with the reporting procedure of that service.

The effect of this is to allow the Master to use his own judgement and discretion. If he departs from the recommended route he should be able to show that he has acted prudently. The use of the ship routeing service enables the charterers to be satisfied at modest cost that the chartered ship has followed the optimum route.

When routeing is not a requirement of the charterers it is still open to the Master to request owners or charterers for permission to use a routeing service and some owners and charterers will expect him to do so when benefits can be anticipated.

Individual cases must be judged on their merits, but routeing services for bulk carriers are likely to provide the biggest savings in fuel consumption, and/or the greatest reduction in damage, when one or more of the following conditions are met: voyage is outside the tropics: voyage is through the tropics during tropical cyclone season: voyage runs more east to west than north to south: the shortest route would take the vessel into very high latitudes: voyage is during bad weather period (eg, winter or monsoons); ship is medium- or low-powered; ship is in ballast or has a deck cargo; Master has little experience of the region; ship's facilities for receiving weather data are poor.

Improvements in communications, in computing and in satellite weather observing and forecasting have greatly improved the availability and the quality of meteorological information for mariners and 'do it yourself' shipboard routeing services were, in 2008, available and well regarded.

Cargo ventilation

Speaking generally, bulk cargoes are ventilated to prevent the formation of cargo sweat or ship's sweat which could damage the cargo, to reduce the harmful heating of a cargo, and/or to remove hazardous gases from the cargo spaces. Ventilation in the wrong circumstances can do considerable harm and before a decision is made to ventilate a space it is necessary to consider the requirements of the cargo, the temperature and humidity within the holds and outside and the presence or absence of sea spray. The types and positions of ventilators with which the ship is provided must also be taken into account.

Hold ventilators: Most bulk carriers built since 2000 are provided with two hold ventilators set into the forward end of the hatch covers and a similar pair of ventilators set into the after end of the hatch covers.(Figs. 15.1) These are easy to open or close, easy to clean, cheap to fit and maintain but are more exposed to sea water and spray on deck than are mushroom ventilators, and therefore require more attention. Ventilators of this type do not contain fans. The arrangements within the hatch cover depend upon whether the hatch panels are single (Fig. 15.2) or double (Fig. 15.3) skinned.

Older bulk carriers and any fitted with mechanical ventilation are more likely to be provided with two or four ventilation trunks per hold, with one or two situated at the fore end of the hold, and one or two at the after end. To avoid passing through the topside tanks these ventilator trunks are situated close to the ship's centreline. Within the hold each such trunk often terminates in a simple square, round or rectangular opening in the deckhead (Fig. 15.4). Alternatively trunking may continue down the bulkhead, with slots at intervals to admit air to the hold at various levels. Portable plates can be put in place to close the lower slots, when ventilation at lower levels in the cargo is not wanted.

Above deck the ventilation trunks may stand alone, each fitted with a mushroom cowl which gives some protection from spray and from the direct force of any wind (Fig. 15.5 and 25.6), or they may be built into

Fig. 15.1 Hold ventilator set into hatch panel

Fig. 15.2 Hold vent set into cover, upper side open

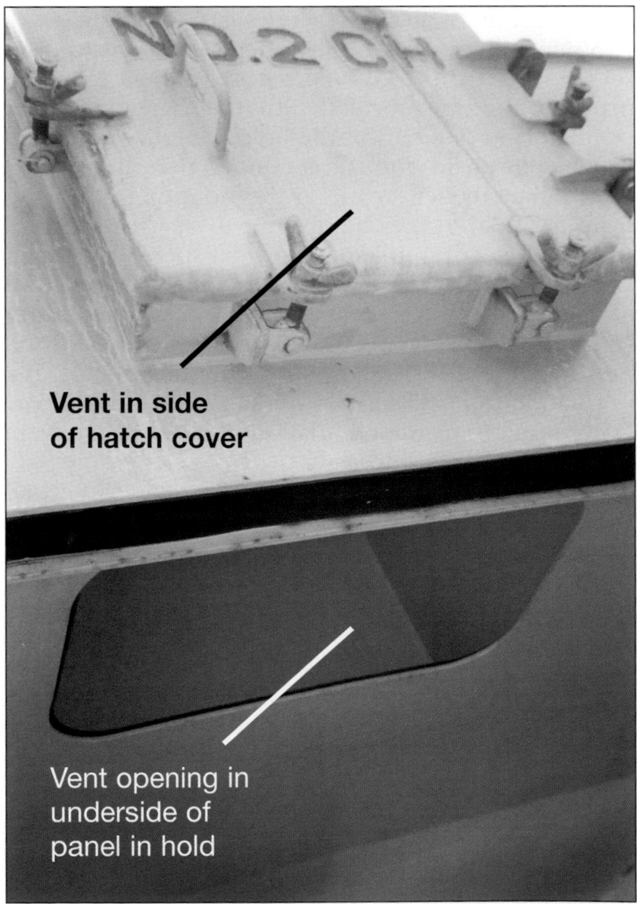

Fig. 15.3 Hold vent in double skinned (sealed) hatch panel

Fig. 15.4 Ventilator opening in deckhead

Fig. 15.5 Mushroom ventilator at the after end of the after hold. Operating wheel and shaft protected by angle iron bracket

the structures of the masthouses with openings situated in the masthouse sides, the masthouse top (Fig. 6.1), or at the masthead (Fig. 6.3).

Every ventilator must be provided with a means of closing so that all ventilation can be stopped in the event of fire. The means of closing may be in the form of a ventilator flap (or 'damper') set within the vent trunk (Fig. 6.3) and operated by an external lever, or a watertight door (Fig. 6.1), or may consist of a cowl which can be screwed down into a closed position by the operation of a valve wheel (Fig. 6.2 and 15.5).

Some bulk carriers are provided with ventilator fans set in the trunks of ventilators. When fans are provided they are normally fitted in the ventilator or ventilators at one end of the hold. Ventilator fans can usually be run in both directions so that they can be used either to deliver air to the hold or to draw air from the hold. It may be possible to vary the speed of the fans, selecting full speed or half speed or a larger range of options. Ventilation assisted by fans is known as mechanical or forced draught ventilation, whilst ventilation which occurs as a result of natural movement of air is called natural ventilation. Natural ventilation can occur as a result of a wind blowing, the ship's motion, or the circulation of air resulting from temperature differences.

The *Regina Oldendorff* is provided with one ventilator at each end of each hold. These ventilators pass vertically through the masthouses with the forward ventilator in each hold being on the starboard side and the after ventilator on the port side. The ventilators terminate on top of the masthouses with grilles which face aft and are provided with watertight doors (Fig. 6.1). No fans are provided, so any ventilation is natural.

Some older vessels are provided with ventilators of the hinged-door type set into the hatch covers, or with portable ventilator cowls, in addition to the mushroom or cowl ventilators at the extremities of the hold. Such additional ventilators are required to provide surface ventilation within the hatch square when a ship is carrying a cargo which fills the hold to coaming level, thereby sealing off the hatch square from the rest of the compartment (Fig. 15.6). The portable ventilator cowls have to be bolted in position on the hatch covers when blank plates have been removed.

Reasons for ventilating bulk cargoes: A number of difficult cargoes have special ventilation requirements to prevent overheating or to remove dangerous gases. In such cases Masters and officers should be guided by any instructions provided by owners, charterers, shippers and/or the *IMSBC Code*[5].

In Chapter 19 the carriage of several typical cargoes is described and these provide a good illustration of the varied reasons for ventilating. Coal is ventilated to remove hazardous gases. With steel a major object is to avoid the formation of sweat, which would damage the cargo. Iron ore has no particular need for ventilation although it is desirable to maintain a dry and healthy atmosphere in the holds for access and to reduce corrosion.

When there is no special need to remove gases, the reason for ventilating is to remove moist air and replace it with drier air to discourage the formation of sweat.

Sweat: Sweat is the name given by seamen to condensation which occurs in a ship's cargo spaces. There are two types of sweat, ship's sweat and cargo sweat. For sweat to occur there must be moisture in the hold atmosphere and a difference of temperature between the air in the hold and the cargo or the ship's steelwork.

The temperature difference usually occurs as the ship moves from one climatic region to another or from a cold to a warm current or vice versa, and the larger the change in temperature the more likely is the formation of sweat.

Sources of moisture in cargo spaces: The most important source of moisture in a hold is the cargo. Most commodities, particularly materials of vegetable origin, possess some natural moisture and create an atmosphere, known as the storage atmosphere, in any compartment in which they are stored[23]. Moisture in a hold can also be the result of rainfall during loading and the air in a hold will be moist if conditions were moist when the hold was closed on completion of loading.

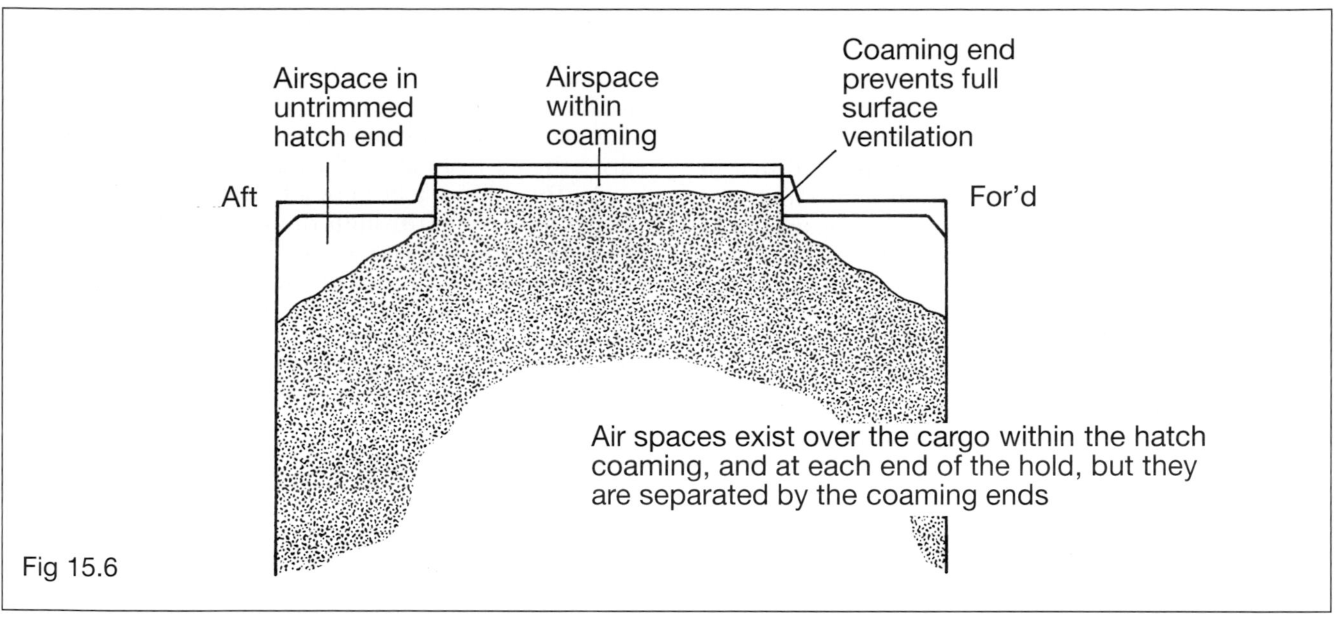

Fig 15.6

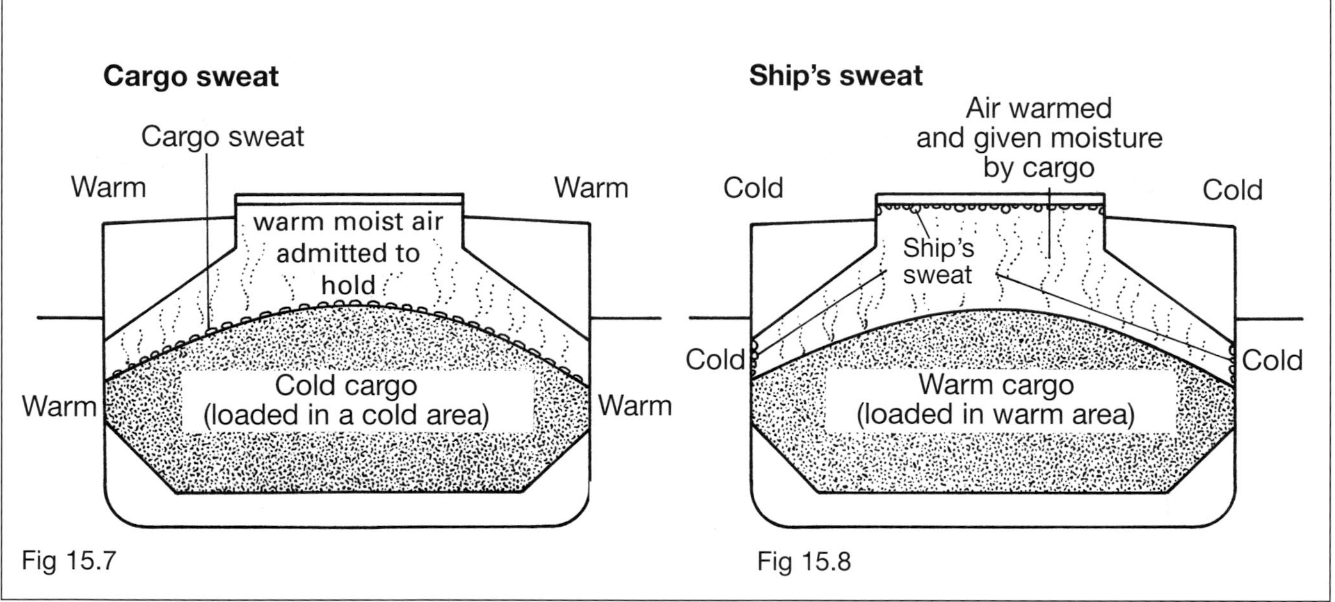

Fig 15.7

Fig 15.8

The amount of moisture in the air is measured by its dewpoint, which is the lowest temperature to which a mass of air can be reduced without condensation occurring. As condensation is a 'bad thing' it is helpful to remember that air with a high dewpoint is a 'bad thing'. Dewpoint is obtained from a table, entered with readings taken from the wet and dry bulb hygrometer.

Cargo sweat: Cargo sweat consists of condensation which forms on the surface of cold cargo when warm moist air comes in contact with it (Fig. 15.7). Cargo sweat will form when the dewpoint of the air in the hold is higher than the temperature of the cargo. This is most likely to occur when the ship has loaded a cargo in a cold region and air is admitted to the hold as the ship is travelling towards a warmer region.

To prevent cargo sweat when passing from a cold region to a warm region all ventilation should be stopped and the hold should be kept closed, with the air unchanged, as far as possible. The temperature of the cargo will only rise very slowly to equal the external atmosphere, and so long as the hold remains closed the air within it will gradually become warmer and able to hold more moisture.

With an inert cargo the dewpoint of the air in the non-ventilated hold remains constant as it warms up. If the cargo contains moisture it will give off moisture as it warms up. However, as the heat will flow from the shell of the ship into the hold atmosphere and from the hold atmosphere to the cargo, the temperature of the hold air stays a step ahead of the cargo temperature. Any moisture given off by the cargo can be held in the air.

It will be safe and desirable to ventilate only after the surface temperature of the cargo has risen to equal that of the air outside the hold or when the external air is exceptionally dry, so that its dewpoint is lower than the temperature of the cargo.

Ship's sweat: Ship's sweat is the condensation which occurs when warm moist air in the hold comes into contact with the cold steelwork which forms the deck and shell plating of the ship (Fig. 15.8). Ship's sweat will form when the dewpoint of the air in the hold is higher than the temperature of the ship's steelwork, conditions most likely to be met when the ship has loaded in a warm region and is steaming towards colder climates. Ship's sweat caused by a low external air temperature is most likely to be deposited first in the vicinity of the hatch coaming and the fore and after ends of the hold amidships, as the topside tanks or double hull, even when empty, provide an insulating layer which delays the penetration of cold from the external air to the plating forming the tank/hold separation.

When a cold current is met, causing a low sea temperature, the side shell plating between the topside and lower hopper tanks will be cooled, providing conditions favourable for the formation of ship's sweat in those areas.

When passing from a warm region to a cold region full ventilation should be continued whenever possible in order to withdraw moist air from the hold and replace it by drier external air. If the cargo contains moisture, the air in the hold will continue to be moist and will condense upon the ship's cold steelwork unless it is continually extracted, and replaced by drier air.

General guidelines for ventilation: Ventilation should be stopped, by stopping fans when in use and closing the ventilators, when the vessel is shipping spray in the vicinity of ventilator intakes. Times of interruption of ventilation should be logged.

On short voyages in small ships such as mini-bulkers employed in the European middle trades it is normal to carry out no ventilation and to keep ventilators tightly sealed. With a low freeboard and regular rough weather the danger of shipping spray into open ventilators is usually found to be far greater than the potential benefits from ventilation.

On longer voyages if the cargo requires ventilation cargo holds should be ventilated when the dewpoint of the external air is lower than the dewpoint of the air in the hold. This will put drier air into the hold, forcing out wetter air and reducing the possibility of sweat forming. Dewpoint readings should be logged. However, dewpoint in the hold may be difficult to measure[172]. The hold may be full or unsafe to enter and when it is safe to enter any airflow will be the result of ventilation, meaning that the true temperature within the hold is not being measured. Another way of deciding when ventilation is needed for hygroscopic cargoes (agricultural cargoes such as grain, timber, animal feedstuffs and woodpulp that have a moisture content that can interact with air) is to use the three-degree rule.

The three-degree rule:[172] says that a hygroscopic cargo should be ventilated when the temperature of the outside air is at least 3°C below that of the cargo temperature taken at loading. This rule avoids the need to take readings in the holds after the voyage has commenced and relies on the fact that the temperature of hygroscopic cargoes, except at their boundaries, changes very slowly during a voyage. However it should be noted that one authority (see Appendix 19.2) advises that the ventilation of grain cargoes is likely to do more harm than good.

Ventilation practice: When natural ventilation is being used with open ventilators at both forward and after ends, the air in the hold tends to travel from aft to forward. When forced ventilation is used it is normal to take advantage of this tendency and to drive the air from aft to forward.

Air forced into a hold by a fan will seek the shortest and easiest route through the hold. If the only route by which the air can leave the hold is through a ventilator at the far end of the hold, the air will tend to flow directly to that ventilator across the surface of the cargo. If an access hatch or other opening close to the inlet vent is left open, the air will leave the hold by the access hatch without travelling the length of the hold. This is known as 'short cycling' and is an inefficient form of ventilation. Short cycling should be prevented by ensuring that only ventilators are left open when the hold is closed.

When a hold is loaded with a bulk cargo the ventilation provided is usually surface ventilation, with air flowing over the surface of the cargo from ventilators at the after end of the hold to ventilators at the fore end of the hold or, in newer ships, from ventilators in the after end of the hatch covers to similar ventilators in the fore end of the hatch covers.

Ventilators situated at the hold ends can provide surface ventilation only for the nearby hold ends when the cargo is a low-density one topped up in the hatch square and preventing a flow of air from one end of the hold to the other. When the hold is filled the hatch square requires separate ventilation. (Fig. 15.6)

Through ventilation of a bulk cargo, when air is forced into the body of the cargo, is not normally required and is difficult to achieve. Some through ventilation can be provided aboard ships in which ventilator trunks extend to the bottom of the hold bulkheads. Through ventilation of coal is likely to cause heating and must be avoided.

The capacity of a ship's hold ventilation fans is normally expressed in the number of air changes that can be achieved in an empty hold per hour. When a cargo is carried the number of air changes per hour will be increased, because the quantity of air which the hold contains is reduced.

Soundings

Importance of soundings: Throughout the loaded voyage, as at all other times, soundings of cargo spaces, ballast tanks, void spaces and bunker tanks should be taken and recorded daily by the same competent person. The readings obtained should be inspected carefully for any unexplained increases or decreases in the values observed. When the sounding positions are located on the open main deck and when the vessel is in adverse weather with a low freeboard, it is often unsafe to obtain soundings on the ship's weather side or even on both sides. This is unfortunate, though unavoidable once the ship's design has been finalised. In these circumstances the chief mate should be alert for any opportunity occurring when in the lee of land or because of an improvement in the weather to obtain a set of soundings. Failing this the hold bilges should be pumped daily until suction is lost. Reasons for any failure to obtain soundings should be logged.

During the 1980s and 1990s there were numerous indications that aboard badly-run bulk carriers a full set of soundings was sometimes not obtained for days or weeks on end. It is true that in almost every case soundings when taken only confirm what the chief mate already knows – namely, that the ship is not leaking. But it is only when soundings are obtained daily, at the very least, that there is a reasonable chance that any damage or oversight will be detected promptly when it occurs. Water ingress detectors, if working properly, should detect serious flooding in forepeak or cargo holds at an early stage but will not detect water at tanktop level. Such water would seriously damage or even destroy a variety of cargoes and in addition would give warning that something was wrong. The safe delivery of cargoes can depend upon this seamanlike precaution and the daily taking of soundings should never be neglected.

High soundings in 'empty' tanks: Warning of a leak is provided by increased soundings in ballast tanks or void spaces and must be investigated promptly. First it may be necessary to pump out the compartment. Provided that the flooding is not too rapid such an investigation will normally involve entering the compartment – taking all the proper precautions when entering an enclosed space (see Chapter 21) – and searching for the source of the leak. When the leak has been found, the problem can be assessed and the correct action chosen.

Interpretation of high soundings in a cargo space: When increased soundings are found in a cargo space loaded with bulk cargo there are a number of possible explanations and each should be considered. The water may have drained from the cargo or leaked through the hatch covers. It may have entered through an unbattened access hatch or an uncapped sounding pipe. Water may have leaked through a fracture in the deck or the hatch coaming or through a damaged ventilator.

It is regrettable that officers of many ships have no accurate idea of the capacity of the hold bilge wells. This means that they cannot say whether an increase in sounding of 0.5 metres represents 1 tonne of water, or 10 tonnes. That makes it more difficult to assess the significance of any increase in hold bilge sounding. The solution to this is simple. Measurements should be taken when the holds are empty to prepare simple calibrations. Of greatest value are the sounding of the bilge when full and the approximate tonnage of water contained by the bilge when full.

When preparing calibrations for the hold bilge wells two important points must be remembered. If the sounding pipe does not run vertically the actual full sounding will be greater than the vertical depth of the bilge well (Fig. 15.9): it is the actual full sounding which is required, since that is what the sounding rod measures. On some ships a number of the bilge wells may have exactly the same dimensions, but every one must be inspected in case the arrangements inside any are different. Details of design near the engine room or in a ballast hold, for example, sometimes require one or two bilge wells to be of a different shape and size to the others or to have the sounding pipe positioned differently and soundings will be very misleading unless this is known.

High soundings caused by drainage from cargo: Aboard a ship which is well operated and well maintained the most likely reason for an increased hold bilge sounding is that water has drained from the cargo into the bilge. If there has been a similar increase in most or all of the bilge soundings this suspicion will be a virtual certainty, particularly if the cargo is known to be self-draining. Water is reported to drain from most mineral and coal cargoes during the course of a long voyage with consequent weight losses of 1 per cent total weight of cargo or more. In a Cape-sized vessel carrying about 22,000 tonnes of iron ore per hold the water draining from the cargo in one

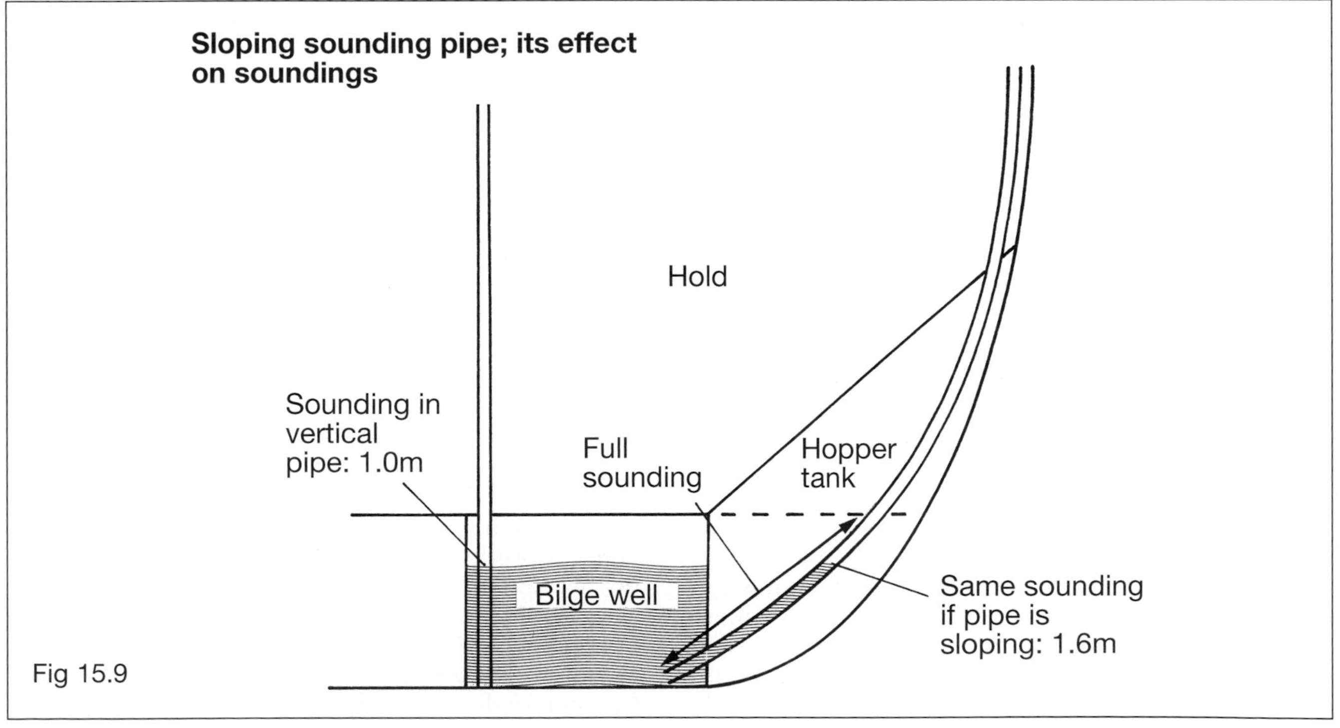

Fig 15.9

hold would average 5 tonnes/day during a 40-day voyage if the 1 per cent figure was found to apply. Water will also drain from a grain cargo which has been sprayed with a wet fumigant during loading.

When water does drain from the cargo there are two important requirements. The water must be pumped out of the bilge and not allowed to flood the hold, and the tonnage of water removed must be recorded. The reason for removing the water is to prevent damage to the cargo and increased corrosion of the tanktop and to reduce difficulties for the trimmers when discharging. It must also be remembered that once the water has filled the bilge well and flooded back over the tanktop, it is much more difficult to be sure how much water the hold contains. Flooding of the hold from a leak would then become more difficult to detect. For all these reasons the bilges must be pumped as frequently as is necessary to maintain them at a safe level – no more than half full.

It is advisable to keep a record of the tonnage of water discharged from the hold bilges, as recommended by the *UN Draught Survey Code*[24] and in some trades it is a charterparty requirement. This can be done by taking soundings before and after each pumping of the bilges if calibration tables for the bilge wells are available, or by pumping all the contents of the hold bilge wells into a holding tank where they can be sounded before being pumped overboard. Such a record, if kept in a seamanlike and professional manner and signed by Master or senior officer, will be evidence of the tonnage of water discharged and will explain apparent loss of cargo weight.

High soundings due to leakage into hold: When one or several soundings are found to be rising for no obvious reason a problem must be suspected and the hold must be investigated for a leak. Whether the hold can be entered will depend upon the amount of space occupied by the cargo and the safety of the operation from the point of view of speed of flooding, shifting cargo and hazardous gases. If the hold can be safely entered, taking all the precautions required for entry into a confined space, it may be possible to find an explanation for the flooding. Evidence of water flowing into the hold may be detectable in the cargo beneath hatch covers or ventilators or below a fracture in the steelwork of deck, coamings or ship's sides.

If the hold cannot be entered, a thorough external inspection should be made of the boundaries of the compartment in search for any fitting which is improperly closed or damaged. If the sounding is found to increase whenever the vessel ships water on deck, a leak at deck level should be suspected. If the flooding continues at the same rate, or an increasing rate, at all times it suggests that the damage is below water level. By using all the information available the most likely explanation for the flooding can be found and appropriate action can be taken. (See below and Chapter 21 for action to take in event of flooding.)

High level bilge alarms: When high-level bilge alarms are fitted and working as intended they provide a useful service to back up the daily soundings and to provide for occasions when adverse weather prevents the taking of soundings. High-level alarms will give prompt warning if hold flooding starts suddenly and proceeds rapidly. However, high-level alarms may not be fitted or may be out of order. Each high-level bilge alarm should contain a delay circuit which prevents the alarm from sounding continually when the water level is low but the ship is rolling heavily. If no delay circuit is fitted the alarm will sound continually during heavy weather and is likely to be switched off. If it is switched off for this reason the sounding must be regularly checked by other means.

Water ingress detector systems (WIDS) and alarms: Introduced in 2004 in accordance with IMO regulations[129] WIDS are now fitted in the holds of all bulk carriers and also in the ballast, dry and void spaces forward of their collision bulkheads. They are designed to give early warning of flooding and to provide an indication of the speed of flooding of a compartment. Flooding is one of the most serious hazards to which bulk carriers are exposed and there are situations in which a flooding bulk carrier can sink within minutes.

High soundings detected by hull stress monitors: It is claimed that hull stress monitors will detect flooding of a bulk carrier because flooding will cause a change in the ship's average level of longitudinal stresses. When an observer at sea notes that the vessel is becoming more heavily loaded there is only one likely explanation: flooding is occurring.

High soundings detected by draught gauges: In at least one instance hold flooding in a forward hold has been confirmed by a high reading on the forward draught gauge. Readings from draught gauges, list indicators and any other devices which indicate a change in the vessel's condition should be promptly and thoroughly investigated.

Action to take when flooding is detected

From the records of bulk carrier losses it can be seen that in many of the cases the ships' Masters appear to have been unaware of the imminent danger they were in. Ship losses were frequently so rapid that the ship did not have time to send a distress signal. Many mariners lost their lives as a consequence[124]. Actions to be taken when flooding is suspected are described in Chapter 21 but can be summarised here. All personnel except those investigating the alarm and keeping systems running should be mustered at abandon ship stations. An URGENCY or DISTRESS signal as appropriate should be transmitted. The decision to abandon ship must be the Master's and the vessel's lifesaving craft must not be launched unless the specific order to do so has been given by him. That order should be based on the knowledge that the vessel is truly sinking, that the depth of water beneath the ship is deeper than the vessel's hull and that the speed of sinking might prevent later launching.

Testing of bilge water for acidity

Cargoes such as high sulphur coals, iron ore, sulphur and salt produce corrosive liquids when wet and can do heavy damage to the fabric of the hold. When cargoes which may be corrosive are being carried the hold bilges should be tested regularly for pH (acidity). This procedure is described in the section of Chapter 19 devoted to the carriage of coal.

Cargo temperatures and sampling of air in holds

When carrying some cargoes such as coal and grain the temperature of the cargo should be obtained regularly to detect signs of heating. Temperatures are usually obtained from thermometers lowered into the sounding pipes on the port and starboard sides at the after end of each hold. An additional temperature pipe may be sited beside the hold ladder at the fore end of the hold. The most accurate and reliable readings will be obtained by making sure that the thermometers are lowered to a level which is well below the surface of the cargo and that they are left in position for several minutes. Where possible there should be a thermometer for each position and thermometers should be left in place permanently and withdrawn rapidly when readings are required.

Mercury thermometers are considered to be less satisfactory for taking cargo temperatures unless fitted with a maximum temperature indicator and reset before the taking of each reading, and one authority[23] recommends the use of suitably calibrated pyrometers.

When carrying coal it is necessary to test the air in the holds for hazardous gases. This process, like the taking of temperatures, is fully described in that part of Chapter 19 which describes the carriage of coal cargoes.

Fumigation to monitor

If the cargo was fumigated before departure from the loading port and if fumigation is continued in transit, regular checks should be made for leakage of the fumigant for so long as it remains active. (Fumigation is described in Chapter 21.) It is essential that ships make a declaration in their pre-arrival notice if the cargo has been fumigated[243] and where possible cargo holds should be ventilated before arrival to ensure that the required safe level of gas has been reached.

Cargo lashings to check

Bulk carriers are required from time to time to carry cargoes which are secured with lashings. Steel coils carried below decks and sawn timber and logs on deck are cases in point. When cargoes are lashed a regular routine of inspecting the lashings daily, or more frequently, is essential. The frequency of the inspections must be increased early in the voyage before the cargo has settled, in bad weather and at any time when each inspection finds noticeable looseness in the lashings.

Lashings can become loose for a variety of reasons. If the ship is pitching and rolling heavily lashings will be stretched as the cargo is accelerated first in one direction and then in another. Wet logs will shrink significantly as they dry out. The cargo will settle as the ship works. Movement and vibration can cause fastenings to slacken or disengage if they have not been locked.

Any slackness in the lashing system will allow cargo to move and once it can move it will further damage the lashings and readily break adrift. It is essential that lashing systems are inspected frequently and thoroughly and that lashings are efficiently retightened as they become slack. When it is necessary to inspect and tighten cargo lashings on deck or in the holds in bad weather, the ship must be hove-to and the inspection must be carried out with the precautions described below.

Inspections

Inspections in good weather: During a loaded voyage a bulk carrier has a low freeboard and is likely to ship spray and seas on deck and over the hatches even during moderately adverse weather. This calls for a high level of alertness from the Master and his officers to ensure that ship's company, ship and cargo are brought safely to their destination.

In good weather it is prudent for the chief mate to carry out an informal inspection of the decks at least once a day and to satisfy himself that all is secure on deck before the end of the working day. Storeroom doors, access hatches and manhole covers if left open during the night can lead to flooding, damage or even, in extreme cases, the loss of the ship if the weather worsens. If bad weather is anticipated lifelines should be rigged along the length of the deck, port and starboard, in good time[124].

Inspections during rough weather: During rough weather the blows which a ship receives from the sea when the bow strikes the swell and when waves are shipped over the decks and hatches can cause damage to her structure and can loosen fastenings and fittings or break them adrift. The ship's violent motion can cause cargo, stores and spares to shift or break adrift. Damage of this sort can be disastrous and every effort should be made to ensure that the ship is all secure. In recent years ship design and equipment has been developed to reduce the need for dangerous physical inspections of holds and forecastle spaces during rough weather. Inspections should never be undertaken recklessly but are a valuable complement to WIDS alarms, gauge readings or information gained from binoculars or closed circuit TV.

Because conditions on deck are likely to be hazardous during rough weather an inspection will require organisation and planning. Wherever possible it should be undertaken during daylight hours. A procedure which can be recommended is for the Master to take the bridge, sending the chief mate, bosun and several seamen to make the inspection. The inspection party dress in high visibility heavy weather clothing and equip themselves with VHF radios, and with hammers, crowbars and such other tools as they anticipate they will need to tighten dogs, cleats, brakes and lashings.

When ready to commence the inspection they report by VHF radio to the Master on the bridge, who is also equipped with a VHF radio. The Master then heaves-to the ship by reducing speed and/or altering the heading as required to provide a deck which is reasonably steady and shipping no water. It is worth waiting for five or ten minutes (or longer on a big ship) for the changes in speed and heading to take effect to ensure that the ship is well hove-to and the decks are safe for the inspection party. When satisfied the Master will inform the inspection party which is the lee side and will instruct them to proceed.

Walking the length of the foredeck on the lee side and also inspecting between the hatches, the inspection party will check that hatch cover cleating is all tight and access hatches properly battened down. Loose fittings will be refastened and damaged items inspected and the damage assessed. If the ship possesses masthouses they will be checked for leakage or for items broken adrift. Soundings located on the lee side of the foredeck can also be taken.

The forward spaces of a bulk carrier are particularly vulnerable to flooding. They will be inspected and the forecastle WIDS alarm and high level bilge alarm, if fitted, will be tested. The proper securing of the anchors will be confirmed, as will the sealing of the spurling pipes to prevent water from flooding the chain lockers. Forepeak and chain locker soundings will be taken.

When all is secure in and on the forecastle, the chief mate will report this to the Master who will decide whether it is safe for the inspection party to inspect the remaining side of the foredeck. Before this can be done safely it may be necessary to put the weather on the other bow and whilst this is done the inspection party will either remain within the shelter of the forecastle or will have returned aft to the accommodation. The inspection of the second side of the foredeck, when it can be undertaken with safety, will be similar to the inspection of the side first inspected.

Hold inspections in rough weather: In addition to the inspection of deck and storerooms described above it will be necessary to inspect the holds if a cargo such as steel products is being carried and may have broken adrift or if the possibility of flooding is feared. Where possible inspections in bad weather should be avoided because of the hazards created by a rolling ship and men who are encumbered with heavy clothing, but when an inspection is necessary the normal safety procedures for entering an enclosed space must be followed (Chapter 21). The inspection is likely to be a slow process, though time will be saved if the inspection party has a really powerful torch and much of the hold can be viewed from the access ladder. When an inspection is undertaken during bad weather and it is necessary to heave-to, these facts should be recorded in the deck log.

Conduct of loaded voyage in rough weather

The seakeeping qualities of bulk carriers: At the conclusion in 2000 of the Re-opened Formal Investigation (RFI) into the loss of the bulk carrier m.v. *Derbyshire* a report[94] containing a large number of recommendations was issued. These led to extensive research into the seakeeping qualities of bulk carriers. An important finding not previously widely known amongst seafarers was that Cape-sized bulk carriers had in 2001 the highest risk of experiencing hatch cover failure in forward hatches because their length causes them to plunge their fore parts into the ocean swells which smaller vessels would ride over. The strength of the No.1 hatch covers of Cape-sized vessels was recognised as being inadequate[95] and it remains true that those Cape-sized bulk carriers which were built to minimum strength requirements before 2004 have insufficient strength in the forward hatch covers to withstand the loads which could be experienced when meeting wave heights greater than 10 metres when loaded to their marks. The Masters of such vessels will be well advised to heave-to or to proceed at very slow speed in severe adverse weather. The trials established that a speed of 7.5 knots (presumably speed over the ground, not engine speed) was too great for handy-sized, Panamax and Cape-sized vessels in severe weather. Trimming the vessel two or three metres by the stern reduces the danger but is seldom an option for a laden Cape-sized vessel.

Research also found that the horizontal loads to which hatch covers and hatch coamings were exposed in extreme conditions were much greater than previously thought[138]. A programme to phase-in tougher requirements for the hatch cover securing arrangements of vessels in service was introduced by the classification societies[133] and has been made mandatory by the International Maritime Organization.

By 2005[134] new Cape-sized vessels being brought into service were provided with hatch covers having a load resistance increased by 40 per cent[131,132].

The research also revealed that some large modern bulk carriers were so low powered that they could make no headway in severe adverse weather[95]. Such vessels need plenty of searoom and must be a cause of anxiety to their Masters.

Condition of a loaded bulker: The condition of a loaded bulker depends to a large extent upon the cargo she is carrying, but one or two general remarks apply. In the loaded condition her propeller and forefoot will normally be well below the surface and her freeboard will be small. As a result she is particularly vulnerable to damage caused by green seas breaking on deck. She will probably be trimmed approximately even keel. If she is loaded with a high-density closeweight cargo such as ore, steel or concentrates she will be stiff. If carrying coal her stability will be comfortable – neither too stiff nor too tender. If loaded with grain she will be tender, and if carrying timber she will be tender and quite possibly not down to her marks.

Movement in a seaway: A ship's behaviour in a seaway depends on the size and shape of the ship and the type of wave system through which she is passing. The factors which affect the ship's behaviour are[27] the significant wave height, the mean wave period, the directional energy spread (which measures whether the waves are all going in the same direction or are fanning out) and the speed and direction of the wind and current. Other significant factors are the ship's size, her form, her condition of loading, and her speed and heading relative to the waves.

As is well known to most seamen, the only factors in the above list which the navigator can alter are the ship's speed and heading, though it may be possible to make some modest alterations to her condition of loading by adjustment to bunkers and possibly to ballast.

When rough weather is met the Master must consider its effect upon his ship and upon the cargo she carries. He must also consider the safety of her crew, particularly when they are required to go onto the open decks and into the holds to carry out inspections and to tighten cargo lashings.

Ship slowed by adverse weather: When a loaded bulk carrier meets a swell from a direction somewhere forward of the beam her speed will fall, even though her engine settings remain constant. The warning given by this forced reduction of speed must not be ignored. The size of the ship and the distance of the bridge from the bows may conceal the violence of the slamming which occurs when the bows meet the swell and may hide the strength of the water shipped over the forecastle, maindeck and hatches, but a bulk carrier can suffer serious damage when forced through adverse weather.

A guideline proposed by The Nautical Institute for this situation is that when adverse weather causes a speed reduction of 25 per cent (for example, from 12 knots to 9 knots) with constant engine settings, the revolutions per minute (RPM) should be substantially reduced to avoid damage from forcing the ship into the weather.

The damage which can be expected if this guideline is ignored includes the setting-in of shell plating around and beneath the bows and damage to anchors, fittings on the forecastle deck and main deck and to hatch covers. The loss of the m.v. *Derbyshire* has been attributed in part to the flooding of forward spaces as a consequence of heavy weather damage to airpipes and to the access hatch on the forecastle[94].

Ship moving violently: Violent movement can take the form of pitching when the swell is ahead, rolling when the swell is abeam and a combination of pitching and rolling (a corkscrew motion) when the swell is at an angle on the bow. When moving violently a bulk carrier's complex structure is comparatively sensitive to cracks developing[27]. Damage from sloshing is also a theoretical danger but is unlikely in practice on the loaded voyage when most, or all, ballast tanks are empty.

When a bulk carrier pitches, she is exposed to longitudinal stresses as successive swells pass beneath her, with the risk of fatigue cracks developing. When the vessel corkscrews, torsional (ie twisting) stresses are caused. Stress concentrations may occur around very large hatch openings. Violent rolling causes rapid pressure changes (panting) in the side shell plating which may weaken the side shell structure. Heavy rolling may also lead to cargo shifting or breaking adrift.

Any motion which occurs as a result of swell from abaft the beam will be much less violent than that caused by swell from forward of the beam, because swell from abaft the beam approaches a moving vessel at a slower speed.

A ship which is pitching, rolling or corkscrewing violently is liable to suffer structural damage. To avoid damage speed should be reduced and/or course should be altered until the ship's motion eases. This action will comply with The Nautical Institute's guideline (see above), since the ship's speed is certain to have been slowed by the motion.

Altering course or speed: When a ship's motion is violent or she is seriously slowed by adverse weather, the Master should choose to ease the motion by reducing speed or by altering course or by a combination of both. When the swell is coming from right ahead, a reduction in speed is likely to be more effective, since a large alteration of course would be needed to put the swell well on the bow and that would result in a lot of extra distance steamed. When the swell is already 20-30° on the bow a smaller course alteration may be sufficient and may be preferable to a reduction in speed.

Alterations of course and reductions of speed in response to bad weather will be the smallest necessary to make the ship's movements safe: they must be sufficient but they should not be excessive. The Master will continue to look for signs that the weather is improving, permitting him to return cautiously and gradually to the original course and to full speed.

Heaving-to: A ship is said to be hove-to when she has been reduced to a slow speed through the water and brought on to a heading on which she lies comfortably. If the wind and swell are coming from different directions a comfortable position for heaving-to is with the swell on one bow and the wind on the other[135]. When hove-to there is no attempt to proceed on the voyage and the ship remains almost stopped over the ground. When hove-to it is advisable to adopt hand steering unless the ship is provided with an 'adaptive' autopilot. A helmsman who is aware of the weather the ship is meeting and the effect which it has on the ship's heading can steer the ship at slow speed with fewer helm movements than an older autopilot would require, and can find the heading on which the ship settles most comfortably. An adaptive autopilot can analyse the ship's movements, however complex, and can steer the ship better and with less use of the helm than can most helmsmen. The Master and officer of the watch must remain on their guard for any change in the conditions which requires a matching change in heading or speed. By night the direction of a heavy swell can often be seen on the radar[136].

Bulk carrier Masters will heave their ships to when crew members are going on deck in bad weather or when exceptionally bad weather is met. The normal attitude for heaving-to is with the vessel's head 20-30° from the direction of the swell and with the engines running at slow ahead, with engine revolutions as for a speed of about 7 knots, which is sufficient to maintain steerage way. The wind normally comes from the same general direction as the swell and loaded bulk carriers, with their accommodation aft, have little difficulty in remaining on the chosen heading. When hove-to with the weather on one bow there is still the danger that green seas will slop aboard on the weather side and spray will continue to be shipped, but the water will arrive less violently than when the vessel is making way.

It sometimes happens in rough weather that the speed of a bulk carrier is so reduced by the adverse conditions that she makes no noticeable progress across the ocean for a period of hours or for several days. In those circumstances she is effectively hove-to, but without having made a deliberate decision to heave-to.

Running before the swell: If the swell is on the quarter during bad weather the ship's motion will usually be much less violent, although it is necessary to beware of a high fast-moving swell which can catch the vessel's stern and push her off course, where she will roll heavily. A wind on the quarter, acting on the after superstructure, will reinforce this tendency. This can be avoided by reducing speed to well below that of the swell, 30-50 per cent of the speed of the swell being advocated by different authorities. In these conditions a ship may pitch slowly and heavily and a high oil level should be maintained in the main

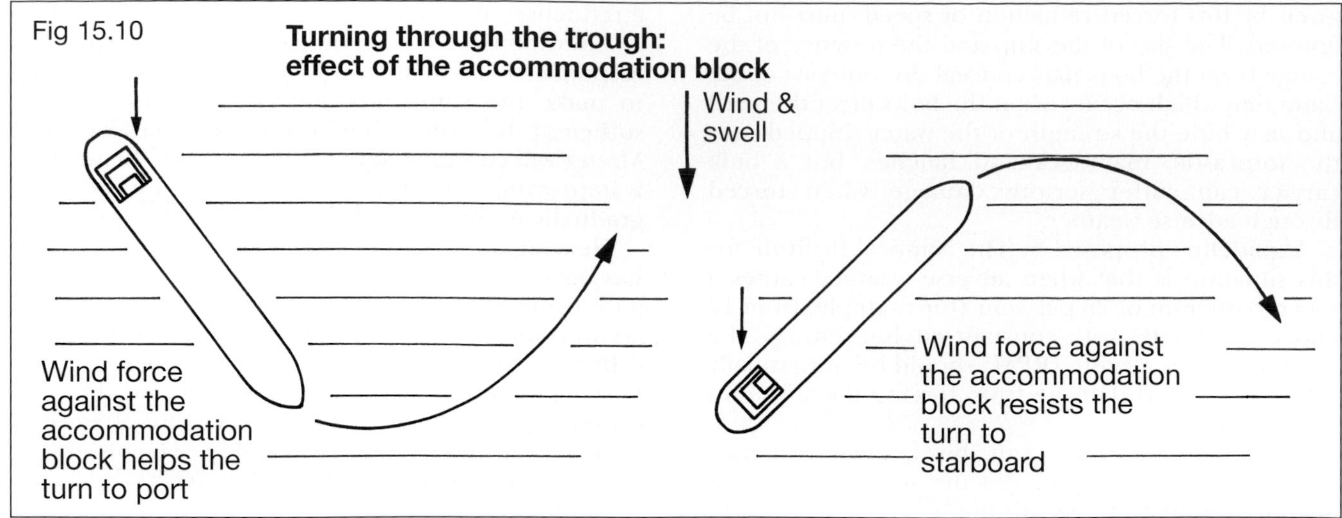

engine sump to ensure that the circulating pump does not draw air[137]. The only other circumstance in which it is necessary to heave-to with the weather on the quarter is if crew members are required to go on deck or into the holds.

When the ship is running with the weather, water is likely to slop onto the main deck on the weather side. Before men go on deck it is advisable to reduce speed, put the weather 20-30° on the quarter, and to ensure that the men remain on the lee side of the deck to avoid water which may be shipped on the weather side. In this attitude the vessel can be regarded as being hove-to with the weather on the quarter.

When rough weather is coming from a position abaft the beam, special care must be taken to secure doors, skylights and hatches facing aft. These are often left open during the day for ventilation purposes and must be secured each and every night as with the weather astern green seas can unexpectedly be shipped, resulting in flooding of machinery spaces, storerooms and accommodation.

Turning through the trough: When a ship is manoeuvring in a heavy swell the most alarming and hazardous manoeuvre is turning from a heading with the weather on the bow to one with the weather on the quarter or vice versa. When lying in the trough of a heavy swell the vessel is liable to roll very heavily. Although this puts no great stress upon the ship's structure in the short term it can cause cargo to shift and create havoc in accommodation and storerooms. For these reasons the manoeuvre should be avoided whenever possible.

Where it is essential to turn the vessel through the trough the Master should first inform the ship's company (particularly the engineroom and galley) of the intended manoeuvre, and the likelihood of heavy rolling. When turning to bring the weather on to the bow the accommodation block, acting as a sail, will assist the turn. A turn to put the weather on the quarter will be more difficult, as it will be necessary to force the stern with the accommodation block into the weather. (Fig. 15.10)

The Master should study the wave patterns for some time in the hope of identifying a period of lower swell. The turn should be commenced at the lowest speed which gives steerage way. The ship should be turned with the helm hard over, and with the use of short bursts of full speed ahead on the engines. This will cause the ship to turn quickly without gathering speed. If the ship does fail to swing through the trough and remains lying beam on to the swell she will stop pitching, which should allow her speed to increase enabling her to complete the turn. Ships with lower power or smaller rudders may require to use continuous full engine power when turning with stern into the wind.

Loss of power:[135] A disabled handy-sized vessel, rolling heavily in the trough in rough seas was brought to a more comfortable condition by lowering six nylon mooring lines over the bows to act as a sea anchor. The drifting rate and heavy rolling were quite effectively minimised, as the bow closed from 80 down to 50° to the wind.

Synchronous rolling:[135] This results from a succession of waves meeting the vessel's side with the same frequency as the rolling period. It can be anticipated by the Master or duty officer who is alerted by a succession of increasing rolling amplitudes. Prompt use of a large rudder angle to alter the vessel's heading is the most effective means of breaking such synchronism following which it may be necessary to choose a different course to avoid further synchronous rolling.

Reporting

During a loaded voyage the Master will be required by owners and/or charterers to submit routine position reports and ETA messages at specified intervals. Fuel consumed, weather experienced, speed made good and engine revolutions and slip may also be required. He may also be instructed to provide reports of cargo temperatures, tonnages of hold bilge water pumped out and of bilge pH values and hold gas readings when sensitive cargoes such as coal are carried, even if the report is no more than 'all normal'. From 1st July 2006 all ships above 500 gt undertaking voyages exceeding 48 hours are required to report their positions daily[139].

It is desirable that ships should also participate in voluntary reporting schemes, such as the worldwide AMVER scheme, and other regional schemes.

Arriving at the discharging port

When arriving at the discharging port the hatches should remain securely battened down until the ship is secured in the berth and the necessary procedures have been completed although, exceptionally, there are circumstances in which hatches can be uncleated or even opened before berthing. (See Chapter 16, 'Arrival in the berth'). Where possible ship's officers should inspect the cargo before berthing for any signs of problems such as wetting from sweat or leakage or deterioration of grain. Such problems should be discovered as soon as possible, so that expert advice can be obtained.

Sources

5, 19, 24, 23, 27, 36, 94, 95, 113, 124, 129, 130, 131, 132, 133, 134, 135, 136, 137, 138 139, 172, 243, 260. (See List of Sources, Page 497)

CHECKLIST – Routine procedures for the loaded voyage

- ☐ Have hatches and mooring lines all secured well before the open sea is reached. Secure anchors when no longer required.
- ☐ Choose and follow the most suitable route for the voyage, taking account of the factors mentioned in the chapter.
- ☐ Determine whether the cargo requires ventilation.
- ☐ Follow any special instructions for ventilation.
- ☐ Take dewpoint readings and ventilate when dewpoint in hold is higher than dewpoint outside.
- ☐ Stop ventilation when shipping spray over vents.
- ☐ Log dewpoint readings and times of stopping and starting ventilation, with reasons.
- ☐ Take a full set of soundings every day and study them for any unexplained increase or reduction in sounding.
- ☐ Investigate promptly any unexplained changes in soundings.
- ☐ When water drains from cargo the bilges should be pumped before they fill, and a record should be kept of the tonnage of water removed.
- ☐ Test hold bilges regularly for acidity (pH) and pump them dry if they are found to be acid.
- ☐ Take cargo temperatures and test air in holds daily when required for the cargo being carried.
- ☐ Check and tighten cargo lashings daily or more often.
- ☐ Inspect the decks daily and ensure that storerooms, hatch accesses, hatch covers and manhole covers are secure at the end of the day and before the onset of bad weather.
- ☐ In bad weather inspect the decks daily, taking all necessary precautions to ensure the inspection is safe and thorough.
- ☐ Rig lifelines on both sides of the main deck when bad weather is expected.
- ☐ When the ship is slowed by bad weather, reduce the engine speed or alter course.
- ☐ Follow safe procedures for heaving-to with the weather on the bow or on the quarter and for turning through the trough.
- ☐ Make routine position reports daily and ETA reports as required.
- ☐ Report cargo temperatures, bilge pH readings and gas readings if required.
- ☐ Submit ballast report – NIL when no ballast aboard
- ☐ Clear anchors, prepare mooring lines and prepare the ship as advised in Chapter 6.
- ☐ Inspect cargo for problems immediately upon arrival.
- ☐ Prepare hatches for discharge immediately upon arrival.

Fig. 15.11 Geared bulk carrier with lumber on deck in heavy weather

Fig. 15.12 A handy-sized bulk carrier meeting a heavy swell

CHAPTER 16

THE DISCHARGING PERIOD

Shipboard organisation during discharge, routine procedures, on first arrival, liaison with the terminal representative, the discharging/ballasting programme, ballasting, discharge by continuous unloading, grab, Cavaletto, vacuvator or ship's gear, care for cargo, the finding, recording and repair of stevedores' damage, crew work

Shipboard organisation during discharge

THE DELIVERY of cargo to the receiver in the discharge port and the importance of the bill of lading is fully discussed in Chapter 14.

The tempo of cargo discharge is normally less hectic than that of the loading. The likelihood that a misjudgement or a brief period of inattention will result in the ship being wrongly loaded is absent: the requirement for a satisfactory discharge can be met by alertness and careful attention to the ship and the cargo at every stage of the discharge.

The supervision of discharge will require a junior officer (second or third mate) on duty at all times as officer of the watch (OOW), with the chief mate monitoring events and intervening whenever necessary to ensure that the discharging programme is observed, standards are maintained and the work is progressed. The Master will be actively involved with the discharge if his officers are inexperienced, or if problems arise. Otherwise he will be able to give his attention to other matters.

Routine duties for the officer of the watch

Described below are a number of particular duties for the officer of the watch (OOW) whilst the vessel is discharging. In addition, the OOW must ensure that the moorings and gangway are tended and the *International Ship and Port Facility Security (ISPS) Code* is observed with a written record kept of all visitors to the ship. Pollution must be avoided, the weather observed and recorded, security for ship and cargo preserved and full records, including those for cargo and ballast, maintained. These requirements are described in Chapter 12, for the loading period. In these respects the discharging period is no different.

Fig.16.1 Using an air hose to clean the hatch coaming

The OOW must also ensure that hatches are always secured to prevent them from moving, whether open or closed. Hatches must only be moved after the coamings have been completely swept clear of cargo residues (Fig. 16.1) and a visual inspection has been made to check that there are no obstructions on the trackway. They must not be moved when any quantity of spilt cargo is lying on them. (The routine closing of hatches is described in Chapter 4. Safe procedures for working cargo are summarised in Chapter 12 and discussed in Chapter 21.)

On first arrival at the berth

When planning the arrival at a discharging berth it is useful to know if a draught survey or cargo survey is to be held, and if discharge is to commence on arrival. When the ship is all fast alongside and a safe access has been provided the immediate priorities are to obtain a full set of draught readings for the ship's own draught survey and at the same time or immediately afterwards to agree the discharging/ballasting programme and the ship/shore safety checklist with the terminal representative as required by the *BLU Code*[110]. The requirements of the receiving country must be satisfied when in-transit fumigation of cargo has taken place. When these matters and any surveys have been completed discharge can commence. Hatches should not be opened until the vessel is in the berth and the above procedures have been completed.

There can be a case for amending the above sequence of tasks and opening some of the hatches in the sheltered approaches to the berth when the weather is favourable, the discharging programme and the ship/shore safety checklist have been fully agreed in advance between ship and terminal, when tonnage is to be decided by shore scales, when no cargo or hatch surveys are scheduled and when no in-transit fumigation has taken place. Occasions when all these requirement will be met are likely to be rare.

Some charterparties and charterers may instruct that all hatches are to be opened before berthing, and these instructions should be followed only provided that it is safe to do so and will not result in damage to the cargo or the ship's equipment, or to neglect of the other requirements mentioned above. When the hatches have been sealed, the weather is adverse or the cargo is sensitive it is prudent to keep all hatches closed until the vessel is berthed and clear information has been obtained from the receivers.

If water is lying on the hatch covers and could spill from them and damage the cargo, it is essential that free water is swept from the covers before they are opened. Rubber squeegees are very effective for this process.

The chief mate should always calculate the deadweight from the draughts on arrival to confirm the quantity to be discharged for the ship's records, regardless of whether or not an independent surveyor is appointed. If there is no formal draught survey he will rely upon his experience and knowledge of the ship to obtain accurate readings of ballast water strippings and bunkers at the first convenient opportunity, not necessarily exactly at the time of berthing.

The Master and his officers should always give high priority to an inspection of the cargo on arrival for any signs of damage from leakage, condensation, shifting, infestation or other cause. Where possible such inspection should be made at the anchorage or during the river transit. Ship's officers should make it a point of professional pride to find any damage before it is discovered by other parties. Minor damage such as slight leakage through the hatch covers should be fully recorded and noted for prompt repair. More substantial damage which seems likely to result in a cargo claim should be immediately reported to the vessel's owner with a view to arranging for the attendance of a P&I club surveyor, who will advise on the best way to minimise the claim.

Liaison with terminal representative

Good communication must be maintained between the terminal representative and the chief mate and officer of the watch. Matters for discussion will be the discharging/ballasting programme, airdraught, new stevedores' damage, stevedores' damage from previous ports if temporary patches have been fitted, as these may impede the work of the front end loader (Fig.16.2), trimming, care of ship's cargo gear if used, and possible causes of interruption of cargo work. Also of interest will be the stevedores' working hours, any specialised equipment or procedures to be used, and the estimated time of completion. The Ship/Shore Safety Checklist specified in the *BLU Code*[110] should be used for the exchange of basic safety information.

If the ship is required to shift along the berth, discharge must stop and cargo gear must be lifted clear of the ship before the move takes place.

Fig. 16.2 A front end loader moving silicon dross into the centre of the hold for discharge by grab

The foreman should be warned if cargo has been spilt on deck, so that trimmers can collect and discharge it. The chief mate should always insist on major spills being cleaned by trimmers to provide a safe access, as coating of some cargoes on a deck wet from rain or dew can make it like an ice rink! In some ports the trimmers will refuse to remove cargo spilt on deck, leaving such residues for the crew to clean at sea, but the attempt should be made to demand that they remove the spillage. A note of protest should be issued for excessive piles of cargo left on the main deck.

The *BLU Code*[148] stipulates that on completion of discharge the Master and the terminal representative should agree in writing that the ship has been unloaded in accordance with the agreed unloading plan, with the holds emptied and cleaned to the Master's requirements. They should should also record any detected damage suffered by the ship.

Discharging/ballasting programme

The discharge and ballasting should be planned to ensure that longitudinal and local stress limits will not be exceeded at any stage, there is always sufficient underkeel clearance and airdraught, and the vessel may leave the berth at any time. The preparation of the discharging/ballasting programme in compliance with the *BLU Code*, following the same procedures as are described in Chapter 9 for the loading/deballasting programme, is normally the work of the chief mate. If the information which the terminal has provided is sufficient the discharging plan should be finalised and transmitted to the terminal before the vessel's arrival. Using the IMO form[110] (Appendix 9.3) or something similar the chief mate will, on arrival at the terminal, deliver copies of the completed programme to the stevedore foreman, and to the officer of the watch, and ensure that it is understood.

When discharging a full cargo of a single commodity at a single berth, the planning normally presents no problems and can be done before berthing, provided that the method of discharge is known in advance. If the cargo consists of several grades or consignments, or if the number of discharging grabs or type of discharging equipment cannot be forecast, it may be impossible to determine which grade or grades will be discharged first. In those circumstances the planning of the discharging and the ballasting must wait until arrival and must then be planned in conjunction with the stevedores. Simple rules of thumb (eg, do not discharge any hold fully until all holds are half empty) are not sufficient to ensure that stresses are never exceeded. Every stage in the discharging programme must be calculated and the stevedores must be provided with a full discharging/ballasting programme to be signed for on the document and on the Ship/Shore safety checklist[110].

Preplanning is only possible when the exact nature of the equipment to be used for discharge and the receivers' requirements regarding sequence of delivery of different marks are known in advance. Preplanning is necessary if a prompt start to discharging is required when the vessel berths because it is a SOLAS requirement[139, 140] that a plan is agreed before unloading commences. A sample discharging/ballasting programme for a Cape-sized bulker is at Appendix 9.3.

If the early completion of the discharge of a particular hold is required for the purposes of survey, repair, cleaning, ballasting or other reason, this requirement should be included in the discharging/ballasting programme and explained to the stevedores.

It may be difficult to ensure that the discharging/ballasting programme is complied with. The stevedores, presented with open holds, may ignore the programme they have been given and move from one hold to another to suit their own convenience. Even if they follow the programme in principle they may be unable or unwilling to keep strictly to the tonnages stated. At a berth where three or four cranes and grabs are used a draught survey made by the ship's officers can provide the total tonnage remaining aboard, but the tonnage in a particular hold can only be estimated.

To assist compliance the discharging programme should be a simple one, relying upon simple proportions which are easy to judge approximately. For example, if each hold was previously filled in two pours then each hold should be 50 per cent discharged and then fully discharged. Where three pours were required for loading the hold should be discharged one third at a time. This allows officers to estimate more easily whether or not the programme is being followed by the stevedores. Towards the end of discharge, as the tonnages remaining become small, the possibility of exceeding stress limits becomes unlikely and strict compliance with the discharging programme is less important.

If three or four cranes are used for discharge it is unusual for longitudinal stresses to cause any problems, because the cargo can be discharged fairly evenly. Stress problems are more likely if there are only one or two discharging cranes.

Because discharge is slower than loading, the chief mate has more time to revise the plan if that becomes necessary because of a change in the number of cranes available. Ballasting, too, presents fewer problems than deballasting and can be reorganised more easily.

A safe discharging/ballasting programme with low levels of longitudinal stress is only difficult to achieve if the discharge is very rapid and uses only one or two unloading devices.

Ballasting

Ballast tanks may be punctured by cargo gear during discharge, and the hopper sides should be inspected where possible before the tanks are ballasted to note damage and avoid pumping ballast water through a punctured tank wall into the cargo. In addition, aboard ships such as the *Regina Oldendorff* where the topside ballast tanks can be used for cargo, the tanks should be checked to ensure that the covers for the feeder ports or dumping manholes are securely closed. If they are not properly closed they will release ballast water into the cargo hold.

Subject to draught restrictions and any other special requirements the ballasting should be planned to start when the discharge is about 25 per cent completed and should be complete well before completion of discharge. The ship's draught should be kept as deep as possible, thereby keeping the airdraught low and minimising the stresses on the double bottom, cross deck and transverse bulkhead structures[145]. A large airdraught slows the discharging rate, and may make it impossible to lift the front end loaders suspended below the grab (Fig. 16.3) into and out of the holds.

Some large bulk carriers have holds which can be partly ballasted in port to reduce the airdraught (Fig. 12.1). These are not true ballast holds and cannot contain ballast water at sea. They do not have the strength to be fully ballasted, nor the hatch cover fastenings to resist the sloshing of water in the hold.

The vessel should be kept upright throughout discharge and ballasting. It becomes difficult or impossible to open and close hatches and to use shipboard cranes against a heavy list or trim.

Water ballast should always be carried symmetrically in port and starboard tanks, with equal levels of filling to avoid torsional loads causing twisting of the hull girder[146]. The ballasting should be carefully supervised to ensure that ballast is not allowed to overflow on deck or overside. (Ballasting is fully discussed in Chapter 7.)

The discharge

Continuous unloading: Discharge by continuous unloading methods such as pneumatic hoses, Archimedes' screw or bucketwheel unloader calls for little comment. By a variety of methods these systems extract a steady flow of cargo from the hold through an enclosed system to the shore. Normally the only source of problems is accidental contact between the unloading equipment and the ship's structure. To prevent damage from contact, the equipment must be operated with care and the ship must not be allowed to surge in the berth. Some continuous unloaders have the operator's cab close to the business end of the system in the ship's hold (Fig. 16.4), and this is to be welcomed as it reduces the likelihood of damage to ship or equipment as a result of accidental contact between them.

Grab discharge: Discharge by grab is by far the most common method of discharging bulk cargoes because of the flexibility of the system, despite the number of theoretical disadvantages from which grabs suffer. In the early stages of the discharge of a cargo such as coal which fills the hold, plenty of cargo is available to the grab in the hatch square, and work can proceed at maximum rate whilst the first 20 per cent of the cargo is discharged. This 'creaming' or 'cream digging' is followed by 'free digging' until 50 per cent of the cargo has been discharged. During free digging the cargo is still accessible but is deeper in the hold, so the discharging rate falls as it continues to do during each stage thereafter.

The cream digging and free digging stages will be reduced if the crane does not have sufficient outreach to plumb the outboard side of the hold. When that occurs, there are three methods[15] which the crane driver can use to reach the cargo on the outboard side. He can swing the grab like a pendulum before lowering it at the limit of its swing, he can slide the grab down the sloping side of the stow, if it has not been trimmed level, or he can use a process known as

Fig.16.3 Lifting a front end loader from the hold

Fig.16.4 A continuous bucket unloader with operator cab just above the buckets

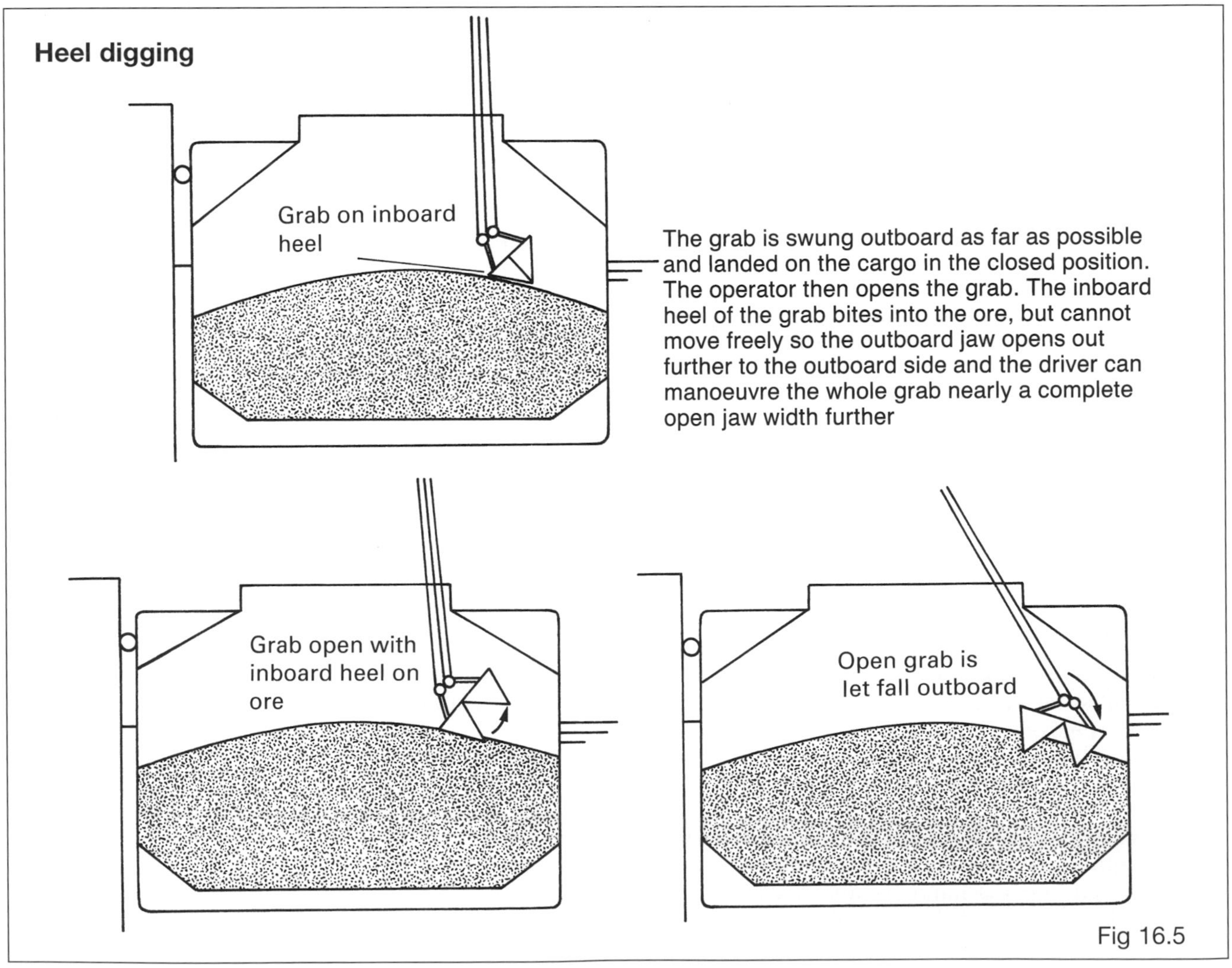

Heel digging

Grab on inboard heel

The grab is swung outboard as far as possible and landed on the cargo in the closed position. The operator then opens the grab. The inboard heel of the grab bites into the ore, but cannot move freely so the outboard jaw opens out further to the outboard side and the driver can manoeuvre the whole grab nearly a complete open jaw width further

Grab open with inboard heel on ore

Open grab is let fall outboard

Fig 16.5

heel digging, illustrated in Fig. 16.5. Stevedores prefer the pendulum method because it is quickest, but when grabbing close to the hopper tanks and tanktop they should use the heel digging method, which is less violent and more easy to control, to avoid damage.

The next stage, 'intermediate digging', requires more care as the cargo is lying closer to the ship's structure and is less accessible. The final stage of discharge is the trimming, a process which must be commenced when the hold is about 85 per cent empty, by volume. During trimming, cargo is brought from the sides and ends of the holds by front end loaders and piled in the square for removal by grab, with the final cleaning and loading of the grab being done by trimmers – men working with shovels and brushes. In some berths the front end loaders may be lifted into the holds and used at an earlier stage to push more cargo into the path of the grab and speed the discharge.

Some cargoes harden during the voyage and stick to the bulkheads and frames in large masses forming overhanging cargo faces[35] which can be dangerous for trimmers in the later stages of discharge. When large quantities of cargo are seen to be clinging to the bulkheads during discharge trimmers should be employed to free the cargo from the bulkheads at an early stage, while the distance for the cargo to fall is small. The OOWs should be instructed to look out for cargo clinging to the bulkheads and to bring it to the attention of the foreman. Stevedores should never be allowed to land grabs or front end loaders on deck or on the hatch covers as they may damage the ship's structure.

Discharge by Cavalletto: The Cavalletto system met in some Italian ports, uses a substantial portable gantry which is lifted aboard ship (Fig. 16.6). First, the hatch coamings are specially strengthened to receive a pair of fore-and-aft beams which are placed on

Fig.16.6 Portable Cavaletto bulk discharge system in use aboard the Panamax Bulker *Asteriks* at Trieste

The system is supported on heavy beams which rest on the hatch coaming

Photograph: Courtesy Captain Pradeep Chawla, MNI

Cargo is raised from the hold by grabs and reaches the barge via the hopper and conveyor system

Photograph: Courtesy Captain Pradeep Chawla, MNI

them. A mobile gantry which houses grab, hopper and chute is then lifted on to the beams by a large shore or floating crane. Cargo is lifted from the hold by grab which is opened over the hopper, tipping cargo into the chute which carries it over the ship's side into barges or coasters lying alongside. The ship may be required to provide electric power for one or more such units.

The process of rigging or shifting the Cavalletto takes six-eight hours and is very labour intensive, so the number of moves from hold to hold should be kept to a minimum.

Discharge by vacuvator: Vacuvators (Photo 11.19) are self-contained mobile suction units powered by diesel motors and usually weighing 3-5 tonnes. Their use is most common in berths where bulk cargoes are not regularly handled and in underdeveloped regions. When lifted on to the deck of a ship they can be used to discharge grain and similar cargoes into barges while at anchor or alongside or into road or rail wagons on the quay. When placed on deck they should be lashed or otherwise secured in position to prevent them from taking charge and rolling across the deck if the list changes or the ship surges at her moorings. Oil leakage from the vacuvator's motor may occur and must be prevented or contained.

Discharge by ship's gear: When ship's cranes or derricks are used for discharge they are normally operated by shore drivers whose level of competence and goodwill is unknown. Their work must be carefully supervised by ship's officers to ensure that they work safely and do not misuse the ship's gear. Continuous cargo work makes a heavy load for the ship's gear and it should be frequently and thoroughly inspected and tested to ensure that all is in order, following the procedures described in Chapters 6 and 23, to ensure that the gear remains operational.

Care for the cargo

During discharge the ships' officers must be alert to ensure that the cargo is not damaged. In the event of damage or dangerous behaviour occurring photographs, particularly digital photographs which are easy to email to interested parties, should be taken. Hatches must be covered promptly for rain or snow if the cargo must not be wetted, and breakbulk and unitised cargoes such as steel, timber and woodpulp must be correctly handled and slung. If there is excessive leakage of cargo from grabs on to the deck or the quay or into the dock, protests must be made by word and supported in writing. High winds may prevent the discharge of some cargoes because of high windblown losses, or because of unwelcome distribution of the cargo over nearby communities.

The OOW should look out for damage to the cargo from oil or hydraulic leaks from shore, or ship's, gear.

Where different parcels of cargo are carried in a single hold, officers must ensure that the stevedores find and observe the separations, whether they be in the form of coloured ropes separating cargoes of logs, thin steel sheeting used to cocoon parcels of minerals from South Africa, or polythene sheeting or netting used between consignments of bagged cargoes. The completion of one parcel, removal of the separation and commencement of the next parcel should be observed by the duty officer to ensure that no mistakes are made and to make a record of the details. Separation material can often be saved to be reused or returned to the supplier.

When two parcels of identical bulk cargo are carried in the same hold, without separation, every care must be taken to ensure by draught survey or other reliable method of measuring the tonnage discharged, that the correct tonnage is delivered to both receivers (see Chapter 14).

Once the cargo has crossed the ship's rail it is more difficult for ship's personnel to prevent it from being damaged, but it is necessary to observe what happens to the cargo ashore. If quantities are spilt, if it is contaminated by loading into dirty trucks or waterlogged lighters, or by placing on contaminated or muddy quays, if different grades are mixed or if cargo which is sensitive to moisture is left in the open, this is cause for concern because an attempt may be made, at a later date, to blame the ship for this damage. The shipowners and/or their P&I club should be informed immediately, so that a surveyor can attend to observe events, and the details should be recorded by the taking of photographs and by an entry in the ship's log book. In addition, a written protest should be issued to stevedores, agents or receivers.

Cargo shortages which occur during or after discharge can also lead to serious problems for the ship and officers should be on their guard for any irregular practices. Losses by leakage from grabs or by spillage from overloaded trucks often occur and weighbridge measurement can be unreliable[143]. In an extreme case a weighbridge was seen to be used to weigh the front end of trailer without uncoupling it, after which it was rolled forward to weigh the rear axle![142]

Care for the ship

Stevedores' damage: A variety of methods for discharging ships are available. Most of them such as suction hoses, Archimedes' screws, or self-unloading by means of gravity feed to shipboard conveyor belt are used for special cargoes or ships and are unlikely to damage the ship. However, by far the most common means of discharging bulk cargoes is by means of grabs rigged on gantry cranes (Fig.11.9), luffing cranes (Fig. 16.7), or ships' cranes or derricks. Grabs are very strongly made from toughened materials and when carelessly used can cause considerable damage to a ship's structure (Fig. 16.8). Crane drivers who are careless or incompetent are also likely to cause damage, and officers must insist that they work more slowly and safely or are replaced by more skilful colleagues.

Damage prevention: The best way to deal with stevedore damage is to prevent it. A procedure which has helped one shipping company is to paintmark the holds prominently with the positions of all the fittings which may be damaged[244]. From the diagram (Fig. 16.9) it can be seen that the inside of the hatch coaming is marked with heavy yellow stripes in way of the forward and after hold ladders. The ladders themselves are prominently painted with yellow paint. The lower stools are marked with yellow symbols close to the bilge wells and the lower hopper plates are similarly marked near the double bottom manhole

Fig.16.7 Level luffing crane being used to discharge into a hopper

Photo courtesy of Walter Vervloesem

Fig.16.8 Grabs with rounded corners like this Valstar grab do significantly less damage to the ship's structure

Photo courtesy of Captain Richard Evans

covers. A thick, white horizontal line runs right around the hold 2.4 m height above the tanktop. These markings, when brought to the attention of the stevedores, have helped to reduce the damage done by discharging grabs and front end loaders working in the holds.

When hold marking of this sort is reinforced by officers who keep a careful watch over the cargo work and protest in the strongest terms when the stevedores appear likely to cause damage that damage can be minimised. Officers who are out on deck keeping a watchful eye on the work are also best placed to notice damage as soon as it occurs or to be told about it by passing crew members or stevedores.

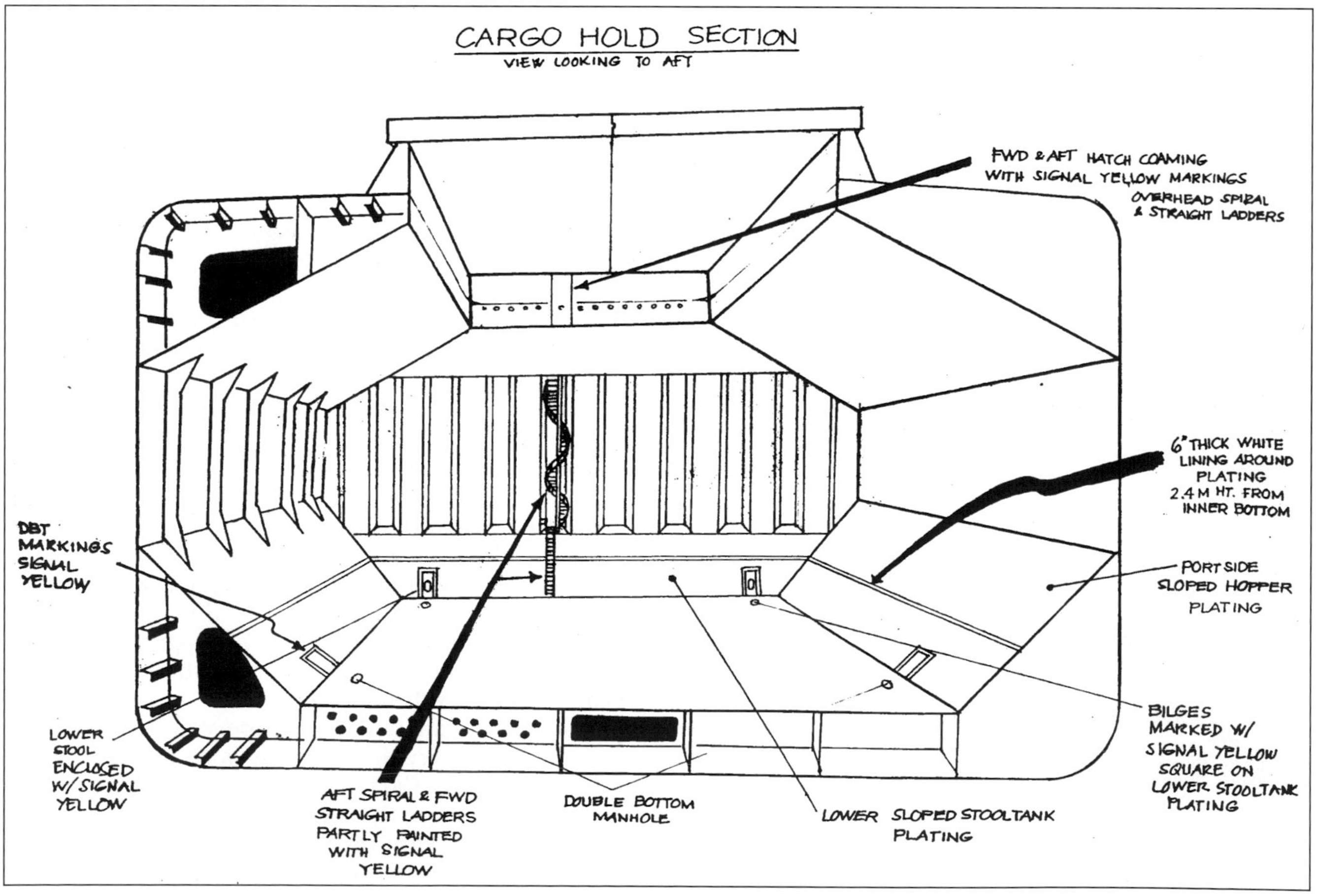

Damage by trimming: Residues from some cargoes cling to the sides and end bulkheads and frames of holds and are difficult to dislodge, and a number of techniques have been developed for removing them. A widespread practice has been for grabs or bulldozers to be used to strike the bulkheads and ships' side frames to dislodge cargo, and pneumatic hammers have been used to vibrate the structure for the same purpose. It has been recognised for some years that these practices are likely to cause fatigue and fractures in the steelwork or the welding of the ship's structure, even when operators are skilful. 'Careful' use of these techniques, if agreed in advance, is condoned by the Ship/Shore Safety Checklist. In practice it is rarely possible to avoid damage and Masters should intervene if necessary to prevent it.

Unfortunately the situation is not straightforward. Although it is known that striking the steelwork causes long-term damage, shipowners are reluctant to forbid the procedure entirely, as they fear that this will make their ships slow and difficult to discharge and therefore unpopular with shippers.

Without clear and definite orders Masters hesitate to forbid hammering, unless damage can be seen, because they fear that unmanageable quantities of residues will be left in the holds for them to remove after the ship has sailed. One Master with experience of this problem advises that the trimmers should be brought into the hold at an early stage to remove cargo from the bulkheads whilst standing on the cargo. If the procedure agreed and signed for (Ship/Shore Safety Checklist, Question 19) is not adhered to the Master should protest in the strongest terms and issue a letter of protest. There is nothing in any charterparty that authorises anyone to damage a vessel.

In recent years systems such as the Caterpillar Hoeram[147] have been used in the USA to vibrate the ship's steelwork less violently. The Caterpillar Hoeram is fitted on the boom of a mobile unit (Fig. 16.10) for cleaning after a cement cargo. It uses a heavy rubber pad.

Finding stevedore damage: Stevedores' damage is sometimes very obvious as when, for example, the corner of a grab punches a hole in a topside tank and ballast water gushes into the hold, or a swinging grab swipes a derrick crutch and bends it through 90°. At other times it is much less obvious, as when the hatch coaming receives a heavy knock and is deflected 50 mm or so out of true or when the damage is concealed by cargo residues. The first rule for detecting stevedores' damage is for the duty officer to remain on deck for as much of the time as possible, to observe the discharging process and to see the way in which the grab is being used. Damage is found when officers or crew members see it occur or when they are drawn to a problem by a clatter of noise or a babble of shouting. Every loud bang must be investigated. Crew members and dock labourers, if consulted, can often draw attention to damage that might otherwise be overlooked and it is worth emphasising this to the crew, who may not previously have been encouraged to help in this way. If the duty officer misses those signs then regular tours of the decks and holds, looking carefully for anything wrong, can help. Loose chips of paint, blobs of grease, traces of cargo in unusual places can all point to damaged structures.

Fig.16.10 Caterpillar Hoeram fitted with a heavy rubber pad to shake down cement dust by vibration
Photo courtesy of Mathieu Baehni MNI

When the main grab discharge is ended front end loaders are usually lowered into the hold to gather cargo from the ends and wings and pile it in the hatch square for discharge by grab. Trimmers – men employed to shovel up the last of the cargo from the positions which the front end loader cannot reach – will also enter the hold at the end of the main grab discharge, to assist in the discharge of the final remaining cargo. Standards of trimming vary considerably and the ship's officers should inspect the holds whilst the trimmers are working there, to encourage them to remove as much cargo as possible. This is unnecessary only if the next cargo is to be the same again, and the ship has received clear written instructions that the holds do not have to be cleaned.

A thorough inspection of each hold should be made as the trimmers are finishing their work, a few minutes before discharge of that hold is completed. That will be the final good opportunity to hold stevedores liable for damage done. The final inspection for stevedores' damage in the hold should ensure that no bilge gratings or manhole cover plates are missing, that the securing bolts have not been damaged, that all sounding pipes, airpipes and ballast lines and their pipeguards are intact, that no new indents can be seen in the plating of the tanktop, lower or upper hopper sides or athwartships bulkheads, that the ship's side frames are regular and undamaged, with brackets undamaged, and that the hold ladders, platforms, rails and other fittings are complete and undamaged.

Classes of stevedore damage: It can be said that there are three classes of stevedore damage. At one end of the scale is serious structural damage which may affect the integrity of the hull structure and the seaworthiness of the ship. This includes all damage to tanktop plating, hopper sides, shell plating and framing, hatch coamings, hatch covers, bulkheads, stools and upper deck plating, air and sounding pipes; in other words all damage that affects the vessel's seaworthiness. Damage of this sort is usually the consequence of an accident and should be reported immediately, directly to the ship's classification society or through the owners or managers, according to company policy. Where possible the written report should be supported by digital photographs to assist Class in assessing the seriousness of the damage. The Class surveyor will make a decision as to whether a permanent repair under his supervision is necessary or a temporary repair, backed by a condition of class, will be sufficient. Certificates for the materials used in the repair and for the welder's qualifications will be required and should be filed with the vessel's Enhanced Survey Programme.

At the other end of the scale is superficial damage which, in the eyes of the Master, is 'fair wear and tear'. Scuffed paintwork, scraped tanktops and coaming edges chafed by crane wires come into this category. It is unreasonable, and unprofitable, to try to make stevedores liable for damage of this sort.

The third class of stevedore damage falls between the two extremes and includes damage to hold ladders or platforms, bilge well or manhole covers, ship's side rails and crane or derrick crutches. Items of this sort do not require supervision by Class but do require prompt repair and competent repair for the sake of the ship's safety and efficiency.

When damage has been found: The foreman or supervisor should be shown the damage and told that stevedores are held responsible. If the damage was caused by carelessness or unsafe practices he should be instructed to prevent any repetition. Owners or managers and charterers should also be promptly informed. The warning should be backed up promptly with a written stevedores' damage report (Appendix 3.1) issued as soon as possible (24 hours is often the time limit given in the charterparty) and supported by photographs. Such written notice is often made on a stevedores' damage report form provided by the charterer. If no such form is available the owners' form should be used, or a suitable letter can be written if no form is available. The report should describe the damage and the cause of the damage. Port, date and time must be stated, and the exact location and description of the damage should be carefully entered, so that several years later the damage can be distinguished from other damage, if necessary. The foreman should sign all copies of the form. He will retain one copy whilst the ship keeps the remainder. Stevedores show great resourcefulness in finding reasons for not signing the damage form, but their resistance must be met by determination on the part of the ship's officers. A signature *'for receipt only'*, or a signature denying liability is better than no signature. If no signature can be obtained the form should be endorsed with *'At (time) on (date) completed form presented to stevedore foreman who refused to accept or sign it'*, and a copy should be given to the ship's agent to deliver to the stevedores.

Stevedores should never be blamed for damage which really occurred in a previous port. They usually have a good idea of what damage they have or have not caused and if an attempt is made to blame them for damage they have not done there will be little prospect of future co-operation. Where damage is suspected, but there are good reasons why it cannot be confirmed before sailing, the stevedores should be issued with a stevedores' damage form holding them liable for any damage found (eg, after completion of discharge of a part discharged hold). The reasons why they are thought to have caused damage should be clearly stated. They should be blamed for damage found after they have left the ship if it is certain that they were responsible. Provided that there is a good reason why it was not discovered sooner the claim will still be valid. The document should be given or sent to the ship's agent.

Repair of stevedores' damage: Those stevedores who are well equipped and well organised usually prefer to make good any stevedore damage which they have admitted before the vessel leaves port. Provided that the repair is a competent one, made by qualified workmen using the correct materials and, in the case of damage to the ship's 'main longitudinal and transverse members and their attachments' approved by a Class surveyor[225], this is the most satisfactory outcome for the ship.

When repairs are completed by the stevedores, they will want a signature to confirm that the repair has been made, or they will demand destruction of all copies of the stevedores' damage form. This is reasonable when a satisfactory permanent repair has been completed, but it should be remembered that further expense will be incurred at a later date if the repair is only temporary. If, for example, a patch has been welded over a hole punched in the hopper side, the stevedores' damage form should not be cancelled, but should be endorsed *'temporary repair made'*.

Stevedores who have made repairs sometimes issue certificates stating, for example *'Repairs to hold ladders in No.3 hold completed to ship's satisfaction'*. If the Master has any doubt about the quality of the repair he should endorse the certificate with a suitable comment such as, *'Repair to be inspected by Class surveyor/Company's superintendent'*.

If the stevedores are unable or unwilling to repair the damage it should, unless minor, be surveyed by a reputable surveyor who should also estimate the repair cost.

Crew work during discharge

There are limits to the work that trimmers can be persuaded or compelled to do in the holds, and it is sometimes in the ship's interests to put crew members to work in the holds on supplementary cleaning. For example, some Masters recommend placing crew members in holds at an early stage in the discharge of grain when it is safe to do so, to stand on the cargo and sweep grain from surfaces such as the flanges of deck frames high in the hold where cargo settles and is later difficult to remove.

Trimmers will often refuse to remove cargo which has fallen into hold bilge wells when a cover plate has been dislodged. If crew members remove the cargo from the bilge the stevedores will normally be co-operative about lifting it from the hold by grab, thus saving time and effort for the crew later. The same applies for completed holds. Extra cargo missed by the trimmers can be gathered by the crew and will usually be discharged by the stevedores, thus saving considerable extra effort for the crew.

As the discharge from particular holds is completed, the crew may be required to clean ballast holds before they are ballasted or in preparation for the loading of the next cargo. (The necessary procedures are described in Chapter 5.)

Sources

15, 35, 110, 139, 140, 142, 143, 144, 145, 146, 147, 148, 244, 285. (See List of Sources, Page 497)

CHECKLIST – Tasks on arrival in the discharging berth

- ☐ Secure vessel in berth
- ☐ Establish safe access
- ☐ Obtain a full set of draught readings
- ☐ Agree Unloading/Ballasting Programme with terminal representative
- ☐ Agree Ship/Shore Safety Checklist with terminal representative
- ☐ Satisfy the requirements of draught surveyor and/or cargo surveyor if appointed
- ☐ Satisfy the requirements of the receiving country regarding fumigated cargo
- ☐ Open hatches when safe and appropriate to do so
- ☐ Commence discharging and ballasting

CHECKLIST – Duties of the officer of the watch in the discharging port

- ☐ Study and understand the discharging/ballasting programme.
- ☐ Monitor the discharge and watch the draught to ensure that the discharging/ballasting programme is followed.
- ☐ Liaise with terminal representative regarding stevedores' damage, work of trimmers, and possible causes of delay.
- ☐ Warn foreman if cargo is sticking to hold bulkheads and trimmers are needed to shovel or brush it down.
- ☐ Ensure correct cargo is discharged and cargo is in good condition.
- ☐ Keep any list within acceptable limits.
- ☐ Monitor the ballasting to ensure it remains symmetrical and no overflows occur.
- ☐ Co-ordinate and supervise the work of the crew to ensure efficiency in shifting of the ship, preparing ballast holds for ballasting, preparing holds for washing, maintaining efficiency of ship's cargo gear, and securing of holds on completion.
- ☐ Keep the terminal representative informed of any developments, particularly of potential problems which may affect the discharging.
- ☐ Note any possible causes of damage to ship or cargo, and make every effort to prevent them.
- ☐ Note and record any damage to ship or cargo and immediately pass details to the chief mate, who will hold the stevedores responsible.
- ☐ Ensure moorings and means of access are tended as necessary.
- ☐ Record full weather observations at least three times daily.
- ☐ Maintain full written records in the port log book and/or deck log book of all relevant events and data (items as detailed in the body of Chapter 12).
- ☐ Ensure that safe procedures are followed at all times.

CHECKLIST – Duties of the chief mate in the discharging port

- ☐ Complete and transmit the discharging/ballasting plan before arrival in discharging berth if possible.
- ☐ Distribute copies of the discharging/ballasting plan to the terminal representative and the OOWs, and ensure that it is understood.
- ☐ Complete the Ship/Shore safety checklist, agree it with the terminal representative and obtain his signature on the document.
- ☐ Give the OOWs additional written instructions regarding the discharging, if the circumstances require it.
- ☐ Liaise with terminal representative regarding stevedores' damage, work of trimmers, and possible causes of delay.
- ☐ Conduct ship's draught survey or undertake draught survey with an independent surveyor, when appointed.
- ☐ Monitor the commencement of discharging and act promptly to deal with any problems.
- ☐ Use 'informal' draught surveys to monitor the tonnages discharged from time to time during the discharge. Figures are often provided by the stevedores at change of shift so draughts should be taken at these times to allow comparison of ship's and shore figures.
- ☐ Supervise the trimming of holds to ensure that they are properly cleaned by trimmers, and minimum work is left for crew.
- ☐ Ensure that appropriate matters receive attention when particular cargoes are discharged.
- ☐ Provide verbal warning, quickly followed by written notice, to stevedores when the ship or the cargo is damaged.
- ☐ Ensure that the ship is properly secured for sea.
- ☐ Ensure that safe procedures are followed at all times.

CHAPTER 17

THE BALLAST VOYAGE

General remarks, departure from the discharging port, choice of route, routine tasks, conduct of the voyage in rough weather, reporting, before arrival at the loading port, partial deballasting before berthing

THE BALLAST VOYAGE is one which takes a vessel without cargo from the discharging port to the next loading port. During such a voyage the vessel will be ballasted to light or heavy ballast draught depending upon the distance between ports, the draught and trim required and the weather anticipated. It may be necessary to change ballast during the voyage in order to reach the loading port with ballast which contains no unwelcome marine life. (Ballast management is discussed in Chapter 7.)

The empty holds may have to be cleaned (a process described in Chapter 5) or if a repeat cargo is to be carried this may not be required. This is a matter on which clear orders are essential. It is reasonable to assume that the holds must be cleaned unless clear written orders have been received to say that they are not to be cleaned. Such orders are most likely when the ship is time chartered for a number of voyages carrying a single commodity. If the Master considers that cleaning is unnecessary for any reason, he will be well advised to obtain confirmation from the charterers for the next voyage before he leaves the holds uncleaned. In any event it will be necessary during the voyage to make sure that the ship and her equipment are well maintained, in good working order, ready for the next cargo. (Chapter 6 contains a description of the necessary processes, whilst Chapter 9 mentions the need to inspect bilges, void spaces and chain lockers towards the end of the ballast voyage and to ensure that they are all empty when the loading port is reached).

If there is time during the ballast voyage and if weather permits, it may be possible to carry out maintenance work in the cargo holds. There may be opportunity to paint in the holds, too, provided that painting is not prohibited by the charterparty. It is also necessary to ensure that the paint has a compliance certificate (Appendix 14.29) if foodstuffs are to be carried, and that fresh paintwork will not harm any other intended cargo. If painting of the holds is permitted, adequate ventilation is essential and there must be sufficient time for the paint to cure fully to ensure that the cargo cannot be damaged.

Departure from the discharging port

A ship on a long ballast voyage has a very different timetable to one which is only 12 or 24 hours away from the loading port. In both cases the essentials must be done and that means that the holds must be made ready for the next cargo. In the case of the longer voyage, the work can be done when the weather is favourable during the normal working day and there will be time for additional maintenance work. When time is short, it is sometimes necessary to work around the clock to have holds ready when required.

When a ship leaves in ballast from the discharging port her condition is different in several respects from that of a ship leaving a loading port. The holds are empty except for any ballast holds which may be filled with water ballast. The ship in ballast has a smaller draught, a greater freeboard and, usually, a larger stern trim. Chapter 15 explains the importance of always keeping a stern trim for safety and efficiency; this is unlikely to be a problem during a ballast passage. The ship will normally have substantial positive stability in contrast to her condition when loaded, when she may be in any condition ranging from very stiff to very tender, depending upon the cargo carried.

Leaving the discharging port, the ship is often very dirty, with cargo residues widely spread on deck and cargo dust covering decks and superstructures. If hold cleaning is in progress the hatches may be secured open or partly open. If closed, they may not be fully secured if the sea is calm and the weather fair. Hatches should always be fully secured at the end of the working day and thereafter hatches should only be unbattened when required for working purposes.

Hazards associated with hold cleaning: The hold cleaning process presents two hazards. Firstly, if hatches are not fully secured and the ship pitches, rolls or heels as a result of meeting swell or a sharp alteration of course, the hatch covers may be disturbed with disastrous consequences. Covers have on occasion been lost overboard or dropped into the hold as a result of being inadequately secured: they must always be properly secured. When it is necessary to open or close hatches the ship should always be put on the heading on which she is steadiest.

The second hazard is the risk of flooding of holds if the weather becomes bad whilst decks and hatches are not secured. A ship in ballast is unlikely to ship quantities of heavy green seas over the decks and hatches, but any flooding should be avoided by keeping the minimum number of working hatches open and by always securing hatches, access hatches and ventilators at the end of the working day and when adverse weather is expected.

Choice of route for the ballast voyage

Much of what is written in Chapter 14 regarding choice of route for the loaded voyage applies to the ballast voyage, too, but there are some important differences. If holds have to be washed the route must take the vessel through waters where the discharge of hold washings is not prohibited (Chapter 25), though this is not normally a problem on deep-sea voyages. If ballast water has to be changed (Chapter 7) an area of deep water as far from land as possible will be required and the route must be considered to see whether such an opportunity can be arranged.

A bulk carrier in ballast will be less likely to suffer

heavy weather damage on deck and will have no cargo to break adrift if she rolls heavily. She will, however, be more likely to pound and to suffer from propeller racing when she pitches in a head swell.

The provision of ship routeing services is less common for ships in ballast than for loaded bulkers. This is because ships in ballast are often not on charter and voyage charterers have no interest in their performance at such times. Time charterers, on the other hand, are always interested in the ship's economic performance and may want to use ship routeing services for ballast voyages. Ships on ballast voyages can sometimes gain significant benefits from routeing services and the charterers may decide to employ ship routeing services. If the ship is not on charter the Master should obtain authority from his owners to use them when some or all the conditions which favour routeing (as listed in Chapter 15) are met.

Routine tasks

The first job when leaving port will be, as always, the securing of the mooring ropes on their reels or if not on reels then below decks. Alternatively, on a short ballast passage ropes not on reels may be left lashed on deck provided that fair weather is expected. Anchors will be secured when clear of the port and of shallow water, and spurling pipes will be sealed.

Washing the ship down to remove cargo dust is a necessary process, but washing with sea water, although the normal practice on most ships, is likely to encourage rust. Where possible other options are to be preferred. For example, the accommodation block can be washed down using a portable high-pressure washing machine and fresh water from a peak tank or from the swimming pool if it has been possible to load fresh water there for this purpose at reasonable cost. Fresh water drawn from the northern Baltic or from the Panama Canal is equally useful for this purpose.

Most modern bulk carriers are able to produce more fresh water than they need at sea and the surplus is sufficient to serve them whilst in port, provided that the sea voyages are long and the port stays are short. However, this does not leave much surplus fresh water for washing decks, superstructure and holds. In the circumstances even a heavy downpour of rain is welcome!

Soundings of all compartments, including bilges and ballast tanks, voids and cofferdams, should be taken daily as they are when the ship is loaded. This helps to identify leaking ballast tanks and leaking ballast holds and provides a check on the reliability of the bilge soundings. If the sounding in a ballast tank is becoming smaller (or the ullage is increasing) the reason must be found. If a visual hold bilge inspection has shown 20 cm of water the sounding book should show a similar figure. Any unexpected readings should be promptly examined.

The decks should be inspected daily in fair and in rough weather, following procedures to ensure that all deck openings are secured at the end of the working day and before the onset of rough weather. (These procedures have been described in Chapter 15.)

Conduct of the ballast voyage in rough weather

Condition of a bulker in ballast: A conventional bulk carrier in ballast will be stiff, but not as stiff as a bulker loaded with a cargo of steel products. At her ballast draught she will have a substantial freeboard, so that her decks will normally be fairly dry and she will ship less spray than does a laden bulker.

A bulker in ballast presents a large area to a wind on the beam. The area is usually roughly balanced about amidships, as the area presented by the accommodation and hull aft is likely to be equalled by the larger hull area forward, which results from the shallower forward draught (Fig. 17.1). As a consequence a bulk carrier in ballast when lying stopped in the water is likely to lie approximately beam-on to the wind.

Pounding and propeller racing: The conduct of a loaded bulk carrier in rough weather was discussed in Chapter 15 and much of what was written there is equally true for the ballast voyage. There are, however, some differences which need to be emphasised.

Because of her shallow draught the forefoot of a bulk carrier in ballast will emerge completely from the water when she pitches. When the underside of the forefoot (the ship's bottom beneath the forepeak and No.1 hold) crashes down on the surface of the water the process is known as pounding or slamming. Pounding can cause serious damage to the shell plating, which appears as dishing of the plating between the double-bottom floors. It is likely that pounding also causes more remote damage in the ship girder. Pounding should be avoided as far as possible. Structural features which overhang in the bow area, such as anchor pods (Fig. 1.35) and deck edges extended to accommodate trackways for deck cranes, will also pound when the bows plunge into the swell.

As the swell increases and the vessel begins to pitch the likelihood of pounding increases. Aboard a small bulker the shock and vibration of pounding can be felt throughout the length of the ship and it is a routine matter, though an important one, to reduce speed and/or course to stop the pounding.

Aboard larger vessels, such as Panamax and Cape-sized bulkers, the forefoot is a long way away from the bridge and accommodation and the pounding is more difficult to detect in those positions, although unmistakable to anyone positioned forward. A number of large bulkers are fitted with hull stress monitors (described in Chapter 8) and these will give warning when the vessel is pounding (slamming) excessively. In vessels without hull stress monitors it is necessary to remember the danger of pounding and the damage which it can do, and to reduce speed when the vessel starts to pitch heavily even if pounding cannot be felt on the bridge.

Whilst at ballast draught the uppermost tip of the propeller will normally be close to the surface when the ship is at rest. When the ship pitches, part of the propeller will emerge from the water and, meeting reduced resistance, the propeller will race and the main engine governor will cut in and temporarily reduce the speed of the engine. When this starts to occur it provides further evidence that the engine speed should be reduced, or course should be altered to reduce the pitching, and thereby to reduce the pounding and racing of the propeller.

Both pounding and propeller racing become worse when the ship's draught is less. This emphasises the importance of having the vessel fully ballasted to heavy ballast condition when adverse swell or weather is expected.

Meeting adverse weather: Chapter 15 offers detailed advice for loaded bulkers when meeting adverse weather and that advice is equally valid for bulk carriers in ballast. If the weather causes a speed reduction of 25 per cent with constant engine settings, the engine RPMs should be substantially reduced to avoid damage from forcing the ship into the weather. Prolonged violent rolling can damage the side shell plating and framing of a bulk carrier, and violent pitching or corkscrewing (ie torsional movement, when the vessel's fore end is forced one way and the after end the other) is dangerous and should be avoided by alteration of course and/or speed.

When a vessel is moving violently, ballast water in part-filled ballast tanks will slosh, a process that can damage the ship's structure. When rough weather is anticipated ballast tanks, and in particular ballast holds, must not be left in any condition other than 100 per cent full. When rough weather persists ballast tanks should be topped up from time to time to replace ballast which has slopped out of airpipes and ventilators. This precaution, too, is particularly important in the case of ballast holds.

Heaving-to: The description of heaving-to contained in Chapter 15 for loaded bulkers applies equally to bulkers in ballast, with one difference. A loaded bulker naturally lies head to wind as a result of the accommodation block which acts as a sail, whilst a bulker in ballast is more likely to lie naturally beam-on to the wind for reasons discussed above. Despite this it is usually possible to use the engine at slow speed and the rudder to heave-to with the wind about 45° on the bow.

Turning through the trough: Turning through the trough (as described in Chapter 15 for loaded bulkers) applies also to bulkers in ballast. Since ballasted bulkers lie naturally beam-on to the wind they will turn easily until they are lying in the trough, but will be slower to continue the turn, regardless of whether they are being turned into or away from the wind and swell.

Action to take when flooding is detected: Emergency action for this situation is discussed in Chapter 21 and summarised in Chapter 15.

Reporting

Since 1st July 2006 all ships above 500 gt undertaking voyages exceeding 48 hours have been required to report their positions daily[139]. In addition, during a ballast voyage, the Master will be required by owners and by charterers if on charter to submit routine position reports and ETA messages to various parties at specified intervals. His voyage orders may also require him to report when hold cleaning has been completed. In some cases owners require a daily report of hold cleaning so that they can prepare for any unexpected delays in the process.

Before arrival at the loading port

A day or two before arriving at the loading port, at the latest moment which allows sufficient time to put right any problems which are found, all holds should be reinspected to ensure that they remain ready for the loading of cargo. Such an inspection may find puddles of water which have formed on the tanktop from condensation or other sources, or undetected cargo residues which have fallen from places high in the hold.

Void spaces, bilges, chain lockers and any other spaces where unnecessary water is being carried should be pumped out to ensure that the ship is carrying no additional weights. Where the next cargo is one which can suffer from water damage the opportunity should be taken, where possible, to test the watertightness of the hatch covers (see Chapter 4) and to record the result in the deck log book. If leakage is found, the fault should be corrected and the covers retested so that a satisfactory result can be logged.

Towards the end of the ballast voyage, when the holds have been prepared for loading, all bilge suctions should be tested and the results of the tests recorded in the deck log book. Surveyors at loading ports have been known to include this item on their pre-loading or on-hire check lists.

Partial deballasting before berthing

When the loading terminal is able to load at a very high speed, the terminal operators may want the ship to discharge part of the ballast before berthing to allow a faster loading rate. When the ship is unable to deballast at a satisfactory rate, the Master may want the ship to discharge part of the ballast before berthing to enable the ship to comply with the required loading rate.

In both cases this want must be balanced against the possible difficulties of manoeuvring into the berth at light draught and the available air draught must be considered. (These matters are fully considered in Chapter 7.) Full account must also be taken of any pilotage or port regulations regarding the draught, trim and propeller immersion which are acceptable to the authorities and of any regulations restricting the discharge of ballast in coastal waters.

The Master must never allow himself to be pressurised into discharging ballast before berthing when he believes it is not safe to do so.

Arrival in the loading berth

Chapter 12 *Arrival in the berth* discusses the arrival at the loading berth and observes that hatches should not be opened until the vessel has been secured in the berth, a safe access has been provided and the necessary procedures have been completed although, in special circumstances when it is safe and prudent to do so there may be a case for berthing with hatches uncleated or even open.

Sources

139. (See List of Sources, Page 497)

CHECKLIST – Routine procedures for the ballast voyage

- ☐ Have mooring lines all secured well before the open sea is reached. Secure anchors when deep water and open seas are reached.
- ☐ Decide what cleaning the holds require, prepare a cleaning timetable and do the cleaning.
- ☐ Close and batten down hatches except for those where work is proceeding.
- ☐ If judged safe to do so, leave open holds which are being cleaned. When open, as when closed, hatch panels must be secured to prevent movement.
- ☐ Take light or heavy ballast according to assessment of weather expected on voyage.
- ☐ Wash down decks and superstructure.
- ☐ Take a full set of soundings every day and study them for any unexplained increase or reduction in sounding.
- ☐ Investigate promptly any unexplained changes in soundings.
- ☐ Change ballast whilst in mid-ocean under safe sea conditions, if so required for discharge port and keep a full record of the process in the Ballast Water Record Book.
- ☐ Change from light to heavy ballast or vice versa during voyage if weather conditions warrant it.
- ☐ Inspect the decks daily and ensure that storerooms, hatch accesses, hatch covers and manhole covers are secure at the end of the day and before the onset of bad weather.
- ☐ In bad weather inspect the decks daily, taking all necessary precautions to ensure the inspection is safe and thorough.
- ☐ When the ship is slowed by bad weather reduce the engine speed or alter course.
- ☐ Follow safe procedures for heaving-to with the weather on the bow or on the quarter, and for turning through the trough.
- ☐ Make routine position reports daily and ETA reports as required.
- ☐ Ensure that all the ship's systems (ventilation, airpipes, hold bilges, water ingress detectors, hull stress monitoring equipment, sounding and hold temperature systems, deck and hold lighting, fire smothering systems, hatch coaming drains, deck machinery, derricks, cranes and grabs) are in good working order.
- ☐ Before arrival at the loading port ensure that the holds and bilge wells remain clean and dry.
- ☐ Before arrival at the loading port ensure that bilges, void spaces, chain lockers and all other compartments which should be empty are empty.
- ☐ Test hatch covers for leakage and log the result.
- ☐ Before berthing at the loading port discharge heavy ballast (eg, contents of ballast holds) on occasions when it is safe and desirable to do so.
- ☐ Clear anchors and prepare ropes for berthing.
- ☐ Arrive in the loading berth with holds closed.
- ☐ Open holds after completion of arrival procedures.

CHAPTER 18

SPECIAL TYPES OF BULK CARRIERS

Operational characteristics of double skinned bulk carriers, self unloaders, mini-bulkers, forest product carriers, log carriers, retractable tweendeck vessels, open hatch vessels with shipboard gantry cranes and combination carriers

Double skinned bulk carriers

PERHAPS the most significant development in bulk carrier design in recent years has been the introduction of double skinned bulk carriers. Attempts to make their introduction mandatory over a period of years were defeated at the Maritime Safety Committee of the International Maritime Organisation early in 2004 but the emergence of a practical, well researched handymax design from Carl Bro AS of Denmark in consultation with Det Norske Veritas for structural and regulatory matters and in collaboration with Graig Investments Ltd of Cardiff for the operational aspects has been welcomed. With 35 of the ships in service in 2008 and another fifty on order they appear to have a promising future (See drawings and technical manuals on CD inside front cover). The Diamond 53 class of handymax vessels has now been joined by the Diamond 34 class of handy-sized vessels, smaller ships but with the same five hold configuration and many of the same features.

The principal benefits[168,169] of double skinned construction are that the second skin provides an additional line of defence against accidental water ingress, too frequently a cause of bulk carrier losses in the past and that holds can be discharged and cleaned more quickly because the sides are flush, with all the steel frames, girders and brackets contained between the skins (Figs. 18.1-3). Another benefit is ease of access for inspection and repair to the entire side structure of the hold from within the double skin (Fig. 18.4 and 5).

Disadvantages of the double skinned design are the additional weight of structural steel required and the small reduction in space available for cargo both of which will reduce slightly the cargo quantity that can be carried. In addition it is feared by some that the great extent of double skin will prove exhausting to inspect and difficult to maintain.

The Diamond 53s: The Diamond 53 class are geared, wide hatched, 54,000 dwt bulk carriers designed to accommodate the latest trends and developments within the handymax bulk carrier trade. It is claimed that they are economical to operate and maintain, environmentally friendly, robust and possessing flexibility in loading. They have been built with features that anticipate future regulations and with safety in mind.

Full speed when laden is about 14 knots and when in ballast 14.5 knots with consumption of about 33.4 tonnes of fuel oil per day. The ships are each equipped with four 36 tonne SWL level luffing cranes designed to operate with electro hydraulically operated grabs. The holds are provided with natural ventilation by way of openings in the hatch cover ends and with permanent lighting. The hatch covers are end folding, double skin and hydraulically operated.

The two ballast pumps, which are operated from the ballast control computer in the deck office (Fig. 18.6) which is duplicated in the engine control room, each have a capacity of 1,000 m^3/hour with a head of 4 bar and the capacity of the two stripping eductors is 50 m^3/hr with a head of 2 bar.

Fig. 18.1 No. 2 hold (S) side with lower and upper hopper tanks

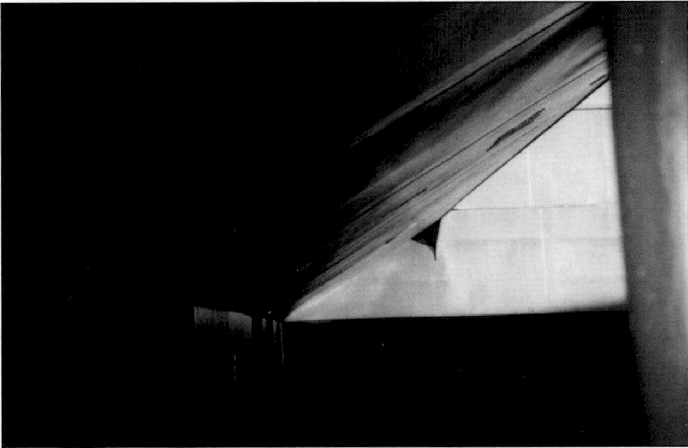

Fig. 18.2 No. 2 hold, aft underdeck area viewed from the Australian ladder. The permanent hold lights are mounted in this sloping plating

Fig. 18.3 No. 2 hold, aft port, looking up to where the corrugated after bulkhead meets the port hopper tank and the crossdeck hopper tank

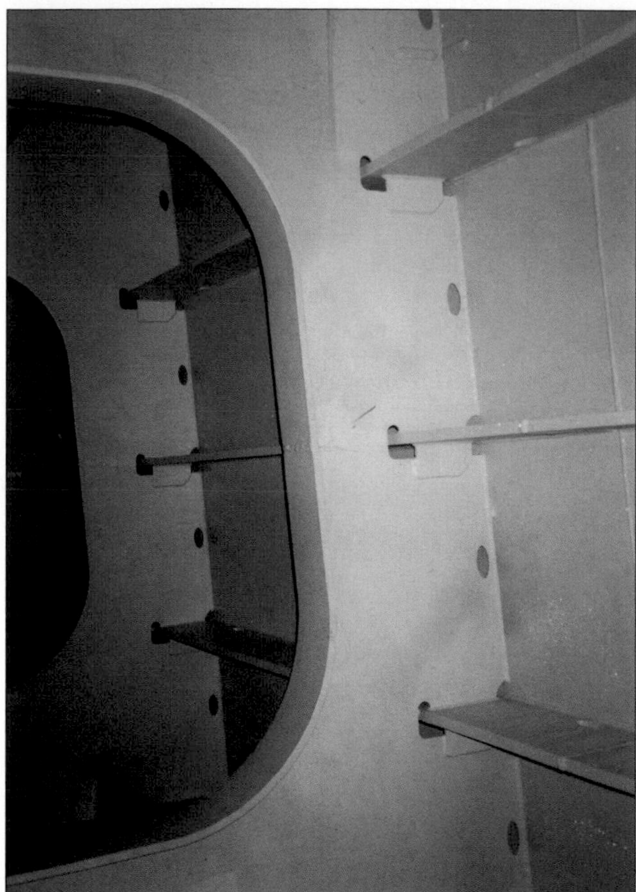

Fig. 18.4 Inside the double skin No. 3 (S) wing tank

Fig. 18.5 Inside the double skin – No. 3 (S) wing tank

Fig. 18.6 The Ballast Control station

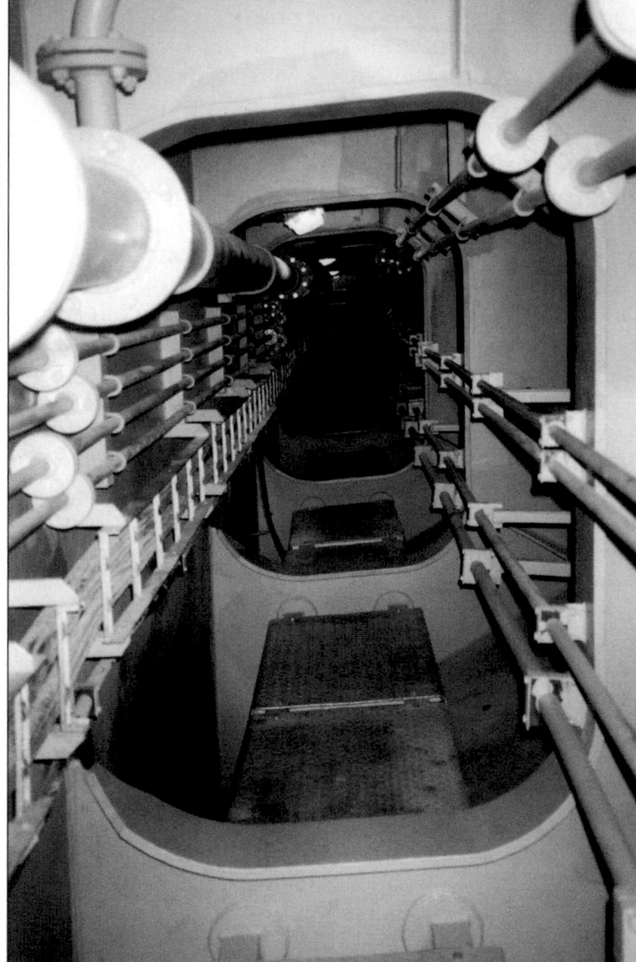

Fig. 18.7 Pipe duct (S)

Fig. 18.8 Ballast vent in No. 3 hatch cover

Below deck pipe ducts run alongside the hatchways, inboard of the wing tanks on port and starboard sides (Fig. 18.7). These contain washdeck and fire fighting lines, compressed air, CO_2, electric cables and hatch hydraulic lines. It seems likely that corrosion in all this pipework will be greatly reduced by these arrangements and that hydraulic leaks on deck will be almost eliminated. Repairs when needed will be done below decks which will be an advantage in adverse weather. Each pipe duct can be entered through three access hatches located on the main deck, one forward, one amidships and one aft. The pipe ducts do not provide a direct sheltered route from the accommodation to the forecastle spaces because they have no accesses in either of those spaces.

Ballast water is carried in five pairs of double bottom tanks and five pairs of wing tanks which extend from the turn of the bilge to main deck level except in way of No.5 hold, where the upper part of each wing tank is a separate tank with a capacity of 377 mt for hold washing water. In addition there are the usual forepeak and afterpeak tanks. The tanks mentioned so far, with a total capacity of 18,126 mt form the vessel's light ballast. When No.3 hold, with a capacity of 13,349 mt is added the vessel's heavy ballast is 31,475 mt, about 50 per cent of her loaded displacement. The light ballast condition is just under 30 per cent of loaded displacement

The danger of sloshing means that ballast in No.3 hold can only be changed at sea by the flow through method but all the remaining tanks can be changed sequentially. A complete mid ocean ballast change takes approximately 24 hours for light ballast and two days for heavy ballast. In fair weather it is possible to leave port with all the wing tanks plus only the No.3 double bottom tanks filled. Depending upon the bunkers carried draughts of about 4.5 m Forward and 6.8 m Aft are achieved. This satisfies the requirement for a minimum after draught of 6.5 m, to ensure that the emergency fire pump has suction, and means that if the remaining ballast tanks are filled once at sea the ballast within them will not need to be changed during the voyage. The No.3 hold has a direct gravitating line to the sea and when gravitating through the direct line and gravitating and pumping as appropriate through the main ballast lines the hold can be completely ballasted or deballasted in about 4.5 hours.

No.3 hold is provided with ballasting ventilators (Fig. 18.8) which must be open when the hold is being ballasted or deballasted to prevent over- or under-pressuring of the hold, as the notice above each ventilator states. It is through these vents that ballast water overflows when a mid ocean ballast change is taking place. The vents are provided with a non-return float mechanism to prevent sea water on deck from flooding into No.3 hold when the vents are open. The No.3 hold access hatches (Figs. 18.9-11) are designed to withstand water pressure from within the hatch.

Given the vessel's heavy ballast tonnage of 31,475 mt, her two ballast pumps each with a capacity of 1,000 tonnes/hr, and the ability to gravitate direct to sea from No.3 hold, these ships appear to have the ability to discharge all main ballast within about 18 hours and to complete deballasting and stripping within 24 hours provided that the deballasting can be co-ordinated with a suitable loading programme.

The Diamond 53 class are fully strengthened to load dense cargoes in alternate holds (ie Nos. 1, 3 and 5) and can also be block loaded in Nos.1, 2, 4 and 5 with a wide range of cargoes such as coal, grain, sugar, urea, cement and other cargoes with densities no more than 1.35 t/m^3. This feature helps to avoid the scramble to convert the ballast hold from cargo to ballast duties. The ships are also fully and unusually up to date in their ability to accept two tiers of 25 tonne steel coils in all holds, enabling them to lift a full deadweight of this commodity. When laden with steel coils the vessel has a GM of about 8.5 m, making her very stiff.

Permanent hold lighting and water ingress detectors are of a certified safe type, allowing the vessels to carry a large range of dangerous cargoes in all holds. The hold lights are set in recesses in the upper hoppers below the cross deck areas (Fig. 18.12 and 13). They are accessible only through manholes in the crossdeck areas (Fig. 18.14).

The water ingress detectors, made by Seamate, are

Fig. 18.9 No. 3 ballast hold access
Photo courtesy of Captain S Kurian

Fig. 18.10 No. 3 ballast hold access open
Photo courtesy of Captain S Kurian

Fig. 18.11 Ballast hold access closing mechanism
Photo courtesy of Captain S Kurian

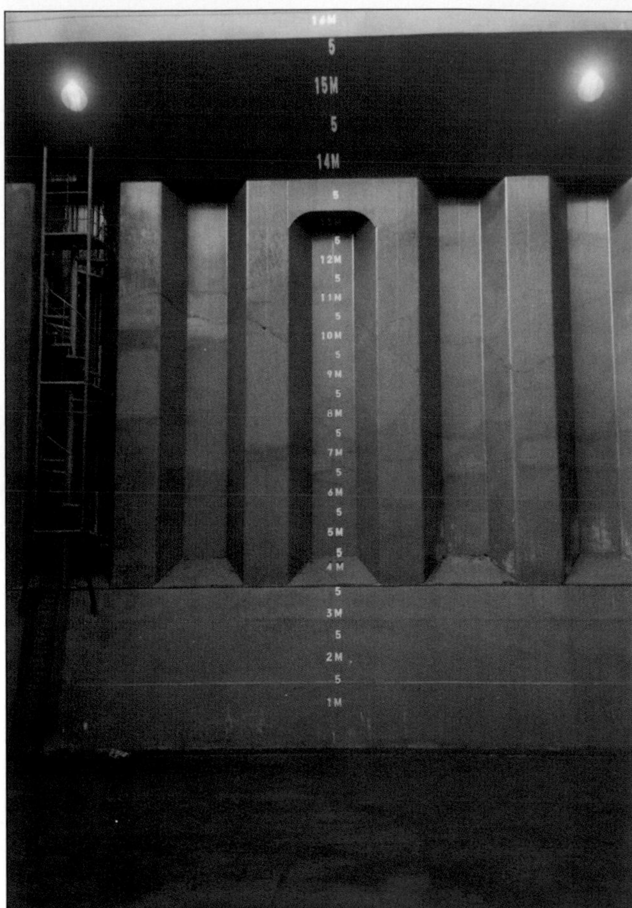

Fig. 18.12 Gas tight hold lighting set into void hopper space below the crossdeck area

Fig. 18.13 A gas tight hold light

Fig. 18.14 Access on deck to permanent hold light

Fig. 18.15 Water Ingress Detector (WID) head set flush in bulkhead stool

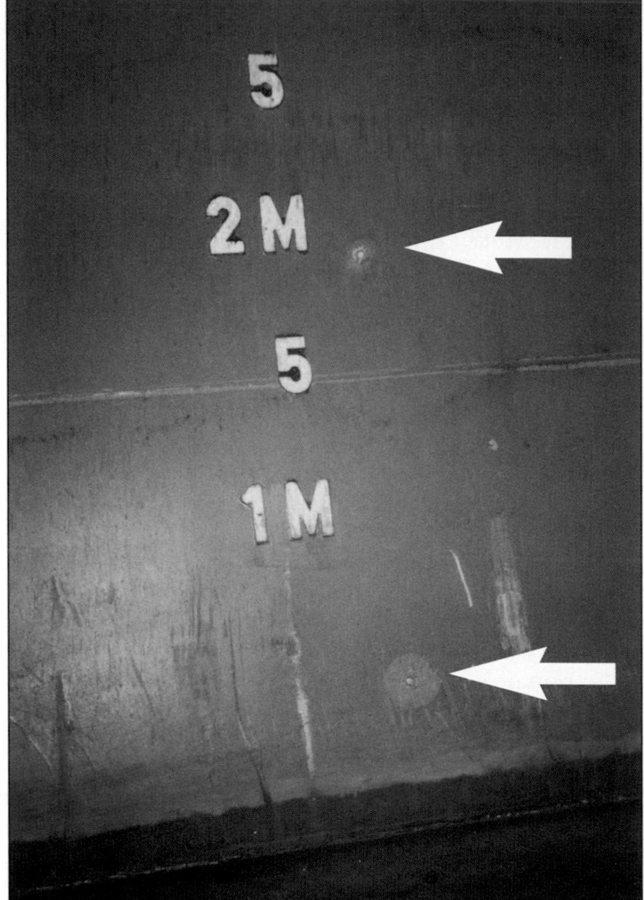

Fig. 18.16 Set of two WID heads in bulkhead stool

Fig. 18.17 Coal ventilator

placed inside the aft bulkhead stool of each hold with their detecting tips in the hold (Figs. 18.15 and 16). They are of a type that detects moisture and are tested by the application of a damp cloth. Alarm panels are situated on the bridge and in the ship's office.

Coal ventilators (Fig. 18.17), set in the hatch lids with two at each end of each hatch, provide ventilation of the hatchways in addition to the ballast vents (Fig. 18.8), unique to No.3 hold. The holds are provided with CO_2 smothering with one delivery nozzle (Fig. 18.18) on each of the four sides of each hatch coaming. The delivery nozzles for the ballast hold are each provided with a valve (Fig. 18.19) so that they can be closed when the hold is ballasted.

Hold washing: The hold structures are entirely boxed in (Figs. 18.1-3), the only departures from smooth surfaces being the forward and after hold ladders and their platforms (Figs. 18.12 and 20), and double bottom airpipes within bulkhead corrugations (Fig. 18.20). This makes hold washing a relatively quick and easy process. Washing is done using a portable combigun. Four pipes run down the after bulkhead of each hold within the corrugation that contains the Australian Rules ladder. One carries salt water to wash the hold and to power the portable ejector (eductor). A second carries compressed air to drive the combigun. Fresh rinsing water runs through the third and the fourth carries the used washing and ejector water from the hold to the collecting tanks abreast No.5 hold. Each pipe ends in a coupling at a point near the tanktop (Fig. 18.21).

Because the hold sides, deckheads and bulkheads are smooth a normal hold cleaning is expected to take no more than four hours consisting of 1.5 hours sweeping up, 1.5 hours washing and 1 hour drying.

The hold cleaning sequence is:

- Sweep up cargo residues, perhaps using compressed air on ladders, and remove them from hold.
- Lower the combigun, hoses and ejector (or sump pump) into the hold.
- Install the combigun in the hold and couple up to the sea water and air deliveries.
- Install the ejector (or sump pump) in one bilge and couple it to the sea water delivery (except in circumstances when there are no restrictions on pumping hold washings overboard and residues will not harm the bilge system, in which case hold washings are removed through the bilge stripping system unless owners' company regulations prohibit this).
- List ship slightly towards the bilge with the ejector (or sump pump).
- Wash hold including undersides of hatch panels and finishing with port and starboard bilges.
- Rinse hold using fresh water delivered by hydroblaster with long lance.
- Unrig and remove combigun, hoses, ejector (or sump pump) and hydroblaster.
- Pump bilges.

The benefits of this system are:

- Washing is quick and easy because the ship's sides and bulkheads are free of obstructions.
- The hold washings, with residues, can be transferred to the washing water tanks through dedicated pipes and need not pass through the ship's bilge system. They can be retained aboard until discharge is permitted.

Fig. 18.18 CO_2 injection into non-ballast hold

Photos courtesy of Captain S Kurian

Fig. 18.19 CO_2 injection into ballast hold. Valve in line must be closed when the hold is ballasted

Fig. 18.20 No. 2 hold for'd end with hold ladder and airpipes in bulkhead corrugations

Fig. 18.21 Lower part of the Australian hold ladder. Connections for hold washing water and air are about 1 metre above the platform

Fig. 18.22 An air driven sump pump
Photo courtesy Capt S Kurian

- No washing water need be put overside.
- Permanent piping in the holds saves time rigging and unrigging the cleaning equipment.

One inconvenient feature is that there is no easy route, such as a trimming hatch, by which to lower equipment into the hold or to remove equipment and sweepings from the hold when the hatches are closed and the cranes are stowed.

There are three routes for the disposal of the hold washing water. When any residues in the water are not expected to cause difficulties in the bilge stripping system and when, in addition, the ship is in a sea area where no restrictions apply (see Chapter 25) the hold washing water can be pumped out by a fixed eductor in the engine room via the bilge stripping system. When those conditions are not satisfied the hold washing water is delivered by eductor via the permanent pipeline system to the washing water tanks which form the upper part of No. 5 wing tanks and can hold about 750 mt. There the water can be retained until the ship is in a sea area where no restrictions apply. The amount of hold washing water used will depend in part upon the condition in which the holds are left by the stevedores but as little as possible will be used when it is to be retained aboard because the more washing water that is retained the less cargo can be lifted at the next loading port if a full deadweight cargo is to be loaded.

An alternative to an eductor (Fig. 22.10) for removing water from the hold is an air driven sump pump (Fig. 18.22) also connected to the washing water tanks through the pipeline. A sump pump is less efficient than an eductor for the removal of washings containing cargo residues, and requires a lot of maintenance to keep it in good working order, but because it is not powered by water the quantity of water sent to the holding tanks is considerably reduced. This is important when the tonnage in the holding tank will reduce the tonnage the ship can lift on her next voyage.

The hold washing water can, if relatively clean and residue-free, be dropped from the hold washing water tanks into the No.5 wing tanks below. Because the holds are easy to sweep clean the hold washing water usually contains little in the way of residues. If the hold washing water is likely to leave residues in the No.5 wing tanks it can, in sea areas where no restrictions apply, be pumped directly into the sea by eductor or sump pump.

Fig. 18.23 Airpipes positioned beside hatch coaming

Fig. 18.24 Wing tank manhole with lid and lightweight flush cover plate

Good design features: Besides the uncluttered holds, the pipelines within pipeducts, the tanks for hold washing water, the fast filling ballast hold and the computerised ballast controls a number of smaller features contribute to the good design of the Diamond 53s. They include well designed protecting brackets for the bottom sections of the hold ladders (Fig. 18.21), all airpipes positioned in from the ship's side (Fig. 18.23), manhole lids protected with light covers flush with the deck (Fig. 18.24) and the quick, easy and effective method of closing the access hatches to the ballast hold (Figs. 18.9-11).

Self-unloaders

Self-unloading bulk carriers which discharge cargo by means of ship-mounted conveyor belts have been known on the Great Lakes for a hundred years and moved into the international trades in the 1980s where they now range in size from mini- to Panamax and there were, in 2008, 11 which are larger than 80,000 dwt. In European waters one of the pioneering shipowners of this trade has been A/S Kristian Jebsens Rederi of Bergen with ships such as the 10,000 tonnes deadweight *Telnes*, built in 1982 and operated by Jebsens' UK subsidiary. (Fig. 18.29.)

After an initial period during which the vessel successfully carried a wide range of traditional cargoes between North Sea ports she was employed mainly in the coal trade, delivering coal to power stations on the Thames estuary from Amsterdam, Rotterdam, Zeebrugge and the North East Coast of England. In this trade she often carried three cargoes a week with loading, loaded passage, discharge and ballast passage each taking about 12 hours. The *Telnes* averaged 100 voyages, or 200 port visits, a year. Recent generations of self-unloaders employed in the European trades have increased in size up to 30,000 dwt with an unloading capacity of up to 3,000 tonnes/hour with boom lengths enabling delivery of cargo up to almost 70 m ashore[160].

The trade is one in which lack of experience on the part of the ships' personnel can lead to considerable delays, since failure of the ship's discharging equipment results in a complete cessation of work with little opportunity for discharge by alternative means.

Self-unloaders have a capital cost which is 20-35 per cent higher than conventional bulkers and provide less space for cargo than do conventional ships of the same size. These disadvantages can be more than balanced by their reduced port time for discharging, so they are most profitable when employed in shuttle services with very frequent port calls.

The International Maritime Solid Bulk Cargoes (IMSBC) Code recognises[247] that self-unloaders have holds fitted at the bottom with non-airtight gravity unloading gates and therefore specifies special arrangements for the atmospheric monitoring and ventilation of the cargo spaces. If methane is detected in the tunnel it must be 'positive pressure' ventilated (more supply than exhaust in the tunnels to remove methane gas) and if carbon monoxide is detected in the tunnel, it must be 'negative pressure' ventilated (more exhaust that supply in the tunnels to remove carbon monoxide).

Fig. 18.25 A self unloader with W shaped hold cross-section similar to mv *Telnes*. Five part closed cargo discharge gates can be seen at the base of the hold

Photo courtesy of Captain L Hesketh FNI

Fig. 18.26 Grain discharging through the forward pair of hopper gates onto the conveyor belts which run below the holds

Photo courtesy of Captain L. Hesketh FNI

Fig. 18.27 A self-unloader. Housing containing the vertical belts and the boom mountings

Photo courtesy of Captain L. Hesketh FNI

Fig. 18.28 Self-unloader's boom being used to discharge grain into a hopper on the jetty
Photo courtesy of Captain L. Hesketh FNI

Ship's particulars: The *Telnes* was a four-hold self-unloading bulk carrier with bridge, accommodation and machinery spaces located aft. She was built by Kleven Mek Verksted A/S of Ulsteinvik, Norway, in 1982, classed by DnV with the notation 1A1 ICE 1A, EO, and was registered in London. Her principal dimensions were length overall 118 metres, breadth moulded 20.5 metres, depth moulded 11 metres and loaded summer draught 8.466 metres with a corresponding deadweight of 10,110 metric tonnes. Her gross tonnage was 6,792 rt and net tonnage 4,249 rt, whilst her trial speed was 14.0 knots.

The four holds have a 'W' shaped cross-section, with the gates for discharge of the cargo being situated at the two base points of the 'W' (Fig. 18.25). Interconnected upper and lower wing tanks for ballast occupy the spaces created by the self-trimming shape of the holds, and double bottom ballast tanks are also fitted.

When discharging, the cargo is gravity-fed from the vessel's holds through a number of hydraulically-operated hopper gates (Fig. 18.26) on to conveyor belts which run forward beneath the holds. It is raised from hold level to boom height by a vertical belt (Fig. 18.27), from where it joins the boom conveyor belt to be discharged. The boom (Fig. 18.28) can unload cargo at any point up to 30 m from the ship's side and up to 15 m above the main deck. The cargo discharging equipment is described in more detail later in these notes.

Loading: Preplanning of the loading is done without the aid of a loading calculator: none is provided since the calculations are elementary. For a normal coal cargo the ship will be filled before she is loaded to her marks, so no decisions as to the distribution of the cargo are required. All holds must be filled. If a denser cargo is to be carried the cargo distribution is planned to ensure a satisfactory trim, and calculations will be routine ones using stability formulae and trimming tables.

The loading sequence, hold by hold, is normally 3, 1, 4, 2, with a final trimming pour of about 400 tonnes in No. 4, aft. This sequence ensures that a stern trim can be maintained throughout loading, thus assisting deballasting. Loading is by shore-based shiploader or grabs.

Before loading the forward hold the boom, which has a length of 40 m and a maximum outreach of 30 m, must be swung out to the offshore side at right angles. Since this would cause a substantial list, ballast must be discharged from an offshore tank to keep the ship upright, this process taking about 20 minutes. When swung out the boom end must be marked with a flashing orange safety light. The purpose of the trimming pour at the completion of loading is to bring the ship upright after the boom has been swung back to its stowage position amidships. Subject to this requirement as much as possible of the remaining space will be filled. The stowed boom is located over Nos. 1-3 holds, but is clear of No.4.

Deballasting takes place concurrently with loading and is arranged by the duty officer – normally the chief mate – from the control room where controls for the ballast valves and pumps are placed.

Steel debris in the cargo loaded, originating from rail wagons or previous ships to carry the cargo, is likely to cause enormous damage to the ship's discharging gear. The system can accept items no larger than a football, but sharp edges are likely to cause damage. Such items of debris cannot always be seen in a bulk cargo but where they are noticed every effort must be made to prevent them from being loaded. In ports where this is a problem powerful electro-magnets, capable of extracting large fragments of iron and steel, are positioned in optimum positions above shore conveyors.

Loaded voyage: Sometime before commencement of discharge the chief mate will inspect the discharging gear to ensure that all appears in good order. If planning a discharge in an unfamiliar berth the chief mate needs to know whether there are any weight restrictions. There may, for example, be maximum permitted loadings for a quay where stockpiling is carried out. Discharge is likely to be to hopper feeding another conveyor belt or to stockpile or barge.

Discharging: A cargo hold tunnel runs along the ship's centreline with, on each side, a main cargo conveyor belt positioned below the gates in the hold bottoms. A selected pair of gates, one port and one starboard, is partly opened to release a flow of cargo on to the main belts which carry the cargo to the fore end of the ship. Here transfer belts bring the cargo amidships to the loop belts situated in the 'cathedral', so-called because of its height. The cargo is compressed between the inner and outer loop belts which raise it vertically to the start of the boom conveyor belt. From the end of the boom conveyor belt, enclosed within the boom, the cargo is discharged ashore.

Communications between ship and shore are usually by means of VHF handsets provided by the shore installation. Alternatively portable telephones may be used. Shore installations accepting cargo direct through a hopper on to a conveyor belt may have a siren to indicate when the belt has stopped.

All discharging operations including positioning of the boom, commencement and stopping of cargo, and rate of discharge are controlled from the ship's cargo control room. Three closed-circuit television cameras are strategically sited in positions in the tunnel, the cathedral and at the boom end to allow

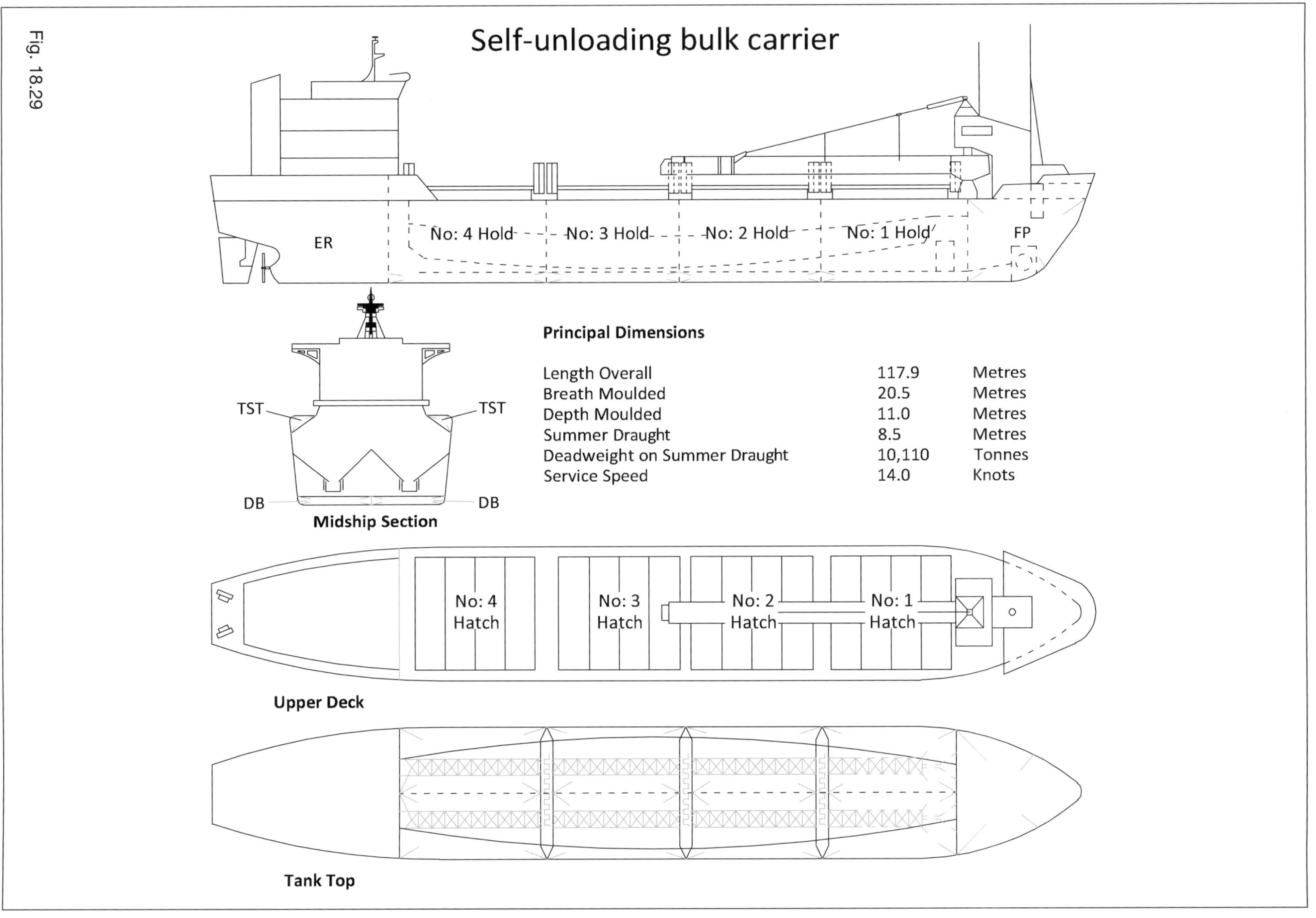
Self-unloading bulk carrier
ER
No: 4 Hold
No: 3 Hold
No: 2 Hold
No: 1 Hold
FP
Principal Dimensions
Length Overall 117.9 Metres
Breath Moulded 20.5 Metres
Depth Moulded 11.0 Metres
Summer Draught 8.5 Metres
Deadweight on Summer Draught 10,110 Tonnes
Service Speed 14.0 Knots
TST
TST
DB
DB
Midship Section
No: 4 Hatch
No: 3 Hatch
No: 2 Hatch
No: 1 Hatch
Upper Deck
Tank Top

Fig. 18.29

the operator in the cargo control room to monitor the flow of cargo. A wandering lead can be used by an officer on deck or ashore to position the boom for discharge into barges.

Operation of the gates at the bottom of the holds to govern the flow of cargo on to the belts requires skill and experience, particularly when cargoes are not free flowing. If there is a mechanical failure of the belts, or if cargo is allowed to flow out too fast, it will jam and overflow the belts. When this happens tonnes of cargo must be shovelled out of confined spaces in the tunnel by hand to free the belts and allow a resumption of discharge. Cargo which overflows in this way will generally be shovelled back on to the belts and discharged.

Control of the flow of cargo is achieved by the amount the gates are opened. For dry coal or for grain the gates are only cracked open. The only indication the operator has of how much cargo is dropping on to the belts is given by the load on the belt motors. If the cargo is sticky, for example moist coal, it may be that initially no cargo drops at all. The flow of cargo can be assisted by operation of the vibrators which are situated next to each gate. These vibrators, also operated from the cargo control room, are in the form of eccentric weights which when activated shake the framework to which the hold plating near the gates is attached.

If cargo starts to overflow a belt at a time when several pairs of gates are open, the operator has no sure way of knowing which pair of gates is releasing too much cargo. A quick-close button permits him to close all gates instantaneously, after which he can gradually reopen the gates in turn. When discharge is interrupted, the belts should if possible be emptied before they are stopped, since it can be very difficult to start the belts when they are loaded. Maximum tonnage likely to be on the belts is 50 tonnes when discharging at maximum rate.

During discharge the ship must be kept even keel as far as possible, with a maximum acceptable trim of 2 metres by the stern, since a greater trim puts an excessive load on the belt motors. If it is necessary to restart the belts when they are fully loaded it may be necessary to trim the vessel by the head to assist the forward momentum of the cargo on the belts.

List must also be kept to a minimum, with a maximum of no more than 1°. A list causes the belts to 'wander towards the list', causing scuffing of the belt edges, which reduces its life. This is expensive in replacement material and in repair time. List and trim are monitored in the control room by means of sensitive inclinometers consisting of weighted 1 metre lengths of line attached to the transverse and fore-aft bulkheads.

Holds may be discharged or part discharged in any convenient sequence calculated to preserve the desired trim. One favoured sequence is: (i) empty No.2 hold; (ii) alternate between Nos.1 and 4 holds until they are empty, keeping trim below 2 m; (iii) complete by discharging No.3 hold. Discharging rates of 1,800 tonnes/hour can be achieved if coal is very dry, and a rate of 1,000 tonnes/hour can comfortably be maintained throughout discharge with most coal cargoes.

On deck and ashore the discharging process is not a dusty one, because the discharging belt is inside the boom. The holds can be kept covered throughout discharge, although the lids must be raised to allow air to enter and they are normally opened for convenient monitoring of progress. When the ship is on a regular coal run, holds are not cleaned between cargoes and the ship sails with some cargo residues between the frames on the transverse bulkheads. The ship's constant, which includes cargo residues and sediment in the ballast tanks, is about 240 metric tonnes.

Discharge can be controlled by a computer program which can be instructed to maintain a stipulated rate of discharge, although with some cargoes manual operation is preferred as it offers more control. Ship's staff find that the program is unable to recognise instances in which the cargo is sticking and will open the gates wider and wider until a large volume of cargo is suddenly dumped on the belts. This can be prevented by setting a maximum permitted opening percentage for the gates. Ballasting is carried out from the control room whilst the cargo is discharged, with care to ensure that list and trim are kept at a minimum.

Two sailors remain on duty throughout discharge. In addition to normal mooring and gangway watch they are responsible for making an inspection in the cargo tunnel at hourly intervals. Any belt roller which is seen to be not turning is freed by tapping or, if that fails, is noted for changing at the first opportunity. A normal 650 mm roller takes about 10 minutes to change. The sailors look out for any spillages of cargo, which must not be allowed to build up under the belts, and they shovel any overflows of cargo back onto the belts or if this is not immediately possible clear of the working area.

Whilst discharging is taking place the tunnel becomes dusty. The tunnel is ventilated by fans and to ensure that it remains well ventilated it is only possible to engage the cargo breaker and commence discharge when the fans have been running for 15 minutes. On completion of discharge the boom is swung inboard and the ship is brought upright with ballast, one tank having been left slack for this purpose.

Belt system: Power to the seven belts which in combination form the discharging system is provided in a variety of ways. The two main cargo belts and the two transfer belts are driven by 440v AC electric motors through Dodge reducers fitted onto the driving rollers. The inner loop belt main drive wheel is driven by two electric motors through two fluid clutches into two Hansen reducers, one each side of the loop casing. The outer loop belt is driven by the inner loop belt by friction. The main boom belt, like the inner loop belt, is driven by an electric motor through a fluid clutch into a Hansen reducer.

The tension in each of the belts is adjustable, and belt tension is an important factor in efficient discharge. Too much tension in the cargo belts will reduce the concavity of their cross-section, and their ability to contain cargo, thus squeezing cargo out of the system. Too little tension will permit the belts to wander. Tension in the main cargo belts is adjusted by adding or removing tensioning weights, whilst screw tensioners are used to adjust tension in the transfer belts and the main boom belt. The tension of the loop belts is adjusted with hydraulic rams, with typical pressures for coal being 1,400 psi (96.5 bar) for the inner loop belt and 1,250 psi (86.2 bar) for the outer loop belt. The belts are automatically stopped if pressure is lost. Suitable tensions for the discharge of a particular cargo have to be found by trial and error, with finer grained cargoes requiring lower belt tensions.

Bins are situated between the transfer belts and the loop belts and between the loop belts and the main boom belt. The bins act as hoppers which feed cargo on to the next belt in the system. Pressure pads fitted in the bins will detect any build-up of cargo and will automatically close the cargo gates to stop discharge. In the bins at belt ends, deflector plates are installed to guide the cargo down on to the centre of the next belt. These have to be adjusted for a change of cargo and may seize up if not operated from time to time. A trip line runs the length of the tunnel and can be used to stop the belts instantly in the event of emergency.

Ballast voyage: Washing of the tunnel is carried out every voyage or at the very least every second voyage. The washing is done with sea water and the objectives are to ensure that the cargo gates are clean and free of any material which might clog them, to wash away any cargo spillage from the tunnel, and to remove the dust. Washing below the gates is done with the gates closed and is difficult, as the space is restricted. The water and all the residues are removed from the bilges by eductors and discharged into the sea when regulations permit. Washing the tunnel normally takes about two hours. Washing the tunnel with sea water encourages corrosion, which may become a problem as this type of ship becomes older, so frequent fresh water rinsing must be carried out.

The cargo holds are not washed if the next cargo is to be similar to the previous one. If holds have to be washed prior to carriage of a different cargo they are washed with seawater from handheld hoses with the gates open, and water draining into the tunnel for discharge by the tunnel eductors. If necessary the seawater wash will be followed by a fresh water rinse.

If a very fine grained cargo, such as nepheline syenite, is to be carried, the hold gates must be lined with polythene sheeting or tarred paper before commencement of loading to prevent cargo from leaking through the closed gates during the loaded passage. This lining will drop through the gates when discharge commences and be discharged with the cargo.

Maintenance: All the deck machinery, including all the discharging gear, is thoroughly greased on a continuous cycle once every six weeks. The full greasing programme takes about four days, with half a day spent on deck fittings including hatch covers and three and a half days spent on the cargo gear. Every large belt roller is provided with a grease nipple at each bearing. The outer nipple is difficult to reach in the restricted space outboard of the belt. Each gate has four greasing points which are not easily accessible.

The ship has the capability to make small repairs to the belts using special clips, but the belts are vulcanised and cannot be permanently repaired by ship's staff.

The cargo belts are connected to the motors by drive belts. If the system is overloaded or if the drive belt is worn, the drive belt will part. It is routine to look behind the guard frequently and to renew the drive belt when it is seen to be worn or damaged.

The main and transfer belts are fitted with skirting at the sides to prevent cargo from falling off the belts, and this skirting must be renewed as it becomes worn. The belts are also fitted with scraper plates to remove residues from the return portion and they, too, require renewal when they are worn out. The main rollers at the ends of each belt are very heavy and difficult to change, chain blocks being required for this process.

The cargo gates are electro-hydraulically controlled. Repairs to the hydraulic pipework, a category of work which becomes larger as a ship grows older, are done by available ship's staff drawn from deck and engine departments.

Cargoes carried: The *Telnes* has successfully carried coal, gypsum, limestone, magnetite, ilmenite, petcoke, chalk, barley, oats, wheat, pyrites, olivin, coke, quartz, salt, stone, iron ore pellets, iron ore fines, cement clinker and nepheline syenite. Alumina, however, was found to be too fine and presented serious problems with the belt tensions in use at that time.

At the other extreme, any cargo which was excessively sticky would be impossible to discharge with ship's gear and would have to be discharged by grab. Such cargoes would not be carried. Cargo which is spout-loaded will generally discharge more easily than cargo loaded by grab, since the latter process tends to compact the cargo.

Hybrid Self-unloaders: These vessels are conventional bulk carriers which have been converted to self-unloading by the fitting of a deck mounted boom conveyor fed by ship's cranes or excavators through a system of hoppers. A number of such vessels with Scandinavian and other North European owners are in service. They are cheaper to buy and to operate than full self-unloaders and can carry the full range of bulk and unitised cargoes when not required for self-unloading. They can also be discharged by shore gear if the ship's conveyor breaks down. They

Fig. 18.30 MV *Clydenes* discharging coal. Travelling platform positioned at the fore end of No. 1 Hold. The ship's excavator is dropping cargo into the ship's hopper while the ship's boom conveyor is delivering coal to the shore hopper
Photo courtesy of Mike Tysoe

cannot compare with conventional self-unloaders for speed of discharge and for the handling of wet-sensitive cargoes when it is raining.

Typical of hybrid self-unloaders[162] is Jebsen's mv *Clydenes* (Fig. 18.30) formerly mv *Arklow Bridge*. She is a 7,182 dwt, two hold vessel. An excavator, a hopper and the boom conveyer are mounted on a platform which straddles the breadth of the holds and travels along rails at each side of the hatches. The boom has an outreach of 22.2 m from the vessel's side and her overall discharging rate, which depends upon the presence of an expert excavator driver, is about 750 tonnes/hr which allows her to berth on one tide and sail on the next. In 2006 she was engaged in the coal trade between Scotland and Ireland. Trimming of the final cargo residues for discharge is done by machine or by hand, a task undertaken by the ship's crew. The ship carries a bobcat for this purpose.

Mini-bulkers

Ships of up to about 10,000 metric tonnes deadweight, when carrying dry bulk cargoes, are often called mini-bulkers though they may alternatively be called multi-purpose ships or general traders. The details of their construction may decide whether or not they are classed as bulk carriers and governed by rules drafted specifically for bulk carriers. Whilst some vessels of this size are engaged in worldwide trading and many are equipped so to do, their main trades are the European short-sea trades. In European waters several thousand mini-bulkers are employed primarily in trades with a draught limitation of about 8 metres or where the requirement is for comparatively small tonnages of cargo. Mini-bulkers can be expected to take the ground more often in berths where this is intended than do larger bulk carriers, and purpose built vessels with low superstructures, shallow draught and folding masts are more likely to make long passages upriver to small inland berths.

Ship types: Mini-bulkers (Drawing 1.6) were, before 1998, normally one- or two-hold vessels of up to 100 metres in length, with large hatch openings and powered steel hatch covers. The trend has been towards vessels of double skinned construction with box holds. Some are fitted with cranes or swinging derricks for cargo loading and discharge, whilst others are gearless. Since the amended SOLAS rules on damage stability for cargo ships took effect in 1998, one- and two hold ships are (by implication) required to have double skins and cannot exceed 80 m in length but ships built earlier will continue to trade.

Intensive trading pattern: The pattern of trade for these vessels is intensive, since a full cargo can in many ports be loaded in 6-12 hours, and will rarely take more than a day, whilst discharge is unlikely to take more than two days unless a weekend is included. Because the sea passages are also short, experienced ship operators are able to plan tight schedules, trying to ensure that ships are at sea over the weekend. A schedule of 50 voyages a year with more than 100 ports visited is normal and will be composed of hectic spells in which three or four ports are visited in a week, interspersed with the occasional longer voyage, often in bad weather, and occasional quiet periods at anchor awaiting a berth.

Communications: Detailed voyage orders will normally be received in printed form by email to the ship or her agents, but most subsequent communications are likely to be by telephone, either via VHF or by mobile telephone.

Ship handling and pilotage: Mini-bulkers require tugs very rarely. It is unusual for such vessels to have cp propellers or bow thrusters, but the traditional use of engines through a clutched ahead/astern gearbox, rudder, anchor and mooring ropes is normally sufficient to allow them to manoeuvre into and out of their berths. Where pilotage is not compulsory the Master will often elect to do his own pilotage, particularly when he is familiar with the berth.

Whilst mini-bulkers are manoeuvrable ships and are usually well handled, the fact that they berth so many times in the course of a year means that they are at risk more often and that they are likely to suffer more contact damage than larger bulk carriers. Some berths are less well suited to mini-bulkers than others. Amongst the most challenging for a 90 metre ship is a jetty with a face of 7 metres, and with a loading structure mounted on top of it! Mooring lines are secured to distant dolphins, or to bollards or even trees on the shore.

Cargoes: Cargoes carried in mini-bulkers include almost every commodity which enters world trade in bulk. Grain including wheat, barley, oats and soya beans is an important trade, as is the transportation of chemical fertilisers. Coal, coke and petcoke is extensively shipped and transhipped in mini-bulkers, as is steel in the form of coils and slabs. Other cargoes widely carried are forest products, quartz, salt, aggregate, ferrous scrap, clay, minerals and sands.

Hold preparation: A feature of the efficient operation of mini-bulkers is the regular occurrence of backloading, whereby a new cargo is loaded in the port or area where the previous cargo was discharged. In European waters this is particularly likely in large and busy ports such as Rotterdam/Europort, Hamburg and Antwerp. This puts particular pressure upon the ship's personnel because of the requirement to prepare the holds for a new cargo without benefit of the ballast passage in which such work is normally done.

It will always be necessary to ensure that the sounding pipes and bilges are clean, that the bilge suctions have been tested and that the bilges have been covered and burlapped before the new cargo is loaded. Usually it will also be desirable to wash the holds but this is seldom possible. The discharge of hold washings is nowadays prohibited within port areas[246] making washing impossible unless washings can be retained aboard in holding tanks, or discharged to reception facilities. When holds cannot be washed they must be swept and the residues lifted and stored on deck. The length of time required for this process will be governed by the labour and equipment available, the nature of the previous cargo, the quality of the stevedores' trimming (ie discharge of sweepings), the size and characteristics of the hold and the level of cleanliness required for the next cargo.

Loading calculations: Stability and loading calculations on mini-bulkers are simplified by the fact that no stress calculations are required. In other respects the calculations are similar to those for larger vessels, except that the number of compartments and the number of loading positions is reduced. The ship's constant, or miscellaneous weights allowance, for a 3,000 metric tonnes deadweight vessel is likely to be 30-50 tonnes, and for a 6,000 mt dwt vessel can be expected to be 50-90 tonnes. These figures can be substantially higher if the ballast tanks contain quantities of mud.

Loading: Loading is normally by means of a loading spout through which cargo is poured into the hold. The spout is frequently fixed, or has only limited mobility, so that the ship must be moved back and forwards along the berth to permit loading in the required positions. A typical loading of a closeweight or heavy cargo for a mini-bulker would involve loading cargo in four positions distributed along the length of the ship (Fig. 18.31). The four pours might be taken in positions 3, 1, 4, 2 in sequence, followed by a trimming pour of about 300 mt if the cargo to be lifted is 3,000 mt. This sequence would be planned to ensure that the ship maintained a stern trim throughout loading, for efficient deballasting and would, of course, be planned and agreed in advance with the terminal as required by the BLU Code.

Because of the requirement to position the ship below the loader for each pour it is necessary to warp the ship along the berth to a new loading position four times during the course of loading. This is a process which will normally require a minimum of five men – namely, two at each end of the ship to handle the mooring ropes and one at the loading position to signal when the ship is correctly positioned. The process can be expected to take about 10 minutes provided the crew are prepared and the working conditions are not exceptional.

Loaded voyage: During the loaded voyage a mini-bulker is likely to have a freeboard of no more than 1-2 metres amidships. She will probably be shipping water on the main deck even in the calmest weather, and in any adverse sea and wind she will be taking spray forward. The hold ventilators of most mini-bulkers operating in the European trades are permanently closed and blanked off.

Keeping water out of the holds and the forecastle spaces is a matter which must never be neglected in mini-bulkers in view of their small freeboard. It is essential that the seals for hatches and for watertight doors and ventilators are well maintained and tightly closed when the vessel goes to sea, and that compartments are frequently inspected for damage, wastage and leakage. It is prudent to heave-to and make an inspection of hatch covers, anchors and windlass, and forecastle store at the start and end of each day when encountering severe weather.

High-level bilge alarms and/or water ingress detectors are usually fitted in the forecastle spaces of mini-bulkers. It is good practice for the officer routinely to test the alarm when he leaves the forecastle head at the commencement of every sea passage. Thereafter, if the alarm sounds an investigation should be undertaken as soon as possible.

The fact that the vessel is likely to be shipping water on deck during loaded passages means that it is seldom possible to obtain direct soundings of hold bilges or ballast tanks. Where reliable remote sounding gauges are available there is no problem, but on many older mini-bulkers it is likely that no soundings can be obtained during normal and worse-than-normal weather.

Discharging: The discharging (unloading) plan must be planned and agreed in advance with the terminal as required by the BLU Code. Objectives will include preserving a reasonable trim and keeping the ship upright. It will usually suit stevedores and ship's personnel if discharge of separate holds is finished in sequence, and not simultaneously. If the ship wishes or requires to commence cleaning holds as soon as possible the planned sequence for completing discharge of individual holds should take this into account.

Discharge, in general, is similar to that for larger bulk carriers. Most discharging methods are liable to damage the ship if carelessly used and the holds should be regularly checked for damage during discharge and on completion.

Sediment in ballast tanks: A result of ballasting the ship 50 times a year is that the build-up of sediment or mud in the ballast tanks is likely to be rapid. This increases the ship's deadweight constant and increases the time required for discharge of ballast. It is necessary to look for any opportunity to remove mud from ballast tanks.

Maintenance programmes: Adverse weather conditions consisting of cold, rain, wind, salt spray and darkness all conspire to reduce the amount of maintenance that can be carried out aboard mini-bulkers in the European trades during Winter. It is realistic to expect very little maintenance work except essential greasing to be done about the decks from December to February, unless unseasonal weather is

Distribution of cargo in mini-bulker

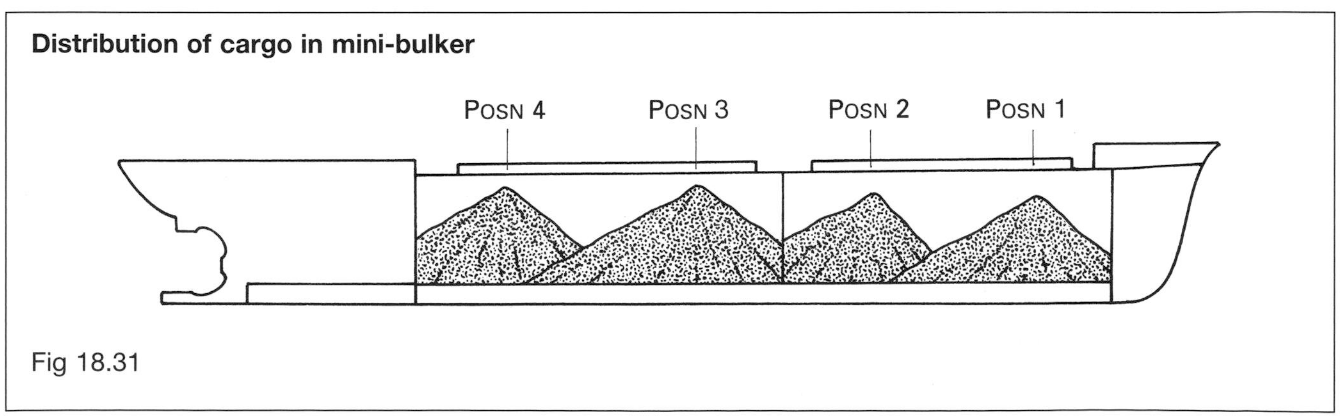

Fig 18.31

met. For this reason it is essential that maintenance and renewal of the ship's safety equipment, hatch covers, deck machinery, cargo gear and paintwork is commenced as soon as the first mild weather is experienced in Spring time, and continued with commitment until the Autumn is well advanced.

Means of access: Access to a mini-bulker, as to larger bulk carriers, is often difficult. Rise and fall of tide, rapid alteration in draught of the ship and the requirement to shift back and forth along the berth all make it difficult to arrange a good means of access. Difficulties are increased because the jetty is often higher than the deck of a mini-bulker, and the stern with its accommodation ladder may be beyond the end of the jetty. Ships are able to provide gangways (also known as brows) and accommodation ladders. Occasionally effective shore gangways are provided, and this is to be welcomed for the improved safety which it offers.

Forest product carriers

Forest product carriers (Drawing 1.10) are handy-sized geared bulk carriers which are able to carry a range of bulk cargoes but which are particularly well suited to the carriage of woodpulp, sawn timber, plywood and newsprint, all cargoes which are relatively light and which can be most easily stowed in rectangular spaces. Some forest product carriers have hold lengths suitable for carrying 40 ft containers and standard length drilling pipes for the off-shore industry. Such vessels have an open hatch layout in which the entire box-shaped hold is open to the sky when the hatch covers have been opened. This permits units of cargo to be landed directly in the intended stowage position. The designers achieve the box-shaped hold configuration by placing ballast tanks ('wing tanks') between the hold and the ship's sides.

Ice strengthening: Forest product ships are often ice strengthened, since many producers of these cargoes, such as Canada, Russia and Scandinavia, are located in areas which experience ice in winter. A bulk carrier fully laden with woodpulp or with sawn softwood will not sink to her winter loadline. Because of this the ice strengthening on some ships is only continued up to the anticipated operating draught. If such a ship loads a full closeweight cargo she will be operating at a draught deeper than the ice strengthened band, and effectively becomes a ship without ice strengthening.

Carriage of deck cargo: Another feature which identifies the forest product ship is the provision for carrying deck cargo. To permit the carriage of the maximum volume of timber on deck the ship's cranes, often capable of lifting units of 25 tonnes or more, will be mounted on pedestals which carry them clear of any deck cargo and which occupy a minimum of deck space. The decks and hatch covers will have been strengthened to allow the loading of a permitted tonnage on deck. Timber deck cargoes may be retained in position by vertical timber stanchions and the box-shaped steel housings, or sockets, for the stanchions are built into the ship's structure along the line of the ship's side rails (Fig. 1.21). Alternatively, the ship may be fitted with permanent tall vertical steel stanchions or pillars at the sides of the deck. (Fig. 18.32.)

Fig. 18.32 Permanent ship's side stanchions abreast of masthouses to retain timber deck cargoes

The IMO *Code of Safe Practice for Ships Carrying Timber Deck Cargoes* provides detail of the regulations governing the stowage, lashing and securing of timber deck cargoes and related matters such as stability and ship handling in heavy weather. A list and description of the ship's cargo lashing equipment can be found in the ship's cargo securing manual. Both these documents should be studied and followed whenever a timber deck cargo is carried.

When such deck cargoes are carried, it is essential that access to safety devices, sounding pipes, remote controls for valves and closing arrangements for deck houses is maintained. To ensure this the deck will be permanently marked with black/yellow stripes in positions where deck cargo must not be placed.

Lashings for timber deck cargoes may be kept permanently aboard a forest product ship or may be provided with the cargo and landed at the end of the voyage. Each lashing must be independent and will consist of wire rope and/or chain, with a quick release mechanism such as a senhouse slip, connecting shackles and a stretching device such as a turnbuckle or speedlashing. (Speedlashings are turnbuckles which can be tightened by use of an air-powered tool.) They must be in sound condition, well maintained and properly certified according to national regulations. In addition they should be visually examined for defects annually, and moving parts must be kept greased and moving freely at all times.

Problems may arise if the national regulations of the shipowners are different from those of the country in which the cargo is loaded – for example, the Canadians will require each and every item of lashing gear to have a test certificate showing a breaking load, whilst the British consider that lashings including lashing chains only require visual examination and need not be certificated.

View from the navigating bridge: One consequence of raising deck cranes high above the decks is that the view ahead from the bridge may be restricted, particularly if twin cranes are fitted side by side. On sea passages the bridge watchkeeper will have to be prepared to move from side to side of the bridge to ensure that he obtains a good view ahead around the stowed cranes. On river passages in sheltered waters it may be possible to put the jibs of twin cranes vertical and to slew the platform for the twin cranes to a position in which the blind sector of the horizon ahead is reduced. Deck cargo may also restrict the view ahead and where necessary it must be stepped down over the forward hatches[181].

(Forest product cargoes are described in Chapter 19.)

Log carriers

The log carrier which provided the basis for this section (Fig. 18.33) was a geared bulk carrier with bridge, machinery spaces and accommodation aft, and having four holds of which Nos 2-4 were provided with twin hatches. Her approximate dimensions were 10,300 tons gross, 6,200 tons nett and 16,000 tonnes dwt with overall length 485 ft, beam 70 ft, moulded depth 40 ft and maximum draught 30 ft. The three cranes and one swinging derrick possessed SWLs of 16 tonnes.

Whilst this vessel was engaged principally in the

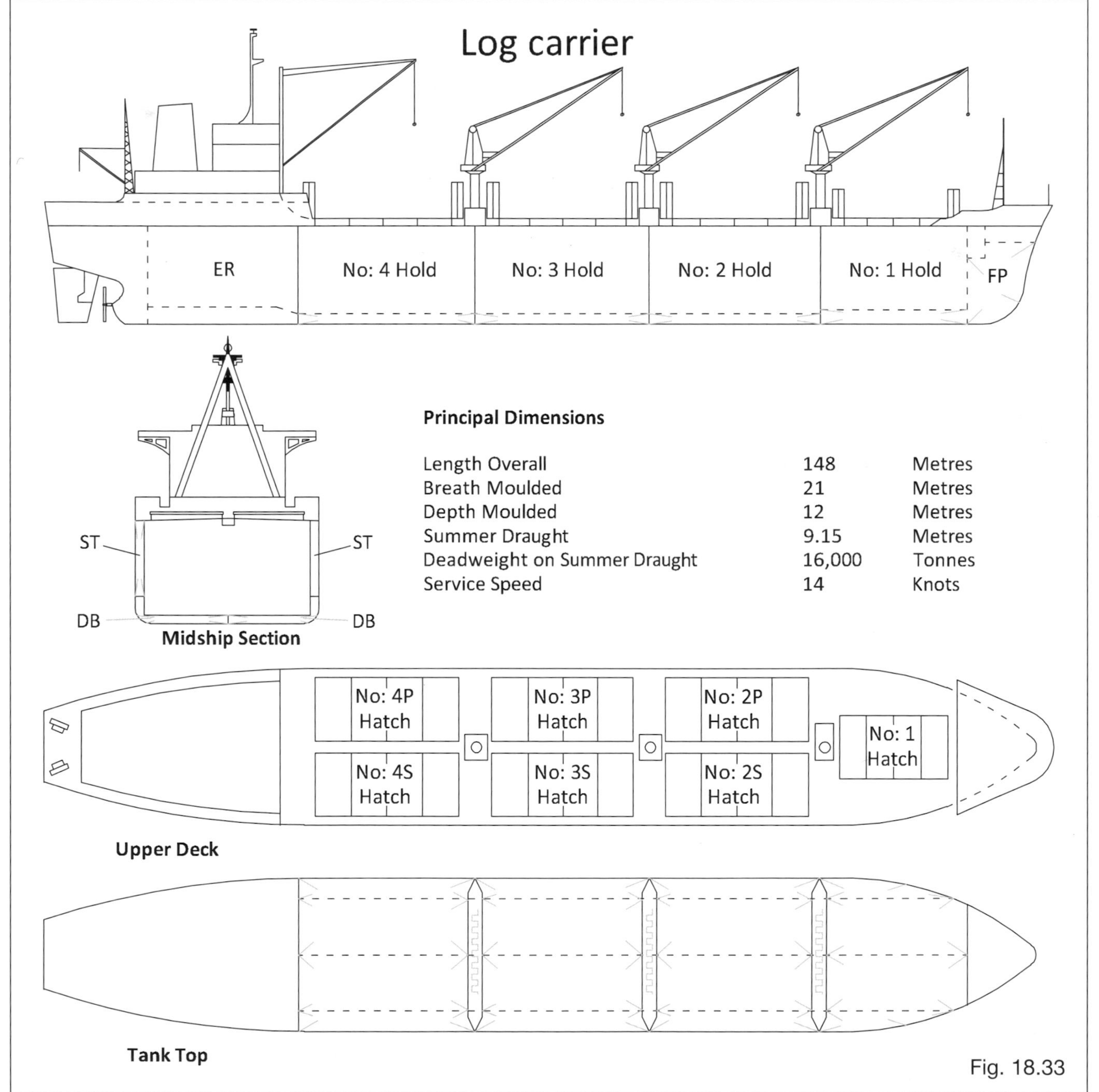

Fig. 18.33

trade between the US/Canadian West Coast and Japan, the operating procedures described are equally valid for smaller two-hold loggers trading in Asian and African waters. These procedures should be read in conjunction with the IMO *Code of Safe Practice for Ships Carrying Timber Deck Cargoes*[4].

Concern was expressed during the 1990s at the substantial number of log carrier casualties which occurred over many years. Contributory factors are thought to have been inadequate initial stability due to taking of excessive deck cargo, shifting of cargo above and below decks due to poor stowage, and flooding of holds due to structural damage suffered when loading and discharging logs. Happily casualties have been very rare in recent years.

Preparation of the vessel: Holds must be swept and free from all debris. Hold bilges must be clean and tested. A portable dewatering pump (sump pump) of capacity sufficient to pump water from holds to deck is useful to deal with flooding if a bilge becomes blocked.

Logs loaded from rafts floated down to the vessel bring on board considerable quantities of water which can lead to hold bilge soundings of several feet. Bilges may need to be pumped several times to remove this water as it has to filter through the logs, and by the time it reaches the bilges it usually contains pieces of bark, weed, mud and other debris. To prevent the bilge strum becoming blocked, the entrance can be stuffed with wire netting (chicken wire) to attempt to filter out the larger pieces of debris.

Any changes to the ballast distribution should be made as soon as practicable, leaving ballast tanks either completely filled or empty to eliminate free surface effect wherever possible. In any event all ballast movements must be completed before loading the deck cargo. Bunkers should be kept to the minimum number of tanks consistent with operational requirements to reduce the free surface effect.

Any bunkering operations should, if possible, be completed before loading the deck cargo. The sounding of tanks and communicating the results are both more difficult with a deck cargo. A spill is bad enough on a clear deck but is virtually impossible to clean up below a cargo of logs. There is also the likelihood of cargo claims from logs impregnated with fuel oil.

All cargo lifting equipment should be thoroughly inspected and any damaged and worn wire ropes replaced. Weights of logs are generally not known, and logs loaded from the water can be much heavier than expected especially if they have been in the water for some time. Cargo gear is likely to be worked hard and any weaknesses will soon be found.

Lines should be painted on the deck in a distinctive colour to indicate the maximum limits of the deck stow and areas to be left clear of cargo. This is to ensure that sounding pipes, devices for remote operation of valves and safety equipment remain accessible, mooring winches remain usable, the pilot can board in safety, and deck lockers and machinery entrances are accessible.

Cargo lashing equipment should be sorted and placed in position, shackles and turnbuckles greased and laid clear of the cargo area so that they are not overstowed. Do not leave this job until the last minute. It is better to sort everything out before arriving in port since after arrival the deck will be cluttered with stevedores. Hatch cover protection should be made available. Some vessels place plywood sheets or dunnage over the hatch covers and then lay old mooring ropes or similar athwartships across the covers to prevent damage.

Following incidents of ships listing heavily when water flooded back into topside tanks, screw-down overboard drain valves fitted to topside ballast tanks (dump valves or drop valves) must be closed whilst loading timber and whilst at sea. Access to the valves must remain free at all times. The internal structure of the holds should be inspected for damage and repaired if defects are found. Hold sparring and pipeguards to protect internal hull members should be in place.

Loading logs in the holds: Logs should be lifted aboard close to the ship and should if necessary be steadied against the hatch coaming before lowering into the hold, to minimise swinging. It is usual to load the logs lying fore and aft, as far as possible, so that in the event of cargo movement logs do not act as battering rams against the ship's side if she rolls heavily.

Care must be taken when placing the first tier of logs on the tank tops so that a good level stow is achieved, broken stowage (ie, empty space between logs) is kept to a minimum and logs are not landed heavily, damaging the tank top plating and internal framing. While it is important that deck officers pay close attention throughout cargo operations so that any damage does not go unnoticed, it is essential that the stevedores are closely supervised during the initial period of cargo operations when any incorrect use of cargo equipment or reckless handling of cargo can be rectified. It also establishes the relationship between the ship's officers and the stevedores and ensures there is no misunderstanding as to the standard of work expected.

Logs stowed fore and aft should be placed towards one end of the compartment. If the space is long enough, a further stow of logs laid fore and aft should be placed towards the other end of the compartment, and any space remaining in the middle of the hold between the two stows should be filled with logs stowed athwartships. If the hold is only long enough for one stow of logs fore and aft, any space which remains at the other end of the hold should be filled with logs stowed athwartships. The athwartships stow should be completed tier by tier as loading progresses. (It is reported that in the West African log trade logs are never stowed athwartships.) Butt ends of the logs should be alternatively reversed to achieve a more level stowage except where excess sheer on the inner bottom is encountered.

Snatch blocks and bull wires should be available to ensure that logs are stowed out to the ship's side and broken stowage is kept to the absolute minimum. The blocks must be attached to suitably reinforced padeyes and eyebolts and the gear must not be overloaded. It is important to stow as much of the cargo as possible in the holds as wasted space can, for reasons of stability, reduce the tonnage of cargo which can be loaded on deck. A tight stow below and within the hatch coamings should be achieved by the use of smaller logs if they are available.

If loading direct from the water or if heavy rain occurs during loading, bilges should be sounded and pumped frequently. Apart from causing errors in stability roll tests and deadweight calculations, significant quantities of water in the holds will when the vessel moves in a seaway mix with bark and other debris and can become a thick emulsified mass which is virtually impossible to pump out.

On completion of loading the holds ensure that all hold lighting is isolated, hold access hatches are securely battened down and cargo will not interfere with the securing of the hatch covers.

Loading on deck: Lighter, longer, logs should whenever possible be kept for deck stowage for both stability reasons and the ease of securing. Shipside timber stanchions should be rigged and secured in position and lashing equipment kept clear of the loading area and free to be pulled over the cargo on completion.

The area between the hatch coaming and the ship side stanchions must be carefully stowed with the longest logs at the ship side and these logs butted-up to each other. This helps to present a smooth surface at the outside of the stow to any seas breaking on board and therefore reduces the likelihood of logs becoming displaced in heavy weather. The stow must be kept as compact as possible.

Loading on the hatch covers must be done with great care to avoid damage. Deck officers must remain conscious of the danger of damage to hatch covers, hold access hatches and hold ventilators. If such damage remains undetected under the stow it could allow large quantities of water to enter the hold in adverse weather with potentially disastrous results.

Experience of the vessel and trade will indicate when checks on the vessel's stability are required, but in general a check should be made before loading of the deck cargo is commenced. Draughts should be monitored regularly and tonnages of cargo loaded should be computed and recorded. From the information thus obtained deck officers will soon gain the ability to estimate the quantity of cargo loaded even if the individual weights of logs are unknown.

The deck stow must be completed with the centre slightly higher than the sides and ideally curved from the centre to the ship side so that the lashings are in contact with the logs across the whole surface of the stow. It may be necessary to stop loading before maximum cargo has been lifted, to ensure that loading ends with a complete tier of logs with the required curved surface.

Hog lashings described in the Timber Deck Cargo Code[4] are wires sometimes used to strengthen and bind the stow and to support the ship side timber stanchions. They are normally used over the second and third tiers and may be set 'hand tight' between stanchions. The result is a series of slack wires running across the logs, secured at each end, which become tight when the next tier of logs is loaded and the wires are pressed down in the curve between the logs underneath. They consolidate the stow, act as a secondary lashing system and pull the ship side timber stanchions inboard at half their height, which reduces the risk of the stanchions shearing at their bases. Wiggle wires[4] are wire ropes about 20 mm diameter, fitted in the manner of a shoelace to tighten the stow. A wiggle wire runs through a series of snatch blocks lying on the top of the stow and secured by wires running alternately to the port or starboard sides of the stow. The wiggle wire is hauled tight with the help of a winch and secured. Turnbuckles fitted between snatch block and lashing wire can be tightened as necessary during the voyage. Chain lashings[4] are passed over the top of the stow and secured to substantial padeyes or other securing points at the outboard extremities of the cargo. Turnbuckles used for tightening the chains at sea are fitted at the mid length of each chain, in positions on top of the stow.

If the deck is completely covered with deck cargo leaving no path along the deck from forward to aft, and if the ship possesses no pipe tunnels or other underdeck walkways extending the length of the ship, a temporary walkway must be provided over the deck cargo.

Stability: In practice there are two possible methods of calculating the vessel's stability when loading a cargo of logs. Conventional trim and stability calculations must be made and these can be checked by calculating the GM from a roll test.

Trim and stability calculations are difficult when the weights of individual logs are unknown. For that reason every item which can be checked should be assessed with care. The contents of tanks and bilges and the ship's constant should be carefully measured and calculated. Accurate figures should be used for the space occupied by the cargo, on deck and below deck, when calculating the positions of the centres of gravity of the cargo. Because some space is always lost below the deckheads it is safe to assume that the cargo is homogeneous, and that its centre of gravity lies at the geometric centre of the hold, unless it is clear that heavier logs have been loaded at the top of the stow.

Frequent checks are required on the vessel's draught during loading to ensure she does not trim by the head, especially if a maximum deadweight cargo is to be lifted and ballasting cannot be used to provide stern trim.

When considering the minimum stability acceptable for the passage to the discharge port several factors should be taken into consideration apart from the minimum criteria stated in the vessel's stability book. Has the deck cargo been loaded in a dry condition? An allowance must be made for water absorbed by the deck cargo. Is the hold cargo very wet? If so allowance must be made for loss of weight as water from the cargo seeps into the bilges and is pumped out. Is the deck cargo tightly stowed? If not can significant quantities of water be held on deck if seas are shipped on board? Ensure there is adequate reserve stability. Will the vessel pass through an area where icing could occur? Allowance must be made for additional weight of ice on top of the stow. Will the free surface effect increase during the voyage due to use of additional tanks? A ballast tank which is full can become slack as a result of spillage caused by rolling, or a large change in temperature.

When loading of the holds is completed, a careful draught check must be made to permit calculation of the weight of cargo loaded. At this point the ship's stability can be calculated with reasonable accuracy and the maximum cargo to be loaded on deck can be established. As a check on the vessel's stability calculation if she is less than 70 m in length[4], a roll test can be conducted and used to calculate the GM.

The vessel must be made to roll and to achieve this, if alongside, all moorings must be slacked, gangway lifted, cargo stopped and all cargo gear brought to as near the seagoing position as reasonable, except for one crane or derrick amidships which should be swung well outboard with a heavy sling of cargo attached. Raising and lowering the sling from the quay will soon induce the vessel to roll, and when rolling gently the sling should either be bought quickly inboard and landed on the centreline, or landed on the quay and the hoist wire kept slack. The size of roll has no effect on the period of roll. As soon as the vessel is rolling freely the period of roll – ie, the time taken from maximum roll one side to that same position again – must be carefully timed over several rolls.

If the vessel is at anchor in calm conditions, the same measurement can be undertaken, the rolling being induced by lowering and raising a sling of cargo in and out of the water. Ensure that all lighters are clear from the ship side as their moorings will affect the period of roll.

The accuracy of the roll test will be reduced if the vessel's freedom to roll is restricted in any way and also if a large free surface effect is present in bunker or ballast tanks. In the latter case it is best to assume that the GM obtained does not include the effect of free surface and to correct the GM for free surface effect.

The formula used to calculate the approximate GM is: $GM = F/T^2$, where GM is the metacentric height in metres or feet (ie, whichever units are specified in the ship's documentation); F is a ship's figure to be determined by the ship's administration and given in the ship's loading manual (this figure is derived from the ship's transverse radius of gyration which depends upon her dimensions and condition of loading); and T is the period of roll in seconds.

When the GM has been calculated from a roll test it is important to consider the other measures of stability for the worst condition before concluding that the ship is entirely safe. These measures include the areas under the GZ curve (the dynamic stability), the range of stability up to the angle when positive stability vanishes and the ship will capsize, and the angle at which the maximum righting effect occurs, which should be above 30° of heel. (Calculation of these values is shown in Appendix 10.9.)

During the voyage: Lashings on deck cargoes of any nature require checking frequently, but deck cargoes of timber and logs in particular require tightening, sometimes as often as two or three times a day during the first days of a sea passage as the vessel's movements cause the stow to settle. Considerable shrinkage can also occur if the logs have been lying in water for some time before being loaded; therefore even after the initial slack has been taken up lashing must be checked and tightened daily and this process recorded in the deck log book.

The ship's period of roll should be checked regularly when the ship is rolling in a seaway and the GM should be recalculated. In these conditions the results can only be approximate since the period of roll may be affected by the waves, by the vessel's speed and by rudder action. If it is found that the positive GM is becoming too small the reason must be sought since at the start of the voyage calculations should have showed that there would be sufficient stability throughout the voyage. The explanation may lie in careless procedures aboard ship, which have allowed too many slack tanks to occur, or inaccurate calculations which concealed a lack of stability. Another possibility is that a compartment has become flooded. When the cause of the loss of stability has been found appropriate steps can be taken.

Holds containing timber should only be entered when they have been ventilated and the good quality of the air has been confirmed. During the entry it is essential that the ventilation is kept running and enclosed space procedures are completed as per ISM. Where doubt remains, and if entry is essential, self-contained breathing apparatus must be worn by all persons entering the space, who should understand that the air bottles will be consumed very quickly while they are climbing up and down ladders. (See Chapter 21).

Retractable tweendeck vessels

Several shipbuilders have produced vessels with tweendecks which can be used in two alternative modes. When the tweendecks are lowered into position the ship operates as a tweendeck vessel; when the tweendecks are drawn up, unshipped or retracted, the vessel becomes a single-deck bulk carrier. This provides a useful flexibility in operating, but naturally incurs a higher initial cost and a greater maintenance requirement. Ships built in the 1990s are described below but retractable tweendecks have also been provided in some more recent mini- and handy-sized bulkers.

One feature shared by several designs of retractable tweendeck vessel is that the space available for cargo is diminished when the tweendecks are retracted (stowed away out of use). This causes no problems when a high-density cargo such as ore is carried, since not all the space is required, but has given rise to disputes when cargoes of sawn timber are carried. When the tweendecks are retracted for the stowage of bundles of sawn timber such space as is available is used more efficiently, but the space available is reduced. The ship's bale capacity is normally quoted for her condition with the tweendecks lowered. With the tweendecks retracted the bale capacity may be reduced by 5 per cent though the precise figure will vary from one design to another.

Freedom Mark II vessels: The Ishikawajima-Harima Freedom Mark II vessels are 17,000 tonne deadweight vessels fitted with hydraulically-operated retractable tweendecks which fold up to the ends of the holds (Fig. 18.34). When the hatches are lowered, tweendeck space is available in the wide hatch square and hatch ends; the small wing spaces are permanently used for pipe passages. When the tweendeck hatches are retracted the tweendeck is converted into a straight-sided graintight feeder space for the hold.

TD15s: The TD15s built by Astilleros Españoles SA are 15,000 tonne deadweight vessels. Hinged portions of the tweendeck are raised to meet the hatch coaming, thereby forming upper wing tanks which

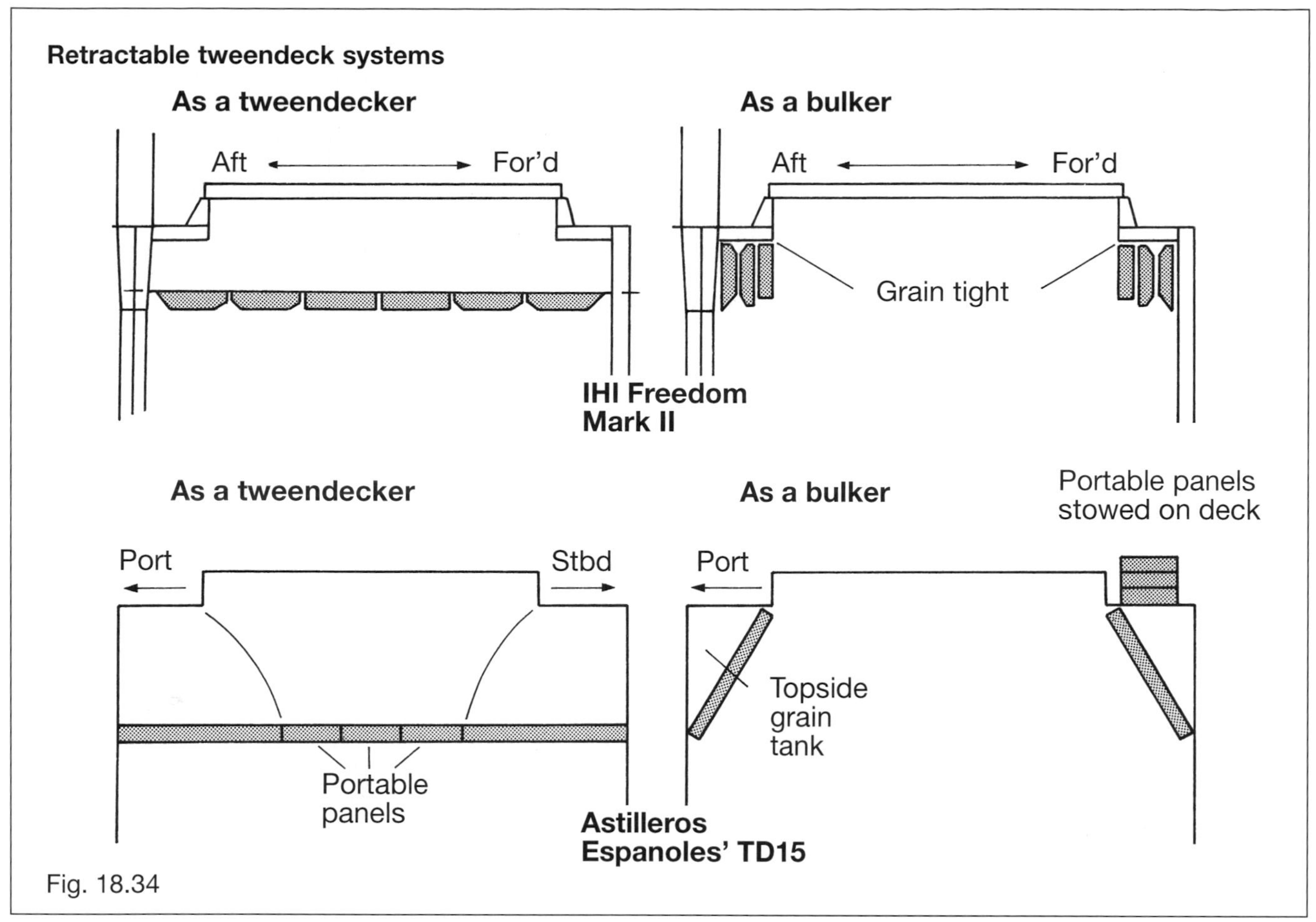

Fig. 18.34

can be used for the carriage of grain (Fig. 18.34). The portable pontoons from the hatch square which form the remainder of the tweendeck must be stowed elsewhere, usually along the sides of the main deck, when the ship is in single-deck configuration. Pontoons which are stowed permanently or semi-permanently on the main deck are liable to suffer from excessive corrosion. On these vessels the removal and replacing of the pontoons and the raising and lowering of the hinged sections of the tweendeck are done with the assistance of the ship's own cargo gear, the lifting of the tweendecks being done by passing hauling wires through manholes set in the main deck and sheaves under the deckhead.

If the ship continues to operate in one mode, particularly the single-deck mode, for a period of months or years as is quite possible, the equipment required for converting the ship and for operating her in the alternative configuration is likely to be neglected. It is important that this is not allowed to happen, and that operating systems are maintained under the ships planned maintenance system and tested from time to time and that equipment is labelled, maintained and kept in safe storage for when it is next required.

Open hatch vessels with shipboard gantry cranes

These versatile vessels (Drawing 1.11), the cargo liners of the twenty first century, are equipped to carry containers, forest products and dry bulk cargoes. They are employed mainly in scheduled services to and between the industrialised regions of Europe, North America and Japan. Such a vessel might load in half a dozen regular ports on the Gulf and East Coasts of the United States for four ports in North West Europe. Two of her ten straight sided holds might be loaded with rolls of newsprint for Rotterdam and Tilbury, three with bales of woodpulp for Antwerp and Bremen, one with 5,000 tonnes of bulk bentonite clay for Rotterdam and the remaining holds and deck space could be occupied with containers for all ports. Whilst some holds are being discharged others are already being loaded with cargoes for the following voyage and the chief mate, often working in collaboration with the owner's supercargo or port captain, must balance the often conflicting requirements of draught, trim, stability, hold readiness, weather and access as well as longitudinal strength considerations. When working with the ship's gear – two gantries – no more than two holds can be worked at a time. When shore cranes are used the need to avoid the ship's gantries dictates, once again, that more than two holds can seldom be worked efficiently. The hatch panels from the open holds, which must be stowed on adjacent hatches, and containers stowed on hatches restrict the options further. The position of each hatch panel at each stage in the loading and discharging must be planned to ensure that underdeck cargo can be accessed when required.

The rig: Aboard mv *Star Istind* (Fig. 18.35) the two Mitsui-Paceco 40 tonne gantry cranes are fitted for the handling of a wide range of cargoes including containers, bales and bulk. Hydraulic rams mounted on their legs are also used for raising, lowering and moving hatch covers. If the gantries are to be used the list must be no greater than 5° and the trim no greater than 2°. In addition the gantries cannot operate if cargo, for example containers stowed on deck, has fallen against the gantry legs.

Each gantry (Fig. 18.36), of open steel construction, consists of a horizontal span supported on two pairs of legs. The gantry straddles the ship's holds, each pair of legs resting on rails (Fig. 18.37) which run the length of the deck to port and to starboard of the hatch covers. The components of the gantry are the gantry frame supported on its legs, the cantilevers (retractable jibs, wings or arms) and the roof with its retractable sections which like the cantilevers, can be extended to port and starboard.

The cantilevers may swing into the extended position from their stowage (Figs. 18.38-40) or may be extended telescopically.

Placed immediately below the gantry roof is the main trolley (Fig. 18.42) which moves to port and starboard on wheels on rails and can travel the full length of the span. Resting on the main trolley is the shift trolley which moves forward and aft and, suspended from the shift trolley, is the lifting head (Fig. 18.43), consisting of a turntable and grab socket which rotates. A large variety of cargo handling heads, carried aboard ship or kept in the terminals which she visits regularly, can be fitted, depending upon the cargo to be handled.

The main trolley also carries the main hoist machinery, the trolley drive machinery, the shift drive machinery, the cable reels for the raise/lower pulley and has suspended below it the operator's cab. Placed high in the gantry is the electrical room consisting of switchboard and electrician's control room,

The controls: Within the operator's cab are master controls for gantry shift and shift of trolley. Movement to port or starboard and rotating, raising or lowering the load are each achieved by one control or foot pedal. A box of buttons provides control of the various electro hydraulic cargo handling heads. The operator can rotate the load in some cases through 360°. The only operation which cannot be controlled from the cab is the lifting, transport and lowering of the hatch panels.

Movement of the gantry along the deck is driven by rack and pinion gears, but the weight of the system is borne on railway-type wheels running on rail tracks (Fig. 18.37). Movement can be controlled from the operator's cab or from the crane leg platform. The crane leg platform (Fig. 18.38) is the position from which the movement of hatch covers is controlled.

Safety devices: Mechanical locks, mostly in the form of heavy steel bolts which are bolted in place, are fitted to secure the equipment when stowed (Fig. 18.41 and 44) and proximity switches ensure that movement cannot be initiated until the mechanical locks have been released.

Automatic 'slow down and stop' limit switches are provided at both gantry ends and there is anti-collision two step protection between two cranes – movement slows down and then stops when they are too close together. The considerable weight of the cranes makes

Fig. 18.35 MV *Star Istind*

Photo courtesy of Star Shipping A/S

Fig. 18.36 Gantry not in use over No. 1 Hold

Fig. 18.37 Gantry leg

Fig. 18.38 Gantry with arms stowed being used to move hatch cover. The operator, in orange overalls, is on the crane leg platform

Fig. 18.39 Arm swinging into position overside

Fig. 18.40 Gantries rigged at Nos. 2 and 6 holds ready to discharge forest products

Fig. 18.41 Gantry leg in position on housing, pins not yet engaged

Fig. 18.42 The main trolley extends the full width of the gantry. It rests on rails and is able to travel the length of the span. The shift trolley travels fore-and-aft on the main trolley and has, below it, the lifting head (black/yellow stripes)

Fig. 18.43 The shift trolley with beneath it the grab socket and turntable and to the right the driver's cab. Below are 40ft containers, stowed on the hatch cover

Fig. 18.44 Gantry leg housed, pins removed from stowage, fitted and secured with locking plates bolted in position

these precautions essential to prevent damage to the crane or the structure collided with. Gantry drive is interlocked so that drive is impossible unless the cantilevers are completely extended or retracted and secured. Gantry drive is available only by slow speed if the trolley is positioned more than 4.6 m outreach from ship's side. Bells and flashing lights are fitted to each leg of the gantries to give warning when they are moved. They should be regularly checked. It has been known for rags to be stuffed into the bells to stop the racket which they create. One portable limit switch striker is provided for each crane.

The main hoist machinery, driven by one electric motor, is provided at both hoist and lower ends with auto stop limit switches.

The trolley drive machinery is installed on the main trolley frame and is interlocked with the cantilever motion so that the trolley drive cannot be operated unless the cantilevers are completely extended or retracted and secured. Automatic stop limit switches are provided at both trolley traversing ends. The trolley shifting motor drives a wire rope drawn system installed on the main trolley frame.

The cantilevers are driven electro-hydraulically from a power unit mounted on the crane, which power unit also operates the hatch cover lifting device and the crane securing device. The cantilevers are extended and retracted horizontally by a folding device the mechanism of which consists of pin-hinges, oil-hydraulic cylinders and gearing. Limit switches to detect completion of cantilever extension and retraction are provided. There are a total of 32 limit switches per gantry.

An overload protection stop and alarm consisting of light, buzzer (and possibly horn) operates at 105% of the rated load. A wire rope slack protection device stops lowering and ignites an alarm lamp if the wire becomes slack. A speed watching device stops the crane when abnormal motion is detected.

Manual safety stop buttons are situated at the base of each leg of the crane and also on the top platform and in the driver's cab. They are clearly marked and are to be used in emergency, such as if someone gets in the way of the moving crane. They have the effect of instantly cutting off power from the hoisting and crane moving motors. Once the safety stop buttons have been operated, they must be reset by ship's staff in the main powerhouse of the crane.

Operating procedures: The cranes are electrically driven, the full range of movements requiring a total of 12 motors (one in each leg, two for athwartships movement, two for fore and aft movement and four for raising and lowering of the lifting head per crane). Electricity for the various powered units is provided by electric cable stowed on special self-tensioning drums which can respond to the various movements of the parts of the crane, paying out and reeling in as necessary.

Hydraulic rams in the four legs of the crane unit are used to raise or lower the hatch lids (covers) which weigh almost 100 tonnes, and must be carefully adjusted to lift uniformly. When raised a lid is moved to another hatch and stacked on top of the lid for that hatch.

Each gantry crane unit fitted aboard a handymax vessel weighs about 400 tonnes without load. Such a bulker with ten or eleven holds will normally be equipped with two gantries. When not in use and when the ship is at sea the gantries are stowed in the aftermost position against the bridge front with their arms retracted.

The gantries and cranes have a reputation for providing a fast, flexible, reliable and efficient service for the handling of bulk cargoes, forest products and containers.

Maintenance: The maintenance required for cargo gear in general is described in Chapter 23 and includes regular greasing and oiling, and inspection of wire ropes, sheaves and other moving parts. Gantries, like other cargo gear, require this treatment. In addition, the self-tension drums for the electric cables must be maintained in good working condition, well greased and free of loose scale, to ensure that the cables do not become slack and get snagged or overtight and broken. The gantries must be kept free of loose scale which could fall on deck and injure someone passing below.

The great quantity of hydraulic piping must be checked and tested periodically for leaks. Since the hydraulics are used for the rigging and unrigging of the gantry and are not required during cargo work, hydraulic repairs are done immediately only when they can be done without interrupting cargo or when they are causing immediate problems. Normally, they are completed during the first normal interruption to cargo to avoid incurring any delay which could be blamed on the ship. The hydraulic rams must be removed occasionally for renewal of rings and packing, a job which is normally done at the time of the vessel's drydocking.

Since each crane uses 12 motors, there is a need for a great deal of high quality electrical maintenance.

Wires and lifting gear: The cranes are fitted with four wires to each lifting head for maximum speed and load. When grabs are used two of the wires are reeled off, since the grabs are designed for two-wire operation. When in use the wires stow on grooved drums.

The cranes can be made multipurpose by the fitting of an assortment of different lifting heads. Bulkers fitted with gantry cranes and employed on regular trades can be provided on arrival in port with appropriate lifting heads which are the property of the stevedores and have been maintained by them. Such heads can include: various types and sizes of grabs: pneumatic vacuum clamps used to lift 12/14 rolls of newsprint (Figs. 18.45-50); pneumatic lock-and-release pulp heads of various sizes; container heads for 20ft and 40ft containers; lumber legs for handling packaged lumber.

Stowage: When parked for sea (Fig. 18.51) the gantries are held in position with a combination of heavy nuts and bolts (Fig. 18.52), locking pins (Fig. 18.53) hydraulic jacks (Fig. 18.54) and heavy pins locked in position by bolted plates (Fig. 18.41 and 44). This prevents damage to the flat tracks and to the racks and pinions whilst the ship and gantries work in a seaway. In heavy seas the top portions of the gantries tend to sway both fore and aft and athwartships due to their height and to the fact that they are only secured at deck level.

Trim calculations: All trim calculations must be

Fig. 18.45 The cargo handling head approaches the hold

Fig. 18.46 Rolls of newsprint for discharge

Fig. 18.47 …poised for lift off…

Fig. 18.48 …out of the hold…

Fig. 18.49 …over the coaming…

Fig. 18.50 …and onto the quay

Fig. 18.51 Gantry leg in position over housing (yellow unit fixed to deck)

Fig. 18.53 Three gantry locking pins ready to fit when securing for sea

Fig. 18.52 Gantry securing bolt secured for sea

Fig. 18.54 Hydraulic powered jack engaging in housing

undertaken with the gantries in the stowed position and with the positions of all hatch covers included in the calculations, since the positioning of these heavy items can have a considerable effect on the trim, for example on a vessel of 204 metres a gantry crane in the furthest forward position can increase the forward draught by 1 metre.

Combination carriers

A combination carrier is a ship which has the ability to carry either a liquid cargo or a dry bulk cargo. Such ships cannot carry the two cargoes simultaneously although when trading as dry bulk carriers a quantity of slops (residual washings of oil and water from which the excess water has been removed) may remain aboard. During the 1990s 42 combination carriers were built but since 2000 only two have been commissioned. There are two basic types of combination carrier.

Ore/bulk/oil carriers: (OBOs) (Drawing 1.8) used to have a basic design which was similar to conventional bulk carriers and were provided with upper wing tanks (topside or shoulder tanks) and with lower wing (hopper) tanks. The lower wing tanks were combined with the double bottom tanks and sometimes were extended up the ship's side to meet the upper wing tanks, thus providing a narrow double skin at the ship's sides. Duct keels were fitted and one main deck cargo hatch opening per hold/tank was provided. The slop tanks were most commonly the after pair of upper wing tanks adjacent to the aftermost hold. OBOs can carry a full oil cargo by deadweight or by volume, or a full dry bulk cargo of high or low density, so that ore, coal or grain can be carried. Since the requirement for double hulls for oil tankers was implemented in the early 1990s, OBOs have also been required to have double hulls, in most cases of 2m width. This requirement has influenced the layout and a number of OBOs built in the 1990s are constructed without hopper tanks.

Ore/oil carriers: (O/O carriers) (Drawing 1.9) are similar in layout to conventional tankers with centre and wing tanks, but the centre tanks are provided with a double bottom, a duct keel is usually provided, and dry cargo can be carried only in the centre cargo spaces. Steel hatch covers are fitted on the main deck but as the centre tanks extend to only about half the beam of the ship the hold length is generally twice that of an OBO hold and each hold will have two hatch openings. The slop tanks in these ships are usually the aftermost wing tanks, adjacent to the pumproom. Such vessels have the ability to carry either a full oil cargo, both by deadweight and by volume, or a full dry bulk cargo by deadweight provided that the dry cargo is heavy (with a stowage factor of no more than 0.57/0.62m^3/tonne – 20/22 ft^3/tonne) and can be accommodated in the appropriate holds/tanks. The ore/oil carrier is less versatile than the OBO, and can carry a smaller range of dry bulk cargoes. Whilst there are variations in the design of combination carriers the two basic types described above are distinct. O/O carriers were generally very large ship but the requirement for double hulls for tankers, mentioned above, has rendered them less efficient and there are by 2008 only four O/Os in service, all above 300,000 dwt.

Combination carriers trading as tankers and bulkers: When considering the operating of combination carriers as dry bulk carriers it is necessary to be aware of the way in which they are operated as tankers. The following paragraphs consider the effects of the carriage of oil and dry bulk cargoes. Whilst oil pollution is an obvious hazard when carrying oil, the greatest danger comes from the explosive gases given off by crude oil. Migration of even small quantities of oil through small fractures into ballast tanks, void spaces and duct keels is often hard to detect, but removal of any such leaked quantities of oil is essential to prevent generation of gas. This matter requires continual vigilance, and a number of precautions are described in the following paragraphs.

Heating coils: Combination carriers when trading as tankers may carry crude or fuel oils. Fuel oils and some crudes have to be heated. This is done with steam coils, which in an O/O carrier are fitted in the wing tanks and in an OBO are usually fitted within the stool spaces (the void hopper spaces at the bases of the athwartships bulkheads) against the plating which forms the hopper side. Leaks can and do occur and oil may be carried back by way of the steam return lines into the condenser. It is good tanker practice to test heating coils by pumping fresh water through them at a time when they can be inspected to detect any leaks. If leaks have been detected or are suspected the lines should be flushed through to remove any gas before changing from oil to dry cargo. Later generations of OBOs are equipped with deep well pumps and heat exchangers on deck through which the cargo oil is re-circulated.

Loading: To load an oil cargo shore pipelines are connected by flexible hoses ('chicksans') to the ship's cargo manifold which is normally located about amidships. The oil is then carried in fixed pipelines aft along the deck and down drop lines into the ship's bottom lines, which lead to all the cargo tanks. The flow into each tank is controlled by main line valves situated on the line itself, with the controls either on deck or in a cargo control room. The cargo quantity loaded is measured by ullage and tanks are filled to about 98 per cent capacity, which usually brings the surface of the oil to the base of the hatch coaming. Ullage measurements are taken from an ullage port which may be set in a pedestal abaft the hatch lid, or may be situated in the centre of the hatch lid.

Official draught surveys are rarely carried out aboard tankers, but it is good practice for the ship's personnel to undertake their own draught survey when an oil cargo is on board, to identify constants and additional weights. The records of such observations will be useful for comparison on a dry cargo voyage if differences arise between ship and shore.

Discharging: On older ships the bulk of the cargo is discharged through the main lines, by way of the main turbine cargo pumps which push the cargo up to the deck lines and through the manifold into the shore line. Newer OBOs have deep well pumps directly connected to the manifold. The final bottom quantity of oil (**ie**, the residue which the main pumps cannot pump efficiently) is discharged by eductor or by stripping pump, the latter being a small reciprocating pump operating through its own line, and drawing oil from a bilge well set into the inner bottom when the tank is placed over a double bottom. The same stripping lines and pumps serve as the bilge system for the cargo holds when the ship is operating in the dry cargo mode.

Inert gas: Before loading an oil cargo the empty cargo tanks will be filled with an inert gas with a recommended oxygen level of 5% or less (directly from flue gas in a steam ship and from a gas generator in a motor ship) and the excess of this gas will be vented as the tanks are filled with oil (to avoid over-pressurisation). The ullage space above the oil will be kept in an inert state, with oxygen levels below explosive levels, throughout the voyage. As the oil cargo is discharged inert gas with an oxygen level of 5% or less is generated and fed into the tanks, so that when empty the tank will still be fully inerted. When the vessel is carrying dry cargo the inert gas lines to the cargo holds will be blanked off, these blanks being fitted in a position adjacent to the hatch coaming.

Crude oil washing (COW): During discharge of a crude oil cargo, to reduce clingage of cargo to the structure, oil is bled from the deck discharge line and fed through a fixed piping system to tank washing machines fixed within the cargo tanks. These machines rotate in two planes in accordance with a time programme to back wash the tank, using cargo for the washing. Whilst washing, the residues are stripped out to one of the slop tanks from where they are discharged to the shore along with the balance of the cargo. The COW procedure is not adopted with fuel oil or heavy, heated, crude oils because remnants of the cargo which cooled in the washing system would block it. When washing with crude oil the inerted atmosphere must be maintained. COW can only be carried out in port whilst discharging an oil cargo.

Load on top: If a full crude oil wash is not carried out the remnants of the last oil cargo clinging to the tank structure (the clingage) can be several hundred tonnes, particularly in the wing tanks of an ore/oil carrier, as most of the structural members are within the wing tanks leaving the centre hold/tank smooth sided. During the ballast voyage some of this clingage slowly flows down and can be stripped into the slop tank. Any slops which remain on board will be in the slop tank when the vessel is presented to load the next oil cargo.

Voyage orders will always contain an instruction as to whether the next cargo is to be segregated from the slops, or can be loaded into the slop tank and co-mingled with the slops, a process known as loading on top of slops. Slop tanks are located aft, and it is usually preferable to load them to avoid any tendency to trim by the head. The slops will, if the ship loads on top then be discharged with the next cargo. If this cannot be done the ship will accumulate an increasing quantity of slops, thus reducing her subsequent cargo lifts.

Water washing: It is necessary to clean the tanks/holds thoroughly when changing to dry cargo or when they have to be entered. A thorough cleaning is achieved by washing with sea water after crude oil washing. The washing is usually done with hot water heated either through a fitted water heater or in one of the slop tanks. When water washing is taking place the strippings are pumped into one of the slop tanks where the oil and water are allowed to settle out, after which most of the water is pumped into the sea leaving the slops, which may be 80/90 per cent oil, with the balance of the water. As on tankers, the slop water passes through a 15 ppm device which will ensure the water is re-circulated back to the slop tank in case the 15 ppm value is exceeded.

Washing machines: In tanks used only for the carriage of oil the washing machines are permanently fixed in position although they can be lifted out (vertically) for maintenance. In tanks/holds which can be used to carry oil or dry cargo the machines must be withdrawn before dry cargo is loaded to prevent damage to them. Before the introduction of fixed machines and COW the normal method of washing was by Butterworthing (a trade name for the machine, for which alternatives include Victor Pyrate and Dasic) using rubber hoses and portable machines that were lowered through holes in the deck.

Some ships still carry a set of these machines which are handy for local cleaning and can be used with chemicals for difficult cleaning jobs such as occur following discharge of fuel oil in exceptionally cold waters. The rule of thumb is that the water should be at a temperature of 180°F (82°C) and a pressure of 180 psi (12 bar), but good results can be expected provided these two values total at least 300.

Hatch covers: The hatch covers on combination carriers are normally of the same basic design as those of conventional bulk carriers, side rolling covers being most common. Such covers on combination carriers possess three distinctive features. They are provided with special oil resistant seals, Butterworth plates (for portable machine washing or portable vents) are fitted at each corner of the hatch covers, and the covers are designed to resist hydrostatic loading from below, an effect which is usually achieved by providing an increased number of cleats.

Some steel weather deck hatch cover panels are plated, fully or partially, on the underside. Any fractures in this underside plating can allow oil and gas to enter the space inside the panel. Such hatch covers must be carefully examined for fractures when they are open and if drain holes are fitted these should be used with an explosimeter to test for hydrocarbon gases. If gas is found the panel air plugs should be removed and the cover should be blown clear with compressed air.

When the fractures have been repaired, the cover should be re-inerted, using vapour phase inhibitor (VPI) tablets. These tablets, which are removed from a canister and poured into the enclosed space via an air hole, have a twofold action: they produce an inert gas and absorb oxygen. Once the gas is seen emerging from both the air holes these holes must be again plugged and sealed, thus effectively inerting the enclosed space.

When changing from dry cargo to oil the normal side rolling hatch covers can only be properly cleaned when in the open position. When making this change particular care must be taken in cleaning the hatch coaming plate and compression bar to avoid dry residues damaging the neoprene seal when the hatch cover is tightly closed.

Instructions: Since the introduction of the Marpol Regulations all ships carrying oil have been provided with an *Operating and Equipment Manual* (otherwise known as the *Procedures and Arrangements Manual – P&A Manual*) which gives full descriptions and capacities of pumps, COW and inert gas systems. Routines for cleaning after oil cargoes are laid down in this manual, and these provide detail of the time required for washing cycles and other routines. Most owners and managements supplement this manual with their own guidance, and the builders often provide a changeover procedure for the change from oil to dry cargo and vice versa. It is essential that all these documents are read with care so that all restrictions which are listed therein can be complied with.

Following a series of explosions which occurred in combination carriers and tankers some decades ago whilst tank cleaning was in progress it has been the practice of prudent owners to lay down a schedule of reports required from the ship at stages in her programme. There is likely to be a requirement to report commencement and completion of tank washing, the gas free status of the ship en route to the loading port and at the time that notice of readiness is tendered, and the times when any maintenance work is being carried out on deck or in the tanks/holds.

Equipment: The equipment and instruments which are provided to enable the combination carrier to operate as a tanker must be in working condition from the moment that she commences to change from dry bulk to oil cargoes until such time as all hydrocarbon materials and gases have been found to have been fully removed and all spaces have been checked daily for gas with negative results for a period of two weeks. Equipment affected by this requirement includes gauges and read-outs, the inert gas system, the crude oil washing system, cargo pumps and oil content monitors.

Of particular importance are the portable gas detectors for explosive hydrocarbon gases (the explosimeters, oxygen meters and tank scopes) which indicate whether at that time and in that condition there is an atmospheric mixture present in the space which is explosive. Equally important are the oxygen analysers used to detect the level of oxygen in a space. When an explosimeter is used to test the atmosphere before entry into an enclosed space the oxygen level must also be checked and confirmed as being safe for entry.

Slop tanks: Every effort must be made to minimise the volume of solid dry cargo residues that are washed into the slop tanks as these will cause problems later. Once in the slop tanks such residues may settle on the tanks' valve seats, or be put back into the cargo tanks by way of the washing machines, or eventually be discharged from the slop tanks together with the oil which has been gathered therein. Each of the foregoing possibilities is undesirable, but tank washing by recirculation (collecting the washings in slop tanks, allowing the oil and water to settle and then using the water again by drawing it from low in the tank) is usually unavoidable. To avoid or minimise these problems a main cargo tank can sometimes be used for the washings. This is possible provided that later in the voyage the ship will pass through an area where the washings can be decanted to the sea, after which this final tank must also be washed.

Older OBOs in particular face problems arising from the fact that the upper wing tanks are used as slop tanks. Such tanks have a small capacity and a shallow depth, which makes it difficult to achieve efficient settling out of the oil and water and results in oil being carried back with the washing water, giving less efficient cleaning. Later generations of OBOs have slop tanks similar to those on tankers. The capacity of the slop tanks is stipulated in MARPOL[245] where capacity requirements for slop tanks in OBOs are slightly relaxed compared to those for tankers.

If at all possible no slops should remain aboard on completion of an oil discharge. If the previous oil cargo was not loaded on top and some slops do remain, every effort must be made through charterers and owners to land these slops before commencing the changeover to a dry bulk cargo. If any slops remain on board they have the effect of putting one of the slop tanks out of service, which will create problems when cleaning after dry bulk and oil cargoes. They also reduce the vessel's cargo deadweight capacity.

When all cleaning has been done and the excess water has been removed from the slops leaving them in one slop tank only, the ventilation arrangements for that slop tank must receive attention. If the slop tank is blanked off from the inert gas system at this time the procedure often consists of fitting an additional section of vent piping to extend the vent to a high position, perhaps under the bridge wing. Alternatively, the tank should be kept inerted if crude oil remains within the slops.

Empty wing tanks: Tanks, such as upper wing tanks in OBOs and side wing tanks in ore/oil carriers that have carried crude oil but are not to be used for the carriage of dry bulk cargo, must be efficiently washed to the point where insufficient traces of oil remain to generate gas. In this connection it must be remembered that a changeover in a cold climate followed by a dry bulk voyage which takes the ship into a hot climate is likely to create conditions which encourage the formation of explosive gas within the empty oil cargo tanks. Consequently, they must be regularly checked during the voyage for any signs of gas. If gas is detected the tank must be ventilated. If the tank is not clean enough to prevent the formation of gas it must be washed again.

The upper wing tanks in an OBO may well be used for a grain cargo and the oiltight manhole covers have to be removed after the compartment has been cleaned and vented. Some ships have grilles to fit in place of the manhole covers. Loose nuts must never be left in these tanks as they will damage grain suckers or ship's pumps if sucked into either discharging system.

Hold washing: The discharge of hold washings into the sea within Special Areas or anywhere within 50 miles of land is forbidden[246]. This makes a change from coal to oil between (say) Antwerp and Rotterdam impossible unless the coal washings can be put ashore or retained aboard. It may be that the long-term solution to this problem is to have a dry cargo washing residue tank in which residues could settle and from which water could then be removed, allowing the solid residues to be disposed of in the open ocean or ashore as appropriate. (Meanwhile this problem is shared with all bulk carriers, and is discussed in Chapter 25.)

Duct keels: A large number of ships have suffered severe flooding and some have even sunk as a direct result of the access manholes of duct keels being left unsecured. The aftermost entrance to the duct keel of a conventional bulk carrier is usually located at the fore end of the engineroom, and a bolted plate is provided to seal and secure it. Access to the duct keel will also be possible by way of a ladder in a trunkway from one or several positions between hatches on the main deck, such trunkways often being built into a corrugation in a transverse bulkhead.

In combination carriers, because the pumproom forms the cofferdam between engineroom and cargo spaces, access to the duct keel is usually gained from the pumproom by a bolted hatch. In some OBOs the stool spaces are common with the duct keel whilst in others access between duct keel and stool space is by manhole.

While oil is being carried and after an oil cargo until the vessel has been found for two weeks to be gas free, any electric lighting in the duct keel must be isolated by withdrawal of the fuses. Under no circumstances should double-bottom access manhole covers located within the duct keel be removed for the venting of tanks when electric lighting or electric fan power sources are live. If the design of the ship makes it necessary to carry out venting by way of the duct keel, the air inlet and not the air exhaust must be provided in the duct keel to prevent gas from entering the duct keel.

Changing from oil to dry cargo must include full checks of the duct keel and the stool spaces, which may be common with the duct keel, for the presence of gas. When the ship is at sea access hatches to duct keels, whether from engineroom or pump room, must be kept fully closed with all bolts in place and fully tightened. The ship may be held to be legally unseaworthy if damage results from the flooding of a duct keel which has not been properly closed.

Miscellaneous matters relating to combination carriers: Some dry cargo ports require a certificate issued by a chemist before the combination carrier is allowed to enter the port or commence loading. Whenever such an inspector can be obtained he will provide valuable support for the ship in the event of any disputes, provided that he takes readings from all spaces regardless of whether they are dry cargo spaces, dry spaces where oil was previously carried, ballast tanks or void spaces.

Enforcement of smoking restrictions that are familiar to tanker crews is best continued when the ship changes to dry cargo. It is generally safer to maintain the routines throughout the trading of the ship.

Between successive dry bulk cargo voyages the cleaning routines will be the same as for a bulk carrier. In addition routine checks of all spaces for gas must continue, particularly when the ship moves to warmer climates.

The standard of hold cleanliness required for most fertilisers including phosphates, and for sulphur, is for all practical purposes the same as for grain. There must be no traces of former cargoes, including oil, and 'no traces' means exactly that. Loose scale is not acceptable but rust coloured steelwork is usually no problem. If traces of oil are discovered during cleaning in positions that are too high to be reached from ship's ladders the owners and/or charterers should be informed so that arrangements can be made for cherrypickers or other suitable equipment for reaching high points to be provided on the ship's arrival at the loading port. Such cleaning is usually done by spraying chemical on to the oil, leaving it for a few hours and washing it off, or in extreme cases by high pressure water washing. Some grain importing countries, eg Japan, place restrictions on OBOs carrying grain after previous voyages with dirty oil.

Areas where fractures often occur on combination carriers lie along the boundaries of hopper tanks and stool spaces, and it is these fractures that may allow some oil migration to take place. Every opportunity should be taken whilst holds/tanks are free of oil and gas-free to examine frames and brackets at the ship's side between lower and upper hopper tanks.

Lower hopper tanks and side hopper tanks in OBOs, if horizontally separated from upper wing tanks, may be found to be difficult to clean. In some ships, access manholes are fitted between the upper wing tanks and the side tanks and it may be necessary to remove these to ventilate the side tanks. Gas readings should never be taken through a sounding pipe as the bottom may not be open and clear. In some of these confined spaces it may be necessary to remove the top of the air (and overflow) vent in order to lower the gas sensing tube into the lower part of the compartment.

Changes of ballast will be required during tank cleaning and when ballasting with clean ballast for arrival in the loading port. Inert gas must be maintained until the water washing is complete in all tanks that previously carried oil. Shear forces and bending moments for each ballast condition and for each change of ballast must be calculated and kept within the permitted limits. The tonnage of tank washings which may be accumulated in an empty cargo hold must be calculated and included in the stress calculations.

Fig. 18.55 shows the areas where particular care must be taken when checking the ship for gas.

Sources

4, 160, 162, 163, 168, 169, 170, 171, 181, 245, 246, 247. (See List of Sources, Page 497)

CHECKLIST – Procedures for changing a combination carrier from dry cargo to oil

NB: The charter party normally allows two days for this process.

- ☐ Check the procedure with the ship's Marpol Operating and Equipment Manual (otherwise known as the Procedures and Arrangements Manual), and with owners' and builders' instructions.
- ☐ Remove all cargo residues by sweeping and by digging out the bilge wells, since holds will usually only have been shovel cleaned.
- ☐ If necessary the tank top and upper levels of the hopper slopes should be hosed off, as should the inside of the hatch covers in the open position, to avoid a build-up of impacted dry cargo and oil. If time permits the holds can be fully washed, but the charter party often allows only two days for converting from dry cargo to oil and experience shows that dry cargo dust which remains on underdeck beams forward of and abaft the hatch coamings causes no noticeable increase of sediment in the next cargo of crude oil.
- ☐ The bilge well covers must be removed and stowed and the oiltight sealing plates for the grain trimming openings must be removed from the main cargo pipelines.
- ☐ Ullage gauges in the upper wing tanks must be refitted.
- ☐ Blank flanges, if of the Whessoe type, should be refitted with wire guide and float.
- ☐ Tank washing machines must be lowered or swung back into position.
- ☐ Blank flanges must be removed from the inert gas lines.
- ☐ Any hatch cover ventilators must be unshipped and blank flanges refitted.
- ☐ Hatch covers must be closed and cleated down.
- ☐ Gas detectors in the accommodation must be switched on and electric sources on deck and in the duct keel must be isolated.
- ☐ Any blank flanges or spool pieces inserted into the stripping line in the pump room should be removed or the line should be reconnected as a stripping system. This system must have no direct connection to an overboard discharge, except through an oil content monitor.
- ☐ Slop tank vent arrangements should be restored to the standard tanker configuration by isolating the high vent line and reconnecting to the main inert gas system (IGS).

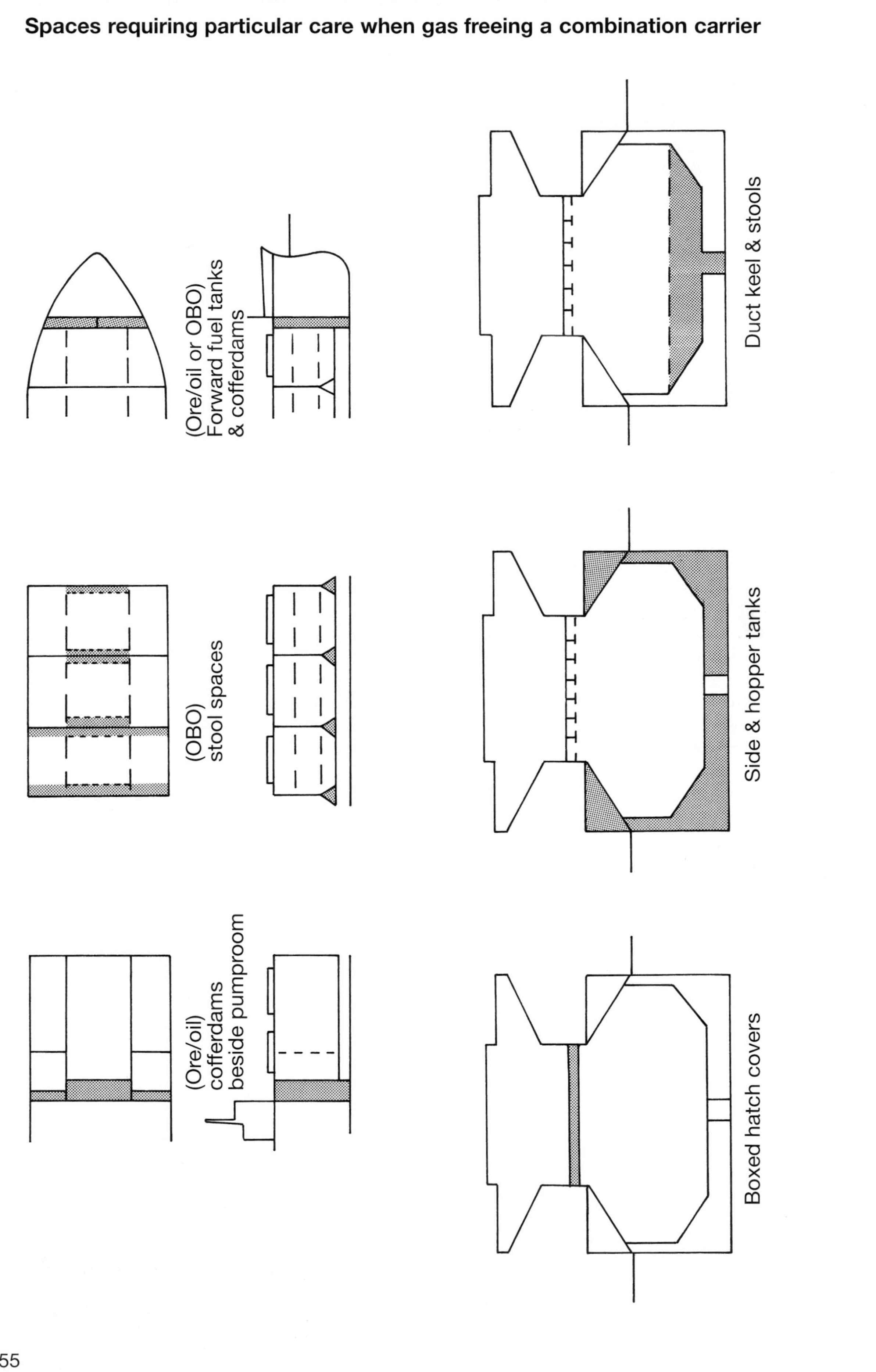
Spaces requiring particular care when gas freeing a combination carrier
(Ore/oil or OBO)
Forward fuel tanks
& cofferdams
Duct keel & stools
(OBO)
stool spaces
Side & hopper tanks
(Ore/oil)
cofferdams
beside pumproom
Boxed hatch covers

Fig. 18.55

CHECKLIST – Procedures for changing a combination carrier from oil to dry cargo

NB: The charter party normally allows four/five days for this process.

- ☐ Check the procedure with the ship's Marpol Operating and Equipment Manual (otherwise known as the Procedures and Arrangements Manual), and with owners' and builders' instructions.
- ☐ A full crude oil washing should be carried out during discharge, provided that crude oil and not fuel or a heated heavy crude oil was the last cargo.
- ☐ A full water wash of all spaces that have carried oil should be carried out, and all empty spaces such as ballast-only tanks, forward fuel tanks, duct keel, stool spaces and cofferdams must be checked for the presence of oil.
- ☐ Once a complete machine washing of cargo tanks has been carried out the spaces should be ventilated before they are entered. Once access with safety is possible each space should be examined for the effectiveness of the washing and if necessary hand washing, or chemicals, should be used to remove all oil traces.
- ☐ All lines including COW lines, deck lines and manifold crossover lines must be washed as thoroughly as possible and vented.
- ☐ Tank washing machines must be withdrawn from cargo tanks and ullage devices must be disconnected and removed.
- ☐ Main cargo lines must be blanked off in the holds.
- ☐ In the pumproom the bilges must be thoroughly washed and any blank flanges or stool pieces must be fitted to convert the stripping system to a bilge system.
- ☐ Inert gas lines must be blanked off beside the hatch coamings.
- ☐ Cover plates for bilge wells must be fitted and grain trimming plates in upper wing tanks must be removed and replaced by grilles where necessary.
- ☐ All spaces including cargo holds, tanks used for oil cargoes only, ballast tanks and void spaces, must be checked and confirmed to be gas free. This checking with a portable explosimeter must be carried out twice daily at first, then daily, for two weeks, and resumed if the ship moves from a cold into a warmer climate. Nothing must allow this procedure to be ignored or neglected. Any spaces in which an explosive reading is obtained must be ventilated. It may be exceedingly difficult to vent lower wing tanks to a gas-free condition, and to obtain a gas-free reading from them, but both these things must be done.
- ☐ The water content of slops should be discharged as far as possible until a minimum remains and the extended vent must be fitted or inert gas must be maintained in the space.
- ☐ Gas detectors in the accommodation can be switched off only after the ending of the testing period of at least two weeks.
- ☐ Any hatch cover ventilators should be refitted.

CHAPTER 19

CARRIAGE OF COMMON AND TYPICAL BULK CARGOES

Grain, coal, iron ore, steel, steel coils, forest products, cement

Carriage of grain

IN 2006 about 262 million tonnes of grain was transported by sea, the principal exporting areas being Argentina, Australia, Canada, the European Union and the United States, which between them accounted for close to 75 per cent of exports. Importing areas include Western Europe, the former Soviet Union, the Middle East, Africa and Asia. Much of this trade is carried in Panamax-sized vessels, with the balance being transported in handymax, handy-sized and mini-bulkers. The term grain covers wheat, maize (corn), oats, rye, barley, rice, pulses, oilseeds and processed forms thereof, whose behaviour is similar to that of grain in its natural state[18].

The carriage of grain presents a number of challenges for the Shipmaster. Grain is a product which flows freely. It is liable to shift and endanger a ship's stability and for that reason the regulations governing its carriage are exacting. In addition, grain is perishable and is intended for consumption by humans or by livestock. This calls for holds that are very clean and for high standards in avoiding contamination, damage or infestation.

Grain stability: When considering grain stability, the Master of a ship required to carry grain has three concerns which do not apply to most other bulk cargoes. He must plan a cargo distribution which satisfies the rigorous stability criteria of the IMO Grain Rules, ensure that the cargo is properly loaded, stowed and where necessary secured in accordance with the Rules, and complete the associated paperwork in a satisfactory manner.

A characteristic of grain is that it flows freely, and the IMO *International Maritime Solid Bulk Cargoes (IMSBC) Code*[5] states in Para. 5.4.3 that 'Non-cohesive bulk cargoes having an angle of repose less than or equal to 30° flow freely like grain, [and] shall be carried according to the provisions applicable to the stowage of grain cargoes', taking account of the density of the material. In other words, bulk cargoes with properties similar to grain must be carried in the same way as grain.

The free-flowing characteristic of grain reduces the stability of any ship which carries it. Grain in a partly-filled cargo compartment displays a free-surface effect similar to that of a liquid in a partly-filled tank. If the ship rolls heavily the grain is likely to flow to one side of the compartment, where it will cause the ship to list or to capsize. Conventional bulk carriers are well suited to the carriage of grain, as their design reduces some of the adverse effects of bulk grain upon stability.

The design of the holds of conventional bulk carriers has been developed to create compartments which can be filled to near 100 per cent of capacity without trimming, except for spout trimming by the shiploader. The upper wing tanks occupy spaces into which cargo would not flow, thereby greatly improving the self trimming character of the conventional bulker hold. (Fig. 1.4)

The area within the hatch coaming on a conventional bulk carrier is much smaller than the hold area below, so that the free surface of the cargo is much reduced when the hold is filled with cargo to the top of the coaming (Fig.9.2). In the *Regina Oldendorff*, for example, the ratio of hatch area to hold area is about 1:3. The coaming, formed of deep vertical plating – with a depth aboard the *Regina Oldendorff* of about 3.0 metres – acts as a feeder from which cargo will flow down to fill any spaces remaining within the hold as the cargo settles during the voyage.

The IMO *Grain Rules*[18] require Shipmasters to load their ships safely. For practical purposes the main requirements are:

- A ship which is to load with grain should plan the loading to leave the least possible number of holds part filled. The calculations will show if the proposed loading is acceptable for stability purposes.
- When the loading plan requires a hold to be full all the spaces under the decks and hatch covers must be filled to the maximum extent possible and all necessary and reasonable trimming must be performed to minimise the effect of grain shifting.
- The ends of the holds of a conventional bulk carrier cannot be completely filled by normal spout loading and if they are allowed to remain unfilled the ship's stability is reduced thereby. This is acceptable only if the ship has been found 'specially suitable', and has been issued with a dispensation from trimming ends. In practice most conventional bulk carriers are found specially suitable. Some modern bulk carriers are constructed with bulkhead top stools which eliminate the 'untrimmed ends' problems (Fig. 18.2)
- The Master must confirm that the ship's stability satisfies the requirements of the Load Line Rules and also the more rigorous requirements of the Grain Rules, which specify that the angle of heel due to the (possible) shift of grain shall not exceed 12°, that the ship's statical stability diagram satisfied specified conditions, and that the initial fluid metacentric height shall not be less than 0.3 metres. For a ship provided with the appropriate tables and computer program these stability requirements can be quickly and easily checked by comparing the actual grain heeling moments with the allowable grain heeling moments (a process described in Chapter 10).
- Before the commencement of loading the Master may be required by the government of the country where the vessel is loading to demonstrate the ability of the ship at all stages of the intended voyage to comply with the relevant stability criteria stated in the Grain Rules. In a number of countries, including the United States, Canada and Australia, this requirement is satisfied by the completion of a form provided by the government concerned. In Australia the completed form must be

submitted to the Authority at least 72 hours before the time when loading is intended to start.

- After loading, all free grain surfaces in partly-filled compartments must be trimmed level.
- The ship must be upright before proceeding to sea.
- Where the ship has part-filled compartments, and the calculations show that her stability is not acceptable, the surface of the stow in the unfilled compartments must be secured in an approved manner by overstowing with bagged grain or other cargo or by strapping and lashing. These methods of securing are described in the Grain Rules and descriptions are often included in the ship's Loading and Securing Manual. Securing of the surface of a grain cargo is seldom required in practice since most ships and cargoes are well matched. Readers who require more information are referred to the IMO Grain Rules.
- There may be a requirement to take ballast during the voyage to preserve sufficient stability as bunkers are consumed.

Stability when loading or discharging: The Ship/Shore Safety Checklist asks if, in emergency, the ship is able to leave the berth at any time. That question deserves careful consideration when loading or discharging grain. The Master of a handymax bulk carrier discharging grain in a Far Eastern port was instructed to put to sea when a typhoon approached. At the time all five holds were part discharged and the Master calculated that the vessel had insufficient stability. He refused to leave the berth and both ship and berth suffered substantial damage. Where possible the loading or discharge should be planned to ensure that the ship will have sufficient stability to leave port at any time. If that is not possible the Master should ensure that the Ship/Shore Safety Checklist records the situation accurately. He should know the times when the ship could safely put to sea and the times when she could not and he and his ship's company should be particularly alert for threats from the weather or any other exceptional circumstances.

Grain stability calculation forms: The governments of a number of the major grain exporting countries require the Master to show, or to be able to show, that the ship will at all stages of the voyage have sufficient stability to satisfy the Grain Rules. This requirement is normally satisfied by completing the required calculations before commencement of loading, and entering the results in a form provided by the government concerned. If it is found that the tonnages actually loaded in each compartment are different to the tonnages assumed in the calculations, as is often the case, the calculations must be repeated on completion of loading to confirm that the ship's stability throughout the voyage is safe. In other words the Master is required to prepare a set of theoretical stability calculations before commencement of loading and a second set, using actual tonnages loaded, on completion of loading.

Copies of the forms provided by the United States, completed for a loading undertaken by the *Regina Oldendorff*, are at Appendix 19.1, accompanied by explanations of some of their more useful and more confusing features. The forms have been completed as though for submission to the Authority before commencement of loading and for convenience the United States forms have been used although the loading was actually in a Canadian Port. The ship's computer printout for stability on completion of loading for the same voyage is at Appendix 10.3 and when the two documents are compared minor differences can be seen because of differences between the tonnages actually loaded in each compartment and the tonnages assumed before loading. The forms provided by different countries are all intended to obtain the same information, but differ in the detail of their designs, and in the way the information is used.

Australia, the USA and Canada all set a tougher test of stability than is required by the International Grain Regulations: they all require the use of tonnages calculated on the basis of the full hold capacity, even when the ends are to be untrimmed. Australia stipulates[159] *For any filled compartment, trimmed or untrimmed, calculations are to be based on the full (ie 100% cubic) capacity and corresponding maximum VCG of the compartment. Untrimmed hold capacities are not to be used in any circumstances.* The United States has similar advice:[117] *Unless there is prior experience to rely on, it is wise to use the full capacities for 'filled, untrimmed compartments' in initial calculations so any differences will be on the safe side and remediable.* Canada specifies[173] *In all cases the weight of cargo in a filled compartment shall be the volume of the whole cargo space divided by the stowage factor.* In other words all three authorities require or recommend that even when the ends are unfilled, tonnages for filled holds are to be used in the calculations, with grain heeling moments for unfilled ends.

This requirement is intended to increase the safety factor in the planning of the loading. The National Cargo Bureau[151] argues with good reason that the effect of untrimmed ends cannot be precisely calculated because the angle of repose of grain varies and the presence or absence of bleeder holes in the coaming ends also affects the extent to which the ends are filled.

Taking a further step the National Cargo Bureau[151] recognises that the loading computers on some ships automatically pair untrimmed heeling moments with untrimmed end capacities (as is the intention of the International Grain Regulations). They advise that such computers can still be used but that *"The vessel should, through experience, develop its own correction table, which would convert the stowage factor provided by the agent and/or charterer, to the vessel specific value suitable for use with the ends untrimmed capacities".*

These requirements are listed in Table 1, opposite.

Trimmed and untrimmed ends: As noted above, a ship which has been issued with a dispensation from trimming ends is not required to have the ends of her holds trimmed full. The advantage of this option is that if trimming is avoided the time and the cost of loading is substantially reduced.

Two disadvantages may be suffered as the result of leaving the ends untrimmed. The ship's stability will be reduced although, provided that the minimum requirements are still satisfied, this need cause no problems. In addition, the volume of grain which can be carried is reduced by the space remaining in the unfilled ends. This may not matter when heavier grain (eg, grain with a SF of 42-47 cuft/tonne) is being carried, since it is likely that the ship will be loaded to her marks before all spaces have been filled.

Country	Before loading	Requirements for the Grain Stability Calculation
Australia	Submit AMSA Form MO33 72hrs before loading and proceed with loading unless told otherwise	*Untrimmed hold capacities are not to be used in any circumstances*
United States	Submit NCB Form before loading and commence when issued with Certificate of Readiness to Load	*It is wise to use the full capacities for 'filled, untrimmed compartments',* *or* *through experience, develop correction table, which would convert the stowage factor provided by the agent and/or charterer, to the vessel specific value suitable for use with the ends untrimmed capacities*
Canada	Submit Transport Canada Form before loading and commence when issued with Certificate of Readiness to Load	*In all cases the weight of cargo in a filled compartment shall be the volume of the whole cargo space divided by the stowage factor*
Other countries	Calculate stability as required by the *International Grain Code*	As far as known: In accordance with the *International Grain Code*

Table 1

Normally the decision as to whether ends are to be trimmed or not will be made by charterers or shippers, who will have chosen a ship which is able to comply with their requirements. If a Master is required to compare the two alternatives (with ends trimmed or untrimmed) for a particular loading it will be necessary to make full calculations for each alternative, since the results may have unforeseen consequences in marginal cases. For example, it may be found to be necessary to leave a different hold slack to achieve the desired trim.

The stowage factor will affect the number and positions of the compartments to be filled and this in turn, in conjunction with the bunkers to be carried and the limiting draught, will affect the deadweight and the stability, which may dictate revision of the first assumptions as to the quantity and position of the cargo to be carried. The ship with untrimmed ends will normally load faster and more cheaply. With ends trimmed and all cargo spaces filled she will load more cargo.

***Regina Oldendorff* with grain from Three Rivers to Oran:** There are several points of interest in the voyage of the *Regina Oldendorff* from Three Rivers to Oran, featured in the grain stability calculation forms (Appendix 19.1) and in earlier documents (Appendices 10.2 and 10.11).

If all holds had been loaded with untrimmed ends the ship's stability would have been insufficient, with grain heeling moments of 14,678 mt.m compared with maximum allowable heeling moments of 11,433 mt.m in the worst condition, arriving in Ceuta. Calculations showed that adequate stability could be achieved by trimming the ends of only two holds, thus keeping the additional cost of trimming to a minimum.

The limiting draught for the berth in Oran was 9.8 m, but the arrival draught for the *Regina Oldendorff* at Oran was 10.3 m before deballasting. However, once she had arrived within port limits complete discharge of ballast from 3 and 4 DB tanks would produce a draught for berthing of 9.8 metres, even keel. The consequent reduction of her positive stability within port limits would be acceptable.

Carriage of grain in topside tanks: Some bulk carriers, such as the *Regina Oldendorff*, are equipped for the carriage of grain in the topside tanks. Loading is done by pneumatic or mechanical hose through manhole lids set in the main deck. Each topside tank is connected to the adjacent hold by feeder ports, or dumping manholes, at the base of the tank (Fig. 1.32). These must be left open whilst grain is carried allowing grain to flow through into the hold as the cargo settles and during discharge. In practice the option of loading in the topside tanks is rarely used though it may be found necessary when the ship is required to load a precise amount of cargo and cannot comply with the Grain Regulations when using the main holds only, or when several grades or types of grain are to be carried. It is not necessary to use the topside tanks when the cubic capacity required is restricted by the high density (low stowage factor) of the cargo or by draught restrictions, and it is not a practical option when loading is to be by grab.

Even when the carriage of grain in the topside tanks is possible it will be viewed with caution because of the practical difficulties. The preparation of the tanks for cargo, when they are normally used for water ballast, is likely to require substantial time and effort from the crew in addition to the routine preparation of the holds. The tanks must be scrupulously cleaned, the feeder ports must be unbolted and the ballast line must be blanked off. Loading grain into the tanks normally presents no problems, but the flow of grain through the feeder openings at the time of discharge is often not as free as is intended, and this slows the process.

Some charterparties state that all extra costs incurred as a result of carrying grain in topside tanks are to be met by owners; this is another factor which discourages their use.

The topside tanks of the *Regina Oldendorff* have been designed for efficient cleaning, and discharge of grain. The ship's side framing (Fig. 19.1) runs horizontally and is canted so that grain will slip from its surface. The underdeck framing (running fore and aft) is without flanges which would catch dirt or cargo residue, and

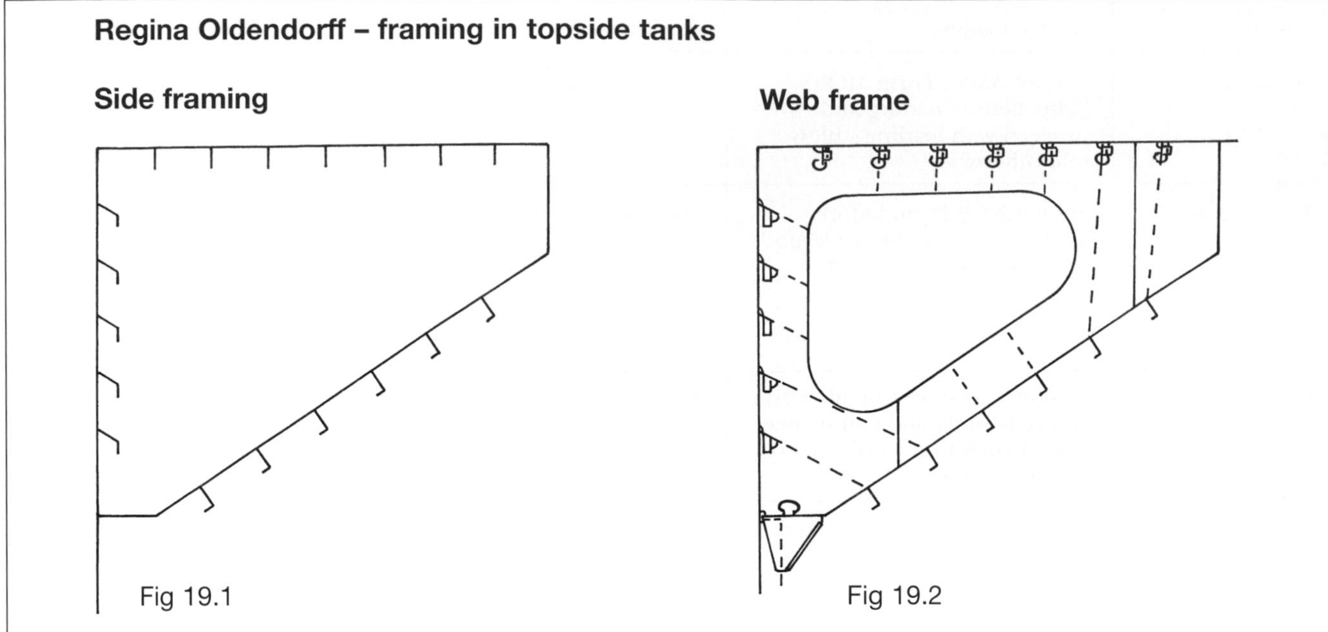

Fig 19.1

Fig 19.2

the hopper side framing (running fore and aft) is in the hold and not within the tank. Each topside tank is partly subdivided along its length by transverse web frames (Fig. 19.2) usually occurring at intervals of four frame spaces. The loading manholes are situated so that every bay can be reached from a manhole by passing through no more than one web frame.

Most of the features mentioned above will help to minimise the amount of cargo which remains in the tank after the contents have fed into the hold by gravity during the main discharge. It is certain, however, that some cargo residues will remain, mostly at the base of the tank, from whence they will have to be removed by hand before discharge is complete and the tank can be ballasted.

The topside tanks must be isolated from the ballast system before grain is loaded in them to ensure that ballast cannot be accidentally flooded into the tanks, and they must be reconnected to the ballast system when the tanks have been emptied and cleaned. The system for isolating the tanks – for example, the fitting of blanks in the ballast lines or plates over the ballast suctions – should be freed and overhauled occasionally even if the tanks are never used for grain, to ensure that it can still be used if required.

When grain is to be carried in topside tanks the tank bilge suctions must be connected up and the cover plates must be sealed with hessian, ensuring a cover which is graintight but not watertight. Serviceable sounding pipes must be available so that the tanks can be sounded daily.

Hold preparation: Procedures for cleaning holds have been described in detail in Chapter 5. When grain is to be carried the hatch covers, holds and bilges must be absolutely clean, dry and free of taint and infestation. A ship can reasonably be rejected for grain loading when the cargo spaces are not absolutely clean, since the cargo is for human or animal consumption and must be protected from contamination. In addition it has often been suggested that when no cargo is ready for loading, the surveyors may inspect the ship with even greater care than is normal looking for any excuse to reject her and thereby to prevent laytime from commencing. It is the ship's responsibility to ensure that surveyors have no valid reason for rejecting the vessel.

All traces of previous cargoes and of loose scale must be removed from hatch covers – especially their undersides, coamings and drains, beam flanges, frames, brackets, casings, manhole covers and bilge wells. Bilge wells should be readily accessible for preloading inspection and for testing of bilge suctions if required by the surveyor.

Any trace of infestation by insects must be found and removed. Such infestation is most likely behind loose scale and within bilge wells and manhole cover recesses. Infestation may be removed with a suitable grain-compatible spray or by fumigation, and expert advice should be requested through the owners for anything more than a minor localised infestation. Taint from any smelly substance must also be eliminated (see Appendix 5.2).

Following cleaning and preparation by the crew the cargo spaces should be reinspected by the Master or chief mate a few hours before the preloading inspection to ensure that all remains in perfect order for that inspection. Grain inspectors have been known to check storerooms and accommodation and can reject vessels if these spaces are found to be infested, even if the holds are acceptable. This action is justified by the possibility of the infestation spreading to the holds.

Loading of grain: Some grain silos are very large structures containing a large number of separate bins. Each bin contains a consignment of grain and the specifications of the grain may vary from one bin to another. The specification required for a particular shipment is achieved by mixing the contents of different bins in suitable proportions. This may be monitored by inspectors, who will board the ship to sample the cargo to ensure that the correct mix has been loaded. If necessary they will order changes in the mix and have been known, in extreme cases, to order a vessel to be part discharged so that the cargo could be remixed to the correct grade. The contents of a bin may be the minimum pour that the vessel can call for.

Condition of cargo: The condition of the cargo should be regularly inspected during the course of loading. Ships' officers cannot be expected to be experts in the condition of grain, but they should have no difficulty in recognising grain which is wet, sprouting, mouldy, discoloured or contaminated with rat droppings or insects, dead or alive. All these and other signs should be a warning that the grain is in poor condition. It is not possible to view all the grain which is loaded, but a good impression of its general condition can be obtained from inspecting cargo in the holds during interruptions in the loading, cargo which is spilt on deck, and cargo within the hatch coaming during the final stages of loading each hold. In addition, it may be possible to inspect grain ashore before it is loaded if the method of delivery alongside allows.

Grain which appears to be unfit for shipment should be rejected altogether and should charterers insist upon the shipment a survey should be held by surveyors acting on behalf of the owners and protest should be promptly noted.

Damage from leakage: Leakage of water into grain is a frequent and serious cause of claims, since any wetting of the grain will damage it. Every effort must be made to ensure that hatch covers and access hatches are absolutely watertight (a subject fully discussed in Chapter 4). When hatch covers are inspected, surveyed and/or tested for watertightness before the start of the voyage, that fact and the results should be recorded in the deck log book.

When grain cargoes suffer from leakage through the hatch covers the Master is sometimes criticised if he did not seal the hatches with bitumastic sealing tape. However (as was noted in Chapter 4 where the subject is fully discussed), its effectiveness is doubtful and the damage which it can cause to the hatch covers in the long term is substantial.

Ventilation: Effective surface ventilation of grain cargoes is often difficult or impossible to achieve because most compartments are filled and there is no route by which air can travel over the cargo from one ventilator at the fore end of the hold to another at the after end (Fig. 15.6). In recent tonnage in which the only ventilators are fitted in the hatch covers (Figs. 4.16, 15.1 and 2), there is no provision for ventilation of the ends of the holds. There is, however, persuasive evidence that healthy grain cargoes require no ventilation[161]. Cargoes of grain remain, unventilated, for months in silos and have been carried successfully in tankers where the tanks are unventilated. When a grain cargo is loaded cool and carried to a warmer area the cargo will be slowly warmed at its boundaries. With no ventilation there will be no danger of ship's or cargo sweat developing. When a grain cargo is loaded warm and carried to a cooler area (a more common occurrence) there is some danger of ship's sweat developing on the steelwork within the hold but it is argued that ventilation to prevent ship's sweat will cool the surface of the cargo and is likely to cause damaging condensation of moisture within the surface layers of the cargo. The removal of one problem will create another. The arguments from ***Carefully to Carry*** are summarised in Appendix 19.2 They conclude that grain cargoes often cannot be ventilated effectively and that it is acceptable for them to remain unventilated.

During the course of an ocean voyage a cargo of grain will settle, perhaps by 5-6 per cent but even this is not likely to be sufficient to permit continuous ventilation along the length of the hold from end to end. Surface ventilation of grain should never take place when the external air (the ambient air) is wetter than the air in the holds, or when spray is being shipped in the vicinity of the ventilator intakes. (For a fuller discussion of ventilation, see Chapter 15).

Infestation: Grain is subject to infestation by insects and the cargo should be inspected with care at every opportunity for any signs of insects or larvae. To emphasise this point, the sad story can be told of the handy-sized bulk carrier which loaded a cargo of yellow corn in Eastern Europe for a North African port. Loading was intermittent and took 18 days. It is probable that insect infestation was present at this time, but it was not noticed. The sea voyage to North Africa took four days and on arrival the vessel anchored to await a berth. Hatches were opened on arrival at the anchorage to inspect the cargo and some infestation was noted.

Unfortunately, the Master took no effective action to deal with the problem, perhaps hoping that the vessel would berth at an early date. Instead she remained a month at anchor and when she eventually berthed the entire surface of the cargo in all holds was covered to a depth of 30 mm with infestation. The full cargo was rejected and eventually sold for one-tenth of its original value and the ship was off hire for months whilst matters were resolved.

As soon as the infestation was noted the Master should have informed the owners and charterers so that expert advice could be obtained on the best way of treating the problem. It is unlikely that the ship had the resources to fumigate the cargo, but suitable materials could have been delivered to her at the anchorage to deal with the infestation.

The IMO *IMSBC Code*[5] recommends that fumigation in-transit should be performed in accordance with IMO MSC.1/Circs. 1264 and 1265 which provide detailed advice on procedures and precautions. (The safety aspects of fumigation are discussed in Chapter 21.) Cases of ineffective fumigation have been reported[198], particularly in instances where the fumigant is delivered only to the top of the stow and when cargo is wheat, which packs very densely,

On occasions a significant quantity of water may be added to a cargo of grain when mixed with a fumigant to dilute it. In one instance a shipper in the USA quoted a figure of 75 mt of water for 45,000 mt of grain.

Heating: Grain can suffer from heating, particularly if its moisture content is too high. It is not normal practice to take daily temperatures of grain cargoes, but it is prudent to take temperatures from time to time, particularly for grain close to the engineroom or to heated fuel oil tanks. Fuel tanks beneath cargo holds are liable to be heated to a maximum of 35°-50°C depending upon the grade of fuel carried and the ship's practice. Grain is a poor conductor of heat (it possesses poor thermal conductivity) so the effects of a heated tank will spread very slowly through a cargo, but it is good practice to arrange where possible for fuel to be drawn from tanks which are not beneath grain laden holds or for heating of the fuel to be minimised.

Cargo inspections: A prudent Master will seek opportunities to inspect the cargo within the hatch coamings from a position on deck from time to time, when it is safe to do so. Suitable opportunities for opening the hatches, provided they have not be sealed by a surveyor, may occur during a mid-voyage canal transit or whilst at the anchorage or in the approaches to the berth at the discharge port. Such an inspection can give the earliest warning of problems with leakage or infestation and provide an opportunity to minimise the damage.

It is important to ensure that any loose water is removed from the hatch covers before they are opened. If it is allowed to fall on to the surface of the cargo it will damage the cargo and give the misleading impression that leakage has occurred.

Discharge of grain cargoes: Discharge is likely to be by suction unloader or possibly by grab. Vacuvators (Fig. 11.19) which are often used in developing areas or berths which do not normally handle bulk cargoes may also be used. In some ports ships may be required to discharge the cargo with ships' gear, using ships' grabs.

Hold cleaning after grain cargoes: When the discharging programme allows it, the thorough cleaning of the holds can be assisted by sending crew members into the holds in the early stages of the discharge. Whilst standing in the cargo they can sweep residues of grain from beam and bracket flanges which are difficult to reach once the hold is empty.

Other precautions: Dust fires and explosions have been known to occur when working grain cargoes. Smoking should not be allowed on deck whilst grain is being worked.

Carriage of coal

The total annual worldwide production of hard coal in 2006 was estimated to have been about 3,080 million tonnes, of which some 755 million tonnes (about 25 per cent) entered world seaborne trade, the major producers for export being Australia, PR China, Indonesia, South Africa and Colombia, in that order, and the main consumers of imported coal being Japan, Western Europe, South Korea and Taiwan. More recently China has become an importer of coal, mostly from Australia and Indonesia.

Coal is carried in bulk carriers of all sizes (Fig. 19.3), from Cape-sized vessels trading between deep-water berths at loading ports in Australia, Indonesia, South Africa and Canada and discharging ports in Europe, Japan and South Korea, to mini-bulkers transporting small parcels between European shallow-draught ports where comparatively small tonnages of coal are required. Since the USA has no deep-draught ports able to accept fully-laden Cape-sized vessels the coal exported from the USA is mainly carried in Panamax-sized vessels (Fig. 19.4), or part-laden Cape-sized vessels, although some vessels were specifically built for the USA East Coast (Hampton Roads) to Europe trade. These vessels have a summer dwt of 115,000 at a draught of 14.5 metres, which was the limiting draught for Hampton Roads at the time of their construction.

Within European waters there is a substantial trade for smaller vessels carrying transhipped cargoes of coal from north west Continental ports.

Economists distinguish two main types of coal which enter international seaborne trade – namely steam or thermal coal which is used for power generation, for industry (including cement making) and for domestic heating; and coking or metallurgical coal, used for steel production. Coal destined for a power station is likely to be steam coal, whilst coking coal will usually be consigned to a steel works.

Marine transportation of coal – the hazards: A number of hazards are associated with the carriage of coal. It can produce explosions, go on fire, corrode the ship's structure, poison or smother those who breathe its gases, and liquefy, causing the cargo to shift and the ship to become unstable and capsize.

Coal may release methane and hydrogen, both of which are flammable gases which can make an explosive mixture with air. Some coals are liable to spontaneous heating, which can cause fire, and may when heated emit flammable gases including carbon monoxide,

Fig.19.3 Loading coal at Richards Bay
Photo courtesy of Richards Bay Coal Terminal

Fig.19.4 Loading coal
Photo courtesy of Captain L Hesketh FNI

which is also toxic. If coal is subject to oxidation within a cargo compartment the oxygen will be depleted and carbon dioxide will increase, creating an atmosphere in which breathing is impossible. The sulphur in coal when combined with moisture can produce sulphuric acid, which is liable to corrode the ship's structure. Some coals when composed of small particles can liquefy and shift when the moisture content is above that of the transportable moisture limit.

The *International Maritime Solid Bulk Cargo (IMSBC) Code*[249] lays down detailed procedures for the safe carriage of coal and these should be followed with care by all engaged in the transportation of coal by sea if the tragic and unnecessary loss of lives which has in the past been associated with this trade is to be ended.

The relevant provisions of the *Code* are summarised below in italics for the benefit of those who merely require an overview. Regular type has been used for explanatory remarks and comments. The contents of the summary have been re-arranged to group together items to consider *Before loading*; *When carrying a coal cargo*; *If methane is forecast or detected*; *If self heating coal is forecast or detected*; and *Before discharging* but it cannot be stated too emphatically that Shipmasters engaged in carrying coal should be familiar with the detailed recommendations of the *Code*.

The *IMSBC Code contains special precautions*[247] for gravity fed self-unloading bulk carriers to allow for the fact that the gates at the bottom of the cargo holds are unlikely to be airtight. These gates, when opened, deliver cargo onto the conveyors in the tunnel below the holds and the *Code* specifies the manner in which ventilation and sampling are to be carried out. The holds and tunnel are to be ventilated as a single unit with positive ventilation (more supply than exhaust in the tunnel) when methane is detected or negative ventilation (more exhaust than supply) when carbon monoxide is found.

All coal cargoes:

Before loading

- A photographic record of hold condition prior to loading coal can be useful and is a wise precaution for claims purposes. Control areas of approximately two square metres can be used at five locations in each hold – one at the after end of each hopper side, one on the tanktop close to each bilge and one on the aft lower stool amidships. These photographs can be used to indicate the preloading condition of the hold plating should the vessel suffer marked corrosion from excessively acid coal.
- *Boundaries of cargo spaces where materials are carried shall be resistant to fire and liquids.* It is dangerous to use water to cool coal cargoes. Liquid from other cargoes, from water ingress or for cooling could cause the cargo to liquefy.
- *Coal shall be separated from other IMO categories of hazardous cargo,* and shall not be stowed adjacent to hot areas. See the *Code* for details of which commodities may not be stowed near coal.
- *The shipper shall provide the Master with a written cargo declaration, before commencement of loading, of the cargo's contracted moisture content, sulphur content and size, and whether it may be liable to emit methane, or to self-heat, and should provide more information if possible.* The Declaration by Shipper form (Appendix 14.10) fulfils this requirement. High sulphur content of coal has been associated with heavy corrosion of the ship's structure. Coal has been said to be potentially harmful when the following values are exceeded: moisture 10.0 per cent; sulphur 1.5 per cent; volatile matter 35.0 per cent; temperature 8°C above ambient. These are matters on which the *Code* offers no guidance.
- *The Master should ensure he receives the written cargo declaration. If the cargo is liable to emit methane or to self heat the Master should read the Special Precautions contained in the Coal section of the IMSBC Code*[249]. Masters should bear in mind the possibility that inaccurate information will be supplied, as has happened on occasions in the past[175]. Furthermore, steam coal shipments are sometimes created with a blend of coals from several different sources. If the different coals have not been properly mixed the characteristics of a particular part of the cargo may be very different from those stated in the shipper's declaration.
- Coal cargoes having a moisture content in excess of the transportable moisture limit (TML) must never be carried. Coal cargoes with a moisture content approaching the TML must never be worked during rain or snowfall and holds which are not being worked should always be kept closed during precipitation. A high moisture content increases the danger of cargo shifting, self-heating, and creating corrosive sulphuric acid. If the moisture content is not near the TML and shippers insist on continuing to load in heavy rain they should be issued with a letter holding them responsible for any resulting damage to ship or cargo.
- *An auxiliary method of testing for the possibility of excess moisture, which could lead to cargo flow is described in the Code*[153] *as follows:*

  Half fill a cylindrical can or similar container (0.5 litre to 1 litre capacity) with a sample of the material. Take the can in one hand and bring it down sharply to strike a hard surface such as a solid table from a height of about 0.2 m. Repeat the procedure 25 times at one or two second intervals. Examine the surface for free moisture or fluid conditions. If free moisture or a fluid condition appears, arrangements should be made to have additional laboratory tests conducted on the material before it is accepted for loading. In other words, if this test reveals a fluid condition the cargo should be rejected unless laboratory tests show that it is safe.
- Shipment of coal from US Gulf ports, particularly in the summer months, have in the past been reported to give special problems when coal was loaded directly from barges. It is recommended that temperatures of the coal in barges be obtained prior to shipment. It has been suggested that problems arise with coal transported in barges because water is retained in the cargo and cannot drain off, the peaked stow of coal in the barge gives high exposure to oxygen and, in addition, steam coal loaded in New Orleans may be a mixture of several grades, some of which are low grades which are particularly liable to self-heating.
- In the 1980s it was said that coal should not be loaded if its temperature is higher than ambient temperature, whilst the South African Department of Transport[22] advised that South African coal should not be loaded at a temperature higher than 45°C, or ambient temperature plus 10°C, whichever is the greater, as measured immediately prior to loading.
- *Holds and bilge wells should be thoroughly cleaned and dry,* and any residues and dunnage must be removed to prevent the formation of air pockets in the cargo, *before loading* commences.
- *All electrical cables and components in holds and adjacent compartments must be free of defects and should be safe for use in an explosive atmosphere, or be isolated* because methane

and hydrogen are explosive, and are much lighter than air, and may escape to adjacent spaces. A recommended method of isolation is by physical removal of the fuses to a safe storage, under the care of a responsible person, so that they cannot be refitted without authority.

- *The ship should be suitably fitted and carry on board appropriate instruments for measuring the following without requiring entry into the cargo space: concentration in the atmosphere of methane; oxygen; carbon monoxide; pH value of cargo hold bilge samples. These instruments should be regularly serviced and calibrated. Ship personnel should be trained in their use.* Procedures for the monitoring of gas in coal cargoes are described in the Coal section of the *IMSBC Code*[249]. (The use and maintenance of sampling instruments is described in Chapter 22 where it is stated that this work is best done ashore by trained personnel.)
- *Means should be provided for measuring the temperature of the coal in the range 0°–100°C during loading and whilst carrying the coal, without the need to enter the holds.* Some ships are provided with special temperature tubes similar to sounding pipes placed midships at each end of the hold. When these are provided the thermometers can be left in position at all times lowered to a level well below the surface of the cargo and withdrawn when a reading is required. Alternatively, hold bilge sounding pipes can be used. Temperatures obtained from sounding pipes which run down engineroom bulkheads will sometimes provide high readings which come from the machinery spaces, and not from the cargo. Where this is a possibility readings should be obtained from several positions. The South African authorities[22] state that temperature measurement of coal in stockpiles and in vessels' holds is best done using suitably calibrated pyrometers, which are easy to use and can reliably indicate temperatures within a body of coal. Mercury thermometers, they say, should not be used unless fitted with a maximum temperature indicator, and reset before use.
- The temperatures of coal cargoes said to be liable to self heating should be monitored before loading and they should be accepted for loading only when the cargo temperature is not higher than 55°C.

When carrying a coal cargo

- The atmosphere over a cargo of coal must be monitored at regular intervals to detect methane, oxygen and carbon monoxide. The necessary preparations, equipment and procedures are described in *'Procedures for gas monitoring of coal cargoes'*[249].
- *Self-contained breathing apparatus (SCBA) required by SOLAS II-2/10.10 must be kept available and used, when required, by trained personnel.* Well equipped ships are provided with compressors for the recharging of (SCBA) air bottles, allowing more training with breathing apparati.
- *Smoking and naked flames near cargo spaces should be prohibited, and suitable notices posted.* It is simplest, and most prudent, not to allow smoking forward of the accommodation.
- *Burning, cutting, chipping, welding and other sources of ignition should not be permitted near cargo spaces unless such spaces have been ventilated and tested free of methane.* Where possible these activities should be avoided forward of the accommodation. The owners' 'safe system of work', including Risk Assessments, Permits To Work etc must be used for any 'hot work'.
- *The cargo shall be trimmed reasonably level to the boundaries of the cargo space to prevent the formation of gas pockets, and to minimise the mixing of air with the coal.* Ventilator trunking leading down the bulkhead into the cargo stow should be adequately sealed. Trimming by spout is an effective way of levelling the cargo (Figs. 19.5 and 19.6).
- *The shipper shall ensure that the Master receives the necessary co-operation from the loading terminal.* This important requirement should, if necessary, be brought to the attention of the shipper and the loading terminal.
- *The atmosphere in the space above the cargo in each compartment shall be regularly monitored for the concentration of methane, oxygen and carbon monoxide in accordance with the 'Procedures for the gas monitoring of coal cargoes'.*[249] Procedures for particular cargoes are decided by the shipper's information and the results of sampling.
- A full record of the methane, oxygen and carbon monoxide readings, along with temperatures, hold bilge soundings, acidity (pH readings), tonnages of bilge water discharged and record of hold ventilation should be retained in the deck log book or elsewhere. Flammable and/or explosive concentrations of gases are as follows: methane 5-16 per cent; carbon monoxide 12-75 per cent; hydrogen 4-75 per cent: All these gases are lighter than air, and carbon monoxide and hydrogen are odourless. The *Code* contains no recommended procedure for testing for hydrogen, which may be formed when coal is mixed with water. In the example (Fig. 19.7) the temperature, O_2, CO, CH_4 and pH readings are recorded for five holds over a 10 day period, along with air and sea temperatures. Times of opening and closing ventilators are shown as are days when water or spray on deck prevented the taking of readings. Fig. 19.8 is the voyage water drainage log and shows the grade and tonnage of coal in each of the nine holds, the bilge capacity in m^3,

Fig.19.5 Rotating spout for loading and trimming coal
Photo courtesy of Captain L Hesketh

Fig.19.6 Start of loading coal
Photo courtesy of Captain L Hesketh FNI

TO :

CARGO TEMP. / GAS / O_2 etc. RECORD

M/V" "

VOY. NO. 2A

Hold	Date	16/05/02	17/05/02	18/05/02	19/05/02	20/05/02	21/05/02	22/05/02	23/05/02	24/05/02	25/05/02
NO. 1	O_2 (%)	19.6		18.0		16.0	19.8	19.9	SEA SPRAY	18.8	19.7
	CH_4 (%)	0		0		0	0	0		0	0
	CO (PPM)	0		2		1	0	0		0	0
	Temp.	27		27		27	28	27		27	28
	BLG pH	–		–		8.1	–	8.1		–	8.1
	Vent'N (O)	0800		–		1300	(o)	(o)	–	–	0800
	(C)	1700	(c)	(c)		–	–	–	0900	(c)	–
NO. 2	O_2 (%)	19.9	ROUGH SEA/SEA SPRAY ON MAIN DECK	19.1	VERY ROUGH SEA/SEA SPRAY ON MAIN DECK	17.0	20.6	20.2	SEA SPRAY	18.9	19.9
	CH_4 (%)	0		0		0	0	0		0	0
	CO (PPM)	2		3		1	0	0		0	0
	Temp.	26		27		27	27	28		28	28
	BLG pH	–		–		8.5	8.5	8.5		8.5	8.5
	Vent'N (O)	0800		–		1300	(o)	(o)	–	–	0800
	(C)	1700		(c)		–	–	–	0900	(c)	–
NO. 3	O_2 (%)	19.7		17.0		16.8	19.4	19.5	18.1	18.2	19.5
	CH_4 (%)	0		0		0	0	0	0	0	0
	CO (PPM)	0		2		0	0	0	0	0	0
	Temp.	25		26		26	26	26	26	26	26
	BLG PH	–		–		7.9	7.9	7.9	7.9	7.9	7.9
	Vent'N (O)	0800		–		1300	(o)	(o)	–	–	0800
	(C)	1700		(c)		–	–	–	1000	(c)	–
NO. 4	O_2 (%)	19.7		18.9		20.1	19.7	19.9	18.5	18.7	19.8
	CH_4 (%)	0		0		0	0	0	0	0	0
	CO (PPM)	3		3		0	0	0	0	0	0
	Temp.	25		25		25	26	26	26	26	26
	BLG pH	–		–		–	–	–	–	–	–
	Vent'N (O)	0800		–		0800	(o)	(o)	–	–	0800
	(C)	1700		(c)		–	–	–	1600	(c)	–
NO. 5	O_2 (%)	19.6		17.5		18.9	19.3	19.4	19.0	18.5	19.4
	CH_4 (%)	0		0		0	0	0	0	0	0
	CO (PPM)	1		2		0	0	0	0	0	0
	Temp.	29		28		27	30	30	29	30	30
	BLG pH	–		–		7.9	–	–	7.9	7.9	7.9
	Vent'N (O)	0800		–		0800	(o)	(o)	–	–	0800
	(C)	1700	(c)	(c)		–	–	–	1600	(c)	–
Air Temp.		20		14		22	14	22	21	20	19
Sea Temp.		18		11		18	13	18	17	15	16

(1) CH_4 (%) : Please enter LEL (%)
(2) CO(PPM) : Please enter PPM
(3) BLG pH : Hold bilge pH(Neutral:7)
(4) Vent'N : Please enter the time of Open(O)/Close(C)

Fig. 19.7

VOYAGE COAL WATER DRAINAGE LOG

HAY POINT, AUS. TO FOS, FRANCE VIA SUEZ CANAL (VOY. 2A)

Vessel	M.V. " "								B = before A = after
Coal Grade	S.W.C.	N/PARK	GREG	N/PARK	GREG	P/DOWNS	GREG	N/PARK	S.W.C.
Tonnage (mt)	16077 m/t	18493 m/t	19557 m/t	19553 m/t	19702 m/t	18529 m/t	19644 m/t	19361 m/t	17284 m/t
Hold	1	2	3	4	5	6	7	8	9
Bilge capacity/m3 (each)	3.888 x 2	4.104 x 2	4.104 x 2	4.104 x 2	4.104 x 2	4.104 x 2	4.104 x 2	4.104 x 2	5.768x4.456
Bilge height/cm	120	120	120	120	120	120	120	120	80

Date 2002 June			Hold 1 Sounding p	s	Tns	Hold 2 Sounding p	s	Tns	Hold 3 Sounding p	s	Tns
8	am	B	38	5	1.23	70	15	2.90	55	18	2.50
		A	0	5		0	0		0	0	
	pm	B									
		A									
9	am	B	21	8		26	31		20	39	
		A									
	pm	B									
		A									
10	am	B	61	21	2.66	65	95	5.47	51	99	5.13
		A	0	0		0	0		0	0	
	pm	B									
		A									
11	am	B									
		A	25	9		20	2		27	2	
	pm	B									
		A									
12	am	B	61	21		57	5		67	5	
		A									
	pm	B									
		A									
Total Tons					3.89			8.37			7.63

Date 2002 June			Hold 4 Sounding p	s	Tns	Hold 5 Sounding p	s	Tns	Hold 6 Sounding p	s	Tns
8	am	B	35	10	1.44	11	11	0.76	19	15	1.16
		A	0	0		0	0		0	0	
	pm	B									
		A									
9	am	B	12	16		7	9		22	20	
		A									
	pm	B									
		A									
10	am	B	43	48	3.11	18	20	1.30	25	41	2.26
		A	0	0		0	0		0	0	
	pm	B									
		A									
11	am	B									
		A	19	0		9	7		18	0	
	pm	B									
		A									
12	am	B	52	0		20	15		31	0	
		A									
	pm	B									
		A									
Total Tons					4.65			2.06			3.42

Date 2002 June			Hold 7 Sounding p	s	Tns	Hold 8 Sounding p	s	Tns	Hold 9 Sounding p	s	Tns	Total Tonnes
8	am	B	105	2	3.59	47	0	1.61	47	47	6.32	21.61
		A	0	2		0	0		0	0		
	pm	B										
		A										
9	am	B	51	14		21	19		31	34		–
		A										
	pm	B										
		A										
10	am	B	115	35	5.13	55	47	3.49	80	80	11.23	39.78
		A	0	0		0	0		0	0		
	pm	B										
		A										
11	am	B										–
		A	31	2		23	0		25	27		
	pm	B										
		A										
12	am	B	59	4		49	1		51	55		–
		A										
	pm	B										
		A										
Total Tons					8.72			5.1			17.55	61.39

Fig. 19.8

the bilge height in cm, the bilge sounding before and after pumping and the tonnage pumped out daily and after five days.

- *Unless expressly directed otherwise all holds should be surface ventilated for the first 24 hours after departure from the loading port. During this period one measurement should be taken from one sample point per hold and for the purpose of the gas monitoring the ventilation shall be stopped for an appropriate* standard *period* of at least four hours before the measurement is taken.
- *If after 24 hours the methane concentrations are at an acceptably low level the ventilation openings shall be closed. If not they shall remain open until acceptably low levels are obtained.* The *IMSBC Code* implies that a methane concentration of less than 20% Lower Explosive Limit (LEL) is an acceptable level. One major ship operator[174] says ventilation should be commenced when levels above 10% are found. *In either event measurements should be continued on a daily basis* following a standard period of at least four hours during which ventilation is stopped. Masters are particularly warned of the dangers of a build-up of methane gas in the holds during times of following wind and in the period immediately subsequent to any enforced shut-down of surface ventilation due to adverse weather.

  The air shall be sampled through methane monitoring points, pipes like sounding pipes set horizontally into the hatch coaming, or through sampling points set into the hatch covers (Fig.4.18).
- *When significant concentrations of methane are subsequently observed in unventilated cargo spaces the appropriate special precautions for coals emitting methane shall apply.* In other words when a cargo is found to emit methane it must be treated like a cargo which emits methane, regardless of its official description.
- *When methane, carbon monoxide or heating is detected, special precautions, described below, should be adopted.* One major shipowner defines safe limits as: methane concentrations not more than 10 per cent of the lower explosive limit (LEL), and temperatures not more than 40°C.
- *The Master shall ensure, as far as practicable, that any gases which may be emitted from this cargo do not accumulate in adjacent enclosed spaces, and that enclosed working spaces such as storerooms, carpenter's shop, passageways, tunnels, etc are regularly monitored for the presence of methane, oxygen and carbon monoxide. Such spaces shall be adequately ventilated.*
- *The hold bilges shall be regularly,* daily is normal, *tested for pH* (acidity). Procedures for testing the acidity of hold bilges are still being developed since this requirement is relatively new. Methods include extracting a sample of bilge water using a narrow cup or beaker attached to the end of a sounding rod or attaching the litmus paper to the sounding rod with a water-absorbing device such as a strip of surgical bandage. The best and simplest method may be to touch the litmus paper with the wet end of the sounding rod or bob once it has been brought back on deck.
- *When excessive acidity is detected the bilges should be regularly pumped dry to reduce corrosion of the tank tops and the bilge system.* The importance of these precautions is underlined by the report of one vessel, in mint condition and on her second voyage, which found 16 mm of a 21 mm hopper plate corroded away by sulphuric acid. The combination of conditions which led to the formation of strong acid were that the cargo was a highly volatile, high sulphur coal which was loaded under extremely wet conditions, due to heavy rain, subsequent self-heating of the cargo serving to aggravate the condition. A record should be kept of tonnages of water discharged from the bilges.

- If the bilge water is found to be excessively acid it is advisable to add some slaked lime to the water before it is pumped out to prevent corrosion of the bilge line system. To do this mix the quantity of lime listed below in a bucket of fresh water and tip the mixture down the sounding pipe.

For 1 m^3 of bilge water with pH	Slaked lime (grams)
2	370.0
3	37.0
4	3.7

It is recommended that a Panamax vessel should carry 200 kg, and a Cape-sized vessel 400 kg, of slaked lime for this purpose. If no lime is available and high acidity of bilge water is detected fresh water can be added via the sounding pipe to dilute the bilge water and protect the system. If this is done it will be necessary to avoid overfilling the bilge or using more fresh water than the vessel can spare. Records of tonnages of water discharged from the bilges must, of course, refer to tonnages found before the addition of fresh water.

- *If the behaviour of the cargo during the voyage is different from that forecast in the shipper's cargo declaration,* for example with respect to emitting methane, or self-heating, *the Master shall inform the shipper, to assist the latter in providing better information in the future.* A form for this purpose has been devised (Appendix 14.11). Some owners take responsibility for passing this information to shippers, on the basis of the records provided by the ship.

If methane is forecast or detected

- *Maintain surface ventilation at all times except in the standard period before gas monitoring* using natural ventilation only, since mechanical ventilation could create sparks. *On no account should air be directed into the body of the coal as this could promote self-heating.*
- *Ventilate spaces before opening hatch covers, and avoid naked lights, and the creation of sparks when opening.*
- *The cargo hold and adjacent spaces shall not be entered by anyone until these spaces have been ventilated, and the atmosphere has been tested and found safe, or unless the person is trained, is wearing a compressed air breathing apparatus, is properly supervised and only equipment safe for use in an explosive atmosphere is used.*
- *Compartments adjacent to holds must be ventilated and monitored for gas, particularly before people enter them, or before equipment is energised and only mechanical ventilation safe for use in an explosive atmosphere shall be used.*

If self-heating coal is forecast or detected

- *If the cargo is liable to self-heat, or an increasing concentration of carbon monoxide is detected,* or the temperature of the cargo is rising rapidly, *the following additional precautions shall be taken.*
- *The hatches shall be closed and kept closed, and can be sealed with sealing tape for increased airtightness. Surface ventilation shall be the minimum to remove methane. Forced ventilation shall not be used, and no ventilation shall be directed into the body of the cargo.*
- *Personnel shall not enter the cargo space. If entry is critical to the safety of the ship or of life the person entering shall wear a compressed air breathing apparatus, and shall be properly trained.* The company's 'enclosed space entry procedures' and relevant Permit to Work must be utilised.
- *When the carbon monoxide level is increasing steadily, a potential self-heating may be developing. The cargo space shall be completely closed down and all ventilation ceased.* Remember to close the coaming drain valves. The Master shall seek expert advice immediately. In no circumstances should hatches be opened to inspect the cargo, since the admission of oxygen could cause a sudden flare-up of fire, making the situation much worse. *Water shall not be used for cooling the cargo, or for fighting a coal cargo fire at sea, but may be used for cooling the boundaries of the cargo space.* Cases have been reported where hot cargoes have been carried safely after the holds had been tightly sealed[215].
- *When the carbon monoxide level in any cargo space reaches 50 ppm or exhibits a steady rise over three consecutive days, a self-heating condition may be developing and the Master shall inform the shipper and the company of, at least, the following information if an accurate assessment of the situation is to be achieved.*
  - *(a) identify of the cargo spaces involved; readings for carbon monoxide, methane and oxygen,*
  - *(b) cargo temperatures and locations, and method used to obtain readings,*
  - *(c) times of readings,*
  - *(d) times ventilators opened/closed,*
  - *(e) tonnages of coal in hold(s) involved,*
  - *(f) type of coal and any special precautions required (as given in cargo information),*
  - *(g) date loaded and ETA at (named) intended discharging port, and*
  - *(h) Master's comments*

Before discharging a coal cargo

- Lightly grease the hatch cover trackways before opening the hatches for the first time after a passage, to prevent sparks which could cause an explosion if pockets of gas exist in the hold.

Detection of heating of coal cargoes: Until recently the accepted method for detecting heating of coal cargoes aboard ship was by thermometer. This, however, was an unreliable method of detecting heating, because heat does not pass easily through coal. If the overheated portion of the cargo is not close to a temperature sampling point the rise in temperature will not be detected. For the last century the coal industry ashore has recognised that temperature monitoring of coal cargo is inefficient and has relied upon the monitoring of carbon monoxide levels for warning that coal is heating. Following experiments aboard ships in recent years[82] the method has been adopted for the marine transportation of coal and the coal section of the *IMSBC Code*[249], summarised above, now attaches less importance to cargo temperatures and warns that if the carbon monoxide level is increasing rapidly a fire may be developing.

Marine transportation of coal – routine operational matters: Despite the numerous hazards which can be met when carrying coal, the vast majority of coal cargoes are carried without serious problem (Fig. 19.9). A variety of practical and commercial considerations should be borne in mind.

Stowage factor: The stowage factor of coal varies considerably, depending upon its origin, type and grade, moisture content, history prior to shipment and the characteristics of the ship. The *IMSBC Code*[249] suggests a range of 0.79-1.53 m^3/tonne (28-54 ft^3/tonne) though other authorities quote a

Fig.19.9 A Cape-sized bulk carrier discharging coal
Photo courtesy of Walter Vervloesem

Fig.19.10 Lump ore
Photo courtesy of Hamersley Iron Pty Ltd

narrower range. It so happens that the stowage factor required to fill a bulk carrier completely whilst bringing her to her summer marks normally lies between 0.95-1.30 m³/tonne (34-46 ft³/tonne), this being a figure which will vary according to the ship's design and also according to the bunkers required for the voyage and the actual mark to which she is permitted to load. Thus some bulkers will be full before they have loaded down to their marks, whilst others will reach their marks before all the holds have been filled. This is a matter of which full account must be taken when the loading is planned, and the Master will require to be provided with a reasonably reliable stowage factor for the cargo before the planning can be completed.

Drainage of moisture: Since coal cargoes may have a moisture content of up to 15 per cent[57] there can be considerable opportunity for water to drain from the cargo into the bilges during the course of the voyage. In some coal trades it has been the practice never to pump bilges because it was feared that the tonnage of water pumped overboard would appear as a loss of weight of cargo. However, as noted earlier, failure to pump bilges can result in the formation of sulphuric acid in the holds and bilge spaces with consequent corrosion of the ship's structure.

When bilges are regularly pumped during an ocean voyage weight loss due to discharge of moisture from coal cargoes is said by one authority[24] to tend to be directly proportional to the level of superficial moisture at the loading point and to the length of the trip. For a high departure level of superficial moisture (10 per cent or more) and a voyage of 40 days or more, with significant climatic changes during the voyage the drainage can, it is stated, be in the order of 1 per cent of the cargo weight measured on departure. For a voyage of 15-20 days with little climatic change and a superficial moisture level on departure of 6-7 per cent, drainage of less than 0.5 per cent is predicted.

It is a recommendation of the UN Working Party on Coal[24] that ships keep a full record certified by Master or officer of all bilge water pumped overboard during the loaded voyage. When bilge calibrations are available this can be achieved by taking soundings of all hold bilges before and after they are pumped. Alternatively, bilges can be pumped first to a holding tank, then discharged after the sounding of the holding tank had been obtained.

An important practical point to remember is that the cap for the bilge sounding pipe should always be removed before the bilge is pumped to ensure a flow of air into the bilge. This will ensure that pumping is not made difficult by the formation of a vacuum and will avoid the risk of unwanted through ventilation of the coal.

Part cargoes: It is quite common for vessels employed in the coal trade to load and to discharge in several ports and for several grades of coal to be carried. This arises partly because the draught restrictions in some coal ports prevent larger vessels from loading or discharging full cargoes and partly because a range of different grades can be loaded at the same port and can conveniently be transported in a single ship with a saving in cost. The relatively low density of coal makes it possible to make a voyage with a number of different combinations of holds full, with others empty, without exceeding longitudinal stress limits, without adopting unacceptable block loading arrangements and without infringing SOLAS Chapter XII Regulation 14 which says, in effect, that older bulk carriers of 150 m or upwards in length when fully laden with a high density cargo must distribute the cargo between all holds.

Carriage of iron ore

World trade: The term iron ore includes all of the oxides or carbonates of iron occurring naturally[15]. In 2006, some 711 million tonnes of iron ore entered into world seaborne trade and this figure has increased substantially since then. The main exporting countries are Australia and Brazil which between them provided over 70 per cent of world seaborne trade, with India, Canada, Sweden, South Africa and Venezuela being other important producers. Asia is the largest market for iron ore, with four countries – Japan, PR China, South Korea and China-Taipei – collectively taking over 60 per cent of world seaborne imports in 2002.

The 1990s saw a continuing trend towards the use of larger vessels for the carriage of iron ore to benefit from the lower transportation costs achieved thereby, this being accompanied by an increase in standard

Cape-sized designs to around 180,000 dwt. By 2002, some 80 per cent of the iron ore entering into world seaborne trade was transported in Cape-sized vessels, VLBCs or ore carriers, whilst sub-50,000 dwt vessels shared a mere 7 per cent of the market[155].

Iron ore cargoes: Iron ore is likely to be carried in one of four different forms:

- **ROM** is run of mine, which is ore of no special grade, shipped as it comes from the mine.
- **Fines** are small screenings of iron ore. They may be **sintered**, which is a fusing together of fines with coke breeze, millstone and limestone fines to make lumps, or **pelletised**, round pellets formed of very fine high grade ores.
- **Lump** is ore larger than a certain size. (Fig 19.10)
- **Concentrates** are obtained when a natural ore has undergone some form of purification by physical separation of undesirable ingredients. Concentrates are like heavy sand.

Preplanning the loading: Iron ore is a high-density cargo, with stowage factor ranging from 0.24-0.8 m^3/tonne. The denser grades require very little space in a hold and when occupying only the bottom of the hold iron ore cargoes lower the ship's centre of gravity and make her very stiff.

There is a variety of ways in which a ship can be damaged by high-density cargoes when badly distributed, and the following errors must be avoided: individual holds must not be overloaded (Appendix 9.2); unsuitable block loading must not be used (Appendix 9.4); excessive shear forces and bending moments must be avoided (Chapter 10).

There are several operational reasons why it is more efficient to carry heavy cargoes such as iron ore only in alternate holds, a system known informally as 'jump loading', and for this reason many bulk carriers have been classified as 'strengthened for heavy cargoes, (alternate) holds may be left empty'. When so classed, it is permissible to load a full deadweight cargo, using only alternate holds, normally the odd numbered ones.

The benefits of jump loading are described below but it is important to recognise the possible deadly consequences of the practice. During the last 25 or 30 years a large number of bulk carriers have been lost when they were jump loaded with a dense cargo and caught in bad weather. This has drawn attention to the severe stresses to which the hulls of ships loaded in this way are subjected and has resulted in a regulation[167] prohibiting most older bulk carriers from jump loading. SOLAS XII/14 applies to bulk carriers of 150 m in length and upwards carrying solid bulk cargo of density 1780 kg/m^3 and above after they have reached ten years of age unless, exceptionally in ships built before 1999, they have sufficient strength to withstand flooding of, and sloshing in, any one cargo hold. The Regulation prohibits these older bulkers from sailing in loaded condition with any hold loaded with less than 10 per cent of its capacity.

The recognition that jump loading increases the danger of foundering has meant that the owners, operators and Masters of many bulk carriers not affected by SOLAS XII/14 have nevertheless stopped using jump loading in recent years.

The benefits of jump loading are as follows: the average height of the cargo in the ship is raised making the ship less excessively stiff; discharging time is significantly reduced because the cargo is higher in the holds, a greater proportion of the cargo can be grabbed from the holds, and there are fewer holds to be trimmed; less hold cleaning is required and it is not necessary to use ballast holds for cargo.

There are disadvantages in jump loading too. It reduces the opportunities for carrying a number of different parcels of iron ore. If segregated parcels or grades are to be carried it may be necessary to use additional holds, thereby introducing block loading with its associated dangers.

Jump loading results in a greater tonnage of iron ore being loaded in each of a smaller number of holds. As a result the ore rises higher up the sides of the holds, reaching the level of the ship's side frames. This makes cleaning more difficult than when the surface of the ore only meets the lower hopper sides.

One major ship operator in the Australian trade requires all holds to be used when carrying fines to lower the height of the cargo for safety reasons. It has been found that because of the nature of the ore it will not run or 'avalanche' when being dug out during discharge. As a result, high vertical faces of cargo form at the ends of the holds where the grabs cannot reach. These faces are dangerous for the trimmers, as there is the danger of the ore collapsing and burying the men[15].

Jump loading exposes the ship to greater longitudinal stresses and higher tanktop loadings. The additional strengthening which is designed into the ship when she is built is intended to take care of the higher stresses, but there is a greater potential for damage if things go wrong. A final problem with jump loading is that the alternate holds may not have been strengthened sufficiently to contain a full cargo of iron ore when the ship is loaded to tropical (rather than summer) marks and carrying only a small tonnage of bunkers.

Hold preparation: Holds must be clean and bilges must be clean and covered with burlap. All the routine preparations described in Chapter 5 must be completed, but no special hold preparations are required for the carriage of iron ore.

Loading and trimming: The loading of iron ore cargoes has traditionally been thought to require no special attention, apart from the basic requirements to place the right quantities in the correct places in the planned sequence, and to keep the ship upright during the process. The traditional method of loading iron ore, still widespread, is to pour the cargo into the hold on the ship's centreline where it forms a broad based cone or heap. This method continues to be favoured because some ports do not have the equipment to load in any other way. Iron ore stowed in this manner is not known to have been the direct cause of any casualties.

When bulk carriers are built the double bottom and cross deck structure are designed based on a 'trimmed cargo distributed symmetrically in a hold space'[146]. For that reason, and because trimming the cargo level in the hold reduces the likelihood of it shifting the *IMSBC Code*[250] states explicitly for iron ore:

> 'As the density of the cargo is extremely high, the tanktop may be overstressed unless the cargo is evenly spread across the tanktop to equalise the weight distribution. Due consideration shall be paid to ensure that tanktop is not overstressed during voyage and during loading by a pile of the cargo'

There is a variety of ways in which heavy bulk cargoes can be trimmed. A shiploader with the outreach to deliver cargo beyond the ship's centreline can distribute cargo in successive heaps across the hold. When the loader has the ability to travel along the quay the cargo can also be delivered along the length of the hold, allowing cargo to be distributed over the entire tanktop. The same result can often be achieved with chutes or splasher plates used with the loading spout. An alternative approach, when either ship or terminal has suitable cranes or derricks, is for the trimming to be completed by a bulldozer or front-end loader lowered into the hold on top of the cargo stow.

The *IMSBC Code*[251] states that many fine-particled cargoes, if possessing sufficiently high moisture content, are liable to flow and earlier editions of its predecessor the *BC Code*[5] list iron ore concentrates, magnetite, sinter feed and pellet feed (all types of iron ore) as commodities which may liquefy. If shipped wet they may shift and put the ship at risk. Officers should, therefore, monitor the amount of moisture in the cargo carefully, and if the cargo is accepted must ensure that it is 'spread as widely as possible to the boundary of the cargo space.'

The benefits of trimming an ore cargo to the ship's side are that it reduces the possibility of cargo shift, reduces cargo oxidation, distributes the weight better over the tanktop and improves the ship's stability and sea kindliness by winging out the weights and increasing her period of roll. The disadvantages, from the point of view of the owners, shippers and crew, are that the procedure is costly, loading and discharging times are increased, the requirement for hold cleaning is increased by the increased contact between the ore and the ship's sides and when the trimming is done by bulldozer or front-end loader the cargo, besides being less accessible to the grabs, will be compacted and more difficult to discharge.

Loaded voyage: No special precautions are required when iron ore cargoes are being carried, but three normal precautions can be emphasised. Bilges should be pumped regularly to dispose of water draining from the cargo. Bilges should be sounded regularly to detect any sign that the vessel is leaking and a hold is flooding. Holds should not be entered except when the oxygen level has been tested and found to be safe and when a Permit to Work has been completed.

Iron ores are self draining. Iron ore loaded in Port Cartier, for example, may in summer be shipped with an average moisture content as high as 5 per cent, but excess water will drain to the bottom of the hold with about 2.5 per cent being retained in the cargo. Excess water remaining in the hold is likely to cause inconvenience during discharge, so bilges should be regularly pumped dry during the voyage.

To avoid disputes in which cargo shortage is alleged after large tonnages of water have been pumped overboard, the ship should keep a record of the tonnages of bilge water discharged. These tonnages can be calculated when the ship has bilge calibrations by recording the bilge soundings before and after pumping bilges. Alternatively, bilges can be pumped to a calibrated tank and sounded therein before discharge.

A number of bulk carriers have foundered when carrying cargoes of iron ore. The foundering was probably preceded by flooding of holds. Hold bilges should be sounded daily to detect any unwanted water. Flooding will be distinguishable from drainage of water from the cargo by the fact that the increase in sounding will be limited to one or two holds and that it will be more rapid.

Iron ores are liable to oxidise, thus reducing the oxygen in the air. The atmosphere in the hold must be tested to ensure that it is safe before the hold is entered or compressed air breathing apparatus must be worn. There is no requirement to ventilate iron ore cargoes, and practices vary. Some Masters keep ventilators closed to exclude rain and spray from the holds. Others ventilate to maintain a healthy atmosphere within the hold.

Discharging: Holds should be well ventilated before they are entered. Iron ore is usually discharged by grab, and spillage from the grabs invariably occurs. Much of the spillage will land on the deck of the bulk carrier, or on her hatch covers if they are side rolling. This damages the paintwork, though chlorinated rubber paint seems to be damaged less easily than alkyd paint. Careful crane drivers spill less cargo from the grabs, so the ship should submit a damage claim in respect of spilt cargo as soon as spillage occurs. This may encourage the drivers to take greater care.

When discharging iron ore normal procedures must be followed to ensure that a safe discharging and ballasting programme is agreed and that no excessive longitudinal stresses are permitted to occur; and a careful watch must be kept for stevedores' damage. The cargo calls for no exceptional precautions.

Carriage of steel

Approaching 200 million tonnes[155] of steel products enter world trade, with much of this trade being transported in handy-sized and mini-bulkers, which offer spacious, unobstructed holds with large hatch openings which are well suited to the loading, carriage and discharge of these products. However, in recent years, handymax and open-hatch vessels have also made inroads into these trades. A detailed guide to the transportation of steel cargoes is available[25]. These notes on the carriage of steel are based in part upon it. A number of P&I clubs, concerned at the high cost of claims for damaged steel, have also issued valuable practical guidance.[156, 157, 158]

Steel products and the likelihood of damage: All steel products are liable to damage from faulty handling and most are liable to damage from rust, a type of damage which can give rise to substantial claims. A claim that the commercial value of the cargo has been reduced by rust is a difficult one to disprove. As a rule of thumb it can be taken that all steel products which are wrapped – ie, enclosed in packaging – should be considered as finished products which must be treated with great care. Any damage whatsoever will make the affected parts or even the entire item of cargo unusable for the purpose for which it was originally intended.

Cold rolled steel products can be damaged easily and will normally be wrapped in packaging which is intended to be moisture proof and to provide some protection from mishandling. Such material requires the highest standard of care. Hot rolled steel products are intended for further processing and if they are not wrapped it can be assumed that rust, when caused by contact with fresh water, is not a problem. If wrapped however, or if loaded from covered storage in prime condition[25], they should be treated as though they were cold rolled steel[156].

Substantial quantities of steel sheeting in coils (steel coils), packages and bundles, structural steel and merchant iron are transported by sea, and a number of other products such as pipes, wire rods, pebble plate, slabs, billets (Figs. 19.11 and 12) and blooms are regularly shipped.

Handling damage may occur in a number of ways. A steel coil should be perfectly circular, but if it is landed too heavily or overstowed by too great a weight of coils or other cargo may become oval in shape. Packaging of steel may be damaged, permitting damage of the contents by contact or by rust. The overloading of slings or the use of wrong lifting gear by stevedores can lead to cargo being bent, chafed or scored. Incorrect stowage can allow cargo to be crushed, warped or bent in the stow. Mishandling of cargo causing damage can occur before shipment, and movement of cargo in the hold can cause damage during the voyage when the ship works in a seaway.

Rusting of steel cargoes can occur as a result of exposure to rain during loading or discharge; the formation of condensation (cargo sweat or ship's sweat) in the hold; or sea water leaking into the hold. Salt water is damaging to all steel and can lead to very heavy claims. No steel should be exposed to contact with sea water or to fresh water which is polluted with chemicals. Any allegations of salt water damage should be carefully checked. When cargo has been washed by a surveyor to find traces of salt a separate sealed sample of the water used for the washing should be preserved for laboratory testing if necessary.

Rain water and condensation are damaging to finished steels even when they are wrapped in moisture-proof packaging, so they should never be loaded or discharged in the rain and ventilation should be controlled to ensure that they are not exposed to sweat.

Rust which occurs on hot rolled steel as a result of rain water or condensation is unlikely to have any adverse effects over a reasonable period of time. It is acceptable to load or discharge hot rolled steel in moderate rain, but the cargo should not be allowed to stand in pools of water in the hold.

Planning the loading: As a starting point for the loading of a cargo of steel products the following points should be borne in mind, in addition to the considerations discussed in Chapter 9.

- Longitudinal stress limits (which affect the larger vessels and those strengthened for loading in alternate holds) and block loading stress limits must not be exceeded at any time. Strictly speaking, the SOLAS restrictions[167] on older bulk carriers of 150 m or upwards in length leaving one or more holds empty when carrying a full high density cargo do not have to be observed, because steel cargoes are breakbulk cargoes, not bulk cargoes, so the requirements in SOLAS Chapter XII do not apply. It is, however, strongly recommended that Masters comply with SOLAS Chapter XII even when steel or other break bulk cargoes are being carried.
- Maximum permitted tanktop loadings must not be exceeded and some steel products are special cases, as described below, because their weight is not distributed evenly over the entire tanktop.
- Steel products such as cold rolled steel coils which cannot tolerate water should not be loaded in the same holds as hot rolled steel coils which can be loaded or discharged in rain.
- When items are loaded by crane and are to be discharged by ship's gear they must be placed in holds served by ship's gear of sufficient capacity. (Steel coils, for example, can weigh as much as 30 tonnes each, so can only be placed in a hold served by a crane or derrick of at least that capacity.)
- When products require lashing the usual approach is to lash the cargo to itself to form a single solid block of cargo. This is the method normally used for steel coils, for example. For some cargoes such as pipes and structural steel it may be necessary to use eye bolts

Fig.19.11 Steel billets well stowed in the tapering No. 1 hold

Photo courtesy of Mathieu Baehni MNI

Fig.19.12 The stow of steel billets at the after end of the No. 1 hold

Photo courtesy of Mathieu Baehni MNI

(padeyes) welded to the ship's side and the tanktop. If not already fitted, eye bolts can only be safely welded in positions where no fuel tanks are located, and it will be prudent to consult Class about their positioning.

- Pebble plate consists of steel offcuts of many sizes, shapes, weights and thicknesses, often buckled and deformed. A block stow of this product at one end of a bulk carrier hold has been secured by welding the cargo to itself and to the ship[248]. Steel plates in contact with others on the upper surface and on the face of the stow were welded together with runs of welding about 1-2 cm in length and were also welded to the ship's side frames where they came in contact with them. At the voyage end the welds were cut with angle grinders.
- It is more difficult to achieve a secure, tight stow of large, symmetrical items in holds such as No. 1, which do not have parallel sides. Where possible such irregular spaces should be used for smaller items of cargo.
- A block stow of cargo in the fore end of the hold is always likely to be less secure than one in the after end, because of the ship's normal stern trim. When the whole length of the hold is not to be used, a stow in the after end is to be preferred to one in the fore end.
- Problems are likely if steel products are stowed in the same hold as cargoes which contain and release moisture (hygroscopic cargoes). Cargoes such as timber contain moisture and have different ventilation requirements to those of steel products, so that there is a high probability of the steel suffering damage from cargo sweat or ship's sweat if they are both stowed in the same hold.
- When no large change in temperature is experienced during the voyage steel and timber can be successfully carried together, but such a combination should never be attempted without careful consideration.
- The special features of loading, stowing, securing and carrying steel coils are discussed separately, following the 'Carriage of steel' section of the chapter.

Hold preparation: Steel is vulnerable to damage from traces of previous cargoes, particularly those which contain sulphur, such as coal, iron ore, phosphates and compound fertilisers, so holds should be carefully cleaned to remove all traces of previous cargoes. Holds which have been washed with salt water should receive a final thorough rinse with fresh water using a portable high-pressure gun to prevent ship's sweat from becoming contaminated with salt. Where possible the fresh hold rinsing water should be produced by the ship's evaporator because water from city mains is often heavily contaminated with chlorides. If the entire wash can be done with fresh water that is even better, of course, and should be done whenever possible.

When carrying steel products it is essential that hatch covers be tight to ensure that no leakage into the holds occurs. The condition of the hatch covers and their seals and fastenings should be carefully checked. If possible the hatches should be tested for watertightness by ship's staff or shore surveyors, an ultrasonic test being considered the most effective, and the results should be recorded in the deck log book.

Preshipment survey: It is common in many steel trades for owners or charterers, prompted by their P&I Clubs, to appoint a local surveyor to conduct a preshipment survey of the cargo. When the ship's personnel are unfamiliar with the trade the surveyor can advise them if the cargo is in satisfactory condition and if clausing of the bills of lading is necessary. The surveyor will normally provide a full written report supported by photographs.

Loading and stowage: Whilst the cargo is being loaded a careful watch must be kept for damage to the cargo and to the ship. Tally clerks or surveyors may be appointed to note defects to each item of cargo on behalf of the owners in the case of high value products such as steel coils, but the Master and his officers must satisfy themselves that such people understand their responsibilities and that they are carrying out their duties conscientiously and recording every item of damage. The appointment of shore surveyors does not relieve the ship of the responsibility to ensure a good stow.

If fork-lift trucks are to be used in the hold for the positioning of heavy items such as steel in the stow it will be necessary to confirm that the weight of the loaded fork-lift truck is not unsafe, and that it is equipped with suitable attachments, for example a circular bar prong, for handling coils without damage. If fork-lift trucks are to be used to work over other cargo, steel plates must be laid to protect the lower layer. This can only be done when it is certain that the lower cargo will not be damaged.

Weather conditions: Loading must be stopped immediately, hatches must be closed, and all cargo must be covered if it rains whilst finished steels in moisture-proofed packaging are being loaded.

Cargo securing: The vessel's cargo securing manual must be consulted to confirm that the correct lashings are ready in all respects to be placed in the required positions. Different steel cargoes require different securing systems. Such systems range from that required for reinforcing bars (bundles of long steel rods) which normally require no lashing, to that for steel coils, which require an elaborate system of chocking and lashing, reinforced with wedges.

The 'California Block Stow' (Fig. 19.13) is a system sometimes used for stowing and securing steel slabs[252]. It consists of loading slabs in stacks interlinked with wooden dunnage and securing only the top tier. It is attractive to shippers because the entire stow can be placed in the hatch square where fork lift trucks are not needed for stowing or unstowing. This system can be acceptable for ships with box shaped holds but has been found to be dangerous when used aboard traditional bulk carriers with sloping hopper tanks as the stacks are insufficiently supported and are liable to topple when the ship rolls. A stow using the full scope of the hold (Fig. 19.14) should be used aboard traditional bulk carriers with hopper tanks..

Chocking is the process of preventing cargo from moving by filling gaps in the stow with lengths of sawn timber set tight by wedges driven between them. Chocking is also the timber which has been used for the process of chocking. The individual pieces of timber which form the chocking should be nailed together to prevent them from falling apart and dropping out of the stow, as is possible when a ship works in a seaway.

The subject of securing steel cargoes is a complex one and is extensively covered in a specialist book[25]. What must be emphasised is that ships carrying steel cargoes are usually very stiff and roll violently in a seaway, frequently rolling 30° or more in each

Fig. 19.13 In a California block stow the slabs are not stowed out to the limit of the hopper tanks. If only the top tier is secured the slabs may fall out of the stow if the ship rolls heavily
Photo courtesy of Mathieu Baehni MNI

Fig. 19.14 The most secure way to stow steel billets in a conventional bulk carrier is a system which brings them right up against the lower hopper tank sides
Photo courtesy of Mathieu Baehni MNI

direction. When the vessel reaches the end of her roll, the inertia of the cargo causes it to wrench at the lashings and chocking which secure it. In these conditions any inadequate lashing or chocking is very quickly exposed.

Steel products which break adrift in a hold can very quickly do enormous damage to surrounding cargo and to the ship. It is essential that every lashing is properly positioned, properly fastened, properly tensioned and complete. Whilst the men employed for the chocking and lashing are usually experienced they do not sail with the ship and see the outturn condition of their work, and they are not infallible. Their work must be checked by the ship's officers, who should insist upon additional or repositioned chocking and lashings when required.

Cargo documents: The bills of lading for steel cargoes and the mates' receipts when issued should provide a true and accurate description of the apparent order and condition of the cargo at the time of loading. The clausing of bills of lading is a matter which can easily cause difficulties for a Master who is not familiar with the steel trade and can give rise to disputes. Some ship operators with experience of the steel trade expect to advise their Masters on the clausing of bills of lading and the Master should consult his owners to ensure that the wording he proposes to use correctly reflects the condition that he has seen. Once the condition of the cargo has been seen and most of it has been loaded, the Master can find a convenient time before completion of loading to talk to his owners. Digital photographs sent by email will assist both the Master and the owner. Other owners who lack special knowledge of the trade will turn to their P&I Club and the club's surveyor for advice, and he should be able to suggest appropriate clausing. A useful booklet[158] seeks to ensure correct and consistent use of a set of standardised clauses.

In general, the clausing should provide an accurate description of any preshipment damage, including any rusting of the cargo. Any preshipment contamination by other matter should also be noted. The clausing should be confined to a factual description of the damage, rusting, or contamination and should not attempt to say how the damage occurred or who caused it. The clausing should not use imprecise or vague terms or quantities. If the Master estimates that about 75 per cent of coils are rusted, and there are 120 coils in total, he should state: *'90 coils heavily rust stained'.*

Another suitable clause for steel coils might be: *'17 coils presented for shipment each with one strap broken'.* A clause suitable for steel reinforcing bars might be: '50 bundles rust stained in patches'. Clausing which criticises loading methods or describes damage done during loading serves no purpose and should not be used, since the ship is normally responsible for ensuring that the cargo is properly and carefully loaded.

Loaded voyage – securing the cargo: During the loaded voyage, securing the cargo and its ventilation are the two matters which should particularly concern the Master and his officers when carrying steel. Lashings are liable to stretch when the ship is rolling in a seaway and lashing screws under tension will slack under the effects of vibration if they have not been secured to prevent this. When lashing wires are stretched by the cargo responding to the movements of the ship, their diameter is reduced and the wire grips which fasten them become slack. Wire lashings should be inspected regularly – at least daily in rough weather provided that the Master considers it safe to do so – and tightened as necessary. The observance of safe entry procedures to cargo holds is paramount.

When the lashings are flat metal strapping bands the ship normally has no method of tightening or renewing them. If lashings are found to have stretched and become slack due to the ship's movement the only available method of resecuring the stow is to force timber between individual items of cargo.

It must be emphasised that entering the holds to inspect the lashings can be a hazardous business. It is always necessary to ensure that the atmosphere is safe and to follow the proper procedures for entering an enclosed space. No attempt should be made to approach cargo in the holds when the vessel is rolling heavily and there is any possibility of movement of the cargo. In rough weather the ship should be put on a course and speed at which she is steady before any close inspection or tightening of lashings is attempted. Time lost due to such manoeuvres is fully justified, as it is necessary to ensure that the voyage is completed with minimum damage to ship and cargo.

Loaded voyage – ventilation: The primary purpose of ventilating a cargo of steel products is to prevent the formation of sweat, which is likely to cause rusting of the product, even when the latter is wrapped in moisture-resisting wrappings. The avoidance of sweat is always to be encouraged and is vitally important when finished (cold rolled) products are being carried.

Cargo sweat forms when the steel is at a lower temperature than the external air and that air is moist when admitted to the cargo compartments. If such air is allowed to come into contact with the steel the air is cooled and water droplets from the air are deposited on the surface of the steel. Cargo sweat will form when the temperature of the steel is lower than the dew point of the air which surrounds it. The temperature of a steel cargo can be measured when it is loaded by placing a thermometer amongst the packaging, hard against the cargo, and specially designed thermometers can be obtained for this purpose.

When steel is loaded in a cold climate and is then transported to tropical regions, as for example on a voyage from Korea to Europe via the Singapore Strait, the temperature of the steel will rise only very slowly in response to increasing sea and air temperatures. For so long as the temperature of the steel remains below the dew point of the external air, ventilator flaps should be closed and no ventilation should take place. The hold should be made as airtight as possible.

If the hatches are opened to load other cargo whilst the steel is at a temperature below the dew point of the external air such air will enter the hold and lead to the formation of cargo sweat. The loading of cargoes such as timber, tobacco and jute which contain moisture will result in an increase of moisture within the hold, increasing the likelihood that cargo sweat will form on the steel. If cargo sweat is to be prevented the safest rule is that moisture-laden cargoes must not be carried with steel and the hatches must be kept closed when the steel is colder than the dew point of the external air. Dusty bagged cargoes containing chemicals, fertiliser or sulphur may cause dust on steel which, when exposed to water, will cause damage[156].

A voyage from a warmer to a cooler climate with the steel loaded warm and meeting cooler air should not cause the formation of cargo sweat. However, these are the circumstances in which ship's sweat can be formed. Ship's sweat is the sweat which forms on the cold steelwork of the ship when warm moist air within the hold comes in contact with it. Ship's sweat can form below the hold deckheads and drip on to the cargo, and ship's sweat which forms on the ship's sides will run down the sides and can form pools on the tanktop if the ship's trim and the alignment of the dunnage do not allow draining into the bilges.

Ship's sweat can, therefore, cause rusting and should be prevented as far as possible by introducing cooler drier air into the holds. Ship's sweat can form on the ship's sides when the ship meets a cold current, even when the air temperature is high, and an officer inspecting the hold should look for signs that this is happening. Ventilation should be operated at all times except when the external air has high humidity and the dew point of the external air is higher than that of the air in the hold, or adverse weather is causing spray in the vicinity of the ventilator intakes.

Records to be maintained: Throughout every voyage in which finished steel products are carried outside temperature and dew point should be recorded in the log book every watch and cargo temperature should be recorded daily where possible. Cargo temperature can be recorded most easily by using a thermocouple connected to a distant reading thermometer situated outside the cargo space, but if this facility is not available readings with a mercury thermometer must be taken direct from the cargo. Every instance of opening and closing ventilation should be logged, as should the tightening of cargo lashings, and any damage found. When the hold is not being ventilated the access hatch should be kept shut as much as possible and times of opening should be logged. Hold bilge wells should be regularly pumped to ensure that no water is allowed to lie on the tanktops and the bilge soundings should be taken and recorded daily.

Discharge of steel cargoes: When a cargo of steel has been lashed the Master may be asked to arrange for the ship's crew to remove the lashings before the vessel berths to save time and labour costs in the discharging port. When the port approaches are completely sheltered – for example, when they are well up a river or fiord – it is safe to remove the lashings in the approaches to the berth. It is never prudent to remove the lashings when a vessel is still in the open ocean. There are many ports where ships roll heavily when they reach the shallow water of the approaches, even when a flat calm has prevailed farther out to sea.

Wire lashings are removed by slackening and unshackling them. Shackles, lashing screws, wire clamps and undamaged wire will be saved for further use. The flat metal strapping bands (when this system of lashings is used) must be cut with bolt cutters or shears and cannot be re-used. The cutting of these straps is reported to have resulted in heavy personal injury claims in the United States. If this work is to be done at all by ship's staff, it must be done with care under experienced supervision and all those involved in the operation must be wearing appropriate Personal Protective Equipment (PPE).

Throughout discharge the ship's officers must be alert for damage to the ship or to items of cargo and must be prepared to insist upon less haste and greater care when that is what is required. All damage must be recorded and immediately brought to the attention of those responsible. It cannot be stressed too strongly that what may appear to be quite minor damage to the ship's officer can, particularly with finished steel products, result in thousands of dollars of claims from the receiver.

Hold cleaning after the discharge of steel cargoes: Remaining in the hold after the discharge of a steel cargo will be the dunnage wood, the timber used for chocks, and the lashing material, and it will often be the responsibility of the ship's crew to remove these materials from the hold. If these materials can be slung in rope slings or gathered into canvas savealls before discharge is complete the crane driver will often co-operate by lifting them out of the hold and placing them on deck or ashore, as required. It should be noted that many ports – particularly in the USA – will not permit the landing of dunnage or old lashings as they may be contaminated.

Carriage of steel coils

Planning the loading of steel coils: The carriage of steel coils is governed by rules made by naval architects. These rules are not well known to mariners,[115, 177, 178, 179, 180] who find the restrictions on tonnage which can be carried difficult to understand and, sometimes, difficult to identify. When the ship's documentation is not clear, or when Masters are in doubt about the tonnage of steel coils they can carry Class should be consulted via the owners or operators. At least one classification society can provide owners with a desktop computer program with which to calculate permissible steel coil loadings for their ships[183]. The following paragraphs have been written with advice from DNV staff who emphasise that if the situation is uncertain Class should be consulted. These paragraphs provide information about the factors involved.

- *The tonnage of steel coils which can be carried in a bulk carrier hold is not, repeat not, governed by the maximum permitted tanktop loading expressed in tonnes per square metre or equivalent units.* That value applies only to homogeneous cargoes (grain, iron ore, coal, etc) which are considered to exert a uniform load on the tanktop.
- *The tonnage of steel coils which can be carried in a hold is governed by the ship's longitudinal strength, double bottom strength, local inner bottom strength and the weights and dimensions of the individual coils.* Many bulk carriers now trading do not have the strength needed to carry a full deadweight cargo of steel coils, although they are built with sufficient strength to carry a full deadweight homogeneous cargo. Ships built recently often have a steel coil loading condition in their stability information manual. Frequently it allows the vessel to carry only a fraction (in some cases 35-50 per cent) of her full deadweight.
- *Ships not provided with a steel coil loading condition have no easy way of finding whether they can load a full deadweight cargo of steel coils.* Crucial elements in the calculation are the weight, dimensions and number of tiers of steel coils, the number of pieces of dunnage placed beneath them and the spacing of the strength members within the double bottom. It cannot be assumed that these ships are built with sufficient strength to load a full deadweight cargo of steel coils even if they have holds strengthened for heavy cargoes (ie heavy homogeneous cargoes) permitting alternate hold loading. If such ships are required to carry steel coils owners should consult their classification society about the tonnage they can load and, equally important, the number of pieces of dunnage required beneath each coil.
- *Nowadays (2007) steel coils are often 25 tonne and 1.2m in length but the steel coil loading conditions for many ships assume 15 tonne coils 1.5m in length.* Consequently the tonnages which can be carried, as stated in the plans, must often be adjusted. Many ships are not provided with the information to take account of coils sizes which depart from the plans. Coil Tables and Maximum Mass Tables (see below) can be provided by classification societies to assist with this problem and they may also be able to provide a desktop computer program for this task.
- *Cargoes often contain steel coils of several different sizes.* When the ship has a steel coil loading condition the document should be studied to find the 'loading per dunnage'. For example if the loading condition specifies *two tiers of 15t coils with a length of 1.5m and three dunnages per coil* that corresponds to a total load of 30t resting on three pieces of dunnage, ie a load of 10t per piece of dunnage. Any arrangement of coils and dunnage which a) puts the same total number of pieces of dunnage beneath the coils on the tanktop and b) puts a load of no more than 10t on each piece of dunnage would be acceptable. Alternatively Maximum Mass Tables (see below) can, if available, be consulted and may show that a greater tonnage can be loaded.
- *Coil Tables.* For cases when the coils are a different size to those assumed in the ship's steel coil loading condition classification societies can provide tables calculated taking account of the details of her construction. The Coil Tables (**Diamond 53 Cargo Loading and Lashing Manual, Para.12.2** – see CD inside front cover) are devised for a stated number of tiers of coils and cannot be used in calculations involving any alternative number of tiers. They are entered with the arguments Weight of Coil, Length of Coil and Number of pieces of Dunnage and provide the answer 'OK' or 'NOT OK'. If the steel coil loading condition specifies two tiers of 15t@1.4m coils and the Coil Tables say 'OK' for 25t@1.4m coils with the same dunnage that means that the ship can carry two tiers of 25t@1.4m coils.
- *Maximum Mass Tables* (Fig. 19.15). These tables from DNV are an alternative to the Coil Tables for calculating what weight of coils of assorted sizes can be loaded. Entered with Length of Bottom Coil and Number of Pieces of Dunnage they give the maximum allowable weight in tonnes acting through the bottom coil. The total weight is calculated by assuming that half the weight of each coil in the second or higher tier acts through each of the coils upon which it rests (Fig. 19.16). This will be only approximately correct if the coils on which it rests are of unequal sizes or if the upper coil is not centred over the middle of two of the lower coils, in which case more complex calculations, which are not described here, must be made.
- *Positioning of coils in the hold.* DNV's calculations assume that coils will be stowed with the axis fore and aft and with a distance of 0.2 length-of-coil – but not more than 0.3m – between two adjacent rows of coils. If only part of a hold contains coils the same rules apply though cargoes stowed in the remainder of the hold, if exceptional, may require special consideration.
- *Plate Fields and Patch Loads.* To understand the explanations which follow it is necessary to know that a *plate field* is an area of the tanktop (inner bottom) bounded by floors and inner bottom longitudinals.

In other words it is an area of the tanktop supported by floors and longitudinal stiffeners only at its boundaries. (In Fig. 19.19 the tanktop is marked with the positions of transverse floors and longitudinal girders. Four longitudinal stiffeners occur between each pair of longitudinal girders, dividing the marked areas into five plate fields supported only at their boundaries). The footprint of the coil relative to the size of the plate field is an important consideration when calculating the rules for maximum weight of coils to be loaded and the number of pieces of dunnage required. Floors are normally positioned at every third frame. This means that the distance between floors is usually 2400 mm which is, therefore, the usual length of the plate field. Coils which are more than 2400 mm in length will always occupy more than one plate field and will overlap at least one floor. This will give them more support than is given to a shorter coil which may not overlap a floor.

- A patch load is the load applied through a piece of dunnage to a small area of the tanktop plating. When three pieces of dunnage are placed beneath a 15t coil three patch loads, each of 5t, will be created on the tanktop. If a second tier of similar coils is loaded above the first the patch loads will increase to 10t.
- *Dunnage beneath steel coils.* Dunnage should be hardwood and, for steel that must be kept free of rust, should have a low moisture content (Less than 14% according to one authority[25]). Neither wooden dunnage nor steel plates are effective in spreading patch loads (see above) uniformly across the tanktop. The load remains concentrated at the point of contact between coil and dunnage. For the purposes of calculating the permissible loading the classification society assumes a specified number and spacing of pieces of dunnage beneath each coil and 'two [pieces of] dunnage' or 'three dunnage' will be stated in class approved loading plans. This is not mandatory but any actual dunnaging that varied markedly from that specified would require recalculation of the permissible loading. It is reasonable to assume that when three dunnages are specified (Fig. 19.17) four would be acceptable but two might not be. It is not a Class requirement for the dunnage to be continuous and gaps

Allowable mass(t)	Number of dunnage						
Length of bottom coil (m)	2	3	4	5	6	7	8
1.00	23.0	23.8	24.1	24.2	24.3	24.4	24.4
1.10	23.8	25.1	25.5	25.7	25.8	25.9	25.9
1.20	25.0	26.4	27.0	27.2	27.4	27.5	27.5
1.30	26.5	28.1	28.8	29.1	29.2	29.3	29.4
1.40	28.3	30.1	30.8	31.1	31.3	31.4	31.5
1.50	30.3	32.2	33.0	33.4	33.6	33.7	33.8
1.60	32.4	34.4	35.1	35.5	35.7	35.8	35.9
1.70	34.4	36.2	36.9	37.5	37.8	38.0	38.2
1.80	36.1	37.5	38.8	39.6	40.0	40.2	40.3
1.90	36.9	38.9	40.8	41.8	42.2	42.3	42.5
2.00	37.0	40.6	43.0	43.9	44.1	44.5	44.7
2.10	37.2	42.4	45.1	45.7	46.2	46.7	46.9

Fig. 19.15 Maximum mass tables
Courtesy of Det Norske Veritas

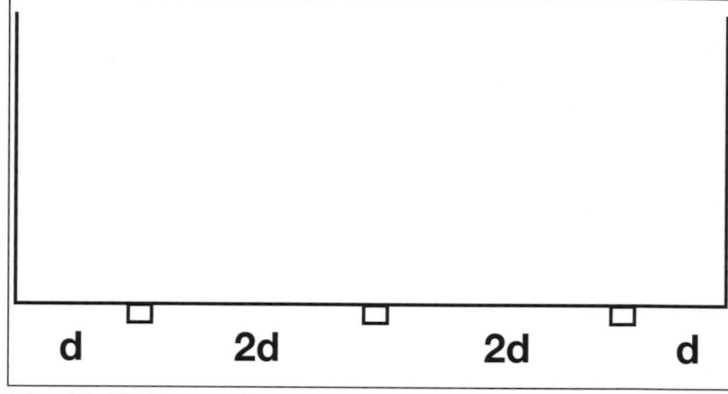

Fig. 19.17 Base of steel coil with positions of dunnage
Courtesy of Det Norske Veritas

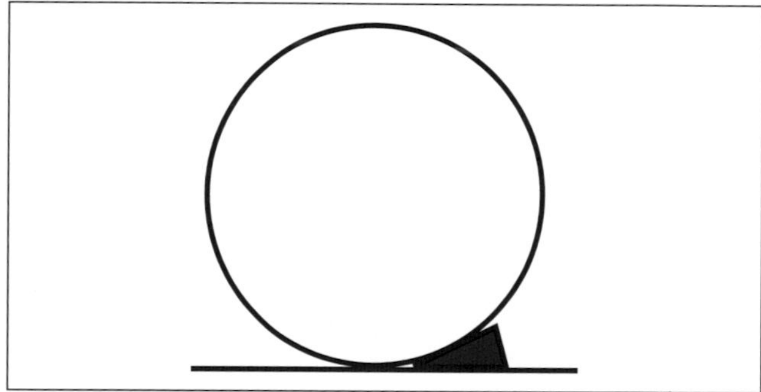

Fig. 19.18 Wedge in position to retain a steel coil

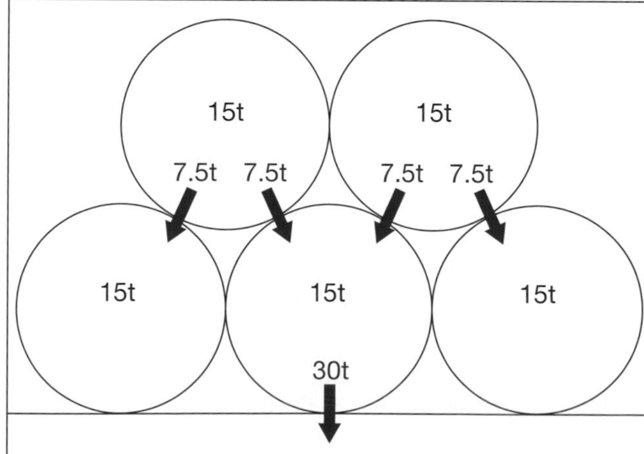

Fig. 19.16 Half weight of coil in second tier acts on each coil in first tier
Courtesy of Det Norske Veritas

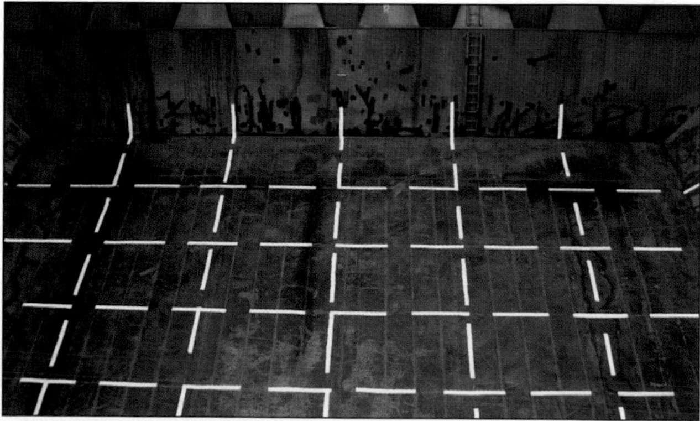

Fig. 19.19 Tanktop marked with positions of transverse floors and longitudinal girders
Photo courtesy of Captain Kaare Lonningen

can be left, between but not beneath coils, to permit drainage of unwanted water to the bilge wells. It is normal practice to wedge the coils in position with wooden wedges nailed to the dunnage. The hypotenuse of the wedge should face downwards (Fig. 19.18). For this process to be effective the dunnage must have a minimum thickness of 40 - 50 mm. All dunnage should be the same thickness and should be 100-200 mm in breadth. The required dunnaging is often achieved by using two pieces of 25 x 150 mm dunnage one over the other.

- *Double dunnage.* Coils are normally stowed with their axes lying fore and aft with the dunnage beneath them running athwartships. If it is thought desirable to place dunnage fore-and-aft on the tanktop to permit drainage of unwanted water then a second tier of dunnage, laid athwartships, should be used beneath steel coils, but this will still deliver patch loads to the tanktop and the stiffeners, and so will have no significant effect on the tonnage of coils that can be carried.
- *Steel billets as dunnage.* If steel billets of sufficient length are used to cover the tanktop beneath steel coils and if the billets are strong enough to carry the coil weight efficiently without deflecting onto the inner bottom plating/longitudinals this arrangement would permit some increase in total tonnage loaded but there are no circumstances in which this would be equivalent to a uniform load because the transverse floors would still be subject to patch loads.
- *Common Structural Rules for Bulk Carriers.* The International Association of Classification Societies (IACS) has introduced Common Structural Rules for Bulk Carriers in which Section 2.7 deals with *Inner bottom loaded by steel coils on a wooden support.* However, since these rules only apply to vessels contracted for construction after 1st April 2006 it will be many years before they have any significant practical effect on current seagoing practice.
- *Coil strength and limits on the number of tiers.* Even when the ship's strength allows the loading of several tiers of coils the strength of the coils themselves may be insufficient and the bottom tier may be squashed out of shape. The shipper's confirmation should be obtained if it is intended to load several tiers. One owner has a rule of thumb that no loading greater than 39 tonnes is acceptable. By that he means three tiers of 13 tonne coils, or two tiers of 15 tonne coils or one tier of 25 tonne coils would all be acceptable but two tiers of 25 tonnes (2 x 25 = 50) would exceed the limit and be unacceptable unless authorised by the shipper and consistent with the strength of the ship.
- *Limits when intending to use fork lift trucks in the holds.* If the vessel is not open hatch, fork lift trucks may be required to position coils in the ends and sides of the hold. A 25 tonne capacity fork lift truck will require a counterweight and the total weight of the loaded truck may be 50 tonnes, applying patch loads to the tanktop. Bulk carriers are not normally provided with guidance as to the acceptable size and loading of fork lift trucks for use in the holds and the ship's permissible tanktop loading values apply only to homogeneous cargoes and not to patch loads such as those imposed by the wheels of the fork lift truck. When in doubt owners and if necessary Class should be consulted, stating the length and breadth of the wheelbase of the fork lift truck, the radius and thickness of its tyres and its loaded weight. Any authoritative guidance on permissible limits would be very welcome.

Dunnage is used beneath all cargoes of steel coils and at the ends and sides of the holds to keep the cargo clear of the vessel's structure. When wire lashings are used it is customary and necessary to use a considerable amount of timber chocking material between the top layers of coils. On the other hand, experience has shown that when as is more common strapping bands are used for lashing and have been tensioned correctly, the use of dunnage belted in between the coils tends to upset the tensioning of the strapping bands. For this reason chocking is not used with strapping bands. This system is found to give satisfactory results.

When steel coils are lashed with wire ropes fastened with wire grips and set taut with lashing screws (turnbuckles) they must be locked or lashed to prevent them from working back – becoming slack – under the effect of vibration. Alternatively and more commonly, such cargoes are lashed with flat metal strapping bands which are set taut to a tension of 2,000 kg with a pneumatic tool and secured with crimped seals. This method of lashing is being used increasingly widely because of its convenience, effectiveness and cheapness but, like any other system of securing, it is only as good as the people who install it and they must be carefully supervised by the ship's officers if a secure stow is to be ensured.

Care must also be taken to ensure that the lashings are in positions where they will not damage the cargo. For example, when a wire lashing passes through a steel coil and bears on the inner edge of the coil that edge should be protected by a custom-made steel plate, or by other suitable material. Such protection is not needed when steel strapping is used, as this will not damage the coil.

Carriage of forest products

Some 160 million tonnes of forest products, including sawn timber ('lumber'), logs, plywood, woodpulp, and woodchips enter into world trade annually. Much of this cargo is carried in specialised vessels such as woodchip carriers, and in log carriers, forest product ships and gantry ships (all described in Chapter 18). All these vessels are handymax, handy-sized, or smaller.

Full cargoes of timber and all other forest products share certain properties. It is regularly overlooked with tragic consequences that they extract oxygen from the atmosphere[166]. A hold containing forest products should never be entered until it has been well ventilated and the atmosphere has been found to be safe. Forest products are all relatively light and bulky cargoes which fill a ship's cargo compartments long before she is down to her marks. In order to carry the maximum cargo it is normal to carry additional cargo on deck, provided that the configuration of the ship and the nature of the cargo permit. The carriage of timber on deck is governed by the *IMO Code*[4], which makes detailed recommendations for the stowage and lashing of the cargo, the stability of the ship, the way to handle her in heavy weather, the tending of lashings and the protection of personnel.

Other special factors are that a timber deck cargo can absorb water from rain, spray or seas, and that ice can form on the deck cargo. These factors can increase the weight being carried on deck, thereby reducing the vessel's stability. When planning the loading, provision must be made for absorption of water by the deck cargo and an allowance must be made for ice if it is to be expected.

Many ships have timber load lines allotted to them and are allowed to load to these deeper marks when carrying a timber deck cargo which satisfies the minimum requirements stated in the International Convention on Load Lines, 1966. When the cargo completely fills the well decks to the full height of the forecastle, when it is correctly secured and when the other requirements in the convention are satisfied, the vessel can load to her timber marks. The deeper loading is permitted in these circumstances because of the additional buoyancy offered by the deck cargo, which resists capsizing forces.

Cargo carried on deck, high above the vessel's centre of gravity, reduces her stability. Because of the buoyancy offered by the deck cargo, the stability criteria for vessels carrying timber deck cargoes are less severe than they are for vessels carrying most other cargoes. Despite this, to maintain the minimum stability required by the regulations it is sometimes necessary to carry less timber on deck than space permits.

The challenge for the ship's Master and for his officers is to ensure that the maximum quantity of deck cargo is carried, consistent with the stability requirements. This is achieved by striking the best possible balance between carrying the maximum permitted volume of cargo on deck and improving the stability by carrying ballast and/or additional bunkers. The first step towards achieving adequate stability is to reduce free-surface effect to a minimum. Next, as much ballast should be carried as the limiting draught permits. Thirdly, extra bunkers can be carried. If that is insufficient to provide adequate stability the proposed quantity of deck cargo must be reduced.

It is worth remembering when carrying timber on deck that too big a GM is almost as dangerous as too small a GM. If the ship is stiff, with a short period of roll, the rolling will be violent and the load on the deck cargo lashings will be increased, with an increasing danger of failure.

The detailed planning of the loading of a full cargo of timber taking account of stability requirements is described in Chapter 10, whilst the characteristics of forest product ships, log carriers and gantry vessels are discussed in Chapter 18, where the carriage of a cargo of logs is also described.

Loading procedures:[163] It is important to remember that the weight of timber and lumber (packaged timber) is seldom known accurately before loading because that depends upon its moisture content which, in turn, is affected by past weather and where the cargo has been stored. It is, therefore, important to conduct draught surveys regularly during loading to check whether the weight of timber loaded corresponds to that expected. If it does not the stability calculations will have to be reworked and the stowage plan will have to be amended.

Any filling or emptying of ballast tanks should be undertaken as early as possible during the loading and should be completed by the time that the deck cargo is being loaded. At this time the ship's positive stability will be approaching the minimum. Normally the deck cargo is not lashed until loading is completed and if a list develops the risk increases that cargo will topple out of the stow.

Fork lift trucks weighing 4-7 tonnes are likely to be used when stowing the ends of the holds of conventional bulk carriers whilst all cargo will be landed directly into position by ship's or shore gear aboard open hatch ships. Preslinging of lumber cargo is now almost universal.

Hatch covers should be fully secured for sea immediately that under deck loading is completed as they will not be accessible for opening and closing once loading on deck begins. Despite the fact that they will be enclosed within the deck cargo the ship will not be considered seaworthy if they are not secured. If ventilation of the cargo holds is considered necessary during the voyage, the ventilators must be accessible for opening and closing. If seasoned timber is to be carried it must be possible to inert the holds with CO_2 and for this the ventilation hatches must be closed.

Deck cargo:[163] It is most important to ensure that any lumber carried on deck is documented as 'on deck cargo' and that all parties involved have given their permission and have authorised the lumber to be stowed on deck.

A timber or lumber deck cargo should be stowed in such a manner as to ensure that the ship has adequate stability, that the stow is tight, that the sides of the stow are continuous, that access to fire hydrants and fire hose boxes, ventilators, deck valves, sounding pipes and other items of deck equipment is ensured and that the view ahead from the navigating bridge is not impeded. Detailed practical advice, written for cargoes loaded on the west coast of Canada but with a wider application is available[163].

On the Canadian west coast packaged lumber is usually loaded two units at a time with one above the other, resulting in a stow composed of successive 'working tiers', each two units high.

Packaged lumber is often supplied with narrow 'attached dunnage' strapped to the base of the package and for this reason some shipowners do not place dunnage over the hatches beneath the deck cargo. It should be remembered that the weight of cargo on the hatch covers may be considerable and that a layer of loose dunnage may be required to reduce the 'line loading' in way of the attached dunnage and spread the weight of the cargo. A second reason for placing dunnage on the hatch covers is to obtain a level surface and take out the camber (ie to remove any slope towards the sides of the hatch covers).

Packaged lumber on deck will normally be loaded on the hatch covers and over the full length of the deck to port and starboard of the hatch covers (sometimes known to stevedores as the 'wings'). Frequent dunnage on deck beneath the packages of lumber should be placed in such a way as to transfer the weight to the deck beams and not to the unsupported deck plating between the beams.

Competent stevedores and/or a competent supercargo or port captain will ensure a tight stow. Recommendations for achieving it[163] include:

- using dunnage at the boundaries of the stow to tilt the packages slightly inwards,

- keeping wrapped packages and custom cut packages (packages with uneven ends because the component planks are of different lengths) 'buried' in the centre of the stow,
- using athwartships dunnage or athwartships packages to tie the wing stow into the stow on the hatch covers,
- using dunnage at every second tier to bind the stow together,
- ensuring that the outside walls of the stow are composed of the longest bundles available and are straight and level,
- ensuring, with the help of dunnage if necessary, that a good level stow is maintained at all times,
- any voids or severe 'cracks' which occur in the stow should be eliminated or chocked off. Where they cannot be eliminated they should be staggered, not continuous.

Consignments for different ports are normally separated with polypropylene rope or 'log marking' paint.

It is increasingly common,[163, 165] particularly on gantry vessels, for isolated 'island' or 'castle' stows of packaged lumber to be placed on individual hatch covers to allow discharge of part cargoes in different ports. The regulations appear to require no special treatment when lashing these castles, despite their lack of the protection which is given by a continuous stow but it is recommended[163, 165] that extra lashings are used or that the cargo is stepped down.

A catwalk over the cargo will be required except when the ship has under deck passageways extending the length of the deck. Deck cargo ladders, giving access to the top of the stow, will be required in any event.

Lashings:[163] The ship's approved Lashing Manual should be consulted. Lumber deck cargoes must be secured with independent overall chain lashings placed at intervals specified in the *IMO Code*[4] and/or the appropriate local code, for example the *Canadian Code*[164]. Every item of lashing equipment must be tested, certified and capable of being identified. The chains lead over the stow and are shackled to padeyes in strengthened positions on deck close to port and starboard of the stow. Corner pieces (corner caps) are put in place to protect the lumber at the points where the chain passes from the side to the top of the stow and to allow the chain to render over the corner when the vessel is working in a seaway. The chain is always longer than the shortest distance over the stow from port to starboard. The slack in the chain is gathered on top of the stow, amidships, and a turnbuckle is fitted between the port and starboard lengths of chain with the help of pear links which slip over the chain and grip it. After it has been first fully tightened at least half the length of the threads of each turnbuckle must remain unused to allow further tightening by the crew during the voyage. The turnbuckles are normally fitted with a pelican hook which can be quickly released by freeing the slip ring. To ensure that the lashing is not released accidentally the slip ring must be moused back to the eye screw ring.

Longshoremen are likely to tighten the lashings using a chain tightener (a chain saw modified to tighten turnbuckles). This device can tighten a lashing to a tension of 10,000 lbs in 30 seconds, a job which would take 10 minutes to complete manually. Such equipment is rarely supplied to ships for use in tightening lashings during the voyage but would be useful, though ship's lifting gear or mooring winches can also be used.

Measurement of forest products: The variety of measurements used for forest products can be confusing. The principal measurements which concern the Shipmaster and his officers are the volume of the cargo, its weight and its stowage factor. Individual unit sizes may be of concern when planning the best stowage.

It is rare for the weight of a timber cargo to be known accurately before loading takes place. Approximate weights per unit volume may well be used by the shipper or charterer and will certainly be used in pre-loading calculations for stability purposes. It is essential that the weights be checked by draught survey during the course of loading. Round logs are listed by weight in some trades and notice is given of heavy units. Care should be taken in estimating stowage factors of logs from equatorial rain forests. Many such logs, such as vitex, have buttressed trunks. Logs sawn from the buttress ends have a star shaped cross-section and occupy considerably more space than conventional round logs.

Volume of cargo: Timber, lumber and logs are always measured by volume. The form of measurement varies according to the locality in which the cargo is loaded. The volume of cargo is the sum of the volumes of each individual piece of timber.

Stowage factors measure the space required in a hold or deck stow for a unit weight of timber or other forest product. Stowage factors take account of broken stowage, which is the space lost when units do not fit exactly into the space available and do not fill it completely. Stowage factors in specialised carriers with box-shaped holds will be better than in bulkers with hopper and topside tanks. The stowage factor of cargo carried on deck will be better than that of the same cargo carried below decks, because in the former case no space is lost above the cargo.

Unit sizes: These are the cargo volumes calculated from the extreme dimensions of the package.

Some examples of measurements used in the timber trade are explained below.

Volume of cargo: Different methods of measuring timber volumes are used in different trades. The following are those most commonly in use:

Board measure Unit of volume based upon a unit of surface area at constant thickness.

FBM (Foot Board Measure) The expression board measure is used on the West Coast of Canada and the United States for what is, more correctly, a board foot, 12 inches x 12 inches x 1 inch, which is the basis for all timber measurements in this trade. It should be noted that the word timber refers, in this area, to baulks (ie, large pieces) of timber. Lumber is the term generally used for sawn wood goods.

1000FBM MBM MFBM M One thousand feet board measure, or Mille. The volume of all shipments from the West Coast of Canada and the United States is measured in units of 1000 feet board measure. The abbreviations are interchangeable.

cbm The volume of timber measured in cubic metres. This is the most common measurement used worldwide. The cbm stated in the shipping documents generally refers to the volume of the timber in the package or unit, and not to the total space which the unit occupies. This is particularly important in the Scandinavian and Russian trades where timber is shipped in 'length' or 'butt ended' packages (all pieces the same length), 'truck bundled' or 'custom cut' packages (random length pieces), or a mixture of the two. Truck bundled packages will occupy some 10-15 per cent more space in the hold and on deck than length packages.

Logs are also measured in cbm. The measurement may reflect the volume of the log but the method of calculating volume varies in different trades. Many such measurements are carried out in conformity with local trade association requirements to calculate the quantity of timber which can be sawn out of the log, rather than to attempt to calculate the true volume of the log. Examples of such systems are *Hoppus measurement* and *Brereton scale.* Many shipping documents, including bills of lading, presented to the ship describe the logs as being so many M/T. This is an abbreviation for *measurement tons* and should not be confused with *metric tonnes.* Such measurement tons are based upon local practices which vary in different trades.

Standard The Petrograd standard of 165 cubic feet was, until metrication, the unit in general use on the Continent and elsewhere. It is now rarely used in Europe but still used in other trades including the East Coast Canadian trade.

Table of equivalent units of volume:

Unit	cbm	cft	FBM	Standard
1 cbm	–	35.3157	423.8	0.2141
1 cft	0.0283	–	12.0	0.0061
1000 FBM	2.3596	83.33	–	0.5050
1 Standard	4.67	165.0	1980.0	–

Stowage factors

cft/cbm Cubic feet per cubic metre – ie, the cubic feet of space required to stow 1 cubic metre of timber. This is in general use worldwide where ships are measured in imperial measure and cargo is measured in metric units.

cbm/cbm Similar to the foregoing. Used when both the ship and the cargo are measured in metric units. For example, sawn timber 1.5 and logs 2.2 means that one cubic metre of sawn timber will stow in 1.5 cubic metres of space, whereas 2.2 cubic metres of space would be required for 1 cubic metre of logs.

cbm/tonne
cft/tonne Cubic metres or cubic feet of space required to stow one tonne weight. Used for pulp, plywood and other manufactured products. In addition to the metric tonne, long tons and short tons (US) are still in use in some places.

cft/std
cbm/std Cubic feet or cubic metres of space required to stow one standard of cargo. In use in East Coast Canada trade and elsewhere where the standard is still used.

cbm/MFBM
cbm/MBM
cbm/M Cubic metres of space required to stow one thousand board feet of cargo. Used on the West Coast of Canada and US trade. Cubic feet can be used in place of cbm in ships measured in imperial units.

Packaged lumber: If the ship's stability manual assumes that the timber deck cargo is composed of loose lumber compactly stowed along the full length of the deck whilst the cargo actually loaded is packaged lumber, the total permitted amount of deck cargo may be reduced, because packaged lumber when stowed will contain gaps in the stow, thus reducing the buoyancy of the deck cargo.

Most West Coast Canadian lumber is shipped in length packages of standard cross-section of 24 x 48 inches. There is, however, a recent trend as more lumber comes from inland forests to make up jumbo packs and to vary the cross section of packages to conform with the requirements of rail wagons.

Kiln-dried lumber, pulp or plywood on deck: Packages of kiln-dried lumber are generally wrapped in plastic or paper coverings although recent experiments with wax dipping have been carried out. Kiln-dried lumber and plywood should be carried under deck. Should charterers require on-deck carriage, special insurance must be arranged. Similar insurance should be arranged if pulp is carried on deck. Such insurances are normally effected through P&I Clubs. Kiln-dried lumber should be stowed apart from cargoes with a high moisture content such as woodpulp and naturally dried lumber.

Woodpulp: Woodpulp is normally shipped in bales, unitised into six or eight bales per unit and lifted aboard or ashore a remarkable 16 units at a time (Fig. 19.20). Some specialised pulp is shipped in rolls which are unitised either by external strapping or by strapping through the cores. For the process of converting woodpulp into paper the pulp must be free of salt. For this reason the hatches, as always, must be watertight and the holds should be rinsed with fresh water at the completion of hold cleaning, prior to loading.

Fig.19.20 Incomplete lift of 13 units of woodpulp being taken ashore. Each unit contains eight bales

Woodpulp is often loaded direct from the pulpmill, at a temperature higher than the ambient temperature. In these circumstances it is liable to produce considerable condensation (ship's sweat) which may drip off the ship's structure and stain the cargo. To prevent the formation of sweat the mechanical ventilation for the cargo hold should be run at full speed whenever the dewpoint of the external air is lower than the dewpoint of the air inside the hold.

The hold dimensions of forest product ships may be designed to accept a number of units of woodpulp exactly, with no gaps, thus making secure stowage a simple process. Unfortunately there are a number of different standard sizes for units of woodpulp and the dimensions of Canadian, Swedish and Finnish units from different suppliers are likely to vary. A vessel which is built to accommodate one standard will find that a tight stow can only be achieved with the help of dunnage when bales of another standard are carried. If the stow is not tight and the ship rolls in a seaway, the bales are liable to be seriously damaged by chafing during a North Atlantic ocean crossing. In some trades the only dunnaging which is permitted is with rubber/polythene inflatable dunnage bags. Timber is forbidden since wood splinters will interfere with the manufacturing process, and plastic sheeting is not acceptable as a separation for similar reasons.

Plywood: Plywood is shipped in bundles which vary greatly in size. The standard area is 2440 x 1220 mm but some larger and small sizes are shipped. Current practice is to unitise bundles into jumbo packs for speedier handling.

Carriage of cement

The world seaborne cement trade was in 2005 about 120 million tonnes, about 4 per cent of total production, with the main exporting countries being found in the Far East and with the Americas and Asia being the principal importers[154].

Cement: The main ingredients of various grey cements are chalk (82 per cent), sand (6 per cent) and fly ash (12 per cent). Fly ash is the residual ash from the burning of coal. In white cement, a speciality of Aalborg Portland, the fly ash is replaced by material with a high content of aluminium oxide. A 'flow promoting' additive is often used in cement manufacture to make it flow more freely during the grinding and transportation processes.

Several characteristics of cement in bulk make it a problem cargo. It is fine grained and potentially very dusty, when contaminated it is useless as a binding agent, when wet it sets solid, when manufactured it is hot and retains its heat and, when aerated (mixed with air) in a pneumatic loading system, it is fluid.

Hold preparation: Much of the world trade in cement is carried in conventional bulk carriers. Holds must be clean, dry and free of all traces of previous cargoes and of rust scale, and regulars in the trade advise that a really thorough cleaning and removal of rust before loading will make the job of cleaning after discharge much easier. Fresh water rinsing, whilst always desirable, is not considered essential. Hold bilges must be sealed with sift proof-material. When cement is to be loaded following a cargo of sugar,

Fig.19.21 Cement loading hose bolted to the hatch cover
Photo courtesy of Aalborg Portland

Fig.19.22 Cement loading hose in place for loading
Photo courtesy of Aalborg Portland

Fig.19.23 Loading hose connected to hatch cover
Photo courtesy of Aalborg Portland

particular attention must be paid to thorough cleaning of the holds as even small traces of sugar can render a cargo of cement worthless.

Loading methods: Loading berths are normally adjacent to cement silos where ships are required to shift back and forwards to bring successive holds under the loader. Loading methods vary considerably. Loading by conveyor belt into an open hold is very dusty and the combination of dust and dew can quickly coat much of the ship with a hard coating. This can be removed by applying a mild acid such as Unitor's Metal Brite HD diluted with fresh water to 50 per cent strength followed after 40 minutes with a high pressure water wash.

The loading system which is most friendly to the environment and to the ship is a sealed pneumatic system. This requires the ship to have two circular holes in the hatch lids, a feeder hole through which to load and an extractor hole for the displaced air. Neither of these holes needs be exactly amidships but the feeder hole should be near to midships. The system used by Aalborg Portland (Figs. 19.21 and 22) requires the holes to be 530 mm in diameter but requirements in other loading ports vary, most conforming to the 'AP' (American Petroleum) or 'D' (Deutsche) norms. At Aalborg three studs welded to the hatch cover in positions 50 mm from the lip of each hole, at 120° intervals, are used to bolt the equipment to the hatch cover (Fig. 19.23).

In some ports it is reported to be the practice to cut the necessary holes in the hatch covers of ships not already so equipped and to reweld them on completion of loading. This is of course easier to do with covers of open web construction than when the hatch panels are double skin sealed units. In either case the work should be agreed by the owners and approved by the vessel's classification society.

To commence loading with a sealed system an electrically powered extractor fan and dust filter unit is bolted over the extractor hole (Fig. 19.24). When running, this maintains a low pressure in the hold which encourages the flow of cement into the space, and ensures that no dust is released into the atmosphere. While the system is in operation all hold accesses, ventilators and coaming drains must be closed. The end of the loading hose is fitted with a trimming spout which extends to 1.5 metres beneath the hatch cover when the hose is bolted in position. A handwheel mounted on and around the hose end (Fig.19.25) allows the spout to be swung through 360°. Tending the trimming spout is a constant task for the duty deck officer who must ensure that the ship remains upright, or nearly so, to avoid the cement flowing to the low side and causing a dangerous list. The sealed system allows loading in all weathers and eliminates atmospheric pollution. Unsealed pneumatic loading systems, on the other hand, deliver the cement to the hold by hose and trimming spout and protect the cargo from the weather, but have no filtering and extraction system, so cement dust will escape from the hold with the displaced air.

The cement, aerated by the hydraulic loading system, flows almost like water to all parts of the hold where it settles, quickly losing its fluid properties. Its final profile is normally gently convex with height of cargo in the centre of the hold of a handy-sized vessel no more than about 0.5 metres higher than the height at the boundaries. There is no stability requirement for cement laden holds to be completely filled and, as cement is a dense cargo with an approximate stowage factor of 0.67 to 1.00 m^3/tonne, it is seldom that they are.

Cargo shift: Masters with many years of experience of carrying cement state that the cargo once settled in the hold does not shift, even in extreme swell conditions, and that the time required for the escape of air trapped in the cargo is a matter of minutes, not hours. Despite this casualties occurring early in the voyage have been attributed to the shifting of cement cargoes. By the time all the air has escaped from within the stow the cargo will have shrunk about 12 per cent[253]. It seems unlikely that this will all happen within the first few minutes of completion of loading. Even when the cargo has settled cargo shift is a possibility if the surface is more than 30° from the horizontal. The *IMSBC Code* warns:[253]

'The ship shall be kept upright during loading of this cargo. This cargo shall be so trimmed to the boundaries of the cargo space that the angle of the surface of the cargo with the horizontal plane does not exceed 25°. Both the specific gravity and the flow characteristics of this cargo are dependent on the volume of air in the cargo. The volume of air in this cargo may be up to 12 per cent'. This cargo is fluid until it settles. 'The ship carrying this cargo shall not depart until the cargo has settled. After' settling, 'shifting of the cargo is not liable to occur unless the angle of the surface with the horizontal plane exceeds 30°'.

On passage: Heat is used in the manufacture of cement and cement is a poor conductor. As a consequence it retains some of its heat and may be loaded and carried for weeks at temperatures of 80°F or significantly higher. Conventional alkyd hold coatings are designed to withstand such temperatures.

Cement is damaged by moisture so the ventilation regime during the voyage must aim to eliminate sweating. The hatch covers must be reliably weathertight to exclude water. In a handy-sized vessel the cargo in each hold will normally settle one metre during the course of an ocean passage.

Discharge: Discharge may be by grab or by bucketwheel unloader but is more usually by pneumatic suction hose working through the open hatch and discharging to a silo. The ship is normally required to shift along the berth to work successive holds. Work must cease and hatches must close during rainfall. A bobcat will be used to move cargo from the wings and ends of the hold.

Hold cleaning: Cement, when wetted, will very readily coat hold surfaces and block bilge lines and valves. The priority is, therefore, to remove the maximum possible quantity of cement from the hold surfaces and discharge it before cleaning is attempted. Methods used include the use in the USA of the Hoeram (Fig. 16.10) to shake residues from surfaces by gentle vibration. A more normal method is for ship's crew wearing face masks to scrape residues from bulkheads and sides using scrapers and manhelps. As cement laden holds are not normally filled to the top the residues do not extend to the full height of the holds. Any residues which are not discharged must be lifted onto the deck. To protect the ship's bilge system from blockage by hard-setting cement hold washing water must not be pumped through the bilge system. Instead it must be pumped directly overside using a submersible pump.

Specialised cement ships

Loading: Specialised cement ships typically have two pairs of cargo holds which are loaded via the ship's cargo transfer line connected to a flexible hose from the silo. The cargo transfer line, running athwartships across a masthouse positioned amidships (Fig. 19.26), has spouts for the delivery of cargo to each of the four holds. The duty deck officer controls the flow of cargo to two holds at a time by adjusting automated valves from the cargo control room. When there is little water beneath the keel No.1 starboard, for example, will be filled at the same time as No.2 port hold to maintain an even keel and the flow to the two holds will be adjusted as necessary to keep the ship upright.

Any blockage in the pipeline which causes the cement to stop flowing and to back up in the shore piping can create serious problems. The cargo has to be dug out of the pipeline by hand so to avoid this constant attention is essential, particularly when topping off the holds. The flow of cargo from the silo can normally be stopped almost instantly, with no more than 10 – 20 mt of cargo 'on the belt'. When a cement ship is loaded to her marks her holds, which occupy a smaller portion of the ship's hull than in conventional bulk carriers, may be almost full. When that point is reached the top layer of cement can be trimmed, ie forced to the far end of the hold, by operation of an exposed Archimedes screw situated horizontally beneath the deckhead. Holds are fitted with high level cargo alarms.

Throughout the loading period air is extracted from the holds and passed through a filter system, permanently fitted in the hold deckheads, which prevents cement dust escaping from the holds and causing pollution.

Deballasting, controlled from the cargo control room, proceeds together with loading. On one 7,000 dwt cement ship 3,000 mt of ballast can be pumped and stripped out in 4–6 hours. Unpumpable strippings are typically 40–50 mt.

Discharging: Specialised cement ships are self discharged by mechanical and/or pneumatic systems. Modern installations are more likely to be pneumatic because that permits a simpler system ashore. In a pneumatic system the delivery of the cement from ship to shore is pneumatic but the transfer of the cement from cargo hold to mixing chamber is by mechanical means.

The cargo holds are like large hoppers contained within the ship's hull. Spaces around the holds, within the hull, contain the cargo discharging system. The hold bottoms have 'VVV' shaped cross sections. Endless cargo drag chains, like the caterpillar tracks used on heavy earth moving equipment, run along the channels at the base of the hold delivering cement to the reloading hoppers. The chains then return through the space beneath the hold to the *'turn around room'* beyond the opposite end of the hold and

Fig.19.24 Loading hose fixed to hatch cover. Grey extractor fan and filter unit to left of hose
Photo courtesy of Aalborg Portland

Fig.19.25 To keep the ship upright the handwheel is used to swing the spout, below the hatch cover, to control the direction in which the cement is poured
Photo courtesy of Aalborg Portland

Fig.19.26 A specialised cement carrier discharging cement mechanically through the midships manifold

thence back into the hold. The reloading hoppers are situated in the elevator room, comparable to a tanker pumproom, extending the full height of the hull in a space between the forward and after holds.

From the six reloading hoppers the cement is transferred by six vertical screw conveyors (Archimedes' screws within pipelines) to the level of the masthouse where it is delivered into the ship's cargo transfer line (a horizontal screw conveyor) and thence by flexible hose into the mechanical system ashore. Alternatively the cement is delivered by mechanical conveyor from the hopper at the end of the ship's cargo transfer line into the mixing chamber where compressed air at 1.5 – 2.0 bars is injected through nozzles. The mixture then forces its way into the shore system through the discharge hose.

Normally all the cargo is removed from the holds by mechanical means, without human assistance but in cold weather the fact that the cargo is hot can cause condensation which will in turn cause the cement to cake and form 'bridges' over the cargo drag chains. A bridge may be composed of as much as 100 mt of cargo. When that happens the crew have to enter the hold and break the bridges down.

Hold cleaning: Holds are not cleaned between successive cargoes of cement except when the next cargo is to be high grade cement such as white cement. To clean a 7,000 dwt ship before carrying white cement takes four crew members assisted by 4–6 shore workers about 24 hours, spread over two days. The whole squad, equipped with face masks and dustproof clothing, works in one hold at a time. Once the previous cargo has been fully discharged the squad use scrapers and manhelps to loosen as much cargo from within the holds as possible. This is discharged to the silo through the ship's self discharging system. Next the holds are hand brushed and cleaned with industrial vacuum cleaners. Even then some traces of hard cement will remain on the bulkheads. This is acceptable. The delivery and discharge lines, hoppers and screw conveyors also have to be scraped, brushed and vacuumed.

The cargo control room: The cargo control room of a specialised cement ship is likely to contain start/stop switches for all the cargo loading and discharging equipment, the ballast pumps, eductors and air ventilator fans, the open/shut switches for the ballast tank valves and the depth gauges for the ballast tanks. It will probably also contain a computer for the planning of loading, the calculation of loading rate and completion time, for draught surveys and for the port log. Closed circuit TV to monitor the gangway and ship/shore connection may also be provided.

Sources

4, 5, 15, 18, 19, 22, 24, 25, 82, 115, 117, 134, 146, 151, 153, 155, 156, 157, 158, 159, 161, 163, 165, 166, 167, 173, 174, 175, 177, 178, 179, 180, 183, 198, 205, 215, 247, 248, 249, 250, 251, 252, 253. (See List of Sources, Page 497)

CHAPTER 20

UNUSUAL CARGOES AND SPECIAL TRADES

Bulk cargo separations, taking the ground in the berth, general and breakbulk cargoes, trading to cold regions

Bulk cargo separations

IN SOME TRADES there is a requirement for parcels of bulk cargo to be carried separately in the same bulk carrier hold for separate discharge. For example, separate parcels of pig iron are shipped from Vitoria, Brazil, separate parcels of minerals are shipped from Durban and Richards Bay, South Africa, and separate parcels of grain are exported from the USA. Separate grades of spodumene concentrate are exported from Australia. When separating these cargoes the objectives are to construct efficient separations as cheaply as possible subject to safety, the design of the ship, the nature of the cargo and the custom of the trade.

Pig iron from Vitoria, Brazil: Consignments of pig iron are separated by vertical fencing supported on steel wire ropes stretched athwartships across the hold. Aboard a handy-sized bulker as many as three bulkheads permit the loading of four different consignments of pig iron in a single hold (Figs. 20.1 and 2). The stevedores erect the fencing, but require ship's staff or supercargo to calculate the position for each fence. The fence must be strong enough to support the weight of cargo on one side until the next parcel is loaded on the other side and must withstand accidental blows from the grab.

In general, each consignment must be allocated ground space (ie, tanktop area) proportional to the tonnage of cargo in the consignment, but this guideline must be modified with small consignments to ensure that the space between the fences is sufficient to provide easy access for the discharging grab. A second variation from strict proportion is required to ensure that no fence is placed too close to the hatch coaming ends. If this precaution is not observed the grabs will be unable to discharge the hold ends without damaging the fencing. The factors governing the position of the fencing are illustrated in Fig. 20.3.

In Fig. 20.3 the tanktop area XXAA may be sufficient for the intended parcel of cargo, but AA is so close to the after end of the hatch square that it would be very difficult to discharge the cargo from that area. The fence must be situated at BB, with the result that the cargo will be stowed to a lesser height in the area XXBB, or a larger parcel must be loaded in that position

The tanktop area AABB may be large enough for a particular parcel of cargo, but it is only about 2 metres wide, which will be difficult for the discharging grab. The fences must be placed wider apart. The tanktop area XXBB is larger than the area DDYY, despite the

Fig 20.1 Separation bulkheads for pig iron

Fig 20.2 Another view of separation bulkheads for pig iron

Fig. 20.3

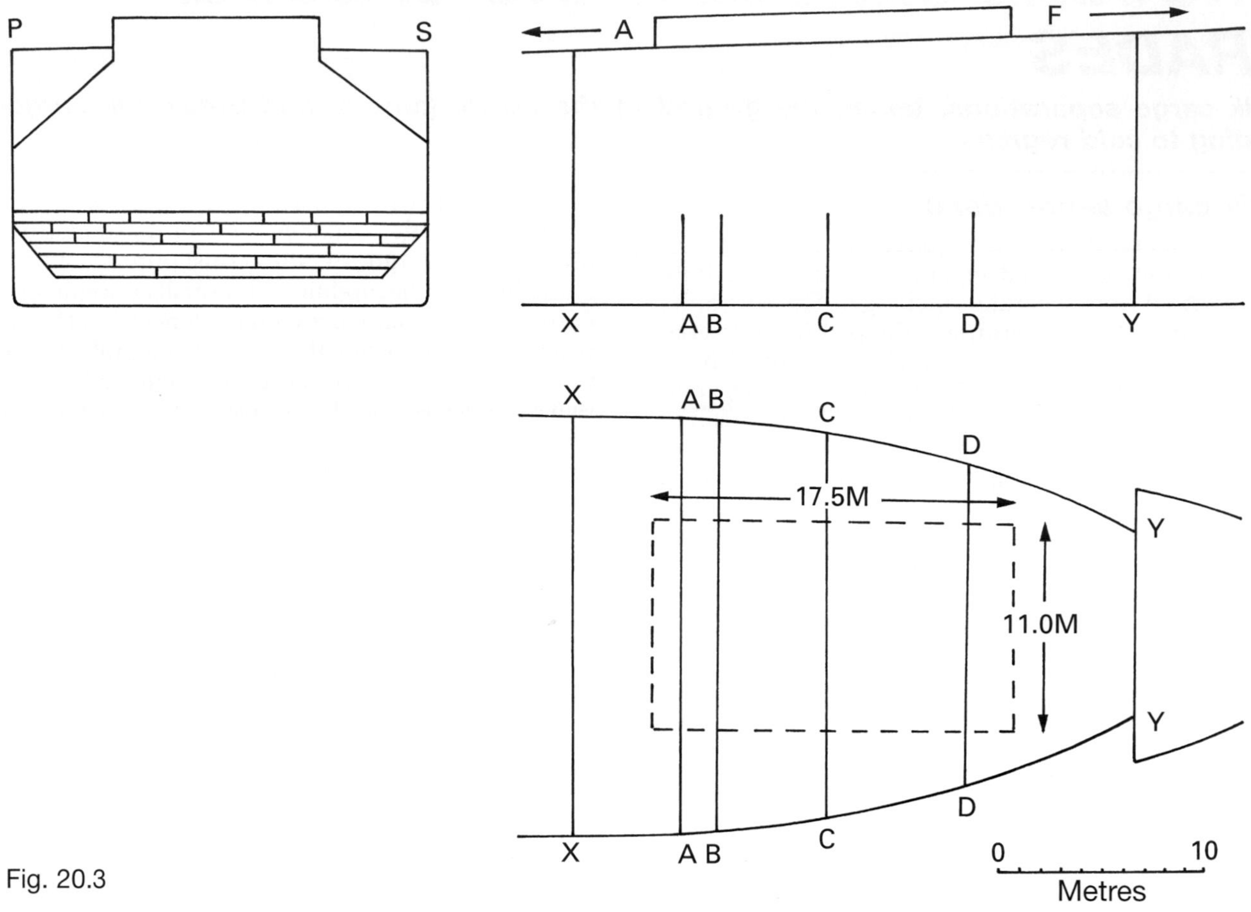

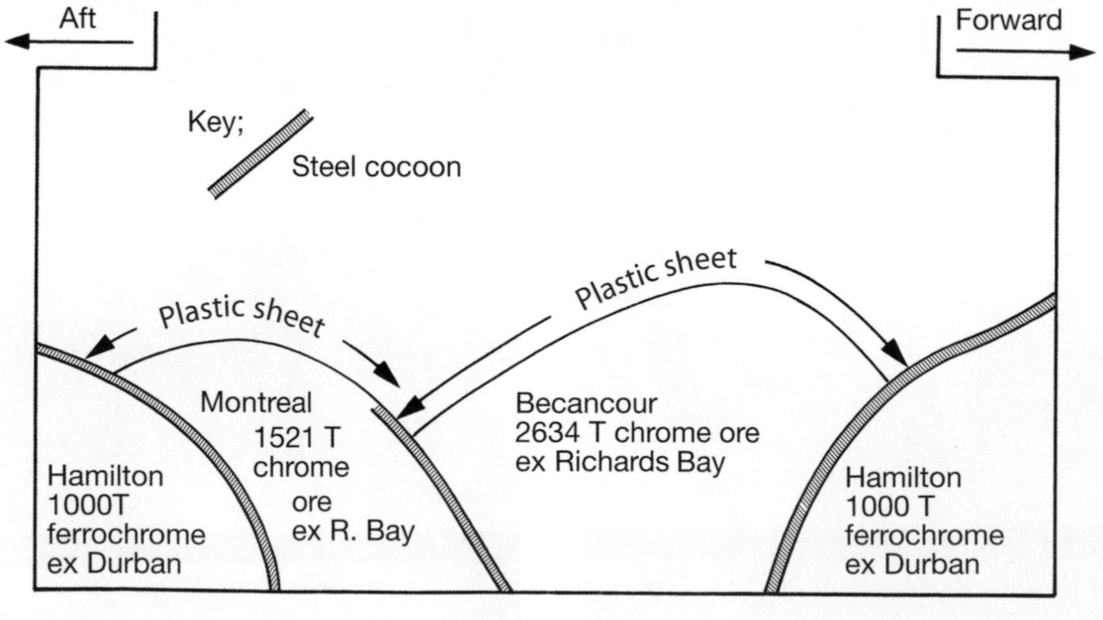

Fig. 20.4

fact that fence DD is farther from the end bulkhead than fence BB. This is because the ship is narrower at DDYY in the bows than it is at XXBB at the after end of No. 1 hold.

The procedure for constructing the separation fences is as follows:

- In positions where fences are required, weld lashing lugs to lower hopper sides and frames at vertical intervals of 0.5 metres to a height of 3.0 metres. (Welding must not be done in way of fuel tanks. Welding will damage the tank coatings of adjacent double-bottom and side tanks. The charterers should be required to sign a letter of indemnity for the cost of later repairing the tank coating. The welded lugs should be primed and painted after fitting, to avoid the formation of rust.)
- Stretch loose doubled 24 mm diameter wire ropes horizontally across the hold between the lugs. Fit a turnbuckle (lashing screw) for tightening each wire rope.
- Weave 100 x 100 mm timber uprights vertically between the wires. Rest the foot of each upright on a length of 100 x 100 mm timber laid fore and aft on the tanktop. Cross the pair of wires between successive uprights. (Fig. 20.6.)
- Tighten the wires with the turnbuckles until the wires hold the uprights rigid.
- Nail 150 x 30 mm planking horizontally to the uprights. (Fig. 20.7.)
- Nail vertical planks at each upright and brace the fence with sloping timber supports, from the timbers laid on the tanktop beneath the foot of each upright. (Fig. 20.7.)

The gratings seen on the tanktop in Figs. 20.1 and 7 are placed there to prevent damage to the tanktop when the pig iron is poured into the hold by the shiploader. They are reduced to rubble during loading and discharged with the pig iron.

Parcels of ore are sometimes separated using wooden fences, as in this mini-bulker (Fig. 20.5).

Parcels of base metals and minerals from South Africa: Parcels of various bulk commodities are exported from Durban and Richards Bay, the products including chrome sand, granulated chrome,

Fig. 20.5 Parcels of ore separated by temporary fences
Photo courtesy of Walter Vervloesem

Fig 20.6 wires for support of uprights

Figs. 20.1, 20.2, 20.6, 20.7 courtesy of CWA Consultants Ltd

Fig 20.7 Construction of fences

Fig. 20.8 South African ore cocooned at one end of the hold

Photo courtesy of Mathieu Baehni MNI

Fig. 20.9 Loading ore in the trench between two cocooned parcels of ore

Photo courtesy of Mathieu Baehni MNI

Fig. 20.10 Pneumatic suction unloader pipes fitted with flexible extensions. Unloading cargo from above a cargo separation constructed from plastic sheet and hardboard

Photo courtesy of Walter Vervloesem

charge chrome, lump chrome, three grades each of ferro manganese, silicon manganese and ferro silicon, andalusite chips, andalusite fines, titanium slag, titanium sand and copper concentrates. When the parcels are between 500 tonnes and 3,000 tonnes it is often impractical to provide separation by hold, and a number of parcels will be stowed in the same hold, separated by a process known as cocooning.

When planning the loading the following factors must be borne in mind.

- As far as possible different parcels of the same cargo or of compatible cargoes should be carried in the same hold to minimise contamination.
- When incompatible cargoes must be loaded in the same hold increased precautions, described below, must be taken.
- The last parcel loaded overlaps the earlier parcels and thus becomes the key to the stow. It must be the first cargo discharged.
- Each parcel will overlap the previous one loaded in the same end of the hold. In general, parcels must be discharged in the reverse order to that in which they were loaded except that once the key parcel is discharged those in the fore end do not interfere with those at the after end and vice versa.
- Every parcel must have some ground space – ie, must be in contact with an area of the tanktop – to allow the cargo to be grabbed out when discharging.

When loading commences the first parcel will be loaded at one end of the hold, where a rubber tyred loader with a long arm will be used to trim or push the cargo upwards against the bulkhead until it is stacked against the bulkhead with a sloping face corresponding to its angle of repose. (Fig. 20.4.)

Parcels of cargo are separated with hot rolled steel sheets measuring 2.4 x 1.2 metres, and with a thickness of 1.6 mm which are fitted over the surface of the cargo like a skin. The sheets are cut with oxy-acetylene torches to fit the shape of bulkhead corrugations, and to allow for ladders and pipework, and are tack welded with stitches of about 25 mm at a spacing of 300 mm. The sheets are welded in position like the tiles on the roof of a house, starting at the base of the stow. When there is no risk of contamination the cocooning will be restricted to the side of the stow where the next parcel will lie and the top of the parcel will be left open (Fig. 20.8).

When the parcels are fines (commodities with small particle size), or when there is a danger of contamination between adjacent parcels, additional precautions are taken to prevent cargo from escaping from the cocoon. Plastic sheeting is placed over the parcel and taped at the boundaries before the steel sheets are put in place, and the welded joints between the steel plates are sealed with a heavy duty adhesive tape.

A parcel can be loaded at the other end of the hold following the same procedure, and thereafter successive parcels can be loaded against the previous ones until the final parcel overlaps cargo forward and abaft it (Fig. 20.9). It is reported that as many as 12 parcels have been loaded in a single hold. At the time of discharge the steel plates are pulled away by cranes, and are reportedly dumped or sold for scrap.

Loading two grades of grain in the same hold: To load cornmeal and wheat, or any two grains, in the same hold the procedure, sometimes known as a Japanese separation because it is used in the trade from the Mississippi to Japan, is as follows:

- Load the heavier cargo (cornmeal) first.
- Spout trim the cargo as level as possible.
- Level the cargo with a bulldozer.
- Stevedores use shovels to complete level trimming, particularly around frames.
- Cover entire cargo with a huge piece of burlap, with small pieces between the frames.
- Cover cargo with stout tarpaulins or plastic sheeting.
- Infill frame spaces and bulkhead corrugations with burlap, tarpaulin or plastic sheeting offcuts.
- Lay standard size plywood sheets on top of tarpaulin or plastic sheeting.
- Cover plywood joins with overlapping plywood strips.
- Secure the plywood sheets and strips to one another and to the tarpaulin or plastic sheeting with staples, tacks or nails.
- Load the next cargo.

The entire process of constructing the separation takes from four to six hours. If discharge is by suction hose this form of separation presents no problems. If discharge is by grab the stevedores must take exceptional care.

The photo (Fig. 20.10) shows the discharge of cargo, perhaps not grain in this case, from above a separation of this type.

Breakbulk cargo stowed over bulk cargo: To load vehicles, containers or general cargo over grain or fertiliser the procedure is as follows:

- Load and trim the cargo as above and cover with tarpaulins and burlap in the same way.
- Provide a robust flooring with extra plywood or a frame of 75 x 75 mm timber or even thin steel sheet.

Empty containers used as a temporary bulkhead: Figs. 20.11 and 20.12 show the No.2 hold of a handymax bulk carrier loaded with two grades of spodumene concentrate which have been separated by a temporary bulkhead constructed of empty containers (Fig. 20.13). The containers have been cut as necessary to match the shape of the hopper tanks. Two wire stays appear to give some support to the centre of the bulkhead and several steel plates appear to have been welded where the bulkhead meets the hopper sides (Fig. 20.14). This system of loading is reported to be in regular use in an Australian port and to have been approved by the vessel's classification society.

Taking the ground in the berth

Most Shipmasters and seamen expect their ships to remain always afloat and imagine that any grounding is cause for concern, but there are berths in many parts of the world where it is the practice of the trade for bulk carriers to take the ground in the berth at low tide.

Mini-bulkers of up to 6,000 tonnes sometimes take the ground in berths where little or no water remains at low tide. Handy-sized and Panamax vessels are required to visit berths where they take the ground during the last low water before they complete loading. The problems for the larger vessels are a less extreme version of those met by smaller vessels. For that reason, the description which follows is of a mini-

Fig. 20.11 Two parcels of spodumene concentrate separated by a temporary container bulkhead. The first parcel to be loaded (on the right) has been covered with sheeting to prevent contamination by dust from the second parcel

Photo courtesy of Mathieu Baehni MNI

Fig. 20.12

Fig. 20.13 Composite photo of a temporary bulkhead constructed from containers

Photo courtesy of Mathieu Baehni, MNI

Fig. 20.14 Temporary bulkhead constructed of empty containers

Photo courtesy Mathieu Baehni MNI

bulker taking the ground in the berth.

The normal sequence of events at such berths is that the vessel berths on one high tide and grounds as the tide falls, an hour or two later. The water may leave the ship completely or, more often, a small depth of water insufficient to float the vessel may remain at low tide. She remains aground for nine or ten hours, working cargo, until the next high tide when she refloats and sails, or the cycle is repeated several more times until the vessel is ready to sail.

Taking the ground in the berth creates a number of problems for ships' personnel. Since many officers only meet such problems very occasionally there are many opportunities for mistakes to be made and it is worth considering the problems in some detail. Loading a cargo whilst aground is more complicated than discharging a cargo, and is also more common. It is that procedure which is described below.

Nature of the bottom in the berth: If the ship takes the ground in a place where there is a hard object projecting below the ship there is an obvious danger that the ship's shell plating will be heavily indented or punctured. If the berth is not plane along its full length, but contains a ridge or a hollow, the vessel could break her back. In most cases there is nothing that the Master can do to guard against such possibilities. It is usually not practical or realistic to make a thorough survey of the berth before berthing, so the Master must assume that there are no such faults in the berth and that the berth to which he has been ordered is safe.

He should, however, keep the possibility of damage in mind and should ensure that a full set of soundings is obtained and that any other signs are carefully considered each time that the ship refloats.

Stability and trim: Taking the bottom presents a number of unusual problems for the chief mate, who is normally responsible for the stability and trim calculations. He must ensure that the ship remains stable whilst taking the ground and he must ensure that she is able to sail at the correct draught and trim without the benefit of regular draught checks with which to monitor the progress of the loading. His calculations will be further complicated by the need for ballast water for generator cooling to be retained until the vessel finally refloats and is ready to sail.

The passage from berth to sea will be undertaken on a falling tide, sometimes with draught limits imposed by the depth of water available downriver from the berth. If sailing is delayed or if the draught after deballasting is miscalculated the vessel could go aground during the downriver passage with consequences which might be disastrous.

Assuming that the ship is to load to her marks with a cargo of coal the sequence of calculations is as follows:

- Calculate the loss of stability which will occur when taking the ground on first berthing and ensure that the ship will retain enough positive stability. The calculation is the same as that for virtual loss of GM when taking the blocks in a drydock (Appendix 20.1). Provided that the initial trim is not too great and the initial GM is large there is not likely to be any problem with stability, but if the initial trim is great or the initial GM is small the vessel may become unstable when taking the bottom. In those circumstances she will list, though it is unlikely that she will capsize. When she lists the bilge on the low side will make contact with the seabed and steady her until she takes the bottom entirely and returns to the upright, if the seabed is level.
- Decide, in consultation with the chief engineer, what quantity of ballast must be retained aboard for use in generator cooling whilst the vessel is aground. Agree which ballast tank is to be used: it will normally be the afterpeak, or a pair of wing or double bottom tanks close to the engineroom.
- Taking account of any limiting conditions and using methods described in Chapter 9 decide the draught and trim required at the commencement of the intended sea voyage. Planning should allow for the possibility that the ballast (cooling water) will be retained aboard on departure from the berth and pumped out during the passage downriver towards the sea. This is necessary because it may be possible to change to sea water cooling only shortly before sailing, allowing insufficient time to pump out the ballast before departure.
- Decide the distribution of cargo to achieve the required draught and trim. If the coal has a high stowage factor (eg, 1.3 m^3/tonne) it is likely that the holds will be filled before the required tonnage can be loaded. In that case the final trim can be calculated with reasonable accuracy, and the ship will not be loaded to her marks. It may be possible to use spare lifting capacity for ballast to improve the final trim.
- If the stowage factor of the coal is lower (eg, 0.95m^3/tonne) space will remain in the holds on completion of loading. It should be assumed in the initial calculations that the stow will be trimmed level, so that the space will extend over the cargo for the full length of the hold. It will be important when loading to ensure that this is achieved, in order to achieve a safe stow (see Chapter 19) and to reach the planned final trim.
- Plan the loading and deballasting sequence. The only times that ballast tanks can be fully discharged and stripped will be when the vessel is afloat and trimmed by the stern, allowing the strippings to drain to the suction at the after end of the tank but it may be necessary to discharge the bulk of the ballast whilst the vessel is aground and approximately even keel.
- When deciding the tonnages of cargo to allow for the trimming pour there are two conflicting requirements. Because it is not possible to monitor the earlier stages of the loading by reading the draughts the tonnage allowed for trimming should be large, to ensure that the correct departure trim can be achieved. However, the time available for trimming will be limited to the short period between coming afloat and the deadline for sailing to avoid grounding in the berth or in the river on the falling tide. It will be necessary to confirm with the stevedores that the planned trimming tonnage is realistic for the time available.
- Whilst difficult to achieve, it is important that stevedores stick rigidly to the Master loading plan and that an accurate tonnage for cargo loaded in each hold is known at all times.

Matters for the engineers: When a bulk carrier enters shallow water and takes the ground the ship's engineers have to deal with several unusual circumstances. Whilst in shallow water the intakes for cooling water for the main engines and for the generators may become blocked with mud or debris. High intakes will be used when the ship is equipped with them, and the engineers will hold themselves ready to change from one intake to another. If an intake becomes blocked the facility for clearing weed from the sea suction grids with compressed air will normally be used. The main engine must be shut down promptly on arrival in the berth, before the tide falls and cooling water becomes unavailable.

Arrangements will be made to use ballast water for generator cooling, with ballast water being returned to the tank from which it is drawn. This arrangement should be tested some hours or days before berthing and will be put into operation before the vessel berths, well before the tide falls and dock water is unavailable as an alternative. Whilst berthing, one generator will normally be cooled with sea water and the other with ballast water, and they will be run in parallel to minimise the problems should any failure occur in the changeover.

Since these arrangements are unusual the valve settings must be checked, and rechecked, with care. Cases have occurred in which the ballast water has been pumped out of the ship and not recirculated to the ballast tank, leaving the ship with no water to cool the generators. Instances have also occurred where cooling water has continued to return to the ballast tank after the vessel has left port, filling a ballast tank which was by that time supposed to be empty. As the time of departure approaches the engineers should be alert for the time when the water level rises sufficiently to again provide cooling water for the main engine.

The generator cooling water should again be drawn from outside the ship when the water level has risen sufficiently. When normal circulation of cooling water has been re-established, and when the vessel is again afloat, all valve settings should be carefully rechecked to ensure that they are correct, and the soundings of bunker tanks, bilges and void spaces should be checked to confirm that the ship has suffered no damage as a consequence of taking the bottom.

Period in the berth: When berthing in a berth where the vessel takes the ground it is normal for the Master to ensure that the engineers are kept fully informed of each step in the programme. They should be told as soon as main engines are not required, when the tide starts to fall, when the vessel first takes the bottom and when she is aground fore and aft.

During the full period that the vessel is in the berth the deck officers and crew must remain alert to tend the moorings and gangway as necessary. As the vessel takes the ground she may assume a slight list, and she may tend to slip away from the quay. The mooring lines must be well adjusted, all bearing an even strain to prevent the vessel from slipping away from the quay. The gangway or accommodation ladder must be properly rigged and carefully watched to ensure that it is not dislodged by an unexpected movement as the ship settles.

If the vessel lists or trims by the head when hard aground some inconvenience is likely to be suffered by the ship's company, with scuppers and drains becoming blocked. It will be impossible to obtain reliable soundings of bilges, and of ballast, fuel and fresh water tanks, and stripping of ballast tanks will be difficult. Problems of this sort must be anticipated and dealt with as necessary.

The loading of the cargo must be watched with care, particularly since ship's personnel cannot check the quantity of cargo loaded by reference to the draught readings. The method which the stevedores will use to measure the tonnages loaded must be understood and checked if possible. Ship's officers must know where cargo is to be loaded and which parts of which holds are to be left empty and must ensure that the plans are followed.

Deballasting must proceed according to the programme as far as conditions allow. If the vessel rests with a list, or without a trim by the stern, it will not be possible to discharge all the ballast according to the programme and final quantities from all tanks will remain for discharge during a period when the vessel is afloat.

If the vessel remains in the berth for the duration of several tides she will refloat at intervals. As the tide rises the engineers should be informed, and the ship's moorings and gangway should be tended as necessary to make sure that the vessel remains secure when she refloats. It is quite common for a vessel which has taken the bottom to be held to the bottom by suction when the water level rises. When she finally breaks free from the suction she often makes a sudden movement which can cause mooring lines to surge or break and disturb the means of access. When she is fully afloat a full set of soundings should be taken and inspected for warning signs, and for the progress made in deballasting.

Final refloating and departure: The final refloating and departure is likely to be an anxious time. In the space of a couple of hours it will be necessary to see the ship safely and securely afloat, re-establish normal cooling of generator and main engines, sound all tanks and spaces and investigate any unexpected soundings, complete deballasting and stripping ballast, complete the main loading of the cargo, conduct a draught survey and calculate the trimming quantities, complete the trimming pours, conduct a final draught survey, test steering gear, main engine and navigation equipment, sign the necessary cargo and other documents on completion and leave the berth in time to catch the tide.

Possible problems which can occur in these circumstances include a failure to have generators and/or main engine ready at sailing time, ship overloaded whilst aground, ship wrongly trimmed or still carrying too much ballast, or ship carrying ballast instead of cargo. In such circumstances it is necessary for the ship's Master and mates to work as a team to gather and exchange information, recheck calculations, maintain contact with the engineers and implement each step in turn.

When there is insufficient depth in the berth but deeper water is available in the approaches the final draught survey and final paperwork can be completed after departure from the berth, for example at anchor in midstream.

General and breakbulk cargoes

Bulk carriers are not designed for the carriage of general cargoes, which are cargoes made up of small units of assorted raw materials and manufactured goods. When crates, cases, cartons, drums, loose machinery or casks are to be carried, often from several loading ports to several discharging ports, the

Stowage of crates, boxes or bales

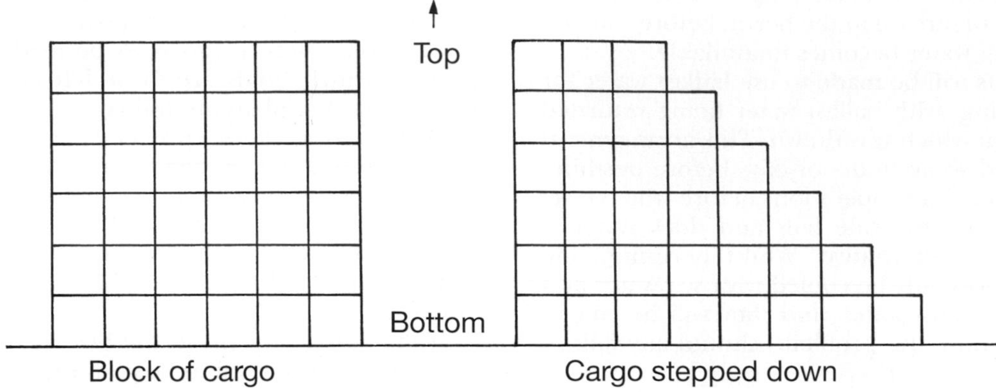

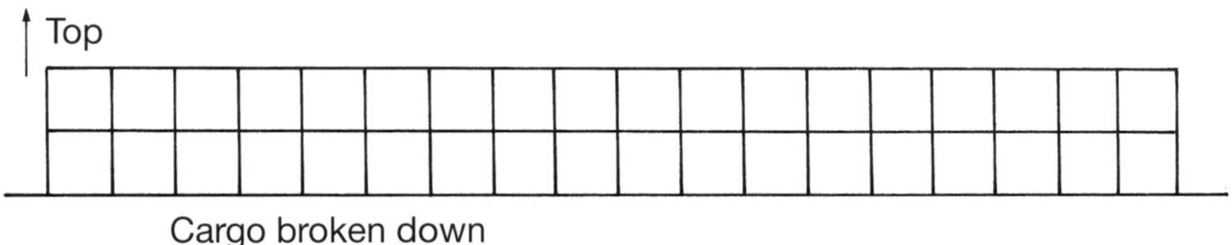

Fig. 20.15

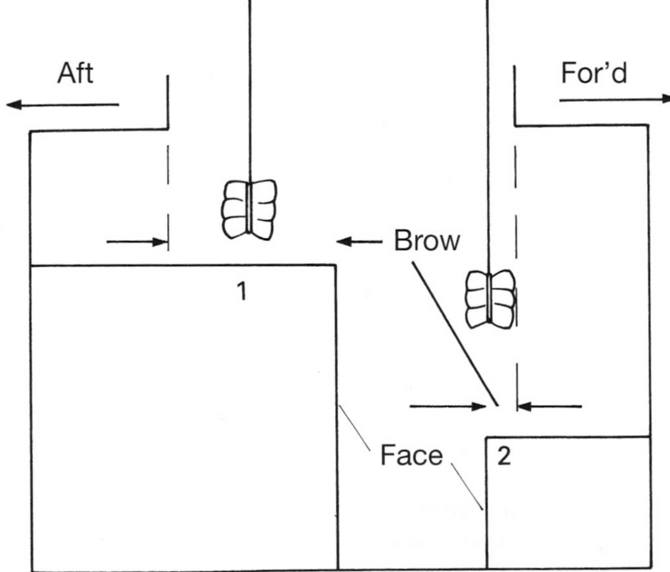

1 This brow provides sufficient room to work safely.

2 This brow is too narrow for safe work

Fig. 20.16

most suitable ship for such products is a tweendeck vessel. Such a vessel offers two advantages over a normal bulk carrier – a tweendeck vessel possesses at least twice as much deck area (ground space) within the cargo spaces, which permits much greater flexibility in arranging the loading and discharging sequence, and the heights of the compartments in the tweendeck vessel are much lower, thus preventing stowage of cargo to an excessive height and consequent crushing.

Despite these disadvantages bulk carriers are required to carry general and breakbulk cargoes from time to time, perhaps because of the decreasing number of tweendeck vessels. In addition a charterer with unused space in his ship may sub-charter one or more holds to another shipper, who may provide such cargo. Full cargoes of rail wagons and of pallets of onions have been carried in handy-sized bulk carriers, with many bagged cargoes, and cargoes of steel products.

Basic rules for the carriage of general cargoes: The following basic rules should be observed when required to carry general or breakbulk cargo:

Planning

- Draught, trim, stress and stability at every stage in the voyage must be planned as for a bulk cargo (see Chapter 9).
- Avoid excessive local loading on the tanktop, deck or hatch covers from cargo or fork lift trucks.
- No. 1 hold, being close to the bows, is not box shaped. It is suitable for small items of cargo and bagged cargoes, but not suitable for large items of cargo. Where possible cargo for discharge by lighter at an anchorage port should not be stowed in No. 1 hold because the water alongside No. 1 hold is usually unsheltered, which will cause difficulties for the lighters.
- Bulky items of cargo such as casks of tobacco should be stowed in large holds where the loss of space due to broken stowage will be least. (Broken stowage is the unoccupied space around items of cargo.)
- Heavy items of cargo such as machinery should be stowed in the hatch square in positions where they can be landed directly and from which they can be discharged directly.
- Different cargoes can damage one another by taint, by dust and sweepings, by leakage of liquid contents, by insect infestation, by condensation from moisture content and by crushing. When stowing different cargoes together these dangers must be borne in mind.
- Hazardous cargoes should be stowed under deck or on deck in accordance with the International Maritime Dangerous Goods (IMDG) Code.
- Heavy cargoes for loading or discharge with ship's gear must be stowed within reach of the appropriate ship's crane or derrick.
- Cargo for each loading port and each discharging port should be shared between all holds or several holds, as far as possible, so that several gangs of stevedores can be employed simultaneously, and the total loading and discharging time can be reduced as much as possible.

Dunnage

- Dunnage, which normally consists of softwood planks with a cross-section of 150x30 mm, or of plywood sheets, should be used with all general cargoes to protect the cargo from moisture, to provide a non-slip base for heavy items and to bind the stow together. Beneath general cargo it is normal to place double dunnage, with the bottom layer consisting of 75 x 75 mm timber running fore and aft, to allow any water to drain to the after end of the hold, and the upper layer consisting of plywood sheets or planks running athwartships. Cargo such as cartons or sacks which could be damaged by contact with the ship's steelwork and the moisture which could collect on it, should be protected with dunnage. Layers of dunnage or single pieces or sheets of dunnage can be placed within the stow to bind it together and stabilise it.

Stowage

- When heavy and light items are stowed together the light items (eg, cartons) must be stowed over the heavy items (eg, crates).
- When cargo is only stowed over part of a hold the vertical boundary of the stow is called the face (Fig. 20.16). The face of the stow must be constructed with skill and care if it is not to collapse during the course of the voyage. A face which faces forward is likely to be more secure than one which faces aft, since the stern trim which is normal for most ships will tilt it slightly in the direction of security. A face in a stow of bags will normally be locked or made more secure, by stowing one tier of bags fore and aft, and the next tier athwartships. Each tier (ie, layer) of bags is started at the face, to ensure that the bags in the face can be placed exactly as required.

Securing

- Cargo securing must be done in compliance with the ship's Cargo Securing Manual. If securing equipment or procedures which are not described in the Manual are required the approval of the authority (the government or classification society which certified the Manual) must be obtained.
- Every item of cargo must be properly secured so that it cannot move and suffer damage when the ship works in a seaway. Cargo must be secured by forming part of a solid stow, by chocking with timber chocks which secure the cargo in position, or by lashing with wire lashings or flat metal strapping bands. Cargoes of steel coils are lashed together to form a solid mass, but are not lashed to the ship. This method of lashing cannot work for items such as locomotives and heavy items of industrial or agricultural machinery. They cannot be fastened tight together and must be individually lashed to the structure of the ship. If cargoes are to be lashed to the ship's structure it is usually necessary to weld a number of lashing eye plates to the ship's tanktop, hopper sides and frames. Project cargoes ('heavy lifts') are often welded to the ship's structure under supervision of Class. Hot work of this sort will damage the coatings in adjacent compartments which should be repaired at the first opportunity.
- A block (ie, a stack) of cargo should never be left unsecured when a ship goes to sea. It must be chocked, or it must be broken down or stepped down. Breaking down a block of cargo means lifting down the upper items and spreading the cargo in a level stow across the tanktop, so that it is impossible for it to fall further. Breaking down and stepping down are illustrated in Fig. 20.15.
- The sloping hopper sides of the holds present problems for the stowage and securing of some general cargoes, though bagged cargoes are unaffected and cargoes such as steel reinforcing bars and girders can be stowed fore and aft across the entire breadth of the hold without difficulty. When square-sided items of cargo are to be stowed in holds with hopper sides, chocking must be used to create a series of steps.
- At various points in the foregoing notes it has been recommended that cargoes be secured with well-placed dunnage, chocking or lashing. In the sheltered waters of

a port it is sometimes difficult to imagine the violence with which a ship can roll and slam in heavy seas, and to take all the precautions necessary to secure the cargo properly. Bulk carriers tend to be stiff ships, and can roll violently in a beam sea. All cargo securing should be done thoroughly and professionally using good quality materials and should be carefully inspected before it is accepted. If the Master has no previous experience of the cargo and is in doubt as to the securing which is appropriate he should consult his owners and ask them to arrange for a surveyor to advise him.

Safety considerations

- Hold ladders must be maintained in good condition, and must remain accessible.
- Hatch covers, whether open or shut, must be properly secured in position.
- All openings must be guarded with handrails.
- The brow of cargo in the hatch square (Fig. 20.16) must always be wide enough to provide a safe working area.
- The edge of the brow of the cargo should be protected with lashing nets to prevent anyone from falling.

Steel products: Steel products form a special category of breakbulk cargo, and were discussed in Chapter 19.

Trading to cold regions

A number of bulk trades require ships to load, or more rarely to discharge, in cold parts of the world such as Canada, Scandinavia, Russia, Greenland and Spitzbergen, places which can be delightful in summer time, but which present real problems in winter (Fig. 20.17 and 18). For general advice on navigating in ice covered waters readers are referred to IMO MSC/Circ.1056 Guidelines for ships operating in Arctic ice-covered waters[188], to The Nautical Institute's Handling Ships in Ice[9] and Polar Ship Operations (due 2011); *The Mariner's Handbook*[10] and to Canadian Coast Guard publications[11]. The BIMCO Ice Handbook[254] contains a mass of useful facts about navigating in ice in twelve distinct ice areas worldwide. The *Admiralty List of Radio Signals, Volume 3*, gives details of the ice information which is broadcast in each part of the world.

Ships usually trade 'within IWL' (Institute Warranty Limits). These limits have been revised and as of 1 November 2003 they are referred to as 'INL' (International Navigating Limits). In the main these

Fig. 20.17 Snow and ice on the hatch covers
Photo courtesy of Captain L Hesketh FNI

Fig. 20.18 Ice on deck – passing the Aleutian Islands
Photograph courtesy of I.D. Smith, MNI

limits refer to ice trading and the areas contained in INL are those areas that are excluded from trading. It is important, therefore, to be fully aware of those limits so as to ensure that the vessel does not venture into an ***excluded*** area unintentionally, or does not enter an excluded area without having taken appropriate precautions.

It must be remembered that vessels may face extended periods manoeuvring in pack ice and, when conditions are severe, should carry sufficient diesel and fresh water for delays possibly amounting to a number of days. The other main problems which face the crews of ships trading to frozen areas are efficient ballasting and the operation of hatch covers, deck machinery and domestic services and the maintenance and operation of fire fighting equipment and life saving appliances, and it is these problems which are discussed in the following paragraphs. The recommendations which follow are based upon experience of bulk carriers of all sizes from mini-bulkers to Cape-sized vessels and also of tankers[186]. Serious problems should be anticipated any time that air temperatures remain significantly below freezing for several days in succession, and the likelihood of problems will be greatly increased if the sea temperature is also at or below freezing.

Icing: Icing of the deck machinery, decks and hatches as a result of meeting spray is a serious inconvenience and a potential hazard. It should be minimised where possible by reducing speed or altering course.

Pilot ladders: Should be stored under cover except when in use, to ensure that they do not become coated with ice. To avoid becoming coated with frozen spray they should not be put in place over the side until required[184].

Inspecting for ice damage: On arrival in port after a passage through ice it is always prudent to inspect the hull as carefully as possible for ice damage which can occur without obvious sign at the time. Such damage usually occurs near to waterline level around the bows, where the shell plating may be dished, and inspection in the forepeak at waterline level may show fractured frames. The rudder and propeller are also easily damaged, particularly when a vessel is in ballast and they are near the surface. Any inspection and its results should be recorded in the deck log book. Any damage found should be reported to the owners, who will inform the classification society and charterers.

Ballast: In freezing conditions if no special precautions are taken it is likely that airpipes, sounding pipes and ballast valves, particularly topside dump valves, will freeze up. Since these items are often inaccessible and since it may be difficult to establish what, if anything, is wrong when sounding pipes are frozen this has in the past resulted in ships sailing with unmeasured quantities of ballast sometimes weighing thousands of tonnes on Cape-sized vessels and with much less cargo than they were intended to load.

A variety of steps can be taken to minimise problems in freezing conditions.

- Before arriving in freezing conditions all air vents should be fitted with canvas covers to be removed only when emptying or filling tanks. Savealls should be kept free of water and ice.
- Any ship which is carrying fresh or brackish ballast should exchange all her ballast whilst in the open ocean for the warmest available salt water ballast (for example, from the Gulf Stream), which will not freeze so readily. If for some reason it is difficult or impossible to change all the ballast, the topside and peak tanks, which are above water level, should be changed since it is the tanks above water level which are normally most likely to freeze as a result of exposure to cold winds.
- A few tonnes of water (say, 10-15 per cent) should be pumped out of each tank to ensure that no water remains in the airpipe, where it may freeze. In double-bottom tanks which extend into the lower hopper sides (the normal arrangement) this will create very little free surface, and have very little effect upon stability. The free surface created in topside tanks by the removal of a few tonnes of ballast is likely to be much greater and should be calculated to ensure that the ship retains sufficient positive stability, although calculations normally show that this is no problem.
- As an alternative to discharging a few tonnes of ballast from each topside tank, the Canadian Coast Guard[11] recommends completely deballasting the topside tanks to ensure that they will not freeze up. This is a possibility well worth considering provided that the weather is fair and the sea is not ice infested. If the weather is foul the deeper draught will be required to reduce pounding and to reduce windage when berthing.
- If the sea is ice infested it is most important to maintain the deepest possible draught in the ballast condition in order to keep the propeller and rudder as far below the surface and below the ice as possible.
- The Canadian Coast Guard recommend that where possible 'ballast should be circulated', since movement of the ballast will inhibit the formation of ice. On most bulkers this is not possible except by filling and emptying tanks, which is not a satisfactory procedure. However, circulation of ballast is possible on some specialist cold weather traders where ballast water can be used to cool the main engine cooling water, a process which also warms the ballast water.
- As a further means of preventing the freezing of bilge and ballast sounding pipes 5 litres of antifreeze or a quantity of brine (very salt water) should be put into them during freezing conditions. Of the two salt is much cheaper, but antifreeze will cause less corrosion. The procedure for adding brine is to pour buckets of heavily salted water, containing as much salt as can be dissolved, down the sounding pipes. This should be done frequently during deballasting. (Any draught surveyor who tries to obtain samples of ballast from the sounding pipe to measure the density should be warned if salt or antifreeze has been added.)
- When deballasting, tanks should as far as possible be pumped right out in a single operation. Stripping of the final small tonnage should not be left until a later time in the loading, although this is less important with the double-bottom tanks, which are well below the surface of the water.

If, despite all precautions, it is found that ballast cannot be pumped right out and it appears that some part of the system is frozen up, efforts should be made to unfreeze the system with heat if possible. If the frozen valve, suction or pipeline is not accessible there will be no alternative but to continue the voyage with ballast retained aboard. In cases in which the vessel is sailing fully laden to her marks it will be necessary to reject some of the cargo.

If, on the other hand, the vessel is loading less than a full cargo to comply with a limiting draught at the discharging port it is worth considering the possibility of sailing at a deeper draught, with full cargo plus ballast retained aboard to be pumped out once warmer water is reached and the ballast system unfreezes. There is sometimes an advantage in sailing at a deeper draught with ballast retained aboard – the rudder and propeller are deeper below the surface and less likely to be damaged by ice. This can only be done when it is certain that the ballast can be pumped out when required.

When pumping ballast tanks full or empty in freezing conditions it is important to ensure that the airpipes are clear and that air is flowing through them. Ballast tanks have been ruptured when pumped at a time when their airpipes were blocked with ice.

Emergency de-icing system: A system which can be used to direct hot water (at a temperature of 30°-40°C) or steam to any part of the vessel, for example to the windlass, the winches or the accommodation ladder can be very useful for de-icing when required and the possibilities for achieving this should be considered in advance.

Deck machinery: When in calm waters the anchors should be first walked out one or two metres and then rehoused from time to time to prevent them from becoming frozen in the stowed position.

Before reaching freezing weather moving parts such as anchor stoppers and clutches should be protected with a heavy coating of grease to exclude water and all water should be drained from deck lines, and from anywhere where it collects unnecessarily. If drain cocks have not been provided at the lowest points in the washdeck lines and winch cooling water lines they should be fitted to permit drainage. If there is any danger that the deck hydraulic systems contain any water slugs in the hydraulic oil the oil should be changed or the hydraulics left running and the oil allowed to warm up.

The deck air line and the water trap cups in the pneumatic air system should be kept empty and drained if not in use. Where possible store the hoist motors for the accommodation ladders and lifeboats in heated spaces. A long spare length of airhose with a spare air motor, stored inside a heated space, can be very useful if the lifeboat hoist motor or the accommodation ladder motor fails in extreme conditions.

Chain lockers should be drained of any water and kept dry by carefully sealing the spurling pipes.

Motors for hydraulic deck machinery for hatch covers, winches and windlass should where possible be kept running continuously to circulate hydraulic oil, unless the system has been fitted with oil of viscosity intended for arctic conditions. The motors must be inspected regularly in case of a hydraulic leak, which could spill all over the pumproom and allow the motor to seize up. Some systems such as hatch hydraulic motors may be fitted with trips which cut-out after 15 minutes' use, in which case they should be restarted regularly around the clock. Heater lamps (eg, cargo clusters) should be placed on the hatch hydraulic reservoir tank in the forecastle. Winch and windlass controls should be set so that the machinery keeps turning, thus reducing the build-up of ice.

Controls for deck machinery should be well greased and then covered with canvas covers. The control pedestals should then be fitted with plastic containers (eg old Teepol containers) over the canvas, to protect them from freezing spray. Winch control pedestals which collect condensation in their bases should be drilled to allow this water to drain away. The burning of rags soaked in paraffin is a method of warming a windlass which has literally frozen up. This method must not be used near fuel tank airpipes.

Ship's cargo grabs, if carried, are normally stowed on deck (Figs. 23.5 and 6) liable to freeze and when frozen are difficult to restow. Spray antifreeze on the sheaves. Unship the grabs and stow them in the holds on top of the cargo where possible.

Top and slew derricks and cranes for an hour or two daily when at anchor or alongside to prevent the sheaves from icing up completely. Inspect sheaves regularly: they are cast and will crack or break if overstressed by the conditions. Ice on the runner or topping wires can force the cheeks of blocks open, making them useless and dangerous. Special low temperature grease for use in temperatures below freezing is available from manufacturers. Where possible such a product should be used to grease deck machinery before any lengthy visit to frozen areas.

Any mooring ropes or wires on reels should be covered with canvas before entering cold weather. Seamen can be provided with pickaxe handles with which to break frozen spray on canvas or lines. Mooring lines should be covered again after the ship is moored. Those mooring ropes which are stowed below decks should only be brought on deck in the approaches to the berth. All deck lights should be left switched on day and night.

Hatch covers: Before entering cold weather the hatch rubbers and compression bars can be smeared with low temperature grease to prevent them from sticking or freezing together. If a build-up of ice on hatch covers prevents the opening of the hatches it may be possible to clear the ice away with axes and picks, followed up with the application of rock salt at the cross joints. Commercial firms if called in may use industrial paraffin flame throwers to melt ice.

When hatches have been opened antifreeze should be brushed on to the hatch rubbers, and compression bars and trackways should be sprinkled with industrial salt to prevent ice and cargo freezing thereon. This will make the cleaning of trackways easier on completion of discharge, but make sure that sensitive cargoes are not contaminated with salt. Another procedure with the same objective is to spread heavy duty plastic or canvas sheeting over the hatch coaming trackways in the way of grab discharge. Ensure that no snow or ice remains between the hatch cover panels when closing hatches. If left in place it can prevent correct closing which may allow leakage at a later date[187].

Machinery spaces: On ice-classed ships the sea water for engine cooling must in freezing conditions be recirculated back to the sea suction. Heat must be kept on the main engine continuously, and the boiler must be in good working condition with plenty of spare parts available. Heaters in the steering gear compartment and hydraulic pump rooms should be left on continuously. Steam heaters should be fitted to the engine intakes to prevent slush from blocking them.

If it becomes necessary to drain the main engine to work on it in port it must be remembered that the cooling water which is used to refill it when the work is finished will be colder than usual, so longer than usual will be required for warming through the engine before sailing.

Steering gear motors: Should be kept running at all times to keep the oil warm.

Bunker tanks: Install a clean steam hose complete with couplings in each of the domestic fresh water tanks (if set against the ship's side) or the windward one will freeze up. Fresh water tanks should be filled only to 90 per cent capacity. Crack open the steam lines to all heating coils in the fuel oil tanks. Drain and isolate the heating coils for any empty bunker tanks.

Navigating bridge: Radar scanners should be left running in port to prevent them from freezing. Radars have to be on standby, or running with brilliance and gain turned down, as necessary to ensure that scanners turn. It is against the Collision Regulations to show lights as a ship underway when your ship is berthed but despite this it is a widespread practice in Arctic waters for navigation lights to remain switched on day and night at sea and in port. Light glasses should be coated in petroleum jelly to prevent ice build up. Ship's whistles are to be heated if heaters are fitted and drained if powered by air or steam. Their drain valves should be left slightly open.

The standard magnetic compass should be provided with a plastic cover (eg a bin liner) and a canvas cover and its electric light should be left on continuously. Searchlights should be provided with canvas covers to be fitted when the equipment is not in use.

Wheelhouse window washing arrangements should be drained and not used. Alternatively, they can be fitted with tape heaters, but even when these are fitted it may be found that the nozzles tend to freeze. Wheelhouse weather doors should be taped up with broad masking tape, on the basis that people will only visit the bridge wings in an emergency. Heaters in the wheelhouse should be left on continuously.

The wheelhouse windows can be cleaned externally using methanol car window water fluid –40°C. They are liable to ice up totally. To prevent this at least three fan heaters should be used, directed at the insides of one port, one central and one starboard window to provide a good all-round view. In addition the outside of the windows should be coated with methylated spirits or Rain-X liquid auto windshield wax. Rain-X Anti-fog liquid can be used on the inside of wheelhouse windows to reduce misting. The watertight seals around the edges of windows should be checked: if water gets behind a seal and freezes it can cause the window to shatter. Clear view screens should be labelled 'check that screen is free before switching on', to avoid burning out the motors. Window wiper blades should be kept clear of the windows. Icing can cause wire radio aerials to collapse, so personnel should wear safety helmets and avoid walking under wire aerials in cases where these are fitted.

Firefighting and lifesaving equipment: Electrical heater lamps should be hung around the emergency fire pump[185] and its radiator should be topped up with antifreeze. Low temperature gas oil should be obtained for use in the emergency fire pump and in lifeboat engines. The lifeboat engine must be fully drained and provided with heating, for which heater lamps or a steam hose can be used. Totally enclosed lifeboats can be permanently fitted with a 1 kW black heater connected to the ship's power supply. Drinking water tanks in the lifeboats must be emptied to 80 per cent level or can be drained completely, with drinking water in plastic jerrycans kept in the accommodation close to the boat stations.

Holds: To allow the fitting of blanks in the ballast hold before loading cargo the bilges can be 'boiled' by use of a portable steam line and coil. A vessel which reaches a loading port with ice in her holds may be able to hire large fan heaters with which to dry out the holds, provided that a crane is available, either ship's or shore's, to lift the heaters into the ship and a suitable electrical power supply is available.

Accommodation: Accommodation heating air is to be recirculated. All accommodation doors are to be kept shut at all times. Only one door is to be used as an entrance/exit, clearly marked, with all other doors secured or locked from the inside, but with keys prominently placed nearby. The entrance door must be kept closed except when in use, and wooden doors which fit badly can be screened with blankets.

The air heating and lights should be left switched on in spare cabins to ensure that the temperature is not allowed to fall in these areas. Any pipework or plumbing which is placed near the outside accommodation bulkheads is likely to freeze up and must be insulated or heated. Typical precautions are the following:

- Fit tape heaters to the plastic fresh water pipes in the dry stores or drain them and shut off or blank off the supply.
- Insulate external accommodation toilets with loft insulation. Pour brine or antifreeze into the toilet bowls. Drain all supply lines, lock toilets and label them 'out of order'.
- Provide heating for the hospital toilet and bath if they are in an exposed position.
- Instruct all ship's company to keep bathroom, shower and toilet doors shut but ventilation grilles open to circulate air over pipework.
- Keep the galley stove and ovens warm day and night.

Personnel:
Extreme cold temperatures reduce the crew's efficiency considerably[184]. Low temperatures reduce the crew's physical ability, their effectiveness and can impair their judgement. It is important that ship's personnel are warmly clothed when working in freezing conditions if efficient work is to be expected of them, particularly since the difficulties encountered in such conditions can sometimes call for long periods of work on exposed decks to put right problems caused by the conditions. When working in extreme cold it is advisable to stop work frequently for a short break.

Heads, hands and feet should all be well protected and all protective clothing, boots, gloves and undergarments should be perfectly dry.

Thick quilted boilersuits of a type which can be wiped clean are recommended for wear with thermal underwear and normal outerwear. Insulated overshoes, balaclavas and heavy-duty waterproof jackets and trousers are also to be recommended, as are woollen inner gloves for warmth and heavy duty outer gloves for protection. Such clothing is readily obtainable in good quality in Northern Europe and Canada, though prices can vary considerably from one country to another, with Canada generally reported to be cheap. Personnel should also be provided with sufficient blankets to ensure that they can sleep in comfort.

Ski goggles, double layered and with ultraviolet protection, have been found useful in protecting from glare and high wind chill factor when working in exposed conditions such as on the forecastle.

Safety on deck: To ensure that people can walk safely on deck the ship should be well equipped with rock salt to spread on deck. If the decks cannot be defrosted grit or sand should be spread where people will walk. Boxes containing rock salt, grit or sand should be placed on deck near to gangway and to hatches. Ice and snow can fall from the bridge front dodgers. Personnel should be warned to beware of this danger. Safety helmets worn on deck by ship's personnel and all visitors should be compulsory.

Damaged pipework: The danger of leakage or flooding from damaged pipework is most severe when the vessel is leaving freezing weather and frozen pipework is thawing. A careful watch should be kept on any known or suspected blockages to detect leakage or flooding as soon as it occurs.

Sources

9, 10, 11, 184, 185, 186, 187, 188, 254. (See List of Sources, Page 497)

CHECKLIST – Requirements for visit to freezing area

The following items may be required, with quantities dependent upon the vessel's size:

- ☐ Rock salt, 25 kg bags.
- ☐ Antifreeze, ethylene glycol, 60 litre drums.
- ☐ De-icer, spray cans.
- ☐ Methyl hydrate, for windows, 4 litres.
- ☐ Electric heater lamps.
- ☐ Low temperature grease, tubs, 12.5, 15.0 or 20 kg.
- ☐ Paraffin, 60 litre drums.
- ☐ Methylated spirits, 5 litre cans.
- ☐ Axes, picks, shovels.
- ☐ Air chisels.
- ☐ Canvas sheeting, waterproof, square metres.
- ☐ Auxiliary boiler spare parts.
- ☐ Steam hose, with couplings.
- ☐ Tape heaters.
- ☐ Masking tape, wide.
- ☐ Fan heaters.
- ☐ Cold weather gas oil, 200 litre drums.
- ☐ Loft insulation, metres.
- ☐ Warm protective clothing, two piece skidoo suits or similar.
- ☐ Woollen socks and glove liners.
- ☐ Insulated over-boots.
- ☐ Heavy duty insulated winter rubber gloves
- ☐ Low temperature gas oil for lifeboats

CHAPTER 21

SAFETY CONSIDERATIONS

The ISM Code, responsibility for safety, abandoning ship when flooding occurs, permit to work system, entering enclosed spaces, use of pesticides, access to the ship, hazards from working cargo, use of safety equipment and clothing, unsafe cargoes

IT IS NOWADAYS IMPOSSIBLE to consider safety aboard ship without acknowledging the existence of the mandatory International Safety Management (ISM) Code which provides an international standard for the safe management and operation of ships and for pollution prevention[195]. Each company and its shipboard management are required to operate in accordance with an approved safety management system (SMS) which will usually have detailed checklists of procedures to be followed for routine and emergency situations. The SMS may be unique to a particular ship but will more usually be developed for a class or fleet of ships within that company. There will be procedures for amending and developing the SMS to take account of unforeseen occurrences thereby ensuring that ISM is a cycle of continual improvement.

It is important for all shipboard work to be planned, for hazards that may be met to be identified and for counter measures to be put in place. This process, known as risk assessment, is part of a ship's SMS.

Bulk Carrier Practice concentrates on the special features of dry bulk carriers[196]. ISM, SMS and risk assessment are not special to bulk carriers but are common to all commercial shipping; consequently this book contains few references to them though it shares the ISM Code's objectives of identifying and encouraging best practice in the operation of dry bulk carriers and protection of the marine environment.

Responsibility for safety rests with each individual on board ship. Not only should individuals protect their own health and wellbeing, they should also protect the health and wellbeing of their shipmates and colleagues. Safety is part of the job and it is the duty of everyone to give careful attention to safety, as well as to complete the task in a skilful way.

The risk of death is insufficient to persuade some people of the need for safety. Officers must for economic and humanitarian reasons ensure by example, training and continuing propaganda that safety is never forgotten or ignored when operating a ship. Dismissal from the ship or an adverse report should be considered for persistent offenders against the rules of safety. Company policy on safety will be stated in the SMS documentation and officers should of course have full backing from their head office when enforcing safe practices.

Safe working practices for seafarers have been listed in various useful publications such as the UK's *Code of Safe Working Practices for Merchant Seamen*[31] which deals clearly and thoroughly with many aspects of marine safety. This chapter concentrates on particular hazards which are characteristic of the dry bulk trades. No attempt has been made to consider the full range of safety issues which affect all shipping.

Abandoning ship when flooding occurs

The shipping industry has slowly awoken to the fact that bulk carriers can, and do, sink very rapidly when holds are flooded as the result of serious damage to the side shell plating or hatch covers as a consequence of accident or neglect. In recent years shipping industry bodies have issued warnings that action of the utmost urgency must be taken when flooding is detected.[191, 192, 193] The Nautical Institute has issued a poster which summarises the advice as follows.

Fact: Bulk carriers, designed and built to relevant IMO standards and Classification specifications, properly inspected, maintained and operated in accordance with IMO industry standards are safe, reliable, and have a life expectancy of more than 20 years provided they remain undamaged.

Fact: When bulk carriers are loaded with dense and heavy cargoes such as iron, dense ores or steel products they rely on large empty spaces in holds, ballast tanks, voids and forward tanks as reserve buoyancy to stay afloat. If seawater enters any of these spaces due to damaged hull, hatches, accesses, ventilators or airpipes, the vessel can lose buoyancy and sink very quickly.

Fact: Many seafarers have been lost when bulk carriers have sunk because they did not have enough time to evacuate the vessel, and on a number of occasions vessels have sunk so fast that not even distress signals were sent out.

Advice:

- Crews should be very aware of any damage to the ship's hull, hatches or deck fittings. Such damage can be caused by contact with dockside or tugs; by impact from cargo gear such as tractors and grabs; by damage from corrosion (often accelerated by the chemical actions of certain cargoes); by sloshing forces from ballast; by swinging anchors hitting the hull; or by any damage to hatches by seas, equipment or poor maintenance.
- Crews should be aware that any loss of buoyancy in forward spaces due to flooding will reduce the freeboard forward and dramatically increase the forces of extreme weather on hull structures and hatches. If a ship takes on an unusual trim or list, or if her motions become changed, breach of the hull should be suspected immediately. Visual signs of trouble can include unusual collection of water on decks or dislodged hatch covers.
- On vessels fitted with water ingress detection systems (WIDS), in the event of a WIDS alarm, muster all personnel at the abandon ship stations with the exception of those crew members investigating the alarm and those keeping systems running, and notify authorities of distress. (Remember that a Distress signal can be downgraded later if it is found that the situation is less serious, but there may be no opportunity to upgrade an Urgency signal if the situation is really hazardous.) In the event of a second alarm warning of flooding to a greater depth, ensure that all personnel are recalled and sent to abandon ship stations. Flooding

aboard a bulker can be more dangerous than fire and the crew should be fully drilled to carry out evacuation procedures urgently when the WIDS alarm sounds.

- In the event of a collision, the Master should call the ship's personnel to emergency stations with a strong emphasis on preparing to evacuate the ship.
- Boats, liferafts or other life-saving craft must not be launched unless the specific order to do so has been given by the Master. The decision to evacuate should be based on knowledge that the vessel is truly sinking, the depth of water is deeper than the depth of the hull, and the speed of sinking might prevent later launching.

For more information and guidance please visit www.nautinst.org/bulk

This advice should, of course, be taken very seriously.

Advice developed by BIMCO[193] includes several additional important points. Any investigation of flooding should be carried out responsibly and should not endanger lives. Seafarers have been swept overboard in heavy weather conditions when they have ventured on deck to investigate a known ingress of water. Adverse weather conditions may make such operations extremely dangerous and Masters should not commit crew members to open decks unless there is no alternative. In making such a decision Masters should consider the value of such action. The purpose of water ingress monitoring systems is to make it possible to know the condition in each hold without having to investigate locally.

Permit to work system

In many situations aboard ship the routine actions of one person can endanger others. Before work is started it is necessary to identify the dangers and to remove them where possible. A most useful safety procedure and a tool of the professional ship's officer is the use of the 'permit to work' (PTW). This system obliges everyone concerned with a particular task to concentrate his mind on the work to be done and serves to involve the team in anticipating where things might go wrong. It is also a training aid, since it indicates the correct way to set about and complete various onboard tasks. This makes permits to work most useful when instructing junior officers and ratings.

The operation of the permit to work system is simple. A checklist consisting of a numbered list of questions relating to the proposed work is completed, by entering Y (yes), N (no) or NA (not applicable), or by using a tick (✔) or a cross (x) against each question. The person who is to directly supervise the work will sign the permit only when he is satisfied that all questions on the checklist have been correctly answered. Only after it has been signed should the work commence. The permit should include a description of the work to be done, and should show the time when the permit expires, which should be no more than 24 hours after the issue of the permit. If there is a need for the work to continue after the permit has expired it must be renewed.

A provision which deserves to be included in every permit requires the supervisor to sign when the work is completed. He is required to sign a statement that all tools and equipment have been safely stowed away, that the area in the vicinity of the work is clean, that all means of access to the work have been secured fastened, and that the ship's watertight integrity has been restored.

Permits with suitable wording are required for a variety of different tasks. They can be written aboard ship, or the shipping company can supply them to all their ships. Permits can be produced in duplicate pads, with one copy issued to the person doing the work and a second retained by the person who issues the permit. Aboard many ships nowadays they are computerised and forms can be printed as required with one copy displayed on-site and another on the PTW board. A copy of each permit issued should be retained amongst the ship's papers for legal reasons and to demonstrate to auditors and safety inspectors that safe working systems are in operation.

One word of warning must be sounded with regard to permits to work. If they are badly written and fail to list a necessary precaution, they can be the cause of that precaution being forgotten. A space for remarks should be provided so that additional precautions can be noted, and the permit should be revised from time to time to include necessary improvements.

It has been estimated that 60 per cent of all major claims are attributable to human error, whilst other authorities put the figure as high as 80 per cent. The permit to work system is intended to reduce the opportunity for human error and by 2009 was used by most, if not all, bulk carrier operators as part of the SMS.

Entering enclosed spaces

Many serious accidents, some resulting in death, occur on board bulk carriers because safe procedures are not followed when enclosed spaces are entered. Any enclosed unventilated space which can be sealed off from the outside atmosphere may be dangerous and enclosed spaces must be taken to include cargo holds, battery lockers, paint storerooms and masthouses as well as ballast, bunker and cargo tanks.

There have been numerous cases of seafarers entering a cargo hold which is battened down with little or no ventilation and being overcome by lack of oxygen. In November 2006, for example, a Filipino seaman died in Helsingborg from breathing an atmosphere starved of oxygen when he entered a hold laden with wood pellets from Vancouver. In the same incident two other members of the crew, a dock worker and two medics had to be hospitalised[199]. Only too often deaths have resulted. Particularly dangerous are cargoes which absorb oxygen by rusting, such as pig iron. Seafarers should never rush down into a hold to rescue a shipmate if they see that he has been overcome. A breathing apparatus should always be used and safe procedures must be followed. It cannot be repeated too often that the natural instinct to give immediate help must be resisted.

Two seamen entered a mast house containing access hatches to the holds. The hatches had not been secured and methane from the coal cargo had escaped into the mast house. One of the seamen lit a cigarette. The resulting explosion killed both men. Had no cigarette been involved they could equally well have died through asphyxiation. On another occasion five stevedores entered a hold before the hatches had been opened. The cargo was yellow corn, otherwise known as maize. Much of the corn had started to germinate during the voyage removing oxygen from the atmosphere of the hold. All the stevedores died of oxygen deficiency. Elsewhere a stevedore slipped and fell amongst a cargo of logs in a hold. He was overcome by an atmosphere deficient in oxygen and so were the three colleagues who tried to save him. All were pronounced dead on arrival in hospital[201].

Many explosions have occurred in battery lockers due to the use of naked flames from matches and cigarette lighters. Seafarers who enter storerooms such as the lower forecastle store flat after stores have been left unsecured during heavy weather have suffered serious injuries as a consequence of heavy items toppling on to them. The foregoing are illustrations of just some of the dangerous situations which can be met, quite unnecessarily, if correct procedures are not adopted when entering enclosed spaces.

IMO[197] has produced detailed and extensive advice and recommendations for entering enclosed spaces. Enclosed spaces and people equipped to evaluate them are defined and the possibility of meeting an unsafe atmosphere is explained. The risk must be assessed, entry authorised, appropriate precautions taken and the atmosphere tested. A space must never, never be entered without precautions when an emergency occurs. When the atmosphere is known to be unsafe additional precautions must be taken to ensure complete safety or the space should not be entered.

Bulk cargoes which are known to cause oxygen depletion (a lack of oxygen) include grain and grain products, oilseeds, copra, all forms of wood, vegetable fibres such as jute, hemp, flax, cotton and many others, fishmeal, guano, sulphidic ores and concentrates, charcoal and coal, dry ice, metal wastes, scrap metal and many more.

Officers should take great care to ensure that all involved have a very clear understanding of the instructions. Bulk carriers are manned by people from many cultures and although it is desirable that all members of a ship's company should speak the same language this is often not the case. Full discussion of the information and instructions relating to entering enclosed spaces should be encouraged to confirm that they have been understood and to remove the possibility that a rating is accepting an order that he does not understand or thinks it wrong to question. If the officer in charge suspects that someone does not have a full understanding of what is intended, he should not allow him to be part of the team entering the enclosed space.

It is important that enclosed space entry forms are completed at the site of entry and actual readings of oxygen and other gases are clearly recorded on the form. It is not good practice for the enclosed space entry forms to be completed in the ship's office or be pre-programmed into the computer with all the boxes ticked. These practices are unprofessional and could very easily result in a fatality.

Enclosed spaces should be thoroughly ventilated, using mechanical ventilation when the atmosphere is not explosive and it is safe to do so. The atmosphere should be tested for oxygen and toxic gases before anyone is allowed to enter the space and should be continuously monitored whilst crew members are within. Frequent communication with those inside the tank is vital. Walkie talkies or thunder ball whistles are often used for this purpose. The access to an enclosed space should be fenced off and provided with eye-catching warning notices when it has been opened but not yet proved safe for entry. Safety is just as much a part of the job as the cleaning of the tank, or the repair of a valve, or an inspection.

The tanks of larger bulk carriers are cavernous places with very big brackets, deep frames, floors and stiffeners. It can take 20 minutes to move from end to end of a large double bottom tank, and such tanks may be entered through bulkhead stools or void spaces. A human can be brain dead if deprived of oxygen for four minutes, so the chances of mounting a successful rescue operation for someone who is overcome by lack of oxygen or toxic fumes at a point in the tank remote from the entry manhole are very poor. A useful exercise for inclusion in the ship's regular safety drills is to practice a rescue from an enclosed space, followed by the appropriate first aid and medical treatment.

Safe use of pesticides

In recent years the authorities have become increasingly concerned at the dangers associated with the use of pesticides aboard ships. There is the possibility that edible cargoes will be contaminated by the use of pesticides and that crew members will be harmed by contact with them.

Before describing routine procedures a warning must be given. On at least one occasion ships' personnel and stevedores required treatment when they breathed fumigant laden dust from a grain cargo while it was being loaded! The ship, in a western Canadian port, had received no warning that the cargo had been fumigated before loading. The Master should enquire whether the intended cargo is under fumigation or has been fumigated and should arrange for the supply of suitable approved protective masks if necessary.

Full recommendations for the use of pesticides aboard ship have been published by the IMO[28]. A copy of this document should be held aboard ship and studied before pesticides are used. The following paragraphs indicate the areas covered by the recommendations, but it must be emphasised that pesticides can kill and should not be used except when the full instructions have been studied.

A ship may be infested by insects or by rats. Infestation by insects may exist aboard ship or may be brought aboard with the cargo. The purpose of its removal may be to satisfy the agricultural authorities in the discharge port or to ensure that the cargo remains acceptable to the receiver. Infestation can cause cargo to overheat. Infestation by rats must be eliminated in accordance with International Health Regulations. Infestation is assisted by dirt and cargo residues. Holds, accommodation, storerooms and machinery spaces should be kept very clean to remove any opportunity for infestation.

Prevention of infestation: Cargo spaces and other parts of the ship should be kept in a good state of repair, clean and free of rubbish. Any infested material

Fig. 21.1 Hose for delivering fumigant to grain cargo
Photo courtesy of Captain L Hesketh FNI

Fig. 21.2 Fumigant hose ends in empty hold before loading grain
Photo courtesy of Captain L Hesketh FNI

Fig. 21.3 Fumigating fan installed in access hatch
Photo courtesy of Captain L Hesketh FNI

collected during cleaning should be disposed of or treated immediately so that infestation cannot spread.

Treatment of infestation: An infestation of a cargo space or an infestation of cargo must be eliminated with the use of a fumigant. Fumigants are administered as gases or liquid sprays and the compartment fumigated must be made gas tight. Evacuation of the space being fumigated is mandatory and it may be necessary for the whole ship to be evacuated. The gas may be delivered in pellets which decompose during the voyage and give a slow release of gas. Fumigant gases are poisonous to humans and their use requires special equipment and skills. They should be used by specialists and not by the ship's crew. There are detailed recommendations for the use of fumigants. The illustrations (Figs. 21.1 and 2) show hoses which are led through the access hatches and put in place in the empty, hold where they become submerged in the cargo. When loading is completed and the fumigant has been pumped into the cargo the hose ends on deck are dropped through the access hatches into the hold. The accesses are then closed and sealed.

In some ports of the USA the fumigation process requires the ship to circulate the fumigant gas through the cargo for a set number of days. This is achieved by portable fan units situated inside the access hatches (Fig. 21.3). During the gas circulation strict precautions must be followed to ensure that the access hatch is fully sealed and does not allow any of the gas to escape. (The access hatch remains cracked open about 10 mm to allow the electric cable through and the crack is sealed with heavy duty tape such as Ramnek tape. During heavy weather the circulation is suspended, the power supply disconnected and the access hatch tightly battened down)[263]. Ship's staff must be prohibited from entering any area where gas circulation is occurring. A large NO–GO area must be maintained for safety reasons.

At the end of the circulation period the fans are switched off and unplugged and remain inside the hatch access until the discharge port. Full safety precautions, using breathing apparatus, must be taken when the fans are switched off and the power cable disconnected. At the arrival berth the fans can only be removed from the access hatches when the atmosphere is found safe to do so.

The Master should be provided with full written instructions in a language he can readily understand about the fumigant used and precautions required. The fumigator-in-charge is responsible for evacuating the crew, posting watchmen and warning notices, injecting the fumigant, issuing respirators if required, testing the spaces to ensure they are gas free, and issuing a clearance certificate when all traces of gas and fumigant material have been removed.

Fumigation with aeration (ventilation) should always be carried out alongside or at anchorage. The detailed precautions to be adopted are listed[28].

In-transit fumigation: In-transit fumigation is fumigation which is commenced in port under specialist supervision, but which continues at sea with only the ship's crew aboard to supervise and control the process. It may be proposed if the ship's stay in port is not long enough for the planned fumigation, or if it is found that the fumigant gases have not completely dispersed at the planned time of completion of fumigation and the spaces have to be resealed. It is also likely to be proposed when an infested cargo such as grain is loaded and fumigation can only commence on completion of loading or when it is a term of the contract of sale.

In-transit fumigation is hazardous because of the lack of experience of the crew and the dangerous nature of fumigants, and is forbidden by some flag State administrations. Before he agrees to in-transit fumigation the Master must ensure that he has the permission of the ship's flag State administration, and of the port State administration.

At least one officer and one rating are to receive training to enable them to take responsibility for ensuring safe conditions throughout the ship. They must be familiar with the characteristics and properties of the fumigant and the manufacturer's recommendations regarding methods of detection, symptoms of poisoning, relevant first aid and special medical treatment, and emergency procedures.

The crew must be briefed. The cargo spaces to be fumigated must be inspected before loading and must be certified by the specialist as gastight and satisfactory. The ship must carry gas detection equipment and instructions, at least four sets of appropriate protective equipment, instructions on disposal of remaining fumigant material, medicines and medical equipment and a copy of the latest version of the *Medical First Aid Guide for Use in Accidents Involving Dangerous Goods (MFAG*[194]*)*.

The fumigator-in-charge must provide a written notice of all spaces which are unsafe to enter during fumigation and must check surrounding spaces for safety. He must remain aboard until the fumigant gas reaches sufficiently high concentrations to ensure that any leak can be detected and until such leaks have been eliminated, and must then issue a written statement that these requirements have been met and that the ship's representative is fully trained in the use of the gas detection equipment provided.

Whilst satisfying the above requirements the fumigator-in-charge may be able to leave the ship before she sails or may undertake part of the voyage with the ship, but in both cases he leaves before the ship is free of fumigant gas. Whilst in-transit fumigation is taking place, warning notices should be posted, adequate stocks of gas detection and respirators (with consumables) should be maintained and spaces around the compartment being fumigated should be checked every eight hours or more often, for gas concentrations and the readings obtained should be logged.

Spaces under fumigation should never be entered unless absolutely essential and then only by two persons, both wearing adequate protective equipment, safety harnesses and lifelines. The lifelines should be tended by persons outside the space who should also wear self-contained breathing apparatus.

In normal circumstances the ventilators will remain sealed and no ventilation will be attempted for a cargo under fumigation. This will continue either for a stated number of days after which the spaces are to be ventilated or, less commonly, for the entire passage to the discharge port. When a space under fumigation has to be ventilated every effort should be made to prevent gases from entering accommodation or work areas. In these circumstances ventilation is best undertaken when there is a strong cross-wind, blowing exhausted air away from the ship. When ventilation takes place accommodation and work areas should be checked for gas concentrations and if they ever exceed the threshold limit value (TLV) for the fumigant the space must be evacuated.

At least 24 hours before arriving at the discharge port the Master must inform the authorities that a fumigation-in-transit is being carried out and must provide relevant details. The requirements of the receiving country regarding the handling of fumigated cargo should be established and observed. Personnel employed in opening hatches should wear respirators and the area should be checked for gas concentrations, with readings recorded in the log.

Discharge should be carried out by mechanical means. If anyone is required to enter the hold and at the completion of discharge, it should be checked for gas concentrations and respirators should be worn if required. When discharge is completed and the ship is free of fumigants and certified as such, all warning notices should be removed.

Every step in the fumigation process, including instrument readings obtained when required, should be recorded in the vessel's log book.

Model checklists for in-transit fumigation are available in Appendix 3 to the document[28].

Access to the ship

Provision of a safe access between ship and shore is an essential requirement, a requirement which is endorsed by the laws of most if not all maritime nations. For these reasons the officers and crew of bulk carriers must ensure that a safe means of access is always provided. This is often difficult to achieve.

There is always movement between ship and quay. This occurs in the short term as a result of swell and the passing of other ships, and in the longer term as the result of tide and the loading and discharging of cargo and ballast. Because of this movement only one end of a gangway or ladder can be secured and the other must be free to move. For practical reasons it is preferable to secure the upper end of the gangway or ladder and to leave the lower end free to move but held in place by gravity. When ships' ladders or gangways are used, the fixed end must be the end which is retained aboard the ship and the ladder must slope down from the ship to the quay. This is impossible when the ship's deck is lower than the quay, as is sometimes the case, and alternatives must be found.

Accommodation ladders: Ship's officers will normally choose to use the accommodation ladder in preference to the portable gangway, because the former is rigged alongside the accommodation and clear of the cargo working areas. This is safer and more convenient than using a gangway which usually must be placed somewhere on the maindeck, often adjacent to one of the working holds. In addition, the accommodation ladder is reasonably simple to rig and can usually be raised and lowered by one man using a powered winch, provided that the ladder remains

Fig. 21.4 Accommodation ladder hung from bridle and with good safety net rigged
Photo courtesy of Captain L Hesketh FNI

Fig. 21.5 Bridging the gap between accommodation ladder and quay with a plank is not acceptable
Photo courtesy of Captain L Hesketh FNI

Fig. 21.6 This short ladder used for passing from the foot of the accommodation ladder to the (dirty) quay is good *Photo courtesy of Captain L Hesketh FNI*

Fig. 21.7 A safe route from quay to accommodation ladder *Photo courtesy of Captain L Hesketh FNI*

Fig. 21.8 Accommodation ladder with net rigged

Fig.21.9 The top and bottom outboard manropes on this ladder are too slack
Photo courtesy of Captain Peter Boyle FNI

Fig. 21.10 This is a good example of a well rigged accommodation ladder. The safety net is carried well beyond the foot of the ladder to catch anyone who stumbles at the bottom platform. The top guardrail is rigid and soft, brightly coloured padding makes the bottom platform obvious and protects heads which might strike the bridle
Photo courtesy of Captain Peter Boyle FNI

suspended from its bridle, hanging against the ship's side (Fig .21.4).

Unfortunately, the accommodation ladder cannot be used when the after part of the ship projects beyond the end of the quay, as is often the case. Nor can it be used when the level of the quay is higher than that of the accommodation ladder top, as often happens at low tide and/or when the bulker is deep laden.

Even when the accommodation ladder can be used it is likely to be found that the fenders placed between the ship and the quay are so large that it is not possible to step from the foot of the accommodation ladder to the quay when the ladder is hanging against the ships' side. Improvised arrangements (Fig. 21.5) are not acceptable but properly constructed ones are (Fig. 21.6 and 21.7). Alternatively the foot of the ladder must be swung away from the side of the ship and landed on the quay (Fig. 21.8). Once that is done it requires two or three crew members to move it, as is necessary at some berths every time a new train of rail wagons are brought alongside, or every time that the loading or discharging equipment must be shifted along the quay, or every time that the ship herself must shift.

If the fenders are not wide and the ship lies close to the edge of the quay, it may be found that the bases of the loading and discharging gantries are so close to the edge of the quay that the accommodation ladder must be raised and swung inboard any time that the ship or the gantries are required to move.

Once the accommodation ladder is in place the manropes should be set taut (Fig. 21.9). The bridle should be padded if there is any danger of users banging their heads on it (Fig. 21.10).

Gangways: When the accommodation ladder cannot be used, a heavy ship or shore portable gangway is an alternative. The main disadvantages of such a gangway are that it must usually be rigged somewhere along the main body of the ship where cargo is being worked, and this is less safe and less convenient than an accommodation ladder. Furthermore, it is heavy and must be handled by a crane, either from the ship or from the shore, and this requires more labour and more co-ordination than does an accommodation ladder. A portable gangway is normally rigged sticking out from the ship at right angles, and in this position it is likely to prevent the movement of cranes and shiploaders along the quay and to require unshipping and rerigging at intervals.

When gangways and steps meet over a bulwark it is essential that the handrails or handropes are continuous (Fig. 21.11). Lives have been lost when users have fallen while stepping over the bulwark without a handrail.

Brows: Some bulk carriers also possess a light portable gangway or brow, made of aluminium, 5-7 metres long, and which can be rigged by about four men (Fig. 21.12). This can be used when the maindeck is below the level of the quay. In these circumstances the brow can be rigged from a higher accommodation deck. The brow is normally rigged sticking out from the ship at right angles, which produces the problems already mentioned and, since the brow is short, it must be shifted to a position on a different deck when the ship rises or falls more than 3-4 metres with the tide or with loading or discharge of cargo. Some

Fig. 21.11 The brow and the gangway meet over the bulwark. Only one side of the brow is fenced. There is no fencing between brow and gangway above the bulwark

Photo courtesy of Captain L Hesketh FNI

Fig. 21.12 A light brow wrongly rigged – it has rails on one side only

Photo courtesy of Captain L Hesketh FNI

brows are designed so that they can be hooked on to the bottom platform of the accommodation ladder.

Ladders: In particularly difficult circumstances the ship may use a rigid aluminium ladder, preferably with a handrail (Fig. 21.13), set at an angle of 65-75° to the horizontal to provide a means of access.

Means of access provided by terminal: A fifth method of access is the gangway of some sort which is provided by the shore installation at some bulk carrier berths (Fig. 21.14). The best of these gangways are permanently hinged at the shore end and suspended from one of the loading or discharging gantries or from an independent mast or tower near the stern of the vessel. Such gangways normally come in the form of a walkway with a set of steps hanging from its end. Some ladders can be raised or lowered by use of a push button on an extended lead which can be brought to the foot of the gangway, a most useful feature when fitted (Fig. 21.15). Even better is the gangway fitted with a sensitive detector foot which rests on the ship's deck and sends messages to controls which automatically raise or lower the ladder as the ship rises or falls with the tide and the cargo work.

Boarding ladders – with handrails. To DTI requirements

Based on DRG No 896/83 from the Tyne Gangway Co Ltd.

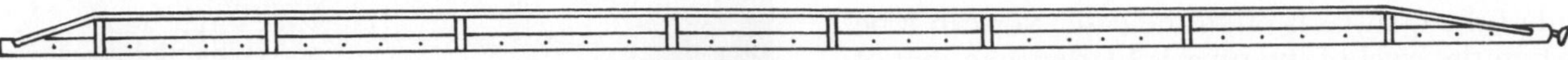

SSA33 HD (handrail) 10m Ladder, weight 70kg.
Lengths may be varied up to the maximum of 10m.
Certificate of conformity issued with each ladder.

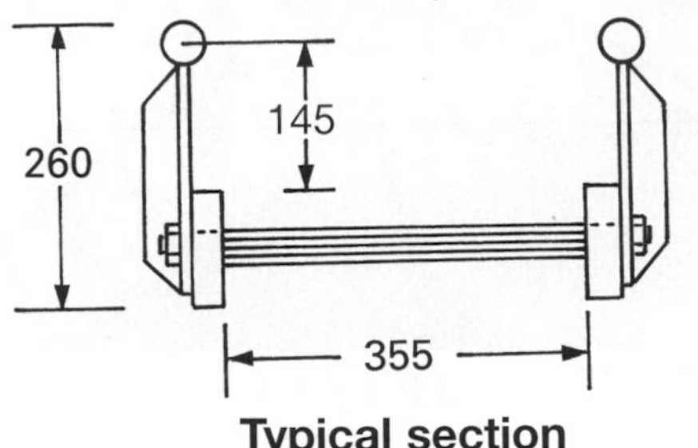

Typical section

Specification

Sides –	aluminium alloy R.H.S.	Non-slip feet rubber suction type
Rungs –	extruded fluted hollow aluminium alloy	Scantlings such that they withstand the loading shown in DTI.DOC[T] 1729.
Handrails –	minimum 25mm x 10g alloy tubes	

Fig 21.13

Fig. 21.14 The terminal's gangway is raised clear to allow the ship to sail

Fig. 21.15 Shore access gangway controlled by a push button on an extended lead

Photo courtesy of Captain L Hesketh FNI

Fig. 21.16 The accommodation ladder meets a dirty quayside

Fig. 21.17 'Max number of persons at any time 5'

If incorrectly rigged, or unsuitable for the ship in the berth, the shore gangway may lie with its fixed steps at quite the wrong angle. This is not acceptable. In most cases the permanent shore gangways, when properly rigged, are safe and convenient. Unfortunately there are many bulker terminals where no gangway of this sort is provided.

When no means of access is provided: Aboard small ships when the deck is level with the quay it is sometimes inconvenient to rig a proper means of access, but easy to step directly from the deck of the ship to the quay. Although this is convenient it can be dangerous. It is forbidden by access regulations and must never be allowed.

Common problems: All means of access are affected by some of the conditions met at bulk cargo berths. Because larger bulk carriers require deep water, many bulk berths are in exposed positions and the ship will surge under the effect of swell or passing shipping, creating a constant threat of damage to the means of access. Some berths are found in a filthy condition (Fig. 21.16), so that there is no choice when stepping off the ship but to step into 5-10 cm of wet cargo residues (sometimes much more!) which make movement along the quay slippery and hazardous and have most unpleasant effects upon clothing.

The ship is required to move position a number of times in loading berths where the shiploader is fixed or restricted in movement, and as already noted there are a number of circumstances in which the access must be lifted out of the way to permit movement of loading or discharging equipment or rail wagons. It is often the case that three or four people are required when the means of access has to be moved, and the need to move the access can occur at frequent but irregular intervals throughout the night and the day.

If no access is possible – for example, when the ship is berthed at dolphins and the policy of the terminal is to withdraw the shore gangway when cargo work stops – the Master should protest at this on safety grounds, as there should always be provision for people to leave or board the vessel in event of emergency. If access is refused the Master must ensure that an emergency escape system is available and may require to use the ship's lifeboats in emergency.

Rules for safe access: The regulations for safe access may vary in detail from one country to another but the main requirements are common to all:

- All access equipment must be in sound repair and properly maintained in good working order.
- All lifting gear used for means of access must be properly certified.
- All access equipment must be used only for the purpose for which it is intended.
- Means of access must comply with regulations in matters such as the angle of incline, the spacing of steps and the height of fencing. Provided that standard items of equipment are correctly used these requirements will normally be satisfied.
- The access must always be properly lit. Ship's lighting should be provided even if shore lighting is adequate in case the latter fails.
- A gangway net must be secured below the means of access in such a way that it will catch anyone who falls from the access or from its approaches (Figs. 21.8, 21.4 and 21.7). This means that the net should extend beyond the end of the access to guard the space beyond. When it is necessary to join two nets together the rope joining them must have the same safe working load as the nets themselves. The requirement to provide a net is often overlooked when the gangway is provided by the terminal.
- A lifebuoy with a self-activating light and a long heaving line with a quoit attached must be placed close to the means of access.
- No more than the permitted maximum number of persons or maximum loading as marked on the equipment should be allowed on the gangway or ladder at one time (Fig. 21.17). In places where a large labour force is used to work cargo it may be necessary to take special precautions to ensure that this rule is observed. A notice stating the maximum number of persons allowed on the gangway should be prominently displayed.
- Arrangements for passing from the head of the gangway to the deck must be safe. When the head of the gangway rests on top of a solid bulwark, steps with handrails must be provided for stepping down to the deck.
- The upper end of a heavy gangway should be housed on a solid part of the ship's structure and not rested on light ship's side railings.
- Stanchions and manropes should be fitted around the lower platform of the accommodation ladder (Figs. 21.6 and 21.7).
- The means of access must be properly adjusted and further adjustments must be made as required when conditions change.
- The proper access must be used and short cuts must not be allowed.
- Safety notices regarding smoking, use of mobile phones and security must be posted.

To maintain the means of access in good working order all moving parts should be carefully lubricated and regularly examined for wear. Rigging should be regularly checked and test certificates should be methodically filed. Machinery for raising and lowering the gangway or ladder should be properly maintained, and safety devices such as pawls and brakes should be regularly tested. When the steps of a gangway or ladder are wasted or worn or when the means of access is otherwise damaged, immediate arrangements must be made for its repair and it must not be used whilst in a damaged condition.

Gangway stanchions are normally provided with keys which ensure that they cannot be accidentally unshipped, but these keys may be damaged or dislodged. Accommodation ladder stanchions may be bent if the ladder is lowered while the manropes are taut (Fig. 21.18). When bent, the stanchions must be straightened and replacement keys must be welded in position. The gangway should be manned by a member of the ship's crew at all times to tend it as required by the rise, fall or surge of the ship and the passage of cranes and vehicles, and to ensure that only authorised persons are allowed on board in line with instructions laid down in the International Ship and Port Facility Security (ISPS) Code, with all persons to be logged on and off the ship.

Instructions about the means of access: The officer of the watch (OOW) must ensure that the access regulations are always observed. An accident could be a personal tragedy for someone and is likely to lead to substantial claims against the ship if it can be shown

Fig. 21.18 Note the manrope stanchions which are bent at the sockets. This is frequently a result of not ensuring that there is sufficient slack in the manropes before lowering the ladder. Additionally the net is not carried around the top platform to meet the ship's guardrails

Fig. 21.19 The bottom platform of the accommodation ladder is over the water and at least 0.6 metres above the quay. Not a safe or comfortable step!

Photo courtesy of Captain L Hesketh FNI

Fig. 21.20 The accommodation ladder is fitted with a spar. When the pin is withdrawn the spar can be extended below the foot of the ladder to prevent small boats from being caught under it

that any reasonable precaution had been neglected. A checklist can assist in ensuring that all is in order.

Whichever means of access is used it will require regular and often frequent attention to ensure that it remains safe, that its adjustment remains correct and that it suffers no damage. Failure to give the gangway or accommodation ladder the attention it requires can lead to prosecution and to the payment of a heavy price in accidents, damaged equipment and injured or irritated users.

The watch on deck should be informed of times of high and low tide, and of anticipated movements of the ship. They must ensure that the gangway is properly secured and the manropes correctly tensioned (Fig. 21.9), and that the height of the accommodation ladder is adjusted to provide an easy step onto the lower platform from the quay (Fig. 21.19).

The OOW should be aware that the gangway or accommodation ladder provides the first impression which a visitor has of the ship. Safety inspectors of various administrations will be impressed favourably by the means of access if it satisfies all requirements. A ship's officer with good professional standards will ensure that the gangway or ladder is well rigged, well illuminated, safe and clean before allowing it to be used for access.

When the accommodation ladder is used at an anchorage a good feature is a spar (Fig. 21.20) which can, on removal of a pin, be slid into a position where it extends beyond the foot of the ladder and prevents small boats from getting caught below the ladder foot. In areas such as the Mississippi, where strong currents are experienced, a lifebuoy is left floating downstream of the accommodation ladder, so that a person falling into the water can grab hold of it. The lifebuoy line is fastened to a secure place on the main deck.

Hazards from working cargo

Cargo falling during loading or discharge: A number of bulk cargoes such as quartz, iron ore, pig iron and steel scrap contain sizeable lumps which can cause injury or death if they fall from a height and strike a person below. From time to time – and frequently in some cases – lumps of cargo will fall from the conveyor belt of the shiploader or from the discharging grab (Fig. 21.21) on to the deck of the ship (Fig. 21.22) or the quay alongside. Such spillage (Fig. 21.23) should be regularly cleared to maintain a safe access route along the deck.

For experienced seafarers and stevedores it becomes second nature to avoid standing below the conveyor or the path of the grab, and this is a rule which should be firmly enforced upon any inexperienced people who have occasion to be in the vicinity of a bulk carrier when bulk cargoes are being loaded or discharged. It is good practice to forbid entry to the working side of the main deck except to those who have necessary work to do in that area. Those required to be on deck during the working of cargo should wear high visibility clothing, hard hats and industrial footwear (Fig. 21.24).

Dust from cargo working: Many bulk cargoes are dusty and some extremely so (Fig. 21.25). The effects of breathing dust can never be beneficial and are probably harmful in some cases at least. Where possible it is always best to avoid exposure to cargo dust and employers and their representatives have a duty to minimise dust (Fig. 21.27). When exposure to hazardous solids, liquids or gases cannot be avoided respiratory protective equipment (RPE) and safety goggles must be worn (Fig. 21.26).

The selection and use of the appropriate RPE is complex and extremely important[32]. It should be part of the risk assessment process. Many different types of RPE are available to give protection against different hazards and the wrong respirator, for example, may be worse than none at all. The advice of a qualified person who understands the circumstances where the RPE is to be used should be obtained.

Anyone required to be on deck when a dusty cargo is being worked and anyone sweeping cargo with a brush or with air should wear a suitable respirator. For a respirator to be effective it must be of suitable design, in good condition and worn by a person who has been trained in its use. For general shipboard use a simple respirator with a disposable filter where the wearer's lungs are used to draw air through the filter should be suitable for cargoes which are not stated to be hazardous. The European (CEN) standard for disposable filtering facepiece (FFP) respirators rates FFP1 as the lowest acceptable standard, removing about 80 per cent of the dust, whilst a facepiece rated FFP3 removes about 98 per cent. All types of respirator are less effective when the wearer is bearded, or unshaven. Filters should be renewed according to manufacturers' instructions or, in the absence of instructions, when soiled.

Respiratory protective equipment (RPE) for use when engaged in spray painting must satisfy requirements quite different from a cargo dust mask as it must exclude gas and vapours, not dust particles. When entering a space which is deficient of oxygen no respirator will be of assistance. The air does not need to be filtered to remove impurities. Air to support life must be provided and in these circumstances a respirator will not do: a breathing apparatus with an air supply is required.

Other safety precautions when working cargo: Smoking should not be allowed on deck when hazardous cargoes are being worked. Grain is a hazardous cargo in this respect: dust explosions have been known to occur in the vicinity of grain. Stevedores must be required to observe the same standards of safety as are required of ships' personnel. Hatch covers, whether open or closed, must always be secured so that they cannot roll in the event of a change in trim or list. A hold should never be entered when cargo is being worked except with the authority of the duty officer and the knowledge of the signaller for the cargo working equipment. Extra care must be taken when slippery cargo residues are on the deck (Fig. 21.28).

Use of safety equipment and clothing

Appropriate protective clothing and equipment must be available to be worn and used aboard ship when the circumstances require it. Appendix 21.1 lists clothing and equipment and the circumstances when it is, or may be, required.

Fig. 21.21 Closed grab leaking cargo *Photo courtesy of Captain L Hesketh FNI*

Fig. 21.22 Deck covered with coal spilt during discharge *Photo courtesy of Captain L Hesketh FNI*

Fig. 21.23 Quantities of grain spilt on deck during discharge *Photo courtesy of Captain L Hesketh FNI*

Fig. 21.24 The route to the open deck

Fig. 21.25 Clouds of dust in Nos. 3 and 6 holds whilst loading grain
Photo courtesy of Captain L Hesketh FNI

Fig. 21.26 Officer wearing protective clothing whilst loading grain
Photo courtesy of Captain L Hesketh FNI

Fig. 21.27 Dust and spilt cargo when loading grain
Photo courtesy of Captain L Hesketh FNI

Fig. 21.28 Deck covered with a layer of soya beans – a slipping hazard
Photo courtesy of Captain L Hesketh FNI

Unsafe cargoes

Many dry bulk cargoes possess features which create hazards for bulk carriers and/or those who serve aboard them. Cargoes which give off explosive or flammable gases, cargoes which may self heat or shift when their moisture content is too high, cargoes which deplete the oxygen content of the surrounding air all present a threat. It is most unlikely that any individual will know all the hazards presented by all the cargoes that may be offered. Masters should study the Declaration by Shipper, relevant entries in the International Maritime Dangerous Goods (IMDG) Code and dry bulk cargo databases such as that provided for members of BIMCO, and should ensure that all those aboard ship are aware of hazards and ways of countering them.

Sources

28, 31, 32, 191, 192, 193, 194, 195, 196, 197, 199, 201, 263. (See List of Sources, Page 497)

CHAPTER 22

INSTRUMENTS AND MECHANICAL EQUIPMENT

Atmospheric test equipment, hydrometers, sea water sampling equipment, psychrometers, mucking winches, mobile cranes, cherrypickers, scaffolding, paint sprayers, portable sump pumps, high pressure washing machines, spray foam systems, hold inspection systems, big area descalers, sand blasting machines, needle guns, pneumatic grease guns, portable fans, power tools

THIS CHAPTER provides a description of instruments and equipment commonly used and/or particularly useful aboard bulk carriers. Important procedures are emphasised, suggestions for making the best of the equipment are offered, and problems commonly met are described. In most cases it is not practicable to provide detailed instructions for the use of the equipment and users are advised always to preserve makers' instruction manuals with care and to study them carefully before using the equipment.

Atmospheric test equipment

Atmospheric test equipment is used to test for the presence of various gases in the atmosphere. The instruments provided for this work have descriptive names such as multi-gas monitor, oxygen monitor, explosimeter, gas monitor and oxygen analyser.

Aboard ship, atmospheric test equipment is used to ensure that the atmosphere in an enclosed space such as a hold, ballast tank, CO_2 room or void space is safe to breathe before the space is entered. It is also used to detect the presence of flammable or toxic gases when these may be released by cargo or by the process of fumigation.

It is not practical to describe the full range of instruments which are available for testing the atmosphere, but these are the questions which a user must ask and which should be first considered before the start of the voyage.

- **Do we have the correct test equipment and sufficient spares for the intended voyage?** The appropriate equipment with sufficient consumable spares must be obtained before the start of the voyage. The instrument should have a valid calibration certificate, preferably from a reputable shore testing establishment and should have been calibrated in accordance with SMS Procedures.
- **What am I testing for? Is it simply to ensure that there is sufficient oxygen to allow comfortable breathing?** Or is it for methane or hydrogen, which are flammable, or for carbon monoxide, which is flammable and toxic? Could CO_2 escape from the gas cylinders in the CO_2 room? Different cargoes produce a variety of gases and it is necessary to know which gases may be present.
- **Is the test instrument correct for the gas to be detected?** The equipment literature must be studied to ensure beyond doubt that the instrument will detect the gas which may be present.
- **Am I familiar with the operating instructions?** The user should have a full knowledge of how to prepare and operate the instrument, and should practice in safe conditions.
- **Is the instrument properly prepared?**
  - * Clean the probe (also known as the sampling line) regularly and be absolutely sure that it is not blocked with anything.
  - * Use the appropriate test procedure to ensure that the battery is fully charged.
  - * If the instrument uses consumables such as filters, sensors or electrolyte jelly renew them as necessary.
  - * Make sure that the instrument has been set to the correct limits for the gases expected.
  - * Confirm that correct readings are obtained in fresh air and that the instrument is properly zeroed.
  - * Reset the instrument after testing.
- **How should the instrument be used?** Can the sensor be placed in an enclosed space to provide a remote reading before the user enters the space, or is it designed to give an alarm if the atmosphere becomes unsafe and to be worn by someone working in a hazardous area? Both types of instruments can be met and many can perform both functions. At least 60 seconds should be allowed for obtaining a reliable reading, a point which should be remembered particularly when an instrument is used to check the atmosphere before the user enters the space.

A quick and simple method of testing an oxygen measuring instrument is to breathe upon it. The air which a user breathes out is low in oxygen and high in carbon dioxide, so this should produce an abnormal reading from the instrument.

Hydrometers

Loadline hydrometer: Most ships are provided with metal hydrometers which measure specific gravity (also known as relative density) in vacuo. These hydrometers (Fig. 22.1) are intended for calculating the vessel's dock water allowance (DWA), so that she can be loaded to her marks and so that she is not overloaded.

The specific gravity of fresh water is 1.000, and that of salt water is 1.025. This number has no units: it is the ratio of the density of the measured water to the density of fresh water. The hydrometer may be graduated in readings from 1.000 to 1.040, from 1000 to 1040 or from 0.00 to 0.25, which is called an 'arbitrary scale'. These alternatives can be rather confusing and it is sometimes helpful to return to basics when calculating the fresh water allowance.

When most of the hydrometer stem is above the water, the device is floating in buoyant salt water and the DWA is small. When most of the stem is below the surface the water is fresh and the DWA is large. The value of the allowance to be used can be calculated from the formula:

Fig. 22.1 A metal hydrometer for use when calculating the Dock Water Allowance

Fig. 22.2 A draught survey hydrometer. The water container is too small. In fresh water the hydrometer will rest on the bottom of the container

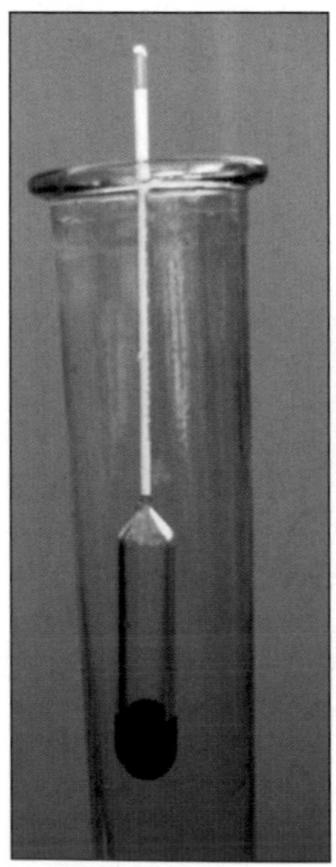

Fig. 22.3 The draught survey hydrometer will always float in this deep container

Fig. 22.4 When the container is filled to the brim the reading is easy to read

$$\text{DWA} = \frac{1025 - \text{Reading}}{25} \times \text{FWA}$$

where DWA= dock water allowance, FWA = fresh water allowance, and Reading = the loadline hydrometer reading.

For example, if the loadline hydrometer reading is 1020, then

$$\text{DWA} = \frac{1025 - 1020}{25} \times \text{FWA} = \frac{5 \times \text{FWA}}{25} = \frac{\text{FWA}}{5}$$

If the hydrometer is marked with one of the alternative scales the reading will be 1.020, or .20 and must be changed to 1020 before being used in the above formula. When calculating the DWA, a correction for temperature taken from a table provided with the instrument should be applied if the temperature of the water is significantly different from that stamped on the hydrometer, which is usually 60°F or 15°C.

A metal hydrometer must be kept meticulously clean at all times. In particular, grease from fingers on the graduated portion of the stem should be avoided. The metal body must not be scratched, cracked or dented. A loadline hydrometer is intended for the calculation of DWA and is not really suitable for use in draught survey calculations, which require readings 'in air' and not 'in vacuo'. However, if the loadline hydrometer is the only one which is available a correction must be applied to the readings obtained. Values for the correction are given in Chapter 13.

Hydrometers for use in draught calculations: For an accurate density (the density in air) of dock water and ballast water, using kilograms per litre (kg/l) as the units. These can be measured directly with a draught survey hydrometer such as the glass instruments manufactured by G H Zeal Ltd (Fig. 22.2), of London, which have a scale which reads from 0.990 to 1.040 kg/l. The hydrometer and water container should be kept scrupulously clean. For accurate readings the water container must be deep and wide enough to float the full length of the hydrometer (Fig. 22.3 and 4). If not transparent the container must be filled to the brim. It should be at the same temperature as the water and shielded from draughts. Readings should be taken without delay to ensure that the water temperature is not allowed to change. The stem of the hydrometer and the surface of the water should be free of grease and oil. The hydrometer should be lowered vertically gently into the water until it floats and the reading should be taken where the level liquid surface meets the graduated scale.

In theory the hydrometer and the ship should be corrected for temperature when draught survey calculations are made. However, it is not practical to correct the volume of the ship for temperature and, since corrections to the volume of the ship and of the hydrometer tend to cancel one another, no corrections should be applied to either in respect of temperature.

Sea water sampling equipment

In some ports, water density may vary with depth, with layers of denser water lying below the less dense surface water. Density can also vary with the state of the tide and can be affected by discharges from installations. To take account of these possibilities, samples of water should be taken from at least three locations on the outboard side of the vessel and from a range of depths. A variety of water sampling devices exist[24] and includes the following.

- A length of metal pipe with threaded caps top and bottom. Holes are drilled in the top cap such that when the pot is placed in water it takes 10 seconds, say, for water to fill it. To obtain an average sample of water through the full water column the pot is lowered steadily from the surface to maximum draught in 10 seconds and will fill as it descends.
- A can closed with a cork stopper which can be jerked free when the can has been lowered to the chosen depth, thus obtaining a sample of water from that depth (Fig. 22.5 and 6).

These sampling devices must be washed in fresh water after use, and kept clean and dry and free from grease and oil. Where sampling equipment for taking samples of water from below the surface are not available, it is still often possible to obtain a sample of sub-surface dock water from a drain cock in the engineroom or from a fire hydrant on deck.

Fig. 22.5 Heavy water sampling bottle closed ready to lower into the water

Psychrometers

A whirling (or aspirated) psychrometer consists of wet and dry bulb thermometers fitted into a rotating case similar to a football rattle. The instrument is designed for use in a shaded, sheltered position such as a cargo hold to find the relative humidity and dewpoint. Because the whirling psychrometer is designed to operate under different conditions to the hygrometer in a Stevenson screen, the relative humidity and dewpoint should be read from a different set of hygrometric tables although the differences are not large. It is important to realise that ventilation of the hold should be stopped before readings are taken. It is the relative humidity and dewpoint of the air in the hold which is required, not the measurements of the external air which is being forced into the hold under ventilation. If ventilation is stopped overnight the best time to take readings is before it is resumed in the morning[172]. The device should be whirled until the wet bulb thermometer gives a steady reading.

There are situations in which it is unsafe or impossible to enter a hold, for example when the hold has been fumigated, when it is sealed or when it has been completely filled with cargo and then, of course, the whirling psychrometer cannot be used.

Battery powered psychrometers are also available and are probably more reliable than whirling psychrometers as they do not rely upon the physical effort of whirling them for up to 60 seconds for each reading. However they do still require access to the hold and a stoppage of the ventilation[172].

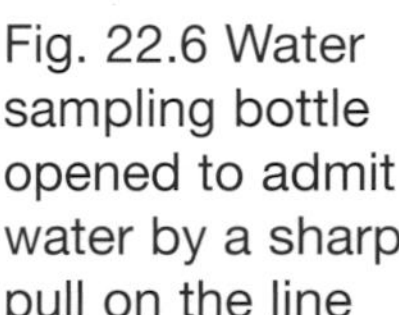

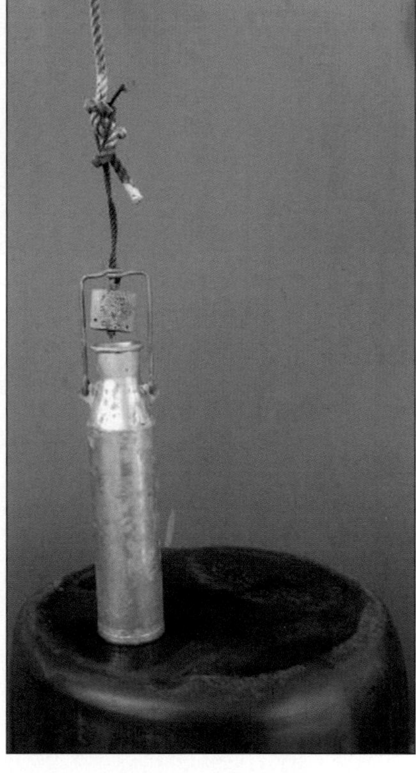

Fig. 22.6 Water sampling bottle opened to admit water by a sharp pull on the line

Mucking winches

A mucking winch unit (Fig. 22.7) is a winch with a davit used for lifting sweepings and rubbish from the holds when they are being cleaned. The winch is usually powered by compressed air from the deck air line, which is used to drive the drum for the winch hoist wire. The equipment is normally portable, which allows it to be used at each hold in turn.

The mucking winch may be worked through the main hatch opening and on Cape-sized and Panamax vessels there may be a suitable mounting permanently fixed at each hatch on a hinged davit which swings into position over the hold. Since hatches cannot be opened when the ship is working in a seaway this restricts the occasions when a mucking winch can be used. Alternatively, it may be positioned to work through a manhole cover in the hatch lids or through a grain trimming hatch (Fig. 1.38) if such is fitted, with the advantage that work can continue in rough weather. A Cape-sized vessel is likely to have a 0.5 tonne winch fitted with 12 mm wires, whilst a mucking winch on a Panamax vessel will probably be of 0.25 tonnes capacity with 8 mm wire. Mucking winches are seldom provided for handymax or smaller bulkers which is surprising as even in these vessels heavy weights require to be lifted in and out of the holds

Fig. 22.7 A mucking winch rigged at the hatch coaming of a Cape-sized bulker

Fig. 22.8 A cherrypicker used for lighthouse maintenance

Photo courtesy of Genie Industries

and the heights are substantial. Although such vessels are usually equipped with cranes or derricks they cannot be used when the ship is unsteady.

Cargo sweepings and the contents of the bilges are lifted from the hold in buckets or old paint drums. The davit is free to rotate so that the load can be swung clear of the coaming and landed on deck or, with smaller davits and lighter loads, the davit may be fixed and the container is pulled over the coaming and landed on deck.

The winch wire may be subjected to rough treatment: it should be inspected frequently and renewed as soon as it is seen to be damaged or worn. The oiler/filter unit (Fig. 6.14) on the air motor should be regularly checked and the unit should be checked for physical damage and greased when being stored away after the voyage's use. Every item of equipment, including the lifting handles fitted to the paint drums, must be in sound condition since the accidental dropping of a drum of rubbish could do fatal damage to a man below. Sufficient spare wires with certificates of test should be kept aboard and spares for the air motor should include a set of air vanes and a set of spare bearings.

Air hoses when used on deck, or indeed anywhere aboard ship, should be undamaged and should have end connections which are sound and secure. The consequences of contamination or pollution from an oil smeared hose could be serious so such hoses should never be used on deck.

Mobile cranes

A mobile crane (stored in a garage under the forecastle head) is a rare sight on Panamax and Cape-sized bulk carriers now that larger bulkers are built with side opening hatch covers which reduce clear deck space in which a crane can operate. On the few ships which carry a mobile crane, a ramp is provided between two of the hatches to allow the crane to cross over the deck pipework from one side of the ship to the other.

A mobile crane provides an alternative to a mucking winch for the removal of sweepings from the holds and a crane has also been used, in port, to hang the painting raft against the ship's side, providing a quickly movable platform from which the ship's overside paintwork can be touched up. A mobile crane is also useful for loading stores into the forecastle store. A mobile crane cannot be used when the ship is unsteady.

The crane wire, sheaves, jib, chassis and winch must be inspected, marked, maintained and certificated like any other item of lifting gear carried aboard ship. The handbrake system and any system for locking the wheels must be maintained in efficient working order. Ships staff appointed to operate the crane should be instructed on its use and be provided with ship's in-house certificates that state that they are certified to operate the equipment.

Cherrypickers

Cherrypickers (Fig. 22.8) are self-contained units for raising a working platform attached to a series of folding arms to a height of 10-15 metres. A small portable cherrypicker suitable for a handy-sized vessel weighs about two tonnes. They are impractical for gearless bulk carriers which have no means of lowering them into the holds, but are standard equipment for some handy-sized geared bulk carriers where they are used for hold maintenance and inspection.

The cherrypicker can be lifted or wheeled into the desired position where solid base plates are jacked down to provide a stable foundation. The working platform can normally accommodate two workers, and controls for raising the platform are duplicated, with one set on the platform and a second set at the base. A cherrypicker provides a quick and efficient means of reaching otherwise inaccessible points high in the hold for cleaning, inspection, repair and painting. A cherrypicker should be maintained in accordance with the manufacturers' instruction manual. Ship's staff approved to operate the equipment should be instructed in its use.

Scaffolding

Lightweight scaffolding tower units made of heavy-duty aluminium and up to 5.0 metres high when assembled have been supplied to some bulkers for use in maintenance and repair work high in the holds. Once erected they can be wheeled from one position to another and then locked in place. They are not popular as they are labour intensive and time consuming to put in position and erect, and they sway when in use unless secured with lashings.

Whilst lashing of the scaffolding with gantlines takes extra time, it is a sensible precaution and suitable lashing points can usually be found, particularly if the gantlines are led over the hatch coaming to positions on deck.

A scaffolding tower consists of up to 30 separate parts, any of which may be damaged or missing, thereby reducing the effectiveness of the complete unit. An added difficulty with scaffolding towers is that because of the hopper tanks in conventional bulkers the scaffolding cannot be erected within reach of the ship's side. Scaffolding towers have been used successfully for welding work, for scaling and for painting, but are not sufficiently stable to provide a platform for high-pressure washing systems.

Paint sprayers

Paint sprayers (Fig. 22.9) are a very efficient means of painting large areas, particularly irregular areas such as the outer sides of hatch coamings and appear to be found on all bulk carriers. However, the preparation and use of paint sprayers is skilled work, and men who do not possess the skill can waste much time and will produce finished work of disappointing quality. If even one person aboard ship such as the chief mate or bosun is thoroughly experienced and competent, he can train others and the benefits will be considerable.

The paint sprayers commonly used aboard ship are known as airless paint sprayers to reflect the fact that no air is ejected with the paint from the nozzle. However, compressed air is used to drive a piston-type air motor which operates a small positive displacement pump. The pump is used to put the paint under pressure, delivering paint at a pressure of up to 5,000 psi at the nozzle tip.

The discharge pressure must be adjusted to the

Fig. 22.9 Hold painting with a paint sprayer

pressure stated in the specification of the paint in use. Adjustment is made by adjusting the inlet air pressure. If the pressure is too high the paint will become like a fine mist. If the paint comes out in blobs the pressure is too low. Spraying should be done using the lowest pressure which gives satisfactory results. The mouth of the suction tube (fitted with a coarse filter) should always be well below the surface of the paint.

Each item of spraying equipment should be earthed (grounded) to reduce risk of static sparking. The supplier's instructions should be carefully observed. When preparing to use the paint sprayer it is essential that the correct spray tip for the type of paint and the correct type and quantity of thinners are used. Failure to get this right will probably result in failure of the equipment to spray and subsequent severe difficulties in cleaning and unclogging it. There is a temptation to use too much thinners because it appears to make the job easier. However, this results in too thin a coating of paint, so must be avoided.

Before paint spraying begins, all washers, 'O' rings and gaskets on the hand gun should be coated in vaseline to prevent excessive wear. The operator must be fully clad in waterproof-type protective clothing which can be wiped clean after use. He must wear a suitable painting respirator – a dust mask is not suitable to exclude vaporised paint. He should also wear goggles and should cover any exposed skin with vaseline or barrier cream.

Since the spray is delivered at very high pressure any direct exposure can result in paint being injected beneath the skin, where it can cause permanent injury. The spray must never be pointed directly at anyone, the safety catch on the trigger should be used any time that spraying is interrupted, and the pressure must be carefully released before the equipment is dismantled and before any attempt is made to clear a blockage.

In the area to be painted, items which must not be painted, such as rubber joints, grease nipples, instruction plates, name plates and safe working load markings must be covered with masking tape or coated with grease. Items like valve wheels can be covered

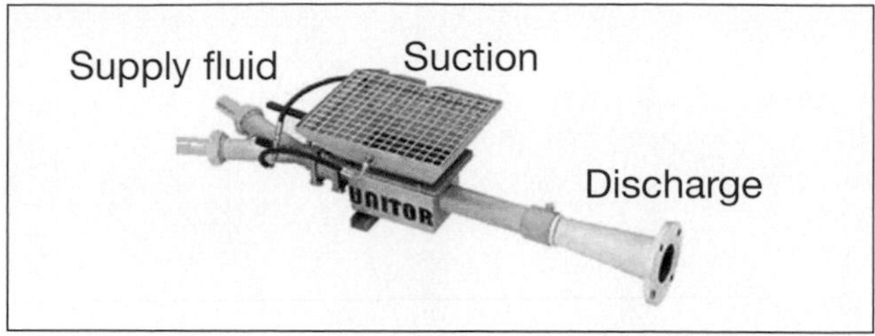

Fig. 22.10 Mucking pump powered by water and employing the venturi system to remove water and solid particles

Photo courtesy of Wilhelmsen Ships Service

Fig. 22.11 Air powered diaphragm (sump) pump

Photo courtesy of Wilhelmsen Ships Service

Fig. 22.12 High powered air driven water cannon for hold washing

Photo courtesy of EMS Ship Supply (Norway) AS

with polythene bags held in place with rubber bands.

Paint spraying must not be undertaken in windy conditions, particularly in port. Claims have been submitted for paint splashed on cars parked 100 metres away from the site of the spraying. The application of an even coat of paint – without curtains, drips or thin patches – is a highly skilled activity which must be mastered before useful painting can be done with the paint sprayer. The secret of good spraying is not to move the wrist; the whole arm should move, thus maintaining an even distance (about 350 mm) from the work.

When paint spraying is briefly interrupted the nozzle of the paint pistol should be left in a bucket of thinners to prevent it from clogging up. At the end of the day the equipment should be depressurised and the paint container should be replaced by a container of solvent (thinners) which is used to flush through the equipment. If the equipment is not to be used for some time oil should be circulated through it as a protection against corrosion. Spares for the paint sprayer are often small and valuable items which can easily be lost. They should remain in the care of a responsible person. Adequate spares should be kept aboard for the intended work programme.

Some officers consider that aboard ship the results achieved with paint sprayers are too unreliable and that unskilled crew members can achieve more satisfactory results with paint rollers. Paint sprayers are normally used in shipyards, which serves to emphasise that this is the most cost-effective option when the skill is present.

Portable sump pumps

Sump pumps (mucking or salvage pumps) are robust and easily portable pumps (Fig. 22.10 and 11) which are designed to work when submerged in water or other liquids. The portable sump pumps found aboard bulk carriers are normally powered by air or water under pressure or by electricity and are of a design which permits small traces of cargo or other rubbish to be pumped along with the water. Most, if not all, bulk carriers carry a sump pump.

About the sump pump shown in Fig. 22.10 a former Master of Cape-sized bulk carriers[264] writes: *Iron ore and coal residues of gravel size down to granular dust and the finest dusts can be shovelled into the hopper and educted directly to the main deck via the 22 cm (approx) heavy duty wire-bound rubber discharge pipe. The venturi outlet has about a 12 cm outlet nozzle so lumpy iron ore or coal could not be shovelled into the hopper as it would block the venturi. If the venturi did get blocked, you simply shut the cock on the inlet side of the hopper (you can just see the black handle of the inlet cock in the photo) and the water in the discharge pipe would run back down and flush out the blocked venturi.*

After the majority of the residues have been educted out of the hold a cover plate is bolted over the top of the hopper. A 15 cm wire-bound rubber suction hose is attached to the removable plate and is used for cleaning and pumping out bilges. It is very effective at this task, as the washing-down hose can be taken directly into the bilge well and swirled around until only clean water remains in the bilge well. While this is going on the crew are having a final sweep and wash down of the tank top directly into the bilges.

We refined our techniques so that with fine iron or coal

cargoes we set the hopper up with the cover plate and bilge suction pipe right from the start and washed and swept everything into the bilges, or one bilge as we would put a 2-3° list on the ship while we were cleaning holds.

The whole rig can take an hour or more to set up, especially the very heavy discharge pipe which needed our mucking davit and winch to hoist and lower it into the hold. But once set up it saved a tremendous amount of work not having to heave the sweepings and residues up onto the deck with the winch and davit, and then having to sweep, shovel or wash it all overboard.

A sump pump is very useful when a bilge or ballast suction becomes blocked or when a ballast line fails, making it impossible to complete discharge of the ballast in a tank or the washings in a hold. The power of the sump pump is normally sufficient to raise water to main deck level for discharge. If problems are experienced and the water is free of debris, a last resort is to use the sump pump to pump the water to the nearest clear suction, opening the appropriate manholes to allow pumping from port tank to starboard tank, or from starboard bilge to starboard ballast tank, for example.

A fresh water wash of external accommodation paintwork has been achieved by filling the swimming pool with fresh water and then drawing it from the swimming pool with the sump pump to wash down. Sump pumps have also been used for applying whitewash to the bulkheads of a hold, drawing the whitewash from a drum standing on the tanktop, but some modern pumps are said to be too powerful for this task. There is, however, more suitable equipment for fresh water washing and for applying whitewash and it is described below.

At times, when the ship is operating smoothly, the sump pump may be unused for months and may be neglected. The equipment normally needs little maintenance, but should be cleaned by flushing through with fresh water before it is stored and moving parts should be oiled with a light oil.

High-pressure washing machines

Three principal varieties of high-pressure washing machine can be met aboard bulk carriers. First, there is the heavy duty portable unit used for washing holds with unheated sea water; next, there are the high-pressure washing machines permanently installed beneath the deckheads of the holds of some ships; and then there are lightweight handheld units, often with mobile power units, used for a variety of washing purposes around the ship. In addition portable Butterworth machines as used on tankers are occasionally found in bulk carriers.

Heavy-duty portable washing machines: Equipment of the Combi-gun or Cleaning Jet (Fig. 22.12) type uses conventional washdeck type hoses and water from the washdeck line, boosted by compressed air at a pressure of about 7 bar injected into the side of the nozzle to produce a powerful water jet which will reach the most remote parts of the hold. Some units are provided with a branch pipe which allows a chemical cleaner to be mixed in with the high pressure water jet.

The unit can be hand-held, in which case it requires at least two men at the gun, one to aim it and a second to help support the weight. Alternatively, the gun can be fastened to a tripod, held in position by the weight of a single operator. An attractive feature of the gun is that it requires no maintenance and has been described as sailor-proof, although this is probably an exaggeration. The hoses which serve the unit are of the same pattern as ships' fire hoses, but fire hoses must never be used in place of washing machine hoses. If fire hoses are used for routine cleaning work they are certain to be damaged by the time they are required in an emergency or to pass a survey.

The units, with associated tripods and lengths of hose, must be lifted into and out of each hold in turn. A standard machine will throw a jet of water about 30 metres. Alternatively more powerful machines, with a throw of up to 50 metres, and requiring air pressure of up to 10 bar, are available for use aboard the largest bulk carriers.

Heavy-duty fixed washing machines: Heavy-duty washing machines are permanently installed beneath the deckheads in some bulkers (Figs. 22.13 and 14), with one placed in the fore end and a second in the after end of each hold. Once the gun has been lowered to the starting position water is piped at high pressure direct from the engineroom to the machines, which complete

Fig. 22.13 Fixed hold washing installation
Photo courtesy of Captain L Hesketh FNI

Fig. 22.14 The on-deck controls and supply line for the permanent hold washing machine. A blank can be fitted in the line to ensure no leakage into the hold
Photo courtesy of Captain L Hesketh FNI

Fig. 22.15 Fixed high pressure washing unit installed in the forecastle space of an open hatch handymax bulk carrier

Fig. 22.16 A mobile high pressure washing machine *Photo courtesy of EMS Ship Supply (Norway) AS*

Fig. 22.17 Upper parts of Butterworth washing machines stowed in the forecastle *Photo courtesy of Captain L Hesketh FNI*

Fig. 22.18 Bottom parts of Butterworth washing machines stowed in forecastle *Photo courtesy of Captain L Hesketh FNI*

Fig. 22.19 Butterworth opening at end of hatch *Photo courtesy of Captain L Hesketh FNI*

Fig. 22.20 A Butterworth coupling in the deck service line *Photo courtesy of Captain L Hesketh FNI*

an automatic cycle probably taking about two hours during which water jets are directed in succession at every part of the hold, finishing with a bottom wash. A good feature of the system is that the holds can easily be washed whilst the hatches are closed.

The washing system is an efficient one, although further washing may be needed after particularly dirty cargoes such as petroleum coke. At the other extreme, when the cargo has been comparatively clean, a wash with handheld hoses completed in an hour may be preferred to a full automatic wash.

Problems occur if a bilge eductor or pump, removing the washing water, becomes blocked. If this happens the water builds up in the hold and the tanktop is not properly washed, so signs of a build up of water must be watched for. The guns are positioned beneath bolted plates or hatches similar to access hatches on the maindeck. These provide access to the gun for inspection and routine greasing, and the gun can be unbolted and moved to a workshop for a complete overhaul.

Lightweight high-pressure washing machines: These lightweight hoses, lances and nozzles deliver a water jet at pressures up to 350 bar powered by an electric pump installed in a storeroom (Fig. 22.15), or on a trolley (Fig. 22.16) which can be wheeled about the decks, and connected to the ship's domestic hot and cold fresh water supplies. A separate branch pipe connected to a knapsack on the operator's back or to a drum of chemical placed on deck beside him allows chemical cleaner or rust remover to be mixed in with the water and a sand injector for rust removal is another option.

The unit provides a thin but powerful jet or spray of water from a convenient lightweight lance. The equipment has numerous uses including the washing of exterior accommodation paintwork, the washing of oily savealls (though care must be taken to ensure that any oil is not washed overboard in contravention of MARPOL), the fresh water rinsing of holds, the loosening of mud in ballast tanks and the removal of rust stains from paintwork.

Butterworth machines: Cape-sized bulk carriers are occasionally provided with Butterworth washing machines for hold washing. The nozzles of these machines complete successive cycles during which water at high pressure is directed in every direction in turn. The machines which can be stored in the forecastle store (Figs. 22.17 and 18) are inserted through deck openings (Fig. 22.19), one forward of and one abaft the hatch and are connected by high pressure hoses to Butterworth couplings on the deck service (washdeck) line (Fig. 22.20). Provided that one hold is washed at a time a normal hold wash using unheated water is completed in about three hours which must be followed by a period spent removing cargo residues from the bilge baskets to the deck[265].

Spray foam systems

Spray foam systems (Fig. 22.21) are portable systems, powered by air, for the delivery of chemical cleaning for holds. They can also be used for limewashing, for applying paint and for fresh water rinsing. The systems include a pressure tank on wheels, air and water hoses, a gun with extension lance and an assortment of nozzles to match the varied uses of the system.

Fig. 22.21 Spray foam delivery system for cleaning and degreasing after dirty cargoes. Also used for limewashing before corrosive cargoes and for fresh water rinsing

Photo courtesy of EMS Ship Supply (Norway) AS

Hold inspection systems

Demands from seafarers and surveyors for simple systems to enable an inspector to reach positions high in the hold of a bulk carrier have led to the development of several systems. Already mentioned have been scaffolding towers and cherrypickers and, when circumstances permit, platforms or cages suspended below a ship's gantry, crane or derrick can be used. Aluminium extending ladders (Fig 22.29) are also regularly used for this purpose. On occasion places high in the hold can be inspected, cleaned and even repaired whilst standing on cargo within the hold but such opportunities are rare. Safety of access including the possible lack of oxygen and risk of damage to the cargo must be taken into account. Positions high in the box shaped holds of bulk carriers with side tanks or double skins are relatively easy to reach with scaffolding or ladders but conventional bulk carrier holds with hopper tanks are still the norm and continue to present difficulties.

Trained climbing technicians have been provided by one specialist organisation to take closed circuit television (CCTV) cameras to positions high in the tank or hold, enabling a classification society surveyor with his feet on the solid deck to complete an enhanced survey of a very large crude carrier (VLCC) during a ballast passage. A drydock specification was composed and 250 tonnes of steel were then successfully renewed in drydock. It has been claimed that the method can be used aboard bulkers too.[202, 203]

One of the benefits claimed for double skinned construction is that every point in the inner skin can be accessed, inspected and if necessary repaired, from within the double skin.

Big area descalers

Big area descalers are scaling machines mounted on wheels and powered by electricity, compressed air or water. They are used for scaling and wire brushing large areas of deck plating. This is achieved by fitting the scaling or the wire brushing head, switching on the machine whilst the machine is tilted and the head

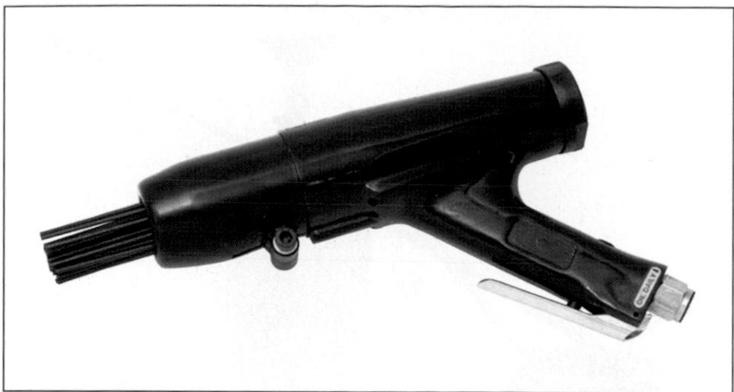
Fig. 22.22 Air powered needle gun
Photo courtesy of Wilhelmsen Ships Service

Fig. 22.23 Air powered grease pump which will be fitted to a drum of grease placed on a trolley
Photo courtesy of Wilhelmsen Ships Service

Fig. 22.24 Space ventilation fan
Photo courtesy of EMS Ship Supply (Norway) AS

is not in contact with the deck, bringing the rotating head in contact with the deck and wheeling the machine slowly back and forwards across the deck. Chipping leaves and brush heads must be renewed when worn and the machine must be lubricated as recommended by the manufacturers. If the machine is not to be used for some time, it should be lightly oiled and greased.

Sand blasting machines

Sand blasting machines are powered by compressed air and used to sandblast steelwork on the maindeck or in other positions to which the machine can be lifted. A cylinder mounted on wheels is filled with sand or other abrasive and is pressurised to a maximum working pressure of 125 psi. A hose and nozzle attached to the cylinder is used to direct the sand blast at the area to be cleaned. To avoid injury the nozzle must be held in the blasting position before the generator (ie, the cylinder) is pressurised. From time to time the machine must be refilled with sand. The sand which has been discharged should be swept up, sieved with a manual sieve to remove rust particles and used again until such time as the rust content in the sand becomes high.

Needle guns

Pneumatic needle guns (Fig. 22.22) have a barrel from which a number of needles project. When the air supply is opened up the needles reciprocate rapidly in a way which is very effective for descaling uneven surfaces. The tool will get into grooves, corners and gaps very efficiently and is well suited for use in spaces which are too confined for other tools.

The equipment operates at 70-100 psi, and should be used with an oiler/filter unit. It should be stored in dry surroundings. After use and before storage, spindle oil should be applied to the air inlet and the tool should be operated for a few moments to distribute the oil throughout the tool.

Pneumatic grease guns

Aboard a bulk carrier one of the most useful pieces of equipment is a pneumatic grease gun (Fig. 22.23). Essentially this consists of a drum of grease on a wheeled trolley. Air pressure from the deck air line is used to put the grease under pressure and to deliver it through the flexible hose to the grease gun. While one man wheels the trolley about the deck the second is able to move briskly from one grease nipple to the next, pumping grease into the places where it is required.

Portable fans

Portable fans (Fig. 22.24) are required for the ventilation of enclosed spaces before they are entered. The fans should be used to blow clean air into the space, driving out the foul air through ventilators or other manhole covers at the extreme far end of the space. It is not a good idea to use a fan to suck air from a space as in these circumstances the air in the vicinity of the fan may become explosive or foul.

Power tools

Pneumatic spanners (Fig. 22.25), chisels, needle guns, drills and angle grinders (Fig. 22.26) are standard equipment aboard most bulk carriers and, when properly used and cared for, help to make the work of the deck crew more reliable and productive. The pneumatic spanner or wrench is perhaps the most useful of all power tools on a bulk carrier, and makes short work of opening and closing tank manholes and ballast hold bilge blanks.

Before using any air powered tool a shot of oil should be put into the airpipe coupling on the tool. When the tool is first used the oil is blown through it and misty oil can be seen coming out of the air vents on the side of the tool. A water trap and lubricator unit is also essential for long life of power tools. A portable unit with three or four outlets is preferable, as it can be stationed close to a convenient compressed air valve, with each power tool having its own flexible hose. This saves moving individual drying units around the deck, which creates a lot of extra work and which is why the crew are reluctant to use them.

After use, the power tools should be dismantled and serviced as per the manufacturer's guidelines. Light greasing and oiling of moving parts is essential if the equipment is to be prevented from seizing. The tools should then be carefully stowed away, preferably by fitting them securely to a display board on a bulkhead. This reduces the risk of the equipment being over-stowed or damaged and is good practice for all tools (Figs. 22.27 and 28).

Sources

24, 172, 202, 203, 204, 205, 264, 265. (See List of Sources, Page 497)

Fig. 22.25 Using a pneumatic wrench to fit a blank over the bilge well in the ballast hold

Fig. 22.26 Air powered wrenches, angle grinders, chisels and needle guns, used aboard ship
Photo courtesy of Wilhelmsens Ships Service

Fig. 22.27 Tools well stored

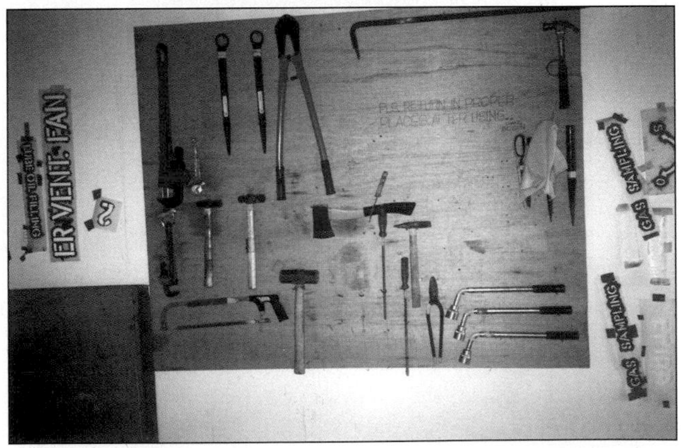

Fig. 22.28 The notice reads 'Pls return in proper places after using'

Fig. 22.29 Using an aluminium extending ladder to reach points high in the hold. A typical example of seamen struggling with inadequate equipment

Photo courtesy of Scanautics

CHAPTER 23

MAINTENANCE

Planned maintenance systems, the planning of maintenance, management of spare parts, greasing and oiling, painting, maintenance of derricks, cranes and grabs, ship's fixtures and fittings, good maintenance

MOST bulk carriers are exposed to demanding working conditions in the unforgiving marine environment. If a bulker is to remain seaworthy, safe and efficient throughout a working life of 20-25 years or upwards she must be designed and built to a good standard and then properly maintained throughout that period. There were some signs by 2008, that the importance of this is becoming more widely accepted with shipowners calling for ships to be built with bigger margins of safety and classed in a manner that gives recognition to ships that were better built[131].

The principles and procedures for good maintenance are stated in this chapter. Everyone aboard ship has his or her part to play in keeping a ship well maintained, but good maintenance also requires owners and managers who are prepared to pay costs reasonably incurred and to provide the support which ships' staff require. Good planning should be encouraged or imposed and the resources in terms of money and manpower must be provided when necessary. Good maintenance also requires competent and reliable suppliers of services, spares and stores, and these are available in many parts of the world.

Good maintenance is not an optional extra. It is an essential part of keeping a ship in a seaworthy condition and should be practiced aboard ship from the day she is delivered by the shipbuilders.

Planned maintenance systems

Value: A planned maintenance system, if well designed, provides a useful scheme for deck maintenance aboard a bulk carrier. The system, which is probably computerised but may rely upon record cards or loose-leaf binders, lists all the maintenance work that the ship requires and the frequency at which it should be done. A single system may include all areas of activity or separate systems may be provided for different areas and categories of work. For example, there may be separate planned maintenance systems for deck, bridge, safety equipment, engineroom and critical equipment as required under the ISM Code[266]. From an inspection of the planned maintenance records it should be easy to see when an item of maintenance was last done, what was done, when it is due for doing again and, possibly, what materials will be required and how many manhours the work will typically take.

Planned maintenance systems are intended to move deck maintenance away from a regime in which tasks are undertaken in response to a succession of crises, or are concentrated on superficial appearances, to a system in which every item of equipment, structure and fittings receives the maintenance it needs to ensure its continued efficient operation. When sufficient resources in terms of equipment, supplies and manpower are made available and when the system is well designed and managed there can be no doubt that a planned maintenance system is the recognised way to ensure that a ship is well maintained.

Even a planned maintenance system which is well designed and well supported cannot always match the difficulties created by foul weather and a hectic succession of short voyages with dirty cargoes, but it will help the ship's officers to make the most of such opportunities as they have.

Not to be accepted uncritically: Planned maintenance systems provide a very useful reminder to the chief mate of work that requires to be done, but the system should not be followed blindly. It is only as good as the people who designed it and important items can be overlooked – for example, one system in use aboard four sister ships did not list the painting of the bridge front. The planned maintenance system should be examined critically and important work which does not appear in it should be done and should be inserted into the system by whatever method is appropriate.

Restarting a planned maintenance system: Some Masters and chief mates will undoubtedly have the depressing experience of taking over a ship with planned maintenance records which have not been kept up to date, with a gap which extends for months or years. In these circumstances it is probably best to resume maintenance according to the plan at the correct intervals. In addition, the items which are listed for attention only at long intervals should be examined at an early date. For example, if the windlass brakes are listed to be opened up for inspection only once a year it would be a mistake to leave them for a further year before inspecting them.

Maintaining planned maintenance records: Planned maintenance records are subject to scrutiny by Port State Control and Class during annual and other periodic surveys and by auditors during internal and external International Safety Management/Safety Management System (SMS) audits. They should be updated methodically and frequently to avoid the inconvenience which occurs if the officer responsible has to leave the ship unexpectedly and fails to bring the entries up to date. Daily updating of the records is to be strongly recommended and encouraged, if adverse comments by Port State inspectors and auditors are to be avoided. Aboard some vessels a particular officer, often the chief engineer, is appointed Technical Manager but each department head has the responsibility for completing the planned maintenance records under his control.

Records when maintenance cannot be done when due: Operational pressures are sometimes so great that there just is not time to complete the maintenance work on schedule. In these circumstances there may be a temptation to make an entry showing that maintenance work has been done when in truth it has not. This should never be done: it is likely to be more damaging to the ship than the failure to do the maintenance on schedule. Reliable maintenance records are essential to a well-maintained ship, and officers should never be penalised for keeping honest records even if they show that scheduled work has not been done.

When it is clear to a chief mate that work cannot be done on schedule he should inspect the area scheduled for maintenance and make an entry in the records such as *No opportunity for maintenance, but item inspected on 27.4.93 and considered fit for service until next due maintenance date.* That makes the situation absolutely clear to a reader and will give added urgency to the attempt to carry out the maintenance on the next due date.

Operational work: Much of the work aboard a bulk carrier is operational, particularly when a vessel is engaged on short voyages. Hold preparation, berthing, unberthing and shifting ship must be done when required and cannot be completed according to a plan.

Despite the introduction of planned maintenance systems the chief mates of many bulk carriers are still required to complete *Monthly Deck Work Reports* for owners which provide an indication of work done, but may not be sufficiently detailed for the purposes of on-board planning.

Planning of maintenance

Work lists: The chief mate should receive from the man he relieves a list of work planned for the coming period. As soon as he has settled aboard ship this list of work should be updated, taking account of the requirements of the planned maintenance system and of any additional work which the chief mate considers to be urgent. The captain and chief engineer and the owner's superintendent may also have useful suggestions as to work which needs to be done.

Priorities: It is useful to sort this list into work to be done in different circumstances, and to list it in order of priority with the most important jobs first. The most difficult maintenance work to complete aboard ship includes the renewal or maintenance of overside paintwork, which requires time in port, permission from the local authorities to paint overside, fair weather and a ship's side free of condensation, so this must be given high priority. Many ports will not allow any painting or maintenance of the ship's side in port and if overside painting is undertaken without permission the ship can be heavily fined. The Master should always seek guidance from the ship's agent prior to arrival and provide a detailed list of exactly what is going to be painted or maintained. As an example re-painting the load line marks and ship's name is likely in most circumstances to be allowed, but the touch up of large areas of the hull may not be allowed. It cannot be stated too strongly that written permission from the harbour master must be obtained in advance. Ships' crews are small and three men are usually fully occupied with gangway security duty to comply with the requirements of the International Ship and Port Facility Security (ISPS) Code. These factors should be taken into account when planning any overside work.

The renewal of hold paintwork requires holds which are empty and clean and a steady ship for a period of days. Work within the double-bottom ballast tanks (DBs) is difficult to arrange aboard small bulkers because these tanks are full when the ship is in ballast and their manholes are overstowed with cargo when she is loaded. Aboard large bulkers the DBs can usually be entered at any time through the stool spaces, so maintenance work can be undertaken during loaded passages, provided the stool spaces can be safely entered from the duct keel or from deck level. During ballast voyage, of course, maintenance is not possible as the tanks are full of water.

Greasing is essential work which, fortunately, can be undertaken on deck whenever it is safe to go on deck and the same is true of the stripping down and overhaul of cargo handling gear aboard geared bulkers. Provided that the ship is not rolling very heavily and that seas are not being shipped, this work can proceed, as can the overhaul of deck machinery and hatch cover fittings and the renewal of pipework on deck.

Scaling and painting on deck, however, require dry conditions which are only found on a loaded bulker in a flat calm or, better still, in a light following wind. In any sort of adverse weather, a loaded bulk carrier will repeatedly ship salt spray over the greater part of the main deck making painting impossible (Fig. 23.1). During ballast passages the increased freeboard provides drier conditions, but the air is still likely to be laden with salt spray during periods of adverse weather.

When the weather is very rough work within and around the accommodation and the machinery spaces is most suitable. This can include the overhaul of the contents of enclosed lifeboats, the cleaning of ventilation louvres in cabins, the tidying of storerooms and the overhaul and refurbishment of spare fittings for hatch covers, and for cargo gear (if carried). In high latitudes in winter, when the weather is cold and dark, work within ballast and fresh water tanks can usefully be undertaken and this applies also during extended periods of heavy rain.

The annual work plan for a geared mini-bulker employed in the European middle trades is at Appendix 23.1.

Confirming requirements: One of the most important reasons for planning the work programme in advance is that the programme can only be put into effect if the necessary tools, spares and consumables are aboard. Plenty of major opportunities for

Fig. 23.1 Part laden, in fair weather, but shipping spray over the starboard bow

maintenance have been lost when it has been discovered once the ship was at sea that the paint spray equipment was damaged or incomplete, or the supply of grit for the grit blasting machine was exhausted after the first day's work. If there is not sufficient paint of the correct type and colour for the area to be repainted the consequence is the same.

A programme of overhauling the quick-acting cleats on the hatch covers cannot be satisfactorily completed if the supply of spare neoprene washers has been used up. If the windlass brakes are opened up for inspection and the linings are found to need renewal the work will have to be repeated if no spare linings are carried. The brakes will have to be re-opened at a later date.

Making requirements realistic: The estimates of the quantities of stores and spares required must be realistic. With paintwork that is not difficult provided that the area to be painted is measured accurately. Manufacturers' literature will show the number of square metres which a litre of paint will cover and stocks must be sufficient to complete the job, with 10 per cent extra for contingencies or for touching up at a later date if not required for the initial painting. With consumable hatch spares, such as the neoprene washers for quick-acting cleats, which have a life of about two years, it is reasonable to carry sufficient for the complete renewal of one hatch or 25 per cent of the ship's total, whichever is greater, unless it is obvious that a great number throughout the ship require renewal in which case more spares should be carried.

Planning the task: If the chief mate is to be sure that the ship has all the necessary tools for the intended work he must have a clear idea of how the work is to be done, and this will sometimes be a problem for the inexperienced chief mate who has need of this advice. It is not possible in this book to provide descriptions of how to organise even the main maintenance tasks, but it is possible to list the questions which the chief mate should ask himself before putting the work into hand and these are given in Appendix 23.2. An experienced chief mate will ask himself these questions, but the process will be a rapid mental one as he will have a clear idea of how the work is to be done and will know many of the answers before he starts.

Confirming that the equipment is ready: When the required tools and equipment have been listed they must be checked to confirm that they are all ready to use. It can never be assumed that equipment is in good working order unless the people who last used it are reliable and are still aboard the vessel. Without this assurance that all is in order, necessary equipment such as paint sprays, scaffolding, chain blocks and grit blasting machines should be tested to make sure that they are complete and working. This will allow time to purchase spares or to plan other work if spares cannot be obtained in time.

Management of spare parts

Maintaining stocks of spare parts: When a ship is provided with a number of identical items of equipment such as cargo winches, roller fairleads, mooring winches, hatch motors, hatch hydrocleats, ventilators or airpipes a minimum of at least one set of spare consumable parts such as bearings, gaskets or complete units should be carried. In many cases, when regular use of spares or renewal of units can be foreseen, a larger number of spares should be carried.

A rule to be remembered in this connection is obvious, but is still often forgotten; as soon as spares are used, replacements should be ordered! A ship which only orders a replacement when the item in use is damaged or worn out will never operate at full efficiency and will always limp from crisis to crisis. Much more time is lost when equipment has to be cannibalised or moved from one place to another than when a replacement can simply be bolted or shackled into position.

The negligent sequence of events which should never be allowed to happen but often does, is as follows. A new ship has no need for spares for several years after being brought into service. Gradually, fittings begin to wear out or break and are replaced by the ship's original stock of spares until the spares are all used. As fittings continue to fail equipment is cannibalised, or is moved from one position to another where the need is more urgent. By this time the ship no longer has a full set of working items, there are no spares, and no spares are on order. Where necessary, ships' officers must be prepared to insist upon maintaining a minimum stock of spare parts to ensure the ship's efficient operation. A requests for spare parts accompanied by a good reason usually produces the right result.

When a ship is provided with a computerised spare parts system, and when that system is understood and kept up to date, the control and reordering of spares is usually easier. The best of such systems are quick to access and, in addition to providing a full specification of the part and the quantity in stock, will recommend the appropriate level of spares taking account of the number used in the past. They will even print an appropriate order for the supplier or chandler.

Ordering spare parts: A good rule to follow when ordering spare parts is to assume the least amount of knowledge and experience on the part of the person supplying the items ordered. Orders should always include: the part number and/or name; the machine number and/or name; manufacturers' name and address; number of items wanted; colour, grade, type of fitting; and sizes and other details of items wanted, if applicable.

Wherever possible spare parts should be ordered from a catalogue or spare parts list, and part numbers should be used in preference to names used aboard ship, which may be incorrect. If the ship does not have a spare parts list that should be ordered from the manufacturer. The catalogue[206] of the International Ship Suppliers' Association (ISSA) provides a useful standard vocabulary and a set of codes which are known and used worldwide.

Caring for spare parts: Spare parts carried aboard ship are useless if they cannot be found or identified when required or if they are kept in damp or dirty conditions and allowed to deteriorate. Spares should be clearly labelled, kept in tidy storerooms and protected from damp.

Records of the spares aboard ship should be maintained. Some ships use a fully computerised, integrated system for spares which automatically generates a replacement order when stocks are used and updates the records of stocks on board, while others use a bar coding system. On older ships records may be in the form of a card index system or a spares and/or stores duplicate book, completed at regular intervals, with one copy for owners and one to remain aboard the ship. However these paper systems are becoming more rare as computer programs are more widely used. Numerous stores management programs are available, some recommended by the Classification Societies.

A useless broken part of equipment or machinery should never be kept unless it is needed as a pattern for the replacement part, to be reconditioned, or needed as evidence for a claim. Parts which are being kept should be clearly labelled. All other discarded parts should be removed from the ship, to prevent overcrowding in storerooms and to avoid later uncertainty. A 'used but good' part must never, ever, be put into the store with new stock in the packaging from which the new part was removed.

Reconditioning spare parts: Many items of equipment such as cargo blocks, hatch hydrocleats and guncleans are suitable for reconditioning. Provided that spares are carried, a defective item of equipment can be replaced by a spare. At a convenient later date the defective equipment can be overhauled and reconditioned in the ship's workshops, by renewing bushes, seals or other damaged parts, thus preserving the value of the item and making it again available as a spare. Alternatively, the item can be landed for reconditioning by the manufacturer and later return to the ship.

Greasing and oiling

Lubrication of moving parts of equipment is essential to prevent gear from seizing up and becoming damaged. As a general rule it must be assumed that whenever there is movement between two or more pieces of metal the area where they make contact must be greased or oiled. Provision for such lubrication is always provided in machinery and fittings. Normally the grease nipples and the oil sumps are readily seen, but occasionally they are very difficult to find and are overlooked though the practice of highlighting them, used aboard some ships, helps to ensure that they are not forgotten (Fig. 23.2). There have been mooring winches on which the nipple for greasing the bearing could only be seen and used after the wire had been removed from the drum, and extended spindles have been installed 'wrong way round' with the grease nipples facing the bulkhead. Grease nipples usually project from the machinery upon which they are fitted and are sometimes sheared off, leaving little to show where they once were.

Fig. 23.2 Mooring winch with grease nipples highlighted in yellow

All the foregoing examples – and many, many others – have led to the failure to grease items as required and to the equipment seizing up (at heavy cost) at a later date. Ratings have no difficulty in recognising grease nipples and applying grease to them, but it is unwise to assume that they will recognise the places which need greasing but which do not appear to have a greasing point. It is the job of a responsible officer to look critically at every fitting on the deck – the hatches, in the storerooms, around the lifeboats and the accommodation – and to make sure that the rule is being followed: if it moves, grease it!

On a bulk carrier, where much greasing must be done on deck, the work is normally done with a pneumatic grease gun (see Chapter 22). Items which are out of reach of the pneumatic grease gun can be greased with a hand-held gun.

For proper lubrication a number of rules must be observed.

- The correct grease or oil must be used for each item. Whilst a general-purpose grease is suitable for most deck fittings and equipment, named high-grade oils and greases are often recommended for particular pieces of machinery and these instructions must be followed. As always the makers' manuals or owners' instructions must be consulted for details. To ensure that the right lubricant is used for the correct equipment a competent crew can be provided with separate grease guns, suitably loaded, for separate jobs. If the crew competence is poor it will probably prove cheaper in total cost to use the better quality lubricant for all the greasing: it may be more expensive in the short term, but will pay for itself in reduced wear.
- Ships operating in sub-zero temperatures for long periods should use greases and oils which are efficient in very low temperatures.
- Grease should be pumped into a grease nipple until grease starts to squeeze out from between the moving parts of the equipment. If grease cannot be forced into the nipple and out between the moving parts the item must be marked for dismantling and cleaning of the grease channel as soon as possible.
- Damaged or missing grease nipples must be replaced.
- Sumps for deck machinery must be kept topped up to the proper level with clean lubricating oil. The correct oil to use must be found from the makers' manuals, and the ship's engineers can usually provide further advice if needed. If the lubricating oil is found to be dirty, contaminated with sea water, or leaking away quickly the cause must be found and the oil renewed.
- If it moves it must be lubricated!

Painting

Correct paint system: Painting is the principal process by which the ship's structure and fittings are protected from corrosion in an environment which is salt laden and hostile. Paintwork also has a decorative function and can give a ship a pleasing appearance. A ship normally leaves the builder's yard fully painted to basic requirements. Thereafter painting is required to repair, renew or reinforce the original paint coating which is often very thin. Repair of paintwork is done by touching up the damaged areas. Renewing paintwork involves removing all paintwork down to the bare metal and applying a full set of replacement coats, and the original paintwork is reinforced by applying additional coats on top of the previous paintwork, a process which should be started as soon as possible after the ship leaves the builder's yard.

A number of different marine paint systems using paint with different chemical structures are nowadays available. These include conventional and bituminous, chlorinated rubber, vinyl, epoxy and antifouling paints and a variety of special coatings. It frequently happens that different systems will be used for different parts of the same ship, with one system used for the topside paint, another for the holds and yet another for the insides of ballast tanks, or with one system for the decks and another for the hatch covers, for example. In many cases paints from different systems cannot be used together, and paint from one system will not adhere to paint from another system. Even when the new paint will stick to the old it is most unwise to change paint type, since there was probably a good reason for choosing the paint which was first used, and problems may arise later.

Before the chief mate starts on a programme of repainting and when he is planning the work, he must be sure which is the correct paint system to use. This is likely to be particularly difficult when the ship has changed paint supplier, or owner, or both. It is quite acceptable to use alkyd (conventional) paint made by manufacturer 'B' to cover alkyd paintwork supplied by manufacturer 'A', but chlorinated rubber paint, say, from any supplier should not be used over alkyd paint unless, exceptionally, the alkyd paint is very old and is coated with an approved 'conversion' primer. When paint is ordered the fullest details should be provided using codes wherever possible to avoid confusion.

Before the work starts the chief mate must be certain which paint system is being used, which are the correct thinners and brush cleaners to use, and whether the paint is intended for application by spray or by brush. He must also be sure that the primer he uses is correct for the surface being covered and that it belongs to the same paint system as the topcoat with which it is to be used.

The necessary information is simple enough and can readily be found in the product literature or from the operators or owners. or on the internet if the ship is provided with internet access, but when the ship has no literature from the paint manufacturer, or when the bosun does not speak the language in which the paint labels are written, there are plenty of opportunities for mistakes to be made and care must be taken to avoid them. When necessary paints, primers and thinners for one painting system should be stowed completely separately from those of another system and someone who can read the paint labels should be employed to mark them with a symbol or letter code to identify each paint type. The paint manufacturers do not want to be associated with painting disasters and will normally be ready to offer information and advice.

Surface preparation: Paint manufacturers advise that by far the best preparation for bare steel is blast cleaning if rusting at a later date is to be avoided. Aboard a bulker equipped with a sand or grit blaster or high pressure water blaster there will be occasions when deck areas, hatch coaming and covers, hold steelwork and other large areas can be blast cleaned, but often it is not practical to use the sand blaster, so surface preparation done by the ship's crew will be carried out with scaling machines, needle guns and powered wire brushes, tools which prepare the surface in a less satisfactory manner. Where possible a surface which has been scaled should be smoothed using a powered grit disking machine before it is painted.

The surface to be painted should always be free of salt. To achieve this the surface must be washed with fresh water, then coated with rust remover and painting must not be done when there is salt in the air as is the case when conditions are windy, or when the ship is proceeding at service speed, causing spray to rise over the fore part of the vessel. If these rules are ignored and paint is applied over salt the paint will peel off after a few days or weeks creating a real mess that will take a lot of time and effort to correct.

The surface must be free of oil, grease and other contaminating substances and, for most paints, it must be absolutely dry. This means that paint cannot be applied to a surface which has not dried properly after washing, nor can a surface which is misted with condensation be painted. The latter condition occurs when a ship carrying cold ballast water arrives in a tropical port: condensation forms on the steel deck and topside plating when the warm air meets the cold plating. Condensation can be prevented by changing the ballast water in the topside tanks when tropical waters are reached. Washing with fresh water can be done with a lightweight high pressure washing machine (Fig. 22.16).

Touching-up: When a paint coating has suffered mechanical damage in places as a result of contact with a grab, a fender, a tug or some other object such as cargo spilt from a grab, or as the result of local rusting, and when the undamaged paintwork remains in good condition the damaged area can be touched up. For effective touching up the area must first be properly prepared by descaling and by smoothing the paintwork at the boundaries of the damage with a disc sanding machine. Next the damage must be wire brushed, washed with fresh water and dried, after which the bare steel can be painted with a rust remover and then primed and coated with gloss.

When the damaged area is on the ship's side and the stay in port is short the descaling may be limited to scraping away loose paint and rust with a scraper before washing, treating with rust remover, priming and painting. However work on the ship's side in a port will in most cases require the permission of the harbour master or local authorities.

Reinforcing paintwork: Paintwork is reinforced by applying an additional full coat of paint over the previous paint. This is the appropriate maintenance when the paint is in good condition, though becoming dull and worn, or when it has been touched up, and looks patchy. Before applying an additional topcoat it is usual to wash the paintwork with a synthetic detergent and then to wash it with fresh water, to remove all traces of salt and contaminants.

Renewing paintwork: When an area of steelwork is badly rusted, or when the paintwork is irregular and badly damaged the only worthwhile treatment is to take it back to the bare metal by blasting or scaling the entire area to remove all paint and rust. When this has been done, the area must be swept free of loose dirt, washed with fresh water, dried, coated with rust remover and then primed and painted. For guidance on the maintenance of coatings in holds and ballast tanks see Appendix 23.3.

Maintenance of ships' cargo-handling gear

The importance of ship's cargo-handling gear – the derricks, cranes, grabs and, in the case of specialist ships, conveyor belts or gantries – is clear. If the equipment does not work efficiently when required the ship will be penalised for time off hire. If the equipment has not been maintained in compliance with the regulations the infringement of regulations may be found by inspectors and, again, the ship may be subjected to expensive delays.

Sometimes a geared bulk carrier may trade for months or years without being required to use the ship's gear for loading or discharging. When this happens there is a danger that other matters may seem more urgent and the cargo gear may be neglected. This should never be allowed to happen, because the expense and time required to upgrade gear will always be more than that required to maintain it in good condition, and because there is always the possibility that circumstances will change unexpectedly and the gear will be required for immediate use.

The maintenance of cargo-handling gear will be included in a planned maintenance system as required by the ISM Code. The programme will specify periodic operation, safety checks and tests and will provide checklists and crane and other logbooks.

Derrick maintenance

There are two basic requirements when maintaining cargo gear: to keep the equipment in good, safe working order; and to keep the supporting documentation in good order. The derricks fitted to some handy-sized and mini-bulkers are composed of a large number of components and are demanding in maintenance time. The maintenance of the derricks and associated gear aboard a ship which has been well maintained can be summarised as follows:

- **Daily, when derricks are being used to work cargo.**

  Inspect runner wires for wear or damage. Check the rig for damage or for fastenings becoming slack.

- **Before arrival in port.**

  Inspect derricks and associated gear to ensure that they comply in every respect with the requirements of the flag State and of the port to be visited.

- **Periodical (visual) survey.**

  The frequency of this survey is decided by the ship's flag state. Most authorities require the survey to be done annually but some, such as the Australians, require surveys at three monthly intervals. The survey must be done by a competent person, often the chief officer, though some authorities require the survey to be carried out by an independent surveyor.

  When the ship's cargo gear is in frequent use all the checks required by the survey should be done by ship's staff more often than once a year, even when the regulations only require an annual survey.

  The main requirements of the survey are summarised hereunder, but anyone intending to undertake a survey should study the full detailed requirements listed in the appropriate government and classification society publications.

  * *The rigging arrangements must conform to the rigging plan.*

  * *Before examination:*

  All assembled items such as goosenecks and blocks should be dismantled so that their component parts can be readily inspected.

  Shackles, links, rings, hooks, triangle plates, chains, etc, must be sufficiently free from paint, grease, scale, etc, to enable a proper inspection to be made.

  Serving must be removed from splices in wire ropes.

  * *The examination is intended to find any of the following:*

  Deformation, wear, scoring, corrosion, scars, dents, or other defects to structure and fittings.

  Free movement and efficiency of lubrication of moving parts.

  To confirm that every item of gear is clearly marked with a safe working load (SWL) and with a unique reference mark (set of numbers and/or letters) which can be matched with a certificate of test.

  * *Items to be examined:*

  Masts, derrick posts, guy posts, and the structure in way of them.

  Derrick boom and mast fittings including lugs, goosenecks, heel pins and heel block anchorages. (If metal appears to be wasted or worn the thickness should be checked, using calipers, against the original specification. In structural members the maximum permitted weardown or corrosion allowed is 10% for structural members[29]. Lugs are particularly prone to wear.)

  Fittings on deck such as stoppers for wire ropes, eyeplates, cleats.

  The derrick boom, particularly at the point where it rests in its crutch, or housing. (Make sure boom is not bent. Hammer test if necessary. Move boom through all working positions if necessary.)

  Blocks.

  Shackles, links, rings, hooks, triangle plates, chains, etc.

  In loose gear the maximum permitted weardown or corrosion allowance is 5% on any diameter and 2% on any diameter 'of a pin in a hole'[29].

  Wire ropes should be inspected over their entire length, with particular attention to end fittings, ferrules (mechanical splices, compressed crimp fittings, Talurit splices) and splices. These must comply with the requirements of Class and/or flag state, for example those set out in Lloyd's Splicing and terminal connections[29] or the UK Code of Safe Working Practice[31]. The condition and security of thimbles and the condition of the wire surrounding them should also be carefully examined. Wire ropes must be renewed if the number of broken, worn or corroded wires in any length of ten diameters exceeds 5 per cent. For example, if the wire rope has a diameter of 30 mm and is of 6 x 24 construction the total number of wires in the rope is 144, of which 5 per cent is 7. If more than 7 broken strands are found in a length of (30 x 10) mm – ie, 300 mm – the rope must be condemned.

Fibre ropes should be examined over their entire length for external chafe and cutting, for internal wear between the strands, for mildew, rot, chemical attack or other contamination.

* *Inspection of test certificates:*

To confirm that the test certificates for shackles, links, rings, hooks, triangle plates and chains show the material used to make the item-mild steel, high tensile steel or alloy steel.

To ensure that there is a valid test certificate for every single item of gear shown on the rigging plan. (To be valid all the details entered on the certificate must be correct for the item of equipment to which it applies.)

* Any item of cargo gear which is repaired must be retested and certified.

- Quadrennial or quintennial thorough survey.

  The quadrennial or quintennial thorough survey (conducted every fourth or fifth year depending upon flag state requirements) must be done by an approved surveyor, who usually represents a classification society. It is more thorough than the periodical survey. Besides including all the work for a periodical survey, the quadrennial/quintennial survey requires the retesting of the derricks and thorough examination of all parts of the derrick and its associated gear. This may involve the removal ashore of the loose gear to a proper workshop where it can be examined, retested and remarked. In some cases the unrigging and rerigging is done by riggers who are familiar with the system adopted by the repair yard and can ensure that all gear is unrigged and rerigged in positions corresponding to the plans which the yard provides for the ship. This is normally completed during the drydocking of the ship

Conduct of the periodical survey: It should not be thought for a moment that a periodical visual survey of a single derrick can be completed in a few hours. Even when all the derrick gear is well maintained and the crew is experienced in the work of dismantling it, the task will be time consuming. A team of three or four experienced crew members will probably require at least two days to lift the heel of a 5 tonne derrick clear of the gooseneck, to release all the shackles, to remove the sheaves of the topping lift, runner and guy blocks and inspect the block swivels, to inspect every item and verify the markings, to make renewals as necessary, to grease and oil and to reassemble the rig.

When the parts of the rig are heavier, when the rig is more complex, when it has been neglected or when the crew is inexperienced the work will take correspondingly longer and for that reason, and because crews are small, such work is usually subcontracted out to specialised firms and nowadays (2008) is seldom undertaken by ship's crew.

Need to keep the documents in good order: An inspector or surveyor of cargo gear when visiting the ship will expect to be shown on demand a certificate for every separate item of gear. If the ship is to comply with such a request the cargo gear documents must be kept methodically and it is essential that the chief mate understands the records and their importance and ensures that they are kept up-to-date.

A variety of systems are used by different shipowners and ship operators for the efficient filing of the cargo gear certificates. The basic requirements of any system are the following:

- If a shackle stamped 'F33 SWL 5T' is found in the cargo gear it must be possible to produce a test certificate for that shackle.
- If asked for the certificate for the derrick-head topping lift block on the No.3 forward starboard derrick it must be possible to produce a test certificate for that block, and the reference number on the certificate must be the same as the reference number on the block.
- A certificate must be held for each wire rope used in the rig.

Methods of keeping the documents in good order: There are a variety of practical difficulties in complying with the foregoing requirements, and the following guidelines may be useful.

- When a number of items of cargo gear are supplied to the ship, each item should be supplied with a separate certificate and this should be stated when ordering the items. For example, if ten 5-tonne shackles are supplied, a single certificate for 10 shackles, Nos. F25-F34 is not acceptable. A separate certificate should be provided for each shackle. Two years later, when three of the shackles are lost, two are unused and remain in store, and five are in use on three different derricks, each certificate can then be placed with the appropriate set of documents.
- Wire ropes may be supplied in coils and the coils may be cut to provide rigging in several different places. For example, a single coil of wire rope might be used to make six guy pennants for different derricks. As the coil is used, a record of the usage must be kept with the certificate. The note attached to the certificate might read, *Certificate No. C13774. 220 metres, 22 mm diameter. 6 x 10 metres used for guy pennants at 1P, 1S, 2P, 2S, 3P and 3S. 160 metres remains in forecastle store. Date: 26.10.06.* As noted earlier any splices must comply with the requirements of Class and/or flag state. It is increasingly common for owners to supply mechanically spliced wires due to the lack of seamanship skills aboard many ships and the smaller crew numbers.
- Records of this sort must be kept up-to-date and accurate. The regulations of most maritime nations require that the ship maintains a full set of certificates for all lifting appliances, including cargo gear. A surveyor will expect to find that the chief mate's records, which for the convenience of surveyors and busy chief mates may actually form part of the Master's filing system, are reliable and up-to-date.
- The records must be kept with the same care and accuracy even if the ship's only derricks are stores derricks or bunker davits.
- A single certificate may refer to items of gear which are in use in a number of different places, like the coil of wire quoted in the example above. In this case a photocopy of the certificate can be placed in records in each place where the certificate should appear. The photocopies should be endorsed with a note stating where the original certificate is filed.
- It is often helpful to write notes, in pencil, on the certificates of test for spare items of cargo gear. Such notes could read *To be used for the renewal of 3P and 3S topping lifts, or Placed in poop store – to be moved to forecastle store.* Such notes can be erased or amended when circumstances change.

Marking of items of cargo gear: Every item of cargo gear is required to be marked with identifying reference numbers and/or letters. Steel items usually have the numbers punched on them and these numbers can become very faint as a result of paint, rust or abrasion. The numbers should be kept clean by wire brushing, and can be painted with a patch of paint of a distinctive colour to help to find them quickly. If the markings become very faint they can be repunched to make them more clear, but it is essential that the markings are not altered in any way.

When wire ropes are manufactured with ferrules (mechanical splices) at their ends or on their splices the reference numbers of their certificates will be stamped on the ferrules, so that the wire rope can be matched with the certificate. When the wire rope has no ferrules (a circumstance that is now rare) it is normally delivered with a metal label with the test certificate reference number fastened to it. When such a wire rope has been put into the derrick rig it can no longer be labelled, so it is essential that the ship's records show which certificate refers to each of the wire ropes in use. The records must be kept up-to-date as the renewal of wire ropes is carried out, because attempts to update the records later nearly always run into trouble. Records prepared after the event are likely to show the same wire rope fitted in two different positions, or a wire rope which is 70 metres long matched with a certificate for a 50 metre wire rope, or other impossible data which discredit the records.

Each derrick boom must be prominently marked with the safe working load of the derrick. When more than one system of rigging the derrick is possible – for example, when the gear can be used as a swinging derrick or in union purchase – the safe working load in each rig must be shown. This is often marked on the boom with lines of weld and painted.

Neglected cargo gear system: When a system for marking every item of cargo gear and providing its certificate needs updating the job is a very big one which is best done by a repair yard using professional riggers. Some owners make it their practice to have the ship prepared even for the annual examination by riggers. If the crew is inexperienced or small in numbers, or if the ship's schedule is a busy one and the cargo gear is often used, this is probably the only practical method of ensuring that the cargo gear and associated records are properly maintained, and it seems likely that this procedure will be adopted with increasing frequency.

Crane design, maintenance and operation

Crane design: Shipboard cranes are usually of electro-hydraulic design (Fig. 23.3). A crane is normally required to perform three functions – namely, to hoist (or lower), to luff and to slew. Hoisting is the raising of the crane wire whilst the crane jib remains in a constant position. Luffing is the raising or lowering of the crane jib, and slewing is the swinging round (or rotating) of the crane. Cranes on a few ships are also able to travel along the deck on rails, but this is unusual.

It is common for shipboard cranes to be level luffing. This means that if the crane is topped from maximum to minimum radius, or vice versa, the crane hook will maintain a level path, allowing the load to move horizontally. The power which enables the crane to hoist, luff and slew is provided by electric motors which drive hydraulic pumps. The hydraulic pumps drive the winches required for the hoisting, and drive the machinery which enables the crane to luff and slew.

Fig. 23.3 Two 25 tonne SWL electro-hydraulic deck cranes, stowed

Twin cranes have been fitted to some conbulk and forest product ships. The basic idea is extremely simple, and consists of two independent cranes of equal capacity mounted on a common platform. The common platform can be rotated independently and the cranes can be slewed relative to the platform. Each crane can be used by itself, with each serving an adjoining hold, but when a heavy lift is required the jibs are slewed parallel to one another and a lifting beam is attached between the crane hooks. This arrangement allows the lifting of loads of up to twice the safe working load of one crane. The speeds of the hoisting and luffing motions of the cranes are synchronised to ensure smooth operation.

When the cranes are operated in the twin mode the individual slewing motions are inoperable and only the platform slewing motion can be used. Operation of the platform slewing motion causes the platform to rotate and with it the two cranes, with their jibs parallel, thus enabling large loads to be safely slewed.

If shipboard cranes are intended to be used with grabs, as *grabbing cranes* they are likely to be fitted with rope-operated grabs, for which the crane will be provided with two rope drums and two wire ropes, one to hold the grab and the other to open and close it. Alternatively, electro-hydraulic grabs are easy to fit to existing cranes and grabs can also be operated by remote radio control. These systems replace the simple but inefficient self-dumping grabs which are used on a single fall of wire rope.

Crane maintenance: The detailed maintenance required by cranes depends upon their construction, and must be learnt from their instruction manuals, which normally provide detailed guidance as to frequency of service, materials to use and items to inspect. The main areas which require attention are the following:

- *Daily, when cranes are being used to work cargo.*
  - * Inspect runner wires for wear or damage. Check the rig for damage and for fastenings becoming slack. Check the limit and cutout switches. Carry out oiling and greasing as necessary. Ensure the ventilation for the crane motors is open, to prevent overheating.

- *Before arrival in port.*

  * Follow the procedures recommended by the crane manufacturers. They should include all the inspections and tests listed below for regular maintenance.

- *Regular maintenance, (normally described in the Makers' Instructions or Planned Maintenance System).*

  * The filters of the hydraulic system must be regularly cleaned or renewed and the hydraulic oil must be changed as required by the manufacturers.

  * The oil in the gearboxes must be kept topped up to the correct level and must be changed at the required intervals.

  * Suitable grease must be applied to all moving parts of the system, such as the bearings of winches and sheaves, the turret bearings, pivot points or hinges for jib and the roller slewing ring. When the crane is required to operate regularly in temperatures below freezing greasing must be done with low temperature grease.

  * Wire ropes should be regreased when they are visibly dry or dry to the touch, when 'bald spots' form in the grease on the outer surface, or when corrosion exists.

  * Wire ropes must be inspected for flattening and kinking, and for broken, worn or corroded wires, and must be condemned when more than 5 per cent of the wires in any length of ten rope diameters are damaged. For example, if the wire rope has a diameter of 24 mm and is of 6 x 37 construction the total number of wires in the rope is 222, of which 5 per cent is 11. If more than 11 broken strands are found in a length of (24 x 10) mm – ie, 240 mm – the rope must be condemned.

  * The brakes for the hoisting winch and for the slewing and luffing machinery must be inspected for contamination with oil, for damage to the adjustments, and for wear. Where necessary they must be degreased – for example, with trichlorethylene – or the linings must be renewed.

  * All parts of the crane must be inspected for damage and for fastenings or fittings which have become loose, worn or fractured as a consequence of blows, vibration or working in a seaway. Loose or damaged slewing ring securing bolts, for example, would seriously reduce the safe lifting capacity of the crane.

  * Crane winch drums must be inspected to ensure that the wire ropes remain firmly attached to them and the attachment must be freed and then refastened to ensure that it can be freed when necessary. Wire must be correctly spooled on to the drum without crossing turns and the reliable operation of spooling and full drum devices and slack wire detectors must be confirmed.

  * Deck cranes are provided with limit switches to prevent over-hoisting, over-lowering, and luffing, slewing or travelling beyond permitted limits. When a limit switch operates the crane cannot pass the limit, but still retains power to move away from the limit. Limit switches and their over-ride keys must be tested frequently and certainly before each port visit to ensure that they work and that they are properly adjusted to operate in the correct position. The over-ride keys for the limit switches should be kept safely in the care of a responsible officer.

  * The emergency cutout stops all power to all controls on the crane, by tripping the main electrical breaker, as soon as it is activated. The brakes on the hoisting and luffing winches are spring-loaded, and will close tight if power is lost, holding the crane and its load fixed. The emergency cutout can be activated by the crane operator and will operate automatically if there is a power failure or if the crane is overloaded. The emergency cutout is tested by hitting the cutout button, and by overloading under controlled conditions when the cranes are retested.

  * High temperature trips and low oil level trips, if fitted, must also be checked regularly and maintained in good condition.

  * The crane cab and machinery must be kept clean and light bulbs must be renewed. Cracked or broken windows, and plastic windows which have become dull or opaque must be renewed. The sun visor is essential to prevent the driver from being dazzled and must be maintained in good condition.

  * Heaters for the crane are normally on a separate power circuit to that for driving the crane. They should remain switched on throughout the voyage to keep the electrical equipment for the crane warm and dry. The correct operation of cooling fans should be confirmed.

  * The crane maintenance programme is likely to depend upon the crane operating hours, so a record of these should be kept.

  * Electrical maintenance should include the occasional checking of all terminal screws in the switchgear cabinets, terminal boxes and on the equipment itself, and tightening them if slack.

  * Sheaves should be inspected for damage from time to time, particularly when the crane is being used with a self dumping grab. The operation of such grabs can cause a 'ripple' in the wire rope fall, which may jump out of its own sheave and finish up in the next sheave, or jammed between two sheaves.

  * The planned maintenance programme for a handymax bulk carrier requires, at six monthly intervals, inspection of the sheaves and the brake linings for weardown. Renewal of hoisting and luffing wires should be when required or every 1,000 working hours or two years, whichever comes first (Fig. 23.4).

- *Spares to be carried.*

  * A minimum stock of all items that could malfunction from the smallest electrical switch or relay to a complete main hydraulic motor and pump must be carried. There is usually a requirement for at least two spare hoisting and luffing wires to be carried by a ship with four cranes.

- *Annual thorough survey.*

  * The annual thorough survey of a crane is carried out by a surveyor representing a statutory authority or a classification society, and the nature and extent of the survey is described in classification society publications[29]. Besides covering all the areas listed above under 'maintenance', the structure of the crane

Fig. 23.4 25 tonne SWL cranes topped up and swung clear of the hatch openings

Fig. 23.5 Ship's grab stowed between two holds

Fig. 23.6 Ship's grab provided with panels which can be locked open to reduce capacity when lifting dense cargo

Fig. 23.7 A clamshell grab opening to deliver cargo
Photo courtesy of Nemag B.V.

Fig. 23.8 A clamshell or Valstar grab, heavily laden
Photo courtesy of Nemag B.V.

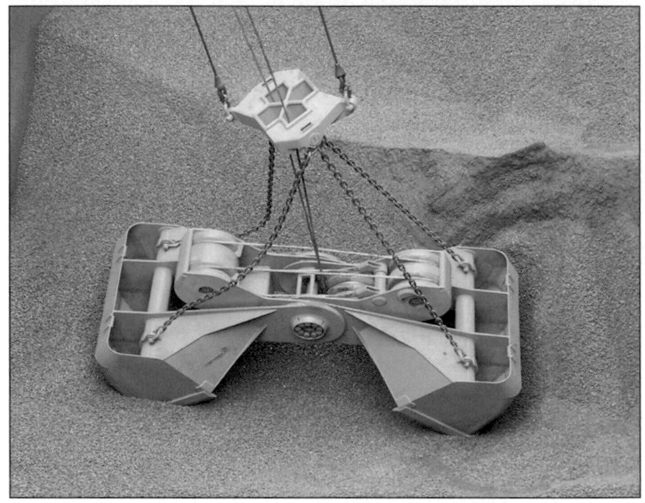

Fig. 23.9 A scissor grab for high productivity and low maintenance *Photo courtesy of Nemag B.V.*

Fig. 23.10 Cactus grab – used for coarse materials
Photo courtesy of Nemag B.V.

will be carefully examined for strength with hammer testing and drilling of the material when found necessary. Sheaves may be unshipped for inspection.

* The cranes must be retested at four- or five-yearly intervals, or more often if found necessary.

Operation of cranes

* The ship's officers can keep the limit switch override keys in their possession, thus ensuring that the limits cannot be overridden without their knowledge. Keys to the cabinet containing the main power breaker should also be kept by the duty officer who can then be certain that the crane cannot be restarted by an unauthorised person after it has been immobilised. It is good practice to immobilise the cranes at the end of the working day and any time that they are being maintained.
* It may be necessary to override a limit switch to stow or unstow the crane jib, or to move it to other exceptional positions whilst it is carrying no load. This must only be done under the supervision of competent ship's personnel.
* When shore drivers are employed to drive the cranes they will require careful supervision from ships' officers to ensure that they use the ship's equipment safely, and do not damage it.
* Cranes should be driven smoothly.

Grab maintenance

Grab design: Some geared bulk carriers are equipped with their own grabs to be used with their cranes or derricks (Fig. 23.5 and 6). Shipboard grabs differ in mechanical design and in the system used to control their closing and opening, but some general points can be made.

The first grabs to be widely used aboard ship with derricks or cranes were self-dumping or hand-released grabs, which operate on a single fall of wire rope. Such a grab is emptied either by pulling on a trip cord or by lowering the cargo-filled grab on to the stockpile, when the release mechanism will operate and the jaws will fall open as the grab is hoisted. However, self-dumping grabs are nowadays uncommon and reputed to be slow in operation and unsuitable for difficult cargoes such as iron ore and rock phosphate. Some crane manufacturers state that all guarantees for their cranes become invalid if self-dumping grabs are used with them, and self-dumping grabs have been replaced by electro-hydraulic grabs and rope-operated grabs in many ports.

Electro-hydraulic grabs are more common and when used with an electric cable reel of the correct type give excellent results. Their principal advantages are that they have a high payload-to-weight ratio, no shock loading occurs during closing or opening, and they are easily fitted to existing cranes.

Rope-operated grabs are few in number and are likely to be fitted when grabs are part of the vessel's initial equipment. They use two winches with independent motors. One winch holds the grab stationary during the opening and closing sequence whilst the other winch pays out to open the grab and winds in to close it. When the grab is being hoisted or lowered both winches operate simultaneously. Another grab control system supplied to ships is remotely operated by radio. Ships' grabs are generally clamshell grabs, the name given to grabs with buckets of a particular shape (Fig. 23.7 and 8).

Fig. 23.11 A trimming grab
Photo courtesy of Nemag B.V.

Grabs used by shore installations: Clamshell (Valstar) grabs are good versatile grabs with some corners rounded which means that they do less damage to ships than do some other designs. They are used for unloading a wide range of products including coal, ore, minerals, grains and fertiliser. Nemag scissor grabs (Fig. 23.9) are also used for unloading and combine very high productivity with very low maintenance – an excellent combination. Cactus grabs (Fig. 23.10) are designed for handling very coarse material such as scrap metal (HMS1-2), pig iron, stones and household waste and trimming grabs (Fig. 23.11) are mainly used for rough granulated bulk with high density such as special ores, granite and pig iron.

Grab capacity: The amount of cargo which a grab can lift is governed by the capacity of its bucket – that part of the grab which holds the cargo. Capacity can be measured flush, or heaped (Fig. 23.12) and a good rule of thumb is that heaped capacity is approximately equal to flush capacity plus 25 per cent. Grabs come in a variety of sizes to suit cargoes with very different densities. A grab intended to lift 5 tonnes of grain would require three times the capacity of a grab suitable for 5 tonnes of iron ore. Grabs carried aboard ship are likely to be a compromise, so if heavy cargoes are to be loaded or discharged by ship's grab, calculations must be carried out to ensure that the weight of grab plus contents will not exceed the safe working load of the ship's cargo gear.

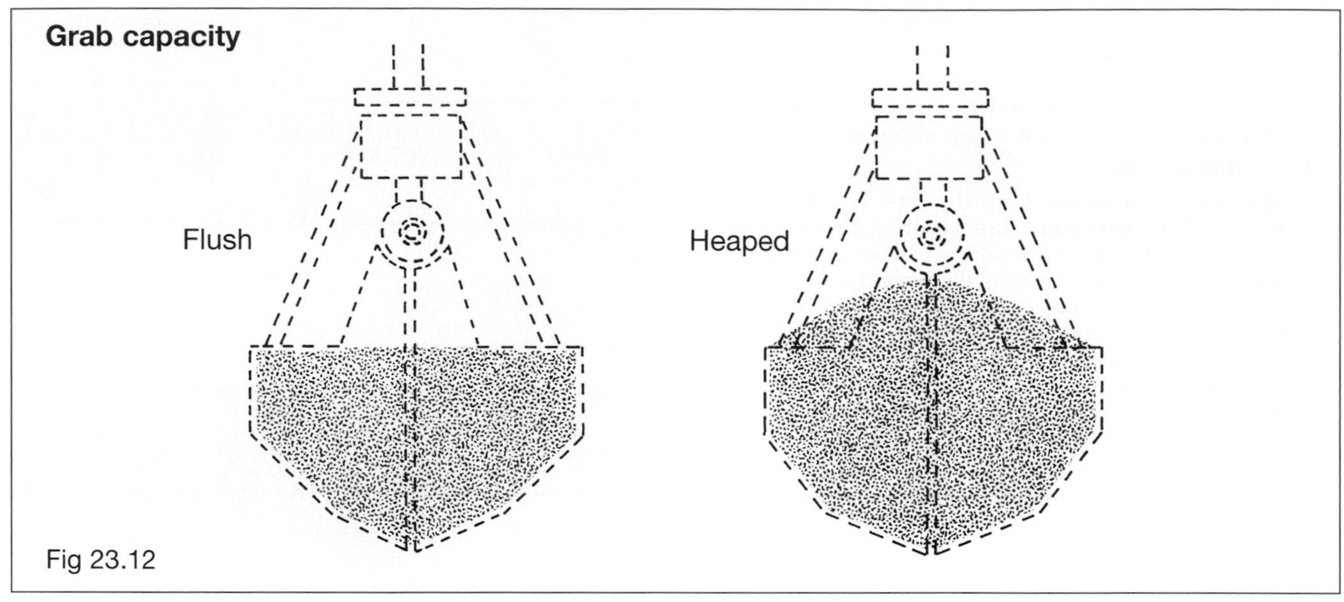

Fig 23.12

The calculation might look like this:

Capacity of grab, flush, (from documentation, or by measurement):	2.50 cbm
Plus 25% for heaped capacity:	.63
Heaped capacity:	3.13
Intended cargo iron ore, (stowage factor 0.45 cbm/tonne), per grabload:	6.96 tonnes
Weight of grab (from documentation)	1.20
Total lift:	8.16 tonnes

Provided that the safe working load of the ship's cargo gear is more than 8.16 tonnes and the safe working load of the grab is more than 6.96 tonnes, the system can be used to lift the iron ore.

Some ships' grabs are provided with hinged flaps which can be secured open or shut to vary the grab capacity (Fig. 23.6). The flaps are to be open when lifting heavier cargoes such as iron ore, to ensure that excessive tonnages are not lifted, and closed for lighter cargoes like coal.

Damage to grabs: Grabs are designed for hard wear, because that is what they will meet when used for handling cargoes. They are likely to suffer damage if they are misused and practices to be avoided include the following:

- A grab which is allowed to land on a steeply sloping face of cargo will capsize, allowing the closing chains or wires to foul the grab's mechanism or structure and to be damaged.
- A grab which makes heavy contact with the ship's structure or a structure ashore is likely to be knocked out of shape, after which it will not close properly. Heavy contact of this sort is likely to be equally harmful to the ship or shore object and to the grab and should never be accepted without protest.
- When a grab is allowed to close upon the ship's frames (for example in No. 1 hold where they are close to the hatch coaming), or upon container sockets or lashing eyes in the hold, it may suffer damage to its closing mechanism or to the grab lips. This is also likely to damage the ship's structure and is to be avoided for this reason too.

Maintenance and inspection of grabs: If grab parts such as bushes, sheaves, wire ropes or chains are to be renewed it will be necessary to unrig and dismantle the grab, partly or completely. Before doing so, full notes or plans should be made, and photos should be taken, to assist with the reassembly and rerigging. Alternatively, another fully rigged grab can be used as a model if necessary.

- Keep a complete electro/hydraulic power pack for a grab as a spare. In the case of grab failure during operations it is easier to replace the whole power pack, rather than trying to repair the motor, hydraulic pump or shuttle valves on deck or even in the hold.
- Inspect the heavy umbilical cable and its control lever and small chain and shackle attachment to the grab head. Check that the self tensioning reel (Fig. 23.13) is operating by pulling down on the umbilical cable. It should rewind slowly.
- All the grease nipples should be found and grease should be applied frequently when the equipment is in use, and regularly at other times, following the procedures described in the general section on greasing and oiling.
- The grab may be fitted with a feature such as a dashpot, used to control the speed of opening. This reduces the violence of the grab's action and so reduces damage. A dashpot, or any similar arrangement of pistons, must have its oil level maintained with the correct clean oil according to the manufacturers' advice.
- When chains are used for opening and closing of grabs they should be lubricated with a light grade SAE 30 oil. This will penetrate to the places where the adjoining links of chain are in contact with one another, providing lubrication and reducing wear. Grease should not be used on chains, as it combines with the cargo being handled and forms a grinding paste which then grinds the chain and the sheaves away.
- Wire ropes when used for grabs should be treated with a suitable wire rope lubricant as approved by the manufacturer.
- Sheaves should be checked for play, and if they move noticeably their bushes must be renewed. The working face of each chain sheave should be inspected (Fig. 23.14). If grooving is found it shows that the sheave has not been turning freely. A normal wear pattern is shown when the working face has a pattern of flats and points.

Fig. 23.13 Self tensioning reel on crane for umbilical cable for control of electro hydraulic grab

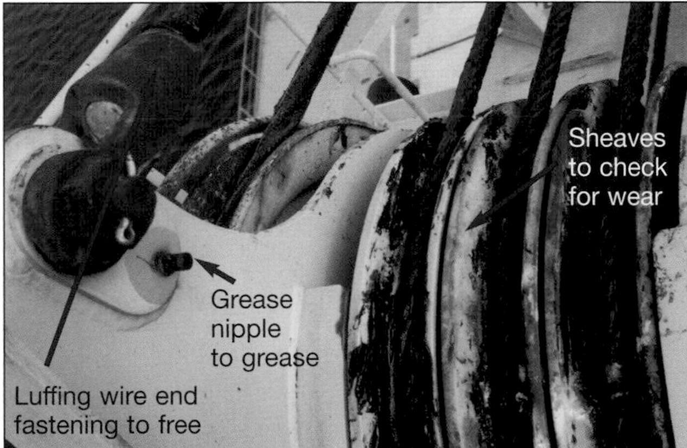

Fig. 23.14 Maintenance required at the crane top

If sheaves are moved to different positions in the grab from time to time the wear on the working face will not become excessive. Badly worn sheaves cause damage to the chain.

- One manufacturer of chain for grabs recommends that grab chain be condemned when the diameter of the links at any point has been reduced by 15 per cent from the original value. Measurement should be made using a vernier caliper, such as the ship's engineers will have. Noticeable stretching of any of the links only occurs when they have been overloaded, and provides another reason for condemning the chain.

Maintenance of fixtures and fittings

All the fixtures and fittings found aboard a bulk carrier are liable to deteriorate. Salt water, vibration, dust and rough treatment all help to ensure that equipment will seize up, waste away or become damaged. A planned maintenance system should ensure that every item is given appropriate treatment at regular intervals. If there is no understandable planned maintenance system, such as when a ship has been taken over from foreign owners the ship's officers must, in the short term, rely upon the system used for centuries – commonsense, experience and practical seamanship. To qualify for a Safety Management Certificate a ship must have a planned maintenance system understood by shipboard personnel so any lack of an understandable system should be brief.

Work should be undertaken methodically, trying to complete one job before starting the next and keeping a record of the work done. To prevent equipment from seizing up or wasting away it should be dismantled (taken apart) once a year or more often. The treatment needed will depend upon the item being maintained, and its condition. Paint coatings should be renewed as necessary to prevent the item from rusting and grease should be applied where needed to prevent seizing up. Damaged parts should be repaired or renewed.

The sort of maintenance which will be needed cannot be fully described within the scope of this book, but can be illustrated by reference to some of the items of equipment mentioned in Chapter 6, which described procedures for ensuring that systems are operational. The object of full maintenance is to ensure that systems remain operational, and to achieve this it is necessary to do rather more than simply to ensure that they are working when required. For this reason the list of jobs is more extensive than when the equipment is simply being checked before use.

The following is not a full list of the maintenance required for fixtures and fittings, but merely a selection of examples:

- To maintain hold ventilators in good condition the moving parts must be moved through their full range and greased regularly, a routine that most ships now include as part of the monthly greasing required by the planned maintenance system. Perishable ventilator parts such as rubber seals and fire gauzes must be renewed when perished, and the steelwork which is liable to rust because of exposure to salt washing water and spray and corrosive cargo fumes must be prepared and repainted as necessary.
- To keep deck lighting in good condition every light should be opened up at regular intervals; bulbs and tubes must be renewed as required, any moving parts such as fastenings must be greased, rubber seals must be renewed when perished, broken glass covers or other causes of leakage must be renewed and wiring and conduits must be inspected. This work must be done sufficiently often to ensure that the lights are always in good condition and that lamps or tubes can be quickly renewed when necessary.
- The non-return valves in the bilge pumping system are fitted to ensure that water can be pumped from the hold bilge wells to the engineroom and overside or into a holding tank for measurement. Their second purpose is to ensure that water cannot travel in the opposite direction, into the hold bilge wells. The system must be tested each voyage to ensure that water can be pumped from the bilge wells, but cannot be pumped into the bilge wells. In addition, the non-return valves must be dismantled, inspected, fitted with replacements for worn or damaged parts and reassembled at regular intervals preferably of 6-12 months or as required by the planned maintenance system.
- The maintenance of CO_2 smothering systems, fire extinguishers and liferafts is often arranged to coincide with the ship's annual inspection or survey of lifesaving equipment. The condition of the equipment must satisfy the surveyor and the required standard is often achieved by employing specialist contractors to carry out the required servicing, including the checking of gas levels in the CO_2 bottles. Annual servicing is not, of course, the limit of the attention which this equipment requires, and

Chapter 6 noted the routines to be followed with this equipment. Fire extinguishers require inspection at intervals of about three months to ensure that they continue to be in good order. It is becoming more common for extinguishers to be inspected each month, with each extinguisher having an inspection tag attached to it. The monthly check tags on each extinguisher are dated and signed by the officer completing the inspection. The inspection process often forms part of the ship's planned maintenance system. Extinguishers should be discharged and recharged in sequence.

- Similarly, the annual freeboard inspection will prompt a careful examination of ventilators, airpipes, watertight doors, hatch covers, skylights and other deck openings. Gaskets for watertight doors, ventilators and access hatches will be renewed if badly compressed. Dogs and butterfly nuts will be greased or renewed if damaged. Floats in airpipe goosenecks must be proved operational. To ensure that the equipment remains in good order and is always able to prevent the entry of water, all the items included in the freeboard survey should receive routine maintenance at short intervals of about three months, or as required by the ship's planned maintenance system when they will be inspected, worked, lubricated and given whatever repairs are needed.

Maintenance of hatch covers and ballast tanks: The maintenance of hatch covers is discussed in Chapter 4, and that of ballast tanks in Chapter 7 and Appendix 23.3.

Good maintenance

To remain safe and efficient a ship must be well maintained with the assistance of an approved planned maintenance system. That requires sensible spending on tools and supplies. It also requires good sense and commitment from a pro-active Master and crew. It has been possible in the foregoing pages to do no more than to show how maintenance work should be approached. The details will vary from ship to ship.

The basic rules of maintenance are:

- Be thorough.
- Be methodical.
- Plan maintenance work well in advance.
- Ensure that all work is completed safely using a Permit to Work System when appropriate.
- Consult with other departments and keep them informed.
- Study the manufacturers' manuals.
- Use the correct tools and materials.
- Do not expect too much from inexperienced crew members.
- Keep full records of the work done.

Sources

29, 31, 131, 206, 266. (See List of Sources, Page 497)

CHAPTER 24

REPAIRS AND DRYDOCKING

Repair of damage and defects, Enhanced Survey Programme, drydocking

Repair of damage and defects

SHIPS, like any other structures, suffer damage and deterioration. As a consequence they need repair from time to time. This chapter does not deal with repairs within the ship's machinery spaces: such repairs are not peculiar to bulk carriers, but must be carried out in every type of vessel. The subject of this volume is bulk carriers and it is the repairs to holds, ballast tanks, hatch coamings, hatch covers, deck services, deck machinery and fittings which are the focus of this chapter.

There is a variety of ways in which repairs can be arranged. A damaged or defective item may be repaired by members of the ship's deck department, by their colleagues from the engine department, by stevedores responsible for the damage, by a repair firm hired in a port of call, by specialists from the firm which manufactured the damaged item, by a riding squad who travel with the ship, or as an item on a drydock repair list.

It is an important matter of principle that no repairs to the vessel's 'primary hull structure' should take place without prior approval of Class. Primary hull structures are defined by the International Maritime Organization[255] as 'main longitudinal and transverse members and their attachments'. A bulk carrier's 'main longitudinal and transverse members and their attachments' are[281] shell plating, strength deck (ie main or upper deck) plating, longitudinal bulkheads (eg inner side of double sided structure), double bottom girders, sloping hopper tank sides, sloping and vertical topside tank sides, longitudinal hatch coamings longer than 0.15L and their end brackets, transverse watertight bulkheads, frames and frame brackets, transverse side structures including ring frames in hopper and topside tanks, upper and lower bulkhead stools, tanktop (inner bottom) plating and double bottom floors. Repairs to 'other hull structural parts' (for example longitudinal framing and stiffeners, transverse hatch coamings, longitudinal hatch coamings no greater than 0.15L, and flanges of cut-outs or brackets) if repaired by riding squads or stevedore repair gangs may be accepted based on examination by the classification society after completion of the repair.

Discovery of damage: It should be impossible for damage and defects to go undetected for any length of time aboard a well-run ship. A system of inspections, testing and measurement should ensure that problems are discovered rapidly.

Wherever possible stevedores' damage should be detected by the duty officer as it occurs. In any event it should be found during hold inspection as discharge is ending. There are further opportunities to detect damage within the holds when cleaning is completed, and during preloading inspections. Routines to ensure that all the ship's equipment is in good order before entering port and the regular sounding of bilge wells and ballast tanks provide further opportunities for discovering defects. Routine thorough examinations of every hold and ballast tank at intervals of 6-12 months should be part of every ship's planned maintenance system and provide further occasions when damage can be found and recorded on company forms. Tank inspections should be well spread throughout the ship and ship's staff must be instructed what to look for[282].

In addition, prudent Masters and chief mates will inspect their ship very thoroughly during the first few days after joining her and should notice defects at that time. Such inspections are advisable because these officers need to possess a detailed knowledge of their ship if they are to perform their duties efficiently, and because defects which they do not discover on joining may be blamed upon them at a later date!

Another obvious warning of damage is received when loud noise, heavy impact or vibration is experienced. It goes without saying that any such should be investigated promptly.

Assessment of damage: Structural damage is generally due to grounding, collision, heavy weather or external contact and in most cases results in the structural integrity of the ship being affected. If this happens the resultant emergency is dealt with between the owner/manager and the classification society's emergency response system, if such an arrangement is in place. The circumstances and details of the incident and the resultant damages should be recorded by the Master/superintendent. On completion of all the surveys, details of structural damages and agreed repairs should be clearly documented. The decision when and where repairs will be carried out must be discussed and agreed with all parties concerned, including the commercial interests of the ship[282].

When damage has occurred the first requirement is to inspect it carefully to determine its extent and cause and to consider its consequences. All damage should be inspected with care. Often damage to the ship's structure will be found to be more widespread than first appears. When an indentation caused by a grab is found in the hatch coaming it is easy to overlook the fact that the entire coaming has been bent out of true, or that coaming brackets have been buckled. A blow on the ship's side, from a tug or a fender, may be transmitted through the ship's internal structure to the hopper sides, causing damage there, remote from the location of the contact. Wherever possible damaged structures should be inspected from both sides of the plating. Inspections are best made by at least two experienced officers to reduce the chance that part of the damage will be overlooked.

Damage can be said to fall into three categories. At one extreme is 'fair wear and tear' such as damaged paintwork and superficial scratches or indentations in steelwork. Damage of this sort is repaired when and if necessary by the vessel's routine maintenance. At the

Fig. 24.1 This damaged hold ladder does not affect the seaworthiness of the ship but must be repaired for the 'health and safety' of users such as crew and stevedores

Photo courtesy of Brookes Bell

Fig. 24.2 These damaged ship's side rails do not make the ship unseaworthy but must be repaired

Photo courtesy of Brookes Bell

Fig. 24.3 This fracture in the shell plating has been temporarily repaired. When the ship reaches port it will be surveyed and permanently repaired. The temporary chalk marking is acceptable because the repair will soon be done

other extreme is damage which affects the vessel's seaworthiness, by reducing her structural strength or watertightness. This damage must be reported to the vessel's classification society which will approve any repairs. The third category of damage falls between the two extremes. It does not affect the vessel's strength or seaworthiness but it needs to be repaired for the safe and efficient operation of the ship. Damage to items such as hold ladders, (Fig.24.1) ship's side rails (Fig. 24.2), derrick or crane crutches and pipe guards falls into this category.

When a first assessment of the damage has been made its consequences must be considered. Is the ship's seaworthiness affected? Can she continue to operate efficiently? What steps can be taken to minimise the effects of the damage? In the case of serious damage these judgements will eventually be made by specialists, but the Master and officers should reach their own conclusions as the people on the spot so that they can provide a full picture when reporting damage. They should also take digital photos of the damage (Fig. 24.3) to accompany their written report.

If ships are to retain their class, shipowners must report to the classification society any damage or deterioration which might affect the ship's class. This is an important requirement and as a first step in observing it the Master should report damage to the owners as soon as it occurs. When damage is found the Master should remember this requirement. If he thinks that there is any possibility that the ship's class is affected he must report the details to the owners immediately, so that they can pass them to the classification society. Any significant damage to the ship's shell or deck plating, coamings, hatch covers or watertight bulkheads, anchors and mooring equipment, watertight openings and their fastenings must be reported immediately to the owners.

Damage also includes 'known defects' such as wastage or fractures. When surveying these the full extent of the defect should be noted, especially relative to all adjacent structure. All relevant details such as tank contents, loading condition and weather condition at the time the defect occurred should also be noted. The cause of such defects should be ascertained ie stress, corrosion, contact damage, etc. The corresponding location on the other side of the ship transversely and either side of amidships longitudinally should always be inspected[282].

Repair documents: When the ship and the ship operator are well organised there will be a system for the recording and reporting of damage and deterioration. An efficient system will:

- provide a record of every defect,
- give full details of the repair required,
- provide the basis for a drydock repair list any time when required,
- inform ship operators of the item, and
- record when the defect has been repaired.

Such systems may use a set of self-carbonating forms or may be computerised in a self contained shipboard system, or with links to head office. To provide a full record of repairs a copy of the form should be completed for every defect, whether the repair has been completed, or remains to be done.

There are several reasons why it is important for head office to have a record of all the ship's defects. A knowledge of items which have suffered damage or failed will help the ship's management to monitor the ship's condition and may provide early warning of similar problems with sister ships. When repairs have been completed by ship's staff it is still important to report that the damage occurred, and the report will ensure that the work of the crew in making the repair will be known and appreciated and can if necessary be inspected by Class. Is is also necessary to ensure that the charterers or other responsible party will be asked to pay.

It is essential for the management to know of unrepaired defects so that they can be sure that repairs are given the priority they require. A further reason why reports of all defects should be sent promptly to head office is that orders for drydocking are sometimes given quite unexpectedly as the result of a complete change of orders or of serious damage from collision or grounding. In these circumstances drydock repair lists must be compiled very rapidly and this is much easier to do when all the details are up to date and immediately to hand.

Reports of defects when made by word of mouth, whether by telephone or face to face, may be forgotten, ignored or overlooked. The completion of a repair form will ensure that the report of the damage remains on record and is considered from time to time. When forms are used one copy will be retained by the originator – the person aboard ship who completes it. A second copy must be sent to the ship manager at head office at the first opportunity. The third copy may be retained to give to a local contractor if the repair is arranged locally. Additional copies may be required by the company's insurance or accounts departments.

Completion of the repair specification: The repair specification form will normally require the details which are needed to arrange for the repair, and to estimate a price for it. It is impossible to design a form which anticipates the details of every item needing repair, and ships' officers must give thought to ensuring that all the information needed to plan the job and to price it is provided. Photos and accurate drawings usually help.

The position of the item requiring repair must be carefully and accurately described with reference to a recognisable feature such as a hold number, port or starboard side, and direction and distance in metres, or number of frames, from an identifiable feature. Additionally the actual position on the ship should be marked with the damage report or drydock repair number, using paint or felt-tipped pen. (Fig. 24.3 and 24.4) It often happens that when the time comes to make the repair the person who wrote the item will have left the ship and no-one will be familiar with it. This makes it essential that sufficient information is given to identify the item for repair.

Dimensions of the damage and of the steelwork or other material damaged must be given accurately or must be labelled 'approximate' in case replacement parts are to be prefabricated. Difficulties of access – difficulties which will be experienced by workmen when required to reach the damage – must be fully explained as this will influence the method of repair and its cost. If the ship has replacement parts aboard and is able to provide the parts needed for the repair, this should be stated. Any need for staging must be stated so that due allowance can be made for this expensive item. If the damage is stevedores' damage or damage sustained in any incident which has been the subject of a report this should be shown on the repair specification.

Fig. 24.4 Fracture in way of weld connection between lower stool and tanktop. The steelwork for renewal has been clearly marked

Photo courtesy of Peter Bryson

Arranging for the repair: The chief mate will normally make the first decision as to who is to make the repair and when and how it is to be done. Minor items of repair, such as the renewal of parts for hatch cover fastenings or cargo gear, will be completed as routine maintenance by the deck department and do not need to be reported in a repair specification.

Stevedores' damage should where possible always be repaired by the stevedores in the port where the damage occurred, and the chief mate (supported if necessary by the Master) will, if Class approves, try to ensure that this is done. The first step is to bring the damage to the attention of the stevedore foreman as soon as it is seen or found, and this must be followed immediately by a written stevedores' damage report, providing details of the damage and how it occurred, and holding the stevedores responsible for making good the damage. Standard forms for this purpose are provided by most owners and charterers (Appendix 3.1). The form should be given to the stevedore foreman and his signature obtained to acknowledge responsibility or, failing that, to acknowledge receipt of the document.

In some circumstances a temporary repair will be allowed by Class or will be necessary for a ship to complete her voyage to a port where repair facilities are available. Temporary repairs may take the form of a steel doubling plate welded over damaged steelwork to prevent leaking, or of a cement box, also usually used to prevent leaking. Such repairs do not return the structure to its former undamaged strength and watertightness and the item which has been temporarily repaired will be listed for a permanent repair at the next drydocking, or sooner. For more expensive and complicated damage Class will be consulted and the chief mate will normally also consult the chief engineer and Master, and enquiries may be referred to the ship's manager or superintendent.

Provided that the ship's staff have the necessary skill, tools, materials and time it is always best for the repairs to be completed by ship's personnel, since this will normally be the cheapest and most efficient alternative. When the ship is at sea or in a remote anchorage or port there is often no alternative to repair by ship's staff.

It should be obvious, but is worth stating, that efficient repairs of deck equipment and fittings by the ship's engineers are most likely to be achieved when there are good working relations between departments. These are most likely to exist when each department keeps the other informed of problems and when the advice of the engineers on the maintenance and operation of mechanical equipment is heard with attention. The training of engineers normally ensures that they have a good knowledge of the principles of using and caring for machinery. This is much less certain in the case of deck ratings and officers: those who have an interest in their work can learn a lot from their engineer colleagues.

When repairs cannot be done by stevedores or ship's staff a decision must be taken as to the best way of obtaining assistance from ashore. This is a decision which the Master and his senior officers are authorised to take on some ships, whilst on others they must refer the problem to the shore-based management. The decision whether to use a local repair firm, a specialist firm or a riding squad to make the repair or to add the item to the drydock list will be influenced by a number of factors. If the ship cannot operate safely until the repair has been completed the work must be done immediately: a major repair to the hatch covers such as the repair of damaged hinges for folding hatch covers would come in this category and would be best done in consultation with the manufacturers. A defect which affects the ship's efficiency or incurs time off-hire, such as a damaged crane, will be repaired as soon as parts and labour can be arranged at an economic price. The more urgently the crane is needed the higher the price worth paying for repairs.

Use of a local repair firm in the port where the ship lies will be a sensible option when urgent work must be done and the ship lacks the equipment, the time or the expertise. This option will be chosen from time to time.

There is a role, too, for riding squads: workers who are contracted to travel with the ship for a period of days or weeks to complete particular items of work. Riding squads may be employees of the shipowner who move from ship to ship within the fleet doing particular work or they may work for repair firms. The benefit of employing a riding squad is that it supplements the ship's work force and can undertake work which the ship's crew do not have the time and/or the expertise to carry out efficiently. If brought aboard at suitable times they can work in favourable conditions, without delaying the ship. Riding squads have been used for jobs such as the renewal of the rubbers in steel hatch covers and the renewal of a ship's deck hydraulic pipework. Such work is usually best done on a ballast voyage when the decks are dry and there is no possibility that a mistake can result in damage to the cargo. They offer a useful solution when there is a major maintenance/repair problem.

When the damage reduces the vessel's value but has little or no effect upon her safety and efficiency, repair is likely to be deferred until the next drydocking. Indentations in the vessel's shell plating sustained from contact with tugs, fenders and dock walls come into this category, as does minor stevedores' damage. Steelwork which has been weakened by wasting is normally renewed in drydock unless it is clear that the need for renewal is so urgent that it cannot be deferred until then. In drydock full repair facilities are available and repair work can usually be done more cheaply.

Supervision of repairs: Defects are a source of worry and inconvenience for those who serve on ships and it is a great relief when the time comes for damage to be made good. The time for celebration, however, comes only when the repairs have been successfully completed. If repair work is not properly supervised there will be plenty of opportunities for mistakes to be made.

It is unwise to assume that repair workers are fully informed, trained in safety procedures, competent in the work they have been given and committed to doing a faultless job. They may be, but it would be a great mistake to rely upon it. The ship's officers should be familiar with the details of the repair which is being undertaken. An officer should be present when the work is commenced to ensure that the right place is found and that conditions are safe for the work to start. The correct repair materials must be used. Special welding rods, for example, are required for the welding of special steels, and this is a fact which could be easily overlooked by a stevedores' repair squad.

The work should be inspected from time to time as it proceeds. Often workers who are having difficulties will say so quite openly. Even an officer who is not an expert in repair techniques can detect when the work is not going according to plan and can obtain expert advice. A messy, irregular repair gives warning that the repairer is incompetent, or is having difficulties.

When a repair has been completed it should be inspected by a ship's officer and, where necessary, by Class. Where possible it should be tested. Moving equipment should be operated to ensure that it runs smoothly as required. Watertight features should be tested by filling the compartment or by hose testing, as appropriate. When the repair is permanent and has been completed satisfactorily, the repair specification should be cancelled and the owners should be informed that the item in question can be deleted from the repair list.

Enhanced Survey Programme (ESP)[282]

Enhanced surveys for older bulk carriers were introduced by the International Association of Classification Societies to monitor vessels' condition more thoroughly as they become older. An integral item of the ESP is the Planning Document. This sets out the owner's/manager's detailed plans for the survey. It should be produced well in advance of the Special Survey, taking account of the fact that 'close-up' surveys and thickness readings can be commenced one year before the Special Survey due date. Once the survey is carried out and the full extent of defects and any necessary repairs is known the repair specification can be produced in sufficient time to obtain costs that can be negotiated with interested shipyards to obtain the best possible price.

- The following information required for ESP should be onboard bulk carriers for the life of the ship.
- Executive hull summary – produced by Class – after the periodic survey has been completed.
- Thickness measurement report, endorsed by the attending surveyor.
- Planning Document.
- Supporting documentation ie main structural drawings, previous repair history, cargo/ballast history and tank condition reports.

One of the main reasons for the introduction of the ESP[282] was to ensure that good access arrangements were available for periodic surveys, especially special surveys. The docking and special survey dates were harmonised resulting in ships being at a repair shipyard where safe and efficient access equipment such as cherrypickers in cargo holds and well constructed staging in tanks and holds are likely to be available. No matter what access equipment is used, the intended method of access should be discussed with the surveyors and technicians before the survey is commenced. Details of the proposed survey access equipment must be stated in the ESP Planning Document.

Management of bulk carrier structure

For the naming of a bulk carrier's structural elements, for a discussion of structural defects, monitoring of the structure and wastage see Appendix 24.1

Drydocking

Before drydocking: The routine drydocking of a bulk carrier is an event which occurs once every two to three years. The ship's Safety Management Systems (SMS) should list the procedures to be followed when preparing for and undergoing drydocking. Drydocking presents the best opportunity for completion of many of the repairs and renewals and much of the maintenance which the ship requires to keep her at a high level of efficiency. This makes it essential that drydocking work is planned well in advance.

If major work and expenditure is required such as, for example, the grit blasting and recoating of holds, the rerubbering of hatch covers or the extensive renewal of deck hydraulic piping, then head office should be warned of the requirement a long time in advance. Major work of this sort will require the allocation of funds and may affect the decision as to which shipyard is to be used for the docking and the number of days required.

The best way to inform head office of each item of work needed is by completion of a repair specification report in electronic or paper format, according to the shipowner or manager's system. With major work there is little purpose in the chief mate or Master attempting to specify the quality of grit blasting they require or the specification of replacement rubber for the hatches. Before the job is finally agreed experts will decide upon the appropriate materials. The chief mate should content himself with stating the requirement in general terms and giving as much information as he reasonably can – for example, the area to be grit blasted, the number and size of hatch panels requiring renewal of rubbers and any difficulties with access.

In addition to ensuring that repair specifications are submitted for major items of expenditure, the Master and his officers should continue to submit forms for all minor defects, including stevedores' damage, so that head office has at all times an up-to-date record of defects which can be used for compiling the drydock specification. Preparation of the next drydock repair list should commence in this manner from the moment that the vessel leaves drydock.

The procedures associated with the planning and supervision of a drydocking and the work done therein have been well described from the viewpoint of a shipmanager for a tanker fleet[30, 226] and it is not intended to repeat those descriptions here. The preparations which the ship's staff should make for the docking can usefully be considered.

- Defects will continue to be found and damage to occur right up to the time of docking. Officers must continue to complete repair specifications and to submit them for inclusion in supplementary repair lists. The Master should retain copies to hand direct to the owner's repair manager, who may not have received copies through the normal channels during the last hectic days before the docking.
- The draught and trim required for the docking should be confirmed and the chief mate must ensure that the required condition can be achieved. The ship's stability must be checked to confirm that the ship will remain stable during the critical period – that period of time which starts when the stern lands on the blocks and ends when she takes the blocks overall. (Appendix 20.1)
- When the drydock has been chosen the Master should consider what can usefully be arranged during the drydock period. It may be found that the period in drydock offers a convenient opportunity for other repairs, renewals or servicing of equipment which are sometimes difficult to arrange during a short stay in port.
- Confirmation should be obtained that the ship's crew will be allowed to carry out maintenance work during the period in drydock and a list of crew work should be compiled. Jobs which are difficult to do during a normal voyage, such as recoating the fresh water tanks and painting the undersides of the hatch covers, should be given high priority.
- Repair processes can provide a variety of hazards calling for unfamiliar risk assessments. These may include:[227]
  - Water at ultra high pressure for plate blasting preparation.
  - Heat, fumes and noise.
  - Scaffolding structures with temporary walkways and lighting.
  - Restrictions on access due to open tanks and compartments.
  - Restrictions on access due to clutter and trip hazards from stripped down machinery.
  - Vehicles such as cherrypickers and fork lift trucks.
  - Confined spaces where entry risks have changed.
  - Grit blasting.
  - Hot working with associated safety measures.
  - Guarded openings.

- Industrial radiography.

- The Master and his senior officers should give consideration to what services are to be maintained in drydock and how this is to be achieved. If the ship's generators are to be used they will need cooling water drawn from and returned to a suitable ballast tank or from ashore. Will water for cooking and washing be available? Can toilets discharging into the ship's sanitary tank be used or must facilities ashore be provided? Can heating, ventilation or air conditioning be maintained? What fire fighting services can be maintained? Will fire and emergency alarm systems remain in operation? Will power be available for manoeuvring hatch covers and driving the deck machinery? If disruptions to services are anticipated the ship's company should be informed and alternative arrangements should be made.
- When ship's staff are to use shore toilet and washing facilities the Master or his deputy should seek the earliest opportunity to inspect them, and ensure that they are adequate, since it is not always that such facilities are of an acceptable standard and conveniently situated. If necessary portable units should be placed on deck.
- The period during which the vessel enters the drydock and takes the blocks must be controlled and monitored with great care to avoid accidents which could cause damage to the ship or the drydock. As soon as the vessel has taken the blocks a full accurate and complete set of soundings must be taken to provide a record of the contents of every tank and to provide the information to enable the ship to be refloated in exactly the same condition as when she was docked.

While in drydock:

- A ship is at greater risk of fire or other accident during her time in drydock, because of the repair work being progressed, the temporary cabling which prevents the closing of doors, the additional people aboard ship and the disruption to safety routines and services. Ship's personnel should be alert for problems and should insist upon the observance of safe working practices. For example, openings must be fenced off. Enclosed spaces must be certified gas free before they are entered. Welding and burning must only be permitted when fire fighting equipment is ready and when any bulkheads subjected to heat have been checked on both sides. It should always be clear to ship's personnel whether they or the shipyard are responsible for safety patrols.
- The established practice of the shipowner or the shipyard, or the laws of the country, will decide whether the Master, the shipowner's superintendent or the shipyard manager has overall responsibility for safety and security whilst the ship is drydocked. The published literature[30, 226, 227] suggests that each of them expects to be fully involved in safety issues and that is how it should be as each will have particular knowledge and experience to contribute. The Master continues to be responsible for the safety of the ship and personnel whilst the ship is in drydock. He should observe the requirements of the ship's International Safety Management (ISM) procedures but in addition should collaborate fully with the shipyard's procedures and, when in doubt, not hesitate to use his own commonsense.
- If any ballast tanks must be emptied after the vessel enters drydock their refilling must be started in good time to achieve completion before refloating. All ballasting and deballasting must be co-ordinated with the dock manager, particularly when the vessel is in a floating dock.
- Officers must be provided with copies of the repair list and must be made familiar with all the work to be done. The details of how this is arranged will depend upon the methods of work adopted by the owner's superintendent, the shipyard and the shipowner. To ensure that he and his officers are kept informed of all the work which is being put in hand and progressed the Master will have to be ready to insist, if necessary, upon daily progress meetings attended by the owner's superintendent and the shipyard manager. Good relations must be maintained with the superintendent and the manager to ensure that the work is well co-ordinated.
- The repair list should be rechecked by the Master and his officers to ensure that no items have been omitted from it by oversight and it should be monitored during the time in drydock to ensure that no work is forgotten.
- Each item on the repair list must be inspected when work on it is started, viewed from time to time whilst the repair is in progress, and inspected and tested on completion, following the guidelines given above.
- Officers may also be given responsibility for monitoring the hours worked by shipyard staff, for checking on the number of drums of paint used on the hull and for keeping track of ship's special equipment and tools used by the shipyard.

Before leaving drydock:

- When the time of undocking is approaching the Master and officers should focus their attention on ensuring that the sites of the repairs are all properly cleared up, with all rubbish and equipment removed from ballast tanks, cofferdams and other spaces before they are closed. Staging and temporary structures must be removed. Manhole doors and other openings which have been closed should where possible be tested for watertightness.
- The chief mate will be required to recalculate the ship's stability and to ensure that the ship has been returned to exactly the same condition of loading as when she entered the drydock. With the agreement of all parties, some amendment to the contents of tanks can be accepted provided that they will affect only draught and trim. Any amendment to the athwartship distribution of weight is unacceptable: the ship must be upright and unlisted when she refloats. If she lists there is a danger that she will cause the blocks and sidebeds to tip over, which could incur considerable expense.
- Before the reflooding of the drydock commences one or more senior officers should tour the dock bottom with a representative of the yard to confirm that all the bottom plugs removed for the draining of tanks have been refitted and that all sea suctions have been correctly reassembled. They should also confirm that the rudder and propeller are clear.
- Machinery, equipment, systems and appliances should be tested where necessary to ensure that they are operating properly.
- The ship's safety and fire protection systems must be checked and found to be operating properly.
- The ship's company should be at a high standard of readiness during the reflooding of the dock and the refloating to deal with any unexpected problem as it emerges. When the vessel has refloated a new set of soundings will be taken to see if any unexpected results are obtained. There have been many cases of problems arising aboard ship in the hours and days following a drydocking as a result of poor or slipshod workmanship, and prudent members of the ship's company will remain alert for anything unusual for some days after the ship's departure from drydock.
- Resume the writing of repair specifications immediately upon departure from drydock, so that an up-to-date record of defects is always ready.

Drydock repairs for bulk carriers: Much of the work for which bulk carriers are drydocked is no different from the work done on other classes of ship. Inspection, repairs and renewals of rudder, propeller, anchors and cables, overhaul of ship's side valves and overside discharges, cleaning of the ship's hull, recoating of the shell plating, renewal of cathodic protection and recutting and remarking of loadlines and draught marks are all tasks performed on any ship which is drydocked.

Within the holds the repair of stevedores' damage is likely to be a substantial item and the repair of stress fractures in side shell frames, welds and brackets will be undertaken if fractures are found. Steelwork, typically in holds and ballast tanks, which has become wasted and weakened by excessive corrosion will be renewed. Drydocking provides an opportunity for heavy deposits of sediment to be washed out of ballast tanks through holes cut in the ship's bottom but alternative methods of sediment removal, described in Chapter 7, may be preferred.

Major repairs of deck hydraulic pipework, often needed when ships are about eight to ten years old, can be completed in drydock as can renewals of hatch rubbers though this work can sometimes be done more economically or conveniently by a riding squad when the ship is on a ballast voyage.

Sources

30, 225, 226, 227, 281, 282. (See List of Sources, Page 497)

CHECKLIST – The repair of damage and defects

- ☐ To discover damage and defects carry out regular inspections on joining the ship, before entering port, on completion of discharge, after cleaning holds, on a regular annual basis and at any other time when damage may have occurred.
- ☐ Inspect damage and defects carefully to note full extent.
- ☐ Does ship retain her structural strength and remain seaworthy and efficient?
- ☐ Obtain Class approval for any repairs to primary hull structures.
- ☐ Report serious damage immediately to the shipowner, who will inform the classification society if necessary.
- ☐ Report minor damage routinely to the shipowner.
- ☐ Reports should be made or confirmed in writing, preferably using a standard defect report and repair specification form and accompanied by photographs of the damage.
- ☐ A repair specification should be completed for every defect.
- ☐ Repair specifications should be completed carefully with full details, including access.
- ☐ When they have the time and when they possess the skill, tools and materials repairs should be done by ship's staff.
- ☐ Stevedores' damage should be brought immediately to the attention of stevedores and repaired by them before the ship leaves the port, supervised where necessary by Class.
- ☐ Temporary repairs of damage may be appropriate.
- ☐ For advice regarding larger repairs the chief mate should consult the Master, chief engineer, ship manager and Class.
- ☐ Repairs can be done by equipment manufacturers, local repair firms, riding squads and drydocks.
- ☐ Repair work should be carefully supervised by ship's staff to ensure that it is done safely and correctly.
- ☐ Completed repairs should be inspected and tested where possible.
- ☐ There should be a procedure for informing owners when a defect has been repaired, and it should be used.

CHECKLIST – Reminders for drydocking

- ☐ Drydocking procedures should be listed in the ship's Safety Management System.
- ☐ Drydocking happens infrequently: every effort must be made to take full advantage of the opportunities it offers.
- ☐ Start reporting defects as soon as the ship leaves drydock, so that data for a repair specification are always ready.
- ☐ Write repair specifications for big and expensive jobs at least a year in advance, so that plans and finance can be arranged.
- ☐ Continue reporting new defects right up to the date of entering drydock.
- ☐ Calculate a stable condition of loading for entering drydock.
- ☐ Take advantage of extended drydocking period in port to arrange for other necessary repairs and services.
- ☐ Prepare a worklist of suitable work for the ship's crew.
- ☐ Consult to find what shipboard services will continue to be available in drydock and make appropriate plans.
- ☐ Prepare risk assessments for anticipated conditions and compose a safety checklist.
- ☐ Ensure that shore facilities for ship's staff are adequate.
- ☐ Carefully monitor the docking and keep a record of tank contents.
- ☐ Ensure that safety is maintained during time in drydock.
- ☐ Establish effective daily consultation with superintendent and yard manager and co-operate with safety measures.
- ☐ Ensure no work is forgotten or dropped from list by mistake.
- ☐ Officers are to monitor and inspect all work and test it on completion.
- ☐ Records of hours worked by dock staff to be kept if required and check to be kept on specialist tools lent.
- ☐ All work areas to be cleaned and closed on completion of work and watertight closing to be tested when applicable.
- ☐ Stability to be recalculated to ensure vessel will refloat upright.
- ☐ Inspect to confirm that bottom plugs and sea suctions are refitted, rudder and propeller are clear, and other external work is complete before refloating.
- ☐ Test machinery, equipment, systems and appliances to ensure all are working properly
- ☐ Ensure that the ship's safety and fire protection systems are working properly.
- ☐ Be alert for problems during refloating and for some time thereafter.
- ☐ Resume reporting defects when the ship leaves drydock, so that data for a repair specification are always ready.

CHAPTER 25

SHIP'S HOUSEKEEPING

Disposal of wastes, the housekeeping problem, excluding dust, dealing with dirt, keeping water out

Disposal of wastes

IN RECENT YEARS concern about the environment and the effect of the activities of mankind upon it has increased considerably. This has led to the introduction, extension and reinforcement of regulations to minimise or eliminate pollution of the environment by shipping. This account describes the situation in 2009. The latest editions of the rules and regulations governing pollution must be consulted by anyone who needs to know the current requirements.

The international regulations which govern the prevention of marine pollution are the International Maritime Organization (IMO) MARPOL 73/78 Regulations as modified by the Protocol of 1997 and as amended, which deal with pollution by oil (Annex I), noxious liquids (Annex II), harmful substances in packaged form (Annex III), sewage (Annex IV), garbage (Annex V) and air pollution (Annex VI). All these regulations apply to dry bulk carriers where appropriate. The regulations which affect bulkers in their day to day operations are those concerning pollution by oil, sewage, garbage and air pollution.

The following paragraphs contain a simplified summary of the main provisions of the regulations, as they applied to bulk carriers of more than 400 tons gross in 2009. The regulations themselves and the ship's Garbage Management Plan should always be consulted to ensure that any disposal of waste complies.

Oily wastes: The oily wastes produced by bulk carriers occur in the ship's machinery spaces. Such wastes usually collect in the machinery space bilges, and become mixed with water. The discharge of unseparated oily wastes from bilges into the sea anywhere in the world is prohibited by MARPOL Annex I.

To comply with the regulations a bulk carrier is normally fitted with an oily water separator which extracts the water from the oily mixture. The waste oil which remains after separation cannot be put into the sea and must either be burned in the ship's incinerator if she is so equipped, or pumped ashore direct to reception facilities at the berth or, more commonly, to a road tanker which will take the waste oil for disposal ashore.

The water which has been separated from the oil may still contain some traces of oil. It can be discharged into the sea, but only under carefully controlled conditions. *Water containing traces of oil can be discharged into the sea only when:* the ship is not within a Special Area, the ship is more than 50 miles from land, the ship is proceeding en route, the oil content of the discharge does not exceed 15 parts per million (ppm), and the ship is using an approved oily-water separator system.

Within a Special Area the discharge of oil or an oily mixture from any ship above 400gt is prohibited.

Special Areas: Special Areas in 2009 for the purposes of discharge of oily water, were the Mediterranean, Baltic, Black Sea, Red Sea, the (Arabian) Gulfs Area, the Gulf of Aden, the Antarctic, the North West European waters, the Oman area of the Arabian Sea and the Southern South African waters. Some Special areas have not yet come into effect[268] because they do not contain adequate facilities for landing wastes. Full records of all activities involving oil or oily water and of the testing, maintenance and repair of the oily water separator and its alarm system[270] must be recorded in the ship's Oil Record Book.

Sewage: Annex IV of the Marpol regulations is concerned with the discharge of sewage. Annex IV entered into force in 2003 and subsequent amendments have been adopted. The requirements for bulk carriers are no different from the requirements for other ships, so require no special comment.

Garbage, cargo residues and associated wastes: Annex V of the Marpol Regulations deals with the disposal of garbage, which includes cargo residues and associated wastes. Fig. 25.1, based on information taken from the Guidelines[210] tabulates the different categories of garbage occurring aboard dry bulk carriers and the places where they can be discharged into the sea. For disposal at sea detergents and hold cleaning chemicals used when washing holds must be on the IMO approved list[267].

Special Areas present particular problems for a bulk carrier which is asked to discharge one cargo and then load another within the same Special Area. All cargo residues and any hold washing water must be landed to reception facilities ashore or retained aboard ship for discharge after leaving the Special Area. In practice suitable reception facilities are seldom found and may be inconveniently positioned, expensive and already in use by another ship. Few ships are built with holding tanks for hold washing water (the Diamond 53 series described in Chapter 18 being a welcome exception) and even this class of ship must accept the penalty that when they are carrying hold washing water their deadweight available for cargo is reduced. For all these reasons it is difficult to comply with the rules and responsible ship operators often avoid the problem by refusing a sequence of cargoes which requires them to discharge and then load in a Special Area unless the outward cargo is one that can be loaded in unwashed holds. They enter or they leave the Special Area in ballast. Alternatively, when it is a practical option, they leave the Special Area to wash holds and then return for the next cargo.

When reception facilities for garbage, including incinerator and cargo residues and associated wastes, are unsatisfactory it is difficult or impossible for ships' personnel to comply with the regulations. This exposes them, and the ship's owners and operators to the serious risk of incurring heavy fines or even imprisonment[212]. Mariners are urged, in their own

Fig. 25.1 Disposal of garbage, including cargo related materials, at Sea

<table>
<tr><th>Garbage type</th><th>Outside Special Area</th><th>In Special Area</th></tr>
<tr><td>Plastics, including packaging, ship construction materials, disposable eating utensils and cups, bags, sheeting, strapping bands, ropes and lines.
Oily rags and contaminated rags (rags saturated with a harmful substance)</td><td>Disposal prohibited</td><td>Disposal prohibited</td></tr>
<tr><td>Cargo associated waste which will float, including dunnage, shoring, pallets, lining and packing materials, plywood, paper, cardboard, wire and steel strapping</td><td>>25 miles offshore*</td><td>Disposal prohibited</td></tr>
<tr><td rowspan="2">Cargo residues, which will sink including the remnants of any cargo left in the holds or spilt on deck during loading or discharge, and also paper, rags, glass, metal, bottles, crockery and similar, ash and clinkers (but not ash from plastic products which may contain toxic or heavy metal residues, which must be put ashore. Ash is usually stored on deck in drums until it is landed)</td><td>>12 miles offshore*</td><td>Disposal prohibited</td></tr>
<tr><td colspan="2">Cargo residues spilt on deck cannot be washed overboard immediately after leaving port but must be retained aboard until the ship reaches a permitted position</td></tr>
<tr><td rowspan="2">Hold washing water containing cargo residues, except when (like petcoke, for example) it contains substances defined or listed under other annexes to the Convention. When hold washing water contains oily or noxious wastes, or detergents or hold cleaning chemicals the composition of the product may determine whether the water should be treated in accordance with MARPOL Annex 1 (Oil) or Annex II (Noxious liquid substance)[211]. If the detergents and hold cleaning chemicals are on the IMO approved list[267] the hold washing water can be treated in accordance with MARPOL Annex V.</td><td>>12 miles offshore*</td><td rowspan="2">Disposal prohibited</td></tr>
<tr><td>Positions of starting and ending washing must be logged</td></tr>
<tr><td>Food waste not comminuted (minced) or ground</td><td>>12 miles offshore*</td><td>Disposal prohibited</td></tr>
<tr><td>All other garbage including paper, rags, glass, etc comminuted or ground</td><td>>3 miles offshore*</td><td>Disposal prohibited</td></tr>
<tr><td>Food waste comminuted (minced) or ground</td><td>>3 miles offshore*</td><td>>12 miles offshore*</td></tr>
<tr><td>Bilge water from the bilges of loaded cargo holds is not treated as cargo residues provided that the cargo material is not classified as a marine pollutant in the IMDG Code and the bilge water is discharged from the loaded hold through the vessel's fixed piping bilge drainage system.
Dishwater and greywater are similarly not treated as garbage.</td><td>Disposal permitted</td><td>Disposal permitted</td></tr>
<tr><td colspan="3">*The regulation states 25 miles (or 12 miles or 3 miles) 'from the nearest land' but this does not mean quite what it says. The distance must be measured 'from the baseline from which the territorial sea of the territory in question is established in accordance with international law', so a greater distance will often be needed and is always to be preferred. Off the Australian coast wider limits apply to protect the Great Barrier Reef.</td></tr>
</table>

interests, to report inadequacies of port reception facilities for garbage using forms available[213].

Each vessel is required to have a Garbage Management Plan which specifies procedures for the collection, sorting, processing, storing and disposal of the garbage. All disposal of wastes is to be recorded in the Garbage Record Book and when the garbage being disposed of is 'cargo residue' the start and finish positions of the ship must be recorded in the Garbage Record Book.

Wherever possible garbage should be landed to reception facilities ashore and a written receipt obtained from the approved receiver. This receipt should be attached to the Garbage Record Book or kept in a clearly marked file. When discharge into the sea is permitted garbage should be discharged as far from land as possible and the correct notations should be made in the Garbage Record Book.

Cargo handling equipment and procedures should be as efficient as possible, to minimise the spillage of cargo on deck and spillage should be landed or put into the hold wherever possible. Shipboard areas where spillage is most common, such as the deck alongside the hatch opening should be protected, by tarpaulins or plastic sheeting, such that the residues are easily recovered.

Special Areas for the discharge of garbage. Special areas for the purposes of Annex V are the Mediterranean Sea area, the Baltic Sea area, the Black Sea area, the Red Sea area, the (Arabian) Gulfs area, the North Sea area, the Antarctic area and the Wider Caribbean Region. These Special Areas come into force when sufficient garbage reception facilities have been provided within the region. In 2009 the Baltic, North Sea, (Arabian) Gulfs and Mediterranean areas are reported to be in operation[268]. The regulations treat the Antarctic as a special case, requiring the flag states from which ships depart to the Antarctic and return from the Antarctic, and the flag states of the ships visiting the Antarctic to undertake that as soon as practicable ships will have sufficient capacity to retain garbage aboard and that adequate reception facilities will be provided in departure and destination ports. Mariners should bear in mind that other areas, such as the USA, may have particular requirements for the environmentally safe disposal of garbage.

In addition to providing detailed information on the disposal of garbage the Guidelines[210] provide a framework for the education and training of seafarers, information on methods of reducing shipboard generation of garbage; shipboard garbage handling and storage procedures; shipboard equipment for processing garbage; estimation of the amounts of ship-generated garbage delivered to port; and actions to ensure compliance with the regulations.

Putting waste overboard at sea: The safest and simplest policy is to dump nothing except food and cargo waste at sea and this policy has been adopted by some major ship operators[269]. Everything is stored on board until the next port of call is reached. To avoid mistakes, safe procedures must be followed when waste is put overboard at sea. The Guidelines[210] provide detailed advice about best procedures and the ship's Garbage Management Plan will set out the agreed procedures for the particular ship:

- The waste must be sorted into (a) plastic, (b) food wastes and (c) other garbage which can be disposed of at sea. Plastic can never be put into the sea. Waste is best sorted by having separate bins, each with its separate lid, in the galley and in other designated places for each type of waste (Figs. 25.2 and 25.3). Cabin waste bins should be metallic, not plastic, to reduce the fire risk.
- The Plan is likely to specify that the person responsible for putting the waste overboard should contact the ship's bridge at a regular time each day for permission to put waste overboard. The type of waste must be stated. Permission should only be given when the ship's position is suitable.
- A full record should be kept, in the Garbage Record Book, of each occasion that waste is put overboard.

Fig. 25.2 Garbage bins marked and colour coded

Fig. 25.3 Garbage bins, marked and colour coded

Fig. 25.4 Incinerator aboard a Panamax bulk carrier

Compacting: When the ship has a compactor it can be used to reduce the volume of waste by as much as 12:1. Compacted waste, if put overboard, will sink much more readily and if stored on board will occupy much less space. Bales of compacted garbage if not put ashore should, where possible, be put overboard in depths greater than 50 metres to minimise their exposure to waves and currents.

Incineration: Disposal of domestic waste in a ship's incinerator (Fig. 25.4) is governed by the requirements of MARPOL Annex VI Regulation 16. Paragraph 4 of the Regulation specifies a short list of prohibited substances which should be noted though most of them are unlikely to occur aboard bulk carriers. The incineration of polyvinyl chlorides (PVCs) is prohibited except in shipboard incinerators which have been IMO Type Approved. Some ships favour disposal of all waste by incineration. Ashes from the incinerator probably amount to no more than 20 litres/week and should be retained for landing, particularly if they include ashes from the burning of oily sludge and plastic. As yet there are no substantial restrictions on the use of incinerators for the disposal of ships' wastes on the high seas. Consequently marine incinerators in current use, usually designed for intermittent operation, typically do not include any provisions for air pollution control. In general the use of shipboard incinerators in ports should be avoided and permission should be obtained from the port authority before any use in port[210].

Putting waste ashore: Receipts must be obtained for any waste which is put ashore as authorities may require evidence of the manner in which the ship disposes of her waste. If necessary a receipt written by the ship for signature and stamping by the person accepting the waste, or even authenticated by the ship's agent will be sufficient proof. Some countries with strict agricultural regulations will not accept dunnage of uncertain or uncertificated origin.

Air pollution from ships is addressed by Marpol Annex VI which, in 2009, requires that the sulphur content of any marine fuel used anywhere worldwide does not exceed 4.5% mass/mass (m/m). The concept of sulphur oxide (SOx) Emission Control Areas (SECAs) was introduced in 2006 when the first such area, the Baltic, was established. Within SECAs ships must burn marine fuel with a sulphur content that does not exceed 1.5% m/m unless an approved exhaust gas system is fitted. In 2007 the Baltic SECA was extended by merging it with a new North Sea SECA such that almost all northern European waters are now included[214].

In a separate initiative the European Community (EC) has introduced a requirement for marine gas oil used and sold within the EC to have a sulphur content of no more than 0.1% by 1st January 2010 and the United States is reported to be considering introducing a similar requirement[214]. Consequently IMO is in 2009 in the process of toughening MARPOL Annex VI.

The timetable adopted by IMO's Marine Environment Protection Committee (MEPC) and entering into force by 1st July 2010 is as follows:

Year	Action
2010	Emission Control Area (ECA) limit for sulphur content in fuel oils reduced to 1.0%
2012	Global limit reduced to 3.5%
2015	ECA limit reduced to 0.1%
2020	Global limit to 0.5% but a review in 2018 (with the authority to delay implementation) will determine if this is achievable.
2025	Global limit to 0.5% notwithstanding the result of the 2018 review.

Ballast water. Restrictions on the discharge of ballast water are described in Chapter 7.

The housekeeping problem

A bulk carrier operates most efficiently and is most pleasant to live in when dust, dirt, seawater, ice and snow are kept out of the accommodation, machinery spaces and storerooms, but this is not easy to achieve. A laden bulk carrier has a small freeboard and her decks are frequently awash (Fig. 25.5), providing opportunities for sea water to enter holds and storerooms.

Bulk cargoes are often dusty and their loading or discharge spreads dust and dirt over a wide area (Fig. 25.6) which can include the entire ship. Bulk terminals are sometimes filthy, with the approaches to the ship covered to a depth of several inches in wet cargo residues (Fig. 21.16). Certain cargoes – such as alumina and quartzite, for example – produce dust which is very abrasive and must be kept out of machinery.

Excluding dust

Alumina is a fine white powder with highly abrasive qualities. It is extremely dusty and liable to cover the ship overall during loading and discharging operations (Figs. 25.7 and 8). Besides overall contamination of accommodation and other spaces, severe damage can be caused by this cargo dust to engineroom and deck machinery, radio and navigation equipment. The precautions recommended by one shipowner for excluding alumina dust are given below. These are extreme precautions for a particularly damaging type of dust: the same precautions can be used, as far as is necessary, for other less harmful dust.

Fig. 25.5 The decks of a bulk carrier are often awash

Fig. 25.6 Cargo residues on deck between hatches Nos 8 and 9

Fig. 25.7 Loading alumina
Photo courtesy of Captain L Hesketh FNI

Fig. 25.8 The alumina dust lies everywhere, even on the flying bridge
Photo courtesy of Captain L Hesketh FNI

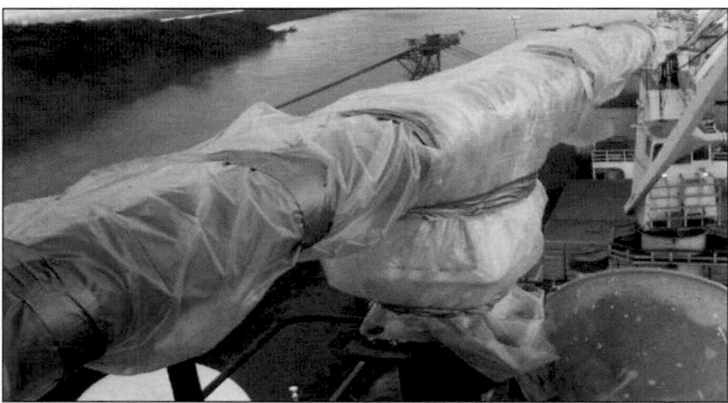

Fig. 25.9 Radar scanner cocooned to protect from dust *Courtesy EMS Ship Supply (Norway) AS*

Fig. 25.10 Liferaft cocooned to protected from dust
Courtesy EMS Ship Supply (Norway) AS

Fig. 25.11 EPIRB cocooned to protect from dust

Courtesy EMS Ship Supply (Norway) AS

- All accommodation and engineroom intake fans must be switched off.
- All intake vents must be screened with a double layer of muslin.
- All fire flaps must be closed.
- All exposed deck motors (eg hatch, windlass, capstan, crane, gangway, lifeboat) must be covered.
- All steel doors, all internal doors, skylights, ports and windows in accommodation, engineroom, cranes, deck stores and other spaces must be closed.
- Because of the sensitivity of equipment in the wheelhouse, bridge wing doors should be sealed with duct tape or masking tape around the frame.
- All exposed navigation aids (eg, radar scanner (Fig. 25.9), satcom aerial) must be protected.
- Air conditioning must be recirculating with outside vents shut.
- Hold bilges must be made 'siftproof' by covering them with double burlap sealed with ramnek or duct tape around the edges.
- Any hatches which are not being worked must be kept closed, thereby avoiding unnecessary exposure of the rubber packing and blockage of the drain holes. Trackways must be scrupulously cleaned upon completion.
- The hatches on enclosed lifeboats must be sealed with masking tape and open lifeboats must be covered.
- Liferafts must be cocooned with plastic sheeting (Fig. 25.10) which must, of course, be removed on completion of cargo work and before the ship sails.
- Lifesaving equipment must be cocooned (Fig. 25.11) and the cocooning must be removed on completion of cargo work and before the ship sails.
- If the instruction books for auxiliary machinery contain advice for running in contaminated areas – for example, if they advise the use of fine air filters or more frequent oil changes – these instructions must be followed.

Precautions of this sort require time and organisation to put in place and to remove. It is necessary for the Master and mates to keep other members of the ship's company fully informed to ensure that the precautions are put in place in good time and are not removed until the exposure to dust is ended.

If the ship is clean and the cargo damaging it may be worthwhile to cover the entire bridge front (Fig. 25.12).

Dealing with dirt

Dirt in the accommodation: Dirt is to be found on the dockside of many bulk carrier berths and is spilt on the decks of bulk carriers by the loading and discharging operations. It is brought into the accommodation on the boots and clothing of ship's crew, stevedores, officials and other visitors if they are not prevented from so doing.

Most of the people who enter the accommodation, both ship's company and visitors, understand the wish to keep the accommodation clean and are prepared to be co-operative. To gain their co-operation it is necessary to make co-operation easy, to provide whatever facilities are needed, and to show clearly what is required. It is useless to post a notice saying 'Clean your boots before entering' if nothing is provided for cleaning boots. Such a notice is equally useless if those entering cannot read English: the best notices use pictures to pass the message.

People who enter the accommodation in port do so through the door which is nearest to the gangway or accommodation ladder. Some bulkers provide a fixed steel scraping bar outside this door on port and starboard sides to be used for scraping dirt from footwear. Some bulkers also have broom heads with stiff bristles fixed in position to one side of the door to be used for brushing dirt from boots before entering the accommodation. (Fig. 25.13)

Inside all accommodation doors the use of checkmats can be recommended. These are rubber-backed mats measuring about 2.0 x 1.3 metres and having a loose pile which soaks up dirt. They can be washed in a heavy-duty domestic washing machine or scrubbed on deck using a portable high-pressure Kew gun and hose, and will dry in a few hours if hung in a warm dry place. If spare mats are carried the dirty mats can be removed daily for washing whilst the ship is in port.

Aboard some bulkers everyone entering the accommodation or some part of it is asked to remove his shoes. Those entering will be very reluctant to comply with this request unless the deck covering is very clean indeed. One major owner of bulkers has adopted an effective way of dealing with this problem.

Fig. 25.12 Bulk carrier's bridge front swathed in sheeting while unloading cement

Photo courtesy of Scanautics

Fig. 25.13 Shoe cleaning facilities at the main accommodation entrance

As people enter the accommodation block they see a notice which invites them to help keep the accommodation clean by wearing the overshoes provided. Two boxes of plastic/fibre overshoes are situated by the entrance. One box contains new unused overshoes, while the other contains used overshoes. These overshoes cost about $1 a pair, and are obtainable from British and European shipchandlers. Provision of overshoes has greatly reduced the amount of dirt being walked into the accommodation. Japanese ship operators achieve a similar result by providing slippers for visitors to wear.

Dirty clothing in the accommodation presents problems unless changing rooms and lockers are available so that all those entering can be persuaded to remove outer clothing for the time they are inside. When a ship is provided with a cargo control room or ship's office close to the main accommodation entrances, movement between the open decks and the control room in dirty clothing is difficult to avoid, but stricter standards can be imposed on anyone needing to pass further into the accommodation, particularly to carpeted areas. A higher standard of cleanliness can be demanded of visitors to cabins and to the Master's office.

The ISPS Code and the ship's Security Plan require no more than one open access to the accommodation in port with other doors closed and locked from the inside. When conditions on deck are dirty this has the added benefit of making it easier to keep dirty clothing and footwear away from clean accommodation areas.

Dirt on deck: For the purposes of these notes dirt on deck includes cargo spillages, hold and bilge sweepings, leaking hydraulic oil and snow and ice. When these substances are to be found on deck officers must consider the danger of people slipping, the possibilities of pollution of dock water, and the likelihood that the substances will be carried into the accommodation on people's shoes.

Where possible trimmers should sweep up and remove cargo spilt on deck, but in many ports they do not accept this as part of their work. If such work is left to the crew they must ensure that nothing is allowed to blow over the ship's side or fall into the sea until the vessel is outside the appropriate MARPOL limit (Fig. 25.1). On occasions sweeping or shoveling all the residues into drums or other containers will be a massive task, which could delay departure. Cargo is usually spilt only on one side of the deck, unless exceptionally the ship is working cargo on both sides, so the side which is not in use besides being safer for anyone needing to walk along the deck is also cleaner. The dirty side of the deck should be roped off. If the decks are unsafe because of cargo residues such as iron ore pellets or slippery soya beans (Fig. 21.28), safe pathways must be swept or shovelled clean.

Hold, deck and bilge sweepings when stored on deck before disposal should be stacked in positions which do not interfere with free passage along the length of the deck. It is sometimes convenient to pile sweepings in the sheltered positions between adjacent hatches, damped down to prevent dust from blowing about and covered if possible with plastic sheeting or tarpaulins.

Leakage of oil from hydraulic systems should never be allowed to lie on deck. Leakage gives the ship a neglected appearance, makes the deck slippery and hazardous and presents a pollution risk since the oil could drain overboard or be washed over by an overflow of ballast or a downpour of rain. Oil leaks should be repaired as soon as they occur, and the spillage should be cleaned up immediately. Oil absorbent granules are better than sawdust for the removal of spillages, and oil absorbent mats are excellent as a temporary means of soaking up minor leakage.

Snow or ice which lies on deck is a hazard for those who have to walk over the decks. It should be shovelled to one side, melted with rock salt or sprinkled with sand or grit to ensure that a safe non-slip surface is available.

Keeping water out

Sea water which enters storerooms, accommodation, machinery or cargo spaces can cause considerable damage to the contents of the space it has entered. Several of the methods of excluding water have been mentioned in previous chapters, but it may be useful to consider them together.

Water in the forecastle space: Water in the forecastle store can destroy the switchgear and motors for the windlasses, hatch opening units and other electric equipment. Stores placed in the space can also be destroyed, and corrosion of the space and its contents will increase. Water can enter the forecastle space by any of the following routes.

- Through watertight doors or hatches which have been left open or carelessly closed or which have defective seals or cleats.
- By leakage from a flooded chain locker.
- By leakage from the deck service/cable washing line.
- Through drains with caps missing in forecastle bulkheads.
- Through a ventilator which has been damaged or left open.
- By flooding from the forepeak tank by way of a loose or open manhole cover or an open sounding pipe.
- Through fractures in the structure of the compartment, most likely to be found around the hawse pipes or in way of contact damage.

The measures required to prevent flooding are the following:

- Keep watertight doors and hatches well maintained with good rubbers and efficient cleats. Make sure they are properly and completely closed at the end of the working day, and when rough weather is expected. Tighten dogs regularly in heavy weather, as they frequently ease back.
- Fit portable covers over the spurling pipes when the ship is at sea to prevent sea water washing into the chain lockers. Keep the chain locker doors closed when the ship is at sea. Sound the chain lockers daily and pump them out when permitted.
- The valves for the washers for the anchor cables should be closed when the washers are not in use.
- Bulkhead drains should always be properly capped or plugged when not in use.
- Ventilators should be carefully closed when bad weather is expected.

- The manhole cover for the forepeak tank should, if it has been opened, be closed and secured before the tank is completely filled and the sounding pipe cap should be left screwed shut.
- Any signs of leakage after washing down, heavy rain or meeting heavy weather should be carefully investigated.
- The high-level bilge alarm, if fitted in the forecastle space, should be tested whenever the ship leaves port and weekly at sea.
- The forecastle space should be inspected daily in rough weather and promptly whenever the high-level bilge alarm sounds.
- The forecastle space water ingress detector should be fully operational

Water in masthouses, deck stores and accommodation: Masthouses, deck stores and accommodation are not intended to contain sea water and it must be excluded by keeping watertight doors, deadlights and ventilators in good operating condition and by ensuring that they are properly closed before the onset of bad weather. Bulkhead drain plugs, when fitted, must be properly capped or plugged when not in use.

The poop deck on all but the smallest bulkers is usually free of water, so doors there are sometimes carelessly left unsecured. On those rare occasions when the vessel is experiencing a high following swell water may be shipped on the poop deck. When that is a possibility the poop deck should be well secured.

Water in holds: Water can leak into holds through the hatch covers, through leaks in the deck or the ship's sides, from ballast tanks, down ventilators, through damaged airpipes or uncapped bilge sounding pipes, and through bilge suction, bilge eductor or ballast lines. Leakage can only occur when the ship or her fittings are defective or misused. Leakage into holds can damage cargoes and even lead to the sinking of ships.

Leakage can usually be detected by a rise in the ship's soundings or by the setting off of high-level bilge alarms, when fitted. The water ingress detectors are fitted to detect serious leakage and will be activated if flood water reaches a depth of 0.5 metres. When holds are empty leaks into the hold can be seen, provided they are below the sea surface. Leakage is prevented by ensuring that the ship's structure is sound and undamaged and that all her fittings are properly maintained, regularly tested and correctly used.

Sources

210, 211, 212, 213, 214, 267, 268, 269, 270. (See List of Sources, Page 497.)

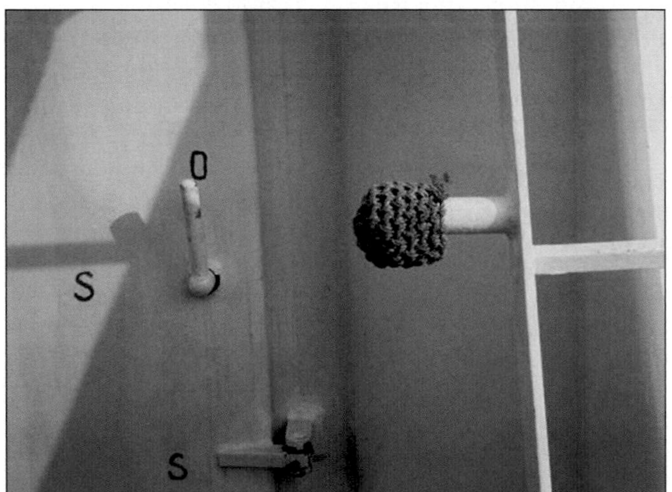

Fig. 25.14 A ropework stop for a steel watertight door, lovingly made by a Greek bosun

CHAPTER 26

BULK CARRIER CASUALTIES

Casualties in the 1980s and 1990s, factors contributing to bulk carrier casualties, the path to safer shipping, improvements introduced, prevention of casualties, casualty prevention by ships' personnel and shipowners, detection of damage, casualties since 1993, conclusion

---

Casualties in the 1980s and 1990s

THE EARLY 1990S were a grim time in which to be serving aboard a bulk carrier. The realisation was gradually dawning on the shipping community that an uncomfortably large number of bulk carriers had foundered or been lost without trace (Appendix 26.1) in the previous fifteen years. That the lost ships had flown many flags and been registered with a number of different classification societies helped to conceal the wide extent of the problem despite the concern expressed during the 1980s by past and current seafarers such as Douglas Foy[37, 40, 58] and Captains Boyle[68] and Richardson[39]. The fact that some of the lost ships were relatively new increased the confusion. In 1990 and 1991 one bulk carrier a month was lost on average. It was abundantly clear that something was wrong, but what was it?

A few fortunate bulk carriers survived serious structural damage and photos appeared in the media of ships with side plating missing from both sides and a view of the scene beyond the ship, framed by the remaining bits of the ship's structure.

When mariners considered their own experience they identified two ways in which, it seemed to them, bulk carriers might be damaged. Big bulk carriers, Panamax, Cape-sized or ULBCs, meet heavy weather ponderously and when the weather worsens and the bow starts slamming into the waves the impacts may not be detected on the ship's bridge, 200 or more metres away. Mariners suspected that some Masters were carelessly driving their ships too hard in adverse weather, thereby fatally damaging them.

Mariners' second concern was the manner in which massive tonnages of cargo, particularly iron ore, were poured into ships at high speed. It was felt intuitively that pouring 16,000 tonnes of iron ore an hour into a bulk carrier must stress her structure. When, finally, the principal causes of casualties were found neither of the mariners' explanations was shown to be significant.

Around about 1990 the classification societies finally recognised that unexplained bulk carrier losses, with the loss of more than 200 lives that year, had become a serious problem and resources were committed to examining the evidence and seeking explanations, individually and collectively within the International Association of Classification Societies (IACS). Early in 1992 Lloyd's Register announced preliminary findings for bulk carriers of more than 20,000 dwt[57] the most significant of which took nearly everybody by surprise. The holds of some bulk carriers were severely corroded but that had not been noticed!

The design of conventional bulk carriers, with their large sloping hopper side tanks (Fig. 26.1), makes it difficult to achieve a close-up inspection of the ship's side plating in the area of vertical framing between the lower and upper hopper tanks. In the 1980s

Fig.26.1 On a big bulk carrier the distance from tanktop to ship's side framing and shell plating is immense

Photo courtesy of Scanautics

Fig.26.2 There is often no way of getting close to the upper parts of the hold

Photo courtesy of Scanautics

inspections by ships' staff and frequently by surveyors too, often consisted of simply standing on the tanktop and looking at the ships frames and plating anything from 5 to 15 metres distant from them. Indented or buckled frames interrupted the symmetry of the construction and were easy to see but corrosion and wastage were not obvious and, it is now well known, were frequently overlooked. A later study[65] concluded 'The higher side shell and bulkhead structures are difficult to reach for close-up inspections. From a distance they may appear in deceptively good condition when actually highly corroded' (Fig. 26.2).

Factors contributing to bulk carrier casualties

The classification societies had, by 1992, concluded[57, 65] that the ships most likely to become casualties were older ships which had carried coal, then iron ore in alternate holds whilst exposed to heavy weather. It appeared that high sulphur coal had caused accelerated corrosion and alternate loading had, in heavy weather, exposed the ships to excessive stresses.

Most surviving casualties had lost side shell plating. Unexpectedly high corrosion levels were frequently found above the lower hoppers and stools in the holds of casualties which survived. Neglected fatigue cracking was often found at bulkhead boundaries and the toes of frame brackets.

The conclusions contained a number of possible causes of damage to bulk carriers. They were: high levels of corrosion from cargoes, weakness in ship design detail, damage to the ship's shell structure by the methods of discharge and inadvertent overloading of compartments. 'Inadvertent over-loading' is the term used to describe a situation in which a ship is properly loaded to her marks but by accident has an excessive tonnage in one hold and too little cargo in another hold.

Corrosion, damage and structural weakness might have been worsened in some cases by the liquefaction of the cargo because of high moisture content or flooding. Flooding through hatchway damage is also mentioned as a possible first event.[42, 65]

The above listed causes of casualties are summarised and also discussed more fully in Appendix 26.2.

Appendix 26.3 contains descriptions of a number of other possible causes of bulk carrier damage and casualties. Most of them remain as valid today as they were when written in 1993, and deserve careful consideration by anyone with a concern for bulk carrier safety.

Discarded theories: It is worthy of note that there has, apparently, been little evidence to suggest that losses have occurred as a result of excessive longitudinal stresses such as might be caused by faulty distribution of the cargo. Readers of The Nautical Institute's *Seaways* were authoritatively told in 1991[84]: 'There is overwhelming evidence that the vast majority of structural failures affecting the seaworthiness of bulk carriers have little to do with longitudinal stresses'. Most failures are fairly evenly distributed along the cargo hold length and originate close to the bending neutral axis. In other words, the damage is not found in the upper deck or double bottom, where longitudinal stress would be expected to show itself. A similar view was expressed ten years later when a shipping forum[257, 258] was reminded that the most significant stresses to which bulk carriers are subjected are transverse, not longitudinal. It is more likely that the side shell plating or the hatch covers will fail than that the bulk carrier will snap in two. Bulk carriers may survive the failure of the 'primary barrier' (ie the side shell or hatch cover) but cannot be guaranteed to survive the subsequent failure of the 'secondary barrier' (transverse bulkhead). When a hold floods and a bulkhead leaks the ship is unlikely to survive the flooding of a second hold. Nor has there ever been significant support from naval architects for the mariners' theory that ships are directly damaged by excessively high cargo loading rates though such rates will be an indirect cause of damage if the deballasting programme cannot keep pace with the loading rate.

The path to safer shipping

Ship Inspections: When in 1992 and 1993 the main causes of bulk carrier casualties had been identified the shipping community set about publicising and correcting the faults in the system. The classification societies' bulk carrier inspection regime was made more rigorous with the introduction, mandated by The International Maritime Organization (IMO) in 1993, of the Enhanced Survey Programme (ESP) for older bulk carriers in Resolution A.744(18). This has perhaps been the single most effective improvement made to the safety of bulk carriers. The P&I Clubs and marine underwriters also introduced or increased condition surveys of the ships in which they had an interest. Shipowners inspected their ships more frequently and instructed their officers to do likewise. In 2004 IMO issued guidance for Port State Control Officers to assist them in inspecting the structure of bulk carriers[262] and part of this is reproduced in Appendix 26.5.

Enhanced surveys[66] of the 'cargo length' of older bulk carriers, were phased in from 1 July 1993. They provide for more frequent and more thorough close-up inspections of hold and ballast tank structures, measurement of steel thickness, and monitoring of the condition of coatings. Thoroughness of inspection increases as the ship becomes older, if substantial corrosion is found, and if hold and ballast tank coatings are not well maintained. A copy of the record of thickness measurements is retained aboard and is available along with the hull survey report, for inspection by all interested parties. These documents were previously confidential between classification society and clients.

Unified Requirements: The classification societies recognised that some of the problems of bulk carriers could have been caused by competition between them to accept designs that minimised shipbuilding costs. 'Unified Requirements', structural rules adopted as minimum standards by all IACS members for different aspects of bulk carrier construction, were seen as a way of preventing damaging competition and have been gradually introduced over the years since 1993 for new tonnage and, to a lesser extent, to ships in service. This ensures that new ships being brought into service are safer than older tonnage, but additional measures were required to improve the safety of bulk carriers already in service.

Guidance and regulation: The International Maritime Organization (IMO) put the issue of bulk carrier safety on the agenda of its Maritime Safety Committee in 1993 and started the development of guidelines, codes of practice and regulations to improve the safety of bulk carriers and those who serve in them. A new SOLAS chapter, Chapter XII, entitled 'Additional Safety Measures for Bulk Carriers' and dealing principally with new buildings, was adopted in November 1997. Bulk carriers were amongst the first categories of vessel to be required to implement the International Safety Management (ISM) Code when it was introduced in 1998. The Code of Practice for the Safe Loading and Unloading of Bulk Carriers (BLU Code), incorporating the Ship/Shore Safety Checklist and the Loading/Unloading Plan was published in 1998.

In 1998 the United Kingdom (UK) Administration proposed to IMO that a full Formal Safety Assessment (FSA) of bulk carriers should be undertaken. The UK also offered to sponsor the study and to act as co-ordinators. This study, reporting in 2002, identified 75 different ways of reducing the risks of bulk carrier operations and concluded that about 20 of them (Appendix 26.4) were cost effective. The FSA ran parallel to the Re-opened Formal Investigation into the Loss of the m.v. *Derbyshire*[94], a 173,000 dwt ore laden British Oil/Bulk/Ore (OBO) carrier which had been lost without trace in a Pacific typhoon when nearing her destination port, Kawasaki in Japan, in September 1980. Her loss was remarkable because she was a well-found ship and only four years old. It was only 14 years later that the ship's remains were identified on the seabed, 2.5 miles below the surface, when it was possible to methodically take about 136,000 photographs of the wreckage which led, eventually, to reliable conclusions as to the causes of the vessel's loss. When the ship had met a long, high swell near the centre of the typhoon and taken green seas over her bows airpipes and ventilators were broken and the forward spaces were flooded. As the forward draught increased, the increased load from the green seas sweeping over the No.1 hatch covers caused them to buckle and collapse allowing the hold to fill with sea water almost immediately, soon to be followed by the other holds in succession. The time from collapse of the No.1 hatch covers until the final plunge to the seabed would have been no more than a few minutes. The Report[94] contains a long list of recommendations for improving the safety of bulk carriers: most if not all the conclusions were applicable to all types of dry bulk carriers, not only to OBOs. At about the same time the IACS announced its 'Eight Initiatives' for existing bulk carriers[259]. They were:

- Early implementation of SOLAS Chapter XII requirements,
- Revision of IACS' Enhanced Survey Programme,
- Installation of water ingress alarms in all cargo holds,
- Improved bulwarks or fitting of a breakwater,
- Increased integrity of foredeck fittings,
- Increased strength requirements for hatch covers,
- Additional requirements for side shell frames in cargo holds,
- Water ingress alarms in forward spaces.

Improvements introduced[138, 256]

This extensive research, investigation, regulation and litigation for bulk carriers has led in the years between 1993 and 2009 to numerous changes in the ways that bulk carriers, primarily single skinned bulk carriers of 150 m in length and upwards, are designed, built, operated and maintained.

Structural: Since 1999 bulk carriers are built to comply with stricter flooding criteria. Their bulkheads are able to resist more severe sloshing and since 2004 they have hatches and coamings with strength sufficient for the most severe weather and seas they can expect to meet[271] (International Association of Classification Societies' Unified Requirement – IACS UR – S21). Hatch cover securing mechanisms have been upgraded where necessary to comply with raised standards (IACS URs S21 and S30). The strengthening of hold framing has been phased in for ships in service and made mandatory for new buildings (IACS UR S31). Minimum standards for foredeck fittings (ventilators and airpipes) have been raised with many of the requirements applicable to tonnage in service as well as new buildings (IACS UR S27). Improved standards for the strength and securing of small hatches on the foredeck have been introduced (IACS UR S26). In a welcome return to ship building traditions bulk carriers are again being built with raised forecastles which contribute to the vessel's buoyancy and give protection to the coamings and covers of the forward holds (IACS UR S28). The structural strength requirements for single side-skin construction in SOLAS have, since July 2006, been applicable to all bulk carriers[272]. The sea water ballast tanks of ships built since 1998 and the double side skin spaces of bulk carriers built since 2006 must be provided with an efficient corrosion prevention system[182]. Standards for protective coatings for holds have also been established (IACS UR Z9).

Operational: Older bulk carriers, unless built with exceptional strength, or specially modified to satisfy the higher standards now required, are forbidden to carry denser cargoes[273]. Unless, in addition, they can satisfy the most demanding flooding criteria in any one hold they are forbidden to carry a full high density cargo in alternate holds[167]. The *International Safety Management (ISM) Code* has introduced safer and more methodical and thorough methods of working to fleets where these were not previously found, but operating standards continue to vary from fleet to fleet and, to a lesser extent, from ship to ship, depending upon the culture of the owner or manager, and upon the calibre of individual managements, Masters and their crews. Since 2006 Masters on voyages longer than 48 hours are required to report their positions daily[274]. Masters have been provided with important and necessary guidance on preparations to abandon ship rapidly if flooding is suspected (See Chapter 21).

Equipment: Every vessel of 3,000 gt and upwards is required to have a voyage data recorder[275]. All bulk carriers must be fitted with water ingress detectors

(WIDs) in their holds and forward spaces with visual and audible alarms on the bridge[129] and with remotely activated pumping systems serving tanks and spaces in the forward part of the vessel[222]. Chain lockers must be watertight with access via bolted doors[276] (IACS UR L4). Windlasses must be strongly fixed in place (IACS UR S27). The industry has been provided with requirements for loading computers[277]. All bulk carrier crew members must be provided with immersion suits[278]. New built bulk carriers must be provided with free-fall lifeboats[279].

Double side skin structure: One of the recommendations of the Formal Safety Assessment of bulk carriers was that double side skin structure was the most effective way of preventing side-shell failure, the single most recorded cause of losses of larger bulk carriers. However this was subsequently rejected by IMO 'as other options were deemed more cost effective per life saved, although with a lower potential risk reduction, there would be less lives saved'[138]. Despite this decision double side skinned bulk carriers are being built in increasing numbers (see Chapter 18) and their performance over the longer term will continue to be of considerable interest to the industry.

'An interesting compromise was reached and a new regulation, SOLAS XII 6.5 introduced to ensure that single side skin ships would have the same benefits as given by double side skin construction, ie cargo friendliness, easy of discharge of cargo, structural continuity and redundancy'[138]. In fact, it is difficult to visualise how the rules can be satisfied, except with double side skin construction.

Prevention of casualties

Since 1991 a great many measures have been put into place to prevent bulk carrier casualties. If all involved in the operation, repair and inspection of bulk carriers do their jobs properly casualties should become exceedingly rare, but risk continues to lie in the fact that individuals do not always do their jobs properly. Seafarers can do no better than remember the simple rule that has prevented so many mistakes – ***always double check.*** This means that plans, procedures, programmes and inspections, if done by one person should be checked by another person or another method.

Of greatest interest to the ships' officers are the measures that they themselves and shipowners can take to reduce the risk of their ships becoming casualties. These measures come in two categories: those designed to prevent damage; and those intended to discover damage so that it can be repaired.

Casualty prevention by ships' personnel and shipowners

The prevention of damage to the ship's structure is of considerable importance to the shipowner and of even greater importance to the seafarer who may lose his life if his ship becomes a casualty. Structural damage is not inevitable, as is illustrated by the fact that sister ships are sometimes found to have quite different levels of damage. This is a matter over which conscientious seamen supported by their owners can exercise considerable influence. Prevention of damage by the use of safe procedures and good planning and by firm dealings with shippers, stevedores, trimmers and receivers is work which is worth doing well.

The recommendations which follow were compiled by The Nautical Institute's Bulk Carrier Working Group in 1992 and most of them remain as relevant in 2009 as they were when first listed. A number of them are now mandatory. They summarise ways in which the International Association of Classification Societies' original brief recommendations for reducing structural failures can be put into effect. Occasional remarks from a 2009 perspective have been added inside square brackets [like this]. Detailed operational and maintenance procedures are described in the body of this book

Where the adoption of any of these recommendations would require a departure from established company policy, The Nautical Institute would expect a Shipmaster to consult his employers before adopting the recommendation.

Minimise corrosion within holds by maintaining paint coatings. The areas most liable to suffer from corrosion are the frames and adjoining areas against the ship's sides, and the transverse bulkheads. These areas are less exposed to scouring by cargo or cargo-handling equipment than are tank tops and lower hopper sides, so paint coatings, if properly applied, can last reasonably well. Paint coatings should be maintained. Holds which have been routinely washed with sea water should where possible be given a final rinse with fresh water. Ships which are continuously employed carrying the same corrosive cargo, where holds are not cleaned between cargoes, have a higher risk of corrosion. A procedure of pumping bilges regularly during the voyage will reduce corrosion at tanktop level and within the bilge system, but will not stop corrosion which occurs as a result of sweat. Extra precautions should be taken when the cargoes are corrosive.

Minimise corrosion within ballast tanks by maintaining coatings. The touching up of mechanical damage and local corrosion is suitable work for a ship's crew, but a complete descaling and recoating probably requires shore labour and equipment.

Prevent stevedores' damage by close supervision of the stevedores to prevent bad practices, and by holding them responsible for any damage done.

Prevent hull contact damage by proceeding carefully when berthing, unberthing, manoeuvring and passing through ice [and check for damages by pushing tugs or cargo lighters lying alongside].

Report damage, and have it surveyed and properly repaired: Ensure that damage, when found, is reported to owners. All except minor damage should be reported to Class and surveyed by a Class surveyor. It should be properly repaired by a competent and suitably qualified person.

Avoid local overloading: Ensure that maximum permissible hold tonnages are known, and are not exceeded. Do not exceed maximum tanktop loadings. Avoid block loading except when approved by Class. Monitor loading and prevent delivery of excess tonnage to hold. Distribute closeweight cargo evenly over the length of the hold.

Provide accurate, accessible stability information: Ensure that the ship's stability and loading information is readily available, accurate and easy for the officers to use.

Prepare a full loading/deballasting or discharging/ballasting plan: Use IMO's form (Appendix 9.3) or a similar one and make sure that every stage is within permitted longitudinal bending stress and shear force limits.

Keep strictly to loading/deballasting or discharging/ballasting plan: Accept changes to the plan only when an amended plan has been fully calculated and found to be safe.

Reduce loading rates when starting an empty hold:[88] While the cargo is being poured directly on to the tanktop the loading rate should be reduced. Cargoes which can cause damage require special care. The first grabloads of scrap should be lowered close to the tanktop before being released. When pig iron is being loaded the tanktop should be shielded from the first pour by temporary sheathing such as pallets.

Ensure that discharging and ballast changes are planned and executed with the same care as loading: High values of longitudinal bending stresses and shear forces can be reached by unplanned or careless operations. They should be avoided.

Reject cargo with excessively high moisture content: Insist on being provided with a certificate of transportable moisture limit, and follow the guidelines laid down in the *IMSBC Code*[5].

Ensure that ship is not twisted whilst loading or changing ballast: Twisting can occur if two loaders do not operate exactly in tandem, or if a single loader distributes cargo unevenly between port and starboard sides. This damage can also be caused by uneven changing of ballast.

Close dump valves immediately deballasting is completed: Ensure dump valves are well maintained and do not leak and have a routine to ensure that they are closed when deballasting is completed.

Trim cargo reasonably level to the boundaries of the cargo space: Cargo should be trimmed in accordance with the *IMSBC Code*[5].

Ensure that cargoes such as steel are well secured: Cargo which breaks adrift can damage the ship's structure. Securing should be in accordance with the *IMO Cargo Securing Code*[38].

All hatch covers should be well maintained and carefully secured: The hatch covers must be in sound condition, with a cleating system which is well maintained and correctly operated.

All deck openings should be in sound condition and properly closed and secured: This applies upon sailing, at night, during adverse weather and any time when there is no need for them to be open.

Speed should be substantially reduced in adverse weather: When adverse weather causes a speed reduction of 25 per cent (for example from 12 knots to 9 knots) with constant engine speed, the rpm should be substantially reduced to avoid damage from forcing the ship into the weather.

Avoid continuous heavy rolling: Heavy rolling results in the repetitive heavy loading (panting) of the side shell plating as the pressure of sea water is applied and removed. Ships are built to withstand this treatment, but can be harmed when rolling is excessive and prolonged. [Continuous heavy rolling is not likely to damage a ship within her normal lifetime].

Sloshing of ballast water in part-filled tanks should not be allowed to occur: As far as possible ballast tanks should be filled or emptied before bad weather is met, this precaution being particularly important in the case of ballast holds and topside ballast tanks, both of which have large open areas which allow sloshing.

Prevent springing by adjustment of course, speed or ballast: Springing, otherwise known as whipping, flexing or wave-excited hull vibration, can be prevented by adjustment of course, speed or ballast. It will disappear with change of loading.

Aboard OBOs follow strict procedures to avoid the possibility of gas explosions: When carrying dry bulk cargoes all compartments, including void spaces, empty ballast tanks and duct keels, must be scrupulously gas freed. Thereafter they must be regularly rechecked for gas to detect any unsuspected gradual build-up.

Additional measures: The following additional measures have been adopted by some shipowners and maritime authorities, and The Nautical Institute lists them for consideration by those who want to provide a greater margin of safety than that which the classification societies require.

Stay within the at-sea stress limits whilst in port: To reduce the longitudinal bending stress and shear force during loading, plan the loading to stay within the at-sea stress limits in port.

Increase the number of loading passes: To reduce the longitudinal bending stress and shear force during loading, increase the number of passes used for loading (eg, make three pours into each hold instead of two).

Insist that a maximum loading rate (eg, 5,000 tonnes/hr per loader) **is not exceeded.**

Avoid jump (alternate hold) loading of closeweight cargoes, and load all holds even when, on newer ships, the regulations permit jump loading.

Detection of damage

Inspections: When damage cannot be prevented it must be detected, reported, examined and repaired. The enhanced programmes of surveys adopted by the classification societies should ensure that they find damage earlier than was previously the case, but as there are intervals between the surveys this still cannot detect all damage. Unexpectedly high rates of corrosion have been reported[82] and it seems that a ship's steelwork can deteriorate rapidly when exposed to corrosive cargoes, excessive loads or mechanical damage. It is therefore highly desirable that ships' personnel should also take an informed interest in the condition of their ships, inspecting carefully for damage and excessive corrosion.

It is unrealistic to imagine that ships' personnel can make a close-up inspection of every hold every voyage, but it should be possible to examine every hold thoroughly about once a year, provided that suitable equipment is available to allow the inspector to make a close-up examination of the full height of the frames. A geared bulker can carry a cherrypicker and

Fig.26.3 The great height, the protruding hopper sides and the ship's movement all make close-up inspections of places high in the hold difficult
Photo courtesy of Scanautics

place it in the hold when required, but for gearless vessels lightweight aluminium ladders are likely to be the only option except for ships built since 2006 which must be provided with a means of having overall close-up access to every part of the cargo spaces. It is necessary that ships' personnel have an efficient means of reaching areas high in the hold, but often they do not (Fig. 26.3).

On occasion it is possible to inspect the higher parts of the hold from the surface of the cargo, and ballast holds when part filled can sometimes be inspected from a raft. However, these possibilities are the exception and cannot be relied upon. The hold must be washed clean for an effective inspection and the hatchcovers must be open to admit daylight. Conditions are likely to be most favourable on a sheltered river or fjord transit or at an anchorage.

It has been argued that such an inspection may only find 40 fractures when there are actually 120 to be found, but that misses the point. Forty fractures are quite enough to alert the Master, the owners and the classification society to the fact that the ship's condition has deteriorated and needs urgent expert examination. Ships' officers cannot replace the classification society surveyor, but they can help to make sure that he overlooks nothing which is important.

Appendix 26.5 contains clear advice for port State control officers on inspecting bulk carriers and this information can be just as useful to ships' officers. Paragraphs 12-17 and the three supporting diagrams are particularly helpful.

Practical advice on the conduct of surveys of damaged holds has been offered by a surveyor experienced in this work whose advice[80] can be summarised as follows. The owner will expect the Master to advise him of any stevedore damage, and any visible cracking in the ship's structure. Wastage due to corrosion is sometimes difficult to detect. In one actual case high-tensile steel had wasted very evenly, without obvious critical spots, so there was little to show that heavy corrosion had occurred. Masters should be alert to this possibility.

The second area of concern reported by the same surveyor is the problem sometimes found in ships' frames, which suffer a high level of 'grooving' or 'necking' right next to the weld where the frame is attached to the ship's side. When the structure is stressed, the frames are cracked or detached from the ship's side at the point of weakness. To inspect this area the Master must first chip away any rust or cargo residues from the vicinity to ensure that he is inspecting sound steel. The areas where damage is most likely to be found in and around the hold of a bulk carrier are clearly shown in diagrams included in Appendix 26.5 and listed in Appendix 24.1.

Bilge soundings: Unexpectedly high bilge soundings can provide the first warning that damage has occurred, and flooding is taking place. Bilge soundings should be taken daily. In bad weather, if remote readings are not available the sounding should be taken when the ship is hove-to for inspection of the decks. Water ingress detectors provide a valuable back-up but cannot give the early warning that high bilge soundings provide. The holds should be checked for flooding if the bilge cannot be pumped dry.

Flood water sloshing: The survivors of several casualties have reported on the odd and unusual motion of the ship when holds were flooded. It seems likely that this odd motion was due to the flood water sloshing in the holds. The motion was described as 'not pitching, not rolling, not corkscrewing, not vibration, but immediately noticeable' (to an experienced seaman). In one case this was the first warning that ship's personnel had that their ship had been damaged.

Casualties since 1993

From the appalling total losses of bulk carriers and their crews in 1991 and 1992 the number of losses due to structural failure diminished until in 1997 there were no bulk carrier losses from this cause (Fig. 26.4). The casualties caused by grounding, machinery fire/explosion and collision occupy the bulk of the records (Fig. 26.5) and are, of course, cause for concern, but are beyond the scope of this book. Since 1997 the number of casualties resulting from structural failure has never been more than three and in several years has been none. It is fair to say that if structural problems have not been entirely eliminated they are under far better control than was the case in 1993 when the First Edition of *Bulk Carrier Practice* was published.

Trends recorded by Intercargo show a continuing decline in casualties (Fig. 26.6) and in lives lost (Fig. 26.7) though the lives lost in 2006 (37) and 2007 (39) are a distressing reminder that when a bulk carrier founders she often sinks very rapidly. That older bulk carriers are at greater risk of becoming casualties from all causes is evident from their prominence in the statistics (Fig. 26.8) where bulk carriers aged more than 15 years account for 85% of losses and those over 20 years occupy 70% of the table.

For most of the last twenty years concern for bulk carrier safety has been focused on the larger vessels, with deadweight greater than 20,000 and/or length more that 150 metres and it is, perhaps, a measure of

Year	Losses due to Structural Failure	Bulkers lost Total	Lives lost
1994	3	14	106
1995	2	5	57
1996	2	14	50
1997	0	11	80
1998	3	19	87
1999	2	14	43
2000	3	14	23
2001	1	4	64
2002	0	5	4
2003	0	4	0
2004	1	5	13
2005	1	6	8
2006	1	7	37
2007	0	8	39

Fig.26.4

Cause of incident	***Losses*** 1998–2007
Structural	12
Fire and explosion	10
Machinery failure	6
Flooding	13
Collision	15
Groundings	21
Contact object	1
Cargo loading/cargo shift	5
Other/unknown	3
	86

Fig 26.5 *Data courtesy of Intercargo*

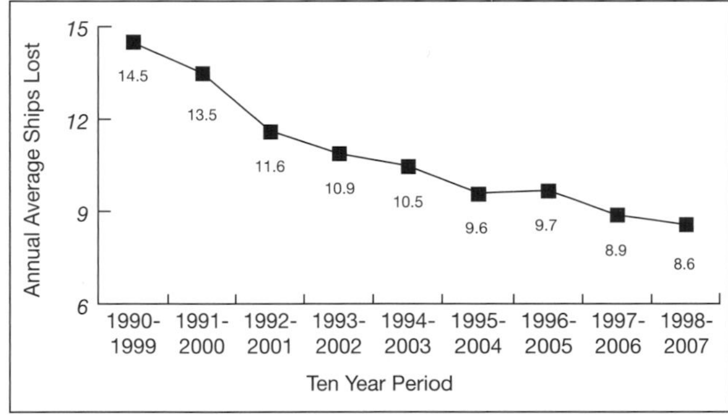

Fig 26.6 Annual average number of bulk carriers over 10,000 dwt lost

Data courtesy of Intercargo

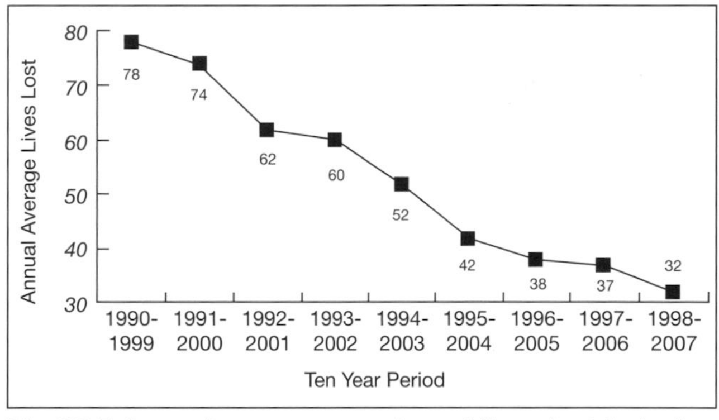

Fig 26.7 Annual average number of lives lost in bulk carrier casualties

Data courtesy of Intercargo

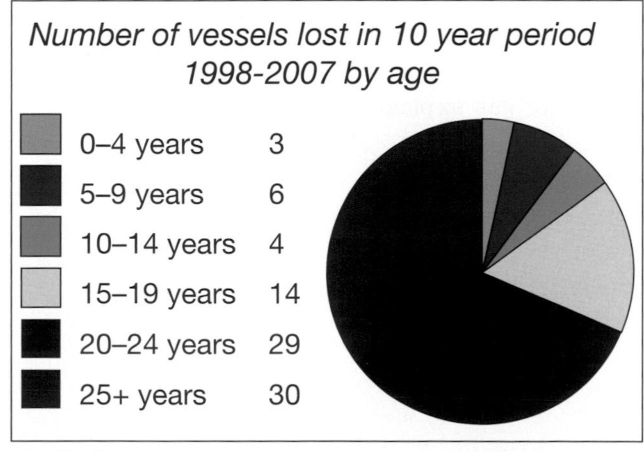

Fig 26.8

Data courtesy of Intercargo

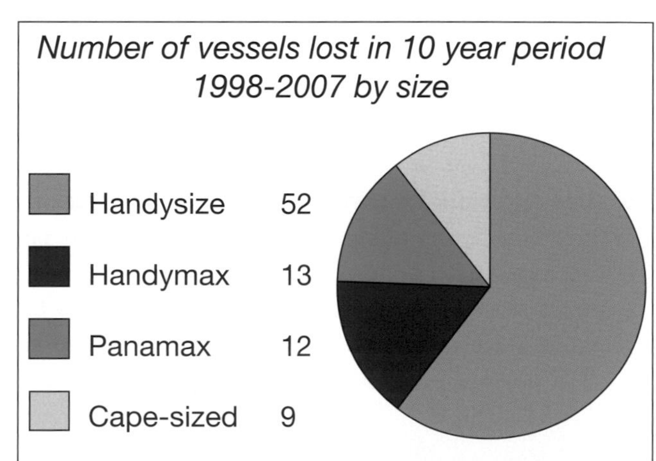

Fig 26.9

Data courtesy of Intercargo

the success of those efforts that it is smaller bulk carriers (handy-sized and handymax) that now dominate the casualty lists and give cause for concern (Fig. 26.9).

Conclusions

A spokesman for the UK Maritime and Coastguard Agency speaking in 2005[138] observed that some of the new requirements, particularly the structural improvements to prevent water ingress, are applicable to new ships only. The overall risk reduction achieved will therefore, he continued, not be evident for some years, when new ships of today reach ages where structural failure becomes more commonplace.

The case for seamanlike precautions, for care, method, thoroughness, prudence and double checking in the inspection, operation and maintenance of bulk carriers remains as strong as ever.

Sources

4, 5, 37, 38, 39, 40, 42, 57, 58, 65, 66, 68, 80, 82, 83, 84, 88, 94, 129, 138, 167, 182, 222, 256, 257, 258, 259, 262, 271, 272, 273, 274, 275, 276, 277, 278, 279. (See List of Sources, Page 497)

CHECKLIST

SUMMARY of measures for preventing casualties

- ☐ Minimise corrosion within holds by maintaining the condition of paint coatings, rinsing with fresh water and taking extra precautions with corrosive cargoes.
- ☐ Minimise corrosion within ballast tanks by maintaining the condition of paint coatings.
- ☐ Prevent stevedores' damage.
- ☐ Prevent hull contact damage.
- ☐ Report damage and have it surveyed and properly repaired.
- ☐ Avoid local overloading.
- ☐ Provide and use accurate, accessible stability information.
- ☐ Always prepare a full loading/deballasting or discharging/ballasting plan.
- ☐ Keep strictly to loading/deballasting or discharging/ballasting plan.
- ☐ Reduce loading rates when starting an empty hold.
- ☐ Ensure that discharging and ballast changes are planned and executed with the same care as loading.
- ☐ Reject cargo with excessively high moisture content.
- ☐ Ensure that ship is not twisted whilst loading or whilst changing ballast.
- ☐ Close dump valves immediately deballasting is completed.
- ☐ Trim cargo reasonably level to the boundaries of the cargo space.
- ☐ Ensure that cargoes such as steel are well secured.
- ☐ All hatchcovers should be well maintained and carefully secured.
- ☐ All deck openings should be in sound condition and properly secured.
- ☐ Speed should be substantially reduced in adverse weather.
- ☐ Sloshing of ballast water in part-filled tanks should not be allowed to occur.
- ☐ Prevent springing by adjustment of course, speed or ballast.
- ☐ Aboard OBOs follow strict procedures to avoid the possibility of gas explosions.

Possible additional measures when a greater margin of safety is required

- ☐ Stay within the at-sea stress limits whilst in port.
- ☐ Increase the number of loading passes.
- ☐ Insist that a maximum loading rate (such as 5,000 tonnes/hour per loader) is not exceeded.
- ☐ Avoid jump (alternate hold) loading, and load all holds.

APPENDICES AND REFERENCE MATERIAL

CONTENTS

REGINA OLDENDORFF

Owner	Egon Oldendorff (Hong Kong) Ltd.
Builder	Dalian Shipyard of China
Kind of ship	Bulk carrier
Service limitation	Oceangoing (Lakes-Fitted)
Date of launching	27 July 1983
Date of sea trial	1 May 1984
Date of delivery	May 1986
Classification	Lloyd's ✠ 100AI and ✠ LMC Bulk Carrier strengthened for heavy cargo, hold 2 and 4 may be empty.
Port of registry	Hong Kong.
Principal dimensions	
Length (overall)	about 195.00m
Length (between BP)	183.00m
Breadth moulded	23.00m
Depth moulded	14.30m
Draft designed moulded	10.00m
Summer draft moulded	10.22m
Timber summer draft moulded	10.59m
Ship's form	
Type of ship	Well deck
Type of stem	Raked stem with bulbous bow
Type of stern	Transom type, cruiser stern
No. of decks	One
No. of bulkheads	Seven
Speed, main engine, etc	
Maximum trial speed (20% dwt)	17.8 knots
Service speed with 15% sea margin	14.5 knots
On full-load condition	
Cruising range at service speed	About 15,000 sea miles
Main engine	B and W 8L55GA
Maximum continuous output (MCO)	10,700 bhp 150 rpm
Continuous service output (CSO)	9,760 bhp 145 rpm
Propeller (keyless type)	Four blade solid type
Material	Mn-Al-Br
Diameter-pitch	5,140 mm–3,392 mm
Tonnage	
Gross	18,121
Net	10,713

Lightweight and deadweight

	Weight	LCG (C)	VCG (KG)
Lightweight	8051.0	12.042	10.119

	Mark	Freeboard	Draft (ext.)	Displacement	Deadweight
Tropical fresh	TF	2.665	10.685	36888	28837
Fresh	F	2.878	10.472	36083	28032
Tropical	T	2.899	10.451	36904	28853
Summer	S	3.112	10.238	36082	28031
Winter	W	3.325	10.025	35263	27212
Timber Tropical fresh	LTF	2.280	11.070	38351	30300
Timber fresh	LF	2.501	10.849	37510	29459
Timber tropical	LT	2.521	10.829	38370	30319
Timber summer	LS	2.742	10.608	37511	29460
Timber winter	LW	3.036	10.314	36375	28324
Timber winter North Atlantic	LWNA	3.325	10.025	35263	27212

Loading capacity

Cargo capacity	Grain (holds only)	34,977.9	cu m
	Grain (inc. TST)	39,399.5	cu m
Tank capacity	Water ballast	10,839.9	cu m
	Fuel oil (100%)	1,729.2	cu m
	Diesel oil (100%)	211.0	cu m
	Fresh water	317.9	cu m

REGINA OLDENDORFF

Hot rolled coil loading capacity Coil: T/PCS 1.5 dia x 1.5L x 1.5 T

	Full bunkers		Half bunkers	
	PCS	Weight (T)	PCS	Weight (T)
No. 1 Cargo hold	223	3,345	230	3,450
No. 2 Cargo hold	345	5,175	345	5,175
No. 3 Cargo hold	230	3,450	253	3,795
No. 4 Cargo hold	345	5,175	360	5,400
No. 5 Cargo hold	207	3,105	232	3,480
Total	1,350	20,250	1,420	21,300

Timber loading capacity

	In hold		On deck		Total	
	Cu m	1,000BM	Cu m	1,000BM	Cu m	1,000BM
No. 1 Cargo hold	6,463.8	1,201.4				
No. 2 Cargo hold	7,421.9	1,379.5				
No. 3 Cargo hold	5,134.1	954.2				
No. 4 Cargo hold	7,662.0	1,424.1				
No. 5 Cargo hold	6,455.9	1,199.9				
Total	33,137.7	6,159.1	9.697.8	2,075.6	42,835.5	8,234.7

Remark Above figures are based on the following stowage factor

In hold 2.5 T/190ft^3/1000 B.M.

On deck 2.5 T/165ft^3/1000 B.M.

REGINA OLDENDORFF

Grain loading capacity

Item	Fr. No.	Capacity (M³) Grain	Capacity (M³) Bale	Centre of gravity G (M)	Centre of gravity KG (M)
Cargo hold					
No. 1 Cargo hold	175-219	6,848.0		-65.67	8.36
			6,463.8	-65.63	8.23
No. 2 Cargo hold	138-175	7,866.9		36.28	7.79
			7,421.9	-36.28	7.70
No. 3 Cargo hold	112-138	5,503.5		-10.12	7.76
			5,134.1	-10.14	7.63
No. 4 Cargo hold	74-112	8,060.5		16.42	7.79
			7,662.0	16.42	7.69
No. 5 Cargo hold	40-74	6,699.1		46.08	8.11
			6,455.9	46.22	7.99
Total		34,977.9			
			33,137.7		
Top side tank					
No. 2 Top side tank (P) & (S)	138-175	1,216.4		-35.87	12.51
No. 3 Top side tank (P) & (S)	112-138	854.8		-9.72	12.51
No. 4 Top side tank (P) & (S)	74-112	1,253.4		16.84	12.51
No. 5 Top side tank (P) & (S)	40-74	1,097.0		46.47	12.60
Total		4,421.6			

Water ballast tank capacity

Item	Fr. No.	Capacity (M³)	Weight (MT)	Centre of gravity G (M³)	Centre of gravity KG (M)
F.P.T. (C)	219-FE	997.2	1,022.1	-86.38	8.58
No. 1 WBT (P) No. 1 WBT (S)	175-219	1,031.8	1,057.6	-65.24	1.44
No. 2 WBT (P) No. 2 WBT (S)	138-175	826.0	846.7	-35.84	1.34
No. 3 WBT (P) No. 3 WBT (S)	112-138	581.6	596.1	-9.72	1.34
No. 4 WBT (P) No. 4 WBT (S)	74-112	857.6	879.0	17.00	1.46
No. 5 WBT (P) No. 5 WBT (S)	39-74	982.8	1,007.4	47.40	1.95
No. 1 TST (P) No. 1 TST (S)	175-219	879.2	901.2	-63.59	13.10
No. 2 TST (P) No. 2 TST (S)	138-175	1,216.4	1,246.8	-35.87	12.51
No. 3 TST (P) No. 3 TST (S)	112-138	854.8	876.2	-9.72	12.51
No. 4 TST (P) No. 4 TST (S)	74-112	1,253.4	1,284.7	16.84	12.51
No. 5 TST (P) No. 5 TST (S)	40-74	1,097.0	1,124.4	46.47	12.60
A.P.T. (C)	AE-12	262.1	268.7	88.72	10.02
Total		10,839.9	11,110.9		

Fresh water tank capacity

Item	Fr. No.	Capacity (M³)	Weight (MT)	G (M³)	KG (M)
No. 1 FWT (P)	4-12	97.9	97.9	86.40	13.20
No. 2 FWT (S) No. 2 FWT (P)	AE-4	125.2	125.2	92.23	13.35
Drinking W.T. (S)	4-12	94.8	94.8	86.40	13.20
Total		317.9	317.9		

REGINA OLDENDORFF

Item		Fr. No.	Capacity (M³)		Weight (MT)	Centre of gravity	
			100%	97%		G (M)	KG (M)
Fuel oil (SG = 0.98 t/m³)							
No. 1 FOT	(C9)	138-175	475.6	461.4	452.1	–35.86	0.74
No. 2 FOT	(C9)	112-138	334.2	324.2	317.7	–9.72	0.74
No. 3 FOT	(C9)	74-112	488.4	473.7	464.3	16.84	0.74
No. 4 FOT	(C9)	39-74	324.8	315.1	308.8	44.26	0.74
FO Service T	(S)	33-36	34.6	33.6	32.9	65.39	12.05
FO Set T	(P & S)	36-39	71.6	69.5	68.1	62.90	12.04
Total			1,729.2		1,643.9		
Diesel oil (SG = 0.85 t/m³)							
DOT	(P & S)	25-39	190.4	184.7	157.0	66.24	1.38
DO Service T	(S)	29-32	10.3	10.0	8.5	68.72	12.02
DO Set T	(S)	29-32	10.3	10.0	8.5	68.72	12.02
Total			211.0		174.0		
Lubricating oil (SG = 0.90 t/m³)							
LO Storage T	(C)	29-35	16.2	15.7	14.1	67.47	0.82
LO Sump T	(C)	20-29	24.4	23.7	21.3	73.70	0.82
LO Set T	(P)	24-27	23.2	22.5	20.3	72.83	8.65
m/e LO ST	(P)	19-24	28.5	27.6	24.9	76.02	8.71
D/G LOT	(P)	13-17	6.1	5.9	5.3	81.37	9.28
D/G LO Set T	(P)	17-19	3.3	3.2	2.9	79.03	8.18
D/G Clean LOT	(P)	17-19	4.1	4.0	3.6	79.06	9.34
Total			105.8		92.4		
Other Tanks							
Oily WT	(C)	17-19	16.2			79.06	1.42
Bilge T	(C)	12-17	24.2			81.56	1.32
Cool WT (FW)	(C)	AF-12	21.6		21.6	85.28	3.53
Cylinder OT	(S)	25-28	20.5	19.9	17.90	72.04	12.02

Definitions of Bulk Carriers, Ore Carriers and Combination Carriers

taken from IACS' Unified Requirements UR Z11

by courtesy of the International Association of Classification Societies (IACS)

Z11
cont'd

2.2 Bulk Carrier

The ship type notation "BULK CARRIER", or equivalent, and the notation "ESP" shall be assigned to sea going self-propelled ships[2] which are constructed generally with single deck, double bottom, hopper side tanks and topside tanks and with single or double side skin construction in cargo length area and intended primarily to carry dry cargoes in bulk.Typical midship sections are given in Figure 2.

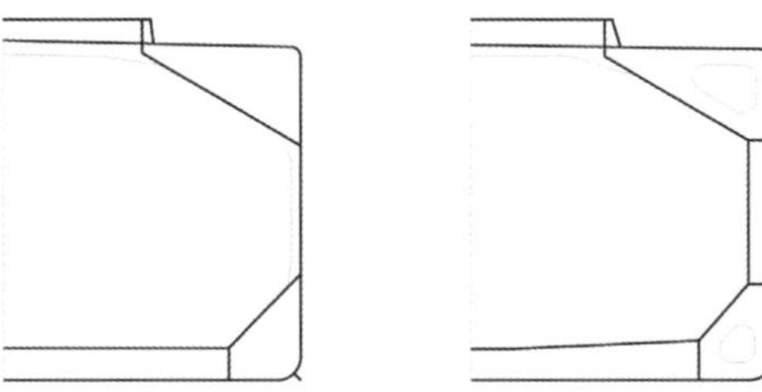

Fig. 2

2.3 Ore Carrier

The ship type notation "ORE CARRIER", or equivalent, and the notation "ESP" shall be assigned to sea going self-propelled ships[2] which are constructed generally with single deck, two longitudinal bulkheads and a double bottom throughout the cargo length area and intended primarily to carry ore cargoes in the centre holds only. Typical midship section are given in Figure 3.

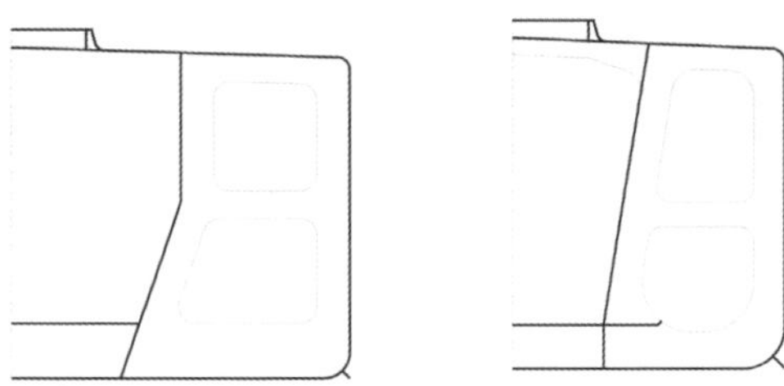

Fig. 3

Z11
cont'd

2.4 Combination Carrier

.1 "Combination carrier" is a general term applied to ships intended for the carriage of both oil and dry cargoes in bulk; these cargoes are not carried simultaneously, with the exception of oily mixture retained in slop tanks. The ship types defined in .2 and .3 below shall be considered to be combination carriers.

.2 The ship type notation 'ORE/OIL CARRIER", or equivalent, and the notation "ESP" shall be assigned to sea going self-propelled ships[2] which are constructed generally with single deck, two longitudinal bulkheads and a double bottom throughout the cargo length area and intended primarily to carry ore cargoes in the centre holds or of oil cargoes in centre holds and wing tanks. Typical midship sections are given in Figure 4.

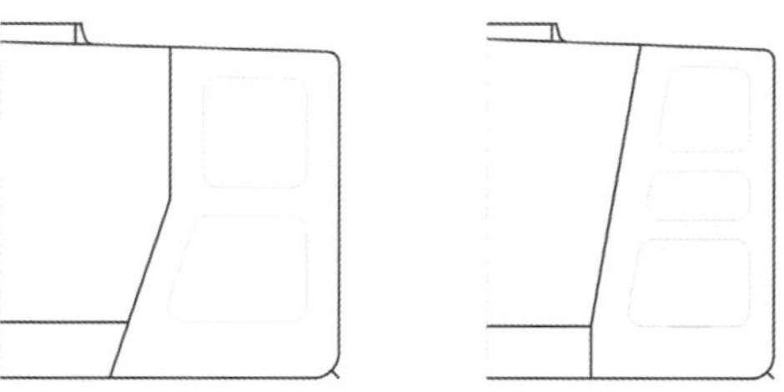

Fig. 4

.3 The ship type notation "OIL/BULK/ORE (OBO) CARRIER", or equivalent, and the notation "ESP" shall be assigned to sea going self-propelled ships[2] which are constructed generally with single deck, double bottom, hopper side tanks and topside tanks, and with single or double side skin construction in the cargo length area, and intended primarily to carry oil or dry cargoes, including ore, in bulk. Typical midship sections are given in Figure 5.

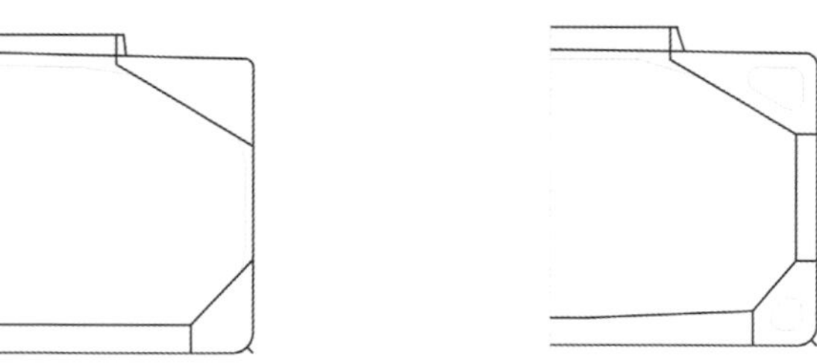

Fig. 5

DAMAGE REPORT

Particulars of damage caused by working cargo.

M.S. ______________________ VOYAGE NO ______________ DATE ______________

1. TIME and DATE OF DAMAGE

2. PORT WHERE DAMAGE OCCURRED
(NAME WHARF OR PLACE WHERE MOORED)

3. NATURE OF DAMAGE (including Cargo) [AND EXACT POSITION]

4. CAUSE OF DAMAGE

5. STATE BY WHOM WORK WAS BEING PERFORMED
WHEN DAMAGE WAS SUSTAINED IE CREW, WHARF
LABOURERS, CONTRACT STEVEDORES ETC

6. NAME OF OFFICER IN CHARGE
AT TIME DAMAGE OCCURRED

7. (1) NATURE OF REPAIRS NECESSARY AND MDR NO.
(2) WHERE AND WHEN TO BE EXECUTED
(3) ESTIMATED OR ACTUAL COST
(4) CODE

DATED THIS ______________ DAY OF __________ 19

RESPONSIBILITY FOR THE ABOVE DAMAGE IS HEREBY ADMITTED, THE CAUSE AND EXTENT OF THE DAMAGE AS STATED ABOVE IS CORRECT

SIGNATURE ______________________ MASTER

______________________ CHIEF OFFICER

______________________ FOREMAN STEVEDORE OR TERMINAL SUPERINTENDENT

______________________ STEVEDORE AGENTS OR TERMINAL OPERATOR

NOTE:	**HEAD OFFICE:**
This report shall be completed in Quadruplicate, original and copies distributed as follows: ORIGINAL to 1. Senior Technical Assistant COPIES to 2. Contract Stevedores or Terminal Operators Office 3. Ship's Agents at port where damage occurred 4. Ship's File	

IACS

Recommendation 83

(August 2003)

Notes to Annexes to IACS Unified Requirement S1A on Guidance for Loading/Unloading Sequences for Bulk Carriers.

Introduction

1 To be of practical use to the ship's officers, any acceptable loading or unloading sequence must, in addition to meeting strength and stability requirements, satisfy operational and commercial requirements as far as possible. Therefore, the following notes have been developed by The Nautical Institute, in association with IACS, Intercargo, BIMCO and the International Bulk Terminals Association. It is recommended that they be taken into account when compiling the typical loading and unloading sequences described in the Annexes to the IACS Unified Requirement.

Loading

2 Deballasting can present difficulties. The process should always be started and finished as early as possible in the loading process and should be planned to proceed in the most favourable circumstances.

3 The easiest ballast tanks to drain should be left until last in the deballasting sequence. In order to take into account the effects of draft, heel and trim and the characteristics of the tanks, the preferred deballasting sequence (subject to the strength requirements of the individual ship) is:

1: ballast holds, 2: double bottoms, 3: topside tanks, 4: peak tanks.

4 A good stern trim should be maintained as far as possible throughout deballasting and final stripping of ballast.

5 The ship should never be allowed to go 'by the head' during deballasting, as the ballast suctions and sounding pipes of most bulk carriers are not designed to cope with this eventuality.

6 Departure draft, when laden, is usually even keel or close thereto. As this trim does not favour the stripping of ballast tanks it should be reached as late as possible in the loading process (See Item 2, above).

7 When loading a homogeneous cargo, one draft survey only will normally be required to interrupt the loading. The purpose of this draft survey, made after some 85-95% of the cargo has been loaded, is to make an accurate calculation of the tonnage remaining to be loaded and to calculate how it is to be distributed between a forward and an after hold, to achieve the desired final trim. Operational factors will influence which specific forward and after holds are used for the trimming.

IACS

8 Draft surveys will normally also be made before commencement and after completion of loading but these surveys need not be included in the loading sequence. If several grades of cargo are loaded it may be necessary to hold a draft survey before commencement and after completion of each grade and, in addition when 85-95% of the grade has been loaded, if the ship is to control the tonnage loaded.

9 If the ship has a ballast hold or ballast holds loading of those holds should be programmed as late as possible in the loading sequence to allow the maximum time for deballasting, cleaning, drying, opening the bilges and closing ballast lines.

Unloading

10 A trim by the stern is easily achieved and is to be preferred throughout unloading to avoid disruption to the ship's machinery and domestic services. Airdraft and strength requirements both usually require that the trim by the stern should not be excessive.

11 Holds which are to be ballasted for the ensuing voyage, or to reduce airdraft whilst unloading, should be the first to be completely unloaded, to allow maximum time for cleaning holds, closing bilges and opening ballast lines.

12 When a full homogeneous cargo is being unloaded, there is no need for a draft survey to interrupt the unloading at any stage, although draft surveys may be required before the start and at the completion of unloading.

13 Unlike deballasting (see above), the tank sequence is not critical when taking on ballast as it is not significantly affected by heel or trim. The sequence will be governed by strength and airdraft considerations and possibly by the desire to avoid taking sediment-laden ballast in double bottom tanks from which the sediment will be most difficult to remove.

****

Emergency opening and closing of hatches

The emergency procedures for a ship like *Regina Oldendorff* can be quoted as an example of the procedures which have to be followed.

The vessel is provided with 'rack back' folding hatch covers, with one pair of panels folding to the fore end of each hold and the second pair folding to the after end of the hold (Fig. 1.8). The covers are operated by hydraulic cylinders powered by two electric/hydraulic pumps, and the cleating is by mechanical wedge cleats which operate automatically in response to the weight of the hatch panel.

When one hydraulic pump is out of order, the covers can be opened by a single pump, but the speed of the operation will be halved. If both hydraulic pumps are out of order or the hydraulic system is damaged the hatches must be opened by mechanical means. In the procedures which follow the item numbers correspond to the numbers inserted in the diagrams and to the diagram caption numbers.

1. At every stage the hydraulic controls must be set in the correct position as if the covers were being moved by the hydraulic system.
2. Jack up the hatch cover with two manual jacks placed in positions provided (Fig.A) This disengages the cleats and relocates the hinge pins in the slotted rack back hinges at the hatch end.
3. Insert emergency retaining pins to hold the hinge pins in the correct positions in the slots of the rack back hinges.
4. Attach a wire pennant to the lug on the covers close to the cross-joint (Fig.A), lead it to the crane or derrick, and haul away to raise the covers.

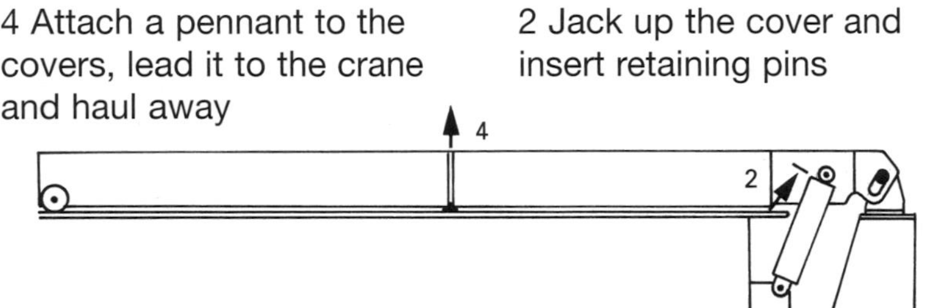

Fig. A

5. Attach the securing wires port and starboard (Fig.B), remove the jacks, and prepare the hatch cover securing hooks in the operating position.
6. Rig tirfor machines (lever-operated devices for hauling on wires) port and starboard, and operate simultaneously until covers are fully stowed.
7. Ensure securing hooks are fully engaged (Fig.B), and disconnect crane hook and tirfors.
8. When hatch covers are opened by wires they must be closed by wires, since the cylinders will be drained of fluid and the panels would otherwise fall uncontrolled.

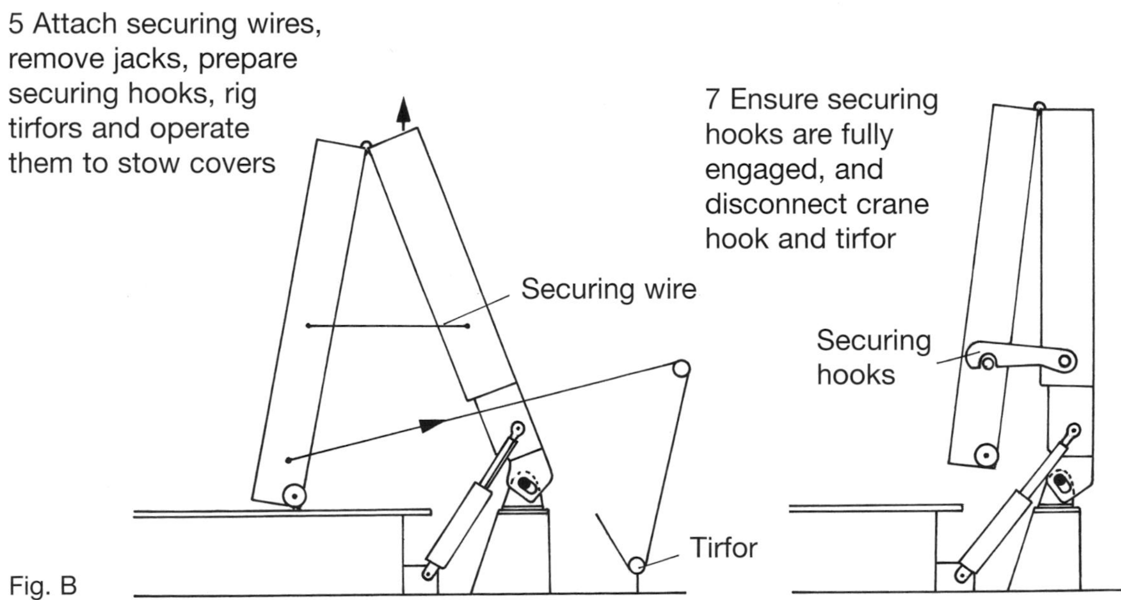

Fig. B

SPAR SCORPIO: EMERGENCY OPENING OF HATCHES

One portable pump unit is supplied for emergency operation when the hydraulic system fails. The ship is supplied with operating procedures.

CLEANING BULKER CARGO HOLDS BY CAPTAIN R.E. SHORE FNI

Based on a paper published in Seaways in November 2000

In this article Captain Shore explains that very severe penalties can be incurred when grain residues are found with fertiliser cargoes (particularly phosphate from Tampa) destined for Australia or New Zealand. He describes in detail a case with which he was involved (mv *Kiukiang Career*), mentions an earlier case (mv *Adelina*) and quotes the recommendations which he subsequently provided for an Australian importer.

Captain Shore's recommendations

- Very strict and detailed instructions on hold cleanliness should be issued to the Master at the time he receives the charterparty. Merely stating the holds should be 'grain clean' through a local agent is insufficient. The Master has to be alerted at the soonest possible time on what is required and the consequences should this fail to be carried out.

- A precise and detailed manual should be drawn up on how to clean and prepare cargo holds for the carriage of US phosphate to Australia. Detail the methods to be used, ie start at the top and work down; air-blow the covers, underside framing and coamings thoroughly with compressed air; wash down with sea water; and fresh down. Detail each and every part of the hatchcovers, coamings and hold, ie frames, pipes, ladders, hatch covers, under side framing, bilges, manhole plates, trackways, drains etc. Clearly state that there should be no past cargo residues, loose scale or paint, debris, insects and/or moisture present. Also ensure that instructions are given to wash down the main deck thoroughly so that it is free of cargo residues. Give this manual to the Master at the last discharge port or earlier if possible.

- A surveyor should attend the vessel at the last discharge port prior to departing for Tampa to generally inspect the cargo holds and discuss/review the above instructions with the Master. This is usually carried out with vessels engaged in the carriage of China clay and kaolin cargoes in the United States and has worked successfully.

- The vessel should be inspected as soon as it arrives at the anchorage. If either the condition of the holds and/or inaccessibility for cleaning and/or close inspection give cause for concern, the vessel should be brought into Tampa and placed at a layby berth for a detailed inspection and subsequent cleaning. Although the Master is under strict time constraints in a volatile commercial market, the Master must be able to exercise this right.

- A piece of lift equipment commonly known as a 'cherry picker' should be placed on board and used in each hold so that the inspector can perform a complete and thorough inspection.

- All inspections must be carried out in daylight.

- Our view on testing the hatchcovers with a water hose has been clearly stated. This exercise could still be carried out with any subsequent repairs being carried out without the use of Ram-Nek tape. The repairs must be again tested. In addition we would be in favour of witnessing the closing and battening down of the hatch covers for sea upon the completion of loading and then testing the hatch cover joints with the use of ultrasonic equipment. This equipment is fast and efficient and can be used with cargo in situ with little or no delay to the vessel on sailing. Any repairs should be carried out and re-tested. The hatch covers should then be taped.

- The double-bottom ballast tanks and top-side ballast tanks should be pressed up prior to loading to ascertain watertight integrity by the way of these tanks.

- Delays at the load berth have to be avoided. The first surveyor on board at the load berth should not be there to instruct the crew on how to clean the holds, as happened at the time of our attendance and, we understand, on the majority of previous vessels. This should be done at the last discharge port prior to departure for Tampa and through the detailed instructions. The surveyor or supervisor should, effectively, be performing a final walk through.

- On completion of loading at each hold, the chief officer should walk the top stow cargo particularly around the periphery in order to inspect the under deck framing and top side beams.

- Do not charter older style bulk carriers; have an age limit of 10-12 years. Do not charter vessels which have just carried grain or sulphur cargoes.

Captain Shore's article then ends with a statement of the detailed responsibilities of the shipowner for ensuring that the condition and security of the cargo is safeguarded by the provision of information and the establishment of appropriate procedures.

HOLD CLEANING AND DEODORISING OF A HANDY-SIZED BULK CARRIER AFTER CARRYING FISHMEAL AND BEFORE CARRYING GRAIN

(The total number of preloading surveys completed is noted in brackets as they occurred)

Day	Cleaning
1-2	The three cargo holds of this handysized vessel were swept then washed with sea water. Holds flushed with freshwater mixed with Alkleen safety liquid, a non-caustic alkaline cleaner.
3	On arrival at the loading port the holds were rejected, then again rejected after more cleaning because of fish odour. (1 and 2)
4	Removed loose rust and paint chips. Washed holds with high pressure fresh water and Airx 60, a cleaner/odour remover. Holds rejected because of strong fish odour. (3)
5	Washed holds with high pressure fresh water and Airx 60, a cleaner/odour remover. Holds rejected because fish odour was present. (4)
6	Cleaned holds, mast houses, winch platforms, decks and coamings. Holds rejected because fish odour still present. (5)
7	All holds washed top to bottom with a 50% solution of Citro Solve Detergent, a citrus oil based detergent and deodoriser which was sprayed onto all surfaces, left for 2-3 hours then rinsed with fresh water.
8	Holds were again rejected for fish odour still present. (6) A shore gang of 4 men working with a freshwater electric powered spraying machine enhanced by compressed air was employed to clean all holds using Gyro AVO Super Corrosive un 1824, a powerful caustic cleaner.
9	All holds were again rejected because fish odour was still present. (7)
10	Local cleaning contractors and the services they offered were considered.
11	A trailer mounted washing unit with a diesel fired water heater capable of achieving temperatures of approximately 210°F and pumps capable of achieving pressures of approximately 3,000 psi was hired. The equipment came with nozzles and extensions that could reach a height of approximately 27 ft, and with rolling scaffolding towers of sufficient height to reach the under deck framing of the ship's coamings and hatch covers. Large amounts of fishmeal were removed from the boat deck drains, adjacent to the accommodation ladder.
12	Cleaning commenced with a shore gang using high pressure, high temperature water blasting with Zep Formula 4089, a concentrated, chlorinated, highly alkaline cleaner followed by high temperature, high pressure water rinsing followed in turn by an application of Amine A, an ammonium based, concentrated disinfectant, deodorant and sanitiser. All the waste water from this operation was pumped into a topside ballast tank. The cleaning resulted in the removal of large amount of fish meal and debris from the kingpost/mast [ie hold ventilator] areas and significant further cleaning of all surfaces in the holds. After each hold had dried it was given a final sweeping by the ship's crew. The ship's entire [open] deck surface, all mast houses and machinery flats were then sprayed with a light coating of Amine A. All rubbish bins and all cleaning tools were removed to the poop. Hold ventilator dampers and access doors were closed. The holds were found to be odour free but a slight residual smell was detected on the hatch covers so all holds were again rejected. (8)
13	The crew spent the day scrubbing the hatch covers. Solid and liquid residues from earlier washings were disposed of.
14	At 1030 hrs No.2 hold was passed but Nos.1 and 3 holds were failed for smell from the area of the masthouses and coamings. (9) The bottoms of the chain boxes located near the holds were scraped and cleaned and the mast house interiors were rewashed. All adjacent surfaces were sprayed with Amine A. At 1530 hrs the vessel was passed as suitable to load grain. (10)

Full ballast change at sea **Appendix 7.1**

The vessel: A Cape-sized bulk carrier with five pairs of upper wing tanks (UWTs), five pairs of double bottom tanks (DBs), one ballast hold and a forepeak tank.

	Sequence	% *SF	% *BM	Draft (m) FOR'D	Draft (m) AFT	TRIM	GM(m)
1.	Drop Nos. 2 and 4 UWTs then pump out No. 2 DBs.	91	56	4.56	10.50	5.94	11.51
2.	Pump in Nos 2 DBs and UWTs	89	35	7.27	9.47	2.20	10.13
3.	Drop out No. 1, 3 and 5 UWTs, then pump out No. 3 and 4 DBs.	87	74	6.55	7.43	1.88	13.10
4.	Pump in No. 3 and 4 DBs.	83	38	6.39	8.98	2.59	12.05
5.	Pump out No. 5 DBs.	94	30	6.96	7.27	0.31	12.51
6.	Pump in Nos. 1 and 3 UWTs and No. 5 DBs.	93	33	7.45	8.90	1.45	10.53
7.	Pump out the forepeak and No. 6 hold.	51	56	5.10	7.05	1.95	15.50
8.	Pump in the forepeak and Nos. 4 and 5 UWTs	48	67	6.59	7.41	0.82	12.22
9.	Pump out No. 1 WBTs.	44	46	5.00	8.35	3.35	13.03
10.	Pump in No. 1 WBTs and No. 6 hold. Press up forepeak and all UWTs.	91	41	7.30	10.26	2.96	9.20

*Shear Force (SF) and Bending Moment (BM) expressed as a percentage of the maximum permitted at-sea stresses.

MOTOR-DRIVEN CENTRIFUGAL PUMPS-TRANSCRIPTION OF MANUFACTURERS' INSTRUCTIONS.

1.0 **Operation**

Operation of the pump after installation or reassembly must be carried out as follows.

1.1 **Preparation before operation**

a. Open the air vent on top of the casing and fill the casing with water until it comes out of the vent.

b. In the case of reservoir-type self-priming pumps, fill the casing with water after removing the plug on top of the casing. After the pump has been started twice there is no need for further priming if water remains in the casing.

c. In the case of a self-priming pump provided with a vacuum pump, fill the replenishing water tank.

d. Open fully the valve on the suction side of the pump (the 'suction valve'), and close completely that on the discharge side (the 'discharge valve').

e. Make sure that the bearings are lubricated.

f. Turn the pump shaft by hand to make sure it turns smoothly.

1.2 **Operation**

a. Start the pump motor and stop it after a few seconds. Repeat this several times, to make sure that it is not faulty. When satisfied that it is working properly leave it switched on.

b. When the pump revolutions and pressure have risen, gradually open the discharge valve until the pressure falls to the specified pressure.

c. Avoid running the pump when no water is passing through it, particularly when the pump is fitted with a mechanical seal. Even when a vacuum pump is provided stop the pump after five minutes if the pump has not been primed, and is still running dry.

1.3 **Stopping**

a. Close the discharge valve.

b. Stop the motor.

c. If the pump stops suddenly during operation, switch off first of all, and then close the discharge valve.

1.4 **Precautions during operation**

a. Operate the pump as near to design settings as possible.

b. Watch for vibration and noise. If an abnormal condition is seen stop the pump immediately. In particular, for pumps fitted with a mechanical seal, guard against vibration, which will shorten the life of the seal.

c. Watch any rise in bearing temperature. If the bearing housing can safely be felt by hand there is no problem. If it is too hot to hold, measure the temperature with a thermometer. The temperature must be kept below ambient temperature plus 40°C, or liquid temperature plus 20°C, and in any case keep it below 75°C.

d. Adding too much grease will cause overheating so, when replacing grease, add it with the drain plug removed during operation, so that the old grease can be forced out.

e. Allow a small amount of continuous leakage, in the form of drops, through the gland. If the packing is tightened too much, overheating and premature wear of the shaft sleeve will occur.

f. When a mechanical seal is used there should be almost no leakage. If continuous leakage is observed the seal should be checked.

g. Never throttle (close) the valve on the suction side. Adjust the flow by means of the valve on the discharge side.

h. Never operate the pump for more than 10 minutes with the discharge valve closed, otherwise the temperature rise of the liquid in the casing will cause the pump to seize.

i. If the pump reverses when on standby the cause will be leakage from the non return valve.

j. If the pump has an automatic starting and stopping device such as a hydrophore system check the pressure when the pump starts and stops, as well as when it is operating and, if the interval is too short, adjust the air amount, water level, etc.

k. If the pump operates automatically under a central control system, monitor the gauge readings on the control panel board.

1.5 **Precautions while the pump is stopped**

a. Keep the discharge valve closed.

b. Keep the suction valve closed if the pump is stopped for a long time.

c. In cold regions drain the pumps if they remain stopped.

CALCULATION OF THE EFFECT ON STABILITY OF WATER IN A CARGO HOLD: WORKED EXAMPLE

THERE are times when it would be convenient to wash one or several holds in port, and retain the washings for later discharge in the open sea. Officers should calculate the effect on the ship's stability of retaining washings in such circumstances.

Such calculations will be approximate, because the water depth will be an estimate and the hold dimensions will be approximate, but the calculations can give a good indication if there is a danger of the stability being reduced too much.

Common abbreviations, if not explained below, are to be found in Appendix 10.1.

Assumption

Assume that the *Regina Oldendorff*, in ballast, has 1.0 m of sea water in No. 4 hold, which is the largest hold. Hold dimensions: B=23.0 m, L=31.0m.

To calculate new displacement

Weight of water = (23 x 31 x 1 x 1.025) tonnes = 731 tonnes, with centre of gravity 0.5 m above the tanktop (Depth of double bottom = 1.5 m, so KG of added weight = 2.0 m)

Effect of added weight on displacement:

Ballast displacement:	21,441 tonnes
Added weight	731
New displacement:	22,172 tonnes

Data for new displacement

From hydrostatic tables, at new displacement:

Transverse KM: 9.70 m.

Shift of CG due to new displacement

Shift of position of ship's centre of gravity as a result of the weight of water in No. 4 hold:

GG_1 = w x d/(W + w), where

GG_1 = shift of the position of the centre of gravity, in metres.
w = is the added weight, (731 tonnes)
d = is the distance between the centre of gravity of the weight added, and the centre of gravity of the ship.
W = is the initial displacement (21,441 tonnes).

From ship's loading manual for ballast condition, KG = 8.23 m.

d = Ship's KG – Hold water KG = 8.23 – 2.0 = 6.23 m.
GG_1 = 731 x 6.23/(21,441 + 731) = 0.20
New KG = KG_1 = 8.23 – 0.20 = 8.03 m.
KM – KG_1 = G_1M = 9.70 – 8.03 = 1.67 m

Effects of free surface in tanks and hold

The calculation so far has taken account of the additional weight of water in No. 4 hold, but the correction for the additional free surface has still to be applied.

Virtual rise of CG (G_1G_0) = FSM/Displacement
(For the derivation of this formula see below)

FSM = $1.025.LB^3/12$, where

L = length of hold = 31 m, B = breadth of hold = 23 m.

FSM for water in hold (tonnes-metres) = $1.025 \times 31 \times 23^3/12$	= 32,217	
FSM for ballast and bunker tanks	= 8,516	(from loading manual)
Total FSM	= 40,733	tonnes-metres.

G_1G_0 = FSM/Displacement (t) = 40,733/22,172 = 1.83 m.
Fluid GM = G_0M = $G_1M - G_1G_0$ = 1.67 – 1.83 = –0.16 m.

Conclusions

In departure ballast condition, with 1.0 metre of water in No. 4 hold, the calculated departure GM of the *Regina Oldendorff* is –0.16 m.

The calculation is an approximate one and includes a generous allowance for free surface in the topside tanks. However, it is clear that the ship's stability does not allow her to put to sea with 1.0 metre of hold washings in the largest hold on the ship. This demonstrates the importance of making the calculation.

Effect on stability of water in hold (continued) *Appendix 8.1(2)*

However, the GM of many bulk carriers in ballast is substantially greater than that of the *Regina Oldendorff,* and individual holds often occupy a smaller part of the ship's hull. The calculation should always be completed, and in many cases it will show that hold washings can be retained in one hold.

Derivation of formula: Virtual rise of CG = FSM/Displacement

Virtual rise of CG (G_1G_0) = $LB^3/12V \times d_1/d_2 \times 1/n^2$ . . . . (1)

V = volume of displacement = displacement (tonnes) x d_2. . . . . (2)

where

L = length of compartment — d_1 = density of liquid in compartment

B = breadth of compartment — d_2 = density of water ship floats in

n = number of longitudinal subdivisions in compartment.

Substitute for V in (1):

$$\text{Virtual rise of CG} = \frac{LB^3 \times d_1}{12 \times \text{Displacement (t)}} \times \frac{1}{n_2}$$

However, $1/n_2$ = 1 when the hold is not subdivided, and
d_1 = 1.025 when the hold contains sea water, so

$$\text{Virtual rise of CG} = \frac{1.025 \times LB^3}{12} \times \frac{1}{\text{Displacement (t)}}$$

$$\text{But} \quad \frac{1.025 \times LB^3}{12} = \text{free surface moments (FSM)}$$

So virtual rise of CG (G_1G_0) = FSM/Displacement

Change of Trim with Change of Density: Worked Example *Appendix 8.2*

For the Regina Oldendorff *the calculation is as follows:*

From ship's hydrostatic data:	Draft (m)	Displ (m^3)	LCB
Initial draft	10.24	35,000	-3.494
New draft (see calc. below)	10.47	35,875	-3.372

If the *Regina Oldendorff* is initially trimmed even keel and floating at her summer draft in salt water, and then passes into fresh water her draft will increase. To calculate the new draft:

$$\text{New displacement } (m^3) = \frac{\text{Old density x Old displacement } (m^3)}{\text{New density}}$$

$$\text{New displacement } (m^3) = \frac{1025 \times 35{,}000}{1000} = 35{,}875 \text{ m}^3$$

From the hydrostatic data, the draft which corresponds to a volume of displacement of 35,875 m^3, is 10.47 m.

New draft: 10.47 m

$$\text{Trim change} = \frac{\text{Displacement (tonnes) x } (LCB_1 - LCB_2)}{MCTC}$$

$$\text{Trim change} = \frac{36{,}090 \times ([-3.494] - [-3.372])}{486.38} = -9.05 \text{ cm}$$

Naming the trim

To decide whether the change of trim is by the head or by the stern keep strictly to the algebraic sign convention, which gives a negative (-ve) answer in this case, as shown above. In the stability documents used on board the *Regina Oldendorff* negative signs signify a trim by the head.

Alternatively, remember this simple rule:

If the position of the CB moves aft the change of trim is by the head. (In the example the CB moves from 3.494 m forward of midships, to 3.372 m forward of miships – ie, it moves aft.)

Loading Orders for a Complex Cargo

THE following emails were sent to the Master of a Panamax bulker, and provide an illustration of the complicated range of alternative programmes that the Master may have to consider. They involve loading in brackish water (BW); bunkering in Tampa, and/or Balboa or Long Beach, or China or Honolulu; working to limiting drafts in Tampa, the Panama Canal and the Chinese discharge port; and loading up to two different grades of cargo in up to three different berths.

From charterers to Master, Message No. 1:

Dear Master

Pls advise (as normal urgently) cargo lift ex Tampa on 38ft BW and 33.5ft BW for phosrock cargo to China. We will bunker vsl after loading Tampa at anchorage with depth 43ft BW. Pls advise bunkers needed for:

AA Tampa – Long Beach

BB Tampa – China

CC Tampa – China – Long Beach

Pls also advise how much cargo would be shut out at 38ft BW due Panama Canal draft of 39ft 6in if take bunkers in plans BB and CC

Await yrs soonest

Brgds

From charterers to Master, Message No.2:

Dear Master

We confirm next voyage is Tampa to China via Panama Canal with phosrock speed 14kts

Pls advise bunker rqmts for AA/BB/CC of our earlier msg basis 14kts

Tampa agents are etc

Pls send ETA on receipt of this cable and 7/4/2/1 days prior arrival to (agents)

Brgds

From charterers to Master, Message No.3:

Dear Master

Tampa now has a tidal berth which allows loading from 38-41ft BW(1.016)

Basis 39ft06 in FW [Fresh Water] for Panama Canal transit and bearing in mind 11.85m SWAD [Salt Water Arrival Draft] China pls advise cargo lift basis:

AA bunker Balboa to reach China.

BB bunker Long Beach.

CC bunker Honolulu.

Pls advise bunkers needed Tampa to reach Honolulu.

Also advise if vessel could safely reach Long Beach using MDO [Marine Diesel Oil] and all going well enroute if we put no bunkers on board at Tampa and if bunkers are suddenly unavailable at Balboa.

What would be IFO [Intermediate Fuel Oil] and MDO ROBS [Remaining on Board] on arrival Long Beach after Tampa – Long Beach at 14kts?

We would appreciate your best efforts to keep weight of lubes [lubricating oil] stores and water as low as possible until after Canal.

Pls note holds must be in grain clean condition for phosrock.

At this time phosrock suppliers are planning to load 2 grades at 3 berths each grade 25000 10 pct moloo [10% More Or Less in Owner's Option] with natural separation. Each berth may have both grades.

Pls advise if need some certain amount of cargo at first two berths to prevent excessive shear stress.

Brgds.

Loading orders (continued) — *Appendix 9.1(2)*

From charterers to Master, Message No.4:

Dear Master

Your programme from agent follows.

First berth load 23500mt.

Second berth load cargo until you reach 34ft BW.

Last berth load cargo to reach max 55000mt available from suppliers.

At last berth 41ft BW available but them must wait for tide to get over 38ft MLW [Mean Low Water] mud bar.

If we put 125mt DO [Diesel Oil] on board pls advise how much IFO you can take and still arrive Panama 39ft06 in FW.

At present will load only one grade but suppliers want two bills of lading if possible. Pls design stowplan so only empty holds are loaded at last berth and it is still possible to have natural separation for 2 lots of 25000 10%MOLOO. Please advise stowplan.

Brgds.

Maximum Tonnage Permitted in Hold — *Appendix 9.2*

WHEN bulk carriers are designed, a maximum tonnage is assumed for each hold, and the ship is then built with sufficient strength to carry the intended tonnage. A ship's loading plan should never propose the loading of a tonnage which exceeds the maximum permitted tonnage.

In recent years it has become a requirement that the maximum permitted tonnage for each hold is stated in the loading manuals of new ships, and this information is given in the manuals of some older vessels, too.

There are, however, many loading manuals in which the maximum permitted tonnages are not stated. Despite this the danger of overloading a hold when carrying closeweight cargoes such as iron ore cannot be ignored.

It may arise when the ship is loaded to tropical marks, and is carrying a small bunker tonnage, or when several grades of cargo are being carried.

There are several ways in which the Master can ensure that no hold is overloaded.

1. When permissible loadings are stated in the loading manual they must not be exceeded.
2. Any loading which appears amongst the standard loadings in the ship's loading manual is permissible. A loading in which cargo tonnages are increased or redistributed, and bunker tonnages are reduced, as compared with the standard loading, may not be permissible.
3. When considering the heavy loading of a hold aboard a ship which has insufficient information about maximum permissible hold loadings the Master should, through his owners, request advice from the classification society.

   It is not possible to give any general advice to enable a Master to resolve this question without reference to the classification society, because both longitudinal strength and local strength must be considered when the maximum permitted hold loading is calculated.

When a hold is being heavily loaded several considerations should be kept in mind.

1. Whilst the classification societies normally allow a margin for error when stating the maximum permitted load for a hold, the margin is usually very small and should never be relied upon. Planned hold loadings should never exceed the hold loadings given in the approved loading manual.
2. The maximum permitted tonnages are calculated on the assumption that the cargo will be trimmed reasonably level to the boundaries of the space and 'the double bottom and cross deck structure are designed based upon a trimmed cargo distributed symmetrically in a hold space'.[111]
3. The maximum tonnage which can be placed in a hold with safety may be considerably reduced when the ship is being block loaded. The separate notes on block loading (Appendix 9.4) should be studied where applicable.

Example Loading/Unloading Plan

The loading or unloading plan should be prepared in a form such as shown below. Worked examples of this form are shown overleaf. A different form may be used provided it contains the essential information enclosed in the heavy line box.

LOADING OR UNLOADING PLAN Version No.	Date	Vessel				Voyage No.
Load/Unload Port	Cargo(es)	Assumed stowage factor of cargo(es)	Ballast pumping rate	Dock water density	Max draught available (HW)	Max. air draught in berth
To/from Port	Last cargo	No. of loaders/ dischargers	Load/ discharge rate		Min draught available (LW)	Max. sailing/ arrival draught

	11	10	9	8	7	6	5	4	3	2	1
Tonnes											
Grade											

Totals: Grade: Tonnes Grade: Tonnes Grade: Tonnes: Total Tonnes

Pour No.	Cargo		Ballast operations	Time required (hours)	Comments	Calculated Values				Calculated Values			Observed Values		
						Draught		Maximum					Draught		
	Hold No.	Tonnes				Fwd	Aft	BM*	SF*	Air draught	Draught mid	Trim	Fwd	Aft	Mid
	TOTAL														

NO DEVIATION FROM ABOVE PLAN WITHOUT PRIOR APPROVAL OF CHIEF MATE
Pours to be numbered 1A, 1B, 2A, 2B, etc when using two loaders.
Abbreviations: PI = Pump In GI = Gravitate In F = Full PO = Pump Out GO = Gravitate Out MT = Empty
All entries within the box must be completed as far as possible. The entries outside the box are optional.

Signed Terminal ______________________

Signed Ship ______________________

*Bending moments (BM) and shear forces (SF) are to be expressed as a percentage of maximum permitted in port values for intermediate stages, and of maximum permitted at sea values for the final stage. Every step in the loading/unloading plan must remain within the allowable limits for hull girder shear forces, bending moments and tonnage per hold where applicable. Loading/unloading operations may have to be paused to allow for ballasting/deballasting in order to keep actual values within limits.

Example Loading Plan

The loading or unloading plan should be prepared in a form such as shown below. A different form may be used provided it contains the essential information enclosed in the heavy line box.

LOADING OR UNLOADING PLAN Version No.	Date 15.05.09	Vessel CAPESIZE				Voyage No. 27
Load/Unload Port BOCA GRANDE	Cargo(es) IRON ORE FINES IRON ORE LUMP	Assumed stowage factor of cargo(es) Both 0.39m³/mt	Ballast pumping rate 4000 t/h	Dock water density 1.025	Max draught available (HW) 17.88	Max. air draught in berth
To/from Port JAPAN F O	Last cargo IRON ORE/COAL	No. of loaders/ dischargers One	Load/ discharge rate 4500 th		Min draught available (LW) 9.42	Max. sailing/ arrival draught 17.88

Tonnes / Grade	11	10	9	8	7	6	5	4	3	2	1
			14765 FINES	17000 LUMP	17380 LUMP	16382 LUMP	16382 LUMP	16900 FINES	15382 LUMP	15766 LUMP	13050 FINES

Totals: Grade: FINES 44706 Tonnes Grade: LUMP 98294 Tonnes Grade: Tonnes: Total 143,000 Tonnes

Pour No.	Cargo Hold No.	Cargo Tonnes	Ballast operations	Time required (hours)	Comments	Calculated Values Draught Fwd	Draught Aft	Maximum BM*	Maximum SF*	Calculated Values Air draught	Draught mid	Trim	Observed Values Draught Fwd	Aft	Mid
1	4	10000	GO 1 and 3 UWTs	2.22	Fines	9.99	10.77	73	49		10.38	0.78			
2	1	7000	GO Upper FP, PO 2 Hold	1.56	Fines. Changeover 2 Hold	10.14	10.48	66	53		10.31	0.34			
3	9	8000	GO 5 UWTs, PO A Peak	1.78	Fines	9.42	12.15	63	59		10.79	2.73			
4	4	6900	PO 1 DBs	1.53	Fines	10.12	12.50	80	43		11.31	2.38			
5	9	6756	PO 5 DBs	1.50	Fines	9.56	13.74	80	45		11.65	4.18			
6	1	6050	PO Lower F Pk, GO 2 UWTs	1.34	Fines	9.61	13.57	75	49		11.59	3.96			
					Change grade to Lump										
7	7	10000	GO 6 Hold to 50%	2.22	Lump	8.94	14.38	–58	55		11.66	5.43			
8	5	10000	PO 6 Hold	2.22	Lump	8.63	13.63	–67	49		11.63	4.00			
9	7	7382	Educt 6 Hold	1.64	Lump. Changeover 6 Hold	9.57	15.24	–64	47		12.41	5.67			
10	3	10000	PO 2 and 3 DBs	2.22	Lump	10.41	14.65	–49	38		12.53	4.28			
11	8	10000	GO 4 UWTs	2.22	Lump	9.58	16.66	–50	43		13.12	7.08			
12	5	6382	PO 4 DBs	1.42	Lump	10.28	16.24	58	37		13.26	5.96			
13	8	6000	Educt as required	1.33	Lump	9.90	17.88	53	38		13.89	7.98			
14	2	8000	Educt as required	1.78	Lump	12.51	16.68	–65	46		14.60	4.17			
15	6	9000	Educt as required	2.00	Lump	13.14	17.80	42	–21		15.47	4.66			
16	2	6000	Educt as required	1.33	Lump	15.06	16.98	33	–14		16.02	1.92			
17	6	3782	Educt ballast lines	1.64	Lump	15.59	17.88	48	–30		16.74	2.29			
18	3	5382	Shut down ballast	1.20	Lump	16.95	17.54	44	–27		17.02	0.59			
					Trim check										
19	8	1000		0.22	Lump	16.94	17.72	49	–30		17.33	0.79			
20	2	1766		0.39	Lump	17.51	17.51	46	–27		17.51	0.00			
					Draft survey										
					Seagoing condition:	17.51	17.51	62	–36		17.51	0.00			
			KEEP CARGO TRIMMED LEVEL IN HOLDS		**KEEP SHIP UPRIGHT AT ALL TIMES**										
	TOTAL	143000													

Signed Terminal ______________________

Signed Ship ______________________

NO DEVIATION FROM ABOVE PLAN WITHOUT PRIOR APPROVAL OF CHIEF MATE
Pours to be numbered 1A, 1B, 2A, 2B, etc when using two loaders.
Abbreviations: PI = Pump In GI = Gravitate In F = Full PO = Pump Out GO = Gravitate Out MT = Empty
All entries within the box must be completed as far as possible. The entries outside the box are optional.

*Bending moments (BM) and shear forces (SF) are to be expressed as a percentage of maximum permitted in port values for intermediate stages, and of maximum permitted at sea values for the final stage. Every step in the loading/unloading plan must remain within the allowable limits for hull girder shear forces, bending moments and tonnage per hold where applicable. Loading/unloading operations may have to be paused to allow for ballasting/deballasting in order to keep actual values within limits.

Example Discharging Plan

The loading or unloading plan should be prepared in a form such as shown below.
A different form may be used provided it contains the essential information enclosed in the heavy line box.

LOADING OR UNLOADING PLAN Version No.	Date 03.07.09	Vessel CAPESIZE				Voyage No.
Load/Unload Port CHIBA	Cargo(es) IRON ORE FINES IRON ORE LUMP	Assumed stowage factor of cargo(es) Both 0.39m³/mt	Ballast pumping rate 4000 t/h	Dock water density 1.025	Max draught available (HW) 17.35	Max. air draught in berth
To/from Port BOCA GRAND	Last cargo COAL 2, 4, 6, 8 IRON ORE 1, 3, 5, 7, 9	No. of loaders/ dischargers Two	Load/ discharge rate 1,250 t/h per grab		Min draught available (LW) 7.59	Max. sailing/ arrival draught 11.30

Tonnes / Grade	11	10	9	8	7	6	5	4	3	2	1
Tonnes			14765	16910	17382	16382	16382	16900	15382	15470	13050
Grade			FINES	LUMP	LUMP	LUMP	LUMP	FINES	LUMP	LUMP	FINES

Totals: Grade: FINES 44706 Tonnes Grade: LUMP 97908 Tonnes Grade: Tonnes: Total 142,614 Tonnes

Pour No.	Cargo: Hold No.	Cargo: Tonnes	Ballast operations	Time required (hours)	Comments	Calculated Values: Draught Fwd	Draught Aft	Maximum BM*	Maximum SF*	Calculated Values: Air draught	Draught mid	Trim	Observed Values: Draught Fwd	Aft	Mid
!A	2	15470	G1 1 and 2 DBs. PI 2 UWTs	13.2	Lump. 2 and 6 Holds MT	13.82	16.29	–72	48			2.47			
1B	6	16382													
2A	5	10000	G1 4 DBs. PI 4 UWTs	8.0	Lump	13.44	14.54	71	56			1.10			
2B	8	10000													
3A	3	9000	GI 3 DBs	7.2	Lump	12.19	13.68	77	78			1.49			
3B	7	9000													
4A	5	6382	GI 5 DBs	5.5	Lump. 5 and 8 Holds MT	12.67	15.22	68	38			2.55			
4B	8	6910	PI 6 Hold to 0.5m ullage												
5A	3	6382		6.7	Lump. 3 and 7 Holds MT	11.05	13.94	–91	59			2.89			
5B	7	8382													
			Draft survey and change grade to Fines												
6A	1	6000	PI 1 x 5 UWTs	4.8	Fines	9.75	14.01	83	42			4.26			
6B	9	6000													
7A	4	8756		7.0	Fines	9.38	10.64	80	52			1.26			
7B	9	8756													
8A	1	7050	GI and PI Lower F Peak	6.5	Fines	7.59	11.30	84	–82			3.71			
8B	4	8144	PI Upper F Peak and 3 UWTs												
1	Please empty No 6 Hold and leave as clean as possible as soon as possible. This will then be changed over and used for ballast during stage 4.														
2	Grab and bulldozer blades must not be allowed to strike the ship's structure. Please instruct drivers to take the utmost care.														
3	Please note there are bilge and eductor plates in the after corners of each hold. Take great cares in these areas.														
					Seagoing condition:	7.59	11.30	84	–82			3.31			
	TOTAL	142614													

Signed Terminal ________________

Signed Ship ________________

NO DEVIATION FROM ABOVE PLAN WITHOUT PRIOR APPROVAL OF CHIEF MATE
Pours to be numbered 1A, 1B, 2A, 2B, etc when using two loaders.
Abbreviations: PI = Pump In GI = Gravitate In F = Full PO = Pump Out GO = Gravitate Out MT = Empty
All entries within the box must be completed as far as possible. The entries outside the box are optional.

*Bending moments (BM) and shear forces (SF) are to be expressed as a percentage of maximum permitted in port values for intermediate stages, and of maximum permitted at sea values for the final stage. Every step in the loading/unloading plan must remain within the allowable limits for hull girder shear forces, bending moments and tonnage per hold where applicable. Loading/unloading operations may have to be paused to allow for ballasting/deballasting in order to keep actual values within limits.

Consequences of block loading

STRUCTURAL DAMAGE TO BULK CARRIERS FROM BLOCK LOADING

THE International Association of Classification Societies (IACS) informed The Nautical Institute in the 1990s that a number of large bulk carriers had experienced structural damage affecting the cross-deck structure which separates adjacent cargo hatchways at the upper deck level. The damage was due to the load distribution adopted.

IACS stated that in all cases the class-approved alternate hatch load distribution had been ignored, and non-standard load distribution had been used. A feature of all the faulty loadings was that two adjacent holds were heavily loaded. The use of two or more heavily loaded adjoining holds, with the adjacent holds empty, is known as block loading.

The Nautical Institute has seen no details of the loadings of the ships in question, but there are several possible reasons for the use of block loading. Such a loading may have been adopted to provide segregated stowage for two or more separate parcels of cargo.

Shipmaster members of The Nautical Institute have, in the past, proposed block loading for two other reasons. The first is to avoid overloading individual holds when the ship is jump loading to Tropical marks and/or carrying only a small quantity of bunkers. In those circumstances the combined maximum permitted tonnage for the ore holds may not be enough to bring the ship to her marks. To a mariner it may seem logical to put the additional tonnage in one of the intervening holds, thus creating a block of three adjoining holds loaded with ore. However, this practice may induce local strength problems particularly if, having made the decision to load an additional hold, the tonnage in it is increased to what is considered a 'worthwhile' value.

The second reason advanced by Shipmasters is to reduce the values of shear forces and bending moments by changing a five hold load into a six or seven hold load. Many Shipmasters believed in the 1990s that excessive static and wave-induced shear forces and bending moments have broken ships and caused their loss and some of them, in discussions on the subject of bulk carrier losses, have advocated reducing static shear forces and bending moments by loading one or two additional holds. In fact it seems that such action, whilst reducing shear forces and bending moments, may increase local loading to an extent which is not acceptable.

The problem with block loading, IACS states, is one of local strength: the ship's longitudinal strength was satisfactory in each of the cases where damage occurred, and the routine calculations for longitudinal strength would have given no warning that damage might occur.

IACS emphasise rules which, if followed, should prevent damage.

1. The maximum permissible load for each hold must never be exceeded.
2. When using an alternate hold loading, the loading condition and distribution approved by the relevant classification society is to be used.
3. When planning to deviate from the approved alternate hold loading by loading additional holds, guidance should be obtained from the relevant classification society. Any non-homogeneous loading condition and distribution which is not shown in the ship's approved loading manual has not been approved, and may be unsafe.

Some ships are provided with standard loading conditions which feature block loading. In such cases the loadings have been checked and approved by the classification society, and can safely be used. If the ship's loading manual does not show the particular block loading that a Master wishes to use, The Nautical Institute strongly recommends that he should follow the IACS recommendation and obtain guidance, through his owners, from the classification society.

A better feel for the factors involved may be gained from guidance given by one of the principal members of IACS to the operator of a class of bulk carriers, although it must be emphasised that the factor quoted was calculated for a particular group of ships, and does not apply to any others. The guidance was as follows:

> *Where block loading is required, ie adjacent holds loaded in association with one or more remaining holds empty, the total maximum permissible load in the two adjacent holds should not exceed 1.25 x maximum corresponding alternate hold load with the double-bottom tanks empty.*

In other words, if the maximum cargo allowed in holds Nos. 3, 5 and 7 is 24,000 tonnes per hold, and if a closeweight cargo is to be block loaded in Nos. 3, 4 and 5, the maximum total permitted in No.3+ No.4, or in No.4+ No.5 is 24,000 x 1.25 (ie 30,000 tonnes), when the double bottom tanks are empty. This applies when the ship is block loaded, despite the fact that the maximum permitted loading of No.4 hold is normally 17,000 tonnes.

IRON SOMERSBY (1976) **LOADING PROCEDURE**

Run	Hold	Tonnes	Ballast
			After draft survey dump all wing tanks.
1	9	8,000	Pump No. 5 hopper (Pt and Stbd).
2	5	10,000	Pump No. 3 hopper (Pt and Stbd).
3	3	10,000	Pump No. 2 and No. 1 hoppers (Pt and Stbd).
4	7	12,000	Strip as required.
5	1	12,000	Ballast out (8 hours) Draft check
6	9	7,000	(If ballast is slow, pouring may continue to end of Run 9, when loading
7	5	8,000	should cease until stripping is completed).
8	3	8,000	
9	7	6,000	
10	1	5,500	
11	9	7,000	
12	5	4,700	Draft check
13	3	2,500	Commence trimming pours (runs)
14	7	3,000	
15	3	1,000	
16	7	1,300	
		106,000	

One loader at 6,000 TPH takes around 18 hours.

Two-loader operation

Loader No. 1				Loader No. 2			
Run	Hold	Tonnes	Elapsed Time	Elapsed Time	Run	Hold	Tonnes
1	9	8,000	0120	0140	2	5	10,000
4	7	12,000	0320	0320	3	3	10,000
6	9	7,000	0430	0520	5	1	12,000
7	5	8,000	0550	0640	8	3	8,000
9	7	6,000	0650	0740	10	1	5,500
11	9	7,000	0800	0820	12	5	4,700
14	7	3,000	0830	0845	13	3	2,500

Identical ballast sequence is followed, although speeded up. When runs 1 & 2 occur simultaneously ballast steps 1 & 2 will usually also occur simultaneously, and so on throughout the loading, subject to the usual strength and stability checks.

On the following page is a diagrammatic explanation of the two-loader operation, in an hour by hour sequence up to the time of the draft check.

(Courtesy BHP)

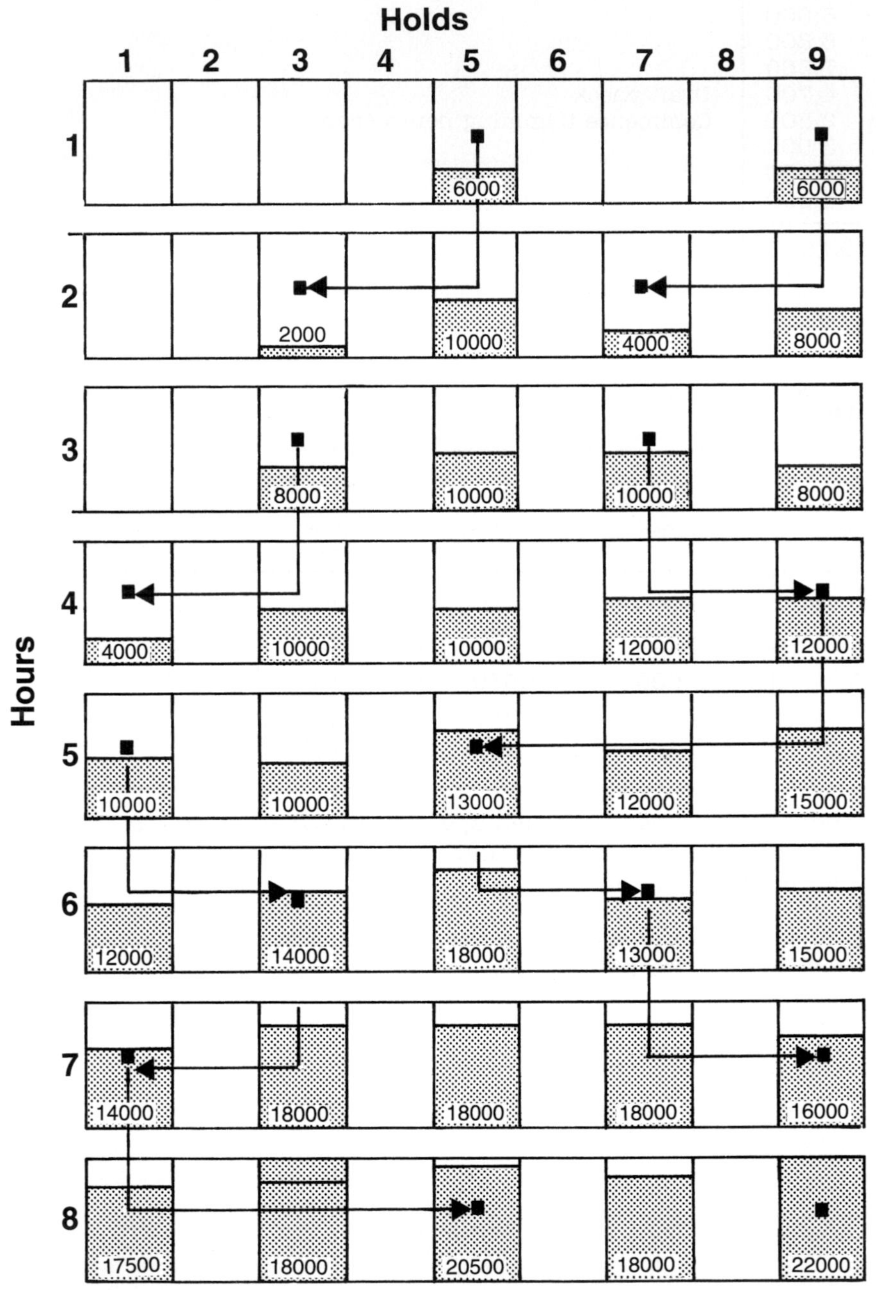

(Courtesy BHP)

TRIMMING POUR – TWO-HOLD, 3,000 TONNE DWT, MINI-BULKER

RESERVE about 300 tonnes for trimming to achieve the required draft. To calculate the trimming pour proceed as follows.

1. Read draft amidships, port and starboard, and take mean.
2. Deduct mean draft from intended loaded draft. (Intended loaded draft should be corrected for dock water density, consumption on passage to open sea, etc.)
3. Tonnes per centimetre immersion (TPC) for this vessel at loaded draft is almost exactly 10, so when a draft increase of 29 cm is required, for example, 290 tonnes of cargo must be loaded.
4. From forecastle head read the forward draft, compare it with draft amidships and from this calculate the present trim. Often it is not easy to read the after draft and even when it is easy to read the draft aft on one side it is not easy to read on the other side, to take the mean, so calculations are best if based upon forward draft plus drafts amidships, port and starboard.
5. The following allowances for loading in different positions in No. 1 hold have been taken from the trimming data of the vessel used for this example. They are used to select the position to be used for the final pour:

100 tonnes at Position:	Change of Trim (cm)
Position One	46
Midlength of No. 1 hatch	34
Halfway between midlength and Two	27
Position Two	20
After coaming of No. 1 hatch	15

6. A typical calculation:

Final mean draft required:	5.45m (corrected for density)		
Mean draft at trimming:	5.16		
Difference:	0.29 . . . to load 290 tonnes		
At trimming, draft forward	4.51		
Mean draft at trimming	5.16		
Half trim:	0.65	. . . full trim	1.30
		. . . trim required	0.50
		Trim change required	**0.80**

From table (above) 290 tonnes at Halfway: 2.9 x 27 = 78.3

7. To keep a check on how the loading is progressing it is helpful to do a succession of calculations like the above, during the last couple of hours of loading, but without stopping loading.

QUANTITIES REQUIRED FOR FINAL TRIMMING
Example based upon a nine-hold Panamax bulk carrier
NB: Trim by head, and trim change toward head: +ve (positive)

		For'd		Aft		Midships	Trim	Mean²
Present Drafts:	P	*.13.41.*	P	*.13.51.*	P	*.13.46.*		
(Corrected)	S	*.13.41.*	S	*.13.51.*	S	*.13.46.*		
Means	F	*.13.41.*	A	*.13.51.*	Mid.	*.13.46.*	*. −0.10.*	
Mean of Means ('Mean²')	[(F+A+6M)/8]							*.13.46.*
Required Draft		***.13.72***		***.13.72***		***.13.72***	***.0.00.***	***.13.72.***
Trim change required (cm)						(+/-)	*.+10.* cm	(A)
Mean sinkage required:								*.0.26.*
	@ TPC	***.68.***		required to load *.1768.* tonnes				(B)

From trim tables:
1000 tonnes in No. ***.3.*** (a for'd hold), changes trim *+**.47.5*** cm (C)
1000 tonnes in No. ***.7.*** (an after hold), changes trim —***.27.0*** cm (D)

Let X be tonnes to be loaded in for'd hold

$$X = [1000A - DB]/[C - D]$$

Substitute for A, B, C and D in the above, taking care to use the correct sign for each of the values, and solve for X.

X = *[1000(+10) – (–**27.0**)(1768)]/**[47.5 – (–27.0)]***

= *[10,000 + 47,736]/**[47.5 + 27.0]***

= *57,736/**74.5***

= *775*

X = *..775..* tonnes and (B – X) = *..993..* tonnes

Check (from trimming tables/

X tonnes	= *.775.* in hold No. ***.3.*** causes trim	*+ 0.30.*F	*−0.07.* A
(B-X) tonnes	= *.993.* in hold No. ***.7.*** causes trim	*+ 0.01*F	*+ 0.28.* A
Trim change		*+ 0.31.*	*+ 0.21*
Present draft		*13.41.*	*13.51.*
Final draft		*13.72.*	*13.72.*

Items shown in italics are to be entered by the user

Items shown in ***bold italics*** can be precomputed and pre-entered.

VARIETY OF ABBREVIATIONS FOR TERMS USED IN STABILITY

These abbreviations have been taken from the loading manuals of five ships, and from several other publications.

	Ship A	Ship B	Ship C	Ship D☆	Ship E	UK DTp	RINA	Derrett
Stowage factor in cubic metres per tonne (or cubic feet per long ton)		SF		SF	SF			
Specific gravity	SG	SG			SG	SG	γ	SG
Volume of Displacement in cubic metres					V		∇	V, ∇
Displacement in tonnes	Dispt	W, Δ		Δ	D	Displ't	Δ	W, Δ
Tonnes per centimetre immersion, in tonnes		TPC	TPC	TPI	TPC	TPC		TPC
Moment to change trim one centimetre, in tonnes-metres		MTC	MTC	MTI	MTC	MCTC		MCTC
Centre of buoyancy from midships (†aft), in metres	LCB	LCB, ⊗B		LCB	MB	LCB, ⊗B	†LCB	
Centre of flotation from midships (‡aft), in metres	LCF	LCF, ⊗F		LCF	MF	LCF, ⊗F	‡LCF	
Centre of gravity from midships, in metres	LCG	⊗G	LCG	MG	LCG, ⊗G			
Centre of gravity above baseline, in metres	KG	KG	KG	KG	VCG, KG	KG	$\overline{KG}$	KG
Longitudinal distance from the longitudinal centre of buoyancy to the longitudinal centre of gravity, metres		BG		BG	BG			
Centre of buoyancy above baseline, in metres	KB	KB		KB	KB	VCB	$\overline{KB}$	KB
Transverse metacentre above baseline, in metres	KMT	T.KM	TKM	TKM	TKM	KM(T)	$\overline{KM}$	KM
Longitudinal metacentre above baseline, in metres	KML	L.KM		LKM	LKM	KM(L)	$\overline{KM_L}$	KM_L
Transverse metacentric height above centre of gravity, in metres, without allowing for free surface effect	GM	GM	GM	GM	GM	GM	$\overline{GM}$	GM
Correction for free surface effect, in metres	GG'	GGo	GGo		GGo			GG_V
Transverse metacentric height above centre of gravity, in metres, corrected for free surface effect, or fluid metacentric height	G'M, GMf	GoM	GoM	⊗GM	GoM	GMfluid	$\overline{GM_F}$	G_VM
Moment due to free surface effect		i	I	i			I_T	I, i
Righting arm, in metres, without correction for free surface effect	GZ	GZ	GZ	GZ	G'Z'	GZ	$\overline{GZ}$	GZ
Righting arm, in metres, corrected for free surface effect		GoZ	GoZ	GZ	GZ	GZ	$\overline{GZ_F}$	GZ
Flooding angle, in degrees	θf	θf			f	θf		
Heeling angle at maximum GZ, in degrees		θmax	θm	θ max	m			
Angle of vanishing stability		θv	θR	θr				
Propeller immersion		I/D	I/D		I/D			
Block coefficient	Cb	CB		Cb	CB		C_B	C_B
Prismatic coefficient	Cp	CP		Cp	CP		C_P	C_P

☆This ship used Imperial measurements

	Ship A	Ship B	Ship C	Ship D☆	Ship E	UK DTp	RINA	Derrett
Waterplane coefficient	Cwl	CW		Cw	CW		C_{WP}	C_w
Midships coefficient	Cm	C MID		Cm	CM		C_M	C_m
Area of waterplane, in square metres		WP		WA			A_W	A
Draft							T	d
Draft (forward), as read	df				d_{fo} dF			
Draft (forward), corrected	dF	dF	DF	d_{FP}	df			
Draft (midships), as read	dm				$d_{⊗}$ dM			
Draft (midships), corrected	dM	d⊗	DC	ds	$d_{⊗}$			
Draft (aft), as read	da				d_{ao} dA			
Draft (aft), corrected	dA	dA	DA	d_{AP}	da			
Mean of forward and aft corrected drafts	dme	dM	dm		dm'			
Mean of mean drafts	dM'				dm			
Forward direction from midships, and trim by head	(+)	(–)	(–)	(–)	(–)			
Aft direction from midships, and trim by stern	(–)	(+)	(+)	(+)	(+)			

☆ This ship used Imperial measurements.

REGINA OLDENDORFF B270/7 Dalian -PRC MACS3 SHIPCOMPUTER....... BY SEACOS GMBH - GERMANY..	VOYAGE NUMBER.....................:WHEAT 5/90 VOYAGE DESCRIPTION................:Bulk Wheat 24/5/90 NAME: kbg 'Regina O' DATE: 02-13-92 TIME: 08:47:31 Three Rivers - Oran

ITEM....................... designation.................	WEIGHT.. ton.....	CENTRE OF GRAVITY....... LONGIT. m.f.AP.	 VERTIC. m.a.BL.	 TRANS. m.f.MS	FREE.... SURFACE. mt......	GRAIN... MOMENT.. mt......	CONTAINER 20ft/40ft units....	WEIGHT DISTRIB.. FROM... m.f.AP.	 TO..... m.f.AP.
)Cargo									
GR.:G-HLD1U 6351M3 1.197M3/T	5305.8	157.170	8.359	0.000		1574.3		142.720	173.650
GR.:G-HLD2T 7865M3 1.246M3/T	6313.0	127.780	7.789	0.000		429.8		112.010	142.720
GR.:G-HLD3U 2858M3 1.246M3/T	2294.0	101.635	4.790	0.000		7165.4		90.430	112.010
GR.:G-HLD4T 8060M3 1.246M3/T	6469.0	75.080	7.790	0.000		439.3		58.890	90.430
GR.:G-HLD5U 6342M3 1.227M3/T	5169.0	45.421	8.103	0.000		1655.7		29.840	58.890
SUM....:Wheat	25550.8	101.531	7.702	0.000	0.0	11264.4		***.***	***.***
LOADING PACKAGE...:BUNK. 5/90	969.7	49.328	6.098	0.112	5453.7	0.0		***.***	***.***
LOADING PACKAGE...:WB 5/90	1450.0	78.698	1.779	0.000	306.6	0.0		***.***	***.***
DEADWEIGHT..................	27970.5	98.538	7.339	0.004	5760.3	11264.4	CONTAINER-TOTAL=		units
LIGHT-SHIP/STANDARD WEIGHT...	8051.0	79.458	10.119	0.000			SUM 20'-CONTAIN=		units
DISPLACEMENT................	36021.5	94.274	7.961	0.003			SUM 40'-CONTAIN=		units

DEADWEIGHT-MAX. TO SUM.FREEB.	28031.0	ton....
DEADWEIGHT-RESERVE TO SUM.FB.	60.5	ton....
DRAUGHT-MAX. TO SUMMER FREEB.	10.238	m.a.bok
DRAUGHT ACTUAL..............	10.222	m.a.bok
DRAUGHT RESERVE SUMMER-FREEB.	0.016	m.a.bok

RHO.SW......= Density of Sea-Water.........= 1.025 t/m3.
GM..........= Metacentric height...........= 1.534 metre
FS.COR......= Free surface correction.......= 0.160 metre
GM.COR......= Metacentric height corrected..= 1.374 metre
GM.REQ......= Limit value of metacen.height.= 0.300 metre
GM.REQ IS VALID ONLY FOR... grain cargo

DRAUGHT CALCULATED metre above bok....	ON PER- PENDIC..	AT THE MARK....	
AFT...............	10.488		
MIDSHIP...........	10.217		
FORWARD...........	9.947		

TRIM.....= 0.169 degree (by stern) = 0.541 metre
HEELING due transverse mom.= 0.125 degree (stbd)

M`WIND......= Moment of wind...............= 2500.0 mt...
A.M`WI+TR...= Heeling due to wind+transv.mom= 3.1 degr.

M`GRAIN.....= Heeling moment of grain cargo.=11264.450 mt...
M`GRAINmax..= Permissable moment of grain...=11749.980 mt...
A.M`GRAIN...= Angle due to grain shifted....= 11.873 degr.
AR.GRAIN....= Area o.residual dyn.stability = 0.218 m*rad

REGINA OLDENDORFF B270/7 Dalian -PRC MACS3 SHIPCOMPUTER....... BY SEACOS GMBH - GERMANY..	LOADING PACKAGE....................:BUNK. 5/90 LPAC DESCRIPTION..................:Bunker etc. NAME: kbg 'Regina O.' 24/5/90 DATE: 02-13-92 TIME: 08:31:26 Three Rivers - Oran

ITEM.......................... designation..................	WEIGHT.. ton.....	CENTRE OF GRAVITY....... LONGIT. m.f.AP.	VERTIC. m.a.BL.	TRANS. m.f.MS	FREE.... SURFACE. mt......	GRAIN... MOMENT.. mt......	CONTAINER 20ft/40ft units....	WEIGHT DISTRIB.. FROM... m.f.AP.	TO..... m.f.AP.
>Fuel Oil									
TANK:1FOT 0.9800t/m3 0.2%	1.0	127.369	0.002	0.000	185.7			112.010	142.720
TANK:2FOT 0.9800t/m3 0.3%	1.0	101.220	0.002	0.000	185.9			90.430	112.010
TANK:3FOT 0.9800t/m3 63.7%	305.0	74.660	0.474	0.000	2981.7			58.890	90.430
TANK:4FOT 0.9800t/m3 11.1%	35.2	47.240	0.082	0.000	1515.2			29.840	58.890
TANK:FOSTP 0.9800t/m3 34.2%	12.0	28.600	11.097	-7.891	25.5			27.350	29.840
TANK:FOSTS 0.9800t/m3 34.2%	12.0	28.600	11.097	7.891	25.5			27.350	29.840
TANK:FOSER 0.9800t/m3 61.9%	21.0	26.110	11.518	7.913	25.5			24.860	27.350
SUM....:Fuel Oil	387.2	66.884	1.694	0.429	4945.0	0.0		***.***	***.***
>Diesel Oil									
TANK:DOTP 0.8500t/m3 22.4%	18.1	24.833	0.408	-3.184	68.3			18.220	29.840
TANK:DOTS 0.8500t/m3 22.4%	18.1	24.833	0.408	3.184	68.3			18.220	29.840
TANK:DOSET 0.8500t/m3 87.9%	7.7	22.780	11.850	7.900	0.7			21.540	24.030
TANK:DOSER 0.8500t/m3 97.1%	8.5	22.780	11.979	6.300	0.7			21.540	24.030
SUM....:Diesel Oil	52.4	24.199	3.963	2.181	138.1	0.0		***.***	***.***
>Lubricating Oil									
TANK:LOS 0.9000t/m3 50.0%	7.3	24.030	0.412	0.000	3.0			21.540	26.520
TANK:SUMP 0.9000t/m3 4.6%	1.0	17.805	0.040	0.000	3.0			14.070	21.540
TANK:MELOS 0.9000t/m3 50.0%	12.8	15.480	8.069	-5.630	12.6			13.240	17.390
TANK:LOSET 0.9000t/m3 90.0%	18.8	18.670	8.538	-6.248	22.7			17.390	19.880
TANK:CYLOT 0.9000t/m3 80.0%	14.8	19.460	11.885	7.100	6.1			18.220	20.710
TANK:DGLOS 0.9000t/m3 91.1%	5.0	10.130	9.066	-5.031	4.4			8.260	11.580
TANK:DGLOL 0.9000t/m3 90.0%	2.7	12.470	7.982	-4.750	1.0			11.580	13.240
TANK:DGLOU 0.9000t/m3 81.3%	3.0	12.440	9.207	-5.396	4.1			11.580	13.240
SUM....:Lubricating Oil	65.3	17.614	8.214	-2.125	56.9	0.0		***.***	***.***
>Freshwater									
TANK:1FWTP 1.0000t/m3 48.0%	47.0	5.118	12.436	-4.404	137.5			2.630	7.430
TANK:2FWTP 1.0000t/m3 49.5%	31.0	-0.552	12.691	-5.089	24.3			-5.770	2.630
TANK:2FWTS 1.0000t/m3 49.5%	31.0	-0.552	12.691	5.089	24.3			-5.770	2.630
TANK:DWTS 1.0000t/m3 42.2%	40.0	5.125	12.345	4.339	118.5			2.630	7.430
TANK:CWT 1.0000t/m3 50.9%	11.0	6.414	2.184	0.000	1.1			4.430	7.430
SUM....:Freshwater	160.0	3.012	11.807	-0.209	305.6	0.0		***.***	***.***
>Sludge									
TANK:OWT 1.0000t/m3 18.5%	3.0	12.440	0.366	0.000	5.5			11.580	13.240
TANK:BILGE 1.0000t/m3 8.3%	2.0	9.708	0.173	0.000	2.5			7.430	11.580
SUM....:Sludge	5.0	11.347	0.289	0.000	8.1	0.0		***.***	***.***
>Stores etc.	250.0	60.000	8.500	0.000	0.0			-4.000	185.000
>Dunnage	49.7	80.000	10.000	0.000	0.0			30.000	180.000
TOTAL SUM.....................	969.7	49.328	6.098	0.112	5453.7	0.0			

REGINA OLDENDORFF B270/7 Dalian -PRC MACS3 SHIPCOMPUTER....... BY SEACOS GMBH - GERMANY..	LOADING PACKAGE...................:WB 5/90 LPAC DESCRIPTION..................:Waterballast NAME: kbg 'Regina O.' 24/5/90 DATE: 02-13-92 TIME: 08:31:55 Three Rivers - Oran

ITEM........................ designation.................	WEIGHT.. ton.....	CENTRE OF GRAVITY....... LONGIT. m.f.AP.	VERTIC. m.a.BL.	TRANS. m.f.MS	FREE.... SURFACE. mt......	GRAIN... MOMENT.. mt......	CONTAINER 20ft/40ft units....	WEIGHT DISTRIB.. FROM... m.f.AP.	TO..... m.f.AP.
TANK:FPT 1.0250t/m3 0.0%	0.0	175.465	0.000	0.000	0.0			173.650	186.250
)Doublebottom									
TANK:1WBTP 1.0250t/m3 0.0%	0.0	155.597	0.000	-2.900	0.0			142.720	173.650
TANK:1WBTS 1.0250t/m3 0.0%	0.0	155.597	0.000	2.900	0.0			142.720	173.650
TANK:2WBTP 1.0250t/m3 0.0%	0.0	127.286	0.000	-7.350	0.0			112.010	142.720
TANK:2WBTS 1.0250t/m3 0.0%	0.0	127.286	0.000	7.350	0.0			112.010	142.720
TANK:3WBTP 1.0250t/m3 82.2%	245.0	101.220	1.037	-8.754	18.1			90.430	112.010
TANK:3WBTS 1.0250t/m3 82.2%	245.0	101.220	1.037	8.754	18.1			90.430	112.010
TANK:4WBTP 1.0250t/m3 97.8%	430.0	74.546	1.398	-8.994	1.4			58.890	90.430
TANK:4WBTS 1.0250t/m3 97.8%	430.0	74.546	1.398	8.994	1.4			58.890	90.430
TANK:5WBTP 1.0250t/m3 0.0%	0.0	45.036	0.000	-6.400	0.0			29.840	58.890
TANK:5WBTS 1.0250t/m3 0.0%	0.0	45.036	0.000	-6.400	0.0			29.840	58.890
SUM....:Doublebottom	1350.0	84.228	1.267	0.000	39.0	0.0		***.***	***.***
)Topwingtanks									
TANK:1TSTP 1.0250t/m3 0.0%	0.0	142.171	9.510	-10.100	0.0			142.720	173.650
TANK:1TSTS 1.0250t/m3 0.0%	0.0	142.171	9.510	10.100	0.0			142.720	173.650
TANK:2TSTP 1.0250t/m3 0.0%	0.0	127.365	9.510	-11.000	0.0			112.010	142.720
TANK:2TSTS 1.0250t/m3 0.0%	0.0	127.365	9.510	11.000	0.0			112.010	142.720
TANK:3TSTP 1.0250t/m3 0.0%	0.0	101.220	9.510	-11.000	0.0			90.430	112.010
TANK:3TSTS 1.0250t/m3 0.0%	0.0	101.220	9.510	11.000	0.0			90.430	112.010
TANK:4TSTP 1.0250t/m3 0.0%	0.0	74.660	9.510	-11.000	0.0			58.890	90.430
TANK:4TSTS 1.0250t/m3 0.0%	0.0	74.660	9.510	11.000	0.0			58.890	90.430
TANK:5TSTP 1.0250t/m3 0.0%	0.0	57.470	9.510	-11.000	0.0			30.670	58.890
TANK:5TSTS 1.0250t/m3 0.0%	0.0	57.470	9.510	11.000	0.0			30.670	58.890
SUM....:Topwingtanks	0.0	0.000	0.000	0.000	0.0	0.0		***.***	***.***
TANK:APT 1.0250t/m3 37.2%	100.0	4.055	8.694	0.000	267.6			-4.570	7.430
TOTAL SUM....................	1450.0	78.698	1.779	0.000	306.6	0.0			

REGINA OLDENDORFF B270/7 Dalian -PRC MACS3 SHIPCOMPUTER....... BY SEACOS GMBH - GERMANY..	VOYAGE NUMBER.....................:WHEAT 5/90 VOYAGE DESCRIPTION................:Bulk Wheat 24/5/90 NAME: kbg 'Regina O' DATE: 02-13-92 TIME: 08:47:42 Three Rivers - Oran

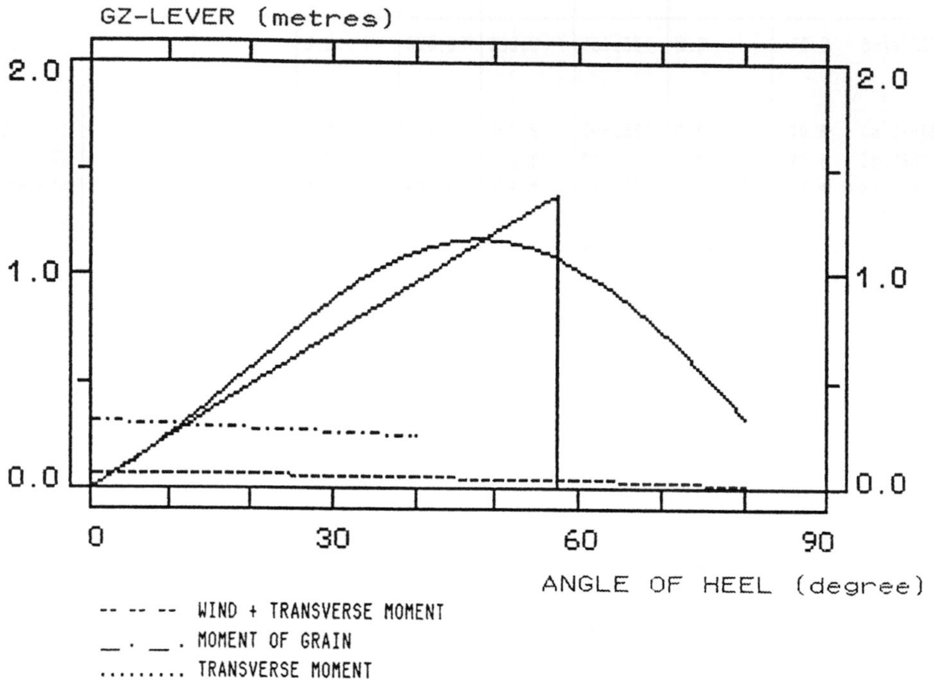

LEVERARM............... RESULTS................ metres.................	PHI = ANGLE OF HEEL (degree)								
	10.000	12.000	20.000	30.000	40.000	50.000	60.000	70.000	80.000
KN-ORDINATE............	1.653	1.989	3.333	4.939	6.321	7.379	8.054	8.357	8.334
KG * SIN(PHI)..........	1.382	1.655	2.723	3.980	5.117	6.098	6.894	7.480	7.840
FREE SURFACE CORRECTION.	0.028	0.033	0.055	0.080	0.103	0.122	0.138	0.150	0.157
GZ-LEVER CORRECTED......	0.243	0.301	0.556	0.879	1.101	1.158	1.022	0.726	0.337
TRANSVERSE MOMENT ORDIN.	0.003	0.003	0.003	0.003	0.002	0.002	0.002	0.001	0.001
WIND+TRANSV.MOMENT ORDIN	0.071	0.071	0.068	0.063	0.055	0.047	0.036	0.025	0.013

ACTUAL VALUES....................................		
GM CORRECTED......................	1.374	metres
ANGLE DUE TO TRANSVERSE MOMENT.....	0.125	degrees
ANGLE DUE TO WIND+TRANSVERSE MOMENT	3.065	degrees
ANGLE DUE TO GRAIN SHIFTED.........	11.873	degrees
AREA OF RESIDUAL DYN. STABILITY....	0.218	m * rad
AREA UP TO 30 DEGREES.............	0.216	m * rad
AREA UP TO 40 DEGREES.............	0.390	m * rad
AREA BETWEEN 30 AND 40 DEGREES.....	0.175	m * rad
GZ LEVER AT 30 DEGREES............	0.879	metres
STATICAL STABILITY RANGE..........	80.000	degrees

LIMIT VALUES.....................................		
GM CORRECTED......................	0.300	metres
ANGLE DUE TO TRANSVERSE MOMENT.....	3.000	degrees
ANGLE DUE TO WIND+TRANSVERSE MOMENT	17.773	degrees
ANGLE DUE TO GRAIN SHIFTED.........	12.000	degrees
AREA OF RESIDUAL DYN. STABILITY....	0.075	m * rad
AREA UP TO 30 DEGREES.............	0.055	m * rad
AREA UP TO 40 DEGREES.............	0.090	m * rad
AREA BETWEEN 30 AND 40 DEGREES.....	0.030	m * rad
GZ LEVER AT 30 DEGREES............	0.366	metres
STATICAL STABILITY RANGE..........	50.000	degrees

REGINA OLDENDORFF
B270/7 Dalian -PRC
MACS3 SHIPCOMPUTER.......
BY SEACOS GMBH - GERMANY..

VOYAGE NUMBER.....................:WHEAT 5/90
VOYAGE DESCRIPTION................:Bulk Wheat 24/5/90
NAME: kbg 'Regina O'
DATE: 02-13-92 TIME: 08:51:38 Three Rivers - Oran

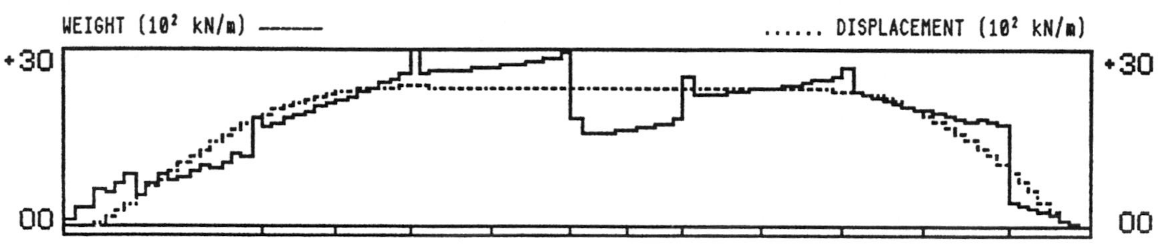

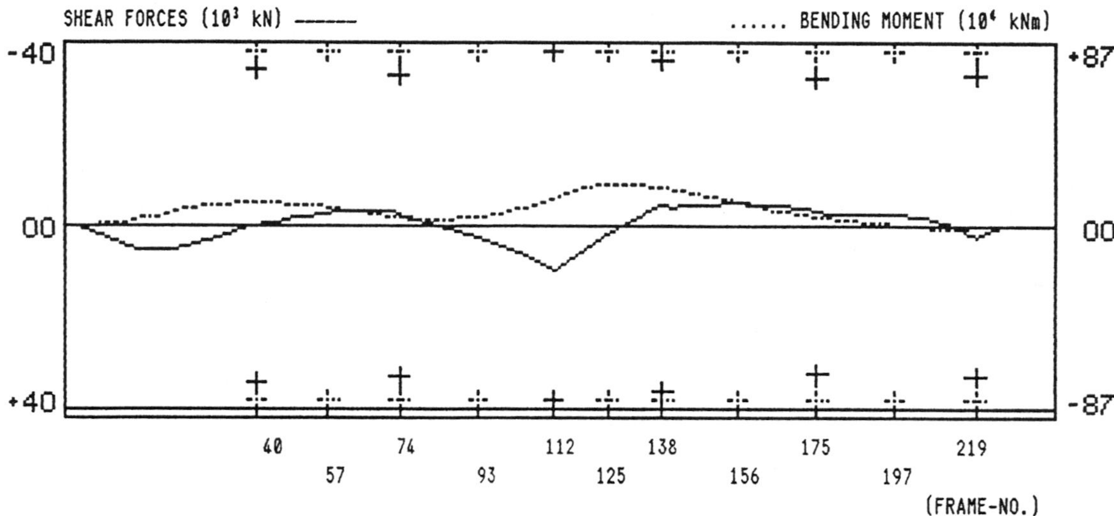

LONGITUDINAL STRENGTH CALCULATION FOR HOMOGENEOUS LOADING

LONGITUDINAL. POSITION.....		.... SHEAR FORCES				.. BENDING MOMENTS ..			..STAT TORSION MOM ..		
				...REL...			...REL...			...REL...	
FRM. num.	DIST... m.f.ap.	EXISTING.. (kN)	CORRECTED. (kN)	SEA (%)	PORT (%)	EXISTING.. (kNm)	SEA (%)	PORT (%)	EXISTING.. (kNm)	SEA (%)	PORT (%)
40	30.670	-27	-27	0	0	106964	13	8			
57	44.780					85851	10	6			
74	58.890	-2688	-2448	7	6	40289	5	3			
93	74.660					42420	5	3			
112	90.430	9564	8155	21	19	132830	16	10			
125	101.220					197444	24	14			
138	112.010	-4658	-4486	12	11	181716	22	13			
156	126.950					112638	14	8			
175	142.720	-3161	-3333	10	8	44023	5	3			
197	158.250					5311	1	0			
219	173.650	2621	2621	8	7	-7544	1	1			

HYDROSTATIC TABLE

DRAFT (EXT) (M)	D (T)	V (M3)	LCB (M)	MTC (T-M)	LCF (M)	TKM (M)	LKM (M)	TPC (T)	KB (M)	AW (M2)	CB	CW	CP	CM	CUT (T/CM)	DRAFT (MLD) (M)
10.100	35551	34477	–3.567	482.70	1.454	9.474	253.68	38.50	5.216	3734	0.8124	0.887	0.817	0.993	0.306	10.082
10.110	35590	34515	–3.562	482.96	1.469	9.476	253.56	38.51	5.221	3735	0.8125	0.887	0.817	0.993	0.309	10.092
10.120	35628	34552	–3.557	483.22	1.483	9.477	253.43	38.52	5.226	3735	0.8126	0.887	0.817	0.993	0.312	10.102
10.130	35667	35689	–3.551	482.49	1.497	9.479	253.30	38.52	5.232	3736	0.8127	0.887	0.817	0.993	0.315	10.112
10.140	35795	34626	–3.546	483.75	1.511	9.480	253.17	38.53	5.237	3737	0.8127	0.887	0.818	0.993	0.318	10.122
10.150	35743	34664	–3.541	484.01	1.525	9.482	253.05	38.54	5.242	3737	0.8128	0.888	0.818	0.993	0.321	10.132
10.160	35782	34701	–3.536	484.27	1.539	9.484	252.92	38.55	5.247	3738	0.8129	0.888	0.818	0.993	0.324	10.142
10.170	35820	34738	–3.531	484.54	1.552	9.485	252.79	38.55	5.253	3739	0.8129	0.888	0.818	0.993	0.326	10.152
10.180	35859	34776	–3.525	484.80	1.566	9.487	252.67	38.56	5.258	3740	0.8130	0.888	0.818	0.993	0.329	10.162
10.190	35897	34813	–3.520	485.06	1.580	9.489	252.54	38.57	5.263	3740	0.8131	0.888	0.818	0.993	0.332	10.172
10.200	35936	34850	–3.515	485.33	1.593	9.490	252.42	38.58	5.268	3741	0.8132	0.888	0.818	0.993	0.335	10.182
10.210	35974	34888	–3.510	485.59	1.607	9.492	252.29	38.58	5.274	3742	0.8132	0.889	0.818	0.993	0.338	10.192
10.220	36013	34925	–3.505	485.85	1.621	9.494	252.17	38.59	5.279	3742	0.8133	0.889	0.818	0.993	0.341	10.202
10.230	36051	34962	–3.499	486.12	1.634	9.495	252.04	38.60	5.284	3743	0.8134	0.889	0.818	0.993	0.344	10.212
10.240	36090	35000	–3.494	486.38	1.648	9.497	251.92	38.61	5.290	3744	0.8135	0.889	0.818	0.993	0.347	10.222
10.250	36128	35037	–3.489	484.64	1.661	9.499	251.79	38.61	5.295	3745	0.8135	0.889	0.818	0.993	0.350	10.232
10.260	36167	35074	–3.484	486.91	1.674	9.500	251.67	38.62	5.300	3745	0.8136	0.889	0.818	0.993	0.353	10.242
10.270	36205	55112	–3.478	487.17	1.687	9.502	251.54	38.63	5.305	3746	0.8137	0.890	0.818	0.993	0.355	10.252
10.280	36244	35149	–3.473	487.43	1.701	9.504	251.42	38.63	5.311	3747	0.8138	0.890	0.818	0.993	0.358	10.262
10.290	36282	35186	–3.468	487.70	1.714	9.505	251.30	38.64	5.316	3747	0.8138	0.890	0.819	0.993	0.361	10.272
10.300	36321	35224	–3.463	487.96	1.727	9.507	251.17	38.65	5.321	3748	0.8139	0.890	0.819	0.993	0.364	10.282
10.310	36360	35261	–3.457	488.22	1.740	9.509	251.05	38.66	5.326	3749	0.8140	0.890	0.819	0.993	0.367	10.292
10.320	36398	35299	–3.452	488.49	1.753	9.511	250.93	38.66	5.332	3750	0.8140	0.890	0.819	0.993	0.370	10.302
10.330	36437	35336	–3.447	488.75	1.766	9.512	250.80	38.67	5.337	3750	0.8141	0.891	0.819	0.993	0.372	10.312
10.340	36475	35373	–3.441	489.01	1.779	9.514	250.68	38.68	5.342	3751	0.8142	0.891	0.819	0.993	0.375	10.322
10.350	36514	33411	–3.436	489.28	1.792	9.516	250.56	38.69	5.347	3752	0.8143	0.891	0.819	0.993	0.378	10.332
10.360	36552	35448	–3.431	489.54	1.805	9.518	250.44	38.69	5.353	3752	0.8143	0.891	0.819	0.993	0.381	10.342
10.370	36591	35486	–3.426	489.80	1.817	9.520	250.32	38.70	5.358	3753	0.8144	0.891	0.819	0.993	0.384	10.352
10.380	36630	35523	–3.420	490.07	1.830	9.521	250.19	38.71	5.363	3754	0.8145	0.891	0.819	0.993	0.386	10.362
10.390	36668	35561	–3.415	490.33	1.843	9.523	250.07	38.71	5.369	3755	0.8146	0.892	0.819	0.993	0.389	10.372

Extract of table from Regina Oldendorff *– for abbreviations see Appendix 10.1.*

FREE SURFACE MOMENT OF INERTIA				
NAME OF TANK	**FRAME NO**	**MOMENT OF INERTIA (M^4)**	**SPECIFIC GRAVITY (T/M^3)**	**FREE SURFACE MOMENT (T-M)**
No.1 F.O.T.	138-175	2962.5	0.98	2903.3
No.2 F.O.T.	112-138	2081.7	0.98	2040.1
No 3. F.O.T.	74-112	3042.6	0.98	2981.7
No 4. F.O.T.	39-74	1546.1	0.98	1515.2
D.O.T. (P. & S.)	25-39	123.4 x 2	0.85	209.8
No 1. F.W.T. (P)	4-12	1973	1.00	197.3
No 2. F.W.T. (P & S.)	–10-4	48.1 x 2	1.00	96.2
DRINKING W.T. (S')	4-12	182.7	1.00	182.7
F.P.T.	219-F	970	1.025	994.3
No 1. W.B.T. (P & S.)	175-219	2008.4 x 2	1.025	4117.2
No 2. W.B.T. (P & S)	138-175	605.3 x 2	1.025	1240.9
No 3. W.B.T. (P & S)	112-138	426.9 x 2	1.025	875.10
No 4. W.B.T. (P & S)	74-112	611.0 x 2	1.025	1252.6
No 5. W.B.T. (P & S)	39-74	547.7 x 2	1.025	1122.8
No 1. T.S.T. (P & S)	175-219	395.3 x 2	1.025	810.4
No 2. T.S.T. (P & S)	138-175	552.7 x 2	1.025	1133.0
No. 3 T.S.T. (P & S)	112-138	388.4 x 2	1.025	796.2
No. 4 T.S.T. (P & S)	74-112	567.7 x 2	1.025	1163.8
No. 5 T.S.T. (P & S)	40-74	508.9 x 2	1.025	1041.2
A.P.T.	–8-12	998.3	1.025	1023.3

SPECIAL NOTES REGARDING THE STABILITY AND LOADING OF THE SHIP

1. As this ship is required to comply with Schedule 4, Part I para. 2 of the 1968 Load Line Rules, it is most important to ensure that in any sailing condition the stability complies at least with the following minimum criteria;-

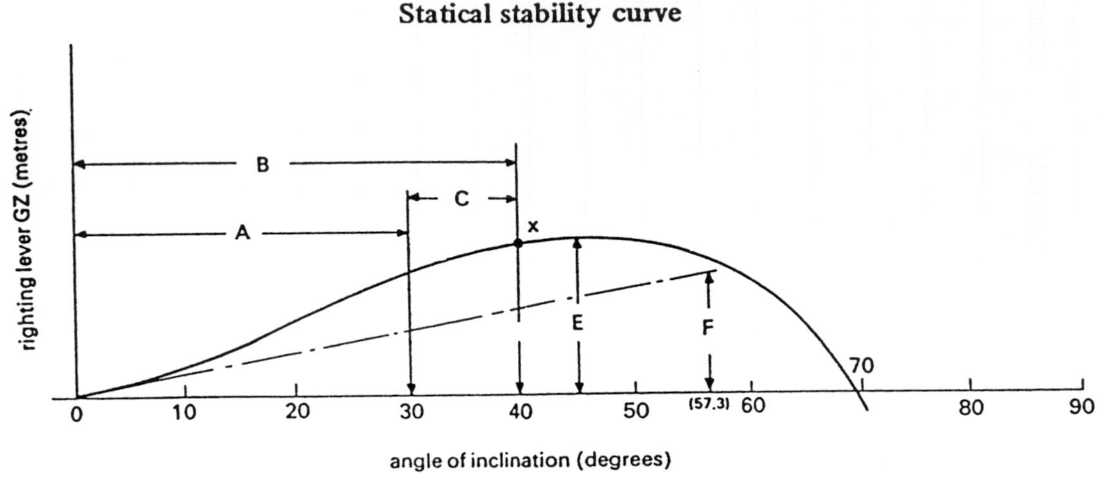

A – area under curve up to 30 degrees to be not less than 0·055 metre-radian (10·34 feet degrees).

B – area under curve up to x degrees to be not less than 0·09 metre-radian (16·92 feet degrees).

C – area between 30 degrees and x degrees to be not less than 0·03 metre-radian (5·64 feet degrees).

x – 40 degrees or any lesser angle at which the lower edges of any openings in the hull, superstructure or deckhouses which lead below deck and cannot be closed weathertight, would be immersed.

E – maximum GZ to occur at angle not less than 30 degrees and to be at least 0·20 metre (0·66 foot) in height.

F – initial GM to be not less than 0·15 metre (0·49 foot). In ships with timber deck cargo 0·05 metre (0·16 foot) will be permitted. The volume of timber deck cargo may be included in the derivation of the cross curves.

STABILITY CALCULATIONS

THIS set of stability calculations has been prepared with the object of providing readers with full, step by step, guidance to all the routine calculations.

The rules and guidelines which apply to all the calculations are given below, and these are followed by a worked example of each calculation, with accompanying notes.

The form provided for each calculation has been specially designed for easy use. It avoids the use of abbreviations as much as possible, to avoid the confusion which comes from the great variety of abbreviations used. Where possible the form also shows the source of the information required for each entry (eg, 'Hydrostatic table', or 'L41 + L49'-meaning the sum of the numbers entered on lines 41 and 49).

Additional detailed explanations accompany each of the forms. They use line references (eg, L27 = line 27) for rapid identification of each item in the form, and reference letters (eg, [B]) to refer to points on the Curve of Statical Stability.

Rules and guidelines for calculations in these appendices

Units

The metric system is used throughout:

Length	Metres
Volume	Cubic metres
Weight	Metric tonnes
Density	Metric tonnes per cubic metre
Moment	Tonne metres
Free surface moment	Metres^4
Areas under curves	Metre radians

Arithmetic functions: symbols used Appendix 10.7–10.14
+ Add; - Subtract; * Multiply; / Divide.

Hierarchy of functions

Each formula has been arranged, as far as possible, so that the order in which it is read is the correct sequence for arithmetic calculation (ie, formulae have been presented to minimise the effect of hierarchy). Care should be taken, however, particularly if using a sequential calculator. (A sequential calculator shows that 1+2*3=9. If correct mathematical sequence is followed 1+2*3=7.)

Arithmetic signs

Formulae have been composed to give appropriate signs, with notes where the convention of the vessel may differ. The sign must be transferred with the element of the formula. (x + -y becomes x - y.)

Conventions used

Distance of longitudinal centres of gravity, flotation and buoyancy must be measured from the midpoint. Sign is negative if centre is forward of the midpoint.
Trim by the head and change of trim forward are negative.

Alternative conventions

The stability and loading manuals of some ships are compiled using conventions which are different from those used in the calculations and forms provided in this book.

Officers on such ships who wish to use the calculations shown in this book must make the following amendments to values taken from the ship's stability and loading manual.

Longitudinal distances. When distance of longitudinal centres are given from the aft perpendicular they must be amended to obtain the distance of the longitudinal centre from the midpoint.

Longitudinal centre from midpoint = LBP/2- LCAP
where: LBP = Length between perpendiculars
LCAP = Longitudinal centre from aft perpendicular

Signs of distances. When the sign of a longitudinal distance is negative when measured aft from the midpoint the sign must be reversed (- becomes +, + becomes -) before it is used in the calculation.

Sign of trim. When trim by the stern and change of trim aft are negative the sign must be reversed before the values are used in calculation.

Worksheets

Items to be entered in the forms by hand are shown in italics and coloured blue.

	Item	Value	Source
1	**Displacement Calculation**		
2	*REGINA OLDENDORFF. Before Loading.*		
3	Item	Value	Source
4	Observations at Draft Survey		
5	Forward Draft Port	*5.06*	Observed
6	Forward Draft Starboard	*5.04*	Observed
7	Midships Draft Port	*6.08*	Observed
8	Midships Draft Starboard	*5.68*	Observed
9	Aft Draft Port	*6.96*	Observed
10	Aft Draft Starboard	*6.92*	Observed
11	Density	*1.013*	Observed
12	Drafts at Marks		
13	Forward	*5.050*	(L5+L6)/2
14	Midships	*5.880*	(L7+L8)/2
15	Aft	*6.940*	(L9+L10)/2
16	Trim between Marks	*1.890*	L15-L13
17	Length Between Marks	*177.62*	Ship's Particulars
18	Distances from Marks to Perpendiculars		
19	Negative if Perpendicular forward of Mark		
20	Forward	*-0.35*	Ship's Particulars
21	Midships	*0.00*	Ship's Particulars
22	Aft	*5.03*	Ship's Particulars
23	Corrections to drafts at Marks		
24	Forward	*-0.004*	L16/L17*L20
25	Midships	*0.000*	L16/L17*L21
26	Aft	*0.054*	L16/L17*L22
27	Drafts at Perpendiculars		
28	Forward	*5.046*	L13+L24
29	Midhips	*5.880*	L14+L25
30	Aft	*6.994*	L15+L26
31	Trim between Perpendiculars	*1.948*	L30-L28
32	Mean of Means	*5.915*	(L29*6+L28+L30)/8
33	Displacement from Table	*19987.00*	Hydrostatic Table
34	Length Between Perpendiculars	*183.00*	Ship's Particulars
35	Distance from Midpoint to Longitudinal Centre of Flotation.		
36	Negative if Longitudinal Centre of Flotation forward of Midpoint.		
37	Longitudinal Centre of Flotation	*-4.161*	Hydrostatic Table
38	Tonnes per Centimetre Immersion	*36.10*	Hydrostatic Table
39	First Trim Correction	*-159.90*	L31/L34*L37*L38*100
40	Mean of Means + 0.5	*6.415*	L32+0.5
41	Mean of Means - 0.5	*5.415*	L32-0.5
42	Moment to Change Trim One Centimetre		
43	at Mean of Means + 0.5	*409.48*	Hydrostatic Table
44	at Mean of Means - 0.5	*396.41*	Hydrostatic Table
45	Difference of MCTC	*13.07*	L43-L44
46	Second Trim Correction	*13.55*	L31*L31/L34*L45*50
47	Difference between Midships drafts	*0.40*	L7-L8
48	Tonnes per Centimetre Immersion		
49	at Midships Draft Port	*36.17*	Hydrostatic Table
50	at Midships Draft Starboard	*35.99*	Hydrostatic Table
51	Difference between TPC	*0.18*	L49-L50
52	List Correction	*0.43*	L47*L51*6
53	Displacement Corrected	*19841.08*	L33+L39+L46+L52
54	Density of Hydrostatic Table	*1.025*	Hydrostatic Table
55	Displacement	*19608.79*	L53*L11/L54

Displacement Calculation.

```
L1  Identity of Worksheet.
L2  Identity of vessel and survey.
L3  Titles of Columns.
L4/
L11 Values observed at survey.
L12/
L15 Drafts at Marks = (DP+DS)/2
       Where:- DP = Draft at Port Mark
               DS = Draft at Starboard Mark
L16 Trim between Marks. Negative if Forward Draft is greater than Aft
    Draft.
    Trim = DA-DF
       Where:- DA = Draft Aft
               DF = Draft Forward,
L17 Length Between Forward and Aft Draft Marks. Extract from Ship's
    Stability and Loading Manual. May be calculated from Length Between
    Perpendiculars and Distances from Draft Marks to Perpendiculars.
L18/
L22 Distances from Draft Marks to Perpendiculars. Extract from Ship's
    Stability and Loading Manual. Negative if Perpendicular is forward
    of Mark.
L23/
L26 Corrections to be applied to Drafts at Marks to find Drafts at
    Perpendiculars.
       Correction = TM/LBM*MtP
          Where:- TM  = Trim between Marks
                  LBM = Length Between Marks
                  MtP = Distance from Mark to Perpendicular
L27/
L30 Drafts at Perpendiculars = DM+C
       Where:- DM = Draft at Mark
               C  = Correction
L31 Trim between Perpendiculars, as Trim between Marks.
L32 Mean of Mean Drafts = (M*6+F+A)/8
       Where:- M = Draft at Midships Perpendicular
               F = Draft at Forward Perpendicular
               A = Draft at Aft Perpendicular
L33 Displacement from Table. Extract from Hydrostatic Table. Value
    corresponding to Mean of Mean Drafts.
L34 Length Between Perpendiculars. Extract from Ship's Stability and
    Loading Manual.
L37 Longitudinal Centre of Flotation. Extract from Hydrostatic Table.
    Value corresponding to Mean of Mean Drafts. Negative if
    Longitudinal Centre of Flotation is forward of Midpoint.
    Distance from Midpoint of Length Between Perpendiculars is
    required. Some tables present distances from Aft Perpendicular; if
    so calculate difference between LCF and LBP/2 and allocate sign.
L38 Tonnes per Centimetre Immersion. Extract from Hydrostatic Table.
    Value corresponding to Mean of Mean Drafts.
L39 First Trim Correction = TP/LBP*LCF*TPC*100
       Where:- TP  = Trim between Perpendiculars
               LBP = Length Between Perpendiculars
               LCF = Longitudinal Centre of Flotation
               TPC = Tonnes per Centimetre Immersion
L40 Draft 0.5 metres greater than Mean of Mean Drafts.
L41 Draft 0.5 metres less than Mean of Mean Drafts.
L42/
L44 Moment to Change Trim One Centimetre. Extract from Hydrostatic
    Table. Values corresponding to Drafts 0.5 metres greater and less
    than Mean of Mean Drafts.
```

```
L45 Rate of change of MCTC per metre. Difference between above values
    of MCTC.
L46 Second Trim Correction = TP*TP/LBP*DMCTC*50
       Where:- TP    = Trim Between Perpendiculars
               LBP   = Length Between Perpendiculars
               DMCTC = Rate of Change of MCTC per Metre
L47 Difference between Midships Drafts = MDP-MDS
       Where:- MDP = Midships Draft Port
               MDS = Midships Draft Starboard
L48/
L50 Tonnes Per Centimetre Immersion. Extract from Hydrostatic Table.
    Values corresponding to Midships Drafts Port and Starboard.
L51 Difference between TPC at Midships Drafts = TPCP-TPCS
       Where:- TPCP = Tonnes Per Centimetre Immersion at Midships Draft
                      Port
               TPCS = Tonnes Per Centimetre Immersion at Midships Draft
                      Starboard
L52 Heel Correction = DMD*DTPC*6
       Where:- DMD  = Difference between Midships Drafts
               DTPC = Difference between Tonnes Per Centimetre
                      Immersion at Midships Drafts
L53 Displacement Corrected = DT+FTC+STC+HC
       Where:- DT  = Displacement from Table
               FTC = First Trim Correction
               STC = Second Trim Correction
               HC  = Heel Correction
L54 Density used in compilation of Hydrostatic Table. Extract from
       Hydrostatic Table. If not stated, assume 1.025 MT/CM.
L55 Displacement = DC*D/DHT
       Where:- DC  = Displacement Corrected
               D   = Density of water
               DHT = Density of Hydrostatic Table
```

Note. This method is the same in principle as that used in the United Nations Economic and Social Council Code of Uniform Standards and Procedures for the Performance of Draught Surveys of Coal Cargoes[60], with the addition of the Heel Correction.

1 **Trim and Initial Stability**
2 *REGINA OLDENDORFF. Summer Marks.*
3 LCG, LCB and LCF from Midpoint.
4 Negative if Centre forward of Midpoint.

	Identity	Weight	Longitudinal Centre of Gravity	Longitudinal Moment	Vertical Centre of Gravity	Vertical Moment	Free Surface or Volumetric Heeling Momnt
5–7	Identity	Weight	Longitudinal Centre of Gravity	Longitudinal Moment	Vertical Centre of Gravity	Vertical Moment	Free Surface or Volumetric Heeling Momnt
8		W	LCG	W*LCG	VCG	W*VCG	
9	*Fuel Oil*						
10	*No 1*	*452*	*-35.86*	*-16209*	*0.74*	*334*	*2903*
11	*No 2*	*318*	*-9.72*	*-3091*	*0.74*	*235*	*2040*
12	*No 3*	*464*	*16.84*	*7814*	*0.74*	*343*	*2982*
13	*No 4*	*309*	*44.26*	*13676*	*0.74*	*229*	*1515*
14	*Service*	*25*	*65.39*	*1635*	*12.05*	*301*	
15	*Settling*	*53*	*62.90*	*3334*	*12.04*	*638*	
16							
17	*Diesel Oil*	*135*	*66.48*	*8975*	*2.42*	*327*	*210*
18	*Lub Oil*	*71*	*74.00*	*5254*	*5.71*	*405*	
19	*Water*	*238*	*88.60*	*21087*	*13.26*	*3156*	*476*
20	*Constant*	*105*	*66.40*	*6972*	*10.17*	*1068*	
21							
22	*Cargo Holds*						
23	*No 1*	*5478*	*-65.67*	*-359740*	*8.36*	*45796*	
24	*No 2*	*6293*	*-36.28*	*-228310*	*7.79*	*49022*	
25	*No 3*	*2283*	*-10.13*	*-23127*	*4.78*	*10913*	
26	*No 4*	*6448*	*16.42*	*105876*	*7.79*	*50230*	
27	*No 5*	*5359*	*46.08*	*246943*	*8.11*	*43461*	
28							
29							
30							
31							
32							
33							
34							
35							
36							
37							
38	Deadweight	*28031*					
39	Light Ship	*8051*	*12.04*	*96950*	*10.12*	*81468*	
40	Displacement	*36082*		*-111962*		*287928*	*10126*

	Item	Value	Source
41	Draft at Centre of Flotation	*10.238*	Hydrostatic Table
42	Longitudinal Centre of Gravity	*-3.103*	L40 LM/W
43	Longitudinal Centre of Buoyancy	*-3.495*	Hydrostatic Table
44	Moment to Change Trim One Centimetre	*486.33*	Hydrostatic Table
45	Trim	*0.291*	(L42-L43)*L40W/L44/100
46	Length Between Perpendiculars	*183.00*	Ship's Particulars
47	Longitudinal Centre of Flotation	*1.645*	Hydrostatic Table
48	Difference of Draft Forward	*-0.148*	-(L46/2+L47)*L45/L46
49	Difference of Draft Aft	*0.143*	(L46/2-L47)*L45/L46
50	Draft Forward	*10.090*	L41+L48
51	Draft Aft	*10.381*	L41+L49
52	Transverse Metacentre	*9.497*	Hydrostatic Table
53	Vertical Centre of Gravity	*7.980*	L40 VM/W
54	Metacentric Height	*1.517*	L52-L53
55	Free Surface Effect	*0.281*	L40 FSM/W
56	Fluid Metacentric Height	*1.236*	L54-L55
57	Permissible Grain Heeling Moment		Hydrostatic Table
58	Volumetric Heeling Moment		Total VHM
59	Density of Grain Cargo		MT/CM
60	Grain Heeling Moment		L58*L59 <L57

Trim and Initial Stability Calculation

```
L1  Identity of worksheet
L2  Description of vessel and condition
L3/
L4  Note regarding Longitudinal Centres
L5/
L8  Titles of columns, abbreviations and formulae.
       Identity of Item
       Weight = V*D
          Where:- V = Volume
                  D = Density
          Value can be otherwise derived, or estimated.
       Longitudinal Centre of Gravity, from Midpoint, negative if LCG
          forward of Midpoint. Extract from Ship's Stability and
          Loading Manual. Value will vary with the position of the
          contents of the space.
       Longitudinal Moment = W*LCG
          Where:- W   = Weight
                  LCG = Longitudinal Centre of Gravity
       Vertical Centre of Gravity. Extract from Ship's Stability and
          Loading Manual. Value will vary with the height of the
          contents of the space.
       Vertical Moment = W*VCG
          Where:- W   = Weight
                  VCG = Vertical Centre of Gravity
       Free Surface or Volumetric Heeling Moment. Extract from Ship's
          Stability and Loading Manual. Value will vary with the height
          and density of the contents of the space.
L9/
L37 Details of individual items. When Grain is carried the Volumetric
    Heeling Moments must be extracted from the Ship's Stability and
    Loading Manual with care, using values for full or part filled
    holds, for trimmed or untrimmed ends, and for volumetric or cargo
    centres as appropriate. The total Free Surface Moment must be
    calculated separately from the total Volumetric Heeling Moment.
L38 Deadweight. The total of the above Weights.
L39 Light Ship details. Extract from Ship's Stability and Loading
    Manual.
L40 Displacement details. Weight; Longitudinal, Vertical and Free
    Surface Moments are the totals of the values entered above. When
    grain is carried care must be taken not to include the Volumetric
    Heeling Moments in the Free Surface Moment total.
L41 Draft at Centre of Flotation. Extract from Hydrostatic Table
    as Draft Extreme. Value corresponding to Displacement.
L42 Longitudinal Centre of Gravity = LM/W
       Where:- LM = Longitudinal Moment, see L40
               W  = Displacement, see L40
L43 Longitudinal Centre of Buoyancy, from Midpoint, negative if LCB
    forward of Midpoint. Extract from Hydrostatic Table. Value
    corresponding to Displacement.
L44 Moment to Change Trim One Centimetre. Extract from Hydrostatic
    Table. Value corresponding to Displacement.
L45 Trim = (LCG-LCB)*W/MCTC/100
       Where:- LCG  = Longitudinal Centre of Gravity, see L42
               LCB  = Longitudinal Centre of Buoyancy, see L43
               W    = Displacement, see L40
               MCTC = Moment to Change Trim One Centimetre, see L44
L46 Length Between Perpendiculars. Extract from Ship's Stability and
    Loading Manual.
L47 Longitudinal Centre of Flotation, from Midpoint, negative if LCF
    forward of Midpoint. Extract from Hydrostatic Table. Value
    corresponding to Displacement.
```

L48 Difference of Draft Forward = -(LBP/2+LCF)*T/LBP
Where:- LBP = Length Between Perpendiculars, see L46
LCF = Longitudinal Centre of Flotation, see L47
T = Trim, see L45

L49 Difference of Draft Aft = (LBP/2-LCF)*T/LBP
Where:- LBP = Length Between Perpendiculars, see L46
LCF = Longitudinal Centre of Flotation, see L47
T = Trim, see L45

L50 Draft Forward = DCF+dDF
Where:- DCF = Draft at Centre of Flotation, see L41
dDF = Difference of Draft Forward, see L48

L51 Draft Aft = DCF+dDA
Where:- DCF = Draft at Centre of Flotation, see L41
dDA = Difference of Draft Aft, see L49

L52 Transverse Metacentre. Extract from Hydrostatic Table (TKM). Value corresponding to Displacement.

L53 Vertical Centre of Gravity = VM/W
Where:- VM = Vertical Moment, see L40
W = Displacement, see L40

L54 Metacentric Height = TKM-KG
Where:- TKM = Transverse Metacentre, see L52
KG = Vertical Centre of Gravity, see L53

L55 Free Surface Effect = FSM/W
Where:- FSM = Free Surface Moment, see L40. Must not include Volumetric Heeling Moments.
W = Displacement, see L40

L56 Fluid Metacentric Height = GM-FSE
Where:- GM = Metacentric Height, see L54
FSE = Free Surface Effect, see L55
For grain cargo this value must be greater than the minimum value (normally 0.30) shown in the Ship's Stability and Loading Manual for the worst condition expected during the voyage, before the vessel can put to sea.

L57 Permissible Grain Heeling Moment. Extract from Hydrostatic Table. Value corresponding to Deadweight and KG.

L58 Volumetric Heeling Moment. Total of Volumetric Heeling Moments of compartments containing grain, calculated separately from Free Surface Moments.

L59 Density of Grain Cargo. MT/CM. MT is weight of entire cargo in Metric Tonnes. CM is volume occupied by cargo in Cubic Metres. Before loading the figure for Density should be the best available estimate. After loading the figure used should be calculated from the actual tonnage, and volume used. When hold ends are untrimmed the reduced hold capacity, read from the Ship's Stability and Loading Manual, should be used. When a space is part filled the actual volume occupied, as calculated from the measured ullage, should be used.

L60 Grain Heeling Moment = VHM*D
Where:- VHM = Volumetric Heeling Moment, see L58.
D = Density of Cargo, see L59.
Once it has been calculated that the Metacentric Height is adequate this is the only additional check which is required. The loading is acceptable provided that L60<L57. If this condition is not satisfied the ship's stability is inadequate and the loading must be replanned or, if the cargo is already loaded, steps must be taken to improve the vessel's stability.

1 **Statical and Dynamical Stability**
2 *REGINA OLDENDORFF. Summer Marks. Grain.*
3 Displacement *36082*
4 Fluid Metacentric Height *1.24*
5 Vertical Centre of Gravity *7.98*
6 Free Surface Effect *0.28*
7 Fluid Vertical Centre of Gravity L5+L6 *8.26*
8 Assumed Vertical Centre of Gravity *7.00*
9 Difference between Vertical Centres of Gravity L8-L7 *-1.26*
10 Righting Arm Curve

	Angle of Heel	Sine	Correction L9*Sine	Assumed Righting Arm	Righting Arm ARA+C
11–13					
14	*0.00*	*0.000*	*0.00*	*0.00*	*0.00*
15	*10.00*	*0.174*	*-0.22*	*0.45*	*0.23*
16	*12.00*	*0.208*	*-0.26*	*0.54*	*0.28*
17	*20.00*	*0.342*	*-0.43*	*0.95*	*0.52*
18	*30.00*	*0.500*	*-0.63*	*1.41*	*0.78*
19	*40.00*	*0.643*	*-0.81*	*1.76*	*0.95*
20	*50.00*	*0.766*	*-0.97*	*1.95*	*0.98*
21	*60.00*	*0.866*	*-1.09*	*1.93*	*0.84*
22	*70.00*	*0.940*	*-1.18*	*1.73*	*0.55*
23	*80.00*	*0.985*	*-1.24*	*1.42*	*0.18*

Line	Item	Value	Required Values *
24	**IMO International Convention on Load Lines 1966**		
25	Righting Arm at 0° Heel [A]	*0.00*	
26	Righting Arm at 15° Heel [DE]	*0.37*	
27	Righting Arm at 30° Heel [FG]	*0.78*	
28	Area to 30° (L26*4+L25+L27)*15/3/57.3 [AFG]	*0.197*	=>0.055
29	Angle of Flooding	*44*	
30	θF, Angle of Flooding L29, or 40°, whichever less.	*40*	
31	Half θF L30/2	*20*	
32	Righting Arm at 0° Heel L25 [A]	*0.00*	
33	Righting Arm at Half θF° Heel L31 [HI]	*0.52*	
34	Righting Arm at θF° Heel L30 [JK]	*0.95*	
35	Area to θF (L33*4+L32+L34)*L31/3/57.3 [AJK]	*0.353*	=>0.090
36	Area 30° to θF L35-L28 [GFJK]	*0.156*	=>0.030
37	Maximum Righting Arm [LM]	*0.99*	=>0.20
38	Angle of Maximum Righting Arm [M]	*47*	=>30°
39	Initial Fluid Metacentric Height L4 [BC]	*1.24*	=>0.15
40	**IMO International Grain Code 1991**		
41	Heeling Arm Curve		
42	Volumetric Heeling Moment of grain	*11100*	
43	Density of Cargo	*0.80*	
44	Heeling Arm at 0° L42/L3*L43 [AN]	*0.25*	
45	Heeling Arm at 40° L44*0.8 [OK]	*0.20*	
46	Angle of Heel due to Grain Shift, [Q], at		
47	Intersection of Righting and Heeling Arm curves [P]	*10*	<=12
48	Angle where difference between		
49	Righting Arm and Heeling Arm curves is maximum [R]	*48*	
50	Limit of Residual Dynamic Stability,		
51	Least value of L29, L49 and 40°	*40*	
52	Midpoint of range (L47+L51)/2 [S]	*25*	
53	Ordinate L51-L52	*15*	
54	Differences between Righting and Heeling Arms		
55	At Angle of Heel due to Grain Shift L47 [P]	*0.00*	
56	At Midpoint of range L52 [TU]	*0.44*	
57	At Limit of Residual Dynamic Stability L51 [JO]	*0.75*	
58	Residual Dynamic Stability (L56*4+L55+L57)*L53/3/57.3 [PJO]	*0.219*	=>0.075
59	Initial Fluid Metacentric Height L4 [BC]	*1.24*	=>0.30
60	**IMO Code of Safe Practice for Ships <100m Carrying Timber Deck Cargoes**		
61	Area to θF L35	*0.353*	=>0.08
62	Maximum Righting Arm L37	*0.99*	=>0.25
63	Initial Fluid Metacentric Height in Departure Condition L4	*1.24*	=>0.10
64	Fluid Metacentric Height to be positive throughout voyage.		
65	* The Ship's Stability and Loading Manual should be checked for		
66	specific requirements, see Note in explanation.		

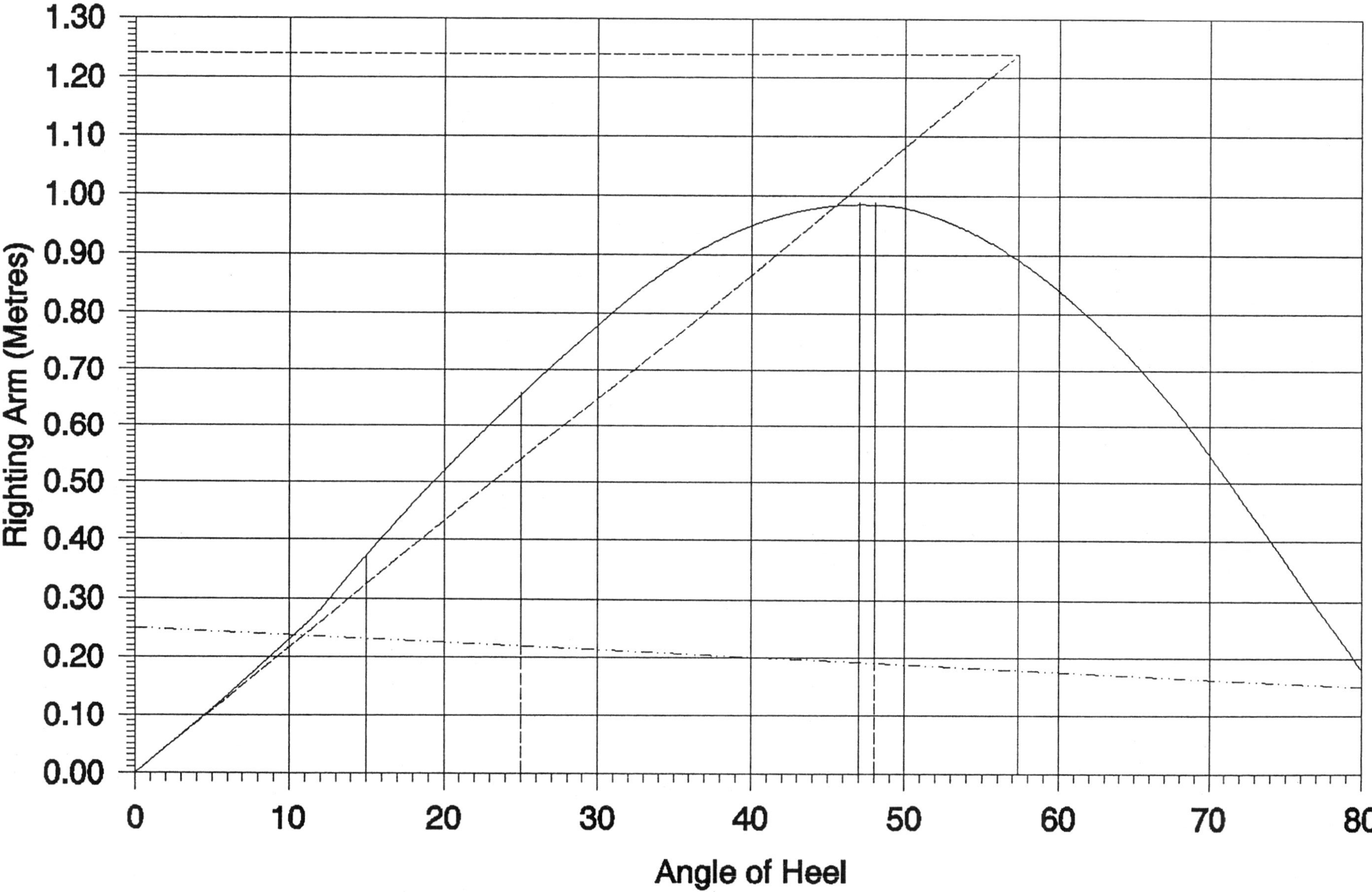
Curve of Statical Stability
REGINA OLDENDORFF
Summer Marks. Grain.
Righting Arm (Metres)
1.30
1.20
1.10
1.00
0.90
0.80
0.70
0.60
0.50
0.40
0.30
0.20
0.10
0.00
0
10
20
30
40
50
60
70
80
Angle of Heel

Statical and Dynamical Stability Calculation.

```
L1  Identity of worksheet.
L2  Identity of vessel and condition.
L3  Displacement, from Initial Stability calculation.
L4  Fluid Metacentric Height, from Initial Stability calculation.
L5  Vertical Centre of Gravity, from Initial Stability calculation.
L6  Free Surface Effect, from Initial Stability calculation.
L7  Fluid Vertical Centre of Gravity = VCG+FSE
       Where:- VCG = Vertical Centre of Gravity, see L5.
               FSE = Free Surface Effect, see L6
L8  Vertical Centre of Gravity assumed when Cross Curves of Stability
    were drawn. This may be zero, in which case the curves are known as
    KN Curves.
L9  Difference between Vertical Centres of Gravity = AVCG-VCG
       Where:- AVCG = Assumed Vertical Centre of Gravity, see L8
               VCG  = Vertical Centre of Gravity, see L7
       Negative if Vertical Centre of Gravity higher than Assumed
       Vertical Centre of Gravity.
L10/
L23 Calculation of data for Righting Arm Curve.
       Angle of Heel. Values of lines given on Cross Curves of
          Stability.
       Sine. Natural Sine of Angle of Heel.
       Correction = DVCG*Sin H
          Where:- DVCG  = Difference between Vertical Centres of
                          Gravity, see L9
                  Sin H = Natural Sine of Angle of Heel.
       Assumed Righting Arm. Extract from Cross Curves of Stability
          the values which correspond to the Displacement.
       Righting Arm = ARA+C
          Where:- ARA = Assumed Righting Arm
                  C   = Correction
    The above values are used to draw the Curve of Statical Stability,
    which is a graph of Righting Arm against Angle of Heel. The initial
    gradient of this curve is given by a straight line from the origin,
    [A], to a point, [B], given by an angle of 57.3° and the value of
    the Fluid Metacentric Height, see L4.
L24 IMO International Convention on Load Lines 1966.
    The calculated values must be checked against the required values
    provided in the Ship's Stability and Loading Manual in compliance
    with the above.
L25 Righting Arm at 0° Heel, from Curve of Statical Stability, [A].
L26 Righting Arm at 15° Heel, from Curve of Statical Stability, [DE].
L27 Righting Arm at 30° Heel, from Curve of Statical Stability, [FG].
L28 Area to 30°, [AFG] = (RA15*4+RA0+RA30)*15/3/57.3
       Where:- RA15 = Righting Arm at 15° Heel, see L26.
               RA0  = Righting Arm at  0° Heel, see L25.
               RA30 = Righting Arm at 30° Heel, see L27.
       To be not less than 0.055
L29 Angle of Flooding. Extract from Flooding Angle Curve in the Ship's
    Stability and Loading Manual the value which corresponds to the
    Displacement.
L30 θF  Angle of Flooding, see L29, or 40°, whichever is less.
L31 Half θF = θF/2, see L30
L32 Righting Arm at 0° Heel, from Curve of Statical Stability, [A].
L33 Righting Arm at Half θF° Heel, see L31, from Curve of
    Statical Stability, [HI].
L34 Righting Arm at θF° Heel, see L30, from Curve of Statical
    Stability, [JK].
```

L35 Area to θF, [AJK] = (RAHθF*4+RA0+RAθF)*HθF/3/57.3
Where:- RAHθF = Righting Arm at Half θF, see L33
RA0 = Righting Arm at 0°, see L32
RAθF = Righting Arm at θF, see L34
HθF = Half θF, see L31
To be not less than 0.090

L36 Area 30° to θF, [GFJK] = AθF-A30
Where:- AθF = Area to θF, see L35
A30 = Area to 30°, see L28
To be not less than 0.030

L37 Maximum Righting Arm, from Curve of Statical Stability, [LM].
To be not less than 0.20.

L38 Angle where Righting Arm has maximum value, from Curve of Statical Stability, [M]. To be not less than 30°.

L39 Initial Fluid Metacentric Height, from Initial Stability calculation, see L4. To be not less than 0.15.

L40 **IMO International Grain Code 1991.**
The calculated values must be checked against the required values if the vessel is loaded with grain.

L41 Heeling Arm Curve. A straight line drawn from the value of the Heeling Arm at 0°, L44 [AN], to the value of the Heeling Arm at 40°, L45 [OK], and projected if required.

L42 Volumetric Heeling Moment of grain. Extract from Ship's Stability and Loading Manual. Value will vary with height of hold contents, degree of trimming, method of measuring hold contents and type of data provided.

L43 Density of Cargo in Metric Tonnes per Cubic Metre, from loading orders, loading port authorities or other source. The figure given may be a Stowage Factor, to be converted as follows:-
Density = 1/SF
Where SF = Stowage Factor in Cubic Metres per Metric Tonne.

L44 Heeling Arm at 0°, [AN] = VHM/W*D
Where:- VHM = Volumetric Heeling Moment, see L42.
W = Displacement, see L3.
D = Density of Cargo, see L43.

L45 Heeling Arm at 40°, [OK] = HA0*0.8
Where:- HA0 = Heeling Arm at 0°, see L44.

L46/
L47 Angle of Heel due to Grain Shift [Q]. The angle at which the Righting and Heeling Arm Curves intersect [P], from Curve of Statical Stability. To be not more than 12°.

L48/
L49 Angle where difference between Righting and Heeling Arm Curves is maximum. From Curve of Statical Stability, [R].

L50/
L51 Limit of Residual Dynamic Stability, whichever is least of:-
Angle of Flooding, see L29,
Angle of Maximum Difference between Righting and Heeling Arm Curves, see L49, and
40°.

L52 Midpoint of range, [S] = (AH+LRDS)/2
Where:- AH = Angle of Heel due to Grain Shift, see L47.
LRDS = Limit of Residual Dynamic Stability, see L51.

L53 Ordinate = M-AH
Where:- M = Midpoint of range, see L52.
AH = Angle of Heel due to Grain Shift, see L47.

L54 Differences between Heeling and Righting Arms at:-
L55 Angle of Heel due to Grain Shift, from Curve of Statical Stability, [P].
L56 Midpoint of range, from Curve of Statical Stability, [TU].
L57 Limit of Residual Dynamic Stability, from Curve of Statical Stability, [JO].

L58 Residual Dynamic Stability [PJO] = (DM*4+DAH+DL)*O/3/57.3
Where:- DM = Difference at Midpoint of range, see L56.
DAH = Difference at Angle of Heel, see L55.
DL = Difference at Limit, see L57.
O = Ordinate, see L53.
To be not less than 0.075.

L59 Initial Fluid Metacentric Height, [BC], see L4.
To be not less than 0.30.

L60 **IMO Code of Safe Practice for Ships <100m Carrying Timber Deck Cargoes.**
When the ship is less than 100 metres in length and loaded with a deck cargo of timber in accordance with the Code the appropriate values must be checked against the requirements of the Code.

L61 Area to θF, see L35. To be not less than 0.08.

L62 Maximum Righting Arm, see L37. To be not less than 0.25.

L63 Initial Fluid Metacentric Height, see L4. To be not less than 0.10

L64 Fluid Metacentric Height, see L4. To be positive throughout the voyage.

L65/
L66 **Note.** The "Required Values" may vary for particular vessels and circumstances. The Ship's approved Stability and Loading Manual should be examined for specific requirements.

SHEAR FORCES AND BENDING MOMENTS

Regina Oldendorff. Ore. Alternate holds

1 Shear Forces and Bending Moments
2 REGINA OLDENDORFF. Ore. Alternate holds.
3 Draft Midships 9.95
4 Trim 0.048

5	Bulkhead. Position P		Frame 12	84.07		Frame 40	60.83		Frame 74	32.61		Frame 112	1.07		Frame 138	-20.51		Frame 175	-51.22		Frame 219	-82.15	
6	Item	Longitudinal	Weight	Distance	Moment	Weight	Distance	Moment	Weight	Distance	Moment	Weight	Distance	Moment	Weight	Distance	Moment	Weight	Distance	Moment	Weight	Distance	Moment
7		Centre of	W	LCG-P	W*D	W	LCG-P	W*D	W	LCG-P	W*D	W	LCG-P	W*D	W	LCG-P	W*D	W	LCG-P	W*D	W	LCG-P	W*D
8		Gravity LCG																					
9	Cargo Holds																						
10	No 1	-64.98																			8450.0	17.17	145086.5
11	No 3	-10.13													9400.0	10.38	97572.0	9400.0	41.09	386246.0	9400.0	72.02	676988.0
12	No 5	45.80							8700.0	13.19	114753.0	8700.0	44.73	389151.0	8700.0	66.31	576897.0	8700.0	97.02	844074.0	8700.0	127.95	1113165.0
13																							
14	Oil Tanks																						
15	No 4 FOT	44.26							89.4	11.65	1041.5	89.40	43.19	3861.2	89.4	64.77	5790.4	89.4	95.48	8535.9	89.4	126.41	11301.1
16	FO Service	65.39				32.9	4.56	150.0	32.9	32.78	1078.5	32.90	64.32	2116.1	32.9	85.90	2826.1	32.9	116.61	3836.5	32.9	147.54	4854.1
17	FO Settling	62.90				34.1	2.07	70.6	34.1	30.29	1032.9	34.10	61.83	2108.4	34.1	83.41	2844.3	34.1	114.12	3891.5	34.1	145.05	4946.2
18	DO Service	68.72				8.5	7.89	67.1	8.5	36.11	306.9	8.50	67.65	575.0	8.5	89.23	758.5	8.5	119.94	1019.5	8.5	150.87	1282.4
19	DO Setting	68.72				8.5	7.89	67.1	8.5	36.11	306.9	8.50	67.65	575.0	8.5	89.23	758.5	8.5	119.94	1019.5	8.5	150.87	1282.4
20																							
21	Fresh Water																						
22	No 1 FWT	86.37	23.5	2.30	54.1	23.5	25.54	600.2	23.5	53.76	1263.4	23.50	85.30	2004.6	23.5	106.88	2511.7	23.5	137.59	3233.4	23.5	168.52	3960.2
23	Drinking Water	86.36	9.5	2.29	21.8	9.5	25.53	242.5	9.5	53.75	510.6	9.50	85.29	810.3	9.5	106.87	1015.3	9.5	137.58	1307.0	9.5	168.51	1600.8
24																							
25	Provisions	88.27	0.8	4.20	3.4	0.8	27.44	22.0	0.8	55.66	44.5	0.80	87.20	69.8	0.8	108.78	87.0	0.8	139.49	111.6	0.8	170.42	136.3
26																							
27																							
28																							
29																							
30																							
31																							
32																							
33																							
34																							
35																							
36																							
37																							
38	Deadweight Weight		33.8			117.8			8907.2			8907.2			18307.2			18307.2			26757.2		
39	Ship Weight		447.5			2611.5			3576.6			4743.7			5644.4			6758.8			7826.5		
40	Buoyancy Even Keel		151.9			2838.3			8956.1			16332.0			21380.6			28559.8			34344.3		
41	Trim Factor		42.3			207.5			377.3			446.1			418.9			276.8			54.9		
42	Trim Correction L4*L41		2.0			10.0			18.1			21.4			20.1			13.3			2.6		
43	Buoyancy L40+L42		153.9			2848.3			8974.2			16353.4			21400.7			28573.1			34346.9		
44	Shear Force L38+L39-L43		327.4			-119.0			3509.6			-2702.5			2550.9			-3507.1			236.8		
45	Difference SF-SF						3628.6			6212.1			5253.4			6058.0			3743.9				
46	Bulkhead Factor						0.19			0.23			0.30			0.23			0.18				
47	Correction L45*L46						344.7			714.4			788.0			696.7			337.0				
48	Lesser Correction								344.7			714.4			696.7			337.0					
49	Corrected Shear Force L44±L48					-119.0			3164.9			-1988.1			1854.2			-3170.1			236.8		
50	Maximum Permitted Shear Force					3550.0			3400.0			3920.0			3740.0			3340.0			3390.00		
51	Shear Force as Percentage of Maximum Permitted L49/L50*100					-3.4%			93.1%			-50.7%			49.6%			-94.9%			7.0%		
52																							
53	Deadweight Moment				79.3			1219.5			120338.2			401271.4			691060.8			1253274.9			1964603.0
54	Ship Moment				2193.1			34761.1			121433.2			253830.7			366539.9			558018.3			785290.0
55	Buoyancy Moment Even Keel				440.2			28672.4			191907.5			590654.9			997596.8			1764640.9			2747861.9
56	Trim Factor				194.1			3000.1			11503.4			24823.5			34278.1			45239.3			50277.2
57	Trim Correction L4*L56				9.3			144.0			552.2			1191.5			1645.3			2171.5			2413.3
58	Buoyancy Moment L55+L57				449.5			28816.4			192459.7			591846.4			999242.1			1766812.4			2750275.2
59	Bending Moment L53+L54-L58				1822.9			7164.2			49311.7			63255.7			58358.6			44480.8			-382.2
60	Maximum Permitted Bending Moment							105400.0			105400.0			105400.0			105400.0			105400.0			105400.0
61	Bending Moment as Percentage of Maximum Permitted L59/L60*100							6.8%			46.8%			60.0%			55.4%			42.2%			-0.4%

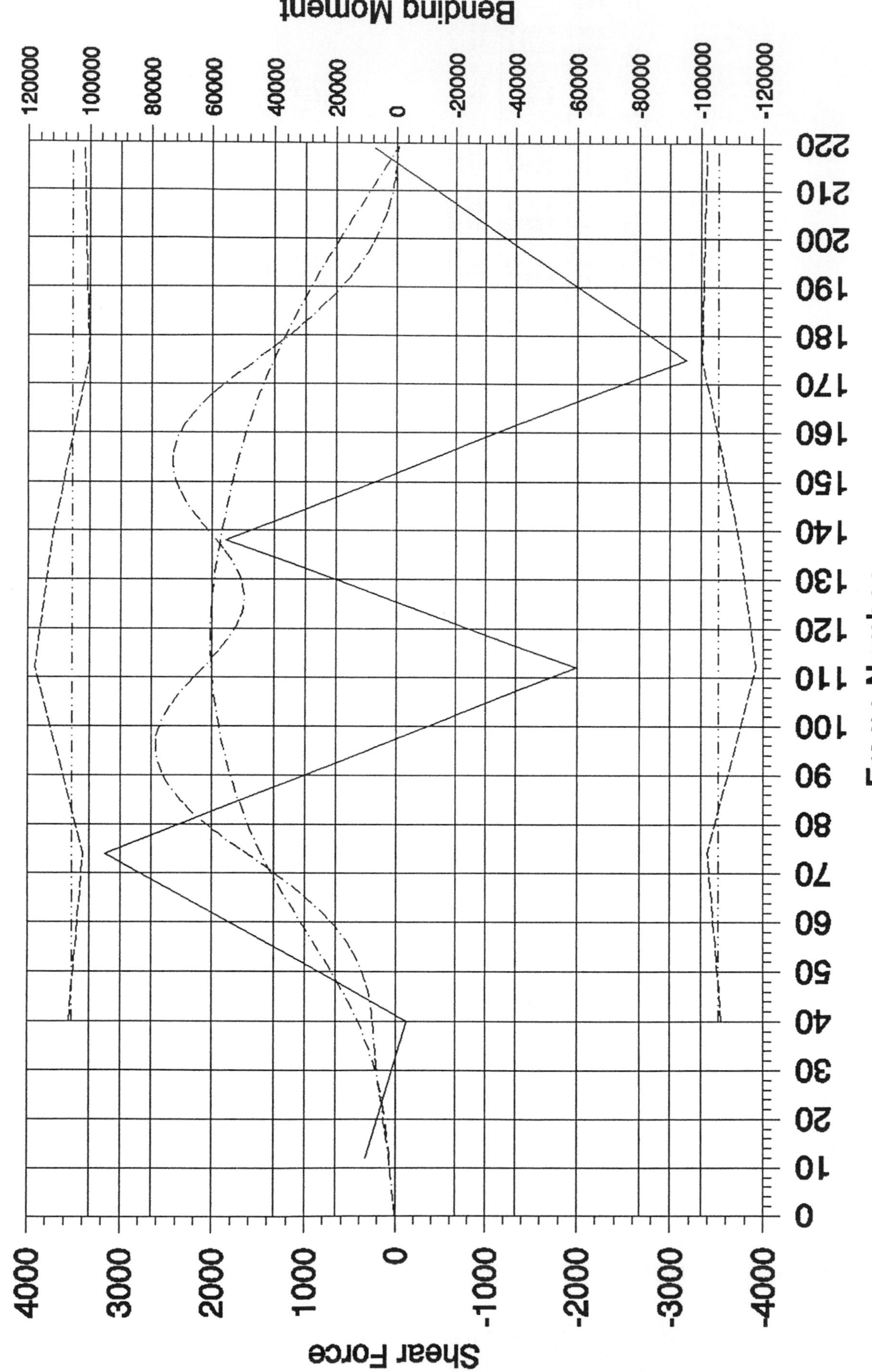
Shear Forces and Bending Moments
REGINA OLDENDORFF
Ore. Alternate Holds.
Bending Moment
Shear Force
Frame Number

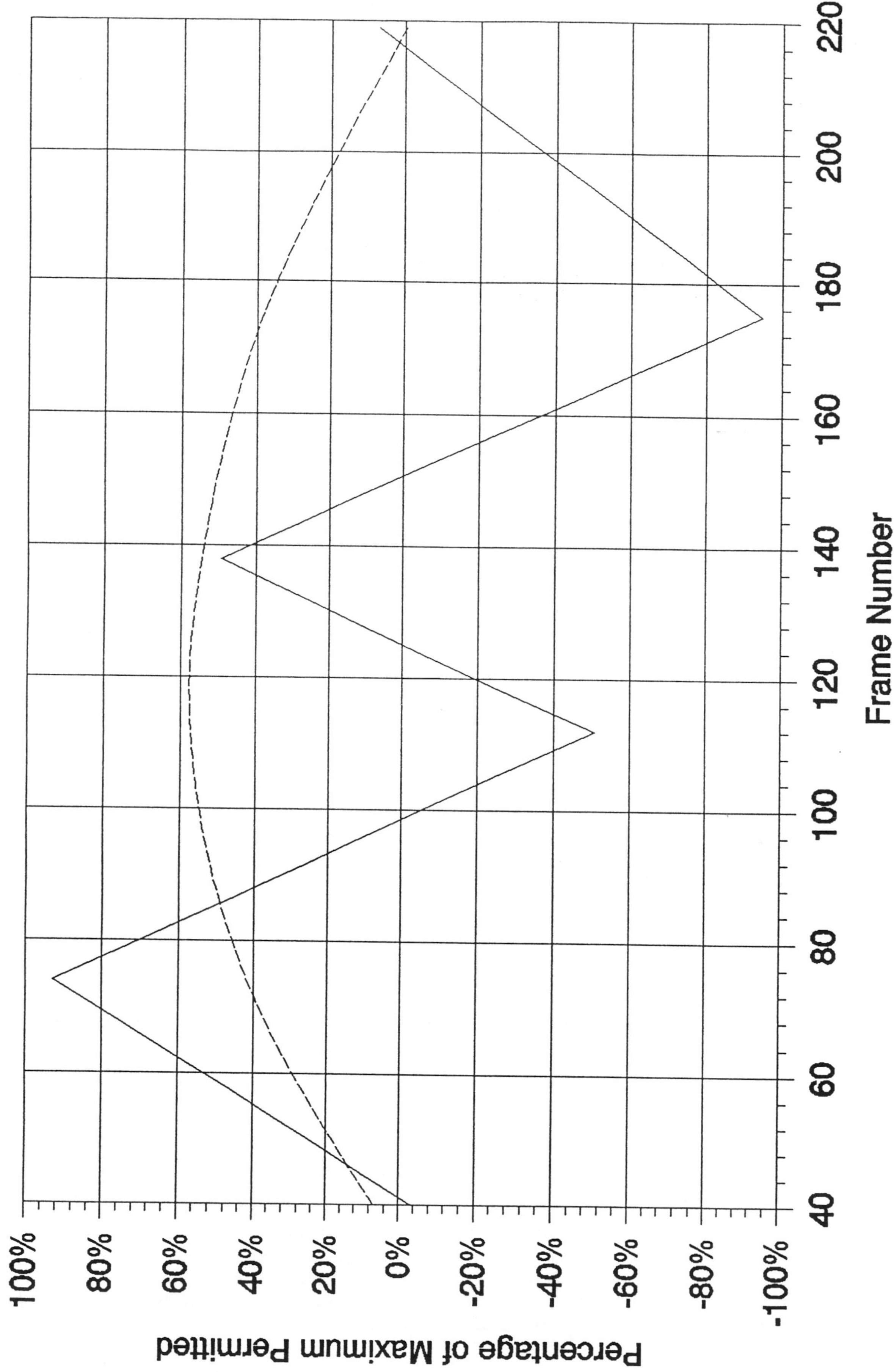
Shear Forces and Bending Moments
REGINA OLDENDORFF
Ore. Alternate Holds.
Percentage of Maximum Permitted
100%
80%
60%
40%
20%
0%
-20%
-40%
-60%
-80%
-100%
Frame Number
40
60
80
100
120
140
160
180
200
220

Shear Force and Bending Moment Calculation

Note. In some Ships' Stability and Loading Manuals the Ship Weight and Buoyancy; Ship Moment and Buoyancy Moment; and Trim Corrections are combined in the structure of the tables and not determined separately. When the information is presented in this way it may be unsuitable for entry in the Form which accompanies these notes.

L1 Identification of worksheet
L2 Identification of ship and condition.
L3 Draft Midships, observed or calculated.
L4 Trim, observed or calculated.
L5 Bulkhead identification by Frame Number.
Position expressed as distance from Midpoint, sign negative if Position forward of Midpoint.

L6/
L8 Titles of columns. Abbreviated formulae.

Item.

Longitudinal Centre of Gravity. Distance from Midpoint, sign negative if Centre forward of Midpoint.

Weight = V*D
Where:- V = Volume.
D = Density.
Value can be estimated, calculated or given.

Distance = LCG - P
Where:- LCG = Longitudinal Centre of Gravity of Weight from Midpoint. Sign negative if LCG forward of Midpoint.
P = Position of Bulkhead from Midpoint. Sign negative if Position forward of Midpoint.

Moment = W*D
Where:- W = Weight
D = Distance

L9/
L37 Details of weights.

All weights which occur in positions abaft (ie aft of) a particular bulkhead must be listed in the column for that bulkhead. For example, if there are 8700 tonnes in No 5 Hold, and No 5 Hold is abaft the bulkhead at Frame 74 (the bulkhead which separates Nos 4 and 5 Holds) the 8700 tonnes must be entered in that column. The 8700 tonnes is also abaft all the bulkheads which are forward of Frame 74, so 8700 tonnes must be repeated in all the columns forward of the first entry.

When every weight has been entered in this manner their distances and moments must be calculated and entered too. A weight entered in several columns will have a different distance in each.

Care should be taken to enter only appropriate items, as some may be included in the Ship Weight and Moment. In the case of the REGINA OLDENDORFF Lubricating Oil, Cooling Water, Crew and Stores are included in the Ship Weight and therefore not entered separately here.

L38 Deadweight Weight. The total of all weights entered above for each section.

L39 Ship Weight. The weight of the ship for each section. Extract from Ship's Stability and Loading Manual. In the case of the REGINA OLDENDORFF this is not purely the Light Weight, certain other weights being included as described above, L37.

L40 Buoyancy Even Keel. Extract from Ship's Stability and Loading Manual. Value corresponding to Draft Midships.

L41 Trim Factor. Extract from Ship's Stability and Loading Manual. Value corresponding to Draft Midships.

```
L42 Trim Correction = T*TF
        Where:- T  = Trim, see L4
                TF = Trim Factor, see L41
L43 Buoyancy = BEK+TC
        Where:- BEK = Buoyancy Even Keel, see L40
                TC  = Trim Correction, see L42
L44 Shear Force = DW+SW-B
        Where:- DW = Deadweight Weight
                SW = Ship Weight
                B  = Buoyancy
L45/
L49 Calculation of Bulkhead Correction for those bulkheads for which a
    Bulkhead Factor is given.
L45 Difference = SF-SF
        Where:- SF = Shear Force
        The lower value is subtracted from the higher to obtain the
        absolute difference between adjacent values.
        NB. -100 is lower than 100.

        For instance:-
        Frame A Shear Force = 1000
        Frame B Shear Force =  100
        Difference = 1000 - 100 = 900

        Frame A Shear Force = 1000
        Frame B Shear Force = -100
        Difference = 1000 - -100 = 1100

        Frame A Shear Force = -1000
        Frame B Shear Force =   100
        Difference = 100 - -1000 = 1100

        Frame A Shear Force = -1000
        Frame B Shear Force =  -100
        Difference = -100 - -1000 = 900

L46 Bulkhead Factor, Extract from Ship's Stability and Loading Manual.
L47 Correction = D*BF
        Where:- D  = Difference, see L45
                BF = Bulkhead Factor, see L46
L48 Lesser Correction. The lesser value of adjacent corrections,
    see L47.
L49 Corrected Shear Force = SF±C
        Where:- SF = Shear Force, see L44
                C  = Correction, see L48
    The sign used is such as to reduce the absolute value of the Shear
    Force.
    For example:-
    Frame 74 Shear Force  3509.6
             Correction    344.7
    Corrected Shear Force = 3509.6 - 344.7 = 3164.9
    Frame 112 Shear Force -2702.5
             Correction     714.4
    Corrected Shear Force = -2702.5 + 714.4 = -1998.1
L50 Maximum Permitted Shear Force. Extract from Ship's Stability and
    Loading Manual. Different values may be given for different
    circumstances. The appropriate value must be used.
L51 Shear Force as Percentage of Maximum Permitted = CSF/MPSF*100
        Where:- CSF  = Corrected Shear Force, see L49
                MPSF = Maximum Permitted Shear Force, see L50
L52
L53 Deadweight Moment. The total of moments entered above.
L54 Ship Moment. The moment for the ship and certain weights not
```

```
    entered above for each section. Extract from Ship's Stability and
    Loading Manual.
L55 Buoyancy Moment Even Keel. Extract from Ship's Stability and
    Loading Manual. Value corresponding to Midships Draft.
L56 Trim Factor. Extract from Ship's Stability and Loading Manual.
    Value corresponding to Midships Draft.
L57 Trim Correction = T*TF
       Where:- T  = Trim, see L4
               TF = Trim Factor, see L56
L58 Buoyancy Moment = BMEK+TC
       Where:- BMEK = Buoyancy Moment Even Keel, see L55
               TC   = Trim Correction, see L57
L59 Bending Moment = DM+SM-BM
       Where:- DM = Deadweight Moment, see L53
               SM = Ship Moment, see L54
               BM = Buoyancy Moment, see L58
L60 Maximum Permitted Bending Moment. Extract from Ship's Stability and
    Loading Manual. Different values may be given for different
    circumstances. The appropriate value must be used.
L61 Bending Moment as Percentage of Maximum Permitted = BM/MPBM*100
       Where:- BM   = Bending Moment, see L59
               MPBM = Maximum Permitted Bending Moment, see L60
```

1 **Trim and Initial Stability**
2 *REGINA OLDENDORFF. Grain. Density 0.803 MT/CM. Arrival Ceuta for Bunkers.*
3 LCG, LCB and LCF from Midpoint.
4 Negative if Centre forward of Midpoint.

5	Identity	Weight	Longitudinal	Longitudinal	Vertical	Vertical	Free Surface
6			Centre of	Moment	Centre of	Moment	or Volumetric
7			Gravity		Gravity		Heeling Momnt
8		W	LCG	W*LCG	VCG	W*VCG	
9	*Crew/Stores*	*372.1*	*54.58*	*20309*	*8.49*	*3159.1*	*0*
10	*No 3 DB*	*490.0*	*-9.72*	*-4763*	*1.04*	*509.6*	*36*
11	*No 4 DB*	*860.0*	*17.00*	*14620*	*1.40*	*1204.0*	*5*
12	*Aft Peak*	*100.0*	*88.72*	*8872*	*8.70*	*870.0*	*270*
13	*FO 3C*	*11.5*	*16.84*	*194*	*0.02*	*0.2*	*3042*
14	*FO 4C*	*1.0*	*44.26*	*44*	*0.00*	*0.0*	*0*
15	*FO Set*	*24.0*	*62.90*	*1510*	*11.10*	*266.4*	*51*
16	*FO Serv*	*21.0*	*65.39*	*1373*	*11.52*	*241.9*	*25*
17	*DO P*	*9.1*	*66.24*	*603*	*0.25*	*2.3*	*63*
18	*DO S*	*9.1*	*66.24*	*603*	*0.25*	*2.3*	*63*
19	*DO Set*	*7.7*	*68.72*	*529*	*11.85*	*91.2*	*1*
20	*DO Serv*	*8.5*	*68.72*	*584*	*12.00*	*102.0*	*1*
21	*FW 1P*	*32.0*	*86.40*	*2765*	*12.20*	*390.4*	*115*
22	*FW 2P*	*25.0*	*92.23*	*2306*	*12.50*	*312.5*	*20*
23	*FW 2S*	*25.0*	*92.23*	*2306*	*12.50*	*312.5*	*20*
24	*Drinking Wtr*	*30.0*	*86.40*	*2592*	*12.20*	*366.0*	*105*
25	*Cooling Wtr*	*11.0*	*85.28*	*938*	*2.18*	*24.0*	*1*
26	*Total Free Surface Moments*						*3818*
27							
28	*Grain Cargo*						*Volumetric*
29							*Heeling*
30							*Moment*
31	*No 1 Hold*	*5305.8*	*-65.67*	*-348432*	*8.36*	*44356.5*	*1882*
32	*No 2 Hold*	*6313.0*	*-36.28*	*-229036*	*7.79*	*49178.3*	*535*
33	*No 3 Hold*	*2294.0*	*-10.12*	*-23215*	*4.80*	*11011.2*	*8900*
34	*No 4 Hold*	*6469.0*	*16.42*	*106221*	*7.79*	*50393.5*	*547*
35	*No 5 Hold*	*5169.0*	*46.08*	*238188*	*8.11*	*41920.6*	*2024*
36	*Total Volumetric Heeling Moments*						*13888*
37							
38	Deadweight	*27588*					
39	Light Ship	*8051*	*12.04*	*96950*	*10.12*	*81468*	
40	Displacement	*35639*		*-103940*		*286183*	*3818*

41	Draft at Centre of Flotation	*10.238*	Hydrostatic Table
42	Longitudinal Centre of Gravity	*-2.916*	L40 LM/W
43	Longitudinal Centre of Buoyancy	*-3.555*	Hydrostatic Table
44	Moment to Change Trim One Centimetre	*483.84*	Hydrostatic Table
45	Trim	*0.471*	(L42-L43)*L40W/L44/100
46	Length Between Perpendiculars	*183.00*	Ship's Particulars
47	Longitudinal Centre of Flotation	*1.458*	Hydrostatic Table
48	Difference of Draft Forward	*-0.239*	-(L43/2+L47)*L45/L46
49	Difference of Draft Aft	*0.232*	(L43/2-L47)*L45/L46
50	Draft Forward	*9.999*	L41+L48
51	Draft Aft	*10.470*	L41+L49
52	Transverse Metacentre	*9.483*	Hydrostatic Table
53	Vertical Centre of Gravity	*8.030*	L40 VM/W
54	Metacentric Height	*1.453*	L52-L53
55	Free Surface Effect	*0.107*	L40 FSM/W Exclude VHM
56	Fluid Metacentric Height	*1.346*	L54-L55
57	Permissible Grain Heeling Moment	*11433*	Hydrostatic Table
58	Volumetric Heeling Moment	*13888*	Total VHM
59	Density of Grain Cargo	*0.803*	MT/CM
60	Grain Heeling Moment	*11146*	L58*L59 <L57

METHOD OF OBTAINING VALUES OF VOLUMETRIC HEELING MOMENTS (VHMs)
(This method must be used when the ship has no loading computer. The way in which the information is presented is likely to vary from one shipbuilder to another.)

The loading used for this example is the grain loading (Three Rivers/Oran) which appears in Appendix 10.11.

Compartment:	No. 1 H	No. 2 H	No. 3 H	No. 4 H	No. 5 H
Compartment full?	*Yes*	*Yes*	*No*	*Yes*	*Yes*
Ends trimmed?	*No*	*Yes*	*N/A*	*Yes*	*No*
VHMs (filled – ends trimmed), values read from hydrostatic table (Appendix 10.12(2))		*533*		*547*	
VHMs (filled – ends untrimmed), values read from hydrostatic table (Appendix 10.12(2))	*1,882*				*2,024*
VHMs (unfilled), value read from graph in hydrostatic table (Appendix 10.12(3))*,			*8,900*		
Summary of volumetric heeling moments:	*1,882*	*533*	*8,900*	*547*	*2,024*

*To obtain the VHMs for the unfilled No. 3 hold proceed as follows.

- Enter the graph with the volume of cargo in No. 3 hold. (No. 3 hold is to contain 2,294 tonnes, at density 0.803, so cargo volume = 2,294/0.803 = 2,856.8 m^3).
- On the graph volume 2,856.8 m^3 correspond to 8.1 m distance of grain surface from top of hatch coaming.
- For grain surface at 8.1 m, the curve of shifting moment value can be read from the scale as 8,900 m^4.

A note on the graph states that shifting moments (ie VHMs) have been increased 12 per cent in accordance with the regulations, to take account of the vertical shift of the grain surface. No further correction is needed for this purpose.

REGINA OLDENDORFF

Grain loading calculation data

Summary table of the grain capacities and transverse volumetric heeling moments for 'filled-ends trimmed' and 'filled-ends not trimmed'.

Notes:
* The whole volume of the compartment.
** The whole volume of the compartment minus the volume of voids in the untrimmed ends.
*** The geometrical centre of the compartment.

Compartment	Filled-ends trimmed				Filled-ends not trimmed			
	Capacity	Centre of gravity		Volumetric Heeling Moments	Capacity	Centre of gravity		Volumetric Heeling Moments
		KG	LCG			KG***	LCG	
	(M^3)	(M)	(M)	(M^4)	(M^3)	(M)	(M)	(M^4)
No. 1 Cargo hold	6,848.0	8.36	−65.67	586	6,351.8**	8.36	−65.67	1882
No. 2 Cargo hold	7,866.9	7.79	−36.28	533	7,562.5**	7.79	−36.28	1762
No. 3 Cargo hold	5,503.4	7.76	−10.12	373	5,264.2**	7.76	−10.12	1333
No. 4 Cargo hold	8,060.5	7.79	16.42	547	7,721.0**	7.79	16.42	1921
No. 5 Cargo hold	6,699.1	8.11	46.08	535	6,344.2**	8.11	46.08	2024
No. 2 TST (P&S)					1,216.4*	12.51	−35.87	451
No. 3 TST (P&S)					854.8*	12.51	−9.72	317
No. 4 TST (P&S)					1,253.4*	12.51	16.84	463
No. 5 TST (P&S)					1,097.0*	12.60	46.47	415

REGINA OLDENDORFF

Curves of Volume, VCG & Shifting Moment for No3 Cargo Hold

Total Capacity	5503m³
Full-hold Heeling Moment	373m⁴
Max Slack-hold Heel Moment	9356m⁴

Note
Shifting moments have been increased 12% of the Transverse Shift as the adverse effect of the Vertical Shift of the Grain surface in accordance with the regulation.

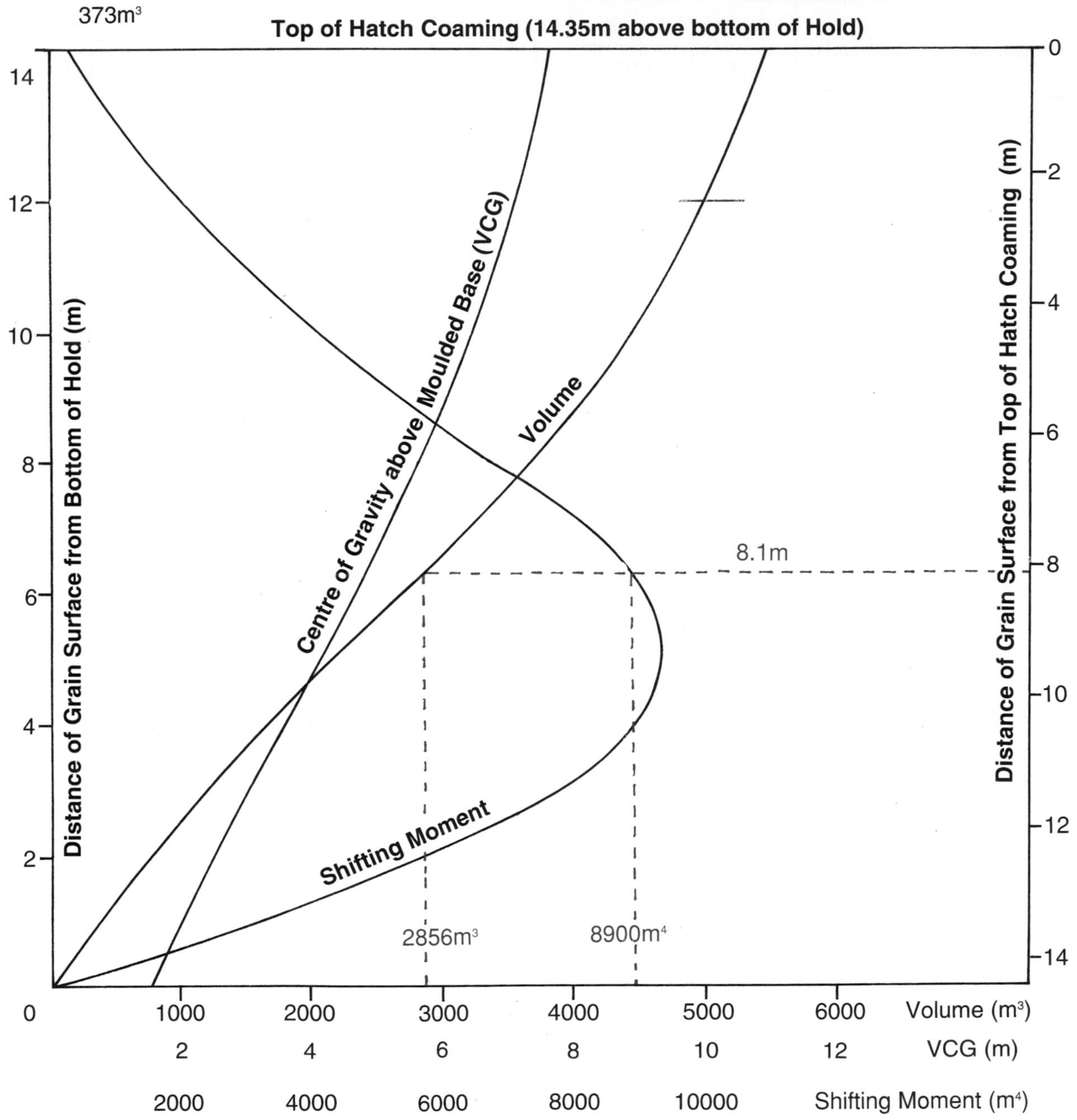

CORRECTIONS TO HEELING MOMENTS TO OBTAIN ACTUAL GRAIN HEELING MOMENTS: THE BACKGROUND

THE grain heeling moments (sometimes called shifting moments or upsetting moments) for each cargo space are a measure of the free surface effect of the grain within that space. Grain heeling moments, like the free surface moments in a ballast tank, are zero when the compartment is empty, and are small when a compartment is almost full. (Filling a hold completely full with grain is not a practical possibility.) The free surface area of grain in the hold of a conventional bulk carrier is greatest when the hold is about half full, and it is at this level that the grain heeling moments are at a maximum.

There are several alternative methods for obtaining accurate values for grain heeling moments. They vary according to whether the ends have been trimmed, the centre of gravity assumed for the grain, the method of assessing the amount of grain in the compartment, whether the compartment is full or part full, the method of calculation of the grain heeling moments, and the units used to describe the density of the grain. The calculations provided in the loading manual for each ship are based upon a particular method, using some of the above alternatives, but the grain stability calculation forms issued by the various national authorities must provide for all the alternatives, and are worded accordingly.

It is not always clear which corrections must be applied to grain heeling moments in which circumstances: the factors which govern this are described below.

Trimmed and untrimmed ends

The values of the grain heeling moments for holds with untrimmed ends are larger than those for holds with trimmed ends, because when the ends are untrimmed the grain has more room in which to shift. A hold with untrimmed ends is a hold in which the grain at the hold ends lies at its natural angle of repose. A hold with trimmed ends is one in which the bulk grain has been trimmed so as to fill all spaces under the decks and hatchcovers to the maximum extent possible[18].

When holds are full, values must always be read from the correct set of tables for the condition of each hold at the time.

Centre of gravity assumed

Volumetric centres of gravity are usually used in loading manuals. The volumetric centre of gravity (CG) is the centre of the volume required to contain the cargo, including broken stowage. For a full compartment the volumetric CG is at the centre of volume of the compartment: this disregards the fact that there will actually be broken stowage in the form of underdeck voids which the cargo has not filled, so the true CG of the cargo will be lower.

CGs which are obtained by measurement-for example, by measurement of the ullage of a part filled compartment-take account of the actual space occupied and do not include the underdeck voids which reduce the vessel's capacity. CGs obtained by measurement are known as 'true' or 'cargo' centres of gravity.

Method of assessing the amount of grain in the compartment

When a proposed loading plan shows a compartment to be full the intended condition is the same as when the compartment has been filled. In both cases the broken stowage is included, and in both cases the heeling moments will require no correction if the volumetric CGs have been used.

A part-filled compartment in a proposed loading plan, calculated with the help of the stowage factor, will not be filled to the same level as the same compartment when filled in reality. This is because the stowage factor does not remain constant throughout the full height of the stow: most of the broken stowage occurs at the top of the hold, under the deckhead. When the height of cargo in a part filled compartment has been obtained by measurement a true or cargo CG will have been calculated, and a correction must be applied to the grain heeling moments to obtain the value as for a volumetric CG.

Whether the compartment is full or part full

As noted above, when a compartment has been part filled the CG calculated from a measured ullage or height of grain will be a true or cargo centre, and not a volumetric centre. A correction must be applied to the heeling moments to take account of this.

Method of calculation of the grain heeling moments

The method of calculation adopted in the loading manual may be to use volumetric CGs. Alternatively, true or cargo centres may be used, in which case they must be corrected for vertical shift of grain surface which occurs as the cargo settles during the voyage. A table of correction factors to allow for vertical shift of grain surface will be provided in the loading manual, or this correction will be incorporated into the tables or curves of shifting moments.

Units used to describe the density of the grain

When the volumetric heeling moments have been calculated they must always be corrected to take account of the stowage factor of the cargo. For this calculation it is essential that the units used are consistent. If the heeling moments are expressed in M^4 they must be divided by the stowage factor expressed in m^3 /tonne, and not by the stowage factor expressed in cuft/ton.

An alternative method of making this correction is to multiply the volumetric heeling moments by the specific gravity of the cargo. This has exactly the same effect as dividing by the stowage factor.

Corrections: a summary

Corrections are made to the tabulated values of the heeling moments by the use of multipliers, with three possible values (1.0, 1.06, 1.12) to be used as required. The occasions for their use are as follows.

(Continued)

Correction x 1.0 (ie no correction), when:

- Compartment is full, and volumetric centre has been used.
- Compartment is not full, but volumetric Centre for full Compartment has been used.
- The table or curve of heeling moments has been adjusted for vertical shift of grain surface by the use of multiplier 1,12 (or + 12%).

Correction x 1.06, when:

- Compartment is full and a true or cargo centre has been used – not a volumetric centre.

Correction x 1.12, when:

- Compartment is part filled, unless volumetric centres for the full compartment have been used, or the table or curve of heeling moments has been adjusted for vertical shift of grain surface by use of the multiplier 1.12.

The ship's loading manual ought to make clear, with explanation and example, which corrections have to be applied.

LOADING CALCULATIONS FOR A TIMBER VOYAGE

Regina Oldendorff, imaginary voyage from Umea, Sweden (in the north Baltic) to Alexandria, Egypt, via the Kiel Canal, bunkering at Brunsbuttel at the Canal exit.

The steps in the calculation are described below, followed by a summary of the data and limits used. Then worked examples of some of the calculations are provided.

Procedure for calculations

Arrival at Kiel is likely to be the worst condition for stability. Stability is likely to be least as the quantities of fuel, carried low in the vessel, will be at a minimum. The shallowest minimum draft also occurs at this point.

Calculation 1: trim and initial stability calculation, attached.

Kiel arrival, with maximum cargo.
The holds and decks have been filled to capacity.
Draft is less than the limit.
However, the fluid metacentric height is negative.

Stability can be improved by filling ballast tanks, thereby adding weight low in the vessel.

Calculation 2: trim and initial stability calculation (not attached).

Kiel arrival, as *Calculation 1*, but with ballast added.
The Nos. 2, 3 and 4 DB ballast tanks have been filled to capacity with water at a density of 1.000 mt/m^3, the dock density at Umea.
The mean draft is 9.595 m, which exceeds the limit.
The fluid metacentric height is still negative.

Free surface effect is already at a minimum, and no further improvements can be made to stability by changing the bunker or ballast tanks. Taking bunkers instead of ballast would not normally help, as bunkers are less dense than ballast water. To achieve a further improvement in stability there is no alternative but to reduce the tonnage of cargo carried on deck.

Calculation 3: trim and initial stability calculation (not attached).

Kiel arrival, as *Calculation 2*, but with deck cargo reduced.
The deck cargo has been reduced evenly until the stability criteria are met. The amount of cargo to remove can be found by trial and error, or by calculation.

Calculation for tonnage of deck cargo to remove.
An approximate value for the amount of cargo to remove can be obtained by solving the familiar equation

GG_1 = w x d/(W –w) for w. Rearrange this to become:

$w = GG_1 \times W/(d + GG_1)$

where GG_1 = the increase required in G_1M
W = Displacement
d = distance of top layer of deck cargo from the ship's centre of gravity (ie KG of layer of deck cargo – KG of ship)
w = tonnage of deck cargo to remove

After removing the unwanted deck cargo the vessel is found to be trimmed by the stern, the draft aft exceeding the limit.
Trim can be reduced by transferring weight of deck cargo forward.

Calculation 4: trim and initial stability calculation. (Not attached.)

Kiel arrival, as *Calculation 3* but weight has been transferred from deck cargo on No. 5 hatch to No. 1 hatch until the appropriate trim is achieved for even keel in dock water. Quantity to transfer is found from trimming tables, or by calculation or trial and error.

Vessel is now at the required draft and trim, and has sufficient initial fluid metacentric height.

Calculation 5: statical and dynamical stability calculation (not attached).

As the vessel is now at a satisfactory draft and trim, and has an acceptable initial fluid metacentric height, it is necessary to ensure that she satisfies all the stability criteria.

The calculation shows that the area under the curve of statical stability from 0° to 30° is 0.051 m-rad, which is less than 0.055 m-rad, so a further improvement in the stability is required.

(When the ship is provided with simplified stability information in the form of a curve or table of initial metacentric height versus draft, or any other measurement of stability, the statical and dynamical stability calculations will not be required.)

Calculation 6: trim and initial stability calculation. and statical and dynamical stability calculation (not attached)

To improve the stability, deck cargo can be reduced with or without the taking of more ballast. However, the ballast tanks are large, and a more economical improvement may be achieved by taking additional diesel bunkers in Umea, and retaining them throughout the voyage. Recalculate as *Calculations 4 and 5*, but with an additional 45 mt in the diesel oil tank, and a reduction of 45 mt of deck cargo.

The area under the curve is now 0.054 m-rad, so a slightly larger tonnage must be transferred.

Calculation 7: trim and initial stability calculation. and statical and dynamical stability calculation (not attached)

Repeat *Calculation 6* using 62 mt in place of 45 mt (a transfer of 15 mt appears to cause an increase of 0.001 m-rad). The area under the curve is 0.056 m-rad, which is acceptable. However, the transfer of weight from the deck cargo to the diesel oil tank has caused the vessel to trim slightly by the stern. This must be corrected by a transfer of deck cargo from aft to forward.

Calculation 8: trim and initial stability calculation, attached.

As *Calculation 7*, but weight has been transferred from deck cargo on No. 5 to deck cargo on No. 1 until the appropriate trim is achieved for even keel in dock water.

Calculation 9: statical and dynamical stability calculation, attached.

As *Calculation 8*. The calculation shows that the condition satisfies all the stability criteria. The deck cargo distribution continues to be acceptable, because all the values in *Condition 9* are less than In *Condition 1*, which used maximum values.

Further calculations.

Using the tonnages in *Calculation 9* as a basis, the bunker quantities must be adjusted to obtain the tonnages aboard at each stage in the voyage. Using these figures the trim and initial stability calculation, and the statical and dynamical stability calculation, must be completed for departure Umea, departure Kiel and arrival Alexandria.

The calculations, which are not attached, show draft, trim and stability to be satisfactory for every stage in the voyage, and confirm that arrival Kiel was the worst condition. Once the Kiel Canal with its draft restrictions has been passed the stability can be further improved by ballasting No. 5 DB tanks.

Allowance for absorption of moisture, and for icing.

In a case such as this one, when the ship's stability condition does not allow any more weight to be carried on deck, the effect of these allowances is to reduce the amount of cargo which can be carried on deck.

When absorption and icing can be expected, as on an ocean voyage in high latitudes, it is reasonable to allow 20 per cent of the weight of the deck cargo for these factors. For a voyage from Umea to Alexandria, on the other hand, it is reasonable to assume that absorption will increase as the voyage goes on, but icing will disappear after the first few days, so an allowance of 10 per cent is appropriate.

Deck cargo tonnage = wx100/110
Where w = calculated value of weight to load on deck
100 = constant
110 = 100 + percentage allowed for absorption and icing

	Calculated weight		Deck cargo tonnage
Deck cargo 1	986	x100/110 =	896
Deck cargo 2	1,091		992
Deck cargo 3	749		681
Deck cargo 4	1,122		1,020
Deck cargo 5	722		656
Total tonnage of deck cargo to be carried			4,245 mt

Data used in the worked example

Consumptions

Fuel oil:	31 mtpd (metric tonnes per day)
Diesel oil:	2.5 mtpd
Fresh water:	nil (vessel has an evaporator)

Distances and consumptions

Umea to Kiel 900 nm @ 14,5 kts = 2.6 days
FO: 81 mt DO 7 mt
Kiel to Alexandria 3444 nm @ 14.5 kts = 9.9 days
FO: 307 mt DO 25 mt
Reserve, 3 days' steaming
FO: 93 mt DO 8 mt

Fuel totals – minimum quantities to satisfy consumption requirements at each point in voyage.

	FO	DO
Umea Departure	174	15
Kiel Arrival	111	6
Kiel Departure	477	26
Alexandria Arrival	111	6

Tank capacities

Fuel oil tanks 95% full with density 0.950 mt/m^3

	m^3	mt
F02	334	301
F04	325	293
Diesel oil tank 95 per cent full with density 0.850 mt/m^3		
DO	190	153
Settling and Service tanks 50% full		
FO Service	35	17
FO Settling	72	34
DO Service	10	4
DO Settling	10	4

Cargo Stowage Factors

Deck cargo: 63 ft^3/lt = 0.56955 mt/m^3
Holds: 68 ft^3/lt = 0.52767 mt/m^3
(NB: these values are useful for this example, but are not typical of timber from Umea.)

Constant weights

Settling and service tanks	59 mt
Lubricating oil	56 mt
Fresh water	50 mt
Other tanks	31 mt
Stores	45 mt

Changes of draft and trim

Dock density at Kiel 1.013 mt/m^3
Limiting draft at Kiel 9.5 m.

To calculate seawater draft corresponding to maximum canal draft:

Draft change = Wx(1 – SD/ DD)/TPC/100
where W = Displacement
SD = Seawater density
DD = Dockwater density
TPC = Tonnes per centimetre immersion
Draft change = 33265x (1-1.025/1.013)/38.0/100
= – 0.102 m

So seawater draft 9.398 m corresponds to 9.5 m in canal.

To calculate seawater trim corresponding to even keel canal trim:

Trim change (m) = (SLCB-DLCB) xW/MCTC/100
where SLCB = Seawater longitudinal centre of buoyancy
DLCB = Dockwater longitudinal centre of buoyancy
W = Displacement
MCTC = Moment to change trim one centimetre
Trim change (m) = ([–3.903] – [–3.855])x33265/467.34/100
= – 0.034 m

This shows that the vessel will trim by the head when passing from sea water to canal water. The trim in sea water must be 0.034 m by the stern for even keel in the canal.

Stability requirements

The stability requirements are governed by the IMO International Convention on Load Lines, the IMO Code of Safe Working Practices for Timber Deck Cargoes, flag State regulations and classification society rules. The minimum criteria are given in the ship's loading manual and should be read with care, because in some cases they are different from the IMO recommendations.

The *Regina Oldendorff* is required to comply with the UK Merchant Shipping (Load Line) Rules 1968, Schedule 4, Part 1, Para. 2. When carrying timber she is permitted to have an initial metacentric height of not less than 0.05 metres.

Deck cargo

Limiting drafts 4.5 m

Limiting height:

	Draft (m)	Density (mt/m^3)	SW Draft (m)
Umea	9.7	1.000	
Kiel	9.5	1.013	9.398
Brunsbuttel	10.4	1.003	
Alexandria	13.5	1.025	

1 **Trim and Initial Stability** Calculation 1

2 *REGINA OLDENDORFF. Kiel. Arrival. Maximum Cargo.*

3 LCG, LCB and LCF from Midpoint.

4 Negative if Centre forward of Midpoint.

Line	Identity	Weight	Longitudinal Centre of Gravity	Longitudinal Moment	Vertical Centre of Gravity	Vertical Moment	Free Surface or Volumetric Heeling Momnt
8		W	LCG	W*LCG	VCG	W*VCG	
9	*Deck Cargo 1*	*1006*	*-63.76*	*-64143*	*17.59*	*17696*	
10	*Deck Cargo 2*	*1290*	*-35.87*	*-46272*	*17.21*	*22201*	
11	*Deck Cargo 3*	*886*	*-9.72*	*-8612*	*17.20*	*15239*	
12	*Deck Cargo 4*	*1327*	*16.84*	*22347*	*17.21*	*22838*	
13	*Deck Cargo 5*	*1014*	*44.82*	*45447*	*17.22*	*17461*	
14	*Hold 1*	*3411*	*-65.63*	*-223864*	*8.23*	*28073*	
15	*Hold 2*	*3916*	*-36.28*	*-142072*	*7.70*	*30153*	
16	*Hold 3*	*2709*	*-10.14*	*-27469*	*7.63*	*20670*	
17	*Hold 4*	*4043*	*16.42*	*66386*	*7.69*	*31091*	
18	*Hold 5*	*3407*	*46.22*	*157472*	*7.99*	*27222*	
19	*W Ballast 1*		*-65.24*		*1.44*		
20	*W Ballast 2*		*-35.84*		*1.34*		
21	*W Ballast 3*		*-9.72*		*1.34*		
22	*W Ballast 4*		*17.00*		*1.46*		
23	*W Ballast 5*		*47.40*		*1.95*		
24	*Fuel Oil 1*		*-35.86*		*0.74*		
25	*Fuel Oil 2*		*-9.72*		*0.74*		
26	*Fuel Oil 3*		*16.84*		*0.74*		
27	*Fuel Oil 4*	*93*	*44.26*	*4116*	*0.74*	*69*	*1469*
28	*FO Ser & Set*	*51*	*58.48*	*2982*	*12.04*	*614*	
29	*Diesel Oil*	*8*	*66.24*	*530*	*1.38*	*11*	*210*
30	*DO Ser & Set*	*8*	*68.72*	*550*	*12.02*	*96*	
31	*Lub Oil*	*56*	*73.74*	*4129*	*6.74*	*377*	
32	*Fresh Water*	*50*	*88.59*	*4430*	*13.26*	*663*	*476*
33	*Other Tanks*	*31*	*82.23*	*2549*	*2.13*	*66*	
34	*Stores*	*45*	*27.33*	*1230*	*16.53*	*744*	
35							
36							
37							
38	Deadweight	*23351*					
39	Light Ship	*8051*	*12.04*	*96950*	*10.12*	*81468*	
40	Displacement	*31402*		*-103314*		*316751*	*2155*

Line	Item	Value	Source
41	Draft at Centre of Flotation	*9.011*	Hydrostatic Table
42	Longitudinal Centre of Gravity	*-3.290*	L40 LM/W
43	Longitudinal Centre of Buoyancy	*-4.085*	Hydrostatic Table
44	Moment to Change Trim One Centimetre	*454.87*	Hydrostatic Table
45	Trim	*0.549*	(L42-L43)*L40W/L44/100
46	Length Between Perpendiculars	*183.00*	Ship's Particulars
47	Longitudinal Centre of Flotation	*-0.333*	Hydrostatic Table
48	Difference of Draft Forward	*-0.274*	-(L46/2+L47)*L45/L46
49	Difference of Draft Aft	*0.275*	(L46/2-L47)*L45/L46
50	Draft Forward	*8.737*	L41+L48
51	Draft Aft	*9.286*	L41+L49
52	Transverse Metacentre	*9.361*	Hydrostatic Table
53	Vertical Centre of Gravity	*10.087*	L40 VM/W
54	Metacentric Height	*-0.726*	L52-L53
55	Free Surface Effect	*0.069*	L40 FSM/W
56	Fluid Metacentric Height	*-0.795*	L54-L55
57	Permissible Grain Heeling Moment		Hydrostatic Table
58	Volumetric Heeling Moment		Total VHM
59	Density of Grain Cargo		MT/CM
60	Grain Heeling Moment		L58*L59 <L57

1 **Trim and Initial Stability** **Calculation 8**
2 *REGINA OLDENDORFF. Kiel. Arrival. Even Keel (Density 1.013).*
3 LCG, LCB and LCF from Midpoint.
4 Negative if Centre forward of Midpoint.

	Identity	Weight	Longitudinal Centre of Gravity	Longitudinal Moment	Vertical Centre of Gravity	Vertical Moment	Free Surface or Volumetric Heeling Momnt
5–8		W	LCG	W*LCG	VCG	W*VCG	
9	*Deck Cargo 1*	*986*	*-63.76*	*-62867*	*17.55*	*17304*	
10	*Deck Cargo 2*	*1091*	*-35.87*	*-39134*	*16.86*	*18394*	
11	*Deck Cargo 3*	*749*	*-9.72*	*-7280*	*16.85*	*12621*	
12	*Deck Cargo 4*	*1122*	*16.84*	*18894*	*16.86*	*18917*	
13	*Deck Cargo 5*	*722*	*44.82*	*32360*	*16.57*	*11964*	
14	*Hold 1*	*3411*	*-65.63*	*-223864*	*8.23*	*28073*	
15	*Hold 2*	*3916*	*-36.28*	*-142072*	*7.70*	*30153*	
16	*Hold 3*	*2709*	*-10.14*	*-27469*	*7.63*	*20670*	
17	*Hold 4*	*4043*	*16.42*	*66386*	*7.69*	*31091*	
18	*Hold 5*	*3407*	*46.22*	*157472*	*7.99*	*27222*	
19	*W Ballast 1*		*-65.24*		*1.44*		
20	*W Ballast 2*	*826*	*-35.84*	*-29604*	*1.34*	*1107*	
21	*W Ballast 3*	*582*	*-9.72*	*-5657*	*1.34*	*780*	
22	*W Ballast 4*	*858*	*17.00*	*14586*	*1.46*	*1253*	
23	*W Ballast 5*		*47.40*		*1.95*		
24	*Fuel Oil 1*		*-35.86*		*0.74*		
25	*Fuel Oil 2*		*-9.72*		*0.74*		
26	*Fuel Oil 3*		*16.84*		*0.74*		
27	*Fuel Oil 4*	*93*	*44.26*	*4116*	*0.74*	*69*	*1469*
28	*FO Ser & Set*	*51*	*58.48*	*2982*	*12.04*	*614*	
29	*Diesel Oil*	*70*	*66.24*	*4637*	*1.38*	*97*	*210*
30	*DO Ser & Set*	*8*	*68.72*	*550*	*12.02*	*96*	
31	*Lub Oil*	*56*	*73.74*	*4129*	*6.74*	*377*	
32	*Fresh Water*	*50*	*88.59*	*4430*	*13.26*	*663*	*476*
33	*Other Tanks*	*31*	*82.23*	*2549*	*2.13*	*66*	
34	*Stores*	*45*	*27.33*	*1230*	*16.53*	*744*	
35							
36							
37							
38	Deadweight	*24826*					
39	Light Ship	*8051*	*12.04*	*96950*	*10.12*	*81468*	
40	Displacement	*32877*		*-126677*		*303741*	*2155*

41	Draft at Centre of Flotation	*9.398*	Hydrostatic Table
42	Longitudinal Centre of Gravity	*-3.853*	L40 LM/W
43	Longitudinal Centre of Buoyancy	*-3.903*	Hydrostatic Table
44	Moment to Change Trim One Centimetre	*464.74*	Hydrostatic Table
45	Trim	*0.035*	(L42-L43)*L40W/L44/100
46	Length Between Perpendiculars	*183.00*	Ship's Particulars
47	Longitudinal Centre of Flotation	*0.311*	Hydrostatic Table
48	Difference of Draft Forward	*-0.018*	-(L46/2+L47)*L45/L46
49	Difference of Draft Aft	*0.017*	(L46/2-L47)*L45/L46
50	Draft Forward	*9.380*	L41+L48
51	Draft Aft	*9.415*	L41+L49
52	Transverse Metacentre	*9.400*	Hydrostatic Table
53	Vertical Centre of Gravity	*9.239*	L40 VM/W
54	Metacentric Height	*0.161*	L52-L53
55	Free Surface Effect	*0.066*	L40 FSM/W
56	Fluid Metacentric Height	*0.095*	L54-L55
57	Permissible Grain Heeling Moment		Hydrostatic Table
58	Volumetric Heeling Moment		Total VHM
59	Density of Grain Cargo		MT/CM
60	Grain Heeling Moment		L58*L59 <L57

Line	Item	Value
1	**Statical and Dynamical Stability**	**Calculation 9**
2	*REGINA OLDENDORFF. Kiel. Arrival.*	
3	Displacement	*32877*
4	Fluid Metacentric Height	*0.095*
5	Vertical Centre of Gravity	*9.239*
6	Free Surface Effect	*0.066*
7	Fluid Vertical Centre of Gravity L5+L6	*9.305*
8	Assumed Vertical Centre of Gravity	*7.000*
9	Difference between Vertical Centres of Gravity L8-L7	*-2.305*
10	Righting Arm Curve	

Line	Angle of Heel	Sine	Correction L9*Sine	Assumed Righting Arm	Righting Arm ARA+C
14	*0.00*	*0.000*	*0.000*	*0.000*	*0.000*
15	*10.00*	*0.174*	*-0.400*	*0.430*	*0.030*
16	*12.00*	*0.208*	*-0.479*	*0.520*	*0.041*
17	*20.00*	*0.342*	*-0.788*	*0.920*	*0.132*
18	*30.00*	*0.500*	*-1.153*	*1.520*	*0.368*
19	*40.00*	*0.643*	*-1.482*	*2.290*	*0.808*
20	*50.00*	*0.766*	*-1.766*	*2.910*	*1.144*
21	*60.00*	*0.866*	*-1.996*	*3.120*	*1.124*
22	*70.00*	*0.940*	*-2.166*	*3.060*	*0.894*
23	*80.00*	*0.985*	*-2.270*	*2.800*	*0.530*

(Header lines 11–13: Angle / of / Heel; Sine; Correction / L9*Sine; Assumed / Righting / Arm; Righting / Arm / ARA+C)

Line	Item	Value	Required Values *
24	**IMO International Convention on Load Lines 1966**		
25	Righting Arm at 0° Heel [A]	*0.000*	
26	Righting Arm at 15° Heel [DE]	*0.065*	
27	Righting Arm at 30° Heel [FG]	*0.368*	
28	Area to 30° (L26*4+L25+L27)*15/3/57.3 [AFG]	*0.055*	=>0.055
29	Angle of Flooding	*47*	
30	θF, Angle of Flooding L29, or 40°, whichever less.	*40*	
31	Half θF L30/2	*20*	
32	Righting Arm at 0° Heel L25 [A]	*0.000*	
33	Righting Arm at Half θF° Heel L31 [HI]	*0.132*	
34	Righting Arm at θF° Heel L30 [JK]	*0.808*	
35	Area to θF (L33*4+L32+L34)*L31/3/57.3 [AJK]	*0.155*	=>0.090
36	Area 30° to θF L35-L28 [GFJK]	*0.100*	=>0.030
37	Maximum Righting Arm [LM]	*1.161*	=>0.20
38	Angle of Maximum Righting Arm [M]	*54*	=>30°
39	Initial Fluid Metacentric Height L4 [BC]	*0.095*	=>0.15
40	**IMO International Grain Code 1991**		
41	Heeling Arm Curve		
42	Volumetric Heeling Moment of grain		
43	Density of Cargo		
44	Heeling Arm at 30° L42/L3*L43 [AN]		
45	Heeling Arm at 40° L44*0.8 [OK]		
46	Angle of Heel due to Grain Shift, [Q], at		
47	Intersection of Righting and Heeling Arm curves [P]		<=12
48	Angle where difference between		
49	Righting Arm and Heeling Arm curves is maximum [R]		
50	Limit of Residual Dynamic Stability,		
51	Least value of L29, L49 and 40°		
52	Midpoint of range (L47+L51)/2 [S]		
53	Ordinate L51-L52		
54	Differences between Righting and Heeling Arms		
55	At Angle of Heel due to Grain Shift L47 [P]		
56	At Midpoint of range L52 [TU]		
57	At Limit of Residual Dynamic Stability L51 [JO]		
58	Residual Dynamic Stability (L56*4+L55+L57)*L53/3/57.3 [PJO]		=>0.075
59	Initial Fluid Metacentric Height L4 [BC]		=>0.30
60	**IMO Code of Safe Practice for Ships <100m Carrying Timber Deck Cargoes**		
61	Area to θF L35	*0.155*	=>0.08
62	Maximum Righting Arm L37	*1.161*	=>0.25
63	Initial Fluid Metacentric Height L4	*0.095*	=>0.10
64	Fluid Metacentric Height to be positive throughout voyage.		
65	* The Ship's Stability and Loading Manual should be checked for		
66	specific requirements, see Note in explanation.		

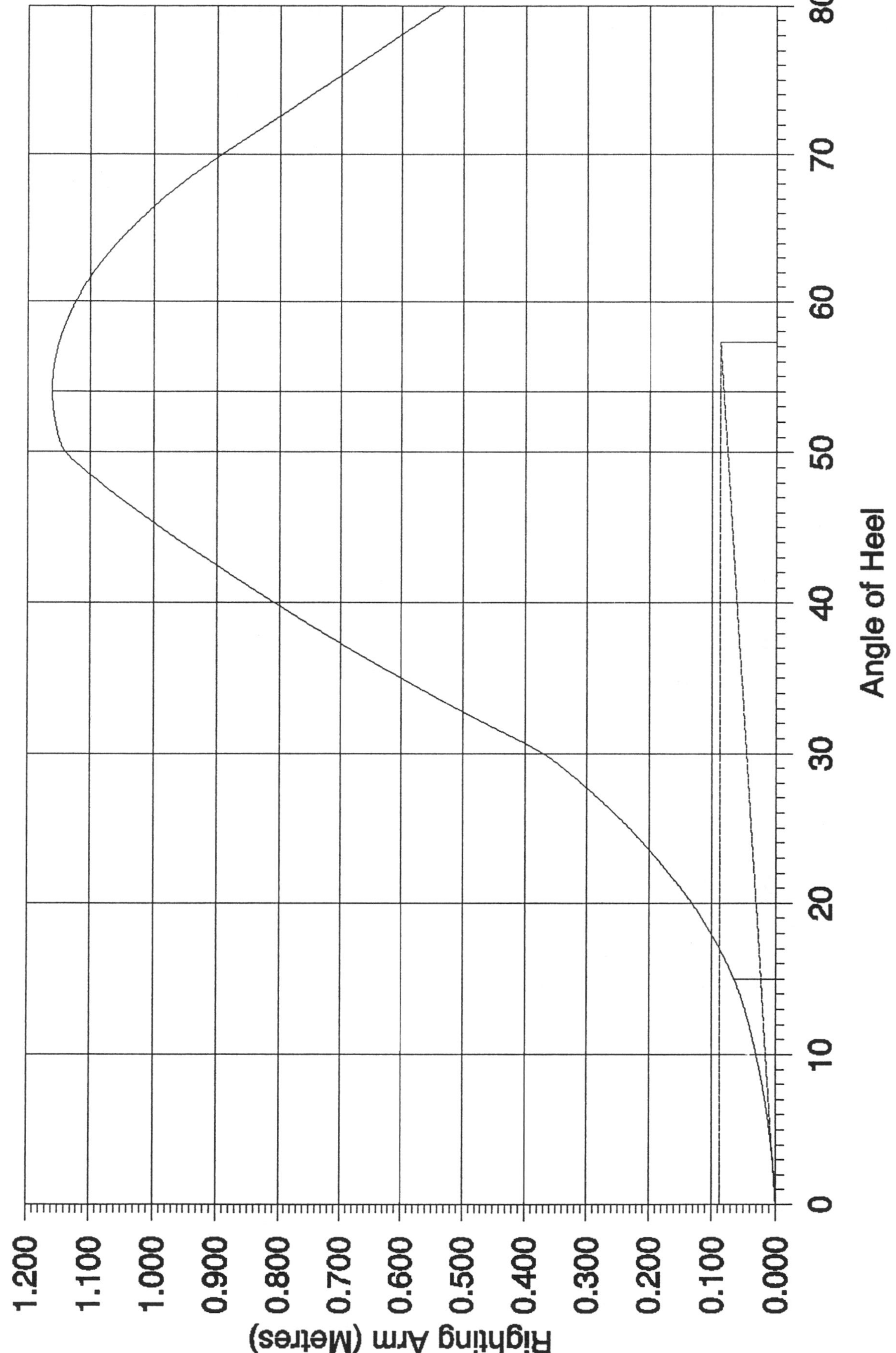
Curve of Statical Stability
REGINA OLDENDORFF
Kiel. Arrival.
Righting Arm (Metres)
1.200
1.100
1.000
0.900
0.800
0.700
0.600
0.500
0.400
0.300
0.200
0.100
0.000
Angle of Heel
0
10
20
30
40
50
60
70
80

GUIDANCE NOTES FOR VESSELS ARRIVING AT AUSTRALIA TO LOAD GRAIN[230]
Notes provided by Captain P. Bruce, Tonand Marine (Australia) Pty Ltd

Vessels loading grain for export in Australia are subject to stringent regulations under the EXPORT CONTROL (PLANTS AND PLANT PRODUCTS) ORDERS 2005, made under the EXPORT CONTROL ACT 1982 to regulate the export of plant and plant products from Australia, effective from 1st July, 2005, under which:

1. Vessels loading grain are subject to survey by a properly qualified marine surveyor and the Australian Quarantine and Inspection Service (AQIS) for cleanliness and infestation or the presence of materials which could lead to infestation.

2. A loading permit will only be issued by the AQIS when the ship has reached the required standards and after the marine surveyor has issued a certificate stating that the holds of the ship are fit for the carriage of grain.

The Masters of vessels intending to load grain in Australia for export should ensure that, prior to the time of inspection:

- Details of the vessel's particulars, the last three previous cargoes and the last grain cargo are available.
- All spaces to be loaded with grain are thoroughly clean and dry, free of odour, gas or fumes, free from previous cargo residues, insects, rust scale and flaking paint. Particular attention should be paid to areas likely to trap previous cargo residues, scale and dirt such as hatch covers, coaming ledges, deck beams, frame knees, brackets, horizontal surfaces, pipe brackets, pipe flanges.
- Bilges are clean, dry, odourless and in working condition. Bilge plate perforations should be clear and the bilges, and any scuppers, should be made grain tight with new, clean Hessian or similar porous material.
- Spaces adjacent to cargo spaces to be loaded, and store rooms, including those for foodstuffs, are free from insects.
- Any wooden structures such as tank top sheathing are clean, completely dry, free from insects and grain tight. Green timber is not permitted.
- If possible, ballast holds are empty and ready for inspection as outlined at the same time as other holds to avoid a costly second inspection.
- Hatches are fully open.
- An aluminium ladder is in place, available for the inspectors use in the first hold to be inspected (usually hold No.1). If a second ladder is available, that should be placed in the second hold to be inspected. Drums, brooms, scrapers and dustpans should also be in place. (In the interests of safety, it is not permitted to lower or raise anything into or out of holds whilst inspectors are in the holds. Thus, a good deal of time can be saved by having the necessary items in the holds before the inspectors enter.)

At the time of inspection an officer with a 'walkie talkie' radio should accompany inspectors in the holds, and another officer with a radio should be standing by on deck at all times. The ship's engineers should be on stand by to operate bilges for testing (dry sucking only). Sufficient crew should be available to carry out on the spot cleaning if necessary.

If the holds are found unfit to load grain, cleaning and/or fumigation may be ordered by the inspectors prior to issuing of a permit to load with subsequent delay and considerable expense.

Cargo spaces used for the carriage of processed grains such as white rice, malt and hulled oats, bagged rice or other grain cargoes which are highly susceptible to discolouration and taint should have a complete paint coat with no bare metal, rust, rust scale, rust powder or rust staining evident at all. All paint must be applied in sufficient time for it to completely dry and be free of odour in accordance with the paint manufacturer's instructions well prior to the arrival of the vessel at the load port (usually, with marine coatings, at least seven days is required for the paint to fully 'cure').

The term 'grain' includes wheat, barley, rice, oats, canola, maize, peas, sorghum, soya beans, sunflower seeds, linseed and rye.

NB The importance of properly preparing cargo spaces to load grain cannot be over stressed. Inspectors will only issue certificates and permits when all cargo spaces are considered fit to be loaded (with the possible exception of holds which have been ballasted). If inspectors consider that further cleaning and/or painting is required, delay and expense are inevitable. Elevated work platforms ('cherry pickers'), high pressure water washing machines and shore labour will usually be needed and the vessel will probably have to shift to a lay-by berth until the work is completed.

These notes are issued for the guidance of shipowners and operators only. No guarantee or warranty is given, or liability accepted, with regard to their comprehensiveness or accuracy.

WEDGE FORMULA: VOLUME IN TANK, ALLOWING FOR TRIM

When a ship is trimmed it is necessary to allow for the trim, to obtain an accurate volume, and tonnage, of liquid in the tank. The tank calibration tables may contain trim corrections, but for an accurate result it is necessary to interpolate carefully between two values for trim. The tank calibration tables for the Regina Oldendorff give readings for every 0.5 m of trim from 0.5 m by the head to 3.0 m by the stern, which is a very useful spread, but many ships are not so well equipped.

Accurate values are important when calculating the tonnage of strippings remaining in ballast tanks, and the wedge formula provides a method for taking account of the trim, when the actual sounding is small.

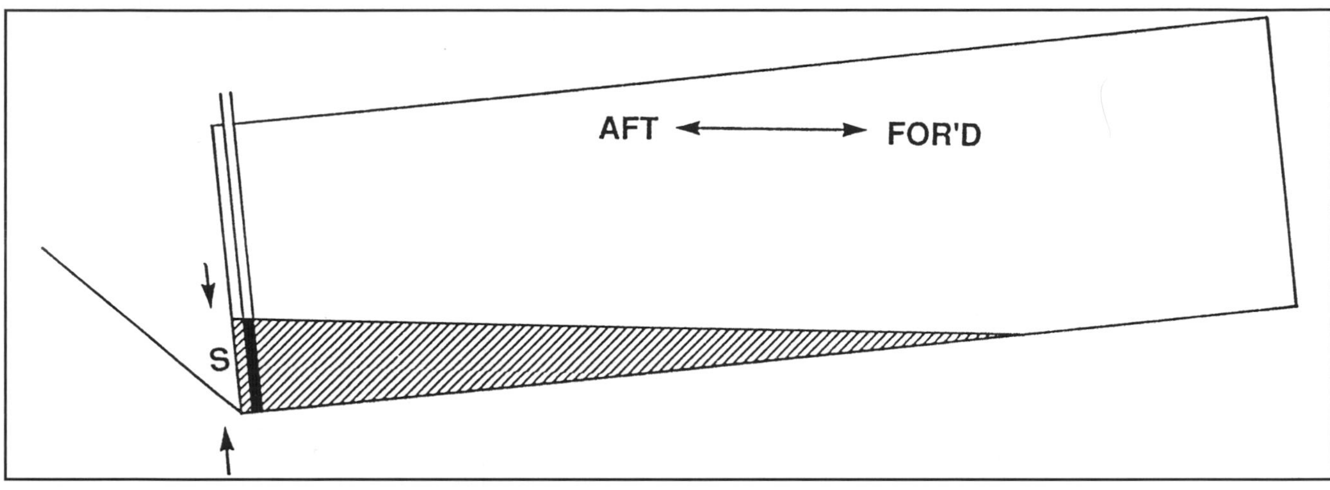

Wedge Formula:

$$V = \frac{LS^2B}{2T}$$

where V = volume of liquid in tank (m^3)
L = vessel's length between perpendiculars (m)
B = breadth of tank (m)
T = trim of vessel (m)
S = sounding (m)

When the volume of liquid has been calculated its weight can be calculated as follows:

$$W = VD$$

where W = tonnage in tank (mt)
V = volume of liquid in tank (m^3)
D = density of liquid in tank (mt/m^3)

The wedge formula:

- Only applies for small soundings below a maximum value which can be calculated (see below),
- Assumes that the tank is box shaped-it ignores the turn of the bilge, and any tapering of the ship along the length of the tank, so its results are only approximate,
- Assumes that the sounding is measured at the after end of the tank. On bulkers this assumption is almost always justified.

The wedge formula does not apply when the liquid in the tank is deep enough to reach the forward end of the tank, ie when:

Length of tank (m) $<$ S x L/T (symbol meanings as above)

Ship Inspection Report and Treatment Order
Export Control Act 1982

Sequence number (Central office) ....
Form number (State Dept.) ....
Original

A. Report

Name of ship .... Registered call signal ....

Previous names ....

De rat Cert. Date of issue: .... Unique number ....

Details of loading

Port	Expected Tonnage	Date
PORT LINCOLN	50,000	8.1.92.

Details of last two cargoes

Commodity	Origin	Date
COAL	AUSTRALIA	DEC 91
MAIZE	U.S.A.	SEPT.91

Details of last grain or oilseed cargo (where applicable): Type of grain .... AS ABOVE .... Origin .... Date ....

Agent .. PATRICK S. LIEGH .... Marine Surveyor ... D. CARLTON

Inspectors . M. RIDGWAY. C. SOUTHAM ... Place of inspection ... PORT LINCOLN

Times and dates of all inspections and re-inspections ... 2h. 30m. 7.1.92.

Site of inspection	No 1	No 2	No 3	No 4	No 5	No 6	No 7							
Hatch covers	C	C	C	C	C	C	C							
Deck beams	C	C	C	C.	C	C	C							
~~Cable casings~~	–	–	–	–	–	–	–							
~~Pipe casings~~	–	–	–	–	–	–	–							
~~Ventilation trunking~~	–	–	–	–	–	–	–							
STEEL bulkheads	C	C	C	C	C	C	C							
~~Spar ceilings~~	–	–	–	–	–	–	–							
Exposed metal surfaces	C	C	C	C	C	C	C							
STEEL tank top ceilings	C	C	C	C	C	C	C							
Bilges	C	C	C	C	C	C	C							
Total infestation for hold (L or H)														

Stores-structure	C	Stores-foodstuff	C	Galley areas	C	Focsle lockers	C	Mast houses	C	Weather deck	C	Other	

Key: L Light infestation; H Heavy infestation; T Trogoderma sp; G Grain; M Mineral residue; R Rodents; S Scale; W Water; O Other; C Clear;
Note more than one letter indicates more than one condition present eg. GS indicates grain plus scale in inspected areas.
*Insert number of insects found in particular sites to 50 then use '50+'.

Residue type

B. Treatment Order

To the master: You are advised that the ship is not to be used for the export of prescribed goods until the action indicated in the following TICKED boxes has been taken, after which a further inspection will be required.

Clean														
Descale**partial														
Dismantle/Remove														
High volume spray														
Gas fumigate														

**delete as applicable

Key for disposal of residues: 1. to be retained for further inspection 2. to be removed prior to treatment 3. to remain in hold during treatment 4. on completion for action, residue to be handed to a Quarantine officer/retained on board for disposal.

Additional Treatment and Remarks

Treatment ordered by Marine Surveyor (Tick appropriate box) Clean ☐ Descale ☐ Other ☐

Date and Time of issue ... 7.1.92 ... 6:00 pm ...... Inspector's Signature .... M. W. Ridgway

Office Use Only
Details of treatment
Spray or Bait
Chemicals used .... % active ingredients .... Treatment carried out by ....
Fumigation
Fumigant used .... Dosage .... Exposure period ....
Insect sample no. holds etc. .... Insect sample no. Storerooms, galley areas etc .... Ships hold Cert. issued (tick) ☑

E 248—3/88

SHIP INSPECTION REPORT AND TREATMENT ORDER: STANDARDS REQUIRED OF VESSELS LOADING GRAIN, PLANTS AND PLANT PRODUCTS

The following notes outline the standards of cleanliness and pest control required of ships presented for loading of grain, plants and plant products in Australia.

1. Grain, Plants and Plants Product Orders
Application for Permission to Load
Ships' masters must apply for permission to load 500 t or more of grain (wheat, barley, oats, sorghum, lupins and dried field peas), or plants and plants products for which the importing country requires a phytosanitary or other official certificate under the provisions of the Ministerial Orders. These commodities are referred to as prescribed goods in the rest of this document.

The application must include details of other cargo, including empty sacks, that could harbour pests, so that this can be inspected prior to loading.

Inspectors
Vessels in which it is intended to export prescribed goods examined by authorised inspectors of the Department Health or State Departments of Agriculture/Primary Industries on behalf of the Department of Primary Industries and Energy. The Orders require that the holds of cargo-loading vessels be free from pests or from residues which could harbour pests. Inspectors are empowered to board ships and order cleaning and treatment, or to require other measures necessary to ensure satisfactory outturn of the cargo overseas, before issuing a permit to load.

For grain loading ships, the holds must also be inspected by an approved marine surveyor. An inspector will not issue a permit to load until he has seen a certificate from the surveyor stating that the holds will not contaminate or otherwise affect the grain.

2. Trogoderma Species
There is a nil tolerance for Trogoderma species (cabinet beetles) on ships loading prescribed goods.

Fumigation is required for any level of infestation by these species in hold spaces.

Cargo-Loading Holds
.ere is a nil tolerance for live pests in holds nominated to load prescribed goods.

All parts of these holds must be free from any previous cargo residue that can harbour pests, including spaces beneath timber linings and the interiors of trunkings and casings.

Masters or agents are legally required to make facilities available to permit inspection of ledges, casings, bulkheads etc. that would otherwise be inaccessible. All non-infestible residue, including loose flaking rust and paint scale, that could conceal pests or infestible residues must be removed to the extent necessary to enable the inspector to carry out a thorough inspection.

Adequate natural light is necessary for all hold spaces and asssociated areas. Inspections are not undertaken before half an hour after sunrise or after half an hour before sunset. Hatch covers must be opened sufficiently to provide good natural lighting.

4. Non-Cargo-Loading Holds
Non-cargo-loading holds are examined when a full cargo is not to be carried.

Pest infestation in non-cargo-loading holds must be controlled to such an extent that the risk of cross-infestation to prescribed goods is eliminated.

5. Ship Stores and Associated Galley Areas
Experience has shown that storerooms are often infested with insect pests to such a degree that a risk of cross-infestation to cargo-loading holds exists. Inspectors are empowered to inspect these areas and to withhold permits to load until that risk has been eliminated.

These areas, being partly or fully lit by artificial light, may be inspected outside the time limits laid down for holds.

6. Other Areas
Areas of ships such as mast houses, fo'c's'le lockers weather deck etc. must not present a cross-infestations or contamination risk to the cargo-loading holds. The permit to load will be withheld until such risks have been removed.

7. Ship Inspection Report and Treatment Order
Following initial inspection of a vessel, a Ship Inspection Report is issued to the master. If cleaning, treatment or other measures are required, this is indicated in the combined Treatment Order. Where hold fitments such as pipe casings, cable casings, spar ceilings and timber bulkhead linings are required to be removed, to facilitate further inspection or cleaning and disinfestation measures, this is also included on the Treatment Order. All procedures in the nomination holds to remove the risk of infestation or infection of the cargo are specified.

Criteria for deciding on treatments followed by inspectors when issuing Treatment Orders are laid down in the Grain, Plants and Plant Products Orders.

Subsequent Ship Inspection Reports and Treatment Orders may be issued as a result of reinspection of a vessel. A re-fumigation is normally ordered following an unsatisfactory fumigation treatment of cargo holds.

8. Permit to Load
When the inspector is satisfied that prescribed goods loaded onto a vessel will not become infested by pests, and, in the case of grain-loading vessels, has seen a certificate from a marine surveyor that the ship is suitable for the carriage of prescribed grain, a permit to load is issued in accordance with the Orders.

LITORAL AGÊNCIA MARITIMA, COMISSÁRIA
DE DESPACHOS E SERVIÇOS CORRELATOS LTDA.

Nº 01

MATE'S RECEIPT

Port of S.Frco.Sul,6th july, de 198 8.-

RECEIVED in apparent good order and condition on board the m/s [redacted]
from Messrs CEVAL AGRO INDUSTRIAL S.A.
the undermetioned goods destined to the port of "ANY IRANIAN SOUTHERN PORTS"

Marks and Numbers	Number of pieces	Class of packages	Said to contain	Gross weight kilos	Cubic measurement
IN BULK			"BRAZILIAN SOYA BEAN		
			MEAL PELLETS		
			IN BULK"	3.028.190 KGS	

"CLEAN ON BOARD"

"Said to be said to weigh"
"quantity and quality unknown"

All terms, conditions, liberties, exceptions, clauses and arbitration clause of Charter Party dated 30-06-88, and any addenda thereto, are herewith incorporated.

THE CARRIAGE OF THE GOODS SPECIFIED HEREIN IS SUBJECT TO THE CONDITIONS AS CONTAINED IN THE BILL OF LADING FOR THIS SHIPMENT

STOWAGE

Hatches	U. T. D.	L. T. D.	L. H.	Total
I				
II				
III				
IV				
V				
VI				

Grand Total

M.V. RUBENS
O.N. 366 308
G.R.T. 17.965.73
N.R.T. 11.236.17
B.H.P. 11200

Port of S.Frco.do Sul,6th july, de 198 8.-

[signature]
Chief Officer

Use Owners' Headed Notepaper
(or state name of Owners)

Specimen Letter of Instruction to Agents

mv................
at................
Date..............

To (Agents)

Dear Sirs

I hereby confirm that you have authority to sign bills of lading on my behalf in strict conformity with mate's or tally clerk's receipts signed by me or by the chief mate*, in respect only of the following cargo loaded at this port and said to be:

Please note that this authority is non-transferable, and that you do not have authority to sign any bill of lading which does not specifically incorporate the terms, conditions and exceptions of the charterparty dated .... and/or the Hague Rules (or rules having a similar effect).

The charterers' instructions/charterparty governing this voyage stipulate that the port of discharge will be .... The destination shown on the bills of lading must be consistent with this provision.

Please ensure that all bills are properly dated.

"Freight prepaid" bills are not to be issued unless expressly authorised by my owners.

Do not hesitate to refer to my owners on this or any other matter concerning the issuance of bills of lading.

Yours faithfully

Master

Signature of any nominated signatory:

Signed for receipt:

*Delete when the cargo is a bulk cargo for which no mate's or tally clerk's receipts have been issued.

MANAGEMENT LTD.

m.v. "......................"

At Sao Francisco Do Sul..

Date 8th July 1988

To: Agencia Maritima Ltda
Rua Almirante Guilhen, 2 - SALA 108
SAO FRANCISCO DO SUL
S.C.
BRAZIL

Dear Sirs,

I hereby confirm that you have authority to sign Bills of Lading on my behalf in conformity with Mates receipts, in respect of the following cargo loaded at this port and said to be:

APPROX 24530 M/T

SOYA BEAN MEAL PELLETS, IN BULK

Please note that you do not have authority to sign any Bill of Lading which does not specifically incorporate the terms, conditions and exceptions of the Charter Party dated 29th June 1988 .... and/or the Hague Rules (or legislation of similar effect).

The destination shown in the Bills of Lading should be consistent with the provisions of the Charter Party governing this voyage/Charterers' instructions, which stipulate that the vessel will discharge at BANDAR ABBAS or BANDAR SHAH BAHAR

Please ensure that all bills are properly dated.

On no account should "freight prepaid" bills be issued without the express authority of my Owners, to whom you should refer on this and any other matter concerning the signing and issuing of Bills of Lading.

Yours faithfully,

MASTER
S.F. Williams

PORT OF REG:
OFFICIAL No:
GROSS TONNAGE:
NETT TONNAGE:

BM6D

Page 2

Shipper:

CEVAL AGRO INDUSTRIAL S.A.

BILL OF LADING B/L No.: 1

Islamic Republic of Iran Shipping Lines

Consignee:

"TO THE ORDER OF BANK SEPAH
TEHRAN IRAN"

Notify address: (carrier not to be responsible for failure to notify)
M/S GOVERNMENT TRADING CO FOR
SANDOGH OMRANEA MARATEA TEHRAN
ISLAMIC REPUBLIC OFF IRAN-185
SEPAHBOD GHARANI AVE TEHRAN 15 -
IRAN

•Local vessel: •from:

(Ocean) vessel: "RUBENS"

Port of loading: SÃO FRANCISCO DO SUL-BRAZIL

Port of discharge: "SEE BELOW"

•Final destination (if on-carriage):

Freight payable at: AS PER CHARTER PARTY

Number of original Bs/L: 4(FOUR)

PARTICULARS FURNISHED BY SHIPPER OF GOODS

Marks & Nos.:

Number and kind of packages; description of goods:

Gross weight kg

COPY NOT NEGOTIABLE

"BRAZILIAN SOYA BEAN MEAL
PELLETS IN BULK" 24.530.000 KGS

"CLEAN ON BOARD"

"FREIGHT PAYABLE AS PER CHARTER PARTY"

- CREDIT NR CA/415515/8
- SHIPMENT THROUGHT ISLAMIC REPUBLIC OF IRAN SHIPPING CO.
- UNDER WRITE: "SHERKATE BIMEH IRAN" TLX 214154

" ONE PORT OUT OF BANDAR CHAH BAHAR, BANDAR
ABBAS IN CHARTERERS OPTION"

Shipper's Ref.:

Freight and charges:

SHIPPED in apparent good order and condition unless otherwise specified on board the aforementioned vessel the goods described above (the particulars given being supplied by the Shipper and the measurement, weight, quantity, brand, contents, marks, numbers, quality and value being unknown to the carrier) for the carriage to the port of discharge or so near thereunto as she may safely go subject to the terms, conditions and exemptions of this Bill of Lading.

In accepting this Bill of Lading the Owners of the goods expressly accept and agree to all its stipulations on both pages, whether written, printed, stamped or otherwise incorporated, as fully as if they were all signed by the Owners of the Goods.

In WITNESS whereof the Master, Purser or Agent of the said vessel has signed the number of original Bills of Lading stated above, all of this tenor and date, one of which being accomplished, the others, stand void. One of the Bills of Lading must be given up, fully endorsed in exchange for the goods.

Place and date of issue: S.Frco.do Sul, 10 JUL 1988

for the Master:

Agência Maritima CARGONAVE Ltda.
ON BEHALF OF MASTER'S AUTHORITY

*) Applicable only when document used as a Through Bill of Lading

CONTI SINGAPORE. 06-09 '91 14:19 P.01

CONTINENTAL GRAIN (S) PTE. LTD.

ORIGINAL

332762

PRIMARY PRODUCTION DEPARTMENT
REPUBLIC OF SINGAPORE

PHYTOSANITARY CERTIFICATE

This is to certify that the plants or plant products described below have been inspected according to appropriate procedures and are considered to be free from quarantine pests, and practically free from other injurious pests; and that they are considered to conform with the current phytosanitary regulations of the importing country.

DESCRIPTION OF THE CONSIGNMENT

Name and Address of Exporter	Name and Address of Consignee
Continental Grain (S) Pte Ltd 10 Collyer Quay #07-09 Ocean Building Singapore 0104	Continental Grain Company 277 Park Avenue New York, N.Y. 10172
Number and Description of Packages 240,000 bags	Distinguishing Marks NIL
Quantity and Name of Produce Rice 12,000 tonnes	

Place of Origin	Name of Conveyance	Point of Entry
Pakistan	MV	Sierra Leone

Botanical Name (if required by importing country)	Date of Shipment
	4.7.91

DISINFESTATION AND/OR DISINFECTION TREATMENT

Date: Treatment:

Chemical: Concentration:

Duration and Temperature

ADDITIONAL DECLARATION

PRIMARY PRODUCTION SINGAPORE

Signature

LIOW CHIN CHOG

Name of Authorised Officer

6 Sep 91

Date of Issue

No liability shall attach to the Primary Production Department or to any officer or representative of the Department with respect to this Certificate
IT SHALL BE UNLAWFUL FOR ANY PERSON TO ALTER, DEFACE OR WRONGFULLY USE THIS CERTIFICATE

SENATOR THE HON. GARETH EVANS Q.C.

MINISTER FOR FOREIGN AFFAIRS AND TRADE
PARLIAMENT HOUSE
CANBERRA A.C.T. 2600

CUSTOMS (PROHIBITED EXPORTS) REGULATIONS
PERMISSION TO EXPORT

Permission No: 2

I, GARETH EVANS, Minister of State for Foreign Affairs and Trade, pursuant to Regulation 13CA of the Customs (Prohibited Exports) Regulations, hereby give permission to the Australian Wheat Board for the export from Australia to Iraq of the goods specified in Part 1 of the schedule hereto, subject to the conditions specified in Part 2 of the schedule hereto, for the reasons specified in Part 3 of the schedule hereto. This permission is Number 2 in a series of 18.

SCHEDULE - PART 1

Up to 65,000 tonnes of Australian Standard White Wheat to be supplied to the Grain Board of Iraq and for delivery to Aqaba Jordan, for road transport to Iraq. This shipment is part of a sale of 900,000 tonnes 10% more or less of wheat by the Australian Wheat Board to the Grain Board of Iraq, with shipments commencing in August 1991 and, with best endeavours, being completed on or about the end of 1991. The indicative specifications of the wheat are:

Test Weight (kg/hl)	78.0
Protein (N x 5.7 at 11% moisture)	9.5%
Moisture	12.0%
Foreign Material	1.0%

SCHEDULE - PART 2

This permission is granted upon the condition that the Australian Wheat Board shall notify the Department of Foreign Affairs and Trade of the name of the vessel which will carry the goods specified in Part 1 of this schedule before the exportation of the said goods.

SCHEDULE - PART 3

This permission is granted because the exportation from Australia to Iraq of the goods specified in Part 1 of this schedule does not infringe UN Security Council sanctions against Iraq.

Dated this 10th day of July 1991

GARETH EVANS
Minister of State for
Foreign Affairs and Trade

UNITED NATIONS  NATIONS UNIES

POSTAL ADDRESS—ADRESSE POSTALE UNITED NATIONS, N.Y. 10017
CABLE ADDRESS—ADRESSE TELEGRAPHIQUE UNATIONS NEWYORK

REFERENCE: SECURITY COUNCIL COMMITTEE ESTABLISHED BY RESOLUTION 661 (1990) CONCERNING THE SITUATION BETWEEN IRAQ AND KUWAIT

30 December 1991

Sir,

On behalf of the Security Council Committee established by resolution 661 (1990) concerning the situation between Iraq and Kuwait, I have the honour to acknowledge receipt of your letter dated 23 December 1991 stating that the shipments of wheat to Iraq, of which you notified the Committee in your letter dated 11 July 1991 and which were originally scheduled to take place by the end of December 1991, will now continue into 1992.

I have the honour to confirm that, according to paragraph 20 of Security Council resolution 687 (1991), the Committee has been duly notified of the shipment of foodstuffs specified in your letter and that prohibitions against the sale or supply of these shipments and financial transactions related thereto contained in resolution 661 (1990) are no longer applicable.

Further, I have the honour to suggest that your Government ensure that copies of this communication are provided to shipping companies for onward transmission to the captains of merchant vessels engaged in the shipment of the specified goods destined for Iraq.

Accept, Sir, the assurances of my highest consideration.

Abelardo Posso Serrano
Vice-Chairman
Security Council Committee established
by resolution 661 (1990) concerning the

His Excellency
Mr. Peter Wilenski
Ambassador Extraordinary and Plenipotentiary
Permanent Representative of Australia
to the United Nations
Permanent Mission of Australia to the
United Nations
One Dag Hammarskjöld Plaza
885 Second Avenue, 16th Floor
New York, N.Y. 10017

44-005

REPUBLIQUE DE GUINEE

MINISTERE DE L'INDUSTRIE
DU COMMERCE
ET ARTISANAT

D.G.C.E. / BUREAU KAMSAR

N° 039 / CO/DGCE /BK/ 93

Kamsar, le 30/3/93

CERTIFICATE OF ORIGIN

We, the undersigned, (Bureau du Commerce extérieur Kamsar)
Certify that the merchandise described below is a product of REPUBLIC OF GUINEA, West Africa -

1) DESCRIPTION OF GOODS : BOKE BAUXITE

2) VESSEL :

3) CROSS WEIGHT : 53388 metric tons Load N° 93057

4) EXPORTER : CBC

5) LOADING PORT : KAMSAR

6) CONSIGNEE : COMALCO

7) PORT OF DISCHARGE : SAN CIPRIAN

SIGNATURE AND STAMP

SURINTENDANT EXPED. / LABO-CHIMIE
ABDOULAYE "SHIPLO" DIALLO

CBG/SHIPPING SUPERINTENDENT

BUREAU COMMERCE EXTERIEUR / KAMSAR

Australian Coal Association

BULK COAL CARGOES

DECLARATION BY SHIPPER

For the guidance of ships' masters in their application of the IMO Code of Safe Practice for Solid Bulk Cargoes

To the Master,

Vessel Name: [redacted]

Port of Loading: NEWCASTLE N.S.W

Commodity to be Shipped: WARKWORTH SEMI SOFT COKING COAL

Port(s) of Discharge: JAPANESE PORT(S)

CARGO CHARACTERISTICS

Transportable Moisture Limit

- [x] This commodity is not considered a cargo which may liquefy during the voyage.

OR

- [ ] This commodity may liquefy. The Transportable Moisture Limit is .... %
  The average moisture content of this cargo is .... %

Estimated Stowage Factor

........(Cubic metres/tonne) ....41....(Cubic Feet/ton)

Contractual Sizing

50mm x 0

Contractual Sulphur Content

.5% Percent

Special Precautions (Refer to the reverse side of this form)

- [ ] This cargo may be liable to emit significant amounts of methane

OR

- [x] This cargo is not considered liable to emit significant amounts of methane

- [ ] This cargo may be liable to spontaneous combustion

OR

- [x] This cargo is considered not liable to spontaneous combustion

EMERGENCY PROCEDURES

For detailed procedures and special precautions, the Master should refer to the entry for Coal (IMO 010) of Appendix B of the IMO Code of Safe Practice for Solid Bulk Cargoes, an extract of which is reproduced on the reverse of this form.

It is certified that for the bulk coal cargo nominated on this certificate, reasonable care has been taken to ensure the relevant information attendant upon its marine transportation has been properly described and that the information given is based upon the latest available experience.

PATRICK SHIPPING AGENCIES PTY LIMITED NEWCASTLE N.S.W. AS AGENTS

Signature ....
By or on behalf of Master acknowledging receipt of the information

Signature [signed]
By or on behalf of WARKWORTH COAL SALES LIMITED
(Consignor)

Date 3.4.92

MASTER'S RESPONSE SHEET

GENERAL REQUIREMENTS SECTION 3-12/COAL ENTRY, B C CODE)

Vessel Name: ______________ Date of Loading ______________
Loadport: ______________ **Aprox. Tonnage:** ______________
Shipper: ______________ **Terminal:** ______________
Type/Name of Coal:

Cargo Specification Given on Shipper's Declaration

Moisture: ______________
Sulfur: ______________
Size: ______________

Additional Information Given on Shipper's Declaration

Special Precautions Indicated by Shipper: ☐ **Coals Emitting Methane** ☐ **Self-Heating Coals**

If behaviour of Coal has differed from above, note below and return to contact address given on Shipper's Declaration.

Commentary on Behavior of Coal During Voyage:

Date: ______________ **Master' Signature:** ______________

CANADA

Empire Shipping   Call Sign. 3EBW4

CERTIFICATE OF FITNESS TO PROCEED TO SEA / **CERTIFICAT D'APTITUDE À PRENDRE LA MER**

GRAIN CONCENTRATES OR A DECK CARGO OF TIMBER / **GRAINS CONCENTRES OU D'UNE PONTÉE DE BOIS**

MV – ~~N.M.~~ Virginia.	P.R. – P.I. Panama.

PORT OF ISSUE – PORT DE DÉLIVRANCE	DATE	TIME – HEURE
New Westminster, B.C.	June 16, 1993	15:00 P.M

ISSUED PURSUANT TO THE CANADA SHIPPING ACT FOR A SHIP WHOLLY OR PARTLY LOADED WITH **GRAIN***, **CONCENTRATES*** OR A **DECK CARGO OF TIMBER***
*(DELETE AS APPROPRIATE)

DÉLIVRÉ EN VERTU DE LA LOI SUR LA MARINE MARCHANDE DU CANADA À UN NAVIRE TOTALEMENT OU PARTIELLEMENT CHARGÉE DE **GRAINS***, DE **CONCENTRÉS*** OU **D'UNE PONTÉE DE BOIS***.
*(BIFFER SELON LE CAS)

CARGO SPACE / ESPACE À CARGAISON	PARTICULARS OF CARGO, MANNER OF STOWAGE AND SECURING / DETAILS RELATIFS À LA CARGAISON, MÉTHODE D'ARRIMAGE ET D'ASSUJETTISSEMENT
All Hatches. on Deck.	3491 M. Tons of log timber loaded on board deck Compactly stowed and secured with 19 m.m. dia. chains spaced at 3 meters, wiggle wire, etc. and access Catwalk from accommodation to Focsle for pilot provided.

CONCENTRATES / CONCENTRÉS	F.M.P. / P.D.A. ▶	T.M.L. / L.E.H.T. ▶	M.C. / T.E.H. ▶	OPTIONAL INFORMATION WHICH MAY BE NOTED BY THE PORT WARDEN / RENSEIGNEMENTS QUI PEUVENT ÊTRE NOTÉS PAR LE GARDIEN DE PORT	
DRAFTS / TIRANT D'EAU	FORWARD / AVANT	9.65 meters		TOTAL CARGO LOADED THIS PORT / TOTAL CARGAISON CHARGÉE AU PORT	3491 M. Tons.
	AFT / ARRIÈRE	10.2 "		OTHER CARGO ON BOARD / AUTRE CARGAISON À BORD	Logs Under Deck ~~2041~~ 14873. on deck 5599
	MIDSHIP / MILIEU	9.925 "		FUEL OIL / MAZOUT	969.18 Tons. Diesel 78.81
FREE BOARD / FRANC-BORD				FRESH WATER / EAU DOUCE	164 Tons.
WATER DENSITY / DENSITÉ DE L'EAU	1.0165			BALLAST / LEST	2300 Tons.
F.W.A. / A.E.D.				CONSTANT / CONSTANTE	121
SEASONAL DRAFT / TIRANT D'EAU SAISONNER	S. / E. — L.S. / B.E.	W. / H. — L.W. / B.H.	WNA / HAN — LWNA / BHAN	G.M. – H.M. 68 Cms.	OTHER / AUTRE — TOTAL DEADWEIGHT / TOTAL PORT EN LOURD: 27599.99 Tons.

I HEREBY CERTIFY THAT INSOFAR AS THE STOWAGE OF THE CARGO IN THE ABOVE VESSEL CONFORMS WITH THE APPROPRIATE REGULATIONS OR APPROVED PRACTICE, THE VESSEL IS FIT TO PROCEED TO SEA.

THIS IS NOT A CERTIFICATE OF SEAWORTHINESS

LE SOUSSIGNÉ ATTESTE PAR LES PRÉSENTES QUE LE NAVIRE EST APTE À PRENDRE LA MER AU POINT DE VUE DE LA CONFORMITÉ DE L'ARRIMAGE DE SA CARGAISON AUX EXIGENCES DU RÈGLEMENT PERTINENT OU À LA PRATIQUE APPROUVÉE.

LES PRÉSENTES NE CONSTITUENT PAS UN CERTIFICAT DE NAVIGABILITÉ

BUT MAY BE USED TO OBTAIN A CLEARANCE TO: / MAIS PEUT ÊTRE UTILISÉ POUR OBTENIR UN CONGÉ À: ▶ Tomakomai, Japan

B Warnd

SIGNATURE OF PORT WARDEN – SIGNATURE DU GARDIEN DE PORT

Canadian Coast Guard / Garde côtière canadienne   Canada

82-0501 (04-90)

DISTRIBUTION ▶ 1. SHIP'S COPY – COPIE DU NAVIRE 2. CUSTOM COPY – COPIE DE LA DOUANE 3. DOCK COPY – COPIE DU PORT 4. FILE COPY – COPIE POUR LE DOSSIER

Certificate of readiness to load — *Appendix 14.13*

CANADA

PORT WARDEN REPORT
CERTIFICATE OF READINESS TO LOAD

RAPPORT DU GARDIEN DE PORT
CERTIFICAT DE NAVIRE PRÊT À CHARGER

MV – N.M. [redacted]	P.R. – P.I. [redacted]	
PORT OF ISSUE – PORT DE DÉLIVRANCE: SEPT-ILES	DATE: Nov 17th 91	TIME – HEURE: 16:25

CARGO SPACE / ESPACE À CARGAISON	PARTICULARS OF CARGO, MANNER OF STOWAGE AND SECURING / DÉTAILS RELATIFS À LA CARGAISON, MÉTHODE D'ARRIMAGE ET D'ASSUJETTISSEMENT
	To be loaded, stowed and trimmed in accordance with the Code of Safe Practice For Solid Bulk Cargoes – Vessel to be loaded with appr. 59000 mT of iron ore concentrate as per attached stowage plan and loading sequence – – Not to be loaded beyond winter load line – Stresses must remain within limits at all time.

I HEREBY CERTIFY THAT THE ABOVE CARGO SPACES WHEREIN IT IS INTENDED TO LOAD ~~GRAIN~~*, CONCENTRATES* OR ~~A DECK CARGO OF TIMBER*~~ HAVE BEEN INSPECTED AND THAT THE REQUIREMENTS OF THE APPROPRIATE REGULATIONS OR APPROVED PRACTICE HAVE BEEN COMPLIED WITH.

LE SOUSSIGNÉ ATTESTE PAR LES AIRES DESTINÉES À RECEVOIR DES ~~GRAINS~~*, DES CONCENTRÉS*, OU ~~DU BOIS EN PONTÉE~~*, ONT ÉTÉ INSPECTÉES ET QU'ELLES SONT CONFORMES AUX EXIGENCES DU RÈGLEMENT PERTINENT OU À LA PRATIQUE APPROUVÉE

*(DELETE AS APPROPRIATE – BIFFER SELON LE CAS)

ISSUED CONDITIONALLY UPON THE METACENTRIC HEIGHT BEING MAINTAINED AT NOT LESS THAN	DÉLIVRÉ SOUS RÉSERVE QUE LA HAUTEUR MÉTACENTRIQUE SOIT GARDÉE À AU MOINS	— ft./ins./cm. – pi./po./cm.	SIGNATURE OF PORT WARDEN / SIGNATURE DU GARDIEN DE PORT	[signature]

82-0522 (05-90)

Canadian Coast Guard / Garde côtière canadienne

DISTRIBUTION: 1. SHIP'S COPY – COPIE DU NAVIRE 2. DOCK COPY – COPIE DU PORT 3. AGENT'S COPY – COPIE DE L'AGENT 4. FILE COPY – COPIE POUR LE DOSSIER

Canada

Certificate of loading — *Appendix 14.14*

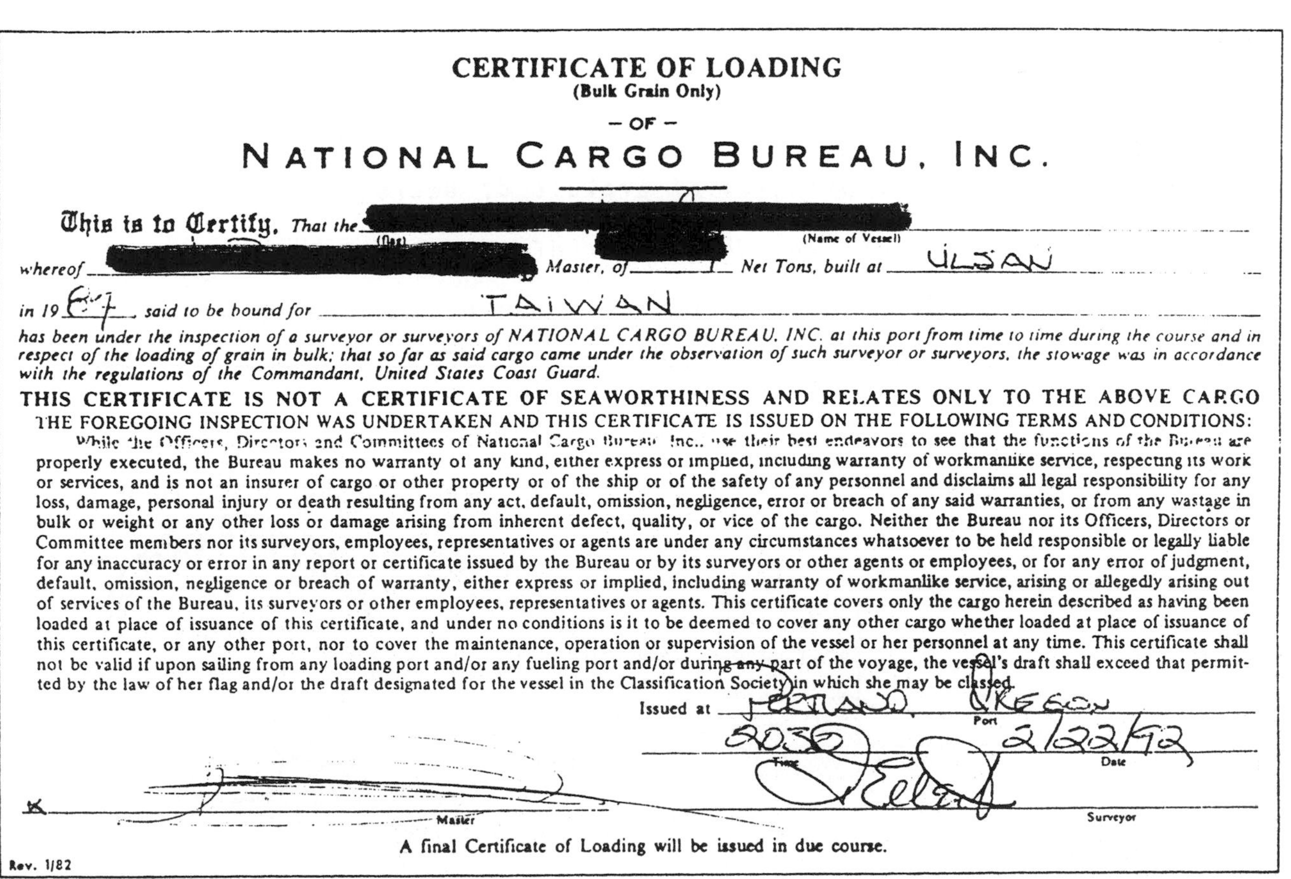

CERTIFICATE OF LOADING
(Bulk Grain Only)
– OF –
NATIONAL CARGO BUREAU, INC.

This is to Certify, *That the* [redacted] (Flag) [redacted] (Name of Vessel)
whereof [redacted] *Master, of* ______ *Net Tons, built at* ULSAN
*in 19*87 *said to be bound for* TAIWAN
has been under the inspection of a surveyor or surveyors of NATIONAL CARGO BUREAU, INC. at this port from time to time during the course and in respect of the loading of grain in bulk; that so far as said cargo came under the observation of such surveyor or surveyors, the stowage was in accordance with the regulations of the Commandant, United States Coast Guard.

THIS CERTIFICATE IS NOT A CERTIFICATE OF SEAWORTHINESS AND RELATES ONLY TO THE ABOVE CARGO

THE FOREGOING INSPECTION WAS UNDERTAKEN AND THIS CERTIFICATE IS ISSUED ON THE FOLLOWING TERMS AND CONDITIONS:

While the Officers, Directors and Committees of National Cargo Bureau, Inc., use their best endeavors to see that the functions of the Bureau are properly executed, the Bureau makes no warranty of any kind, either express or implied, including warranty of workmanlike service, respecting its work or services, and is not an insurer of cargo or other property or of the ship or of the safety of any personnel and disclaims all legal responsibility for any loss, damage, personal injury or death resulting from any act, default, omission, negligence, error or breach of any said warranties, or from any wastage in bulk or weight or any other loss or damage arising from inherent defect, quality, or vice of the cargo. Neither the Bureau nor its Officers, Directors or Committee members nor its surveyors, employees, representatives or agents are under any circumstances whatsoever to be held responsible or legally liable for any inaccuracy or error in any report or certificate issued by the Bureau or by its surveyors or other agents or employees, or for any error of judgment, default, omission, negligence or breach of warranty, either express or implied, including warranty of workmanlike service, arising or allegedly arising out of services of the Bureau, its surveyors or other employees, representatives or agents. This certificate covers only the cargo herein described as having been loaded at place of issuance of this certificate, and under no conditions is it to be deemed to cover any other cargo whether loaded at place of issuance of this certificate, or any other port, nor to cover the maintenance, operation or supervision of the vessel or her personnel at any time. This certificate shall not be valid if upon sailing from any loading port and/or any fueling port and/or during ~~any~~ part of the voyage, the vessel's draft shall exceed that permitted by the law of her flag and/or the draft designated for the vessel in the Classification Society in which she may be classed.

Issued at PORTLAND, OREGON (Port)
2030 (Time) 2/22/92 (Date)

[signature] Master — [signature] Surveyor

A final Certificate of Loading will be issued in due course.

Rev. 1/82

FUMIGATION AND GÁS CERTIFICATE NO 040/88

THIS IS TO CERTIFY, in witness of aproval the terms requested and submitted by L.FIGUEIREDO S/A.-Administração Despachos Representações, registered in the Division of Vegetal Sanitary Defense of Agriculture ' Brasilia, under number 1212750005, hereby certify that in this Superintendence of Vegetal Sanitary Defense (PODEF) of the Ministry of Agriculture, S.Frco.doSul-State StªCatarinaBrazil, at 1130 hours on the 10 JULHO, 1.988, after duly inspected and convenient prepared, the holds nos. 1 / 2 / 3 / 4 / 5 / 6 / / / / / / /, of the vessel 'RUBENS' loaded with PELLETS IN BULK by several shippers, have been fumigated by the process of Methyl Bromid gas (CH3Br) and Chloropicrin 2% (two pct) in the dosage of 50 grames per cubic metre on the total cubic space of such holds during 72 hours of exposure ' and under the permanent supervision of Agronomist Engineers of this Superintendence of Vegetal Sanitary Defense (PODEF) of Ministry of Agriculture- São Francisco do Sul, SC.

Due to the necessity of vessel sailing, as it can not stay moored in port or at anchorage waiting for expiry of the period of the gas, and in accordance with the paragraf of article 8º Decree 675/60 issued by the Ministry of Agriculture, the Master of the above mentioned vessel hereby commits himself to make the exaustion during the voyage, after expiring 72 hours of exposure only, at 1130 hours on the 10 JULY OF 1.988.

Agronomist Engineer. Executive Principal of PODEF in São Francisco do Sul

M.V. RUBENS
PORT OF REG: HAMILTON
OFFICIAL No: 366308
GROSS TONNAGE: 17965.73

In accordance ____________ Master

POSTO DE EXPURGO
L. FIGUEIREDO S.
D.D. SAN. VEGETAL

2

Control Union

GESELLSCHAFT FÜR WARENKONTROLLE mbH & Co. KG
Sworn Cargo Superintendents and Samplers
Technical Inspections and Analysis

WEIGHT- AND QUALITY-
CERTIFICATE No. [illegible]

Contract: Contract 5/85 Messrs. Andre & Cie. S.A.
Lausanne, Switzerland

Parcel: 9.000.000 kos. **YELLOW CORN**, in bulk
Crop 1984/1985

Vessel: M/V "[illegible]" - from Zadar to Tripoli

Sellers: Messrs. Andre & Cie. S.A.
Lausanne, Switzerland

Buyers: The General National Company for Flour Mills and
Tripoli/Libya

****

We, the undersigned **CONTROL UNION**, Gesellschaft für Warenko-
P.O. Box 15 03 26, 2800 **BREMEN / W. GERMANY**, certify that o,
of THE GENERAL NATIONAL COMPANY FOR FLOUR MILLS AND FODDER,
carried out the control of weight quality and inspection of
loading of a.m. parcel.

INSPECTION OF COMMODITY:

Inspection of the above mentioned parcel took place from July 27, 1985 until August 14, 1985.

SAMPLING:

Samples were drawn carefully mixed, sealed and analysed.

WEIGHING:

During our inspection the weight has been ascertained as 9.000 metric tons.

- 2 -

Control Union CERT. No. 8033/85 page - 2 -

26

continued from page - 1 -

ANALYSIS:

Specifications of YELLOW CORN

Physical Specifications:

Sound loyal merchantable yellow corn. Free from alive and dead insects, of natural odor and free from fermentation. Free from poisonous seeds and weeds not lumpy or rotten. Not treated with chemicals harmful to animal and poultry consumption. Crop 1984/1985.

Analytical Specifications:

Moisture:	13.34 %
Protein:	9.18 %
Fat:	3.22 %
Fibre:	2.90 %
Ash:	1.22 %
Sound grains:	91.20 %
Broken grains:	7.60 %
Foreign materials:	1.2[illegible] %

INSPECTION OF VESSEL:

The M/V " KRPAN " was nominated to carry this parcel and arrived at loading berth in Zadar on July 22, 1985 at 17:20 hours.

Details of vessel were ascertained as follows :

Name:	" KRPAN "
Flag:	Yugoslavia
Built:	1966
G.R.T.:	9.080.89 tons
N.R.T.:	5.122.76 tons
Deadweight:	14.499 tons
De-rate Certificate:	issued at Sibenik/Yugoslavia on May 16, 1985.

We carried out one inspection of holds regarding cleanliness, dryness and foreign smell, presence of living insects and residues of previous cargo.

The vessel has in total 6 holds / no tweendecks which were found clean, dry, free from foreign smell, presence of living insects and residues of previous cargo.

As we had no objections, loading started accordingly..

- 3 -

Control Union CERT. No. [illegible] page 3

continued from page - 2 -

LOADING OF VESSEL:

Loading commenced: July 27, 1985 at 11.00 hrs.
Loading completed: August 14, 1985 at 17.00 hrs.

This parcel was stowed as follows :

Hold 1	- YELLOW CORN, in bulk	297.745 kos.
Hold 2.	- YELLOW CORN, in bulk	2.116.541 kos.
Hold 3	- YELLOW CORN, in bulk	1.438.950 kos.
Hold 4		e m p t y
Hold 5	- YELLOW CORN, in bulk	2.650.125 kos.
Hold 6	- YELLOW CORN, in bulk	2.296.639 kos.
		9.000.000 kos.

B/L-DETAILS:

The B/L (Bill of Lading) for this parcel was issued as follows:

B/L - No. 1: dated August 13, 1985
Vessel sailed: August 14, 1985 at 20.00 hours.
For Destination: Tripoli / Libya
Expected time of arrival: August 18, 1985

Bremen, August 22, 1985

CONTROL UNION
Gesellschaft für Warenkontrolle mbH & Co. KG

[Stamp: CONTROL-UNION ... 28 Bremen 1 ... 150326]

This certificate does not release the parties concerned from their own contractual

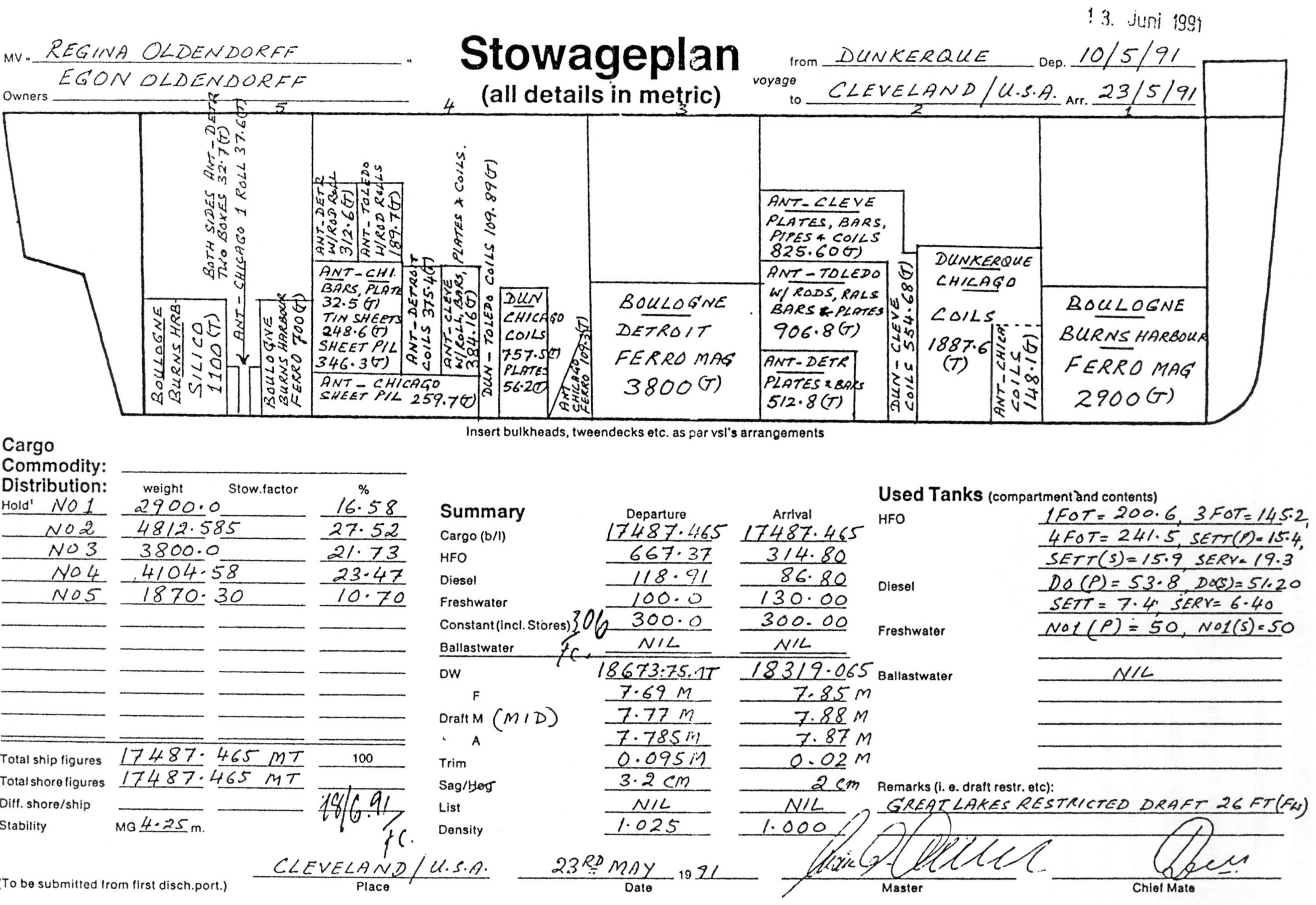

1 3. Juni 1991

Stowageplan

(all details in metric)

MV „ REGINA OLDENDORFF "

Owners EGON OLDENDORFF

voyage from DUNKERQUE Dep. 10/5/91

to CLEVELAND / U.S.A. Arr. 23/5/91

Insert bulkheads, tweendecks etc. as per vsl's arrangements

Cargo Commodity:

Distribution:

Hold[1]	weight	Stow.factor	%
NO 1	2900.0		16.58
NO 2	4812.585		27.52
NO 3	3800.0		21.73
NO 4	4104.58		23.47
NO 5	1870.30		10.70
Total ship figures	17487.465 MT		100
Total shore figures	17487.465 MT		
Diff. shore/ship			18/6.91 f.c.
Stability	MG 4.25 m.		

Summary

	Departure	Arrival
Cargo (b/l)	17487.465	17487.465
HFO	667.37	314.80
Diesel	118.91	86.80
Freshwater	100.0	130.00
Constant (incl. Stores) 306 f.c.	300.0	300.00
Ballastwater	NIL	NIL
DW	18673.75.1T	18319.065
Draft M (MID) F	7.69 M	7.85 M
M	7.77 M	7.88 M
A	7.785 M	7.87 M
Trim	0.095 M	0.02 M
Sag/~~Hog~~	3.2 CM	2 cm
List	NIL	NIL
Density	1.025	1.000

Used Tanks (compartment and contents)

HFO	1FOT = 200.6, 3FOT = 145.2, 4FOT = 241.5, SETT(P) = 15.4, SETT(S) = 15.9, SERV = 19.3
Diesel	DO(P) = 53.8, DO(S) = 51.20, SETT = 7.4, SERV = 6.40
Freshwater	NO1(P) = 50, NO1(S) = 50
Ballastwater	NIL

Remarks (i. e. draft restr. etc): GREAT LAKES RESTRICTED DRAFT 26 FT (FW)

CLEVELAND / U.S.A.	23RD MAY 1991	[signature]	[signature]
Place	Date	Master	Chief Mate

(To be submitted from first disch.port.)

STOWAGE PLAN

Agência Marítima CARGONAVE Ltda.

M. V. " R U B E N S " - VOY. 1-1734

SAILED FROM S. F. S. ON JULY 10th, 1988.

LOADED: 24.530.000 KGS BRAZILIAN SOYA BEAN MEAL PELLETS IN BUL

SHIPPER: CEVAL AGRO INDUSTRIAL S/A.

DESTINATION: "ANY IRANIAN SOUTHERN PORTS"

ARRIVAL DRAFT: FWD 03,98 Mts AFT 05,72 Mts

SAILING DRAFT: FWD 09,46 Mts AFT 09,63 Mts

HOLD	CUBIC FEET	STOWAGE FACTOR
1	151.497	55.3
2	198.483	51.9
3	261.167	52.3
4	203.281	54.0
5	260.810	52.8
6	225.064	52.5

6	5	4	3	2	1
4.281.765 KGS SBMPELLETS, IN BUIK. FULL.	4.938.505 KGS SBMPELLETS, IN BUIK. FULL.	3.750.655 KGS SBMPELLETS, IN BUIK. FULL.	4.990.245 KGS SBMPELLETS, IN BUIK. FULL.	3.824.335 KGS SBMPELLETS, IN BUIK. FULL.	2.735.495 KGS SBMPELLETS, IN BUIK. FULL.

Stowage plan (showing cargo separations)

OCT 1 1991

M/V ERIKSVANN VOYAGE 17

CHARTERER WEYERHAEUSER CO
SUB-CHARTERER
AGENTS SUNRISE SHIPPING
STEVEFORES TWIN HARBOR-SSA
CAPTAIN A.R. TINSLEY
CHIEF OFFICER S.E GINER
SUPERCARGO GENE EVERSON

ARRIVED AT ABERDEEN 9-22-91 AT 1240 HRS
COMM LOADING 9-23-91 AT 0800 HRS
COMPLETE LOAD 9-27-91 AT 0930 HRS
FIRST LOG 9-23-91 1100
LAST LOG 9-27-91 0910
FINISH LASHING 9-27-91 1400
SAILED FOR NAOETSU, JAPAN
ON 9-28-91 AT 1300 HRS

DISCH PORT	NO. 1	NO. 2	NO. 3	NO. 4	ON DECK	TOTAL FBM	PIECES
NAOETSU-KOB					724540	724,540	4685
NAOETSU-C.I					484,650	484,650	2531
NAOETSU-C.I	38,890	94 350	98 000	90270		321 510	2570
NANAO-HAY	216 140	290,000	275 390	277 030		1,058,530	9653
TSURUGA-KOB	234 160	224,910	210,070	340,000		1,009,140	3765
TOTALS	489,190	609 260	583,460	707,270	1209190	3,598,370	23204

ON DECK 1 209 190 SCRIB. 5832 TONS 7 216 PIECES
BELOW DECK 2389,180 SCRIB. 11 470 TONS 15988 PIECES
TOTAL CARGO 3,598,370 SCRIB. 17 302 TONS 23 204 PIECES
STOW FACTOR 441.1 WEIGHT FACTOR 4.8

BY DRAFT CHECK NAOETSU
DK. CARGO · 5900 M/T

CARGO RATIO
DECK/HOLD
WEIGHT 50.8%
VOLUME 50.6%
487,315 CF

On deck:

NAOETSU-KOB
L-10A 860 Pcs FIR 108,360 FBM
L-9 419 Pcs SS 2 FIR 143,780 FBM B/OFF
L-13 A/B 1269 Pcs SC 6 HEM 150,730 FBM
L-12 967 Pcs SL③ HEM 114,550 FBM B/OFF
L-11 879 Pcs SL FIR 109,180 FBM B/OFF
— PURPLE — ROPE —
NAOETSU-C.I.
L-18 497 Pcs SC6 FIR
63,720 FBM B/OFF
— GREEN —
L-8 291 Pcs RS 1 FIR 97,940 FBM B/OFF
— PURPLE — ROPE — PURPLE — ROPE — PURPLE — ROPE — PURPLE —
L-19 600 Pcs IS 25 FIR 193 730 FBM B/OFF
L-14 300 Pcs SS 2 FIR 97 870 FBM B/OFF
L-17A 1134 Pcs SC 6 FIR 129,330 FBM

SAILING CONDITIONS
FUEL IFO 1157 M/T
MDO 120
FWATER 419
CONSTANTS 200
BALLAST 2921
CARGO 17302
TOTAL 22119 M/T

DECK HEIGHTS
1. 7.02 m
2. 7.62 m
3. 7.67 m
4. 7.66 m

1053 824 CF

4	3	2	1
NAOETSU-C.I. L-15 A/B 702 Pcs SL 3 FIR 90,270 FBM — GREEN — NANAO-HAY L-7 A/B 2543 Pcs SC 6 FIR 277,000 FBM — WHITE — ROPE — ORANGE TSURUGA-KOB L-4 447 Pcs GC $15 FIR 164,000 FBM B/OFF L-2 535 Pcs SS 2 FIR 176,000 FBM B/OFF	NAOETSU-C.I. L-15 A/B 762 Pcs SL 3 FIR 98,000 FBM — GREEN — NANAO-HAY L-7 A/B 2543 Pcs SC 6 FIR 275,390 FBM — WHITE — ROPE — TSURUGA-KOB L-4 344 Pcs GC $15 FIR 126,350 FBM B/OFF L-2 254 Pcs SS 2 FIR 83 720 FBM B/OFF	NAOETSU-C.I. L-17 196 Pcs SC6 FIR 22,350 FBM — PURPLE — L-16 591 Pcs SL 3 FIR 72 000 FBM B/OFF — GREEN — NANAO-HAY L-7 A/B 2692 Pcs SC 6 FIR 290,000 FBM — WHITE — ROPE — TSURUGA-KOB L-4 370 Pcs GC $15 FIR 136 000 FBM B/OFF L-5 715 Pcs SC 6 FIR 88,910 FBM	NAOETSU-C.I. L-16 319 Pcs SL 3 FIR B/OFF 38,890 FBM — GREEN — NANAO-HAY L-6 A/B 1875 Pcs SL 3 FIR 216,140 FBM — ORANGE — ROPE — L-3 A/B 640 Pcs SL 3 FIR 77,830 FBM L-1 460 Pcs RS 1 FIR 156,330 FBM B/OFF
276 841 CF	275 757 CF	275 635 CF	225 591 CF

CUBIC SPACE PER HOLD: 276 841 CF | 275 757 CF | 275 635 CF | 225 591 CF

SAILING DRAFT FWD 9.49 AFT 9.60 MEAN 9.545 GM 72 GoM 40 ROLL PERIOD 23 SECONDS

FORM 283913 1/90 Printing Service TP-1 Tacoma

DENSITY - 1008 = 9.395W - 27870 D/PLACE
5800 LT SHIP
22070 KT

gencia Maritima CARGONAVE Ltda.

M A N I F E S T

NATIONALITY	NAME OF SHIP	VOY.No.	NET TONS	MASTER NAME	FROM	TO	SHEET
BRITISH	RUBENS	JULY	11236	WILLIAMS STEPHEN	SAO FRANCISCO DO SUL	ONE PORT OUT OF BANDAR CHAH BAHAR, BANADAR ABBAS IN CHARTERERS OPTION	1

B/L No.	SHIPPER	CONSIGNEE	MARKS AND NUMBERS	C O N T E N T S	GROSS/WEIGHT KILOS	FREIGHT
1	CEVAL AGRO INDUSTRIAL S.A.	TO THE ORDER OF BANK SEPAH TEHRAN IRAN.	IN BULK	BRAZILIAN SOYA BEAN MEAL PELLETS IN BULK	24530000	PAYABLE AS PER CHARTER PARTY
				T O T A L	24530000	

SAO FRANCISCO DO SUL , JULY 09TH [illegible]

AGENCIA MARITIMA CARGONAVE LTDA.

PACIFIC SHIPPING SERVICES, INC.

TO: United States Coast Guard
Long Beach / Los Angeles

Date: 05-06-92

In compliance with section 148.02-1 USCG Regulations, we provide the following in reference to the cargo being loaded for shipment aboard the M/V ____________ Official #
Nationality: ________

1) Petroleum coke, uncalcined ORM-C
2) Approx. Metric Tons
3) Shipper: Applied Industrial Materials Corp.
100 First Stamford Place
Stamford, CT. 06904-2388 (24HR) 310 436-5235

This is to certify that the above named hazardous material is properly named, prepared, and otherwise in proper condition for bulk shipment by vessel in accordance with the applicable regulations of the U.S. Coast Guard.

DANGEROUS CARGO MANIFEST

PETROLEUM COKE, UNCALCINED ORM-C

HOLD #	QUANTITY
____	________ METRIC TONS
2	8600 METRIC TONS
3	8700 METRIC TONS
____	________ METRIC TONS
5	8800 METRIC TONS
6	8570 METRIC TONS
____	________ METRIC TONS
TOTAL ON BOARD:	________ METRIC TONS

For AIMCOR
Pacific Shipping Services, inc.

Master M/V

200 Oceangate, Suite 530, Long Beach, California 90802
PH (310) 436-6221 FAX (310) 436-4433 TLX 140424

0730E

MATERIAL SAFETY DATA SHEET

MSDS # 3013

TOSCO CORPORATION
10100 SANTA MONICA BLVD.
LOS ANGELES, CALIFORNIA 90067

24 HOUR EMERGENCY ASSISTANCE
TOSCO:
CHEMTREC: 800-424-9300

SECTION I — GENERAL INFORMATION

TRADE NAME AND SYNONYMS: Coke

CHEMICAL NAME AND SYNONYMS: Coke

FORMULA: Carbon and hydrocarbons

CAS#: 64741-79-3

MATERIAL HAZARD:
FIRE HAZARD — RED
HEALTH HAZARD — BLUE
REACTIVITY — YELLOW
SPECIFIC HAZARD — WHITE

HAZARD RATING
0 ——→ 4
LEAST EXTREME

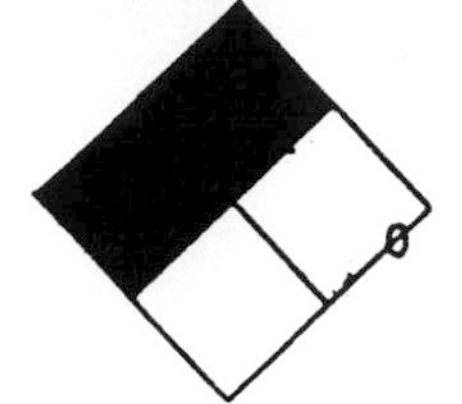

SECTION II — HAZARDOUS INGREDIENTS

COMPONENTS	%	OCCUPATIONAL EXPOSURE LIMITS
Solid carbonaceous material resulting from high temperature treatment of petroleum fractions. It contains some hydrocarbons having a high carbon-to-hydrogen ratio.	100	10 mg/M3 TWA (Cal-OSHA PEL - 1981)

SECTION III — HEALTH HAZARD INFORMATION

Petroleum coke does not present any unusual health hazards. Skin painting studies conducted by the American Petroleum Institute have found no evidence of tumorigenic activity. A chronic inhalation study initiated in August, 1981 has to-date shown no adverse effects.

ROUTE OF EXPOSURE	EFFECTS OF OVEREXPOSURE
EYE CONTACT	Solid particles can cause physical eye irritation.
SKIN CONTACT	
INHALATION	Inhalation of dust may lead to respiratory irritation; observe nuisance dust PEL of 10 mg/M3.
INGESTION	
SKIN ABSORPTION	

SECTION IV — EMERGENCY AND FIRST AID PROCEDURES

EYE CONTACT: Flush eyes with large amounts of low pressure water.

SKIN CONTACT: Wash with soap and water.

INHALATION: N.A.

INGESTION: N.A.

15 001 (11-82)

TLV — THRESHOLD LIMIT VALUE
PEL — PERMISSIBLE EXPOSURE LIMIT
L.T. — LESS THAN
N.D. — NOT DETERMINED
mg/M³ — MILLIGRAMS/CUBIC METER
ppm — PARTS PER MILLION
G.T. — GREATER THAN
TWA — TIME WEIGHTED AVERAGE
C — CEILING
S — SKIN

Page 1 of a two-page document

COTECNA SERVIÇOS LTDA.
Rua Riachuelo, 121 - 9.° Andar - Conj. 93
11100 - Santos - SP - Brasil
Tel.: (0132) 34-2982
Tlx.: (013) 1608 COTV BR

S.F. do Sul.. 10 07.88.

To the

MASTER M/V Rubens

In Port S. F. do Sul - Brasil

Dear Sirs:

This is to inform you that hatchs cover and manholes of the vessel have been sealed with nylon and plastic seal ' "COINS". As per figures below:

HOLD 1..9410999...STAR..................PORT..........................

MANHOLES..

HOLD 2..9723999...STAR..................PORT..........................

MANHOLES..

HOLD 3..[illegible]...STAR..................PORT..........................

MANHOLES..

HOLD 4..3038443...STAR..................PORT..........................

MANHOLES..

HOLD 5..9504009...STAR..................PORT..........................

MANHOLES..

HOLD 6 - 6971776.

MASTER/CHIEF OFFICER

COTECNA SERVIÇOS LTDA.

AGÊNCIA MARÍTIMA **CARGONAVE** LTDA

SAO FRANCISCO DO SUL, JULY 1988

VESSEL	:	RUBENS
TYPE	:	SELF TRIMMING BULK CARRIER
OWNERS	:	BOLTON MARITIME MANAGEMENT
CHARTERERS	:	ISLAMIC REPUBLIC OF IRAN SHIPPING LINES
CARGO	:	BRAZILIAN SOYA BEAN MEAL PELLETS IN BULK
NEXT PORT	:	PARANAGUA
DESTINATION	:	ANY IRANIAN SOUTHERN PORTS

SHIPPERS	QUANTITY	COMMODITY	BERTH
CEVAL AGRO IND. S/A	24530000 KGS	SBMPELLETS	COCAR

STATEMENT OF FACTS

VESSEL ARRIVED AT PILOT STATION	WEDNESDAY	06TH	0742 HRS
PILOT ON BOARD	WEDNESDAY	06TH	0742 HRS
DROPPED ANCHOR INNER PORT	WEDNESDAY	06TH	0912 HRS
NOTICE OF READINESS TENDERD	WEDNESDAY	06TH	0912 HRS
FREE PRATIQUE GRANTED	WEDNESDAY	06TH	1030 HRS
HOLDS CLEARED BY MINISTRY OF AGRICULTURE	WEDNESDAY	06TH	1030 HRS
NOTICE OF READINESS ACCEPTED	WEDNESDAY	06TH	1145 HRS
VESSEL BERTHED AT COCAR TERMINAL	WEDNESDAY	06TH	1530 HRS
COMMENCED LOADING	WEDNESDAY	06TH	1925 HRS
COMPLETED LOADING	SUNDAY	10TH	1115 HRS
COMPLETED FUMIGATION	SUNDAY	10TH	1130 HRS
VESSEL SAILED FOR PARANAGUA	SUNDAY	10TH	1200 HRS

-*-*-*-*-*-*-*-*-*-*-

RAIN PERIODS :

THURSDAY 07TH - 1700/1955 HRS
SATURDAY 09TH - 1455/2030 - 2105/2400 HRS
SUNDAY 10TH - 0000/0600 HRS

-*-*-*-*-*-*-*-*-*-*-

DAILY LOADING REPORT

WEDNESDAY	06TH	1530/1925	WAITING THE LOADING OPERATION
		/1925	COMMENCING LOADING
		1925/2400	LOADING - TOTAL LOADED 3028.190 KGS
THURSDAY	07TH	0000/1700	LOADING
		1700/1955	RAIN
		1955/2400	LOADING - TOTAL LOADED 10492.915 KGS
FRIDAY	08TH	0000/1700	LOADING
		1700/1900	NO WORKED - MEAL TIME
		1900/2400	LOADING - TOTAL LOADED 9080.830 KGS
SATURDAY	09TH	0000/0400	LOADING
		0400/0700	NO WORKED SHIFTING GANG
		0700/1130	LOADING
		1130/1255	TRIMMING CARGO
		1255/1350	LOADING
		1350/1445	TRIMMING CARGO
		1455/2030	RAIN
		2030/2105	TRIMMING CARGO
		2105/2400	RAIN - TOTAL LOADED 1655.150 KGS

M.V. RUBENS
PORT OF REGI HAMILTON
OFFICIAL No: 346308
GROSS TONNAGE: 17965.73
NETT TONNAGE: 11336.17

PARANAGUÁ · SÃO FRANCISCO DO SUL

AGÊNCIA MARÍTIMA **CARGONAVE** LTDA

SUNDAY 10TH - 0000/0600 - RAIN
0600/0700 - SHIFTING GANG
0700/1115 - LOADING
/1115 - COMPLETED LOADING: TOTAL LOADED: 242.915 KGS

-*-*-*-*-*-*-*-*-*-*-

BUNKERS ON ARRIVAL	F.O. 292 MT	D.O. 51 MT	FWATER 80 MT
BUNKERS ON SAILING	F.O. 292 MT	D.O. 42 MT	FWATER 50 MT

DRAFT ON ARRIVAL :	FWD 03,98 MTS	AFT 05,72 MTS
DRAFT ON SAILING :	FWD 09,46 MTS	AFT 09,63 MTS

-*-*-*-*-*-*-*-*-*-*-

MASTER mvRUBENS

AGENCIA MARITIMA CARGONAVE LTDA.
AS AGENTS

M.V. RUBENS
PORT OF REG: HAMILTON
OFFICIAL No: 366308
GROSS TONNAGE: 17965.73
NETT TONNAGE: 11236.17

Agência Marítima Laurits Lachmann S. A.
SÃO FRANCISCO DO SUL - SC

AGENCIA MARITIMA L. LACHMANN S.A

SUBJECT TO ALL TERMS CONDITIONS OF GOVERNING CHARTER PARTY

PARANAGUÁ · SÃO FRANCISCO DO SUL

Fig. 14.ACC

mv. . . . .
at. . . . .
Date. . . . .

To (Receivers)

Dear Sirs

Alleged Stoppages due to Crane Breakdown

I refer to the attached "Stoppage due to crane breakdown" sheet. This document, dated 17.8.88, refers to stoppages of ship's cranes Nos. 3 & 5 at hatches 4 & 6 on 17.8.88 from 0700 to 0930 hrs.

During this period, which occurred at the commencement of discharge, the cranes were being adjusted for height of travel, and the crane hooks and associated linkages were being removed. This was found to be necessary to compensate for the fact that the hoppers on the quayside, into which the cranes were required to discharge, were so high that the grabs could not enter them while the cranes were rigged in the normal manner.

In other words, the cranes had to be adjusted to suit the equipment on the quayside, and this took 2 5 hours.

If we had been warned whilst at anchor of the height of the hoppers we could have made these adjustments before berthing, and no time would have been lost on berthing.

I must inform you that neither my vessel nor owners can accept any responsibility for the delays incurred due to this matter, as the cranes in question were in normal working condition at all times during the period in question

Yours faithfully

Master

Fig. 14. ADD

Port. . . . .
Date. . . . .

To the Master

mv. . . . . (Own vessel)

Dear Sir

Empty Hold Certificate

I hereby confirm that holds Nos. have been completely discharged, and that no further cargo remains in them.

Yours faithfully

for the discharging stevedores.

Trimming certificate

Appendix 14.27.1

To the Master / ~~Ist Officier~~

S/S : _

Destination : Kenya

Commodity : EEC milling wheat in bulk – empty bags.

I being, Master / ~~Ist Officier~~ of the above mentioned vessel hereby agree that the trimming on the hold/Tween deck n° 1.2.3.4.5. has been made to my satisfaction.

Hold n°	1	2	3	4	5	6	7	8	9	Total
Tonnage	2538.560 Full	5026.155 Full	1857.000 Full	4970.330 Full	2718.405 Full	X	X	X	X	17510.355 (wheat)

Tween deck	1	2	3	4	5	6	7	8	9	Total
Tonnage			42.000 empty bags / 399.910 wheat in bulk			X	X	X	X	254.300 (Bags)

+ 1 pallet n° 178.

Rouen, date : The 02nd of November 1992

Signature : Master

MON C
PIRAEUS
LIBER

CAPITAINES-EXPERTS
ROUEN

CERTIFICATE OF LOADING/DISCHARGING
ZEN-NOH GRAIN STEVEDORES

M/V m/v AMAZON
VESSEL

10-01-2002
DATE

I HEREBY ACKNOWLEDGE THAT THE CARGO OF

US NO.2 YELLOW SOYBEANS

HAS BEEN PROPERLY LOADED, STOWED, TRIMMED AND SEPARATIONS LAID ACCORDING TO MY SPECIFICATIONS AND SATISFICATION.

NO SEPARATION OR TRIMMING REQUIRED

VESSEL'S CAPTAIN/CHIEF OFFICER

CLEAN BALLAST DISCHARGE PERMIT

Permit No. 162-92 Issue Date May 1, 1992

Expiration Date May 1, 1993

REQUEST OF: Vessel M/V [redacted], and her master, owner, operator, charterer, or agent

REQUEST FOR: DISCHARGING CLEAN BALLAST WATER

AT: 212 LB ON: MAY 7, 1992

Date Commence-Terminate 1800/7 - 0300/11

DISCHARGE FROM: (Check One) SBT's X TYPE OF BALLAST: SEA WATER

CBT's X LOADING PORT:

OTHER (SPECIFY)

REQUESTED BY: Name: A. R. MADLEM, OPERATIONS MANAGER

Company: GENERAL STEAMSHIP CORP., LTD - As Agents

Address: 302 W 5TH STREET, SUITE 101 SAN PEDRO, CA. 90731

Phone No.: (310) 832-0314

Signature: [signature]

Pursuant to request of the above vessel, her master, owner, agent, or permittee, discharge of CLEAN BALLAST WATER TANKS into the waters of the Long Beach Harbor District is authorized upon the following conditions:

1. Violation of the pollution or ballast regulations, Tariff No. 4, Item 748 and all other applicable Items; 33 CFR Part 157; and all other applicable federal, state, and local rules and regulations, shall result in a revocation of this permit.

2. Port Security must be notified at (213) 590-4185 of each intent to discharge clean ballast water 24 hours prior to the vessel's arrival.

3. Ballast may be discharged from ABOVE THE WATER LINE with a visible OUTFALL or BELOW THE WATER LINE. In all cases, an hourly check of discharge shall be made to ascertain the cleanliness thereof. Record of all checks and condition of discharge shall be kept during a vessel's stay in port and shall be posted at the gangway. The discharge location shall be designated by a bunting secured at the vessel's side at the main deck level directly over the discharge location, with sufficient illumination at night so that the water surface at the discharge point may be clearly seen. Where access is available, the master, prior to discharge of ballast, shall ensure that ballast is not discharged unless he finds that there is no oily mixture or other prohibited material after visually examining the top of the ballast contents of each tank or testing the ballast contents of each tank with an oil/water interfacedetector or other device. (Note: In certain situations Federal Regulations regarding tank vessels require constant visual monitoring.)

4. In the event that the discharged ballast water is not clean, and contains visible settleable solids, floating solids, oil sheen, or other visible residue, the vessel, her master, owners, charterers, operators managers, agents, or permittee shall immediately notify the Chief Wharfinger and desist from further discharge and at its or their cost, shall immediately remove or cause to be removed, such matter to the satisfaction of the Executive Director or designee, and if not immediately removed, the Executive Director or designee may cause the removal of such matter and invoice the parties mentioned above for the cost thereof, including interest at the maximum rate allowed by law from the date of the discharge, which shall be immediately due and payable. The enumerated parties shall also be liable as further set forth in Tariff No. 4, Item 748, copy of which is attached hereto and made a part hereof.

EXECUTIVE DIRECTOR
LONG BEACH HARBOR DEPARTMENT

[signature]

MUST BE POSTED AT GANGWAY

DJK RESEARCH CENTER INC.

DJK Ref. No. N9-0023

CERTIFICATION

DJK Research Center Inc., Testing Laboratory hereby certifies that the following product covered and manufactured by

NIPPON STEEL CHEMICAL CO., LTD., No. 13-16
Ginza 5-chome, Chuo-ku, Tokyo 104, Japan

complies with the specification outlined in Code of Federal Regulations (CFR), Title 21, Food and Drugs (By Food and Drug Administration, Department of Health and Human Services, USA), Section 175.300 (Resinous and Polymeric Coatings) and Section 177.1680 (Polyurethane Resins).

1. Uses: For Dry Solids

2. Product Covered: NB-COAT 3000GW

DJK Research Center Inc., Testing Laboratory certifies that a search was made under Code of Federal Regulations (CFR), Title 21, Parts 100-199 for NIPPON STEEL CHEMICAL CO., LTD., for the purpose of determining compliance of the above product under Section 175.300 "Resinous and Polymeric Coatings" and Section 177.1680 "Polyurethane Resins" for the safe use of such coating as an indirect food additive, and that said search revealed each component to be listed under Section 175.300 and 177.1680 for use as the food contact surface of articles intended for use under conditions prescribed in Section 175.300 and 177.1680.

Validity

This Certificate Report will be valid only for two(2) years after issuance of the Report. Any formulation change will forfeit validity of the Report.

Independent and third party

International Testing Laboratory

Date: July 29, 1990

Bolton Maritime Management

To: Agencia Maritime Laurits Lachmann
Racre 30
P.O. Box 1629
20.081 Rio de Jineiro
Brazil

Name of Vessel: M.V. "RUBENS"
Port of Sao Francisco do Sul
6th July 1988

NOTICE OF READINESS

Dear Sirs,

Please be advised of the arrival of the above vessel at the port of Sao Francisco do Sul at ......0912......... hrs today the 6th July 1988.

The vessel is in all respects ready to commence LOADING a full cargo of 24530 M/T ,of SOYA BEAN MEAL PELLETS in Bulk.

Time to commence in accordance with the terms and conditions of the Governing Charter Party

Please acknowledge receipt of this Notice ~~of Readiness~~ by signing and returning duplicate copies herewith.

Yours very truly,

....
S.F. Williams Master

M.V. RUBENS
PORT OF REG: HAMILTON
OFFICIAL No: 366308
GROSS TONNAGE: 17965.73
NETT TONNAGE: 11236.17

Received By:
AGÊNCIA MARÍTIMA LAURITS LACHMANN S.A.
SÃO FRANCISCO DO SUL — S. C.
....

per: ....

Date and Hour JULY 06th., 1988 AT 11:45 HOURS.

SUBJECT TO ALL TERMS CONDITIONS AND OR EXCEPTIONS OF THE GOVERNING CHARTER PARTY.

Form 130

NIPPON KAIJI KYOKAI

BC CODE FITNESS CERTIFICATE

No. XXXX

THIS IS TO CERTIFY that

M.S. "   "

Call Sign:

Port of Registry:

Gross Tonnage:

Class Number:

is fit for the carriage in bulk of all the materials listed in the appendices A and C of the Code of Safe Practice for Solid Bulk Cargoes and coal listed in the appendix B of the Code in all cargo holds in accordance with the provisions of the Code provided that the construction and equipment listed in the attached table are maintained in good order and that all relevant operational provisions of the Code including the following are observed:

1. Any cargo should be loaded and distributed in pursuant to information provided in the approved loading manual and the stability information booklet provided onboard the ship;
2. The nominal specific gravity of any cargo should not exceed the allowable value indicated in the loading manual; and
3. The moisture content of any material listed in the appendix A should not exceed the transportable moisture limit as defined in the Code.

This certificate remains valid until 13th June,   , the relevant requirements of the Code are amended or the interpretations of the requirements are changed, or the class assigned by the Society is withdrawn, whichever is earliest.

Issued at O   on 14th June, 2001 on behalf of the Government of

NIPPON KAIJI KYOKAI

This Report is issued subject to the condition that it is understood and agreed that neither the Society nor any of its Committees is under any circumstances whatever to be held responsible for any inaccuracy in any report or certificate issued by this Society or its Surveyors or in any entry in the Record or other publication of the Society or for any error of judgment, default or negligence of its Officers, Surveyors or Agents.

95. 7. 15000 (K)

DET NORSKE VERITAS

CERTIFICATE OF COMPLIANCE FOR THE CARRIAGE OF SOLID BULK CARGOES

Issued under the authority of the Government of:

_   _ _ _ _ _ _ _ _ _ _ _ _ _ _ _ _ _ _

Name of Ship	Signal Letters	Port of Registry	Gross Tonnage

This is to certify that:

The ship is suitable for the carriage of cargoes listed in Appendix A or C of IMO's "Code of Safe Practice for Solid Bulk Cargoes", Res. A.434 (XI) subject to the assumptions and conditions given in the "Appendix to Classification Certificate" being complied with.

The following limitations apply:

a) The following cargoes in Appendix A are excluded unless covered by a Certificate of Compliance, Appendix B Cargoes:

- Zink sulphide (consentrate)
- Cargoes listed under A.3.3

b) The moisture content of Appendix A cargoes is not to exceed the transportable moisture limit as defined by the Code or by and Administration.

c) When loading mineral concentrates reference is made to the entry "Metal Sulphide Concentrates" in Appendix B of the BC Code.

Place: _ Date of issue: 1998 _ _ _ _

DET NORSKE VERITAS AS

DET NORSKE VERITAS 1864

It is agreed that save as provided below Det Norske Veritas, its subsidiaries, bodies, officers, directors, employees and agents shall have no liability for any loss, damage or expense allegedly caused directly or indirectly by their mistake or negligence, breach of warranty, or any other act, omission or error by them, including gross negligence or wilful misconduct by any such person with the exception of gross negligence or wilful misconduct by the governing bodies or senior executive officers of Det Norske Veritas. This applies regardless of whether the loss, damage or expense has affected anyone with whom Det Norske Veritas has a contract or a third party who has acted or relied on decisions made or information given by or on behalf of Det Norske Veritas.* However, if any person uses the services of Det Norske Veritas or its subsidiaries or relies on any decision made or information given by or on behalf of them and in consequence suffers a loss, damage or expense proved to be due to their negligence, omission or default, then Det Norske Veritas will pay by way of compensation to such person a sum representing his proved loss.* In the event Det Norske Veritas or its subsidiaries may be held liable in accordance with the sections above, the amount of compensation shall under no circumstances exceed the amount of the fee, if any, charged for that particular service, decision, advice or information.* Under no circumstances whatsoever shall the individual or individuals who have personally caused the loss, damage or expense be held liable.* In the event that any provision in this section shall be invalid under the law of any jurisdiction, the validity of the remaining provisions shall not in any way be affected.

DET NORSKE VERITAS AS, VERITASVEIEN 1, N-1322 HØVIK, NORWAY, TEL. INT: +47 67 57 99 00, TELEFAX: +47 67 57 99 11
Form No.: 7SCB.102a Issue: January 96 Page 1 of 1

DET NORSKE VERITAS

Certificate No.: ·
DNV Id. No.:
IMO No.: 8·

CERTIFICATE OF COMPLIANCE FOR THE CARRIAGE OF DANGEROUS GOODS

Issued in pursuance of the provisions of paragraph 3 of Regulation 54 of Chapter II-2 of 1981 Amendments to the International Convention for Safety of Life at Sea, 1974 under the authority of the Government of:

by Det Norske Veritas AS.

Name M/S "!		Signal Letters I	Date on which keel was laid
Port of Registry	Gross Tonnage	Type of ship BULK CARRIER	

THIS IS TO CERTIFY:

1. That the construction and equipment of the above-mentioned ship have been found to comply with the provisions of Regulation 54 of Chapter II-2 of 1981 Amendments to the International Convention for the Safety of Life at Sea, 1974;
2. That the ship is suitable for carrying dangerous goods as specified overleaf on page 2, subject to any provisions in the International Maritime Dangerous Goods (IMDG) Code and the Code of Safe Practice for Solid Bulk Cargoes (BC Code) for individual substances also being complied with.
3. In respect of dangerous solid bulk cargoes, the cargo list also includes cargoes designated class MHB in the "Code of Safety Practice for Solid Bulk Cargoes" for which the vessel is suited.

Note Regulation 54 does not address for the carriage of dangerous goods of Classes 6.2 and 7 in bulk or packaged form, and carriage of dangerous goods in limited quantities, as defined in chapter 3,4 in the IMOG Code.

This Certificate is valid until

Place: Date of issue:

for Det Norske Veritas AS

DET NORSKE VERITAS * 1864 *

Head of Section

RENEWAL OF CERTIFICATE

THIS IS TO CERTIFY that at the periodical survey required for renewal of the Certificate, the ship was found to comply with the relevant provisions and that this Certificate is reinstated with validity until (max five months), pending the issuance of the new Certificate.

Place Date

Surveyor's signature Stamp

DET NORSKE VERITAS AS, VERITASVEIEN 1, N-1322 HØVIK, NORWAY, TEL INT: +47 67 57 99 00, TELEFAX: +47 67 57 99 11
Form No.: DG 47.71a Issue: April 2001 Page 1 of 4

Inspectorate Watson Gray (SA) Ltd
P O Box 10608
Jubail Industrial City - 31961
Email : 5584855@mcimail.com
Tel : (03) 361 3330
Fax : (03) 362 0065

Report No WGJBL/ 194 - 00

Vessel : STAR SEA COSMOS
Port : King Fahd Industrial Port, Al-Jubail
Product : Bulk Urea
Date : 11 MAY 2000

HATCH CLOSING CERTIFICATE

This is to confirm that the undersigned Surveyor of Inspectorate Watson Gray (Saudi Arabia) Ltd has observed the closing of the vessel's hatches after loading and prior to the vessel sailing from the berth.

The sealing devices, rubbers, tarpaulins, locking bars and/or other devices pertinent to the Vessel's construction appeared to be adequate for the prevention of any ingress of water under normal circumstances. We make no guarantee as to the watertightness of any hatch closure.

Any diversion or abnormality from the above statements is noted below.

The following hatches were seen to be securely closed on completion of loading and prior to the vessel sailing from the berth:-

Hatch # 2, 3 + 5

The following hatches were considered not fully secure at the time of sailing from the berth:-

Hatch # ______

Reason for abnormality ______

Certificate issued at : 1000 hrs 11 MAY 2000

STAR SEA COSMOS

For vessel (Chief Officer/Master)

Date :

For and on behalf of
Inspectorate Watson Gray (SA) Ltd

Revised Guidelines to the Master for Avoiding Dangerous Situations in Adverse Weather and Sea Conditions – A digest of IMO MSC.1/Circ.1228

For a full understanding of the dangers of ship motions in adverse weather the IMO Circular should be read

1. General
For the purposes of this document 'adverse weather' includes wind induced waves or heavy swell, with breaking crests.

Different ships have different dimensions, different stability characteristics and travel at different speeds. As a consequence different weather conditions are dangerous for them.

The wave period T_W: the time in seconds between two wave crests passing the same point, such as the foam from the first crest.

The wave length λ: in metres is determined either by visual observation in comparison with the ship length or by reading the mean distance between successive wave crests on the radar screen.

The encounter wave period (period of encounter) T_E: the interval in seconds between the ship pitching to successive waves.

The ship rolling period T_R: port to starboard and back to port, in seconds, timed by observing roll motions in low sea or swell conditions.

2. Cautions
This guidance is general, so not necessarily right for all ships.
It is concerned only with capsizing or heavy rolling in adverse weather, not other hazards.
A ship at sea should always be stable, seaworthy and well secured for sea.

3. Dangerous phenomena
A ship sailing in following or stern quartering seas encounters the waves with a longer period than in beam, head or bow waves. The principal consequent dangers are:

- Surf riding and broaching-to.
- Reduction of intact stability when riding a wave crest amidships
- Synchronous rolling motion.
- Parametric rolling motions.
- Combinations of dangerous phenomena

4. Operational Guidance
Surf riding and broaching-to

In adverse weather, when the ship is situated on the steep forefront of a high wave in following or quartering sea conditions the ship can surf ride (be accelerated forward). In these conditions broaching-to can occur – a sudden change in direction and heeling putting the ship at risk of capsizing.

Table 1 (obtained by solving the formula from the MSC Circular for ships of different lengths) shows dangerous ship's speed for a range of ship sizes with the seas right astern. For ships with seas on the quarter values have been extracted from Fig. 2 of the Circular. In all cases the minimum dangerous speeds are greater than those reached by any bulk carrier.

To avoid the danger of surf riding and broaching-to, high speed vessels should decrease their speed or alter course when they have rough seas astern. Because of their modest speed it is unlikely that any bulk carriers will be affected by this danger.

Table 1	Ship length (Metres)	Dangerous ship's speed (Knots)	
		Seas right astern	Seas 45° to port or stbd of right astern
Cape-sized	289	30.6	43.4
Panamax	256	28.8	40.8
Handymax	196	25.2	35.7
Handy-sized	144	21.6	30.6
Mini	100	18.0	25.5
Mini	81	16.2	23.0

Successive high wave attack

Successive high wave attack can create the circumstances in which a variety of dangerous conditions (reduction of intact stability, synchronous rolling motions, parametric rolling motions or a combination of various phenomena) can occur, endangering the ship. Table 2 shows the minimum wave conditions in which these risks are likely for ships of different sizes. For example a handy-sized bulk carrier of Length BP 144 m may experience problems when the wave length is greater than 115 m and wave height greater than 5.76 m.

Table 2	Ship length (metres)	Wave length 0.8 L (metres)	Wave height 0.04 L (metres)
Cape-sized	289	231	11.56
Panamax	256	205	10.24
Handymax	196	157	7.84
Handy-sized	144	115	5.76
Mini	100	80	4.00
Mini	81	65	3.24

Conditions will be dangerous when, in addition to the wave heights and lengths listed above, the encounter wave period (the interval between the ship pitching to successive waves) is about 1.8 to 3.0 times the wave period (the interval between two wave crests passing a 'fixed point' such as a patch of foam).

When these conditions occur course and/or speed should be altered to change the encounter wave period.

Synchronous rolling and parametric rolling motions

Synchronous rolling with large rolling motions can occur when the encounter wave period is about the same as the ship rolling period. This may happen in following or quartering seas when the ship's transverse stability 'is marginal' ie when the GM (metacentric height) is small.

Parametric rolling with large and dangerous roll amplitudes can occur in seas meeting the vessel from any direction, when the encounter wave period is about the same as, or is about half of, the ship rolling period.

When these conditions occur course and/or speed should be altered to change the encounter wave period.

Grain Stability Calculation for the United States: The National Cargo Bureau Form — *Appendix 19.1(1)*

The reference numbers used below match numbers found in the appropriate places in the completed copy of the NCB Form which follows.

[1] This loading actually took place in Canada but for convenience the United States form is used here.

[2] In Holds Nos.1 and 5 the ends have not been trimmed. Despite that the Americans, like the Canadians and Australians, insist that the full capacity of the hold must be used when calculating the weight of cargo that will be loaded into the hold. The affected weights have been printed **bold** in the form. Authorities which keep strictly to the International Grain Regulations would expect the grain cubics used for Nos. 1 and 5 Holds to be the figures taken from the ship's tables for untrimmed ends, namely 6352 and 6344 respectively. The corresponding weights would be 5306 and 5169.

The vessel was loading to Summer draft so the consequence of assuming extra weight in Nos.1 and 5 holds is that less weight is assumed in No.3, the part filled hold.

[3] The blank cargo plan in Part I is hardly adequate to show the information required, especially for a Panamax vessel. A copy of one of the ship's plans, suitably completed, will probably be acceptable as an alternative.

[4] The intermediate section of Part II is to be completed if the arrival section shows ballast which is not listed in the departure section, because the worst condition will occur as ballasting commences. This is equally true for the time that bunkering commences, if bunkers are taken between the loading and discharging ports, so it is sensible to complete the intermediate section if the arrival section shows bunkers which were not listed in the departure section. The intermediate section of the completed form shows 3C and P and S DO tanks before bunkering, but with free surface effect, as the form requires.

[5] Half way down Part III is as far as must be completed for ships with full conventional grain documentation.

NATIONAL CARGO BUREAU, INC.
GRAIN STABILITY CALCULATION FORM

[1]

* (Required for vessels loading bulk grain in the United States of America)

M.V. / S.S. *Regina Oldendorff*			YEAR BUILT *1982* AT CITY *Dalien* IN COUNTRY *China*
COUNTRY OF REGISTRY *Hong Kong*	NET TONNAGE *10713*	IMO NO. *8120707*	
AGENT			

GRAIN LOADING BOOKLET APPROVED BY *Lloyd's Register*

ON BEHALF OF (FLAG STATE) *Hong Kong*

DRAWING NO. *DL413G3-050-006JS-1* DATE OF APPROVAL *(Provis) 06-05-86*

APPLICABLE REGULATIONS

ADDENDUM FOR UNTRIMMED ENDS APPROVED BY

DRAWING NO. DATE OF APPROVAL

LOADING PORT(S) *Three Rivers, Canada*

BUNKERING PORT(S) *Ceuta, Spanish Morocco*

DISCHARGE PORT(S) *Oran, Algeria*

STEAMING DISTANCE *3350* MILES MILES PER DAY *348* TIME *9.6 days*

DAILY CONSUMPTION: FUEL *37* DIESEL *2* WATER *10*

	DISPLACEMENT	DEADWEIGHT	DRAFT	FREEBOARD
**WINTER				
SUMMER	*36,082 mt*	*28,031 mt*	*10.238 m*	*3.112 m*
**TROPICAL				

FRESH WATER ALLOWANCE *234 mm* TPC/TPI (AT SUMMER DRAFT) *38.6*

* EXCEPT FOR EXEMPTED VOYAGES

** IF APPLICABLE

THIS IS TO CERTIFY THAT:

1. THIS CALCULATION IS PREPARED IN ACCORDANCE WITH THE REQUIREMENTS OF THE VESSEL'S GRAIN LOADING BOOKLET AND THE APPLICABLE GRAIN REGULATIONS.
2. THE STABILITY OF THE VESSEL WILL BE MAINTAINED THROUGHOUT THE VOYAGE IN ACCORDANCE WITH THIS CALCULATION.

CALCULATION PREPARED BY:
(TO BE COMPLETED IF THE FORM IS PREPARED BY OTHER THAN SHIP'S PERSONNEL)

NAME (PRINT)

COMPANY

SIGNATURE

DATE

MASTER'S SIGNATURE

MASTER'S NAME (PRINTED)

EXAMINED BY:

N.C.B. SURVEYOR'S SIGNATURE

N.C.B. SURVEYOR'S NAME (PRINTED)

DATE:

NOTE: ORIGINAL STABILITY CALCULATION AND GRAIN ARRANGEMENT PLAN TO BE SUBMITTED TO THE N.C.B. SURVEYOR. ALL TONNAGES USED IN THIS CALCULATION SHALL BE SHOWN IN THE SAME UNITS AS USED IN THE GRAIN LOADING BOOKLET.

REV 07/06 HTTP://WWW.NATCARGO.ORG (212) 785-8300

SHIP AND CARGO CALCULATION

PART I

TYPE OF GRAIN *Wheat* STOWAGE FACTOR *1.246* M³/MT *N/A* FT³/LT

COMPT. NO.	CARGO (1)	S.F. (1)	GRAIN CUBICS (2) TOTAL	GRAIN CUBICS (2) USED	WEIGHT (3)	V.C.G.	MOMENT (3)
1			*6848*		***5496***	*8.36*	*45947*
2			*7866*		*6313*	*7.79*	*49178*
3	[2]		*5503*	*2362*	*1896*	*4.30*	*8153*
4			*8061*		*6470*	*7.79*	*50401*
5			*6699*		***5375***	*8.11*	*43599*

S.F. $\frac{M^3}{MT}$	S.F. $\frac{FT^3}{LT}$	DEN $\frac{MT}{M^3}$
1.171	42	0.854
1.184	42.5	0.844
1.198	43	0.834
1.212	43.5	0.825
1.226	44	0.816
1.240	44.5	0.806
1.254	45	0.797
1.268	45.5	0.789
1.282	46	0.780
1.296	46.5	0.772
1.310	47	0.763
1.324	47.5	0.755
1.338	48	0.747
1.352	48.5	0.740
1.366	49	0.732
1.380	49.5	0.725
1.393	50	0.718
1.407	50.5	0.711
1.421	51	0.704
1.435	51.5	0.697
1.449	52	0.690
1.477	53	0.677
1.505	54	0.664
1.533	55	0.652
1.561	56	0.641
1.589	57	0.629
1.616	58	0.619
1.644	59	0.608
1.672	60	0.598
1.700	61	0.588
1.728	62	0.579

THIS CALCULATION IS PREPARED IN:

☐ METRIC UNITS

☐ ENGLISH UNITS

	WEIGHT	V.C.G.	MOMENT
CARGO TOTALS	*25551*		*197278*
LIGHT SHIP	*8051*	*10.119*	*81468*
CONSTANT	*372*	*8.49*	*3158*
SHIP AND CARGO TOTALS	*33974*		*281904*

(1) COMPLETE THESE COLUMNS IF MORE THAN ONE TYPE OF CARGO IS LOADED.

(2) FOR PARTLY FILLED COMPARTMENTS, SHOW THE CUBICS USED IN ADDITION TO THE TOTAL CUBICS.

(3) WEIGHTS AND MOMENTS SHOULD BE SHOWN TO THE NEAREST WHOLE UNIT.

CARGO PLAN: INDICATE HOLDS, TWEEN DECKS, ENGINE SPACES, FITTINGS, STOWAGE, TONNAGES, ETC.

[3]

--------------------Topside Tanks------------------

5	*4*	*3*	*2*	*1*
Empty	*Empty*	*Empty*	*Empty*	*Empty*
F - UT	*F*	*PF*	*F*	*F - UT*
Full	*Full*	*Slack*	*Full*	*Full*
5376 mt	*6470 mt*	*1896 mt*	*6313 mt*	*5496 mt*

REV 07/06 HTTP://WWW.NATCARGO.ORG (212) 785-8300

FUEL AND WATER CALCULATION

PART II

THE **INTERMEDIATE** SECTION MUST BE COMPLETED IF THE **ARRIVAL** SECTION SHOWS BALLAST THAT IS NOT LISTED IN THE **DEPARTURE** SECTION. THE **INTERMEDIATE** CONDITION IS IMMEDIATELY BEFORE BALLASTING AND MUST INCLUDE THE EFFECT OF FREE SURFACE, BUT **NOT** THE EFFECT OF A [4] EIGHT. ADDITIONAL FUEL TAKEN AFTER DEPARTURE MUST BE SHOWN IN THE **INTERMEDIATE** SECTION IN THE SA IER AS BALLAST.

		DEPARTURE: *Three Rivers*				INTERMEDIATE: *Arrival Ceuta for bunkers*				ARRIVAL: *Oran*			
TANK	TYPE LIQUID	WEIGHT	V.C.G.	MOMENT	F.S. MOM.	WEIGHT	V.C.G.	MOMENT	F.S. MOM.	WEIGHT	V.C.G.	MOMENT	F.S. MOM.
3DBs	*WB*	*490*	*1.04*	*510*	*36*	*490*	*1.04*	*510*	*36*	*490*	*1.04*	*510*	*36*
4DBs	*WB*	*860*	*1.40*	*1204*	*3*	*860*	*1.40*	*1204*	*3*	*860*	*1.40*	*1204*	*3*
AP	*WB*	*100*	*8.70*	*870*	*268*	*100*	*8.70*	*870*	*268*	*50*	*7.90*	*395*	*65*
3C	*FO*	*305*	*0.47*	*143*	*2982*	*12*	*0.02*	*0*	*2982*	*137*	*0.21*	*29*	*2982*
4C	*FO*	*35*	*0.08*	*3*	*1515*	*1*	*0*	*0*	*0*	*1*	*0*	*0*	*0*
SetsP&S	*FO*	*24*	*11.10*	*266*	*51*	*24*	*11.10*	*266*	*51*	*24*	*11.10*	*266*	*51*
Serv	*FO*	*21*	*11.52*	*242*	*26*	*21*	*11.52*	*242*	*26*	*21*	*11.52*	*242*	*26*
P	*DO*	*18*	*0.41*	*7*	*68*	*9*	*0.25*	*2*	*63*	*47*	*0.85*	*40*	*118*
S	*DO*	*18*	*0.41*	*7*	*68*	*9*	*0.25*	*2*	*63*	*47*	*0.85*	*40*	*118*
SET	*DO*	*8*	*11.85*	*95*	*1*	*8*	*11.85*	*95*	*1*	*8*	*11.85*	*95*	*1*
SERV	*DO*	*9*	*11.98*	*108*	*1*	*9*	*11.98*	*108*	*1*	*9*	*11.98*	*108*	*1*
1P	*FW*	*47*	*12.44*	*585*	*138*	*32*	*12.20*	*390*	*115*	*19*	*12.00*	*228*	*100*
2P	*FW*	*31*	*12.69*	*393*	*24*	*25*	*12.50*	*313*	*20*	*20*	*12.40*	*248*	*15*
2S	*FW*	*31*	*12.69*	*393*	*24*	*25*	*12.50*	*313*	*20*	*20*	*12.40*	*248*	*15*
DrW	*FW*	*40*	*12.35*	*494*	*119*	*30*	*12.20*	*366*	*105*	*20*	*12.00*	*240*	*90*
CoolW	*FW*	*11*	*2.18*	*24*	*1*	*11*	*2.18*	*24*	*1*	*11*	*2.18*	*24*	*1*

TOTALS

	WEIGHT	MOMENT	F.S. MOM.	WEIGHT	MOMENT	F.S. MOM.	WEIGHT	MOMENT	F.S. MOM.
LIQUIDS	*2048*	*5344*	*5325*	*1666*	*4705*	*3755*	*1784*	*3917*	*3622*
SHIP AND CARGO	*33974*	*281904*		*33974*	*281904*		*33974*	*281904*	
DISPLACEMENT	*36022*	*287248*		*35640*	*286609*		*35758*	*285821*	

SAILING DRAFT *10.222* AT DENSITY *1.025 tm3*

DEPARTURE KG	*7.97*	INTERMEDIATE KG	*8.04*	ARRIVAL KG	*7.99*
(1) FREE SURFACE CORR. (+)	*0.15*	(1) FREE SURFACE CORR. (+)	*0.11*	(1) FREE SURFACE CORR. (+)	*0.10*
(2) VERT. S.M. CORR. (+)	*n.a*	(2) VERT. S.M. CORR. (+)	*n.a*	(2) VERT. S.M. CORR. (+)	*n.a*
DEPARTURE KG_V	*8.12*	INTERMEDIATE KG_V	*8.15*	ARRIVAL KG_V	*8.09*

DEPARTURE KM	*9.49*	INTERMEDIATE KM	*9.48*	ARRIVAL KM	*9.48*
DEPARTURE KG_V	*8.12*	INTERMEDIATE KG_V	*8.15*	ARRIVAL KG_V	*8.09*
DEPARTURE GM	*1.37*	INTERMEDIATE GM	*1.33*	ARRIVAL GM	*1.39*
REQUIRED MINIMUM GM	*0.30*	REQUIRED MINIMUM GM	*0.30*	REQUIRED MINIMUM GM	*0.30*

(1) FREE SURFACE CORR. = $\frac{\text{SUM OF FREE SURFACE MOMENTS}}{\text{DISPLACEMENT}}$ (THIS CORRECTION MUST BE APPLIED TO ALL SHIPS.)

(2) VERT. S.M. CORR. = $\frac{\text{SUM OF VERTICAL SHIFTING MOMENTS}}{\text{DISPLACEMENT}}$ (THIS CORRECTION APPLIES WHEN THE VOLUMETRIC HEELING MOMENT CURVES OR TABLES DO NOT SPECIFICALLY STATE THAT THE CORRECTION FOR THE RISE IN VERTICAL CENTER OF GRAVITY HAS BEEN INCLUDED, AND THE MANUAL PROVIDES VERTICAL SHIFTING MOMENTS.)

REV 07/06 HTTP://WWW.NATCARGO.ORG (212) 785-8300

HEELING MOMENT CALCULATION

PART III

COMPT. NO	STOWAGE (1)	GRAIN ULLAGE OR DEPTH	VOLUMETRIC HEELING MOMENT	S.F. OR DENSITY (2)	GRAIN HEELING MOMENT	VERTICAL SHIFTING MOMENT (IF PROVIDED) SEE NOTE 2 IN PART II	
		M/FT	M^4/FT^4		MT– M / FT– LT	M^4/FT^4	MT– M / FT– LT
1	F - UT		1882	1.246			
2	F		535	1.246			
3	PF	D:6.4 m	9100	1.246			
4	F		547	1.246			
5	F - UT		2024	1.246			
		TOTALS	14088		11307		

(1) UNDER STOWAGE INDICATE "F-T" FOR FILLED COMPARTMENTS TRIMMED, "F-UT" FOR FILLED COMPARTMENTS UNTRIMMED, "PF" FOR PARTLY FILLED COMPARTMENTS, AND "SEC" FOR SECURED OR OVER-STOWED COMPARTMENTS.

(2) THE STOWAGE FACTOR USED IN PART III SHALL NOT EXCEED THE ONE BASED ON THE WEIGHT PER UNIT OF VOLUME (TEST WEIGHT) OF THE GRAIN. IF THE STOWAGE FACTOR IS THE SAME IN ALL COMPARTMENTS, DIVIDE THE TOTAL VOLUMETRIC HEELING MOMENT BY THE STOWAGE FACTOR OR MULTIPLY BY THE DENSITY TO OBTAIN THE GRAIN HEELING MOMENT. IF THE STOWAGE FACTOR VARIES, OBTAIN THE GRAIN HEELING MOMENT FOR EACH COMPARTMENT.

A. FOR VESSELS APPROVED UNDER

INTERNATIONAL GRAIN CODE, Part A, 7.1
REGULATION 4, CHAPTER VI, SOLAS 1974 or
REGULATION 4, IMCO RESOLUTION A.264(VIII), NEW CHAPTER VI, SOLAS 1960
REGULATION 4, IMCO RESOLUTION A.184 AN EQUIVALENT TO CHAPTER VI, SOLAS 1960

STABILITY SUMMARY

	DEPARTURE	INTERMEDIATE	ARRIVAL
DISPLACEMENT			
KG_V or GM			
TOTAL GRAIN HEELING MOMENT	11307	11307	11307
MAXIMUM ALLOWABLE HEELING MOMENT	11595	11433	11981
* ANGLE OF HEEL (12° MAX.)			
* RESIDUAL AREA 0.075 METER-RADIANS (14.1 FT° OR 4.3 M°) MINIMUM			[5]
* GM (0.3M OR 1 FT MINIMUM)			

* TO BE COMPLETED IF VESSEL'S GRAIN LOADING BOOKLET DOES NOT INCLUDE A TABLE OF ALLOWABLE HEELING MOMENTS. IN SUCH CASE, STATICAL STABILITY DIAGRAMS DEMONSTRATING THIS INFORMATION SHALL BE ATTACHED HERETO.

B. FOR SPECIALLY SUITABLE SHIPS APPROVED UNDER

INTERNATIONAL GRAIN CODE, PART A, 8. 2
SECTION V (B) , PART B, CHAPTER VI, SOLAS 1974
SECTION V (B) , PART B, IMCO RESOLUTION A.264 (VIII), NEW CHAPTER VI, SOLAS 1960
REGULATION 12, CHAPTER VI, SOLAS 1960

$$\text{ANGLE OF HEEL} = \frac{\text{GRAIN HEELING MOMENT} \times 57.3}{\text{DISPLACEMENT} \times \text{GM}}$$

	DEPARTURE	INTERMEDIATE	ARRIVAL
TOTAL GRAIN HEELING MOMENT			
DISPLACEMENT			
GM			
ANGLE OF HEEL (5° MAX.)			

REV 07/06 HTTP://WWW.NATCARGO.ORG (212) 785-8300

The carriage of grain

Appendix 19.2

A Summary of Grain notes from the UK P&I Club's **Carefully to Carry**
With acknowledgements to Thomas Miller P&I Ltd

The properties of grain

Grain has a comparatively low moisture content and a protective outer skin which is relatively impermeable to water.

Normally in the grain trade, from harvesting to the discharge of cargo, there is a tendency for grain to lose moisture to the surrounding atmosphere.

Air currents can carry moisture more rapidly through a less compact cargo such as pellets than through a powdered cargo.

It is possible to transport unventilated grain without damage in tankers and to store it safely for long periods in unventilated silos.

Grain possesses low thermal conductivity - heat moves slowly through grain.

Moisture in grain

All biological materials normally contain a certain amount of water. When a material is put in contact with dry air it will tend to lose a certain amount of its water to the air in the form of water vapour. This process will continue until equilibrium is reached between the material with that particular moisture content and the surrounding air at that particular temperature.

In cargoes such as bulk grain, when air movement within the cargo is very restricted, the moisture content of the air within the cargo is, under normal conditions, completely controlled by the moisture content and temperature of the cargo.

If the initial moisture content of the grain is lower the difference in equilibrium vapour pressure resulting from a temperature difference will be less and a much greater quantity of water can be absorbed by the cooler grain before water content is raised to a level at which spoilage will begin to occur.

To quote a typical example: in a cargo of bulk maize with a moisture content of 14% and a temperature of 25°C the vapour pressure of the atmosphere within the cargo, which occupies 40% of the volume of the cargo, will quickly reach equilibrium with the maize. A relative humidity of 68% will be reached and the water vapour pressure in the air at that time will be 16.3mm Hg. A change in the temperature of the maize will result in a change in the equilibrium relative humidity and the vapour pressure.

Moisture migration

When a temperature difference exists within a grain cargo moisture moves slowly through the cargo in a process known as moisture migration. Regardless of what causes the temperature difference, when the moisture content is uniform, moisture always moves from areas of higher temperature to areas of lower temperature.

Moisture migration is an important factor in cargo care because too much moisture in a particular area can damage the cargo. It is important to avoid any actions which will encourage moisture migration within the cargo.

Moisture migration will be greater when temperatures are higher and when the sites of the different temperatures are closer together. The lower the thermal conductivity of the cargo the slower heat will move through the cargo and the less the opportunity for moisture migration. Under normal conditions the rate of moisture migration in grain is low.

For grain loaded warm and subjected to boundary cooling the major amount of moisture migration will be upwards because of the tendency for hot air to rise. More moisture will pass to the top of the cargo than to the sides. In cases where damage from sweat occurs more damage can be expected at the top of the cargo than at the sides.

(Continued)

Ventilation
A bulk cargo of grain, if stowed in accordance with SOLAS regulations, cannot be significantly affected by surface ventilation or by lack of it. An objective of the grain regulations is to eliminate or minimise space over the grain: this makes surface ventilation difficult or impossible.

Surface ventilation of grain cannot affect heating which is occurring more than one metre below the surface, because the transfer of heat is so slow.

Surface ventilation can do nothing to reduce or eliminate moisture migration in bulk grain. Continual surface ventilation will maintain the temperature differential and encourage moisture migration to the surface.

Because of the many factors involved it would be unwise to attempt to formulate any general rules for the ventilation of cargo to minimise the effect of moisture migration. However in most instances moisture migration within a healthy cargo is slow and is therefore not a problem.

If ship's sweat would occur without ventilation then cargo sweat is likely if ventilation is used! Without ventilation ship's sweat will occur only if the ship's steelwork becomes cold enough to cool the air over the cargo to the dew point. With ventilation the surface of the cargo is cooled and warm air rising through the cargo may condense just below the surface layers causing caking and/or encouraging microbiological activity.

Virtual loss of GM when grounding or docking **Appendix 20.1**

When a vessel takes the ground in a berth, or takes the blocks in a floating or drydock, she experiences an upthrust at the point where she first makes contact. If the vessel is trimmed by the stern this point will be the sternpost. The effect of the uprthrust is to reduce the vessel's stability (ie to cause a virtual loss of GM). The value of the loss of stability is:

$$GG_1 = \frac{MCTC \times t \times KG}{d \times W - MCTC \times t}$$

where:

GG_1 = virtual loss of GM. (metres)
MCTC = moment to change trim 1 cm (tonnes. metres). The value used should correspond to mean draft when afloat.
t = difference between trim when afloat and trim when aground (centimetres).
KG = height of centre of gravity of ship above keel (metres).
d = distance of centre of flotation from point at which vessel first touches (metres).
W = weight (displacement) of ship (tonnes).

When a vessel is to take the blocks in a dock, or the ground in a berth, the above formula should be used to calculate the loss of GM which will occur during the critical period, which is the time between first touching and finally settling on the blocks or ground.

The loss of stability will be at a maximum immediately before the vessel takes the blocks, or the ground.

If the loss of GM is greater than the initial GM the vessel will become unstable, and will list, during the manoeuvre. This is completely unacceptable when docking, or when taking the ground, as the list cannot be controlled, and is likely to lead to damage to the ship, dock or berth.

This calculation must be repeated each time that the vessel takes the ground or refloats, using the calculated draft, trim, deadweight and GM for the condition of loading at that time. A part laden ship will usually be more stable than a fully laden one, as the centre of gravity of the cargo will be lower.

Any loss of stability will be minimised when the vessel is trimmed even keel, so a condition close to even keel should be the objective on each occasion that the vessel grounds or refloats.

	Boilersuit	Safety shoes	Helmet	Ear defenders	Harness	Goggles	Leather gloves	Chemical gloves	Visor	Safety line	Flotation aid	Dust mask/Filter mask	Flashlight	Winter jacket	Skidoo suits, winter gloves/boots	Warning signs	Isolate/check	Drain/vent	Permit to work
On deck	■	■	■																
Machinery space	■	■	■	■															
Mooring ops	■	■	■				■												
Anchoring ops	■	■	■			■	■					■							
Cargo ops	■	■	■				■												
Crane ops	■	■	■																
Wire handling	■	■	■				■												
Lifeboats	■	■	■		■					■	■								
Ship's side	■	■	■		■					■	■								
Height>1.5-2.0m	■	■	■		■					■									■
Descaling	■	■	■	■		■	■												
Painting	■	■	■																
Cleaning equipment	■	■	■			■		■											
Chemicals	■	■	■			■		■	■										
Welding	■	■	■			■	■												■
Power tools/Angle grinders	■	■	■			■			■							■			
Electrical	■	■	■																
Hydraulic	■	■	■			■		■	■							■	■		■
High pressure air	■	■	■			■			■							■	■	■	■
Cold areas	■	■	■											■					
Extreme cold areas	■	■	■												■				
Steam	■	■	■				■									■	■	■	■

■ Use at all times □ Use as required

Strategy for deck maintenance on a geared mini-bulker employed in European middle trades

Appendix 23.1

Deck maintenance on these vessels is greatly affected by trading pattern and weather. It is impossible to carry out any extensive maintenance when engaged in a hectic shuttle service over short distances, or when deep laden in rough weather, even in the height of Summer. Even when this is acknowledged, however, it is possible to suggest guidelines, and to indicate where the emphasis can best be placed.

Spring time: March-May
Weather expected: mainly cold, or cool and damp.
Strip down and grease all moving gear throughout the ship following the reduced opportunities for maintenance during the winter: cargo blocks, derrick goosenecks, fairleads, deadmen, lifeboat davit sheaves, accommodation ladder gear, etc. Clean FW tanks. Hold painting if ship's employment permits. Check hatch rubber and cleats.

Summer time: June-August
Weather expected: some mild or warm dry weather, suitable for painting.
First priority to be given to the painting of the topsides, deckhouses, decks, etc. Routine greasing. Hold painting if ship's employment permits. Check hatch rubber and cleats.

Autumn: September-November
Weather expected: mainly cold, or cool and damp.
Strip down and grease all moving gear throughout the ship in preparation for the winter. Clean FW tanks. Overhaul/renew lifeboat wires and ropes every second year. Hold painting if ship's employment permits. Check hatch rubber and cleats in preparation for Winter trade.

Winter: December-February
Weather expected: bitter weather, with little work possible outdoors.
Routine greasing throughout ship. Overhaul and maintain: power tools, spare cargo gear, spare anchoring and mooring gear, manual pumps in forecastle, galley and steering flat. Check and clean safety equipment. Overhaul and check small gear within enclosed lifeboats. Renew pilot ladders and lifeboat ladders. Recoat ballast tanks.
Unship and take under cover for maintenance: portable hold ventilators, accommodation ladder platforms.
Hatches, ventilators, lifelines, watertight doors, etc ready for annual freeboard survey. Clean out and tidy storerooms.
Grease ports, windows and deadlights within accommodation. Painting within accommodation store rooms and engine room.

What result do I want to achieve?
The gritblasting and repainting of the main deck abreast No.3 hold, port and starboard sides.

What is the sequence of steps required to achieve this result?

Step 1. Move gritblasting machine from the forecastle head to No.3 hold starboard side.
Step 2. Move sacks of grit from forecastle head to No.3 hold starboard side as required.
Step 3. Use gritblasting machine to gritblast deck plating.
Step 4. Gather up grit for re-use and filter using a manual sieve.
Step 5. Sweep deck. Wash down with high pressure fresh water.
Step 6. Apply metalbrite to deck plating with light weight high pressure washing machine or by hand with a roller or paint brush.
Step 7. Apply primer coats to deck plating with rollers.
Step 8. Apply deck paint to plating with rollers.
Step 9. Move gritblaster across deck to port side.
Step 10/15. Repeat Steps 3-8 on port side.
Step 16. Clean equipment and tools and prepare for storage.
Step 17. Return gritblasting machine to forecastle head.
Step 18. Return filtered re-usable grit to forecastle head

Taking each step in turn, the following questions should be asked:

What are the necessary conditions?
Gritblasting machine ready to use.

What tools and equipment are needed?
Ramp or chainblocks for lifting machine over sill of forecastle store.
Air lines in good condition with the right type of connections.

Do we have them aboard?
Yes.

Are they all in good order?
To be checked.

What difficulties may we meet?
If ship is rolling the machine could 'take charge' and break adrift, causing damage and injuries

What safety precautions are required?
Complete the Permit to Work form.
Ensure ship's staff are provided with personal protective equipment.
Ensure operation of equipment is fully understood.
Ensure manufacturer's instructions are followed in full.
Move the machine only when the ship is steady.
Make sure that an officer, or an experienced petty officer, is in charge of shifting the machine
Secure the machine when it is in position on deck.

Action arising from the above review:
Gritblasting machine to be checked to ensure it is in good working order.
Ramp or chainblocks to be checked to ensure that they are in good working order and can be used to move the machine.
Officer or experienced petty officer to be instructed to supervise the shifting of the machine, and to make sure that it is secured against movement when in position.
Person using the equipment to be fully conversant with its operation and to have received instruction and 'in house' certification.

This appendix contains edited extracts from the excellent practical paper ***'Management of Bulk Carrier Structure'*** by Peter A Bryson presented at the RINA Design and Operation of Bulk Carriers Seminar, London, October 2005. These extracts focus on information likely to be most useful to ships' personnel, but the paper is written from the perspective of a Fleet Manager – Hull and anyone wanting that level of detail is well advised to read the original paper.

Coatings

The major barrier preventing structural deterioration onboard ships, especially in the very corrosive environment of water ballast tanks and to a slightly lesser extent cargo holds is the tank/hold coating. Since the establishment of the Enhanced Survey Programme (ESP), water ballast tanks and cargo holds of all new ships must be fully coated. Such coatings should be 'hard coating' and preferably light in colour.

Compared to the previously applied tradition coal tar epoxy coatings that were black in colour, light coatings are ergonomically more desirable and the identification of structural defects is easier.

The progressive failure of coatings will vary dependent on the standard of the original application, the paint specification and the numbers of full/stripe coats applied. The 'in service' conditions are also significant. Coatings will first fail in way of edges of openings, slots and welds (Fig.23A) – all locations that 'as a good coating standard' should be stripe coated at the newbuilding stage. Stripe coating, normally applied by brush, is the application of additional coating in way of edges to compensate for the dry film thickness reduction at the edges when the coating is applied by airless spray.

Fig. 23A Coating breakdown in TST in way of slots and airholes.

Photo courtesy of Peter Bryson

Coating breakdown also occurs in way of 'holidays' (areas where painting has been missed, and areas of low paint film thickness) behind flanges of stiffeners/brackets, etc. As the ship gets older local coating breakdown also occurs in way of areas of increased stress concentration. Local coating breakdown in way of otherwise intact coating will result in so called 'accelerated corrosion'. If left un-repaired, local coating breakdown will result in a more general coating breakdown, and eventually in structural diminution and wastage.

On bulk carriers the coating on the underside of the tanktop is regularly damaged by cargo grabs striking the tanktop during cargo discharge operations (Fig. 23B).

Fig. 23B Coating on the underside of the tanktop damaged by impacts from grabs.

Photo courtesy of Peter Bryson

To maintain a good and efficient standard of coating is an important function of structural condition management. If coatings are kept in good condition, the structure will be effectively protected and the original scantlings will be available to resist 'in service' loads and stresses. Sea staff therefore should meaningfully report the condition of the tank/hold coatings during routine tank inspections and conditions found should be documented in the owner's or manager's Safety Management System (SMS) tank condition report forms in order that any remedial work can be discussed and planned. If coatings are in poor condition, annual structural surveys will need to be carried out, possibly including thickness readings.

(Continued)

As part of the ESP, the International Association of Classification Societies (IACS) produced definitions of tank coatings conditions:

- **Good** – A condition with minor spot rusting affecting not more than 20% of areas under consideration.
- **Fair** – A condition with local breakdown at edges of stiffened and welded connections and/or light rusting.
- **Poor** – A condition with general breakdown of coating affecting 20% or more of areas under consideration or hard scale affecting 10% or more of areas under consideration.

The most effective method of protecting the structure of a bulk carrier is to maintain the coatings and carry out coating repairs in good time. The installation of anodes, subject to the tanks being regularly ballasted, is an effective 'back up' that will prevent accelerated corrosion in way of local coating breakdown. In a paper produced by the Exxon Corporation many years ago, it was concluded that it was seven times more cost effective to maintain structural coatings compared to letting the coatings deteriorate and repairing the resultant structure diminution.

Water ballast tank coating repairs

The right time to commence coating repairs on a bulk carrier is a matter of judgement. However timely coating repairs will result in minimal structural renewals and hence in the effective management of the structure. If coating repairs are started at an early stage it is also more likely to be within the capability of the sea staff. (Fig.23C)

Sea staff can carry out local coating repairs in water ballast tanks whilst the ship is in service but such work needs to be thoroughly and sensibly planned. In some cases staging will be necessary. This work will generally be limited to surface preparation by power tool to a standard of St.2 or St.3, after all surfaces have been fresh water washed. It is more than likely the coating breakdown will be in way of edges, welds, etc, hence brush applied stripe coating will be required before the application of a surface/ moisture tolerant epoxy coating. Painting sub-contractors can also sail with the ship and carry out this work. The same basic procedure will apply but the work will be done more efficiently.

Fig. 23C Topside tank coating repairs carried out by sea staff in way of slots and drain holes
Photo courtesy of Peter Bryson

The most effective time to carry out coating repairs in water ballast tanks is during a routine repair period of reasonable duration. The coating repair, ie fresh water washing, surface preparation and coating application, can be done by experienced coating companies. Safe and adequate staging for access (if required) can also be arranged.

During a repair period various surface preparation methods are available. In all cases the tanks need to be initially cleaned and fresh water washed to remove all salt contaminants. On completion of the specified surface preparation the tanks should be cleaned and a suitable coating system applied, including stripe coating by brush.

Open full grit blasting: The most effective surface preparation is full open grit blasting to SA $2^1/_2$ standard. This is the most expensive method but it is definitive and will give the best in service performance.

Open spot grit blasting: Local spot blasting. Spot blasting local areas of coating breakdown to SA $2^1/_2$ standard. This results in over blasting in way of the areas of breakdown and adjacent intact coating being damaged by ricochet from blasting grit. For example an original 5% local coating breakdown could result in as much as 70% of the coating either blasted or damaged and needing repair. Hence the resultant method should be spot blasting in way of the local coating breakdown and grit sweeping the remaining areas.

Power tool cleaning: Using mechanical power tools to surface prepare the local areas of coating breakdown to a St2 or St3 standard. The surface preparation can be limited to the local areas of coating breakdown and abrading edges of prepared surfaces. This method is very labour intensive and for this reason is not favoured by some shipyards.

Ultra high pressure water (UHP) water blasting: The use of UHP water blasting in confined spaces such as water ballast tanks creates excessive misting and this makes it difficult to see while working. In addition the size of the blasting lances makes blasting behind stiffener flanges, etc, very difficult. It is also heavy work. For this reason it is not a preferred option in many shipyards.

Cargo hold coating repairs

At some stage in the service life of a bulk carrier the cargo holds will need to be re-coated, especially in way of the cargo heap area. In almost all cases the cargo holds are fully staged and the structure is open grit blasted. As with all grit blasting operations, care should be taken to ensure that the backs of stiffener and bracket flanges and face flats are fully blasted to the same standard as more easily accessed plate surfaces. UHP water blasting or a combination of both is also possible. The blasted surfaces should be fully coated with a suitable coating. Consideration should be given to applying an abrasion resistant coating.

This appendix contains edited extracts from the excellent practical paper ***'Management of Bulk Carrier Structure'*** by Peter A Bryson presented at the RINA ***Design and Operation of Bulk Carriers*** Seminar, London, October 2005. These extracts focus on information likely to be most useful to ships' personnel, but the paper is written from the perspective of a Fleet Manager – Hull and anyone wanting that level of detail is well advised to read the original paper.

The names of a bulk carrier's structural elements

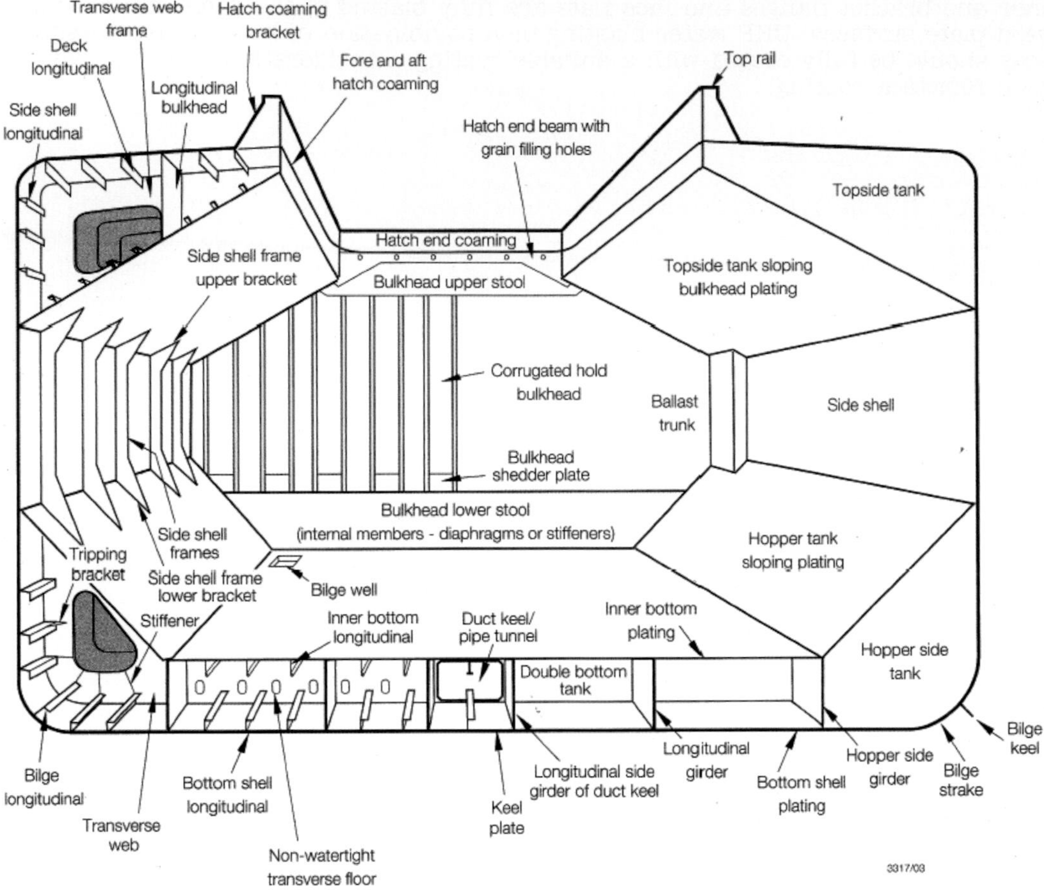

Fig. 24E Bulk carrier hold showing the names of structural parts.

Drawing courtesy of Peter Bryson

Structural defects

Structural defects: These are caused by poor design detail, poor detailed design, local stress concentration, poor repair workmanship, corrosion, operational incident and wear and tear.

Where to look for structural defects:

In general:

- Note the condition of the access ladder
- Always check both sides – port and starboard
- Ullage spaces – a very corrosive environment
- Common bulkheads between water ballast tanks and heated fuel tanks/warm machinery spaces
- Excessive amounts of accumulated loose scale and/or residual ballast mud lying at the bottom of a tank entraps water ballast, creates a damp and corrosive environment that results in coating breakdown and subsequent structural diminution. Excessive amounts of loose scale also suggest diminution has occurred at some location(s) within the tank.
- Bottom plating in way of suction bell mouth and sounding pipe striking plate.
- Bottom plate pitting ie microbial water ballast contamination.
- Where internal members fail, plating becomes unsupported. This leads to further detachment of adjacent internal members and subsequent failure of the plating.
- Areas of stress concentration, usually with associated local coating breakdown.
- Both sides of internal structural elements in water ballast tanks are subjected to corrosion. The boundary plating only one side.

The upper deck:

- The connection of the outboard strake (stringer plate) to the sheerstrake is one of the most highly stressed connections on a bulk carrier. It is important that no attachments are welded to the upper edge of this upstand, hence avoiding any stress-raising notches.
- Forward topside tanks underdeck structure. This structure is subject to 'green sea' loading especially during heavy weather voyages. This also applies to the forecastle deck structure.
- Main hatch opening corners. Look for grab wire damage and possible fractures in way of the shedder plates, if fitted.
- Between main hatches – undulated and/or pitted plating. Also the corners and edges of the small access hatch deck openings.

The ship's aft end:

- Connection of transverse floors to side shell plating, especially in way of the propeller aperture, due to propeller induced vibration.
- Connection of rudder horn webs to side shell plating especially in way of the so-called 'transition area'. Defects are more likely if the rudder horn is a fabricated construction and not a casting.
- More extensive surveys are required in way of the deckhead and forward areas of aft peak tanks, if the engine room extends across the top of the tank and ventilation trunks pass through the tank. This can be the case on smaller ships.
- If the lower area of the aft peak tank is partially ballasted for stern tube cooling purposes, such structure can only be surveyed during a dry dock repair period when the tank can be fully drained.

Machinery spaces:

- Forward bulkhead structure in way of the topside structure on the forward side of the bulkhead.
- Underdeck structure in way of generators – for vibration induced defects.
- The connection of side shell structure to the engine room tank top, especially if the bilges are not kept in a clean and dry condition. This also applies to the lower area of the forward bulkhead.
- Structure in way of leaking machinery, such as seawater pumps and pipes.

Double bottom tanks:

- Bottom plating in way of the ballast suction pipe(s) and sounding pipe striking plate.
- Connection of transverse floors and longitudinal girders in way of the bottom stool plating on the hold side of the tanktop, especially in way of the ballast hold.
- Structure in way of the bilge wells.
- Cargo handling damages in way of the inner bottom plating, ie indented plating and/or tripped inner bottom longitudinals.

Cargo holds, especially in the water ballast hold:

- Connection of the sloping hopper plating (P&S) and the forward and aft bulkhead bottom stool sloping plating to the tanktop plating, in way of the hopper space transverse web frames and double bottom longitudinal girders respectively.
- Tanktop plating at bilge well openings.
- Shedder plates on transverse bulkheads in way of bottom stool upper shelf plate.
- Side shell frames: upper, mid and lower areas for general condition and connection to associated plating. More especially in way of the cargo heap area.
- Pneumatic hammers and bulldozers are used to free the last remains of entrapped cargo. Such a practice results in mechanical damages to the structure, including indents, detachments and even holes.
- The general condition of the transverse bulkhead especially in way of the cargo heap area. Also the connections to the upper and lower stools.
- Structure supporting the upper deck, ie cross deck strips, including hatch end beams.
- Cargo handling equipment damages in way of bulkheads and side shell frames.

Topside tanks:

- Sloping plate in way of lower area. Also the remaining sloping plate, especially in way of the sloping plate longitudinals – for possible necking.
- Transverse web frames in way of large opening radiused corners and the slots for longitudinals.
- Connection of transverse web frame stiffeners to upper deck and sloping plate longitudinals.
- Scarphing structure at aft end of aftermost tank and forward end of forwardmost tank.
- Structure immediately adjacent to air pipes.

Hatch covers and coamings:

- Hatch cover cross joints, for local wastage
- General wear and tear of compression rubber, running wheels, chains, etc.
- Coaming top bar grooving, ie rubbing of lower edge of covers due to hull girder bending.
- Coaming end bracket toe connection to the deck, especially in way of 0.5 L [ie the ship's mid length].

Forward end:

- Ullage space in fore peak tank.
- Horizontal stringers, including openings, slots, etc. The slots for passing through side shell frames are subject to local stress concentration, especially the aft upper half of the tank (P&S) just forward of the collision bulkhead.
- Scarphing structure on the forward side of the collision bulkhead in way of the topside tank sloping plate (P&S).
- General side shell structure which is subject to slamming forces.
- Forecastle deck structure subject to green sea loading.

External hull, whilst in drydock:

- Bottom and side shell plate indents, ie operational contact damages – routine dock inspection.
- Underside of rudder horn and topside of rudder recess – surfaces that are seldom painted.
- Rudder recess corners, ie relatively small radius corners. Fractures are common.
- Rudder 'soft nose' plating – pitted surface due to propeller induced cavitation.
- Corrosion/erosion of external welds, both butts and seams. Also welds in way of drain plug housings.
- Bilge keel endings, either single length or shorter multi-length bilge keels. Also crack arresting holes in way of bilge keel butt welds.

Monitoring the bulk carrier's structure

- Plan structural surveys in advance
- What information is required?
- Identify areas to be surveyed
- Ensure conditions are favourable - area accessible, clean and well lit
- Likely defect locations (including previous defects) should be known
- Discuss the survey in advance with all involved

Structural surveys include:
- Routine inspections
- Planning surveys
- Survey of known defects
- Damage surveys
- Classification surveys
    - Annual surveys
    - Intermediate surveys
    - Special surveys
- Port state control surveys
- Condition surveys
    - On-hire/Off-hire survey
    - Asset protection survey
    - Pre-entry insurance survey
    - Planning survey
    - CAP survey
    - Hull renovation survey
    - Life extension survey

Wastage

Structural Diminution (Wastage): Is greater with ships regularly carrying coal than those carrying grain. There are detailed requirements for thickness measurements and the treatment of the results obtained.

Locations most susceptible to diminution: The following areas are those most susceptible to excessive structural diminution and hence should be specifically inspected during structural surveys
- Forward bays of the aft peak tank adjacent to the aft end of the engine room
- Aft bays of the topside tanks/hopper spaces/double bottom tanks – all adjacent to the engine room
- Double bottom tanks adjacent to heated fuel oil tanks
- Ullage space of topside tanks
- Cargo heap area of cargo holds, especially the lower half of transverse bulkheads and side shell framing. Also, to a lesser extent, the sloping hopper and bottom stool plating. In many cases the structure in way of the cargo heap is covered with loose and hard attached scale while the coating in the upper areas of the hold is intact, almost like two different compartments.
- Under deck structure of cross deck strips ie the cargo hold deckhead.
- Ullage space of fore peak tank

For notes on the repair of coatings, see Appendix 23.3

Year	Vessel	Flag	Year Built /Age	Remarks
1977	*Eurobulker*	Cyprus	1963/14	Posted Missing
1978	*Vitasea Araba*	Greece	1958/20	Posted Missing
	Araba	Panama	1955/23	Posted Missing
	Munchen	W. Germany	1972/6	Presumed Sunk
1979	*Sea Pine*	Japan	1978/1	Posted Missing
	Kairali	India	1967/12	Posted Missing
	Myrina	Greece	1971/8	Posted Missing
	Berge Vanga	Liberia	1962/17	Presumed Sunk
1980	*Maria Bacolitsa*	Greece	1962/18	Found Sunk
	Mount Horizon	Panama	1970/10	Posted Missing
	Sam Kwang	S. Korea	1970/10	Posted Missing
	Hae Dang Wha	S. Korea	1968/12	Posted Missing
	Georgios G	Panama	1965/15	Posted Missing
	Derbyshire	UK	1976/4	Posted Missing
	Dunav	Yugoslavia	1973/7	Presumed Sunk
	Artemis	Liberia	1973/7	Presumed Sunk
	Poet	U.S.A.	1944/36	Posted Missing
	Sandalion	Italy	–	Abandoned/Sunk
1981	*Golden Pine*	Liberia	1968/13	Presumed Sunk
	Antiparos	Greece	1963/18	Presumed Sunk
	Delfovos	Greece.	–	Sunk
	Don Aurelio	Panama	1976/5	Posted Missing
	Onomichi Maru	Japan	–	Broke Up
	Mezada	Israel	–	Sunk
	Rugwardersand	W, Germany	1969/12	Posted Missing
	Rio Bravo	Greek	–	Sunk
	Leslie	Greece	1965/16	Posted Missing
	Marina di Equa	Italian	–	Abandoned/Sunk
	Wheststar	W. Germany	1966/15	Posted Missing
	Delta	Greece	1964/17	Posted Missing

ALL ABOVE DETAILS FROM LIVERPOOL UNDERWRITERS ASSOCIATION

ALL BELOW DETAILS FROM LLOYD'S REGISTER

Year	Vessel	Flag	Year Built /Age	Remarks
1982	*Academy Star*	Panama	–	Abandoned/Sunk
	Orient Treasury	Panama	–	Posted missing
1983	*Marine Electric*	USA	–	Capsized/Sunk
	Elena	Greek	–	Sunk
1984	*Themes K*	Greek	1961/23	Sunk
	Tito Campanella	Italian	1962/22	Posted missing
	Antacus	Liberia	1973/11	Abandoned/Sunk
	Char Ye	Panama	–	Abandoned/Sunk
	Hennigsdorf	DDR	1966/18	Abandoned/Sunk
	Kalliopi A	Greek	1969/15	Abandoned/Sunk
1985	*Hope Star*	S. Korean	1970/15	Abandoned/Sunk
	Tanfory	Panama	–	Abandoned/Sunk
	Winners Bee	Panama	–	Abandoned/Sunk
	Pab	Panama	–	Abandoned/Sunk
	Arctic Career	Panama	1966/19	Posted Missing
	Karin Vatis	Greek	1973/12	Abandoned/Sunk
1986	*Luchana*	Spain	1964/22	Broke up/Skunk
	Riviera Sky	Panama	–	Abandoned/Sunk
	Alexandros F	Panama	1978/8	Exploded/Abandoned
	De Bao	China	–	Sunk
	Brave Themis	Cyprus	1973/13	Abandoned/Sunk
1987	*Testarossa*	Philippines	1970/17	Sunk
	Cathay Seatrade	Liberia	1973/14	Sunk
	Tina	Cyprus	1974/13	Abandoned/Sunk
	Skipper I	Panama	1973/14	Abandoned/Sunk
	Cumberlande	Hung Kong	1973/14	Abandoned/Sunk
	Dayspring	Panama	1970/17	Abandoned/Sunk
	Star Carrier	S. Korea	1967/20	Abandoned/Sunk
	Alborada	Chile	1969/18	Sunk
	Queen Jane	Panama	1968/19	Presumed Sunk
1988	*Korean Star*	Panama	1984/4	Stranded/Broke
	Singa Sea	Philippines	1976/12	Sunk
	Mega Taurus	Panama	1980/8	Presumed Sunk
1989	*Kronos*	Bahamas	1973/16	Presumed Sunk

Year	Vessel	Flag	Year Built /Age	Remarks
1989	*Star Alexandria*	Gibraltar	1965/24	Sunk
	Sevasti	Bahamas	1971/18	Sunk
	Huron	Cyprus	1972/18	Sunk
	Lung Hao	Panama	1966/23	Stranded/Broke
	Pan Dynasty	S. Korea	1968/21	Sunk
	Porn Udom	Thailand	1969/20	Presumed Sunk
	Norsul Trombetas	Brazil	1984/5	Stranded/Broke
	Vulca		1968/21	Sunk
1990	*Orient Pioneer*	Liberia	1971/19	Sunk
	Charlie	Greek	1975/15	Sunk
	Walter Leonhardt	W. German	1966/24	Sunk
	Alexandre P	Panama	1967/23	Sunk
	Azalea	Greek	1969/21	Sunk
	Tao Yuan Hai	China	1977/13	Sunk
	Silimna	Liberia	1978/12	Sunk
	Petingo	Vanuatu	1967/23	Sunk
	Corazon	Malta	1972/18	Sunk
	Pasithea	Liberia	1971/19	Sunk
	Algarrobo	Monaco	1973/17	Sunk
	Elounda Day	Panama	1973/17	Sunk
1991	*Protektor*	German	1967/24	Sunk
	Continental Lotus	India	1967/24	Sunk
	Salvia	S, Korea	1979/21	Sunk
	Vasso	Bahamas	1967/24	Sunk
	Starfish	Argentine	1970/21	Sunk
	Mineral Diamond	Hong Kong	1982/9	Presumed Sunk
1991				
June	*Brant Team*	Norwegian	1976	Foundered. All 17 crew rescued
July	*Manila Transporter*	Philippine	1976	Abandoned. 24 rescued
July	*Choba*	Malta	1969	Sunk. 8 lost, 12 saved
July	*Ruth Riis*	Denmark	1988	Sunk in storm, 5 crew rescued
August	*Sunset*	Cyprus	1970	Sunk, flooded. Crew saved
August	*Blooming Orchard*	Taiwan	1970	Cracked, flooded and salved
August	*Petchomphoo*	Thailand	1969	Flooded forward. Found safe
August	*King William Ex-Pacifico-It)*	British	1974	Flooded, salved 27 crew
August	*Melete*	Greece	1975	Sunk rapidly, 25 missing, 2 rescued
August	*Anemi (Drycargo)*	Malta	1969	Flooded, salved
August	*Atlas Pride (0/0)*	Liberia	1973	Cracked, flooded, salved
October	*Erato*	Malta	1968	Sunk. 19 rescued, 6 lost
November	*Sonata*	Panama	1969	Cracked flooded under tow and sunk
November	*Hanjin Karachi*	S. Korean	1973	E.R. flooded; abandoned; 22 saved
November	*Entrust Faith*	Greek	1973	Flooded salved abandoned sunk
December	*Scaieni*	Romanian		Sank in Med storm, 10 missing from 26
1992				
January	*Captain Veniamis*	Greek	1967	Flooded, beached, refloated ctl Dec 92
January	*I. Van*	St. Vincent	1966	Hull leak repaired
January	*Arisan*	Panama	1974	Cracked and sunk
March	*Karadeni Z. S.*	Turkey	1969	Flooded and sank
May	*Golden Promise*	Cyprus		Heavy list (bad ballasting)
May	*Great Eagle*	Panama	1968	Cracked, flooded, sank, all 19 saved
August	*Trave Ore*	Panama	1968	Structural failure
October	*Dayang Honey*	Korea	1970	Believed sunk during typhoon
December	*Lika*	GRC	1976	Sprang leaks to cargo holds and hull; repaired
1993				
March	*Gold Bond Conveyor*	Liberian	1974	Sank. 32 missing from 33
May	*Nagos*	Panama	1969	Sank. 17 missing from 33
July	*River Plate*	Panama		Hole appeared in hull all rescued

This summary of the Classification Societies' casualty findings, as announced in 1991 and 1992, is followed by a discussion of the background to the findings, and their implications

The tentative findings[57], most of which were subsequently confirmed by more extensive studies[44], were:

- The great majority of the ships that became casualties were more than 15 years old.
- Many of the casualties which reached port had lost side shell plating.
- A number of the casualties had carried coal followed by iron ore.
- Iron ore had mainly been carried in alternate holds.
- The ships could have been damaged by the methods used in discharge.
- The rates of corrosion of the lower side framing and its connection to the hopper side plating appear to have been high.
- Rates of corrosion appear to have accelerated with the age of the ship and/or to be associated with the carriage of coal with a high sulphur content.
- Inadvertent overloading of compartments can occur.

A further report published by IACS[65] a year or so later added several more items to the list of conclusions about bulker losses.

- The rates of corrosion of vertically corrugated transverse bulkhead plating appear to have been high in some casualties.
- Fatigue cracking at the boundaries of the bulkheads and at the toes of the frame brackets had often occurred.
- It is possible that some cargoes had liquefied, either as a result of high initial moisture content or of flooding.
- Details of design at main frame bracket toes and the termination of topside tank platings at the forward and aft ends of the cargo region may have contributed to structural failure and ship loss.
- There had been a lack of awareness that seemingly minor damage to the side shell structure could spread and lead to flooding of the holds through the side shell plating.
- The higher side shell and transverse bulkhead structures are difficult to reach for close-up inspections. From a distance they may appear in deceptively good condition when actually highly corroded.
- Extreme weather conditions may contribute to the loss of a ship.

The findings discussed

Age of ship: Ships are progressively weakened by corrosion and metal fatigue as they become older and it is not surprising that most casualties are older ships. Judgements vary as to the age at which ships become a significantly higher risk, but 15 years is widely quoted[54]. It should be noted that the procedures agreed by IACS for enhanced surveys[66] for bulk carriers require a more extensive survey for all bulkers over ten years old. IMO, indeed, recommends that more rigorous inspections be introduced from the time of the intermediate survey following the first special survey, effectively when the ship is seven years old[71]. A ship which has been cared for, well maintained and safely operated can be expected to trade safely for years longer than one which has been mismanaged and neglected. The trading history is likely to be important, too, and it is significant that sister ships are sometimes found to have very different amounts of damage, suggesting that such damage is not inevitable[52].

Loss of side shell plating: A number of the bulk carrier casualties which survived are known to have suffered serious damage to their side shell plating[48]. In several reported cases large areas of side shell plating became detached, leaving gaping holes in the ships' sides, whilst in other instances the plating fractured and leaked. The damage occurred because the ship's shell plating and associated framing had become weakened by corrosion and stevedores' damage in the areas between the upper and lower hopper tanks, and these weaknesses had not been found and corrected.

Carriage of coal followed by iron ore: Coal and iron ore, with grain, are the three main commodities which enter world seaborne trade so the carriage of coal followed by iron ore is common, particularly in Cape-sized and Panamax vessels. It is now recognised that both commodities have or may have properties which can damage bulk carriers. High sulphur coal when wet produces highly corrosive sulphuric acid which can cause rapid corrosion of the ship's steelwork, particularly on older ships where the hold coatings have deteriorated and offer little protection to the steelwork. Iron ore is a high-density cargo and stress levels reach the highest values that a vessel normally experiences when she carries a cargo of iron ore, jump loaded in alternate holds.

Iron ore mainly carried in alternate holds: Most conventional bulk carriers of handy-size and upwards are strengthened to carry heavy cargoes with alternate holds empty. (The advantages and disadvantages of jump loading are discussed in Chapter 19.) The use of jump loading for the carriage of iron ore cargoes has in the past been almost universal when ships are suitably strengthened.

There are some exceptions, however, such as Australian bulk cargo operators BHP[15] who insist that iron ore fines must be carried in all holds to lower the height of cargo in the hold and thereby reduce danger to the trimmers who can be injured by residues falling from bulkheads during discharge. In addition, resistance by Shipmasters and shipowners to jump loading has increased since the link with bulker casualties has been recognised. The owners of two Cape-sized bulk carriers are known to have instructed their Masters that iron ore should whenever possible be loaded in all holds. A number of individual ship Masters[62,63,64] serving in a variety of fleets have individually taken the same decision.

Ship damaged by stevedores during discharge: Ships can be and frequently are damaged during the discharging process. Damage occurs when the discharging grab or the bulldozer makes heavy contact with the ship's structure. Damage can also be done by hydraulic hammers or grabs used to free residues from the sides of holds. If the damage is incorrectly repaired or the quality of the workmanship is poor, the damage may be made even worse. For example, the correct materials may not be used for the repair of high-tensile steel. A ship which is damaged and badly repaired or which remains unrepaired is at greater risk than is an undamaged ship.

High and increasing rates of corrosion[82,87] of the side structure[41] and athwartships corrugated bulkheads:[65] High-sulphur coal is corrosive and this is particularly so when it is wet and warm. When the coal is loaded wet, or when sweating occurs because the coal is warm and the sea water on the other side of the shell plating is cold, corrosion is encouraged. In these circumstances the corrosion can be highly localised, affecting those portions of the frames and lower bracket connections that lie closest to the ship's sides.

Athwartships bulkheads which form the boundaries of ballast holds are particularly exposed to corrosion from the damp and salty atmosphere. In addition, all bulkheads (like the ship's side structure) suffer from corrosion caused by problem cargoes. This problem occurs particularly when hold coatings have broken down leaving the steelwork unprotected, a situation found mainly in older ships. Other commodities – such as sulphur and salt, for example – may have a corrosive effect even greater than that of high sulphur coal.

Ship damaged by unintentional overloading of particular holds.[65,86] There are a number of ways, some of them not widely known amongst ships' officers, in which particular holds or blocks of holds can be overloaded. Local overloading of this sort may cause cracking and buckling of structure in both the double bottom and deck areas. An example quoted to illustrate this is cracking of the deck plating at the hatch corners and deformation and/or buckling of plating between the hatchways.

Local overloading can occur when bulk carriers are loaded in ways not foreseen by their classification society or shown in their loading manual[60]. For many years, mariners have assumed that they can adopt any loading distribution unless the loading manual says plainly that they cannot. Unfortunately, the classification societies work on a different basis. They consider that no loading has been approved unless it is shown in the loading manual as having been approved. This has led to misunderstandings and to the adoption by seafarers of unsafe cargo distributions.

A faulty distribution of weights can occur when:

- A ship jump loads to her tropical marks and carries less than full bunkers. In that situation some or all of the strengthened holds may carry a greater tonnage of cargo than they were designed to carry.
- Particular holds are loaded with greater tonnage than the tonnage for which the hold was designed. In older ships the design tonnage for each hold is seldom stated and the loading instrument does not warn when local overloading is programmed.[42]
- The vessel is block loaded.

Block loading, fully discussed in Appendix 9.4, is the name given to a loading in which the ore holds are loaded and one or more of the alternate holds are also loaded. The effect is that two or more adjoining holds are heavily loaded with the adjacent holds empty. The longitudinal strength with such a loading is usually satisfactory and this may lead Masters to think that the loading is acceptable, but the problem is actually one of local strength. It has been reported[72] that a number of large bulk carriers have in the past experienced structural damage affecting the cross-deck structure which separates adjacent cargo hatchways at the upper deck level. The single common feature present in all cases was the existence of block loading of cargo holds. Block loading is likely to be considered when the ship is required to load several parcels of ore, possibly in different loading ports or for different destinations.

Fatigue cracking at the boundaries of bulkheads and at the toes of frame brackets: Since surveyors have started making close-up inspections of these areas fatigue cracking has often been found in the bracket toes at the connection of the main frames to the hopper and topside tanks and in the boundaries of the vertically corrugated transverse bulkheads with the upper stools, lower stools and topside tanks. Fatigue cracking is often found in areas which are badly corroded.

Poor design detail: This is a matter for naval architects to resolve, and it is to be expected that class surveyors will look closely at the poorly designed areas of bulkers whilst such ships remain in service. Owners and Masters should be informed when weaknesses have been identified, so that they, too, can monitor the condition of the structure in these areas with particular care. The *Executive Hull Summary* or *Planning Document* required as part of the enhanced survey procedure should help to fill this need.

Neglect of minor damage to the side shell structure: Seemingly minor damage to the side shell structure, usually caused by stevedores' discharging operations or by berthing contact, can become more severe (perhaps as a consequence of the ship working in a seaway) and result in flooding of the hold.

Difficulty in making close-up inspections: The difficulty of making close-up inspections of the higher shell and transverse bulkhead structures is now well known. Very often the need for such inspections was not apparent because from a distance the structure could appear to be in a deceptively good condition, whilst actually highly corroded.[65]

Extreme weather conditions: It has been reported[49] that 70 per cent bulker losses occurring between 1980 and 1991 occurred in heavy weather, though no definition of 'heavy weather' is given. Ships should be built and maintained in a condition to survive heavy weather and should do so provided that they are not handled incompetently. A weakened ship will be at greater risk if she meets extreme weather conditions, but such conditions must be expected.

Some cargoes may have liquefied as a result of high initial moisture content or of flooding: If the cargo in a hold liquefies and shifts it will cause the ship to list; if it shifts violently it can cause a severe impact load on the ship's structure. Sliding and liquefaction of cargoes are two processes which have features in common.

Sources
15, 41, 42, 44, 48, 49, 52, 54, 57, 62, 63, 64, 65, 66, 71, 72, 82, 86, 87.
(See List of Sources, Page 497)

Other possible causes of bulk carrier losses — *Appendix 26.3(1)*

The items discussed below were identified in 1993 as other possible causes of bulk carrier damage and losses. Most remain as valid in 2009 as they were sixteen years ago.

[Comments added in 2009 have been placed in square brackets]

Introduction: When a ship is lost without trace, as a number of bulk carriers were in the 1980s and 1990s, it is not possible to be certain how the ship was lost. When the loss occurs without any distress message, it is reasonable to conclude that the loss must have been very sudden, which suggests the possibility of the ship breaking in two or capsizing. Final foundering, with holds flooded, can also be rapid and will be unexpected if the flooding has not been detected because of darkness and adverse weather.

Even if the problems identified by the members of IACS account for most of the bulk carrier losses which occurred during the period, the possibility remains that some ships have been sufficiently damaged in other ways to cause their loss and many possible causes of damage and loss have been suggested. Some theories undoubtedly have a sound scientific basis, whilst others may not. Theories from a number of sources were reported in the First Edition of ***Bulk Carrier Practice***, and are repeated here for information, but with no guarantee as to their validity.

Ship badly operated by inexperienced or incompetent crew:[12,45,46,50] Many commentators have suggested that the problems of bulk carriers are increased by officers and crews who are inexperienced and/or incompetent. There is no doubt that a failure to follow safe loading and discharging routines can damage a ship.

Twisting the ship:[15,60,69] If a ship is loaded with extra weight to starboard of the centreline in one hold, and to port of the centreline in another, stresses which tend to twist the ship will be created. This problem is known to naval architects as cargo torque and can easily occur if the ship is loaded using two loaders which do not both plumb the centreline. It can also occur with a single loader if the deballasting of double-bottom tanks is done unevenly and cargo is used to correct the list introduced by uneven ballast distribution.

Twisting the ship can also occur during ballast changes if diagonally opposite tanks are emptied to reduce longitudinal stresses. Whilst reducing one set of stresses a second set are introduced/ Uneven transverse distribution of cargo and ballast, if of large magnitude, can result in damage to the cargo hatchway corners and cross-deck structure whilst working cargo or in a seaway.

Ship damaged by berthing impact: Ships can be damaged by landing heavily on the quay or on the fenders during berthing. This is primarily a problem for vessels berthing without the assistance of tugs. Ships can also be damaged by contact with fenders or wall when passing through locks, by violent contact with a tug, or by contact with ice. Like stevedore damage, contact damage can be made worse by a faulty repair and a ship which is damaged and badly repaired (or which remains unrepaired) is at greater risk than is an undamaged ship.

Water pressure against unsupported side shell plating:[52,54] When a vessel is jump loaded with iron ore some holds are empty and the remainder contain iron ore which is usually untrimmed and piled in the centre of the hold, making little or no contact with the ship's sides (Fig. 1.5). Since there is no cargo resting against the side shell plating, supporting it against the pressure of sea water on the outside, this plating can flex more, increasing the risk of cracking and failure. This problem can be reduced by trimming the cargo reasonably level to the boundaries of the space. However this has a variety of consequences.

Sliding solid bulk cargoes:[55] Solid bulk cargoes can shift by sliding or liquefying. Whilst the consequences – listing or capsize, and structural damage – may be the same, the two processes are different.

Sliding occurs when the cohesive strength of the cargo, its 'stickiness', is insufficient to withstand the effects of rolling. Unfortunately cohesive strength is a property which varies according to moisture content and the height of the stockpile as well as other factors. In addition, the moisture content of a cargo can vary during the voyage – for example, if a cargo drains the surface may dry out and the bottom become wet, leaving both top and bottom with no cohesive strength. The accurate measurement of the cohesive strength of a cargo requires expertise, is a time-consuming process and the result is of limited value since it may change during the voyage.

A good illustration of how cohesive strength varies is provided by sand which, when damp, can be used to make sandcastles with heights of up to about 30 cm. Dry or very wet sand has no cohesion and cannot be used for sandcastles: any steep slope will collapse. Even when the sand is damp the cohesive strength does not allow the building of structures which are more than about 30 cm in height.

The angle of repose of a cargo (the slope which it assumes when poured) was previously used to decide which cargoes needed to be trimmed. This measurement is now considered to be unsatisfactory, since it ignores the cohesive strength of the cargo.

It is not practical routinely to make all the tests and calculations necessary to confirm that a particular cargo will not slide, so the IMO Sub-committee on Containers and Cargoes [now the Sub-Committee on Dangerous Goods, Solid Cargoes and Containers – DSC] now recommends[55] that all solid bulk cargoes be trimmed reasonably level unless there are very sound reasons for doing otherwise. Trimming a cargo reasonably level does not guarantee that it will not slide, but it goes a long way in that direction.

'Reasonably level' is meant to convey that the surface can be like a ploughed field and need not be like a billiard table. Trimming only within the area of the hatch square is better than no trimming, but the side slopes remain a hazard.

Liquefying of solid bulk cargoes:[280,61,79] Certain bulk commodities generally those with a small particle size, are liable to liquefy if they contain too much water. Cargoes most at risk are those which contain water as a result of the way they are processed before loading, iron ore concentrates being an example of this. Even though they may appear to be in a relatively dry granular state when loaded, such cargoes may contain sufficient moisture to become fluid when compacted and subjected to vibration during a voyage.

When fluid the cargo can flow to one side of the ship, causing a dangerous heel and capsize. One authoritative paper,[70] reporting research done in conjunction with Lloyd's Register, states: 'Cargo can shift due to it sliding on a saturated base layer caused by the downward migration of its water content, without liquefaction occurring. The effect of this on ship stability could be serious, but if liquefaction also occurred and a virtual landslide was let loose in the holds, the effect on ship stability could be catastrophic. In addition to the safety hazard presented by reduction in stability, a virtual landslide of cargo could impose a severe impact load on the ship structure, when brought to rest from its sudden and rapid movement'.

This danger should be avoided by obtaining details of the moisture content of the cargo and ensuring that it is less than the transportable moisture limit. If there is any reason to suspect the reliability of the details provided, the moisture content must be rechecked using the procedures given in the *[IMS]BC Code.*[5] All cargoes which are liable to liquefy should be trimmed reasonably level to the boundaries of the cargo space. A cargo which is well trimmed is less likely to shift. [The handy-sized *Sea Prospect* which capsized in 1996 en route from Indonesia to Japan was only four years old. Her cargo of nickel ore was believed to have liquefied.]

Failure to trim cargo reasonably level: The IMO recommendations for the trimming of bulk cargoes have become more exacting with the passage of years and the 1991 edition of the BC Code recommends that all bulk cargoes should be trimmed reasonably level to the boundaries of the cargo space, except when the history of past shipments shows that, because of the properties of the material, a lesser degree of trimming is safe. In 1993 it was still normal practice for iron ore cargoes not to be trimmed.[74]

There are five alternative methods of trimming bulk cargoes level – namely, by free pour, by integral spout machine trimmer, by deflectors, by separate machine trimmers, and by hand trimming. The cargo within the hatch square can be trimmed reasonably level by free pouring successively in every part of the hatch square, building a series of small peaks all to the same height. Spout trimming, with a trimming shoe or rotating head on the end of the spout, is used for coal and grain and can be used for ore and concentrates. Separate deflectors can be used, like the spout, to direct cargo into the corners of the hold. The fourth available method of trimming is to use a machine trimmer – for example, a bulldozer lowered into the hold on top of the cargo to trim the cargo out to the ship's side. This process compacts the cargo, which may make it more difficult to grab out at the time of discharge. Hand trimming with shovels is unsuitable for closeweight cargoes, except for small parcels.

When a cargo is not trimmed, but is poured amidships and forms a cone in the centre of the hold, there are benefits. The ship remains upright throughout the loading. On most ships this helps with the deballasting, except whilst stripping. The danger of twisting the ship during loading is reduced. If trimming is not required no trimming equipment is needed. The ship will suffer no delay caused by trimming. The cargo is well placed for the normal grab discharge and is not compacted. Since little of it comes in contact with the sides of the ship, more of it can be grabbed directly and there is less need for bulldozers and trimmers at the time of discharge to remove the cargo from the ship's sides. Stevedores' grab damage ought to be less, since there is less need for the grab to work close to the ship's sides. Cleaning should be less, since less cargo comes into contact with the ship's structure.

To summarise, if the cargo is not trimmed there are savings in equipment needed and the capital cost thereof, in time spent loading and discharging, and in the work which has to be done. These benefits must be weighed against the possible risk associated with a failure to trim.

When the cargo is trimmed reasonably level to the boundaries of the cargo space, as recommended in the *[IMS]BC Code*, it is less likely to shift as a result of sliding or liquefying. That makes it less likely that the ship will develop a heavy list, or even capsize. An additional benefit is that the weight has been winged out – ie, moved into the wings (or sides) of the hold – and this reduces the speed of the ship's roll, making the motion less violent and uncomfortable. The cargo also provides support against water pressure for the ship's side shell plating.

Flooding through dump valves:[12] A considerable number of bulk carriers are fitted with dump valves (drop valves, or screw-down overboard drain valves) which allow them to discharge the ballast held in topside tanks by gravity through an opening at about the level of the load waterline.

Serving seafarers have reported that on loaded passages during heavy weather, water has entered the lower ballast tanks through these openings and the ducting which, on some ships, connects the topside and lower hopper tanks. Such flooding, due to leaking valves or the failure to close them properly or at all, would be slow and in heavy weather hardly noticeable. It will remain undetected if soundings are not taken because of heavy weather or for any other reason.

The amount of water which can enter can be thousands of tonnes over the course of some days, with the rate increasing as the ship sinks deeper. While the loss of buoyancy and freeboard may be insufficient to cause a casualty the resultant increase in stress, from local overloading, could be catastrophic.

Failure of hatch covers:[52] In a laden bulker with a low freeboard, no raised forecastle and virtually no foredeck, the forward hatch is likely to be more or less permanently awash in heavy weather. Total failure of hatch covers, it has been claimed on the basis of plastic analysis, can occur in a new ship with about 4.0 metres of water over the hatch. If the hatches have been corroded, failure will occur with a smaller depth of water. Damage to covers can also be sustained by overloading when carrying deck cargoes, and by over pressure or under pressure of the ballast holds when used to carry water ballast.

A forward hold loaded with iron ore would contain plenty of empty space, so a very large amount of water could enter. This would trim the bow down, allow green seas to roll up the main deck and place all the hatch covers at risk. During rough weather this could happen at night on a large bulk carrier without anyone on board realising what had happened. The additional trim due to flooding of the forward hold would only be about 1 degree on a large vessel, almost imperceptible in a heavy swell with the vessel pitching. Once the second and possibly third holds had flooded, the vessel would nosedive and sink very rapidly.

Failure of hatch cover fastenings due to inadequate maintenance, or faulty operation: This is a fault which most certainly can occur in some systems of hatch cover as a result of loss of pressure in the hatch hydraulic system coupled with poor adjustment of the hydrocleats and lack of renewal of cleat washers. This could lead to flooding of a hold and consequent loss of the ship. The ill-fated *Marina di Equa*, a handy-sized bulker which was photographed in the Bay of Biscay shortly before she sank in 1981, appeared to have her No. 1 hatch covers partly open and to be heavily down by the head. Her loss could have been due to hatch covers sprung open by flexing or to inadequate maintenance or faulty operation.

Failure of transverse watertight bulkheads:[52] The transverse watertight bulkheads which separate a bulk carrier's holds can be damaged by cargo operations, by corrosion and, in the case of the ballast holds, by the sloshing of ballast water. The failure of such a bulkhead would not lead directly to the loss of a bulk carrier carrying a dry bulk cargo, but it might allow sufficient flexing of the side shell, bottom and/or deck to induce cracking and loss of watertight integrity.

Once a hold is accidentally flooded for this or any other reason the danger of progressive collapse of bulkheads becomes much greater. The flood water, which may have its density increased by cargo in suspension, can exert on the bulkhead a pressure which is much greater than its design load, a problem made worse by sloshing of the liquid. If the source of the flooding is the sea it is likely that several bulkheads will fail progressively, allowing a large amount of cargo space to flood and threatening the loss of the ship.

Failure of structure in ballast compartments due to sloshing:[69,77] Ballast water sloshing in a part-filled ballast tank or ballast hold can damage the ship's structure, and naval architects advise that it should not be allowed to happen or that any occurrences should be kept as brief as possible whilst the tank is filling or emptying. The maximum damage is likely to occur in rough weather when the compartment is about half full, and some classification societies advise that ballast holds should not be left filled to 25 per cent-75 per cent of capacity. The documents issued to many older ships contain no such warnings and it is likely that some older ships have suffered weakening of their structures from ballast water sloshing in part filled ballast compartments.

Fatigue cracking of the steel structure:[52] Fatigue cracking occurs at points such as hatch corners where stresses are locally high. Such cracking is the result of cumulative damage caused by cyclic loading of the structure and invariably starts at the welded joints. The fatigue life is the time required in service for the structure to experience enough stress cycles for a crack to occur, and a bulker is designed so that with proper maintenance cracking should not occur until a fatigue life in the region of 20 years of operation has been used up.

Fatigue life, once used up, cannot be regained except by complete replacement of the welded joint, so life extension programmes carried out on bulkers do not extend the fatigue lives of welded joints that have not been replaced.

The consequences of fatigue cracking can range from a completely benign crack which relieves a stress concentration without overloading or endangering any other detail, to side shell cracks which allow water ingress. It is even possible for a crack to start a major brittle fracture at low temperature which could break the hull in two, though the quality of special grade modern steel, welding techniques and detailed designs make such brittle failures extremely rare, though not impossible.

High loading rates: Loading rates of up to 16,000 tonnes/hour, achieved by using two loaders, have been quoted for the iron ore ports of Punta Madera and Tubarao and recently (1993) for the coal port of Richards Bay. Many people in the shipping community have suggested that these rates may in themselves damage bulk carriers,[54] but this suggestion has been described[52] as unrealistic because the rate of loading required to induce dynamic hull flexing is of the order of 1,000 tonnes/second, and the ports with the highest loading rates do not have the worst casualty records.[47] High loading rates do, however, create other problems such as the inability to keep to the loading/deballasting programme.

Consequences of using high-tensile steel:[52] High-tensile steel (HTS) has been increasingly used in the construction of bulk carriers because it greatly reduces building costs by reducing the manhours required for welding. It also allows the handling of larger prefabricated units without increase in weight. HTS has a significant weight advantage when compared with mild steel of the same strength. The reduction in hull weight has the additional benefit of allowing a ship of a given size to carry additional cargo.

However, the use of HTS incurs penalties. HTS structures are subject to higher levels of stress than those of mild steel because they are thinner and hence more flexible. In addition, because HTS is thinner, each millimetre lost by corrosion is a greater percentage loss and corrosion is also likely to be faster because HTS is more flexible. Since the fatigue properties of HTS are similar to those of mild steel, the higher level of stress to which HTS structures are subject considerably shortens the fatigue life of HTS components [designed according to standards used with mild steel[255]].

Failure of ship designers to take account of the fact that ships are flexible structures:[59] Those who support this theory say that ships are flexible structures which are subjected, whilst in service, to steady and also irregular loads, distortions and stresses. The hydroelasticity theory has been developed to predict the effects of these varying loads and stresses.

When the still water and dynamic stress variations along the hull are predicted using the hydroelasticity theory, the results show that dynamic loads and stresses induced can be several times larger than the corresponding still water loads, and that large stresses may occur away from midships and, in particular, towards the end of the hull. This is noteworthy because a number of reported casualties to bulkers and tankers have involved the ship breaking in two in way of the collision bulkhead or in the vicinity of the bridge front. This theory remains controversial and its basis and conclusions are not accepted by many traditional naval architects.

Areas particularly prone to cracking:[42] The fore and aft end transition zones – ie, the side shell areas in the forward part of No. 1 hold and the after part of the aftermost hold – are particularly prone to cracking. Several factors contribute to this:

- Discontinuities between longitudinal hold structures and the structures in the foreship and in the aftship.
- The shape of the hull cross-sections forward and aft causes increased slenderness and flexibility of side structure near the more rigid end structures.
- Complete prefabricated portions of the ship are often joined (hand welded) close to the collision bulkhead and the engineroom bulkhead.
- Because of the finer shape of the hull cross-sections in these regions the hopper side tanks are closer to the hatch square and thus more exposed to rough loading and discharging procedures.

Wave-excited hull vibration:[51] Hull vibration which occurs when a ship meets waves comes in two forms. Springing is the name given by naval architects to continuous vibration caused by wave action, whilst slamming and pounding are names for the transient or short-term vibration which occurs when a ship meets waves during heavy weather.

Ships are more likely to suffer from springing, which is a form of heavy vibration otherwise known as flexing or whipping, when the hull possesses low damping properties as is the case when high-tensile steel has been used in their construction. Springing in low sea states is reported to be common for ships over 200 metres in length.

Any form of hull vibration will cause fatigue in the hull, thus reducing the vessel's fatigue life, and it has been suggested that wave-excited hull vibrations could be of considerable importance in relation to structural failures of ships, this applying in particular to bulk carriers on account of the low damping properties which their hulls are reported to possess. (The procedure for preventing springing is described in Chapter 8.)

Ship driven too hard in adverse weather:[39,43] Aboard a Panamax or Cape-sized bulker the stem of the vessel is likely to be more than 200 metres from the navigating bridge. When a laden ship meets bad weather her blunt bows will *slam* the swell, this being the name given to the violent collision between ship and sea. When in ballast and meeting rough weather the bows rise clear of the water and smash down on the sea surface from above, in a process known as pounding. Both slamming and pounding will damage a ship, but the bows of a larger bulker are so far distant from the bridge that the violence of the slamming or pounding in rough weather is not easily detected. In these circumstances it is easy to fail to notice or to ignore the severity of the conditions the ship is meeting, particularly at night or if there is a deadline to meet.

One sign which warns of adverse conditions is when the ship slows down whilst the engine settings remain unaltered. If the ship is slowed 25 per cent by adverse weather – for example, if she is reduced in speed from 12 knots to 9 knots whilst at constant engine settings – The Nautical Institute recommends that the rpm should be substantially reduced to avoid damage from forcing the ship into the weather.

A few ships have been fitted with equipment (described in Chapter 8) for the monitoring of hull stresses. Such equipment is intended to give warning at any time that the ship's hull is being overstressed, enabling the officer of the watch to adjust course or reduce speed to avoid excessive stress.

Ship damaged by unsuitable distribution of weights: If the weights aboard a ship at any time are badly distributed it is possible for the ship to be subjected to excessive longitudinal bending stresses and shear forces. In these circumstances the stresses, if correctly calculated by those on board, would be found to be excessive and likely to lead to structural damage.

It is the responsibility of the ship's Master and officers to make sure that a ship never is overstressed, but there are a number of situations in which they may fail to do so. Such situations are most likely to occur when a ship is loading, discharging or carrying a high-density cargo, such as iron ore or mineral concentrates, but can occur with incompetent loading when the cargo is a commodity such as grain, or when the ship is in ballast.[12,45,54,69,77,85,86]

Such mistakes can occur in any of the situations listed below, and doubtless there are others:

- When the Master and his officers fail to calculate a full, safe loading/deballasting or discharging/ballasting programme. This might happen because: they make errors in their calculations; they fail to realise the importance of the calculation and do not bother to do it; they are unable to make the calculation because the loading instrument is out of order and they cannot do the longhand calculation; the loading manual is written in a language they do not understand; the loading manual contains errors; they overlook warnings which are contained in the loading manual, but which are not prominent; they think that the ship when in ballast is subject only to low stresses, which do not need to be calculated; they are so inexperienced that they are unable to devise a safe loading, or to recognise that the loading they have chosen is unsafe.
- When there is a departure from the loading/deballasting or discharging/ballasting plan. This can happen when: the ballast operations get out of step with the cargo operations; mistakes are made in the quantities delivered; the needs of the terminal change and they fail to inform the ship, or force the change on to an unwilling ship; the needs of the ship change and they fail to inform the terminal and to produce a revised programme; ship's personnel fail to monitor the programme and the terminal staff depart from it.
- When ballast or cargo compartments are accidentally flooded, particularly when the ship is jump loaded.

Classification society rules for wave loadings: Correspondence[75,76,81] in *Lloyd's List* has quoted Professor Soeding, a leading wave load expert, to the effect that when deciding upon the proper design and scantlings of side shell structure 'the rules of most of the classification societies are totally unreasonable' with reference to the wave load assumed to be acting on the ship's side shell. The main criticisms put forward by the correspondents are that different societies make very different assumptions which are difficult to compare, and that the values assumed in most cases are unrealistically low.

If the values used are indeed unrealistically low this would make the structure weaker than is necessary to withstand the swell conditions met at sea. The classification societies state, however, that this criticism fails to take account of the full extent of their calculations, and that known failures are not consistent with this theory.

Faults in construction of vessel:[73] A ship which has been badly constructed, with defects built into her, is at greater risk of becoming a casualty. An allegation often made about the *Derbyshire*, the British OBO lost in the Pacific in 1980, and her sister ships is that they had a structural fault around frame 65. [This was eventually found to have played no part in the vessel's loss[94].]

Use of grade 'A' steel (which has no guaranteed fracture toughness) to build bulkers: It has been stated[56,67] that grade 'A' steel has no proven fracture toughness and that substantial quantities of it are still used in the construction of bulk carriers, although its use is being reduced. It is said to be an unnecessary risk to have ships which have large or multiple fatigue cracks, but which have no proven fracture toughness in the material at the crack tip.

Corrosion in topside tanks:[52] The topside tanks are continuously subject to a salty atmosphere and it is well known that they are particularly prone to corrosion, which reduces the thickness of plating and thereby reducing the longitudinal strength of the ship. The topside tanks, which are formed by the deck, topside shell plating and sloping internal bulkhead of the tanks, are the only parts of the ship's structure which resist longitudinal compressive bending loads whilst the vessel is in sagging condition. If this part of the ship's structure fails the ship will fold up and probably sink.

Damage to double bottoms:[52] The double-bottom structure is built very strongly to allow for the heavy loads to which it is subjected. These include the effects of water pressure acting upwards and the downward pressure of the cargo. This latter has its greatest local effect when the ship is jump loaded with a closeweight cargo, the cargo is peaked in the hold, and the hold is overloaded, as can happen in practice[53]. The effect of loading alternate holds is to induce large bending shear stresses in the double bottom, stresses for which allowance is made in the design. Double bottoms can be damaged by the impact of heavy grabs[41] which nowadays commonly have an unloaded weight of 35 tonnes, by the tipping of heavy items of cargo such as pig iron or scrap metal into the holds from a height,[83] and by corrosion within the double-bottom ballast tanks. It is also suggested[67] that the dropping of iron ore on to the tanktop from height of more than 27 metres may do harm on impact. Corrosion of and damage to the double bottom could lead to collapse, resulting in failure of the hull girder and the ship breaking in two.

Hatch cover fastenings sprung open by flexing of the ship: It has been suggested that hatch cover fastenings could be sprung open by the flexing of a bulk carrier in rough weather. If covers opened in such circumstances it could lead to flooding of a hold and consequent loss of the ship. If such an event were possible, then instances of the fastenings being sprung open without the ship being lost could also be expected, but little has been published to support this theory.

Unexplained hull flexing: One report[21] tells of excessive and alarming hull flexing which occurred on a Cape-sized bulk carrier on several occasions when she was part loaded with coal, with some holds full and others empty, and on passage between the first and second discharge ports. The observer suggested that this phenomenon may have been caused by stresses locked into the ship's structure by the uneven loads on the shell plating along the length of the ship. Another possibility is that this was an example of wave-excited hull vibration, triggered by the unusual weight distribution.

Explosions aboard combination carriers:[43,78] Explosions can occur in combination carriers due to explosive gases in ballast compartments or void spaces. This danger is well documented, but continues to present practical problems for ships' personnel, particularly in the cases of those OBOs which have combined side and double-bottom tanks with a single air pipe at the forward end. Such ballast tanks cannot easily be cleaned or gas freed.

Sources

5, 12, 15, 21, 39, 41, 42, 43, 45, 46, 47, 50, 51, 52, 53, 54, 55, 56, 59, 60, 61,67, 69, 70, 73, 74, 75, 76, 77, 78, 79, 81, 83, 85, 86, 94, 255 280. (See List of Sources, Page 497)

6. Conclusion

6.1. Ranking of Risk Control Options

The 75 risk control options included in this cost benefit analysis cover a wide range of measures that in many cases substitute or supplement each other. The risk control options also differ strongly with respect to risk reduction, cost and benefit.

The determination of risk reduction was performed on information produced at earlier steps in the Formal Safety Assessment of Bulk Carriers. The fault trees delivered to the cost benefit assessment were populated with data only at their higher levels. Lower levels of the trees were unpopulated. Risk reduction was therefore assessed directly using the PLL figures relating to each component of a tree. Estimates of risk benefit were made as a percentage reduction in PLL.

The study concludes that the following risk control options, considering their large risk reduction, are the most cost effective to implement:

Handy (Newbuilding)
- Free fall life boat
- A06 Improved coating systems on hatch covers
- A24 Port State inspector training
- A25 Enhanced survey and inspection
- A50 Bilge alarms

Panamax (Newbuilding)
- Free fall life boat
- A06 Improved coating systems on hatch covers
- A25 Enhanced survey and inspection
- B05 Double side skin
- B10 Control standards of steel repair

Capesize (Newbuilding)
- Free fall life boat
- A06 Improved coating systems on hatch covers
- A20 Positive indication of openings
- A25 Enhanced survey and inspection
- B05 Double side skin

Handy (10 & 15 years old)
- A24 Port State inspector training
- A25 Enhanced survey and inspection
- A26 Weather routing
- B10 Control standards of steel repair
- C08 Improved ship/shore communication

Panamax (10 & 15 years old)
- A24 Port State inspector training
- A25 Enhanced survey and inspection
- A26 Weather routing
- B10 Control standards of steel repair
- C08 Improved ship/shore communication

Capesize (10 & 15 years old)
- A24 Port State inspector training
- A25 Enhanced survey and inspection
- A26 Weather routing
- B10 Control standards of steel repair
- C08 Improved ship/shore communication

6.2. Sensitivity analysis of risk control options

Of the above-mentioned risk control options the following are relatively cost sensitive and do become less attractive if they are implemented where the cost level is high:

On newbuildings
- A50 Water ingress alarms in cargo holds and remote spaces

On existing bulk carriers
- A25 Enhanced survey and inspection
- B05 Double side skin

- C11 Design ship to meet criteria of loading terminal

The following RCOs are relatively sensitive to changes in the discount rate and become less attractive at high discount rates:

On newbuildings

- A50 Water ingress alarms in cargo holds and remote spaces

On existing bulk carriers

- B05 Double side skin
- C11 Design ship to meet criteria of loading terminal

6.3. Stakeholder analysis

The stakeholder analysis shows generally a little difference in the origination of the costs and benefits for the risk control options however, the RCOs dealing with the implementation of double hull and ban alternate hold loading clear differences are revealed.

6.4. Cost Benefit Assessment model

A Cost Benefit Assessment model has been developed on a standard Microsoft Office package. The CBA model uses the spreadsheet program Excel in combination with Visual Basic Programming and comprises of three separate applications:

1. The RCO Generator
2. The RCO Analysis Engine
3. The RCO Report Generator

The CBA model manages the CBA process and provides a range of information for input to the later stages of the Formal Safety Assessment of Bulk Carriers.

ANNEX

GUIDANCE FOR CHECKING THE STRUCTURE OF BULK CARRIERS

1 This guidance is to assist port State control officers (PSCOs) in checking the structure as well as the operational aspects of bulk carriers during port State control inspections.

2 In addition to this guidance, PSCOs should refer to the following documents:

.1 SOLAS chapter XII - Additional safety measures for bulk carriers;

.2 resolution A.862(20) - Code of Practice for the Safe Loading and Unloading of Bulk Carriers;

.3 resolution A.866(20) - Guidance to ships' crews and terminal personnel for bulk carrier inspections; and

.4 resolution A.744(18) as amended – Guidelines on the enhanced programme of inspections during surveys of bulk carriers and oil tankers.

3 PSCOs are further invited to consult the following IACS publications, if available:

.1 Bulk Carriers: Guidelines for Surveys, Assessment and Repair of Hull Structure;

.2 Bulk Carriers: Guidance and Information on Bulk Cargo Loading and Discharging to Reduce the Likelihood of Over-Stressing the Hull Structure; and

.3 Bulk Carriers – Handle With Care.

Documentation

4 While checking the ship's documentation, PSCOs should pay particular attention to the loading plan, cargo distribution and loading/unloading sequences to ascertain that the ship is loaded in accordance with the approved loading manual.

5 PSCOs should pay particular attention to the tank top limitation, the bending moments and shearing forces as well as the cargo distribution. Past experience shows that ships often load in patterns not approved in the stability manual. For example, on board a nine-hold bulk carrier, the approved stability manual often has an annotation stating that holds 2, 4, 6 and 8 may be empty. This implies that all even number holds must be empty at the same time. In many cases, ship officers believe that such an annotation allows for any combination of these holds to be empty, which is not the case.

6 PSCOs should remember that loading patterns not included in the approved stability manual should not be accepted since this might create excessive local stress to the ship's structure regardless of the fact that the bending moments and shearing forces are within the permissible values.

7 When it is established during a PSC inspection that a ship loading pattern is not per the approved stability manuals, the PSCO should request confirmation in the first instance by the ship's officers, by the flag State administration, or the recognized organization working on behalf of the flag State, that the proposed loading plan/distribution is acceptable. In the event that a ship is found non-compliant with the approved stability manuals during unloading operations, the PSCO should inform the master and chief officer that future loading should be within the limitation of the approved stability manual.

8 Initially, a check of the survey report file may identify possible suspect areas requiring inspection. The provisions contained in resolution A.744(18) as amended, require a specific survey programme which includes access arrangements and, when necessary, the requirements for a close-up survey and thickness measurements. A survey report file is required to be held on board consisting of:

.1 reports of structural surveys;

.2 condition evaluation reports;

.3 thickness measurement reports; and

.4 survey planning document (or equivalent) containing the following information:

.4.1 main particulars;

.4.2 plan of tanks and holds;

.4.3 list of tanks and holds and usage, corrosion protection and condition of coating;

.4.4 corrosion risk in tanks; and

.4.5 design risk of structures.

Inspection

9 Ideally, inspections should be carried out by a team of at least two PSCOs and include, at least, one person with an in-depth knowledge of ship structures. In a loading port they should be ready to board the ship on arrival. In a discharge port, information on the likely discharge sequences should be obtained, where possible, so that the inspection can be carried out when holds become available.

10 Access to the upper parts of holds is problematic. Ladders may help and experience has shown that using binoculars along with high-powered torches can assist in making an initial assessment of the condition of inaccessible parts. If the condition of other parts of the hold and the hull structure in general give rise to concern, the flag State/recognized organization should be consulted to consider the need for a more detailed survey.

11 The impression of hull maintenance and general state on deck, the condition of items such as ladders, hatches, air pipes, guardrails, visible evidence of previously effected repairs, and the condition of deck machinery should influence the PSCO's decision on whether to make the fullest possible examination of the hull.

12 Special attention should be given to areas of high stress and bending moments, such as:

.1 immediately forward of the engine-room bulkhead;

.2 over the midships half-length; and

.3 no.1 hold side shell framing and top and bottom connections (panting region).

13 Particular attention should be given to areas where fracturing, cracks, distortion or excessive wastage can occur. These areas are illustrated in the diagrams in appendices 1 and 2*. The weather tight integrity of hatches and closures is particularly important on ore carriers with minimal reserve buoyancy.

14 Common defects are:

.1 cracking at hatch corners;

.2 plate panel buckling of cross deck strips and stiffening structure;

.3 cracking of hatch coamings;

.4 cracking at intersection of the inner bottom plating and the hopper plating;

.5 grab and bulldozer damage to the side shell frames lower brackets;

.6 grab damage to the inner bottom plating, hopper and lower stool plating;

.7 cracking at side shell frame bracket toes;

.8 both general and localized corrosion of side shell frames and brackets;

.9 cracking at fore and aft extremities of topside tank structures;

.10 corrosion within topside tanks; and

.11 general corrosion and cracking of transverse bulkheads.

---

* Diagrams in the appendices are reproduced with the kind permission of IACS, Lloyd's Register and Nippon Kaiji Kyokai.

15 If tanks or holds are to be inspected, the PSCO should ensure it is safe to enter. The requirements of the Code of Safe Practice for Solid Bulk Cargoes, Appendix F, apply. Additional safeguards could include carrying personal devices capable of determining the safety of tank atmospheres or employing the services of a chemist to check the atmosphere.

16 Permanent seawater ballast tanks represent one of the most likely problem areas and, if inspected, the following aspects should be considered:

.1 the paint condition in coated ballast tanks and condition of anodes. In ballast tanks, rates of corrosion in the order of 1mm per year may be encountered, depending on whether they are coated or protected by anodes. In some ships, only the ullage space is coated with the remainder protected by anodes. During empty periods, this can result in corrosion on uncoated structures, which remain wet;

.2 in tanks used for ballast that may be subject to variable depths of seawater, for example forepeak tanks, it is often the case that there is little wastage top and bottom, but significant wastage over central regions. Attention should be paid to longitudinal stiffeners and brackets at the collision bulkhead to shell junction;

.3 longitudinal shell stiffeners in dedicated ballast tanks, particularly in areas adjacent to bulkheads and web frames; and

.4 underdeck longitudinals in ballast tanks. Wastage is usually the most severe close to the deckhead. This may result in the fillet welds, attaching longitudinals to the deck, being wasted thus leading to detachment of the longitudinals and consequent buckling of deck plates.

17 Where a fracture, which has not been caused by contact damage, is found in the main hull structure on one side of a ship, the corresponding structure on the opposite side should be examined to see if a similar failure has occurred. Fractures of this nature are of concern, especially where corrosion is associated with the failure and may have been a contributing factor.

18 If relevant, the PSCO may check that the necessary calculations have been made to ensure bending and shear stresses are maintained within maximum limits both during loading/discharge and the ensuing voyage. This is especially important where high density cargoes are carried or where the loading/ballasting arrangement is of a different configuration to that described in the ship's loading manual.

19 In reaching any decision regarding a detention, the PSCO should consider the seaworthiness and not the age of the ship, making allowance for fair wear and tear over the minimum acceptable scantlings. Where there is doubt, the classification society should advise the accepted diminution rates of structural members. Damage not affecting seaworthiness should not constitute grounds for judging that a ship should be detained, nor should damage temporarily but effectively repaired for a voyage to a port for permanent repairs. However, in his assessment of the effect of damages, the PSCO should have regard to the location of crew accommodation and whether the damage substantially affects its habitability.

20 Any proposals from the flag State or classification society should be considered carefully. Specification of repairs is the responsibility of the classification society surveyor and need only be agreed to by the PSCO. In the event that the proposals are acceptable, care should be taken to ensure that the flag State and classification society oversee the repairs and clear the ship before a request to lift the detention is made.

21 Any proposal by the flag State to allow the ship to make a single voyage to a repair yard should be in accordance with chapter 4.7 of resolution A.787(19) as amended by resolution A.882(21) on Procedures for port State control.

APPENDIX 1

WHAT TO LOOK FOR IN HOLDS

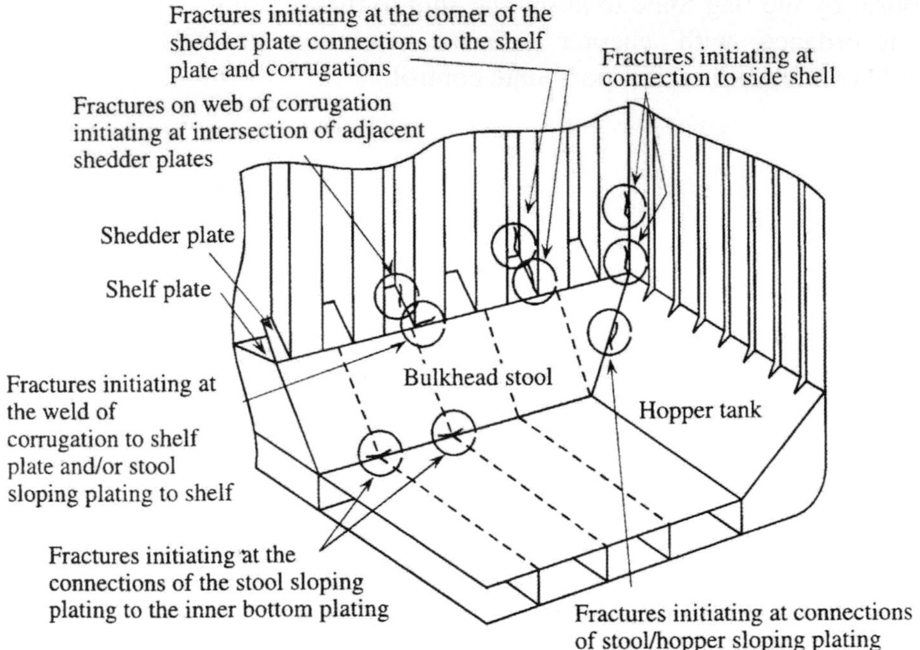

Typical fracturing at the connection of a transverse bulkhead structure

WHAT AND WHERE TO LOOK FOR IN HOLDS

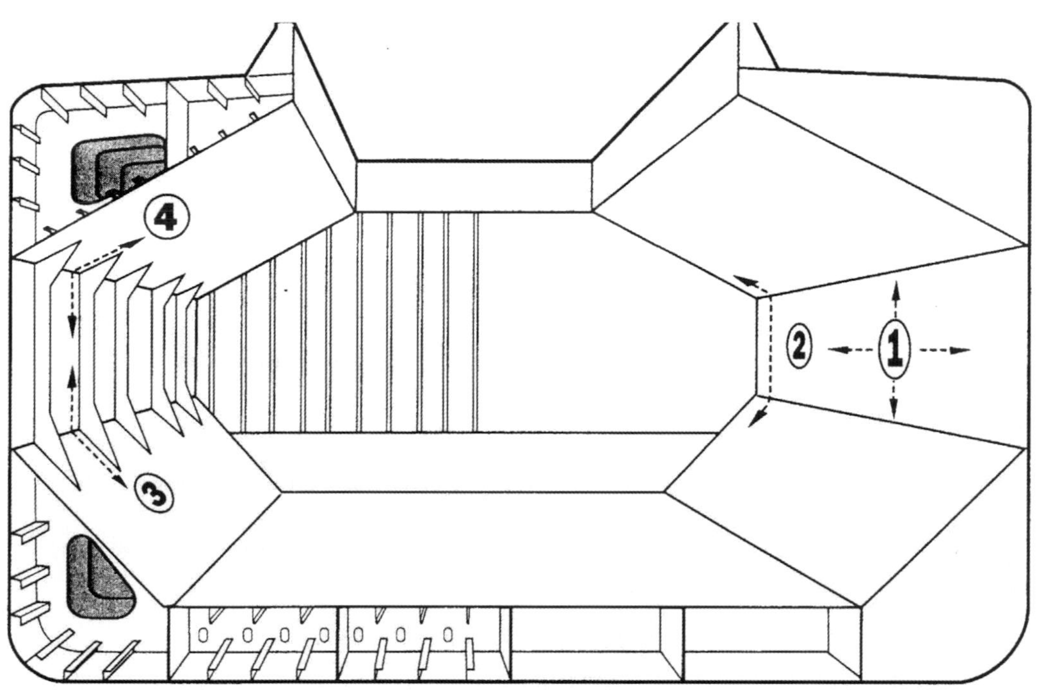

Typical cross section of bulk carrier through cargo hold.

Where to look	What to look for
① Side shell plating.	Cracks in welds or plates. Leaks in welds or plates. Distortion of plating.
② Connection of bulkhead plating to side shell.	Punctured plating. Cracked plating. Heavily indented plating. Buckled plating. Corrosion and wastage.
③ Connection of side shell frames and end brackets to the shell plating and hopperside tank plating by close-up inspection.	Cracks. Corrosion and wastage. Excessively deformed frames or brackets. Detached frames or brackets.
④ Connection of side shell frames and end brackets to the shell plating and topside tank plating.	Cracks. Corrosion and wastage. Excessively deformed frames or brackets. Detached frames or brackets.

APPENDIX 2

WHAT TO LOOK FOR ON DECK

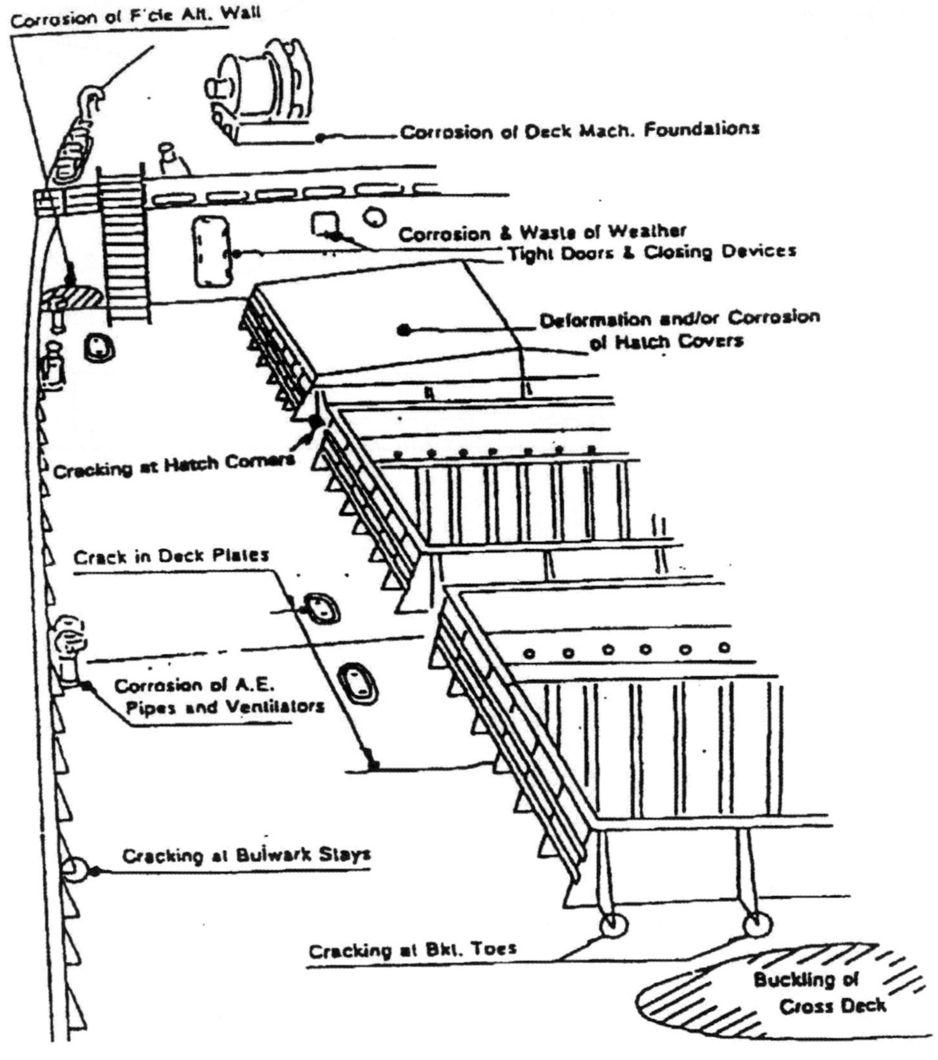

LIST OF SOURCES

1. Parker, Captain K., MNI. 'Measurement of Bulk Cargoes.' *The Mariner and the Maritime Law.* The Nautical Institute North East Branch, November 1990.
2. 'The Measurement of Bulk Cargoes.' *Carefully to Carry No. 13.* UK P&I Club. April 1989.
3. 'Care and Survey of Hatch Covers of Dry Cargo Ships.' The International Association of Classification Societies. *Work of the Nautical Surveyor.* The Nautical Institute. 1989.
4. 'Code of Safe Practice for Ships Carrying Timber Deck Cargoes.' International Maritime Organization. 1991.
5. 'International Maritime Solid Bulk Cargo (IMSBC) Code.' (Formerly the BC Code). International Maritime Organization. 2009.
6. Gilfillan, A. 'Developments in Bulk Carrier Design.' Bulktrans '89. CS Publications Ltd. 1989.
7. Buxton, I. L. and Logan, J. A. 'The Ballast Performance of Ships with Particular Reference to Bulk Carriers.' RINA. 1986.
8. Muckle, W. 'Naval Architecture.' Butterworths. 1987.
9. Buysse, Captain J., MNI. 'Handling Ships in Ice.' The Nautical Institute. 2007.
10. 'The Mariner's Handbook', Eighth Edition. NP100. The Hydrographer of the Navy. 2004.
11. 'Ice Navigation in Canadian Waters.' TP5064. Canadian Coast Guard. September 1999
12. Caro, J. P., and Spink, H. E. 'Hong Kong Administration's View of Bulk Carrier Casualties and Losses.' *Intercargo/IBJ Seminar.* Hong Kong. 1991.
13. Bulk Cargo Committee Document BC 30/17/Add.1. Annex 3, p. 54. International Maritime Organization.
14. Logan, J. A., and Chreseson, P. J. 'The Application of Controllable Ballasting to Cargo Carrying Ships.' NECIES. 1986.
15. Lynch, R. J. 'Steel Industry Bulk Cargoes – a guide for BHP personnel.' BHP Transport Ltd. 1980.
16. Fawbert, J. 'Bulk Port Design – An Expert Overview.' *Bulktrans '91.* CS Publications Ltd. 1991.
17. Merchant Shipping Notice No. M. 1122. UK Department of Transport. February 1984.
18. 'International Grain Code.' International Maritime Organization. 1991.
19. Thomas, Capt. R.E., Pepper, Capt.G.M. 'Thomas' Stowage – The Properties and Stowage of Cargoes.' Brown, Son and Ferguson Ltd. 2008.
20. Rigby, Dr G., and Hallegraeff, Dr G. 'Ballast Water Exchange Trials and Marine Plankton Distribution on the mv *Iron Whyalla.*' BHP Research., 1992.
21. Phillips, C. 'Ship Stresses when Carrying Coal.' Seaways. October 1991.
22. 'Code of Practice for the Safe Handling and Ocean Transport of South African Coal'. South African Department of Transport.
23. Lower-Hill, B. J. 'Lloyd's Survey Handbook.' Lloyd's of London Press Ltd. 1991.
24. 'Code of Uniform Standards and Procedures for the Performance of Draught Surveys of Coal Cargoes.' United Nations Economic and Social Council. Economic Commission for Europe Committee on Energy, Working Party on Coal. 1992.
25. Sparks, A. FNI. 'Steel Carriage by Sea.' Lloyd's of London Press Ltd. Fourth Edition, 2003.
26. Llewellyn, T. J. 'The Master's Role in Signing Bills of Lading.' Nautical Institute North East Branch. 1990.
27. Robertsson, S. and Lindemann, K. 'An Introduction to Ship Handling in Rough Weather.' Veritas Report No. 81-0215. DnV. 1981.
28. 'Recommendations on the Safe Use of Pesticides in Ships Applicable to the fumigation of cargo holds.' *MSC.1/Circ.1264.* International Maritime Organization. June 2008
29. 'Code for Lifting Appliances in a Marine Environment.' Lloyd's Register of Shipping. Jan 2003.
30. Hutchinson, J. L., C.Eng, MIMarE. 'Planning a Dry Dock.' *The Nautical Institute on Command.* 2nd Edition. 2000
31. 'Code of Safe Working Practices for Merchant Seamen Consolidated Edition.' Maritime and Coastguard Agency. TSO. 2007
32. 'Respiratory Protective Equipment at Work: a Practical Guide.' UK Health and Safety Executive. 2005.
33. 'International Maritime Dangerous Goods (IMDG) Code.' International Maritime Organization. Consolidated Edition, 2008.
34. Rayfield, R. 'Nature and Function of the Bill of Lading and Mate's Receipts.' Nautical Institute North East Branch. 1990.
35. Curline, J. R. (Editor). 'Safe Loading, Ocean Transport and Discharge Practices for Dry Bulk Commodities.' The Australian Coal Association et al. 1992.
36. 'Ocean Passages of the World', 5th Edition. NP 136. Hydrographer of the Navy. 2004.
37. Foy, D. B., MRIN, FNI. 'Disasters at Sea and their Prevention.' RSA Journal. December 1987.
38. 'Code of Safe Practice for Cargo Stowage and Securing.' International Maritime Organization. 2003.
39. Richardson, Captain J., MNI. 'Total Loss: Some Possible Causes.' Seaways, April 1986.
40. Foy, D. B., MRIN, FNI. 'Bulk Carrier Losses – Unanswered Questions.' *Safe Ship – Safe Cargo Conference.* 1987.
41. Ferguson J. M. 'Bulk Carriers – The Challenge.' *Lloyd's Register Seminar.* May 1991.
42. 'Bulk Carrier Losses.' Det norske Veritas. November 1991.
43. Beetham, Captain E. H., FNI. 'Loss of Bulk Carriers.' *Seaways.* May 1991.

44. Robinson, D. W. 'Bulk Carrier Casualties – A Classification Society's View.' *Intercargo Seminar*, Oslo. June 1991.

45. 'What is the World Coming To?' Anon. *Journal of Master Mariners of Australia Inc.* Winter 1991.

46. Isbester, Captain J., ExC, FNI. 'Bulk Carrier Casualties and Losses – the Shipmaster's Point of View.' *Intercargo/IBJ Seminar.* Hong Kong. October 1991.

47. Nunn, A. S. 'Bulk Carriers.' *Intercargo Seminar*, Oslo, June 1991.

48. Bau, Huyng duc. 'Bulk Carriers Structural Damage.' *Intercargo/IBJ Seminar.* Hong Kong. October 1991.

49. Jones, D. K. and Roe N. P. 'Bulk Carrier Casualties – an independent consultant's view.' *Intercargo/IBJ Seminar.* Hong Kong. October 1991.

50. Barnet, Captain S., MNI. 'What the World has Come to.' *Seaways*, July 1993.

51. Ørbeck F. 'Wave-excited hull vibration reduction using hull vibration damper.' Institute of Marine Engineers. March 1992.

52. Corlett, B. J., and Colman, J. C. 'Bulk Carrier Losses – A Naval Architect's Viewpoint.' *MLAANZ Conference.* 1992.

53. Isbester, Captain J., ExC, FNI. 'The Operation of Bulk Carriers – the Seagoing Perspective.' Royal Institution of Naval Architects. December 1992.

54. Avrin, K., and Spence, N. 'The Harland and Wolff New Bulk Carrier Design for Improved Safety and Longevity.' Royal Institution of Naval Architects. December 1992.

55. Kruszewski, Dr A. 'Sliding Solid Bulk Cargoes: How to Avoid Them.' *ICHCA Annual Review.* 1992.

56. Jubb J. E. M. 'Bulk Carriers – Fatally Flawed?' *Welding and Metal Fabrication.* May 1992.

57. 'Losses of Bulk Carriers during 1990.' *Lloyd's Register Press Release.* January 1991.

58. Foy, D. B., MRIN, FNI. 'Combination Carriers, Ore Carriers and Sudden Sinkings.' *Safety at Sea.* February 1983.

59. Aksu, S. et al. 'Load and Stress Distributions on Bulk Carriers and Tankers in Various Loading Conditions.' Royal Institution of Naval Architects. December 1992.

60. Isbester, Captain J., ExC, FNI. 'Tankers and Bulk Carriers: the Way Ahead.' *Seaways.* February 1993.

61. Investigation Report on the Capsizing of the Pusher Vessel *Finn* and the Barge *Baltic* off Hanko. *Accident Report No.2/1990.* Helsinki. 1992.

62. Keith, Captain B. F., MNI. 'Loading of Large Bulk Carriers.' *Seaways.* February 1993.

63. Isbester, Captain J., ExC, FNI. 'Bulk Carrier Practice.' *Seaways.* May 1992.

64. Baillod, Captain F., MNI. Personal correspondence. 31 October 1992.

65. 'Bulk Carriers: Guidance and Information to Shipowners and Operators.' International Association of Classification Societies. April 1992.

66. Burton, J. A. 'Enhanced Surveys for Tankers and Bulk Carriers.' Lloyd's Register. January 1993.

67. 'Safety Aspects of Ship Design and Technology.' House of Lords' Select Committee on Science and Technology (The Carver Committee). HMSO. February 1992.

68. Boyle, Captain P., FNI. 'Bulk Carriers: Operational Aspects which Might Lead to Loss.' Safe Ship Safe Cargo Conference, September 1987.

69. Lanham, Captain B. D., MNI. 'Bulk Carrier Losses.' *Seaways* September 1991.

70. Skinner, Dr A. E. et al. 'Notes on Bulk Carrier Cargo Liquefaction.' *RINA London branch seminar.* August 1991.

71. Annex to IMO Resolution A.713 (17). International Maritime Organization. November 1991.

72. Isbester, Captain J., ExC, FNI. 'Structural Damage to Bulk Carriers from Block Loading.' *Seaways.* July 1993.

73. Price, Prof G. Second Wakeford Maritime Lecture. February 1991.

74. 'The Structural Price of Port Pressures.' *Lloyd's List.* 17 September 1991.

75. Hachmann, D. 'Wave Load Rules Unreasonable.' *Lloyd's List.* 9 October 1991.

76. Björkman, A. I. C. H. 'Big Bulkers Should be Stronger.' *Lloyd's List.* October 1991.

77. Baillod, Captain F., MNI. 'Shipping's Deep Crisis.' *Seaways.* October 1991.

78. Knight, Captain R., MNI. 'Focus on Bulk Carriers.' *Seaways.* October 1991.

79. Skinner Dr A. 'Cargo Liquefaction.' *MER.* October 1991.

80. Noble, J. M., BSc, FNI. 'Bulk Carrier Losses.' *Seaways.* March 1992.

81. Björkman, A. I. C. H. 'Weak Bulk Carriers.' *Seaways.* March 1992.

82. Ferguson, J. M. 'Informed Opinion is Crucial for Bulk Carrier Safety.' *Lloyd's List.* 19 August 1992.

83. Foy, D. B., MRIN, FNI. 'Marine Enquiries and the Public Interest.' Trans IMarE. November 1982.

84. Robinson, D. W. 'Bulk Carrier Research – LR Project.' *Seaways.* October 1991.

85. 'Pilot Study into Loading of Bulk Carriers.' Report from Australia to IMO Maritime Safety Committee. MSC 60/20/5.

86. 'Safety of Ships Carrying Solid Bulk Cargoes.' Document submitted by the Government of France to the IMO Maritime Safety Committee. MSC 60/20/8.

87. McDowell, D., AMNI. 'Bulk Carrier Corrosion – Recent Experiences.' *Seaways.* August 1991.

88. 'The Management of Safety in Shipping.' The Nautical Institute. 1991.

89. 'The Mariners Role in Collecting Evidence.' Third Edition. The Nautical Institute. 2006.

90. 'Bills of Lading: Delivery of Cargo Against one Original Bill of Lading Carried on Board.' The London Steam – Ship Owners' Mutual Insurance Association Ltd. *Circular.* July 1990.

91. Harris, Jennie. 'Building Lower Rates.' *International Bulk Journal.* June 2001.

92. SOLAS (as amended). International Maritime Organization. 2009

93. De Rose, J. 'Enhanced surveys of bulk carriers and tankers – an update.' *RINA London branch meeting.* January 2002.

94. Colman, The Hon. Mr Justice. 'Report of the Re-opened Formal Investigation into the loss of the mv *Derbyshire.*' The Stationery Office. 2000.

95. Isbester, Capt. J, ExC, FNI, MCMS. 'Design and operation of bulk carriers post mv *Derbyshire.*' *Seaways.* The Nautical Institute. February 2002.

96. 'Inchon reports first boxed grain' *Lloyd's Register – Fairplay web links.* 25 February 2008

97. Beetham, Capt. E.H, FNI, FRSA, FRMetS, FRIN. Personal correspondence. 28 October 1999.

98. Strømme Ships Equipment [Now EMS Ship Supply (Norway) AS] literature. Haslum, Norway. 2002.

99. RBM HoldSolutions product literature. Vancouver, British Columbia. 2002

100. BIMCO, Denmark. Confidential reports. 1997.

101. Dixon, Captain R, MNI. Personal correspondence. 19 December 1999.

102. 'Bulk carrier hold cleanliness.' *BIMCO Bulletin* Volume 92 No.2 97

103. 'BIMCO Standard Scrap Metal Clause for Voyage C/Ps.' *BIMCO Bulletin* Volume 94 No.1 99

104. Shore, Capt. R.E, FNI. 'Cleaning bulker cargo holds.' *Seaways.* November 2000

105. Asmyhr, D. Torvald Klaveness Group. Personal correspondence.11 January 2003.

106. 'Seafarers' Training, Certification and Watchkeeping' (STCW), as amended. International Maritime Organization. 2001.

107. International Safety Management (ISM) Code. International Maritime Organization. 2002

108. 'Guidelines for the control and management of ships' ballast water to minimize the transfer of harmful aquatic organisms and pathogens.' Resolution A.868(20). International Maritime Organization. November 1997

109. 'Ballast water convention.' International Maritime Organization. February 2004

110. Code of Practice for the Safe Loading and Unloading of Bulk Carriers' (BLU Code). International Maritime Organization. 1998.

111. 'Bulk Carriers. Guidance and Information on Bulk Cargo Loading and Discharging to Reduce the Likelihood of Over-stressing the Hull Structure.' International Association of Classification Societies. 1997.

112. Barber, Capt. D, FNI ARINA. Personal correspondence. 03 March 2004.

113. Sole, G.H and Milne, S. 'Test Results and the Risk Context.' *Design and Operation of Bulk Carriers: Post MV Derbyshire.* RINA. October 2001.

114. 'Guidelines for the on-board use and application of computers.' *MSC/Circ.891.* International Maritime Organisation. December 1998

115. Swerke, A.G. 'Challenges on steel coil loading.' *Bulk Carrier Update.* DNV. November 2003.

116. McNamara, J. National Cargo Bureau. Personal correspondence. 21 August 2002

117. 'General Information for Grain Loading.' National Cargo Bureau Inc. 2007.

118. 'Guidelines for bulk carrier hatch cover surveys and owner's inspections and maintenance.' *MSC/Circ.1071.* International Maritime Organization. 13 June 2003.

119. 'Hatch Coaming Drains.' *Loss Prevention Bulletin 261.* UK P&I Club. September 2002.

120. Isbester, Capt. J, ExC, FNI, MCMS. 'Bulk Carriers – Safe loading and unloading: whose rules apply?' *Seaways.* The Nautical Institute. February 2004.

121. 'Safe Loading and Unloading of Bulk Carriers 2003.' Maritime and Coastguard Agency. July 2003

122. Dibble, W.J. and Mitchell, P. 'Draft Surveys – A guide to good practice.' *Loss Prevention Guides.* North of England P&I Association Ltd. 1994

123. SOLAS (as amended) II-2/19.4. International Maritime Organization. 2009

124. 'Guidelines on early assessment of hull damage and possible need for abandonment of bulk carriers.' *MSC/Circ.1143.* International Maritime Organization. 13th December 2004.

125. Mullins, C. *Loss Prevention Bulletins Nos. 309, 368.* UK P&I Club. 2003/04

126. Evans, Capt. R. Personal correspondence. 30th June 2005

127. Baenhi, Capt. M. Personal correspondence. 20th April 2005

128. SOLAS (as amended) VI/2.1. International Maritime Organization. 2009

129. SOLAS (as amended) XII/12. International Maritime Organization. 2009

130. 'Advice on the dangers of flooding forward compartments.' *Marine Guidance Note 210(M).* Maritime & Coastguard Agency. December 2001

131. Isbester, Capt. J. ExC, FNI, MCMS. 'Design and Operation of Bulk Carriers.' *Seaways.* The Nautical Institute. December 2005

132. Dahl, T. 'New Rules for Safer Bulk Carrier Hatch Covers.' *Design and Operation of Bulk Carriers.* The Royal Institution of Naval Architects. October 2005.

133. Hatch Cover Securing Arrangements for Bulk Carriers not Built in accordance with UR S21 (Rev.3)' IACS UR S30. August 2003

134. Evaluation of Scantlings of Hatch Covers and Hatch Coamings of Cargo Holds of Bulk Carriers, Ore Carriers and Combination Carriers (Rev. 4)' IACS UR S21. October 2004

135. Baillod, Capt. F. FNI. 'Ship handling in heavy weather.' *Seaways.* The Nautical Institute. February 2004

136. Barber, Capt. D. FNI. 'Bulk carriers: real results from the big testing tank.' *Design and Operation for Abnormal Conditions II.* The Royal Institution of Naval Architects. November 2001.

137. Richardson, Capt. J. FNI. 'Some feedback from extreme sea experiences.' *Design and Operation for Abnormal Conditions II.* The Royal Institution of Naval Architects. November 2001.

138. Milne, S. 'The New Regulatory Regime for Bulk Carriers.' *Informal meeting, 28 April 2005.* Royal Institution of Naval Architects, London Branch. April 2005

139. SOLAS (as amended) VI/7.3. International Maritime Organization. 2009

140. 'Bulk Carriers – Guidance and Information on Bulk Cargo Loading and Discharging to Reduce the Likelihood of Over-stressing the Hull Structure', Para.4.1.4. IACS. 1997.

141. 'Improper Bulk Measurement – Chittagong (Bangladesh).' *Bulletin 393.* UK P&I Club. December, 2004.

142. 'Weighbridge Accuracy – Dar Es Salaam – Tanzania.' *Bulletin 258.* UK P&I Club. August, 2002

143. 'Problems with Alleged Shortage Claims – Morocco.' *Bulletin 360.* UK P&I Club. May, 2004.

144. 'Bulk Carriers – Guidance and Information on Bulk Cargo Loading and Discharging to Reduce the Likelihood of Over-stressing the Hull Structure', Para.4.2.3. IACS. 1997.

145. 'Bulk Carriers – Guidance and Information on Bulk Cargo Loading and Discharging to Reduce the Likelihood of Over-stressing the Hull Structure', Para.5.2. IACS. 1997.

146. 'Bulk Carriers – Guidance and Information on Bulk Cargo Loading and Discharging to Reduce the Likelihood of Over-stressing the Hull Structure', Para.5.4. IACS. 1997.

147. Baehni, M, MNI Personal correspondence. 10th April 2006.

148. 'Code of Practice for the Safe Loading and Unloading of Bulk Cargoes.' (BLU Code), Para.6.1.3. International Maritime Organization. 1998.

149. SOLAS (as amended) XII/11. International Maritime Organization. 2009

150. SOLAS (as amended) VI/7.2, International Maritime Organization. 2009

151. Kaminski, Capt.M. 'Loading bulk grain in the US.' *Seaways.* The Nautical Institute. March 2005

152. 'ISM Code', Para.1.2.2.1. International Maritime Organization. 2002.

153. IMSBC Code, Section 8. International Maritime Organization. 2009

154. Adigüzel, Emir. 'Maritime Cement Trade Outlook.' *The Dry Bulk Shipping Market Outlook Conference.* Lloyd's List Events. April 2006.

155. Rogers, Dr.P. 'Dry Bulk Freight Market Outlook.' *The Dry Bulk Shipping Market Outlook Conference.* Lloyd's List Events. April 2006.

156. 'Carriage of steel.' *Loss prevention bulletin 3/1993/94.* West of England Ship Owners Insurance Services Ltd. December 1993.

157. 'Carriage of steel cargoes.' Assuranceforeningen SKULD (Gjensidig). January 1998.

158. 'Steel Preshipment Surveys.' North of England P&I Association. 2003

159. 'Loading, or sailing after partial discharge, of bulk grain.' Note No.5. *Marine Orders Part 33 (Cargo and Cargo Handling – Grain).* Australian Marine Safety Authority. July 2005.

160. Konow, T. Personal correspondence. 1st November 2006.

161. 'Carefully to Carry', Volume 1, Part 2. Thomas Miller P&I Ltd. October 2002

162. Tysoe, M. Personal correspondence. 22nd November 2006.

163. Fothergill, Captain M.G, FNI. 'Lumber Deck Cargo Loading Manual.' The Nautical Institute. 2002

164. 'Canadian Code of Safe Practice for ships carrying Timber Deck Cargoes.' Transport Canada. January 1992

165. Beetham, Captain E.H, FNI, FRIN, FRSA. Personal correspondence. 28th October 1999.

166. 'Timber Cargo – Stevedore Deaths.' *UK P&I Club Bulletin 346.* February 2004.

167. SOLAS (as amended) XII/14. International Maritime Organization. 2009

168. Johnson, A and Harrison, I. 'Pros and Cons of Double Side Skin Bulk Carriers.' *Design and Operation of Bulk Carriers.* RINA. October 2005.

169. Brazdis, S, Anghel, L, Dimitriu, C.V and Alexandru, G. *'New Innovative and Safety DSS Bulk Carrier Design.'* Design and Operation of Bulk Carriers. RINA. October 2005.

170. Ballast Water Management Manual for Diamond 53 Class. Carl Bro AS. September 2006.

171. Cargo Loading and Securing Manual for Diamond 53 Class. Carl Bro AS. October 2006.

172. Anderson, D and Sheard, D. 'Cargo Ventilation.' *Loss Prevention Guides.* North of England P&I Association. 2006.

173. Canada Shipping Act Grain Cargo Regulations, Schedule 1, Part 1, Note 2.(3) on Table 1. November 1979.

174. 'Precaution for Carriage of Coal in Bulk.' Notes issued by major bulk shipping operator. October 2001.

175. 'Carriage of Coal Cargoes – Updated' *LP Bulletin 368.* UK Club. June 2004.

176. Hesketh, Capt. L, FNI Personal correspondence. 29th May 2003.

177. Isbester, Capt. J. ExC, FNI, MCMS. 'Carriage of Steel Coils.' *Seaways.* The Nautical Institute. May 2003

178. Isbester, Capt. J. ExC, FNI, MCMS. 'Carriage of Steel Coils.' *Seaways.* The Nautical Institute. September 2004.

179. Isbester, Capt. J. ExC, FNI, MCMS. 'Steel Coils.' *Seaways.* The Nautical Institute. November 2007.

180. 'Steel coils No2.' *Bulk Carrier Update.* Det Norske Veritas. April 2004.

181. SOLAS (as amended) V/22. International Maritime Organization. 2009.

182. SOLAS (as amended) II-1/3-2. International Maritime Organization. 2009.

183. Strobel, Christian. Senior Maritime Advisor, DNV. Personal correspondence. 9th May 2003.

184. 'Ice as a danger to shipping.' *BIMCO Bulletin.* October 2007

185. Duggal, Capt. B.S., MNI. 'Ice class ships.' *Seaways.* The Nautical Institute. August 2006.

186. Rodericks, Capt. R.P. BSc, MNI. 'Breaking the ice.' *Seaways.* The Nautical Institute. November 1996.

187. 'Operations in extremely cold climates.' *Gard News.* Gard AS. April 2002.

188. 'Guidelines for ships operating in Arctic ice-covered waters.' *MSC/Circ.1056.* International Maritime Organization. 23 December 2002.

189. Cooper, Capt. N, FNI. Personal correspondence. 1st September 2004.

190. SOLAS (as amended) VI/7.7. International Maritime Organization. 2009.

191. 'Advice on the dangers of flooding of forward compartments.' *Marine guidance note 210 (M).* Maritime and Coastguard Agency. December 2001

192. 'Guidelines on early assessment of hull damage and possible need for abandonment of bulk carriers.' *MSC/Circ.1143.* International Maritime Organization. 13 December 2004.

193. 'Water ingress monitoring' *IMO MSC 79/INF 3* submitted by BIMCO. 19 August 2004.

194. 'Medical first aid guide for use in accidents involving dangerous goods.' *IMDG Code supplement.* International Maritime Organization. 2008.

195. Kidman, P and Anderson P. 'A seafarers Guide to ISM.' *Loss prevention guide.* NEP&I. April 2002.

196. Isbester, Capt. J. ExC, FNI, MCMS. Introduction. *Bulk Carrier Practice.* The Nautical Institute. November 1993.

197. 'Recommendations for entering enclosed spaces aboard ship.' *IMSBC Code Supplement.* The International Maritime Organization. 2009

198. 'Ineffective fumigation of wheat – USA' *LP Bulletin 552* – 11/07 UK P&I Club. November 2007.

199. 'Seafarer dies of CO_2 from woodchips.' *Fairplay Daily News.* 16 November 2006.

200. MARS 200812. *Seaways.* The Nautical Institute. February 2008.

201. 'Timber cargo – stevedore deaths.' MARS 200404. *Bulletin 346 – 2/04.* UK P&I Club. 2004.

202. Constantinis, D.A., and Richardson, A.J., 'Enhanced surveys – a cost effective method.' IMarEST. November 1994.

203. Constantinis, D.A, 'New methods for survey and maintanance' EM&I. March 1995.

204. Product literature, DVDs, website and personal correspondence, Stromme A/S becoming EMS Ship Supply (Norway) AS. Various dates to February 2008

205. DVDs, website, and personal correspondence. Wilhelmsen Ships Service. Various dates to February 2008

206. International Ship Suppliers Association: http://www.shipsupply.org/admin/cat.htm

207. 'Rules for certification of lifting appliances.' Det Norske Veritas. January 2007.

208. 'Cranes – Wire ropes – Care, maintenance, installation, examination and discard.' ISO 4309 International Organization for Standardization. 2004

209. Hanily, C.A.M, MNI. 'Draft survey accuracy' *Seaways.* The Nautical Institute. May 2008.

210. 'Guidelines for the Implementation of Annex V of MARPOL 2006 Edition.' International Maritime Organization. 2006.

211. 'Implications of Cargo Residues as Garbage.' *LP Bulletin 425* – 08/05. UK P&I Club. August 2005.

212. 'MARPOL not being taken seriously.' *Fairplay Daily News.* 7th January 2008.

213. Forms for reporting deficiencies in reception facilities: a) IMO Revised consolidated format for reporting alleged inadequacies of port reception facilities, Appendix 1 to the Guidelines to Annex V of MARPOL b) BIMCO 'Adequacy of port reception facilities' form

214. 'North Sea SECA in force 11 August 2007 – Europe.' *LP Bulletin 536* – 08/07 UK P&I Club. August 2007.

215. 'Heating of Coal Cargoes during Loading – Worldwide' *LP Bulletin 590* – 07/08 UK P&I Club. July 2008.

216. 'Get the low-down before loading.' *Signals Newsletter.* NE P&I. April 2007.

217. SOLAS (as amended) XII International Maritime Organization. 2009.

218. SOLAS (as amended) XII/10 International Maritime Organization. 2009.

219. SOLAS (as amended) XII/8.3 International Maritime Organization. 2009.

220. SOLAS (as amended) XII/1 International Maritime Organization. 2009.

221. King, M. 'Size does matter.' *Cargo Systems Americas.* November 2007.

222. SOLAS (as amended) XII/13 International Maritime Organization. 2009.

223. Barber, Capt. D. FNI. 'Bulk Carriers Post FSA: Variations on Compliance.' *Design and Operation of Bulk Carriers.* The Royal Institution of Naval Architects. October 2005.

224. Gratsos, G.A. and Zachariadis, P. 'Life Cycle Cost of Maintaining the Ship's Structure.' *Design and Operation of Bulk Carriers.* The Royal Institution of Naval Architects. October 2005.

225. 'Ship design, construction, repair and maintenance – Guidelines for the survey of repairs.' *IMO MSC/Circ.1070.* 12 June 2003.

226. Chandorkar, Capt. S., MNI. 'Managing dry dock maintenance' *'The Nautical Institute on Command'.* 2nd Edition. 2000.

227. Smith, Capt.D., CMIOSH, MNI. 'Dry-docking safety.' *Seaways.* The Nautical Institute. June 2006.

228. 'World Shipping Encyclopaedia' *Lloyds Register/Fairplay.* July 2008.

229. 'M.S. Berge Stahl.' *Wikipedia, the free encyclopedia.* October 2008.

230. Bruce, Capt. P. 'Guidance notes for vessels arriving at Australia to load grain.' Tonand Marine (Aust) Pty Ltd. July 2005

231. King, M. 'New equipment comes to rescue.' *Cargo Systems.* August 2008.

232. IMSBC Code, Section 5. International Maritime Organization. January 2009.

233. ISL Shipping Statistics and Market Review, Volume 52 No 4. 2008.

234. 'The Bulk Carrier Register 2008.' Clarkson Research Services Ltd, London. 2008.

235. www.imo.org/home.asp/marine_environment/ballast_water_management

236. IACS Unified Requirement (UR) S28.

237. IACS Unified Requirement (UR) S21.

238. BLU Code. Para.2.1.1 International Maritime Organization. 1998.

239. 'Weighbridge Accuracy.' *Bulletin 258.* UK P&I Club. August 2002.

240. 'Improper Bulk Measurement.' *Bulletin 393.* UK P&I Club. December 2004.

241. 'Problems with Alleged Shortage Claims.' *Bulletin 360.* UK P&I Club. May 2004.

242. 'Further Problems with Alleged Shortage Claims.' *Bulletin 331.* UK P&I Club. November 2003.

243. 'Declaring Fumigation of Bulk Cargo Worldwide.' *Bulletin 488.* UK P&I Club. September 2006.

244. Evans, Capt. R, MNI. Personal correspondence. 15th September 2008.

245. MARPOL 2006, Annex I, Regulation 29. International Maritime Organization. 2006.

246. MARPOL 2006, Annex V. International Maritime Organization. 2006.

247. IMSBC Code. Appendix 1, Coal, Special Precautions, Para.3. International Maritime Organization, 2009.

248. Cooper, Capt. N, FNI. Personal correspondence. 1st January 2008.

249. IMSBC Code. Appendix 1, Coal, International Maritime Organization, 2009.

250. IMSBC Code. Appendix 1, Iron ore, International Maritime Organization, 2009.

251. IMSBC Code. Appendix 3 Para.2. International Maritime Organization, 2009.

252. 'Block stow reminder.' *Stoploss Bulletin Issue 49.* The London P&I Club. May 2008.

253. 'IMSBC Code.' Appendix 1, Cement, International Maritime Organization, 2009.

254. 'BIMCO Ice Handbook.' BIMCO. 2005.

255. Hachmann, D. Personal correspondence. 15th December 1994.

256. Mortensen, N.B.L. 'Bulk Carrier Safety – the latest IMO developments.' *Bulk Carrier Update.* DnV. April 2004.

257. Isbester, Capt. J. ExC, FNI, MCMS. 'Dry bulk shipping – current issues.' Seaways. The Nautical Institute. June 2001.

258. Ferguson, J.M. 'Structural strength studies for bulk carriers.' International dry bulk shipping forum. Lloyd's List Events. February 2001

259. 'IACS takes action to improve the safety regime for bulk carriers.' International Association of Classification Societies' *Press Release,* 15 March, 2002.

260. 'Participation of ships in weather routeing services.' *MSC/Circ.1063.* International Maritime Organization. December 2002.

261. SOLAS (as amended) II-1/3.7 International Maritime Organization. 2009

262. 'Guidance for checking the structure of bulk carriers.' *MSC/Circ.1117.* International Maritime Organization. June 2004

263. Hesketh, Capt. L, FNI Personal correspondence. 29th January 2009

264. Cooper Capt. N., FNI. Personal correspondence. 8th March 2008

265. Hesketh, Capt. L, FNI Personal correspondence. 24th August 2008

266. 'ISM Code', Section 10. International Maritime Organization. 2002.

267. 'Cleaning additives evaluated and found to meet the requirements of Regulation 13.5.2 of Annex II of MARPOL 73/78.' *Annex 10 to MEPC.2/Circ.14.* International Maritime Organization. January 2009

268. 'Special Areas under MARPOL.' http://www.imo.org/Environment/mainframe.asp?topic_id=760 February 2009

269. Cooper Capt. N., FNI. Personal correspondence. 10th September 2008

270. Oil Record Book Entries – Machinery space operations (Part 1) *Technical Bulletin 24* UK P&I Club August 2007

271. Regulation 16. Load Lines Consolidated Edition 2005. International Maritime Organization. 2005

272. SOLAS (as amended) XII/5.1-2. International Maritime Organization. 2009

273. SOLAS (as amended) XII/6. International Maritime Organization. 2009

274. SOLAS (as amended) V/28. International Maritime Organization. 2009

275. SOLAS (as amended) V/20. International Maritime Organization. 2009

276. Regulation 22-2. Load Lines Consolidated Edition 2005. International Maritime Organization. 2005

277. 'Assessment of longitudinal strength.' *MSC/Circ.1108.* International Maritime Organization. May 2004

278. SOLAS (as amended) III/32. International Maritime Organization. 2009

279. SOLAS (as amended) III/31. International Maritime Organization. 2009

280. IMSBC Code. Section 7. International Maritime Organization, 2009

281. International Association of Classification Societies. Personal correspondence. October 2008-February 2010.

282. Bryson P A. 'Management of Bulk Carrier Structure.' *Design and Operation of Bulk Carriers.* The Royal Institution of Naval Architects. October 2005.

283. Clark, I.C, MSc, MNI. 'Mooring and anchoring ships Vol.1.' The Nautical Institute. November 2008.

INDEX